D1367585

FUTURE ENVIRONMENTS OF NORTH AMERICA

The Natural History Press, publisher for The American Museum of Natural History, is a division of Doubleday & Company, Inc. Directed by a joint editorial board made up of members of the staff of both the Museum and Doubleday, the Natural History Press publishes books and periodicals in all branches of the life and earth sciences, including anthropology and astronomy. The Natural History Press has its editorial offices at The American Museum of Natural History, Central Park West at Seventy-ninth Street, New York, New York 10024, and its business offices at 501 Franklin Avenue, Garden City, New York.

FUTURE ENVIRONMENTS OF NORTH AMERICA

Being the record of a Conference convened by The Conservation Foundation in April, 1965, at Airlie House, Warrenton, Virginia

Edited by
F. FRASER DARLING
and JOHN P. MILTON

The Natural History Press / Garden City, New York / 1966

3/8/67 pb. 12.50

To

EDWARD H. GRAHAM

whose inspiration remains for
all those endeavoring to harmonize
the works of nature and of man

Foreword

The Conservation Foundation is fortunate to have among its supporters a family that has been devoted among other things to wildlife protection over the years. They are also aware, as a family, that the protection of wildlife in the future depends upon an adequate, suitable, and healthy habitat.

They are concerned that the advancing technological, social, economic problems and expansion of human numbers in our countries—on this continent—will very shortly increase the damage that is occurring to all sorts of habitats.

Our Steering Committee has called for our consideration of a great many of these factors that influence human conduct in the treatment of environments. Indeed, I doubt that so many relevant factors have been marshaled before by such able discussants at so high a philosophical yet practical level.

We are here exploring ways to create and conserve the health of a continent for the well-being of all life. The human spirit, like life, is many wondrous things. As we ponder these papers before us, we shall find joy, I think, not merely in observing and studying the wondrous, but in analyzing its factors and relishing them and, hopefully, directing their content to our honor. It will be our purpose to expand our thought and apply our understanding to enhance environmental health and thereby human sanity.

This should be an uplifting experience. We welcome you here with all our hearts.*

S. H. Ordway, Jr.

* From opening remarks by Mr. S. H. Ordway, Jr., President 1962–65, The Conservation Foundation.

Preface

In April 1965 over forty scholars of many disciplines met to consider the future environments of North America. The Conference was convened by The Conservation Foundation to provide an opportunity for thoughtful men to ponder the implications of the increasingly dominant influence of man upon his own environment. With rapidly growing numbers and an increasingly sophisticated technology, man is changing the life systems of this continent. The effects—those which can now be perceived and those which can be foreseen—are of such magnitude as to warrant a most profound appraisal.

Commissioned papers prepared for the Conference examined some of the forces which are shaping the environment and described their present and potential impacts. The deliberations elicited and sharpened proposals for modifying the existing patterns of environmental change in order to secure an environment of order and diversity, health and beauty. Implicit in all the papers and discussions was a consciousness of man's responsibility to himself and to the future, and an unspoken consensus that the freedom of future generations to make a meaningful choice about the kind of world they want to live in is the responsibility of each generation.

In preparing for the Conference the Foundation was fortunate to secure a distinguished Steering Committee composed of Ian McTaggart Cowan, A. Starker Leopold, E. M. Nicholson, and Christopher Tunnard. Each contributed significantly to the definition and development of the four-day Conference. As Chairman of the Conference, F. Fraser Darling had major responsibility for its planning, and John Milton, Conference Secretary, for its execution. The efforts of many persons within the Foundation staff—notably Samuel H. Ordway, Jr., George E. Brewer, Jr., Fairfield Osborn, and Wallace D. Bowman—were essential to the Conference and to the successful completion of this volume.

The vision and generous support of the late Mrs. Alan M. Scaife made the project possible. The Foundation wishes to record its special gratitude to her.

Russell E. Train
PRESIDENT, THE CONSERVATION FOUNDATION

Contents

FUTURE ENVIRONMENTS OF NORTH AMERICA

Introduction

by F. Fraser Darling, CONFERENCE CHAIRMAN AND VICE PRESIDENT, THE CONSERVATION FOUNDATION

My President, my lady, and gentlemen: We have said how glad we are to see you here. This undertaking is one that I was in some measure responsible for, but I can't say that I have done very much of the work. That has been the responsibility of my colleagues in the Foundation, particularly John Milton and Noel Eichhorn and our secretary, Harriet Bennett.

It might be interesting to give a glimpse of the obvious, as it were, and find out why we are here; why this agglomeration of skills and their bearers are incarcerated for four days in this delightful enclosure of Airlie House.

If we equate our several skills as so many species, what sort of a biological community is going to evolve in four days? After all, we are not quite a chance collection of creatures thrown together to sink or swim, but a selected group, thought out by a Steering Committee sweating for a couple of days eighteen months ago.

A very few of our chosen organisms could not be enticed into our net and one or two have slipped out of it during that difficult evolutionary period when expression of skills has to be exercised in producing papers.

You see how teleological we are, molding the beginnings of the evolution of this biological community! But at that the Steering Committee has ceased meddling like a would-be beneficent deity, and with only the slightest directional irritant pressure, I hope, from myself, these forty or so species in five or six separate phyla have been quietly expressing themselves in the written word. They are now present, fully aware—again I hope—of what the other species have been thinking, and they face that evolutionary phase of the spoken word, a phase of competition and cooperation.

Standing here before you, like neither a teleological deity nor a mischievous devil, I am wondering whether this evolutionary experiment is going to produce a harmonious ecosystem, the cooperative complexity of which is going to produce a resource wealth comparable with those accumulated resources of the organic world by which man has gained the leisure to civilize and gather together as we have today.

Four days hence we shall know whether we have attained to being an intellectual ecosystem, but only the future can say whether we shall have created a rich resource. To use Derrick Ovington's language, we shall know more about our primary and secondary productivity.

Ten years ago I was one of the fortunate members of the Wenner-Gren Conference on "Man's Role in Changing the Face of the Earth." A few veterans of that immensely rewarding intellectual occasion are here today. All of us know the big volume that came from that conference.

All of us have used that book, and thousands more. There can be no doubt of the rich resource of coordinated knowledge and quickened thinking the Wenner-Gren Conference generated.

I confess to you how closely our own gathering here has followed the Wenner-Gren idea. Then, the assembled company of about seventy-five with thirty-four papers was concerned with the whole planet and the past. We are to think about the North American continent and the future. We are not going to indulge in attempts at finite projectionism at any one date in the future, but rather will examine trends in our various fields and how this gathering of skills can ameliorate, prune, amplify, and possibly validate the thoughts of each.

The game of projectionism, as I like to call it, makes deductions from what may or may not be facts: projections are made with owllike solemnity and the listener is half expected to believe them.

As we go through these papers we find a minimum of definite projection but a lot of ideas about the future, and ideas will draw us forth in these four days.

I think Pierre Dansereau puts it beautifully when he closes his essay:

"A valid imaginary reconstruction of our world is now our greatest task. It may even be the condition of our survival."

Why are we here? you ask. First, let us acknowledge our debt to a benefactress who wondered what was the future for wildlife in North America. We might have been optimistic or depressed—individually we may be—and gathered a group of wildlife biologists to argue this way and that.

But this would have been too simple an ecosystem, like that of an oceanic island, to have built up a biological community that could have withstood contact with the many other disciplines whose thought and activities are going to influence the future of wildlife in North America.

Obviously, we must become more complex and here we are, thirty-four papers with the minds behind them, and a few additional free minds coming fresh to the Conference.

These few individual "species" have been asked because we wished to honor them, but were I the mischievous devil mooted above, perhaps they are the wild cards in the pack who will provide a lot of fun.

No, I prefer to keep our evolutionary analogy, and let us think of Starker Leopold's paper and admit that our guests show that lack of specialization which will make them highly adaptable species in successional rather than climax states in the general environment of our Conference.

What mutations, modifications, and adaptations shall we bring about in these four days of evolution?

We have called this a Conference on "The Future Environments of North America." Please note the philosophical modesty of the plural, "Environments."

We have thought in terms of the human habitat throughout, not because we are anthropocentric, but for the stark reason that we now know our awe-full and awesome condition of being the dominant animal species on the planet.

We have choice, decision, and responsibility, and we are beginning to feel this last increasingly toward those other habitats of other living things, plant and animal, with which we share. We want our dominance to be an expression of the aristocratic ideal, that of being the servant of those less able to care for themselves, not a tyrannical despotism of looting, crushing levies, and destruction.

But our desire to do right by the planet and its denizens and our own posterity cannot be a pious wish and an expression of a philosophy of *laissez-faire*. All through these papers—which I hope we have all read—runs the same thread, that of management. In short, we seem agreed on the necessity of a positive approach toward the several environments of North America. So I do not greatly fear that our evolutionary experiment will produce that figment "nature red in tooth and claw."

There should be no predatory extinctions, though it is almost certain that some of our species will have gained greater lissomeness and perspicacity through contact with the more complex world of disciplines represented here. This is one of the prime reasons for the Conference.

Preserve us from wildlifers talking in an ivory tower of conservatism which Kenneth Boulding has deplored, from planners and landscape architects who have no biological knowledge though they are dealing with the living landscape, and from economists who fail to realize the biological desire which man shares with most animals, of just loafing.

Man's most creative moments may be in his loafing time. Loafing and lethargy are not the same thing at all. Perhaps Marion Clawson will agree with reservations to this.

My friend Charles Elton, a senior ecologist, was asked to this Conference, but as a species he lurks in deep cover among the dreaming spires, or at least in Whytham Wood, and could not be enticed or frightened out of it to enter our net. Sparse as may be our glimpses of his physical presence, we are fortunate in being able to follow "sign" and read something of what he is thinking, much of it pertinent to our concern in these four days.

Clarence Glacken has recalled Elton's case for the preservation of variety and of diversification in the landscape, in Elton's beautiful essay *The Ecology of Invasions by Animals and Plants*. I would quote Elton a little further, in that he shows quite apart from any esthetic satisfaction in the varied scene, there is definite ecological advantage to be gained from diversity. There is a stability in such landscapes somewhat comparable with the ecological qualities of wilderness.

Elton finishes his book by quoting John Muir—and I wish he could be with us today—who spoke of the abundance of wild beauty across the continent of North America, and Elton asks, "Will we be able to talk like this in fifty years' time, as he could fifty years ago?" There is no doubt at all that Charles should have been here.

For myself, I found particular fascination in reading the legal and organizational approach of our only woman member, Ann Louise Strong, to achievement of maximal variety in the human environment. Two quite different minds come to a large common ground of understanding.

Forgive me for dwelling already on the subject of landscape as if I were looking back over my shoulder. Indeed I am not wishing to do that; rather am I, with you, interested in the future.

We have Paul Waggoner among us. He works at an Agricultural Experiment Station that has almost ceased to be primarily concerned with the financial welfare of farmers and is thereby allowed to use his imagination. This is a splendid evolutionary phenomenon in itself.

Two years ago he called a conference at New Haven in which the small company dealt with the Suburban Forest. The theme developed of the eastern hardwood and mixed forest on the edge of Megalopolis, being a biological community no longer supplying timber, no longer exercising minds as to how it could be converted into profitable softwood forest, but now fulfilling an entirely different social function of being an important ameliorative factor in the way of recreation and re-creation for the human inhabitants of Megalopolis.

This is symptomatic of what is happening in many other parts of America from Alaska to Panama, and very markedly in Britain, though I would suggest that too few of our legislators have woken up to the phenomenon. The fate of a hedgerow tree in Britain should no longer rest on the criterion of how much more wheat or barley would grow if the tree were removed, but on how much amenity would be lost for a crowded population needing and desiring what I have called the therapy of the green leaf.

Urban folk have come into the countryside in our time in a new way, calling it theirs and ready to give brains, time, and treasure to its care, although we all know of the apparent majority ready to give none of these. Neither farmer nor industrialist is quite free any more to do exactly as he likes, and he will do well to listen to the voice of the people.

Max Nicholson, one of our guests, who organized the continuing British Conference "The Countryside in 1970," will doubtless have something to say about the forward thinking of some industrialists, how the British Coal Board is spending more than a tithe of its gross income on rehabilitation of landscape after opencast mining. The Board is not troubling itself too much that the cost of such work vastly exceeds the immediate agricultural value of the ground, but is thinking of the land and the quality of the landscape for posterity. Amortized in this way the cost is small.

Ray Fosberg's mind has been working in the same way. With that slightly cynical twist so many of us use to hide our depth of feeling, he suggests that the next "fringe benefit" organized labor may be asking for will be decent ecological and esthetic conditions in which to live.

We have these dreadful degraded habitats in America and in Britain. Their redevelopment in Ian McHarg's sense, fashioning Capability Brown landscapes with our improved ecological knowledge, could be one of the most uplifting things for our civilization providing that unification of ideal and physical effort which might be one of the stress-relieving influences described by Seymour Farber.

As I said before, the British Coal Board has made a wonderful start.

If, being British, I have proudly alluded to the unselfishness and foresight of a nationalized industry, let me now just as proudly in the country of my semiadoption bow to that great man President Lyndon Johnson, who could make natural and man-made beauty the keynote of his address on the State of the Nation, in January, and who in May will call a White House Conference on beauty in town and country. This is tremendous.

The President's Conference will be entirely different from ours in numbers and modes of procedure. It will be primarily a practical Conference designed for action to get under way, whereas we are more relaxed, discussing principles and ideas. But there could scarcely be a happier coincidence and I feel our Conference will be quickened and given fire by the assurance that the President is eager for action in the field of environment in the United States.

The President, shrewd and hard-headed, has had the insight to bring forth what many men would have been shy to express: these stirrings of the mind of the people declaring respect for nature and a desire that man-made beauty, truly an emanation of nature, should be a living, integral part of the whole.

As Ray Dasmann puts it, "pathways of understanding are being built more rapidly today . . . the losses in the quality of our living are being noticed soon enough to be remedied."

The automobile junk yard has been much quoted from the President's speech. Its cure is largely a mechanical job rather than an ecological, but there are ample opportunities for ecological therapy in degraded landscapes in lifting the depression from slag heaps, fume-killed landscapes, subsidences, strip- and auger-mining sites, dredger-mining gravel heaps, and the terrible landscapes of derelict housing which did not quite cover the terrain but hopelessly degraded that which was not covered.

These are nineteenth-century black spots, canker-producing within our society. If some of our earth-moving equipment got busy in these places instead of shearing off pristine sites, some of us would be happier.

Christopher Tunnard opens his paper with a reasoning for his use of the word "patrimony." I like this emphasizing, as it does, the continuity, our identity with those who came before.

I am sorry in a way that we have no structural engineers with us or any of those people concerned with the physical problems of industry. I hope, nevertheless, that we shall remember such geographical facts that the Great Lakes region is the greatest industrial region in the world, yet the areas just north of it in the United States and Canada are depressed or slow to prosper. Again, what is going to be the water situation in the continent? Shall we have to pipe water from the Yukon to California, Texas, and Mexico in the further future? Texas may well run short of fossil water before her oil is done.

When we look around our continent, seeing so much spoliation, through ignorance, through increase in numbers of people and increase in pressures from land-using agencies, our hearts are apt to fail, but there can be no doubt of those "pathways of understanding" which were not apparent so few years ago. How soon can they be used?

One essay in our collection gave me real pain, that of Gerardo Budowski analyzing the condition of Central America. He has been entirely courageous, not only in giving us the truth but of facing up to it himself in the spirit of science, expressing a fine contempt for the unctuous do-gooders who prolong the agony of a country in need of those drastic fundamental reforms which can come only from a change of heart and will within a country. They are so near to us, those countries, and yet in so different a condition from ourselves.

William Vogt's essay could be another source of pain. He and Budowski are aligned and to both of them the net increase in populations of human beings is the major problem. Vogt is a pessimist, I think, easing his own pain and ours by his gift of withering satire and positively desiccating dry humor. His zenith of wit I find in his having dug up the aspirations and the prognostications of the Golf Foundation. I hope you remember these. They are very funny. These are the narrow-visioned inanities which should show us where we can get if we are content to ignore most other things than golf.

You might equate with golf the ideas and activities of that questionable breed the conservationists, or the anthropocentric economists. Kenneth Boulding has enlarged on this theme in his essay and I am much looking forward to the discussions in Section III, because I think that is where we are going to have the toughest arguments and where there may be some modification and evolution of the species taking part. Optimists and pessimists will come to the bit, and maybe the fulcrum of the seesaw will be the subject of human population. Can the ostrich modify its fabled habit of head-burying?

Whatever we call ourselves, we are probably all trying in our own small ways to bring about human betterment, though some of us—ecologists, of course—may secretly be more bothered about the restoration of this choice jewel of our imagination, the planet, than about the ruck of its human inhabitants. But most of us have put such jejune and fallacious daydreaming on one side and are ready to meet and take part in a dynamic evolution. One thing troubles me a little and this Conference may give some help—how far does our concern for human welfare lead toward homeostasis for the species? Is there such abundant variety of genetic possibility within us that homeostasis is no threat?

Yet, remember the degrees of uniformity being forced on us by our numbers and the powers of dialectic and mass communication. The ecologist's concern for the planet can be a valuable corrective to the tendency toward the hell of homeostasis.

The name of Pierre Teilhard de Chardin has come into several of our papers. Père Teilhard was to have been present at the Wenner-Gren Conference at Princeton in 1955, but his sudden death deprived us. His idea of the noösphere has affected most of us, but we part company with him when he thinks the actual quantity of the stuff of the noösphere can mean significant evolution of the spiritual quality of man, the one species that can carry this forward. Physically, here is the rich gene pool again, and its value in evolution.

The British geneticist Penrose even questions the eugenic validity of removing mental deficients and idiots from the population. Perhaps out of this welter of genetic combination and segregation of the population explosion will come the new man of the millennium. None of us can say yes or no or what measure of catastrophe must intervene between our suffering present and that far future, but the ecologist still holds by the vision of Wordsworth "On the solid ground of Nature rests the mind that builds for aye."

The ecologist's concern with the future of the face of the planet, with its plants and animals, their lives as members of societies, and the evolutionary dynamic of biological community in which man joins, seems to me to be the necessary concomitant of acceptance of the idea of the noösphere.

In the conjunction of disciplines within this Conference we reach forth intellectually to contemplation of the future of one small section of the planet's surface, North America, the future environments of North America. We have not put a term on our future, but the far future rests on what we do in the near future and our academic and intellectual approach is no indication, I feel, of any lack of the sense of urgency in our concern. We wish only to be scholarly.

It behooves me to stand down for I see you "like greyhounds in the slips, straining on the start." My task is immeasurably lightened by my several colleagues who will chair the sessions.

I shall now hand over to Ian Cowan, who will give us his understanding of the papers grouped under "The Organic World and Its Environment."

Thank you very much.

I THE ORGANIC WORLD AND ITS ENVIRONMENT

---

* Professor Cowan, one of the world's leading animal ecologists, is Dean of the Faculty of Graduate Studies at the University of British Columbia. He received his Ph.D. in vertebrate zoology from the University of California in 1935 and has devoted the years since to studying the ecology and speciation of the Canadian ungulates.

Introductory Statement and Summary Remarks

COWAN: By way of introduction to our consideration of the organic world and environments of North America, the first point I would make is that our concern has been for the human environment in its entirety, the environment of the dominant animal species of the planet.

It is our thesis that as man expands his occupancy and varies his use of the North American continent, he can do so heedlessly, and so contribute to the further degradation of landscape, the pollution of the air, the land, the water, or he can do so with sensitivity and enlightenment, with a determination to conserve around him the greatest possible combination of the biological treasures that are end products of the eons of evolution that have preceded the present.

An expansion of this view, that is at the same time a particularization, can be found in the objective that we seek to maintain for the interests and use of future generations of men, at least some examples of all the organisms now alive. Preferably, they should be wild-living and in their native habitats.

However, we can not now really achieve this because we are ready at the same time to admit that the task of even identifying the world's creatures is perhaps not more than two thirds complete, and probably never will be completed.

There are many lesser forms we know so little about that any objective as broad as that which I have framed is impossible of achievement.

For the moment, we proceed on the faith that if we maintain intact and uncontaminated adequate segments of the various communities, we shall lose but few of the lesser forms. Specific and species-oriented conservation will, in most instances, it seems to me, be directed toward the large, the obvious, the beautiful, or the bizarre, that attract our attention and challenge our interest.

The knowledge we have gained in our search for understanding that could lead to mastery of our environment has led us to vital discoveries—those that give us the power to manipulate mortality. We know that, in the passage of years, many creatures have become extinct. There is no doubt at all that, among these species we want to maintain in our environment, there were those that were on the way to extinction without the impact of man. Our discoveries challenge us in a unique way. They offer us an opportunity to marshal our understanding, our technology, and our ingenuity in an attempt to outwit not just the death of individuals, but the passing of species. This kind of test presents us with the biological drama that quickens the spirit as it enriches our competence. I suggest that we gain far more than we give as we learn to regulate our own impact upon our environment and to reverse the inexorable course of nature.

We are aware that as our populations increase, so will our demands on the energy resources of the continent. Wild acres will be tilled and turned to food production. Increasingly, perhaps, we will become vegetarians as we seek to turn to our own needs the energies that we now convert to animal products for our later use. But the pattern that I see is not one of continuous expansion. The movement of man on this continent has been amoebalike, with pseudopods thrusting in one direction, withdrawing from another. The increasing efficiency of our agricultural adventures will return vast acreages to wild-land uses as it expands on to other acres. By the very nature of things, the exchange of unproductive or poorly productive acres for productive ones will, for many years, lead to an over-all reduction of the areas of intensive environmental change.

These alterations will greatly benefit the plants and animals of the successional stages of the forest habitats in particular. Conversely, the climax communities, especially those of the grasslands, the shrub lands, and the tundra, will be severely altered and will absorb the largest part of our attention as we seek to adjust our activities to the larger objective of conserving environmental variety.

In this panel we will review the present state of the art of conservation as it concerns the living elements of the human environment. Fundamental to this is an examination of the principle that underlies all the discussions of biological conservation. This is that the maintenance of the best possible environment for future generations of men includes the maintenance of the entire gamut of variety in the living biota. Our reasons for maintaining this view are:

(1) The biota stands as the world's complement of DNA in all its complexity. In the past, we have found entities in this gene pool that have been of the greatest economic value to us as we have selected and recombined to provide the richness of cultivated and domesticated species that support our culture.

We are well aware that much has yet to be gained as we seek further recombinations that will extend even further the adaptive capacity and the yield of both our crops and our animals.

Economic self-interest, then, cautions us to husband all the potential genetic raw material. We know not when we may need it.

(2) We are only just beginning to acquire an understanding of the mechanisms that are woven into the simpler ecosystems. The more complex are largely not understood.

Organisms that appear to us now to have no function may occupy important niches in vital food chains. Their elimination might slow down the energy flux in an environment, eliminate an essential step, or pave the way for replacement by less useful or even baneful genotypes.

(3) The challenge to control mortality, that I have already referred to, stands as a very potent reason for seeking to maintain tenuous and fragile species, and those lacking the adaptive capacities to cope with alternate habitats; as I have already said, it is my impression that we shall gain more than we pay in attempting to cope with these very interesting problems.

(4) There are larger moral issues separated from mere self-interest that suggest caution before we decide to commit to oblivion any single unique product of evolution on this continent.

We must be able to point to a better, a happier, a fuller form of life for man. But we have all too little evidence to assure us that without the conservation of variety, man will not lead a deprived existence. The concepts we should be searching for depend upon direct comparative evidence of man in and out of contact with the living environment.

We hope that you will give these reasons and the thesis itself critical examination.

In providing the groundwork for the further discussions that will follow, we have sought to establish some common grounds of understanding. To this end Stanley Cain, who unfortunately will not be attending, has in the first half of his paper presented a series of definitions of basic ecological terms applied to the structural elements in the living world. He concludes with the point that the ecosystem is the key to preservation.

Turning to the species level of conservation, he expresses the view that the real problem for the survival of selected species is likely to involve cases of genetic poverty and thus of limited adaptability. This theme is developed in greater detail by Starker Leopold.

We would point out also that animal species in the arctic and tropical communities appear to be much more vulnerable to changes in their ecosystems than are most temperate-zone species. In the latter we find an abundance of subspeciation and of epigenetic variation. In many also the distribution is wider, and the variations in the physical environment encountered are correspondingly diverse. These features of the temperate-zone fauna and flora suggest to us that the species there have evolved with a complex gene pool, with flexibility of response, and perhaps also a higher mutation rate than is characteristic of the species of arctic and tropics.

In discussions within our panel it came to light that successful introductions have almost all of them involved species from the temperate zones, rather than from the arctic and the tropical areas of the world.

If this is true, while we may face more difficult tasks in coping with the consequences of human impact on the fragile communities of the arctic and tropics, we have an even greater self-interest in maintenance of the temperate complexes with their greater gene complexity.

The paper by Dr. Ovington introduces a new orientation to our discussion of ecology. He views the plant communities in their role as primary producers of chemical energy in the form of protoplasm. This is a most fruitful concept, certain to make major contributions to our capacity to predict and to manipulate. One thing we might examine with profit is the apparent discrepancy between the production of plant biomass and the related abundance of animal forms. These do not seem to relate directly in the somewhat superficial discussions that we have had to date within our group.

The paper by Waggoner examines objectively one of the much publicized possibilities of manipulating the physical environment by altering precipitation patterns. The limitations of present and likely capacity to do this successfully return to us the task of assessing the critical boundaries of survival for the ecosystems as we know them.

There is evidence in various parts of the continent that changes in the mean minimum, the mean maximum, and even the mean annual temperatures of as little as one or two degrees can have measurable results on the competitive survival and distribution of various plants and animals. Much more precise information on limiting factors is needed for all of the ecosystems.

This is my introduction to the panel. I am going to call now upon the first of the panelists, Dr. Durward L. Allen, to bring to your attention the major items of his review.

ALLEN: I have viewed this problem of endangered habitats and species against a background that has already been discussed by every speaker, I think, that of the population increase, and most of our resource problems will need to be related to that context for the reason of course that every resource must be evaluated in terms of the number of people it is going to serve. This obviously involves cultural level, a thing that man has found it possible to change.

I view the natural ecosystems that we have left as perhaps the most vulnerable and fragile of all our resources. They have many uses, many of which we don't even need to try at this time to foresee.

I think a point brought out by Dr. Cowan is of fundamental importance, that of future scientific learning. We have only begun to investigate the relationships and the natural mechanisms that are at work within our natural ecosystems. It would be foolhardy to deny the more competent scientists of the future the opportunity to learn from these devices that have developed through millions of years and which have proved their durability by survival.

I view population control, control of the human population, as inevitable. However, we cannot wait for it as a means of preserving the things that are endangered now. Therefore our programs to review the biota, especially the endangered biota, must be immediately undertaken through strenuous effort, both private and public.

We are attempting now, through much improved means in the federal government, and at the state level, to bring about this rescue operation with much better equipment and resources than we ever had before, and with much better public understanding. We are, however, still contending with programs that are tax supported and sponsored by the government. I refer particularly to the kind of reclamation programs that are subsidizing the destruction of some of our important wildlife habitats and ecotypes. As examples of some of these, I have cited the widespread destruction of wetlands. The Everglades can be cited as a particularly important wetland type, one that is unique in North America, and in great jeopardy at present; dependent upon the Everglades is a wide assortment of birds, mammals, and other forms of life in southern Florida.

This example is being debated widely. While the debates go, the draglines are working.

Various forest types are obvious kinds of primitive ecosystems that need to be preserved—e.g. the redwoods in California. Every open space and every resource that we have is under demand, to be used by someone. Actually all of our lands and waters are already being used—just as open space, if nothing else. The mountaintops and the unwatered deserts and the tundras are of use to us right now, even a negative use in that they are not growing people.

The efforts we are making to turn these into habitats that can grow more people are to a great extent at odds with this program of preserving ecosystems and outdoor areas for recreation.

Grasslands are another example of land types and biota that we are not preserving well. One of the greatest needs we have, I think, one of the greatest challenges in wilderness restoration and preservation, is that of creating at least one major national park in our grasslands. The ones we have are too small. We have the challenge of restoring, insofar as possible, a primitive biota of which some species are extinct and which will be altered by the presence of exotics. But a next-best grassland community that is a fair facsimile of the original could be reconstructed, and it would be vastly better than anything we have now.

We are wiping out unique types of brushland, and I have cited the chaparral areas of the Rio Grande Valley as a good example of this. Those are now down to a thousand acres within the United States. There is a program under way to conserve those areas that are left.

Ecosystems are the basic problem in our nature preservation system because individual species can only be preserved in their respective environments. Many, taken as individual species, have declined through the destruction of their habitats. This has been the most widespread trend. Other species, however, have declined through such attrition as shooting and even government control programs.

Perhaps an even greater issue, ultimately, is one that Leopold has developed, concerning the genetic jeopardy of some of our species now being managed by methods much different from the conditions that existed in primitive times. I have cited particularly the bison on our public areas that is now being culled every year by the human, whereas at one time it was culled by the wolf, acting with other factors in the environment.

Other ungulates, such as the deer, are being managed by the gun, without the attention of their natural enemies to do a realistic job of ecologic selection as in times past.

We have these problems of genetics and speciation to deal with ultimately. What we are trying to preserve now is a very good philosophic question.

COWAN: Thank you. Next I will call upon Dr. Starker Leopold to outline his paper.

LEOPOLD: In North America we have now had an active wildlife conservation program for approximately sixty years. A few beginnings preceded that. It was actually in the era of Theodore Roosevelt that wildlife conservation became a specific function of government, and subsequently of many private groups as well.

It became clear at an early stage in this endeavor to conserve wild animals that some species responded to this protective management, and other species did not. Now, as we look back upon the differential success we have had in restoring different kinds of wild animals, it is clear that some of these are associated ecologically with climax types of vegetation and are dependent upon these very fragile climax ecosystems for their livelihood. These are, of course, of the species that today are scarce or in a few cases extinct.

Conversely, other species, often closely related, seem to have responded very positively—not merely to our endeavors at conservation and management, but to the very changes in the landscape that grew out of our occupancy and development; the deer, white-tailed and mule deer, are classic examples of this.

Our problem in managing deer in many parts of North America today is that we have too many of them. The problem is one of reducing numbers. Yet in the same mountain range we will be attempting to build up a small component of bighorn sheep that do not respond at all to the basic protection program which has been the key to conservation over much of the last half century.

This concept that animals are differentially tied to plant successional stages I have found useful and applicable in every continent in the world in which I have worked. Last spring, for example, I was in Australia, an entirely new experience for me. Yet within a few weeks of cruising around with Harry Frith and looking at the different problems in Australia, I found that at the time the white man moved into Australia and brought with him his sheep and his agriculture, some of the native species had started in a decline to a point to where they had become practically extinct, or reduced to tiny areas that have not been seriously affected by agricultural or pastoral industry. Others have increased with disturbance and become pests.

In the first category are some of the bandicoots and wallabies and the small marsupials that mysteriously disappeared when the sheep came into the country. Some of the larger kangaroos have increased, conversely, and the big job today is controlling the kangaroo.

Here you have exactly the same parallelism to the sorts of things that we have observed here, that I have seen in Mexico, Frank Darling and I in Alaska, and so on—and similarly in Africa the problems are of this nature.

In trying to understand what is the component of adaptability that permits some species to respond favorably and others very unfavorably to human occupancy, we discover that several components seem to be involved. The most obvious one is the nutritional relationship between an animal and where it gets its food from an ecosystem.

Animals that are able to utilize second growth obviously are the ones that are going to be favored by a management program that creates second growth, be it weeds on the prairie or scrub forest or shrubs that grow when a forest ecosystem is cut or cleared or burned.

The nutritional tie is the easiest one to see, and the one I think that we have studied the most. But there are other components here, too, that I understand much less myself. One of them is what may be called genetic adaptability, or plasticity, the ability of a species to evolve quickly to meet a new situation by changing, literally changing, genetically. We have lots of examples of species that we know to be genetically plastic, constantly shifting their genetic base to meet a new situation.

I think one of the best examples, and one that has not been studied, is the ring-necked pheasant in North America, an introduced animal coming from the Orient that now is established over roughly half the continent. I am convinced that the pheasant that lives on the Saskatchewan prairie and the pheasant that lives in the Imperial Valley in southern California are today not genetically the same animal at all. Yet they have evolved from the same stock. This has happened in roughly forty years, or a little more than that.

Lastly, and the component that I understand least, is the ability of individual animals to adjust as individuals, without implying any genetic change in the strain. We can give examples of this. I have cited a few known to me—animals that apparently have the capacity to learn, as individuals, to catch on to nutrition, to fit into a given ecosystem by virtue of their individual cleverness. This ability is hard to separate from the genetic component because, for one thing, the ability to learn is certainly a genetic trait.

These three components—and perhaps many more that I don't even recognize—I think will give us, as they are studied, a much better clue as to why some of these animals do adapt and do fit in and respond to management; our management ideas and concepts of the future will then be adjusted accordingly.

COWAN: Dr. Ovington?

OVINGTON: It is becoming clear that conservation can be expressed in a great variety of ways. On the one hand, we have emphasized this morning that because of man's great capacity to change and pollute his environment, there is need to set aside special areas for the protection or preservation of endangered species or communities.

On the other extreme, there is a growing appreciation of the advantages that are to be gained from applying conservation principles to practical problems of land use, forestry, and agriculture.

If conservation is to succeed in contributing to man's welfare, it is essential that it is placed on a sound, scientific footing. The problems of conservation are often problems of ecology, and we have to view these against the background of human ecology, recognizing particularly that there is a biological limit to the world's resources and the growing requirements of the world population.

We are dealing with such complex situations and such a variety of situations that it is also vital, since our time is limited, to identify the main ecological problems that need to be tackled, and how best to tackle them in order to get the answers we need.

Boulding, in his discussion of economics and ecology, suggests that ecology has not had any regard to the gross production of ecosystems. I think he is mistaken in this, for there is a large and growing literature available in which attempts are being made to produce budgets showing income and outcome for organic matter, for energy, for water, and mineral nutrients in a great variety of ecosystems.

At the same time, he is undoubtedly right in that this approach, which contributes greatly to our knowledge of the functioning of the ecosystems, is incomplete and has been neglected in the past. We are only just beginning to elucidate the factors of climate, of soil, and of human intervention and of community structure that control the functioning of ecosystems.

In my paper I have tried to show such differences that occur, for example, between prairie, savanna, and woodland—differences not only in the total production, but in the quality of production and in the position of that production within the ecosystem.

We should not overlook the fact that ecologists are now getting used to tackling these complex problems. We have computers, the use of radioisotopes, analog systems.

One other point I would like to stress is that there is urgent need to improve field techniques, and that conservationists are being slow to adopt the idea of setting aside areas where experimental ecology can be developed, areas in which the ecologist must destroy ecosystems in order to understand better how they function.

These field experiments need to be carefully designed, to give us insight into how ecosystems function. It is important that the administrators realize their value, since the ecological problems are essentially long term, and these field experiments must be protected so that they are not lost because of administrative inconvenience.

It is possible in our management of natural areas, of national parks, to carry out field ecological experiments on a grand scale, but I have also in mind very detailed, precise field studies.

Therefore the main emphasis in my paper is this need to try to examine ecosystems by these various techniques in order to understand their functioning and to develop both the lab and field techniques to make this a more critical science than it is at present.

WAGGONER: This morning Dr. Leopold has demonstrated the difficulty of wild-game management by failing to produce a grizzly bear on the hill behind you, and I have demonstrated for you the difficulties of weather modification by failing to inspire you with the bright sun.

This is the first point of my paper: Weather modification has become rational and it has become scientific. There are good reasons why we might someday change the weather. We now test, experimentally and correctly and conservatively, whether we have changed the weather. If we stick to the facts, little if anything can yet be claimed for weather modification. This should reassure conservative people, and I am sure disappoints the radicals.

The second point of my paper is that if the meteorologist could change the weather, could the physiologist or ecologist, after a century of research, say precisely how the landscape would then change? This certainly tests our ecological capacity on the anvil of practicality or use. I offer humbly some examples of attempts to make these predictions in my paper on page 87 and following.

Esthetic and moral motives exist in our present affluent society for this luxury of enlarging or preserving natural areas, unpaved and untilled. My third point concerns whether there are any measurable and hence scientific reasons for this luxury.

There are any measurable and hence scientific reasons for this luxury. I offer two in my appraisal here of what difference to man, if any, would follow a change in our landscape caused either by weather modification or by the ax or the plow.

First, how would our water supply change? Second, how would our energy budget, or the energy budget of any other mammal, and hence perhaps the comfort, or even the survival of this or that species be endangered?

I extend to you two invitations. The first is to try your hand at saying specifically and rationally how our landscape would change if I can change the weather.

The second invitation is for you to say specifically and quantitatively how the changed landscape would affect animals and plants.

COWAN: Finally, I wish to present a brief review of my own paper entitled "Management, Response, and Variety."

In this I tried to present as a first thesis that the birth of the concept of conservation probably marked one of the most important turning points in human ideas, that it marks the point at which man, who up to that time had been acting as if he were a struggling species, barely surviving in an inhospitable environment, suddenly realizes that he can control his survival, that he can influence his mortality, and that there are other things that he can turn his interests to. He can extend the umbrella of his competence over a number of the creatures that surround him.

I suggest that this idea first arose in affluent societies living under aristocratic forms of government. I hope this can be challenged.

To a large extent we find our conservation motivated by the probability of use, and I think in the general attitude of the nonecologist, the moral issues do not predominate.

In directing my attention to management and the possibility of obtaining response, it seemed to me that we devote ourselves to three kinds of management: management for survival, for distribution, and for abundance.

Under the heading of survival we can point to certain dramatic attempts today, such as the trumpeter swan, which has been a success, the whooping crane, in which the success is still dubious, the attempts to preserve certain of the rare species of antelopes from other parts of the world.

In general, we have the greatest likelihood of success where we are dealing with a single factor that is limiting the population and this factor is the consequence of human action.

We bring to bear captive rearing in an attempt to help us. When we do this, we must acknowledge that there is such a thing as inherited wildness, and that species or individuals that prove to be rearable in captivity may have lost this capacity for going wild again when later released.

There is the very interesting possibility of recreating species that have vanished, such as the present attempt to recreate the original European wild ox, which seems to show indications of considerable success. These, of course, can only be attempted where considerable variety of extant genotypes exist that can be recombined.

Management for distribution concerns itself with the importance of dispersal. I think this rests on two things. First, that no small group contains the entire genetic complement of the original species. A grab sample is not a random sample. Second, that by distributing the population we divide the hazards. Introduction and reintroduction are also tools of this attempt to manage for distribution. Here again we must be constantly alert that we do not destroy locally adaptive genotypes in our attempts to introduce or reintroduce.

Management of numbers is primarily what we are concerned with when we attempt to produce crops of wildlife. What we are interested in here is the production of a surplus which can be used by man. We do this largely by regulation and rule. We do it by attempts to manage populations so that they conform with the carrying capacities of the environments in which they live. Our success rests on the detection and manipulation of the elements in the environments that are limiting. These are usually regarded as seven in number and it is not usually very easy to detect which is the one. In looking to the future, it seems to me that technology is expanding even faster than our population and that we can be certain that this expanding population will greatly alter our way of life; that land-retirement will perhaps increase faster than the extension of new land breaking; that specific chemical manipulation of species will become a growing element in our capacity to manage the environment; that changes in our domestication pattern and in our manipulation of genotypes to expand areas of tolerance will continue.

We face in the long run probably the most difficult problem of all in a democratic society, the constant collision between public benefit versus private gain in the use of the resources. We are making poor headway in resolving this one.

I think we must admit that man can continue to survive without utilizing our concepts of conservation, and we must show (or try to find out) what the consequences are to man if either one of these courses is followed—either the course leading to destruction of what we regard as valuable and valid or the course that leads to the preservation of the most abundant variety of biota.

This is the substance of my contribution.

THE PRESERVATION OF ENDANGERED HABITATS AND VERTEBRATES OF NORTH AMERICA

Durward L. Allen*

Around the earth, vast land and water areas have been developed to specialized uses as a means of supporting increasing numbers of human beings. Under primitive conditions strategically located men could subsist quite well in small numbers at the carnivore end of the food chain, as exemplified by the Eskimo, plains Indian, and tribes of interior Africa. Providing for more people required a shortening of the food chain, an increased dependence on plant foods, and a situation in which man himself formed a greater portion of the earth-based biomass.

In cultural developments for mass subsistence there have been no visible incentives for preserving natural ecosystems in the forms produced by millions of years of adaptive change. The unchecked increase in population creates demand for a continuous intensification of land and water use in the immediacy of support problems or make-work projects. In North America "growth" has become a self-justifying economic end which makes no distinction between quantity and quality living. In application it invokes the combined power of technology and taxation to "develop" natural assets and open spaces as rapidly as possible, the implied

assumption being that quantity production of consumer goods can outrun human reproduction and achieve a better life for the individual.

In a finite world, this outlook has shortcomings, since it can be effective (if at all) only temporarily. An ecological appraisal suggests that if a steadily improving living standard is the proper objective, there must be a limit to the number of people served. We have justification for a viewpoint that the world is waiting for population control.

While orderly social mechanisms for bringing this about are being developed, it appears the better part of scientific valor to examine carefully the human habitat. Unguided traditional types of enterprise can easily destroy natural assets that should be a part of our future, since the onrush of utilization has no built-in limitation. Forbearance in the exploitation of resources is seldom an individual virtue. It is effectuated through public policy as a result of public enlightenment and understanding.

Any farsighted concept of man's relationship to the earth must deal with the dynamic involvement of population, culture, and resources. Somewhere quantity must give way to quality, and "growth" to stability. This is to affirm, with Lucretius, that "nothing from nothing ever yet was born." It is prudent to assume that the human species is in the throes of a

* Dr. Allen is Professor of Wildlife Ecology in the Department of Forestry and Conservation at Purdue University. A practiced mediator between the wolf and the moose, he is the author of *Our Wildlife Legacy* (1954).

temporary phase in developing a higher civilization wherein want and conflict can give way to comfort and dignity. If this is a valid perspective, men should achieve greater wisdom in using natural wealth of every kind—which means that we are not ready to appraise the ultimate worth of any living thing or commit to extinction any of our remaining biota. The dwindling of certain vertebrates and native ecosystems poses a challenge for emergency consideration and action.

In summary, it is evident that, at the least, all forms of life have "scientific" value. The holdover of living things *in situ* from primitive times is an indispensable biological record which has been inadequately studied. Portions of the record have been destroyed, perhaps inevitably in some cases and not so in others. In terms of extractive technology, we have much to learn of productive biological mechanisms that developed through ages past; but beyond this, the way should be left open indefinitely for further research and accessions to the fundament of knowledge. In actuality, what we may call nature preservation needs no more telling justification than this. Such a concept obviously has scientific and philosophical, rather than utilitarian, appeal, and hence it is unlikely to be implemented by general public demand.

Despite this limitation, preserving an endangered species or habitat almost invariably requires a public effort, and a variety of agencies and organizations have concerned themselves with these problems. Government at any level may be involved, but such responsibilities probably are implicit in the functions of the Canadian Wildlife Service, the United States Fish and Wildlife Service, the National Park Service, and the Forest Service. The Mexico Department of Wildlife appears to have a similar mission. Among citizen groups of North America the National Audubon Society, the Boone and Crockett Club, the Izaak Walton League,

the Nature Conservancy, the Sierra Club, and the Wilderness Society have been particularly active in this field.

The present appraisal comes at a time of widespread concern for declining wildlife and environmental types. In particular, a committee of the Bureau of Sport Fisheries and Wildlife is compiling detailed information on a long list of North American vertebrates which are rare or in threatened status. This committee has extensive resources, and its report will constitute the most complete and up-to-date documentation available on individual species. The preliminary findings have been a useful background for my own more generalized consideration of biological and administrative aspects of problems affecting endangered life forms. In addition, I have consulted many authorities on situations in various parts of the continent, and their valued contributions are acknowledged in a section at the end of this paper.

FUNCTIONS AND MEANS IN
NATURE PRESERVATION

Three measures enacted by the 88th Congress are likely to have far-reaching influence in the United States on efforts to save for the future our surviving primitive areas and vertebrate species. The Wilderness Act has promoted a national recognition of the need for such a program. For the present, it may have done little more, but with supplemental legislation presumably to follow, it should provide a framework within which efforts to preserve specific units of primordial range can be formalized. Congress also revised the formula through which counties share in revenues accruing through the management of lands on the National Wildlife Refuges. A primary requisite for jeopardized species is undisturbed living space, and this action should help, in some situations, to counter the local opposition which, with increasing frequency, besets attempts to establish new refuges, parks, and other public areas.

The Land and Water Conservation Fund is designed primarily to stimulate the development of outdoor recreation facilities. However, this recent act has a provision relative to the use of funds by several federal agencies "for any national area which may be authorized for the preservation of species of fish or wildlife that are threatened with extinction." It should be noted that this does not enable a federal bureau to use funds on a project of a type not already authorized. Notably, the Fish and Wildlife Service has statutory responsibility for managing migratory wildlife, but there is no general authorization for expenditures on problems of nonmigratory species. To effect a more flexible federal program, it is expected that in 1965 the Congress will consider legislation which will, in particular, enable the Bureau of Sport Fisheries and Wildlife to contribute to projects for endangered nonmigratory species.

Land and Water Fund allocations to the states will provide another means of purchasing and developing critical areas. These funds are administered by the Bureau of Outdoor Recreation. They must be matched from sources within the state and can be made available to any local unit of government. This device should open the way, in a manner not heretofore available, to support local projects which can be sponsored in part through private subscription.

In the work of preserving remnant biotypes and habitats, the efforts of citizen organizations and foundations have an importance that can hardly be overestimated. Private individuals are without bureaucratic limitations in publicizing problems. They speak with authority at any level of government, and their money-raising can catalyze an action at any time. Some visible public backing is essential to the success of nearly any preservation project undertaken by an agency of government, since counterpressures with political support frequently are involved.

In individual states, actions in favor of wild fauna and flora are most likely to be taken by conservation or fish and game departments. Their policies commonly are decided by commissions, and their funds usually are license money. Sometimes it is a critical question whether such an agency can use its resources in aiding a species which obviously will not furnish public hunting. The "safest" answer for a commission in deciding this matter is to assume that the sportsman is interested only in hunting. On the other hand, a broader outlook is evident in states where the conservation function has matured through many years of service, where competent commissioners have a high degree of political independence, and where sportsmen are organized in a state federation of sufficiently long standing to develop its own broad and responsible outlook on outdoor problems.

Every state now receives an annual allotment of "federal aid" funds to be used for wildlife and fish restoration as provided by the acts of 1937 and 1950, respectively. This program requires the matching of three federal dollars with one state dollar, and it encompasses acquisition, development, and research. It is totally supported by sportsmen, since the federal share originates with arms and tackle taxes and the state share with license fees. Recognizing the stake of the general public in wild lands and waters for recreation, many states are supplementing the federal-aid land-acquisition program with bond issues, special taxes, and *ad hoc* appropriations. The first allocations under the Land and Water Fund Act will become available in fiscal year 1965.

In an era of burgeoning land prices and costs of all kinds, the total financial base for outdoor projects will not be great in most states. However, the situation is improving, and policy makers with understanding and concern now have considerably increased leeway in giving the state a share in the salvage of disappearing biota. It is generally true that where local or state handling of a project is possible, this is also preferable, since federal attention can then be concentrated on major efforts requiring national resources. However, it seems a valid principle that, in default of other protective action, the federal government should consider any unique area or animal population to be a national charge.

DIMINISHED SPECIES WITH
AVAILABLE RANGES

The extirpation or reduction to rare status of many kinds of wildlife has taken place by the direct killing of populations rather than the destruction or degrading of ranges. Where this has happened to legally commercialized species, the evident need is for restriction of the kill. Thus, the scientific husbandry of whales of the world, certain fisheries, the green turtle, the walrus, and possibly the polar bear is today awaiting the negotiation of effective international agreements and control. The northern fur seal and sea otter are outstanding examples of the successful restoration of species once endangered. The conservation of maritime forms has a major advantage in that the environment may be largely unchanged since primitive times. Obviously this is not true in polluted coastal waters, and even the open oceans are not quite the same in a world pervaded by radioactive fallout and chlorinated hydrocarbons.

Shooting as a factor

Particular vulnerability to the gun and lack of restrictions on shooting probably account for the disappearance of the Carolina parakeet. Likewise the Eskimo curlew was reduced from millions to a few individuals—if, indeed, any now sur-

vive, since the last sightings on Galveston Island were in 1962. Direct killing, coupled with drainage and disturbance on breeding marshes, probably eliminated trumpeter swans and whooping cranes from most of their former range.

Fortunately, the swans held out in the remote Red Rock Lakes area of Montana, and the refuge created there is providing breeding stock for reintroduction to other protected areas. With a well-distributed population of around two thousand, the trumpeter is not in imminent danger. The whooping crane has achieved a more precarious survival, also through the existence of an isolated breeding ground, this one in Northwest Territories. The concentration of wintering birds in a small area on the coast of Texas proved to be an advantage, since acquisition from a single interested landowner permitted establishment of the Aransas National Wildlife Refuge. With a total known population of forty-two, this species hangs in the balance, shooting on the fall flight southward being the greatest annual hazard. Some added security probably could be achieved through enlargement of the Aransas refuge.

Students of the California condor have concluded generally that indiscriminate shooting played a major role in wiping out the bulk of the condor population, which originally was distributed on the coast from Baja California to the Columbia River. It is evident also that the species is extremely sensitive to disturbance of its nesting, and this may have influenced the decline. By the time Koford's monograph was published in 1953, there were some sixty survivors which nested largely on the Los Padres National Forest and ranged over a few counties in that region north of Los Angeles. The Forest Service set aside the Sespe Wildlife Preserve, encompassing nest and roosting sites, in 1941, and the Secretary of Interior placed restrictions on gas and oil leasing in fifty-five square miles of the forest.

The National Audubon Society, long a guardian of this species, sponsored a review of the situation in 1964, which was reported on by Miller (1964) at the annual meeting. There is little cause for optimism. Two seasoned observers, Ian and Eben McMillan, calculated the present population at forty, indicating a one-third decline since the early fifties. The birds are reproducing but evidently not replacing annual mortality. Losses probably can be attributed to continued shooting and possibly to secondary poisoning in ground-squirrel control operations. In this area within twenty-five miles of Los Angeles, human disturbance constitutes a growing harassment of nesting birds. A greater regulatory effort obviously is needed if the reduction of condors is not to proceed, as Miller stated, "below some critical level necessary for successful social response, pairing, and group feeding procedures essential to the conduct of a normal nesting cycle."

Parallels to the condor situation are seen in the plight of the southern bald eagle (*Haliaeetus leucocephalus*), of which the National Audubon Society supports a continuing study and inventory (Sprunt, 1963). For many years the shooting of eagles, especially first-year birds, has been well documented. Now there is increasing evidence that reproductive failures may be associated with the intake of pesticides biologically concentrated in fish fed upon by the eagles. This phase of the problem is under investigation (Buckley and DeWitt, 1963), and it is too early to reach firm conclusions.

The build-up of hunters in all parts of the continent poses an increasing threat to large and conspicuous birds. Even a few of the heedless can take the annual increase of condors, whooping cranes, or bald eagles. Many reviews of this situation have stressed the need for "public education," and this doubtless is an important approach to the problem. But more effective laws and a greater enforcement effort are indicated as a means of reaching irresponsible elements.

Valgene Lehmann, King Ranch biologist, informs me that he has seen a marked decline in birds of prey in south Texas, a wintering ground for numerous species breeding in the North. Evidence on many fronts indicates a general reduction of raptorial birds, probably resulting in large part from shooting by increased numbers of gunners afield with effective long-range weapons. The peregrine falcon, in particular, may soon be on our list of endangered species. Clement (1965) cited a recent record of 200 Swainson hawks found shot at their perches on telephone poles along a Kansas highway. Predacious species are not biologically geared to the replacement of these heavy losses. Some nineteen states give legal protection to birds of prey, always allowing for control by landowners with damage problems. States which except the Accipiters and great horned owl have, in effect, no protection at all, since hunters seldom know one species from another. Even legal protection may not be meaningful if there is no enforcement, which is our present situation in Indiana.

Hunting according to scientifically based regulations is a legitimate use of certain wildlife resources, but indiscriminate shooting of nongame species is an infringement of public rights. In nearly all states wanton gunnery, in common with trespass of many kinds, needs more serious attention by lawmakers, enforcement staffs, and the judiciary.

Restoration through transplantation

A part of the security of an endangered species may well rest in the existence of multiple colonies or populations. Thus, available ranges should not be left unstocked if there are breeders to spare.

As mentioned previously, the transplanting of trumpeter swans is well under way and should do much to place this, the largest of our waterfowl, out of danger. Forty years ago the status of the sage grouse, eastern wild turkey, and pronghorn was cause for alarm, but adequate protection and progressive restocking of old ranges re-established all three on a scale whereby they can now support public hunting. As a result of similar management, the fisher and marten are taking their places in forested regions where they once were extirpated.

Bighorn sheep are so evidently sensitive to range conditions and density that continued study and attention to range improvement—largely through control of competition from domestic sheep, feral burros, and overnumerous deer—will be required for the indefinite future. It should be noted that herd thinning through regulated hunting may be called for as a safety factor, and this measure does not merit the categorical opposition it sometimes receives.

Surveys of Jones (1950) and Buechner (1960) indicated that in California the Sierra bighorn (*Ovis canadensis californiana*) has maintained a total recent population of less than 400 animals. The primary present range is the Sierra Nevada adjacent to Kings Canyon and Sequoia National Parks and southward. This subspecies formerly occupied a geographically separate northern range from northeast California through Oregon and Washington into British Columbia. Various bands in British Columbia now total possibly 1200 head, but the animal was completely eliminated from Washington and Oregon. Buechner remarked, "That they could disappear from the wildest country in Oregon should be an object lesson in conservation."

Obviously, an opportunity for benefiting this race lies in its re-establishment in suitable ranges from which it was killed out. A start was made by the Fish and Wildlife Service with the introduction of Sierra bighorns to the Hart Mountain Antelope Refuge in Oregon in 1954, and plans now are under way for a similar stocking on the Charles Sheldon Antelope Range in Nevada. In 1957 the Washington Department of Game moved animals from British Columbia to the north-central region of the state. These operations help to improve the outlook for the most precariously situated of our surviving wild sheep.

The Audubon bighorn (*Ovis canadensis auduboni*) is a subspecies that did not survive; it was exterminated from the Black Hills and badlands of the upper Missouri region early in this century. However, the habitats are available, and the South Dakota Department of Game, Fish and Parks has undertaken a "restoration" program using the Rocky Mountain bighorn (*Ovis canadensis*) a closely related race (Lee, 1964). This appears to be the best possible expedient in creating, insofar as possible, a facsimile of the native ecosystem.

A timely transplanting program may well be the means of preserving one of our two recognized races of American bison. The wood bison (*Bison b. athabascae*) in historic times occupied a boreal range from central Northwest Territories southward into the parklands of western Canada and through the Rocky Mountain region into western United States. In 1922, south of Great Slave Lake, the Canadian government set aside Wood Buffalo Park to protect the one herd of *athabascae* that survived the great slaughter of bison prior to 1900.

In the twenties, a large herd of plains bison (*Bison bison bison*) was rapidly overstocking its range near Wainwright, Alberta, and in three years more than 6000 animals were shipped north to Wood Buffalo Park. This infiltration of the wild wood bison introduced several new diseases and gave rise to a genetically mixed herd. Fortunately, it was discovered in 1957 that some 200 wood bison had remained isolated in the northwest region of the park (Banfield and Novakowski, 1960). To ensure the continued existence of "pure" wood bison, in 1963 the Canadian Wildlife Service airlifted sixteen animals by helicopter across the Mackenzie River to a new sanctuary near Fort Providence. Surveys are now under way to find other suitable areas within the ancestral range. Since this subspecies evidently was the "mountain buffalo" often referred to in early literature of the western states, it should receive consideration for restoration to available public areas in Montana and southward in the Rockies before any new herds of plains bison are established.

Exemplifying a local effort of this kind, reintroduction of the long-missing masked bobwhite (*Colinus virginiana ridgwayi*) is being attempted by the Arizona-Sonora Desert Museum. With financial backing by the Allegheny Foundation of Pittsburgh, several birds were brought from Mexico for liberation on a square-mile tract allocated to the purpose by the Bureau of Land Management. Other quail from aviary stock were reared in captivity at Tucson in 1964, although most of these were lost through an act of vandalism. This restoration effort is eminently worthwhile, since the subspecies evidently has been reduced to rarity in Sonora by heavy grazing. Preserving the bird also means rehabilitating an area of grassland in a region almost devoid of this habitat in its primitive condition.

THE QUANTITY AND QUALITY OF WILDERNESS

The overwhelming impetus of government drainage programs, other types of agricultural reclamation, and the high price of any kind of standing timber are among the major barriers to preservation of important representative samples of primitive ecosystems. Though little publicized, it is widely recognized that large annual appropriations for water projects are in part a device for returning federal tax funds to business interests in the various states, often with minimum consideration for the economic feasibility of projects (Haveman, 1964). Local or even national conservation groups have particular difficulty in countering, with social and economic logic, projects whose ultimate frame of reference is largely political.

The Everglades of southern Florida are a semitropical wilderness whose ecology is minutely adjusted to the slow movement of surface waters from marshes and lakes of the interior southward into coastal estuaries. The principal public area, set aside in 1947 to protect an array of unique animal life and biotopes, is Everglades National Park, third largest park in the national system.

About the time the park was established, a program of engineering developments was launched by the Corps of Engineers aimed initially at flood control north and south of Lake Okeechobee (Tilden, 1964). This complex of channels and dikes has since been elaborated into a comprehensive drainage system which diverts water quickly to the sea. A primary reclamation purpose is evident in that the vast interior wetland will be converted to agricultural uses. Water releases to Everglades National Park are provided for in structures, but such operations have not been scheduled, and the future is in question, since competition for water is inevitable with the continued growth of population in urban centers. Desiccation of the Everglades is already under way with consequent oxidation of organic soils, changes in plant succession trends, and alteration of communities dependent on a seasonal balance of fresh and brackish waters. Park biologist William B. Robertson (personal communication) pointed out another portent of the agricultural future: Without a flow of water the deterioration of habitats is predictable, and with it come pesticide residues.

A resurvey of water needs of the Everglades is urgent, and a mandatory provision for adequate seasonal releases of water to the park and associated areas is the least that can be done if the national interest in this singular area is to be protected. Tied into the fate of the Everglades region are such rare or declining vertebrates as the crocodile, alligator, manatee, panther, everglade kite, bald eagle, Florida sandhill crane, white ibis, and roseate spoonbill. Increasing jeopardy for these and other species would inevitably attend the destruction of this ecologically unique wilderness. Southern Florida and the Keys still support high-quality units of other habitat types which should be in public custody, among which are the tropical hammock forest of the Upper Keys, and the royal palm—bald-cypress forest of Fahkahatchee Strand (Collier County). Both have been surveyed by the National Park Service.

It is timely to consider that in North America our food production is still well ahead of present population requirements. With the possible exception of specialty crops, price supports and reclamation incentives are a make-work kind of enterprise that frequently adds to national surpluses. If and when food consumption actually outruns supply in any important way, the pressures on remaining units of natural habitat are likely to grow beyond anything yet seen.

Agricultural reclamation plays a prominent part in other nature preservation issues, an outstanding example being the disappearance of brushlands in the lower Rio Grande Valley. Mature chaparral north of the river is being cleared for cotton and vegetable fields and citrus groves. Remaining units support concentrated nestings of the white-winged dove and are a unique habitat in the United States for jaguarundi and ocelot, several species of hawks, and various Mexican birds. Only about a thousand acres of this brush, in scattered stands, remain. More extensive areas occur south of the border, but clearing is in progress there also. It is estimated that $400,000 is needed immediately for land purchase in Texas and $100,000 in Mexico. The World Wildlife Fund has undertaken this project with initial grants from the Caesar Kleberg Wildlife Foundation of Kingsville, Texas. It is expected that acquired lands will be turned over to an appropriate public agency for administration.

These same organizations are active on a project farther north on the coast of Texas. The Attwater prairie chicken (*Tympanuchus cupido attwateri*) has been in steady decline occasioned by reduction of the native prairies that supported it (Lehmann and Mauermann, 1963). As of 1963 the total population estimate was 1335. The only hope of preventing the disappearance of this "heath hen of the South" is intensive protection and management of remaining flocks through the negotiation of landowner agreements, improvement of habitat conditions, and acquisition of native prairie as a refuge. Through a fortunate circumstance, 3500 acres of the best remaining grassland have been optioned at half the market price. Immediate action is needed, and whether it can be mustered in time is a question soon to be answered.

With few exceptions existing populations of prairie chickens are under the attrition of intensified land use and the disappearance of grasslands. While various small areas approximating natural conditions have been set aside in midwestern states, they are generally too small and scattered to be an important benefit to chickens. Fortunately, there are exceptions, a recent notable project being the purchase of 1680 acres of native prairie by the Missouri Conservation Commission specifically for purposes of a prairie-chicken sanctuary. Provision for the observation of booming grounds in spring will help to popularize and justify this area to the public.

The creation of major reserves in representative zones of the grassland biome has long been recognized (by biologists) as a national need. Although this is more difficult today than ever before, it should be considered an imperative in the national wilderness preservation system. A unit of half a million acres probably is a minimum standard for such an area.

The National Park Service carried out a survey relative to creation of a Prairie National Park in the tall-grass region (Flint Hills) of northeastern Kansas. This was opposed so strenuously by landowners and other local interests that in 1963 a Senate investigating committee tabled the proposal indefinitely. It now appears that specific authorization and funding by the new Congress would be helpful in activating the search for and establishment of a prairie unit in the national park system. While a nucleus of native vegetation is desirable, the inclusion of broken lands need not be a deterrent, since plants will in time assume their proper distribution and function under a technically designed regime of burning, grazing by bison, and other dynamic features of the ecosystem. A missing component (an important one to be discussed later) is likely to be the wolf, unless a means of confining such an area is found. A day's ride over one of our superhighways suggests that this might be feasible both in terms of cost and engineering.

Our present areas of public grasslands have almost invariably been salvaged from a condition of heavy overgrazing. Yet the perennial grasses are growing again as floras re-establish themselves. Their south-to-north variations can be seen on the Wichita Mountains National

Wildlife Refuge (Oklahoma), Wind Cave National Park (South Dakota), and Theodore Roosevelt National Monument (North Dakota). These areas have value, but they are small and their faunas are influenced by such activities as the control of rodents and predators on surrounding lands. The national-park concept should make possible a larger and biologically self-contained ecosystem. It would appear that at least two such units are needed, one in the tall-grass region, probably in the Kansas-Nebraska latitude or southward, and another to the north in mixed-grass country. Of all the nature preservation jobs awaiting action, this probably is the most challenging.

Any discussion of grasslands and their fauna recalls the position of the black-footed ferret, sometimes referred to as the "most endangered" of our mammals. It is likely that this mustelid always was sparsely distributed, but in the past half century it disappeared from the bulk of its range, which evidently coincided closely with the distribution of black-tailed prairie dogs on the high plains. It is assumed that this rodent is a primary food species, and that ferrets succumbed to widespread poisoning of the prairie dog.

The most important recent information on black-footed ferrets has been gathered by the Bureau of Sport Fisheries and Wildlife through observations of predator and rodent control agents. Over the past decade, several dozen sightings have been reported in South Dakota to Mark D. Worcester, District Agent at Mitchell. A study has been initiated by the Cooperative Wildlife Research Unit at the University of South Dakota, and the prospects seem good for the fact-gathering on which a restoration program would need to be based (Kittams, 1964; Springer, 1964).

Another national-park possibility exists in the redwood strip of northern California, and here a contested value is in standing timber (Miller, 1965). On some two million acres of well-watered coastline, the last of the world's redwoods (*Sequoia sempervirens*) survived into the present era, including trees more than 2000 years old. The bulk of this land passed into private hands, and some 1,750,000 acres now support an active redwood-management industry important to the economy of the region. The National Park Service (1964) reports that about 300,000 acres of virgin growth remain, of which 48,000 acres are in twenty-eight state parks. Some of the stands are too small or broken by highways and adjacent cutting for ecological stability, being exposed to wind, flood, and public-use damage.

The park units containing redwoods which have been set aside in California represent a preservation effort beginning in 1902. This is largely the work of the Save-the-Redwoods League, which enlisted widespread support for the movement and raised ten million dollars in private contributions. Lumber companies cooperated in selling choice old growth for park purposes, and the state frequently matched money in a total acquisition program costing more than nineteen million dollars. Recently there has been a controversy over plans of the State Highway Commission to route a new freeway through the giant redwoods of the Jedediah Smith State Park. In view of the trust accepted by the state relative to redwood preservation, it is hardly likely that this will happen.

Of the remaining virgin stands, 62 per cent is in private ownership with the prospect that the bulk of it will be cut. There is widespread interest in preserving the better part of this dwindling old growth for public use. Aside from scientific values, sight-seeing demands are increasing, and the tourist dollar looms large in the regional economy. A National Park Service study (1964) financed by the National Geographic Society proposes three alternative plans for federal acquisition

of privately owned lands to block in a major park area in Humboldt and Del Norte counties. Federal grants would also assist in adding desirable tracts to state parks. The number-one plan calls for acquisition of approximately 55,000 acres of which about half would be virgin forest. However, the National Parks Association, the Sierra Club, and the Save-the-Redwoods League question the adequacy of the proposal in terms of watershed protection and other respects.

Plans for the expansion of parks are opposed by the lumber industries (Anon., 1965) on the grounds that enough redwood lands are now publicly owned and for economic reasons no more should be retired from timber management. This viewpoint is understandable, although development of the details of such a program should reveal opportunities for land exchanges which would mitigate stresses growing out of the removal of limited tracts of virgin growth from commercial management. Effective long-term protection of the mature redwood forest from damage and degrading influences requires the administration of a much larger unit than is now available. In decades past, other proposals to establish a national redwoods park have been successfully opposed. However, growing nation-wide interest and a recognition that another failure would be irrevocable provide a favorable climate for action.

Questions of private versus public interest and ownership are much involved in many preservation problems. Local and regional planning frequently gives preferment to any use which promises greater tax returns. Native habitats are commonly regarded as "waste" areas and may be especially vulnerable to expropriation for industrial, road building, and real estate purposes. This situation places a premium on quick action and total cooperation among groups and agencies concerned with endangered species and habitats.

The "Great Swamp" of New Jersey, an 8000-acre wetland within thirty miles of New York City, was retrieved from development as a jet-age airport by just such an effort. Under the aegis of the North American Wildlife Foundation, contributions totaling more than $600,-000 were collected from 3407 individuals and 197 clubs and societies. The area was acquired and turned over to the Bureau of Sport Fisheries and Wildlife for management as a national wildlife refuge (Gale, 1963).

Real estate values were a primary consideration fifteen years ago when a national effort was required to halt the rapid decline of the key deer (*Odocoileus virginianus clavium*) on its island range off the southern tip of Florida. A national wildlife refuge has been established and dedicated on the basis of 763 acres owned by the government and 6200 acres leased. The deer population, which was as low as thirty-five animals, is now between 250 and 300. But its future hinges on means being found to perpetuate protection on land under leases which can be terminated easily by the owners. This obviously is a holding action.

More problems of ownership are seen in the situation of the tule elk or dwarf wapiti—once plentiful in the grasslands of California's central valley but reduced to a remnant in gold-rush days. It survived under the protection of sympathetic ranchers, but numbers built up, competed with livestock, and had to be reduced by "hunts" to prevent overpopulation.

A public range is needed, and the alternatives characterize difficulties in attempting to devote land to public, noncommercial uses. Tule elk are doing well in Owens Valley, and a range of 240 square miles in the valley is potentially available as a refuge—it is a public-land withdrawal on which the City of Los Angeles owns water rights. But there are grazing leases, and termination of these in favor of wild animals is opposed by stockmen (Amaral, 1964).

Another site suitable for a limited herd is San Luis Island, a river floodplain marsh of some 7000 acres near Los Banos. Acquisition of this area for a refuge is opposed by the Merced County Board of Supervisors, who are concerned about possible tax losses (Rock, 1964). Possibly a technical study now under way, and the watchful custody of the Committee for the Preservation of the Tule Elk, in Los Angeles, will provide an answer.

STATUS OF CARNIVORES

Attempts to preserve or restore large units of primitive ecosystems frequently must presuppose that important endemic components will be missing and that numerous exotics, both plant and animal, will be present. The vertebrates most commonly absent and difficult, or impossible, to provide for are the species originally dominant in the animal community—the large carnivores. Patently the cougar, grizzly, and wolf are true "wilderness" animals, capable, wide ranging, and at odds with the livestock industry. Their status merits continuous scrutiny, since a few years of intensified "control" can make a major difference. Fortunately, a survey by Cahalane (1964), on behalf of the Boone and Crockett Club and the New York Zoological Society, brings facts on these species up to date, and I have relied principally on this report. Cahalane does not, in this case, concern himself with subspecific forms, a realistic policy also followed here.

The cougar has held its own remarkably well in western states in the face of long-standing control operations, although there is little doubt that over most of the range it is gradually losing ground. A few are to be found as far east as western Oklahoma and the western Dakotas. The eastern "panther" holds out in northern Florida and the Everglades, probably with scattered individuals between. O. E. Frye (personal communication) estimates a state-wide population of fifty to a hundred. Bruce S. Wright continues to observe the small relict population of *Felis concolor* in New Brunswick (1948 and personal communication) which has persisted and may be extending its range. On a basis of reports over the past decade, he suggests that a thin population of cougars is continuous from British Columbia to Nova Scotia. Cahalane mentions that the big cat is protected in Florida and South Dakota and that bounties recently were removed in British Columbia, Washington, Oregon, and California. This animal is in a position of tenuous security, and its status would be further improved if it were recognized as a high-quality sporting species and placed under appropriate hunting regulations in states where any continued annual kill is deemed necessary.

The grizzlies of western Canada and Alaska are generally thrifty and holding their own (Cahalane, 1964). In the Canadian arctic, the barren ground race actually is dispersing eastward to occupy new range (Banfield, 1958). In the western United States grizzlies have been largely extirpated, excepting some few hundred that persist in the vicinities of Glacier and Yellowstone National Parks. Less than a dozen animals each are estimated for Washington and Colorado, and possibly two dozen for the mountains of Chihuahua.

It is notable that grizzlies still are being killed as livestock marauders, and it is a stimulating philosophic question whether a way might be found, at least in remote mountainous country, to remove the sheep rather than the bears. If a large grassland park were established on the northern plains, the "white" badlands grizzly is one species that would not be there and which could hardly be replaced with anything similar. This was the first of our grizzlies to be collected (by Lewis and Clark in 1805), and it was extinct before the end of the last century.

From the Canadian border northward the wolf, in various described races, is in no present danger of extinction, but the situation in the contiguous states is worthy of attention. I use the term "wolf" as referring to *Canis lupus,* the gray wolf, and excluding the coyotelike "red wolf," *Canis niger,* of the South.

So far as is known, there are no breeding wolves in western states, although a declining population of unknown number exists in the Sierra Madre Occidental of Mexico (Cahalane, 1964) where they are, in part, protected. Except for stragglers across the Canadian and Mexican borders, the only surviving wolves in the United States are in the northern Great Lakes region. As a result of long-standing bounty hunting, the species declined to what are evidently a few nonbreeders in the area south of Lake Superior. There, since 1960, Wisconsin has provided legal protection and Michigan has removed the bounty—probably too late to preserve this population. Isle Royale National Park (Michigan) in upper Lake Superior supports about two dozen wolves, which are the only truly protected animals of this species in the forty-eight contiguous states (Allen and Mech, 1963).

With the latter exception, the several hundred wolves now found in northern Minnesota constitute our only breeding population. There the situation appears precarious, since Minnesota still pays a bounty. Snaring was legal until the fall of 1964, when it was outlawed by executive order. The famed Boundary Waters Canoe Area might logically function as a retreat of the wolf, but this country has experienced a rapidly growing influx of snow mobiles which traverse lakes and portages far to the interior, contributing to a build-up of bounty hunting. While this situation exists in the Superior National Forest, it is notable that on the Canadian side, in Quetico Provincial Park, the only legal wolf hunting is by Indians, and no bounty is paid.

Wolf control and the bounty have a deeply entrenched tradition in Minnesota, where regulations originate in the legislature. Biologically, the wolf can only help to preserve deer range and other features of the canoe country in a naturally productive condition, and esthetically it is a valuable attribute of the wilderness. Yet a national effort to point up these values probably will be necessary to change the regulations. A development now under study which might be helpful is the creation of a Voyageurs National Park on the old fur-trade canoe route between the Superior National Forest and International Falls. The boundary country supports a forestry program and a growing recreational use by the general public; but with time the processes of natural succession could restore a semblance of primitive conditions, with the dominant carnivore playing its proper role. Of course, this could come about only if a portion of the area, at least, were under a "wilderness" classification.

PRESERVATION, ENVIRONMENTS,
AND EVOLUTION

In preservation parlance it is common to speak of species *and* ecosystems. However, this is with tacit understanding that no individual biotype is likely to be preserved in its present form except *within* its native association of plants and animals. Thus the ecosystem is our basic preservation unit.

Evolutionary changes are easily seen against the scale of geological time. Actually, in postglacial North America racial modifications must have proceeded rapidly, and with the accumulation of records they probably can be appraised in terms of thousands of years. An example which seems likely to hold is the emergence of *Bison b. bison* and *Bison b. athabascae* from their late progenitor *Bison occidentalis* (Skinner and Kaisen, 1947; Forbis, 1956). Now, we may ask, under modern conditions what divergence in the direction of speciation can be expected? The situation of the plains bison on public ranges exemplifies the question of what we are attempting to preserve and how.

Three representative herds which I have visited recently are on the National Bison Range in Montana, Wind Cave National Park in South Dakota, and Wichita Mountains Wildlife Refuge in Oklahoma. In each case a population of around 500 animals is reduced annually (by butchering and live sales) to hold numbers within range capacity. All herds were built up from small beginnings, but there is no evidence that the gene pool is not representative of wild bison a century ago.

A problem which greatly concerns management biologists is what "standards" to apply in selecting animals for removal. What kind of bison are we going to have 100 and 500 years from now? Early reduction programs were strongly influenced by the livestock experience of locally recruited managers. More recently scientific study has brought improvements, but the truth is that an ecologically realistic "culling" is beyond possibility. There are no criteria for selection which will remove annually the same individuals in the same age groups which would have been eliminated from a wild herd on the plains.

The predator of major influence in primitive times was the wolf, and available information indicates that its effect was especially selective against calves and superannuated animals. No life table is available for a bison herd under a regime of wolf predation. Such a study should be made when the requisite conditions can be met; they do not now exist in Canada or Alaska. While an authentic survival series would be useful in management, it is not an ultimate solution. The long-term biological problem probably requires a large Great Plains park confined to accommodate an unmanaged bison herd and a population of wolves. The gray wolf of the Midwest would need to substitute for the extinct "prairie" wolf.

Even broader questions concern the integrity of such species as deer, elk, pronghorns, and other ungulates in many areas of North America where they exist under primary control by the gun and without biologically adequate attention from natural enemies.

While ecosystems can be modified by the absence of essential species, they can also be changed by the presence of aliens. The widespread introduction of nonendemic fishes to streams and lakes of western states is a notable example. The effects of such "management," plus watershed damage and alterations in the nature of waters through damming and diversions have wrought major changes in aquatic life. From these causes, Miller (1963) records the extinction of eight species of fish in the Southwest and considers thirty-one others to be in jeopardy. These thirty-nine species, he points out, represent nearly 40 per cent of the known native fishes of western states.

NOW AND THE FUTURE

Probably the greatest unrealism in policies governing our evaluation and use of resources is the short-term view. This inheres in the nature of the problems. A biologist suspects (and a mathematician might prove) that social and economic complexities aggravate as the square of the population. Since the growth of human numbers already has exponential characteristics, it is evident that the trou-

bles of the day are sufficient thereto. In such a fast-moving world, predictions of need beyond the century become abstract and tedious.

Yet there are certain provisions for the future which seem undeniably right. One is that we should avoid irreversible damage to the environment with which all humans must henceforth live. The most fragile and vulnerable elements in that environment are the open "undeveloped" lands and waters which are under suspicion as "going to waste." Certain of these have critical significance in that they are unique and irreplaceable. The definition of problems and furnishing guidance to necessary programs of preservation and restoration are a realm of applied biology which merits an increased scientific effort.

ACKNOWLEDGMENTS

For advice and information concerning many problems of declining habitats and species which are discussed in this paper, or which serve as background for it, I am indebted to numerous observers and authorities in various parts of the continent, the following of whom have been particularly helpful:

In Canada: A. W. F. Banfield of the Canadian National Museum, C. H. D. Clarke of the Ontario Department of Lands and Forests, W. A. Fuller of the University of Alberta, and Bruce S. Wright of the Northeastern Wildlife Station.

In the United States: many members of the Washington staff and field stations of the Bureau of Sport Fisheries and Wildlife, including John W. Aldrich, Watson E. Beed, Milton C. Caroline, Francis C. Gillett, Arthur F. Halloran, Cordia J. Henry, Daniel H. Janzen, Calvin W. Johnson, David R. Klein, Charles H. Lawrence, James O. Lee, Jr., Urban C. Nelson, Paul T. Quick, Lansing A. Parker, and Mark D. Worcester; of the National Park Service, Walter H. Kittams, Robert M. Linn, Wilfred D. Logan, Robert J. Murphy, Neil J. Reid, William B. Robertson, Jr., E. Lowell Sumner, and John A. Tyers; Roland C. Clement of the National Audubon Society and Ian McMillan of the California Audubon Society; Valgene W. Lehmann and William H. Kiel, Jr. of the King Ranch; Clarence Cottam of the Welder Wildlife Foundation; Alex Calhoun, Ben Glading, Fred L. Jones, and Dale R. McCullough of

the Resources Agency of California; Bill T. Crawford of the Missouri Conservation Commission; and O. Earle Frye, Jr. of the Florida Game and Fresh Water Fish Commission.

Several others of my consultants are mentioned more specifically in references to their publications. Only selected recent references have been cited; no attempt is made to present a comprehensive bibliography on these subjects.

BIBLIOGRAPHY

Allen, Durward L., and Mech, L. David. 1963. Wolves versus Moose on Isle Royale. Nat. Geog. 123(2):200–19.

Amaral, Anthony A. 1964. Struggle in Owens Valley. Amer. Forests 70(8):26–27, 53–55.

Anon. 1965. Our Growing Redwoods. Amer. Forest Prod. Indust. and Calif. Redwood Assn.

Banfield, A. W. F. 1958. Distribution of the Barren Ground Grizzly Bear in Northern Canada. Nat. Mus. Can. Bul. 166:47–59.

———— and Novakowski, N. S. 1960. The Survival of the Wood Bison (*Bison bison athabascae* Rhodes) in the Northwest Territories. Nat. Mus. Can., Nat. Hist. Pap. 8:1–6.

Buckley, John L., and Dewitt, James B. 1963. Pesticide-Bald Eagle Relationships. Nat. Aud. Soc., 58th Ann. Conv. Proc.:15–20.

Buechner, Helmut K. 1960. The Bighorn Sheep in the United States, Its Past, Present, and Future. Wildl. Mon. 4:5–174.

Cahalane, Victor H. 1964. Cougar, Grizzly and Wolf in North America. N.Y. Zool. Soc.

Clement, Roland C. 1965. Last Call for the Birds of Prey. Aud. Mag. 67(1):37.

Forbis, Richard G. 1956. Early Man and Fossil Bison. Sci. 123(3191):327–28.

Gale, Joseph. 1963. How the "Great Swamp" of New Jersey Was Saved. Nat. Parks 37(191):10–14.

Haveman, Robert. 1964. The Postwar Corps of Engineers Program in Ten Southern States: An Evaluation of Economic Efficiency. In: Whitman, Tate and Greenhut, Melvin, eds., Essays on Southern Economic Development. Univ. N. Carolina:450–72.

Jones, Fred L. 1950. A Survey of the Sierra Nevada Bighorn. Sierra Club Bul. 35(6):29–76.

Kittams, Walter H. 1964. Search for Black-footed Ferrets. 26th Midwest Wildl. Conf. (unpub.).

Koford, Carl B. 1953. The California Condor. Nat. Aud. Soc., Res. Rep. 4.

Lee, O. B. 1964. To Recoup Man's Error. S. Dakota Cons. Dig. 31(3):6–9.

Lehmann, V. W., and Mauermann, R. G. 1963. Status of Attwater's Prairie Chicken. J. Wildl. Mgt. 27(4):712–23.

Miller, Alden H. 1964. The Current Status and Welfare of the California Condor. Nat. Aud. Soc., 60th Ann. Conv. (mim.).

Miller, Don C. 1965. Last Stand of the Giants. Nat. Wildl. 3(1):12–15.

Miller, Robert R. 1963. Is Our Native Underwater Life Worth Saving? Nat. Parks 37(188):4–9.

National Park Service. 1964. The Redwoods. U.S. Nat. Park Serv., Prof. Rep.

Rock, Maxine A. 1964. Needed: A Permanent Refuge for California's Tule Elk. Nat. Parks 38(201):3–11, 15.

Skinner, Morris F., and Kaisen, Ove C. 1947. The Fossil *Bison* of Alaska and Preliminary Revision of the Genus. Amer. Mus. Nat. Hist. Bul. 89(3):127–256.

Springer, Paul F. 1964. Plans for Field Study of the Black-footed Ferret. 26th Midwest Wildl. Conf. (unpub.).

Sprunt, Alexander IV. 1963. Continental Bald Eagle Project, Prog. Rep. III. Nat. Aud. Soc., 58th Ann. Conf. Proc.:2–7.

Tilden, Paul M. 1964. The Water Problem in Everglades National Park. Nat. Parks 38(197):4–9; 38(198):8–11.

Wright, Bruce S. 1948. Survival of the Northeastern Panther (*Felis concolor*) in New Brunswick. J. Mamm. 29(3):235–46.

BIOTOPE AND HABITAT

Stanley A. Cain*

I

In view of the theme of this Conference and that of the first study session, I have elected to treat my assignment in a broad frame of reference. As a consequence, I will discuss several concepts and terms associated with them, rather than confine myself to the two of the title.

With some justification, ecology has been accused of having an unnecessary burden of terminology. This situation has arisen in part because the phenomena dealt with are complexes of merging and overlapping features of environment, species occurrences, community structure, and behavior patterns. This complexity resides in the inseparable aspects of all ecosystems. Under such conditions there is a large element of abstraction and subjective judgment shown by students of nature who approach ecosystems primarily as taxonomists, biosociologists, physiologists, environmentalists, or geographers.[1]

Biotic communities of whatever rank are never studied in their entirety and throughout their geographic extent, with the result that partial descriptions and incomplete understanding are the best that we have. The investigator is forced to some method of sampling within the complex whole. This is usually done at some place which is judged to be typical, and often the sampling is not conducted in a manner that would warrant generalization about the whole community. A further difficulty arises from the indefiniteness of boundary which often is a more or less broad transition with contiguous communities.

Natural areas[2]

Nearly two decades ago I wrote a symposium paper on "Characteristics of Natural Areas and Factors in Their Development" in which I offered the following definition: A natural area is a geographic unit of any order or size with sufficient common characteristics of various sorts to be of some practical usefulness in biogeography—and I added that wildlife managers, grazing and forest administrators, and other working ecologists approach such a usage in common

* Dr. Cain, one of the leading plant ecologists in the new world, is Assistant Secretary of the Interior in charge of the Fish and Wildlife Service and the National Parks. He was formerly Charles Lathrop Pack Professor of Conservation at the School of Natural Resources, University of Michigan. He served as President of the Ecological Society of America in 1958. This paper was written when the author was associated with Resources for the Future, Inc., Washington, D.C.

[1] Ecological literature is rife with confused concepts and imprecise terminology as well as synonyms. It is not the purpose of this paper to demonstrate this but, rather, to suggest a clearer and perhaps more rational set of terms to coincide with useful concepts without creating any new ones.

[2] The term *natural area* is widely used to refer to relic tracts of land which are more or less free of human interference, especially in connection with the nature-protection movement. This is not the subject that is under consideration here.

practice (Cain, 1947). It does not follow from this argument that students should discontinue their efforts toward analytic studies of the environment, the fauna and flora, and the communities, or that efforts toward synthesis and classification are to be abandoned. It is suggested, however, that it be kept in mind that single-factor operation does not occur in biological nature, that the environment apparently cannot be completely analyzed, and that diverse analytic data cannot at present be synthesized back again into anything like the natural whole of the ecosystem.

However loose the term may be, a natural area will have one or more specified natural characteristics. It occupies space and within the specified area the ascribed characteristics generally are prevalent. It follows that a natural area has boundary, even though at an ecotone, and is contiguous with other areas.

Such remarks raise the question as to how natural are the areas that are being discussed if man must exercise some judgment as to their extent, boundaries being more or less arbitrary. Also there is the suggestion that such areas are natural only in a few characteristics that man selects for some practical purpose. Furthermore, there is the question of homogeneity throughout the area, even as to the selected characteristics. How much can an environmental character (or complex) vary in space and one still use it as a criterion of identification of a natural area? How much can fauna and flora and community structure vary from place to place and one still be warranted to refer to the area as natural? Let us examine some of these awkward facts.

A watershed is one kind of natural area. Whether the term is applied to the Mississippi River basin from headwaters to the Gulf of Mexico, to a portion of this tremendous river system, or to the few miles of a stream that flows southward on Long Island from the terminal moraine to the Atlantic, a watershed is characterized by at least one natural feature—the surface flow of water is within the drainage basin. A molecule of water falling anywhere onto the watershed will, if it does not fly off by evaporation or drain off by some subterranean route, eventually arrive at the bottom of the drainage system. A watershed does not have to be homogeneous in any other regard and, in fact, it is unlikely that it will be. It may be similar to or different from adjacent watersheds in climate, soil, and wildlife. Nevertheless, a watershed does have a precise boundary except rarely where there are wide, flat interfluves.

Soils are natural phenomena that occur in geographic patterns. Soil types are defined by many physical, chemical, and biological characteristics in combination. Two related soil types are distinguished by degrees of difference in the sizes of physical particles, by being more or less acid, having more or less humus, varying depths of the different horizons, and so on. As a consequence, soils nearly always present a boundary problem no matter the scale of the mapping or the level in the hierarchy of soil classification. When, as one moves in space, has the combination of the complex characteristics of soils changed enough that one no longer has the same type with which he started? Despite this, soils are usefully classified and mapped on large scale or on one small enough to represent the entire global pattern.

Various parts of the world have typical weather and describable climates, but what combinations of what conditions of the atmosphere, and what periodicities and irregularities of factors, are to be employed in defining a given climate? The temperate zone has very intemperate weather and it can be "hot as hell" at one time and, paradoxically, "cold as hell" at another time in the same place.

In one sense it can be said that climates are man-made, for he selects "types" from the varying conditions, basing them on selected criteria, and expresses them in averages and probabilities. Sometimes he gives up on the problem of integrating the physical data from weather instruments and lets living organisms do it for him. Thus he speaks of "desert climate," "rain-forest climate," and "hemi-cryptophytic climate."

Ecosystems may be expected to present even greater difficulties than topographic, edaphic, climatic, and biological areas (species areas, communities areas, etc.), for ecosystems combine the variability of the biotic and the abiotic. What species in what abundance and with what organization and what environmental conditions at what level of intensity are required for one to determine where one ecosystem stops and another commences? That this question is a real one can be illustrated by the great American-Mexican desert. Is the desert boundary to be drawn where the average annual precipitation is six or ten inches? Is it to be drawn where evapotranspiration exceeds precipitation? Is desert determined by the existence of cacti and other succulent plants and microphyllous and aphyllous shrubs together with numerous annual plants? Is percentage of bare ground a criterion? Or wind-swept pavements and sand dunes? Obviously deserts are not one thing, yet they do have their peculiar adaptations to xerophytic conditions and constitute ecosystems that are recognizably different from grassland, woodland, and forest.

We can reach certain conclusions about natural areas. No natural area has more than a degree of naturalness in the sense that it has more than a degree of homogeneity over space and, consequently, generally has an indefinite boundary. When a natural area is defined by two or more characteristics in a certain combination, the areas of these characteristics usually are not coincident in space. They overlap in the defined natural area, but their boundaries are different. Whatever the scale of our view of nature, we are met by the phenomena of variability in all regards. The consequence is that one deals in probabilities and generalizations, not with certainties and definiteness. This is useful to keep in mind in the following discussion which deals first with life categories and then with environmental ones.

HIERARCHY OF LIFE CATEGORIES

Ecological terminology is awkward because some concepts do not make a distinction between the biotic and the abiotic. I will first deal with a series of terms that are strictly biotic (remembering, of course, that all life is associated with environment) and then take up some that concern the physical world in relation to life.

The purpose of considering a hierarchy of life categories from the global to the organism is that a system of classification can provide a useful frame of reference for geographic understanding of natural patterns, provide suggestions, even guidelines, for biogeographic studies and for human manipulations of nature. There can be direct benefits to agriculture, range management, forestry, wildlife management, nature protection, and so on, resulting from an understanding of natural categories.

As has been emphasized already, any system of categories will have a subjective element because it exists more for human purposes based on partial understandings than it does on units with complete objective reality in nature. Nevertheless there is a degree of objective reality to the categories to be discussed shortly despite the existence of ecotones or transitions between units and because of the continuum phenomenon of gradual internal change with distance. These difficult matters result from the lack of coincidence of the separate areas of all of the parameters of each category. Specifically, this means that the areas of the component species of plants and animals which may be used to characterize a category (or an example of it) are not coincident in space and hence do not have the same boundaries as the area of the category. The physical structure of the biotic communities is not constant in an absolute sense over any considerable distance; and the abiotic factors of climate, soil, and topography which influence the biotic members also show different mixes over space.

Despite such difficulties, actual units representing all of the categories of the hierarchy can be recognized on the ground and can be usefully studied (and manipulated by man) as local examples,[3] or in local portions which can be taken as more or less typical of the whole.

Because of the lack of clean-cut parameters and because of the statistical nature of the data on the parameters, biogeographers, ecologists, and others have come up with an array of concepts and terms some of which are simple synonyms but others a consequence of different interpretations of nature.

Although bearing a strong resemblance

[3] It is useful to bear in mind the difference between a type and an example of the type. Take the category of association: an example is specific and concrete, it exists somewhere; the type of which it is an example is an abstraction formed by synthesizing data from several concrete associations which are sufficiently similar, in someone's judgment and for certain purposes to be grouped together. Gleason (1939) in proposing the "individualistic association concept" and Curtis and his associates (1951) in developing the "continuum concept of community structure" have questioned the objective reality of the type. This does not negate the convenience and practical usefulness of forest types, for example, in the practice of forest management where approximate similarity of several stands is sufficient for certain purposes.

to other systems, such as Dansereau's (1957, p. 127), the hierarchy proposed here does have some distinct features. There is a consistent effort to characterize the categories by biological phenomena. At the same time, any biological system will of necessity have associated physical determinants in the climatic, geological, and pedological conditions and will itself be a consequence of the historical record of migrations and evolution, and for any biological type, time, too, has been a factor and sometimes even elements of pure chance, yet in a rational system of biological classification, biological facts should be primary and all other associated facts should be relegated to secondary consideration.

The biosphere

The biosphere is the thin global "shell" of all living matter. It occurs in the free-water zone essentially at the interface of the lithosphere and the atmosphere. It includes all terrestrial life and that in fresh and salt waters. Living organisms occur to the bottom of fresh waters and to great oceanic depths; they occur in soil to relatively shallow depths, and grow up from the soil to the height of the tallest trees; and they may fly or be carried temporarily up into the air. But considering the radius of the earth and its enveloping atmosphere, the biosphere is a relatively thin layer.

Vernadsky, Teilhard de Chardin, and others have added the concept of the *noösphere* (within the biosphere) as the conceptual, communicative, and operative "shell" of the human intellect.[4]

[4] Pierre Teilhard de Chardin, "The Antiquity and World Expansion of Human Culture," pp. 103–12 in Thomas (1956). He wrote: "More than a half century ago the great geologist Suess took a bold and lucky step when, in addition to describing our planet by the classical sequence of concentrical, spherical shells (barysphere, lithosphere, atmosphere, etc.), he decided to add the biosphere, in order to affirm, in a concise and

Whatever the operative scope of the human intellect, it is a phenomenon of man that emanates only from his physical person and, as a consequence, can be considered a special aspect of the biosphere. I include the concept at this point for two reasons: (1) the significant evolution of man is not now physical but cultural, and a consequence of intellect; and (2) man is an all-pervading influent throughout the entire range of this hierarchy of life categories.

Major world subdivisions

The biosphere divides naturally into three parts: salt-water life, fresh-water life, and terrestrial life. Each subdivision requires its own complex of ecological adjustments. These major world divisions have been termed *biocycles*. This is not a satisfactory term for a category of this sort because "cycle" suggests process, as in the great geochemical cycles: the hydrologic cycle, for example, involves the oceans, continents, the fresh waters, and the atmosphere above.

vivid way, that the frail but superactive film of highly complex, self-reproducing matter spread around the world was of decided geological significance and value. Since Suess' time, the notion of a special planetary envelope of organic matter distinct from the inorganic lithosphere has been accepted as a normal basis for the fast-growing structures of geobiology. . . . But then, why not take one step more and recognize the fact that, if the appearance of the earth has undergone a major alteration by turning chlorophyll-green or life-warm since the Paleozoic period, an even more revolutionary transformation took place at the end of Tertiary time, when our planet developed the psychically reflexive human surface, for which, together with Professor Edouard Le Roy and Professor Vernadsky, we suggested in the 1920s the name 'noösphere'? . . . Ultimately, neither earth nor man can be fully understood except with regard to the marvelous sheet of humanized and socialized matter, which, despite its incredibly small mass and its incredible thinness, has to be regarded positively as the most sharply individualized of all the planetary units so far recognized. . . ."

Biochores

The terrestrial part of the biosphere, for example, can be divided into biochores. They are the major subdivisions of vegetation (and associated animal life) characterized by physiognomy—the "look of the landscape" that results from the dominant life forms which are ecologically adjusted to the world climatic types. Grassland, desert, and forest are examples of biochores.

Formations

The forest biochore, for example, is composed of formations which have readily apparent physiognomic differences, as in the case of the broadleaf, evergreen, tropical rain-forest formation, the broadleaf, winter-deciduous forest formation of moist temperate regions, and the needle-leaf (conifer), evergreen forest formation. The term "formation" originated in the description of vegetation. *Biome* is a term for the equivalent category that is meant to include the animals which are associated with the vegetation.[5]

Climax areas

Within a formation (or biome), which is broadly characterized by the general climate and the life forms of the dominant organisms, as in the eastern American broadleaf, winter-deciduous forest formation, several climax areas can be distinguished on a floristic and faunistic basis. Although a climax area is a mosaic of communities, it is characterized by a climatic climax association which occurs here and there throughout the climax area. The *climatic climax association* is a biotic community that is not subject to progressive change but is in a fluctuating equilibrium with the prevailing climate and mature soil. The climax association has been arrived at by a series of com-

[5] See F. E. Clements and V. F. Shelford *Bioecology*, John Wiley & Sons, New York, for a treatment of biomes.

munities replacing one another of which it is the termination capable of replacing and restoring itself. It is to be found mainly on mature soils which are themselves a consequence of the long interaction of climatic-biological-geological influences.[6]

A climax area also contains some long-enduring *subclimax communities,* which, measured in human life spans, seem to be as stable as climatic climaxes. They differ from them, however, by being held back from further succession (perhaps for centuries) by topographic-edaphic conditions and even by recurrent disturbances. To distinguish them from climatic climaxes they are sometimes called "edaphic" climaxes, "fire" climaxes, etc. For most purposes, including management, it is the present stability of a community that is important, and not whether the primary control of the stability is climatic or edaphic, or whether there ultimately will be change. Hence the arguments about mono- and poly-climax are largely academic.[7]

Climax areas also contain numerous *successional communities* which more or less rapidly develop and succeed one another in *seres* from bare rock and soil, open water, abandoned agricultural land, cut and burned forest, etc., to the climax. In any seral stage the ecological action system (actions, reactions, and coactions) results in a changing habitat that eventually becomes less favorable for the community of the given stage and more favorable for the next succeeding stage of the sere. This is in contrast to climaxes which maintain their composition and structure, the plants and animals reproducing, as it were, under their own shade. Change in a climax community is cyclic

or haphazard, within the fabric of the community, and not inimical to its continuance.

Associations

The term *association* has been variously used. It is proposed here to apply it to all of the types of communities mentioned in the discussion on climax areas. Associations of whatever rank and dynamism are distinguished by biotic characteristics, that is, by the kinds of plants and animals which comprise them. An association, then, is a plant-animal *community* or *biocoenosis.*

The term *ecosystem* in this context refers to a biocoenosis together with its inseparable environment. It is a real unit in nature because life and environment are inseparable. Tansley, who is responsible for originating the term, applied it at the level of the biocoenosis; it is applicable, however, to all levels of this classificatory hierarchy from the biosphere to the individual.[8]

Synusiae

The terms *community, association, biocoenosis,* and *ecosystem* are usually applied to the entire complex of life that occurs at a given place, occupying area and space. These life units are usually complex and subdivisions that are called *synusiae* can be recognized within their total structure. Synusiae have greater homogeneity than a biocoenosis as a whole because they are based on one or a few ecologically related life forms. As a structural subdivision of a biocoenosis, synusiae also have fewer species and the environment shows less variability of habitat factors than does the whole biocoenosis.

The phenomenon of the synusial struc-

[6] The dynamic ecology of Frederick E. Clements was reviewed by Cain (1939), where several of Clements' original works are cited.

[7] Discussion of the mono-climax question will be found in Cain (1959).

[8] The term *ecosystem* was originated by Tansley (1935). The first clear exposition of an ecosystem, especially in terms of fundamental energetics of food chains, seems to be by Lindeman (1941–42).

ture of biocoenoses is most apparent in the layers of vegetation, but a complex community may contain synusiae other than the layers, such as those of rotting logs, boulders, and pools on the forest floor, vascular epiphytes on the upper branches of the trees (especially those forming "nests" and "tanks"), bryophytic mats on tree trunks, and termitaria, for instance.

Local communities

Within a synusia, such as the herbaceous layer of a forest floor, there may occur local communities, sometimes called *alternes,* which are dominated by one or a few species of plants. Such *societies* or *colonies* often result from vegetative reproduction and localized seed distribution. Colonies occur in the animal world also—corals, certain birds with gregarious nesting, and prairie dogs. The behavioral biologists are using the term *local community* for monospecific (sometimes polyspecific) aggregations that are organized by sociopsychological coactions leading to dominance order, as in troops of primates, and pecking order among birds (Klopfer, 1962).

Population

The term *population* is most precisely used in a statistical sense for the sum total of units which conform to a given definition. In biology one speaks of a species population (or a lesser taxon, such as a variety or subspecies) in its entirety, or that portion of it which exists in a given circumscribed area. For some purposes one may speak of the ungulate population of a given savanna area, consisting of several different species all of which are ungulates, as well as of the population of antelopes or any other ungulate species.

Organism

The organism is the discrete individual living entity—a single bacterium, amoeba, fir tree, or man.

CONCEPTS AND TERMS OF THE ENVIRONMENT

For precision and clarity I would like to see the concepts and terms of the environment kept distinct from those of the biological classificatory categories which have just been discussed.

Environment

For any spot on earth there is a complex of things, conditions, and forces the totality of which composes the *surroundings.* The environment may be taken as somewhat less than the total surroundings and given a biological pertinence by the following definition: Environment consists of all of the things, conditions, and forces to which living matter is sensitive and capable of responding, including changes in intensity and direction of stimuli. The rest of the surroundings, whatever they may be, have no significance for life because no stimulus to protoplasm is a consequence of their existence and they elicit no biological response.

It is stimulus and response that are important in this concept of environment. Awareness of the environment, in the sense of conscious perception of it by an organism, is not requisite. For example, a man's body may be affected by radioactive isotopes without his knowing of the stimulus and response that occurs; and the question of conscious perception does not arise for plants although their protoplasm may be affected by the same isotopes.[9]

[9] An interesting comment on the problem of perception is made by Donald K. Adams in his foreword to Klopfer (1962). He says: "It would seem self-evident that an animal can respond only to the environment that its sense organs, its motor equipment, and its central nervous organization, both innate and acquired, make accessible to it; and hence that

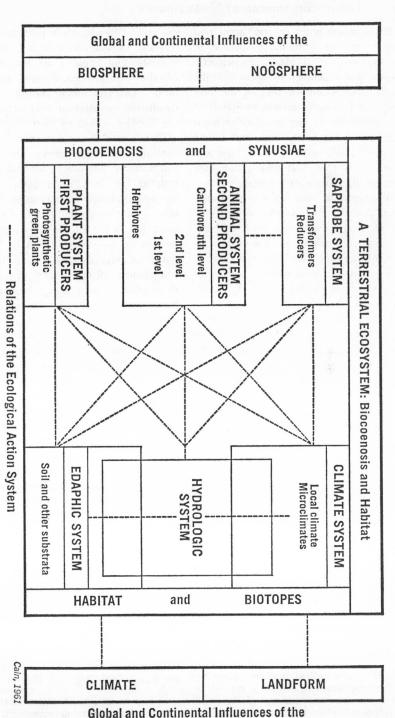

FIG. I-1. Relations of the ecological action system.

Environment is a "generic" term that may be applied to the different levels of the organization of life. It is perfectly proper, for example, to speak of the desert environment or that of the rain forest. It is equally proper to speak of the differences in environment of communities on the north- and south-facing slopes of a hill, or between the base and crown of a tree, that within a hollow tree, or the burrow of a rodent.

Biogeographic and ecological studies often describe environment in terms of the physical factors only, such as heat, moisture, and acidity, but the ecological-action system includes biotic coactions as well as such abiotic actions. Other organisms are invariably a part of the environment of any organism.

For analytic purposes one can consider the *factors* of the environment individually. For example, precipitation can be examined in terms of kind, of amounts during a stated period of time, or as an average amount per month or year. It can be examined in terms of intensity, as "drizzles" and "cloudbursts," or as to

cycles and trends, while precipitation in relation to evapotranspiration and the water-holding capacity of the soil are certainly also ecologically important conditions. Other factors of the environment —radiation, substratum chemistry, etc.— are likewise subject to analytical study.

The factors of the environment are in constant interaction among themselves. Furthermore, any one factor that may be isolated for study never acts alone in nature but always in conjunction with all other protoplasmic stimuli. For these reasons, the action of the environment is said to be *holocoenotic* and to have a concerted impact on the organism.[10] The complicated, diverse mixes of environmental factors have always been an embarrassment to ecologists because of the difficulty of reassembling analytical data into meaningful wholes. However, the fact of successful life of an organism or the existence of a biocoenosis in typical form has often been taken by ecologists to represent the integration of the environmental factors. This is a sort of "biological assay" or "indicator" phenomenon based on the fact that the totality of responses to the totality of the effective environment produces an automatic integration that is the phenomenon of successful life. It is in this sense that the climatologists speak of a "laurel climate" or a "grassland climate." Dubos (1964, pp. 11–14) recognizes the holocoenotic nature of the environment when he says: "The physician could not deal with the problems of disease if he did not concern himself with the integrated reactions of man to environmental forces. He would have little chance to help his patient if he did not try to comprehend the effects of the total environment on the human condition. . . ."

any inquiry designed to describe, understand, or explain its behavior would necessarily use this environment as one of the variables that condition the behavior. But it has taken psychologists a long time to arrive at the recognition of this seemingly obvious state of affairs. This recognition was long impeded by a conviction derived from the mistaken epistemology, namely the conviction that we could not know the relevant, effective, or psychological environment of another animal. Actually, of course, this knowledge is subject to no epistemological difficulties that do not apply equally to our knowledge of the physical world. The latter is also dependent upon elaborate and still mysterious processes in our nervous system. . . . Perceiving any object as an object involves processes which, if they were conscious, would be called reasoning. . . . If it is considered that our knowledge of the environment of another is derived by analogy to our own experience of the world . . . this perception is just as mysterious as our perception of depth, color contrast, or objects in general *and not one bit more so.*"

[10] Two recent general papers on the environment contain useful discussion of the holocoenotic nature of the environment: Platt (1960, 1964).

Habitat

Habitat is a term sometimes used interchangeably with environment. However, environment is used in a general sense and habitat is usually taken more specifically to refer to the living conditions of an organism, a population, or a biocoenosis. It is common to speak of the dune, bog, floodplain or alpine-meadow habitat, or that of an oak-hickory or spruce-fir forest. It is also proper to speak of the swamp habitat of skunk cabbage or a certain kind of frog, and of the different habitats which a bird may occupy when nesting and feeding and at different places during migration.

Biotope

Biotope is yet another term used for biological environments. It is a *micro-habitat* or the smallest natural area or space characterized by a particular environment. Although a single biotope might exist by itself, it is commonly only one of several life areas within a biocoenosis or heterogeneous community. As straightforward as this term seems to be, there is confusion between the environmental conditions and the typical assemblage of organisms that occupies a biotope.[11] I believe that biotope should be used in the strict sense of living conditions (granted that organisms themselves participate in the production of the particular set of living conditions) and not in the sense of the ecosystem. However, this does not preclude the application of the concept of ecosystem to the biotope

[11] *Biotope* has also been used to indicate place where an organism is to be found. It seems that the term *place* should be used as *station* is, merely to indicate location, and not to suggest the conditions at the place. In technical literature, *site* is used to suggest the quality of the environment at a place. This is the sense in which it is used by foresters, for example, when they refer to *site quality* of a given place. Differences in site quality are determined by differences in tree growth-rate in different habitats.

and its community any more than it does to the more complex biocoenosis and its environment. A biotope, then, is not the ultimate subdivision of a biocoenosis but of the habitat of a biocoenosis. Living conditions within a biotope are presumably more homogeneous and less variable than within a habitat. It is clear, however, that neither the particular mix of environmental conditions nor the size of the area or volume of space separate habitat and biotope, but the relationship of environment to life. It is the structural subdivision of a biocoenosis—the synusiae and local communities—that enables one to divide the habitat into biotopes. In other words, a biotope unoccupied by organisms would be a meaningless term. Rarely, it may be some structural boundary that delimits a biotope, such as a termitarium, the hollow in a tree, the water-filled cavity of a pitcher-plant leaf, or the alimentary tract of a mammal.

Niche

There are three ways that the term *niche* has been used:

(1) as a synonym for biotope—that is, as a strictly environmental term for a small or least space with described physical characteristics;

(2) as an ecosystem—that is, as a biotope in the first sense together with the occupying organisms; and

(3) as a term applied to the function performed in an ecosystem by an organism, a population, or a group of mixed species which have the same role.

A statement by Dice (1952) is illustrative of the first usage: "The term niche includes . . . a consideration of the habitat that the species occupies for shelter, for breeding sites, and for other activities, the food it eats, and all other features of the ecosystem that it utilizes. The term does not include, except indirectly, any consideration of the functions that the species serves in the community."

Platt[12] states clearly the second usage: "The whole system of interaction between a particular organism and its physical and biotic environment is the niche of that organism. The term indicates not only the habitat, or microenvironment, but also the activity of the organism." Kendeigh says that the term emphasizes "the relation of the organism to both the physical and biotic factors of its environment. The restriction of a species to a particular niche depends on its structural adaptations, physiological adjustments, and developed behavioral patterns." He attributes the term originally to Grinnell, who spoke of animals generally and birds in particular as having preference for a particular niche, choosing surroundings consistent with their needs. At about the same time, Elton defined niche in functional terms of an organism's food and enemies, and it is this point of view which has led to the third usage which is common in behavioral science.

This third usage is made explicit by Clarke,[13] who says: "Different species of animals and plants fulfill different functions in the ecological complex. The role of each is spoken of as its niche. The term so used stresses the function of each organism in the community rather than its physical place in the habitat. . . . The 'functional niche' is more fundamental than the 'place niche,' but both concepts exist and should eventually be given different names." The broadest use of the functional niche is for an entire trophic level such as that of primary producers, including all photosynthetic plants in an ecosystem, or the herbivores collectively, the primary carnivores, the secondary carnivores, and the decomposers and transformers. In this sense, each step in a food chain is a different niche —the prey occupying one niche, the predator another. A narrower use of the term refers to how, within a trophic level, organisms have different ways of "making a living." Clarke illustrates this by saying that "among herbivores that feed on trees, for example, some fill the niche of eating the leaves whereas others use the twigs, sap, bark, or roots as a source of food."

Cole[14] also subscribes to the functional concept of niche when he says: "All ecological niches, or roles in the economy of nature, tend to be filled, and, if there is a way for another species to make a living in a community, we expect some species to evolve the mechanisms for doing so even if it requires drastic morphological and physiological modifications. [Some empty niches may get filled by immigration rather than by evolution.] Thus, all ecologists are aware of marsu-

---

[12] See reference in note 10. Other references referred to in the text are Grinnell (1917, 1924, 1928), Elton (1927), Kendeigh (1961).

[13] Clarke (1954). The reductionist use of the concept of *niche* is well illustrated by this quotation from Clarke: "Minute differences in function are exhibited by the niches of birds that obtain food organisms from crevices of bark. Small woodpeckers characteristically fly to the base of a tree and climb the trunk looking for grubs. When they reach the top, they fly diagonally downward to the base of the next tree and again work their way upward. In contrast, nuthatches common in eastern United States ordinarily fly to the top of a tree and work toward the base, clinging upside down to the trunk. In this way woodpeckers readily remove grubs and other food from crevices easily reached from below, whereas the nuthatches obtain their prey from cracks in the bark more accessible from above. In the Galápagos Islands a finch that has evolved toward the woodpecker type fills this niche, but having no barbs on its tongue it wedges grubs out of crevices by means of a

thin twig held in its beak." Incidentally this latter case is one of the few examples of tool using by animals below the primates.

[14] See Cole (1964). Cole is treating the filling of empty niches by evolution; it needs to be remembered that empty niches can be filled by immigration of a "preadapted" species from elsewhere, as well as by adaptive evolution.

pials and placentals occupying comparable niches, even specialized ones such as the mole and anteater niches, in different regions. We teach about the finch that has learned to exploit the woodpecker niche, of lizards that substitute for grazing mammals, and of euphorbias that look like and live like cacti. . . ."

In the foreword to *Behavioral Aspects of Ecology*, by Peter Klopfer, Adams[15] says, "The concept of niche is clearly playing an increasingly important role in ecology and is involved in a number of problems Dr. Klopfer poses. The corresponding concept in psychology has had a number of names: it has been called behavioral environment, psychological environment, life-space, psychological situation, and subjective environment or subjective situation. The term subjective in these last two merely refers to the fact that the environment in question can be described only in relation to a specific organism. That is to say, a physical description of the environment will not suffice."

Hutchinson[16] has used the concept of *niche space* as consisting of all those variables whose limits determine the presence or absence of a species. Klopfer follows this line when he says that a smaller niche is the measurable range of conditions determining the occurrence of one species that is less than that which determines the presence of another. Niche space, then, seems to be the exact equivalent of ecological amplitude or the breadth of a species' tolerance to a range of environmental conditions.

The experimental population ecologists state unequivocally that two species of

ecological equivalence cannot occupy the same niche because, if they are really two species, each will have individual niche requirements which may be similar but which are sufficiently different that when mixed in a physical niche (biotope) one will fit better and as a consequence eliminate the other. When this line of reasoning is followed to its end, the conclusion is reached that competition among species results in a sort of one-species, one-niche rule or, conversely, one-niche, one-species.

Clarke, as noted above, suggests that the different concepts of niche should eventually be given different names, and he uses *place niche* for the concept that is clearly the equivalent of biotope. I would prefer *environmental niche* as a term because the connotation of place might well remain the neutral one of geographic designation, like "station." The second usage, in the sense of ecosystem, might be referred to as *ecological niche*. After all, ecology is the science of the environmental relationships of organisms. The third usage is well designated as *functional niche* because it is concerned with the role that an organism plays in an ecosystem.

II

In addition to discussing biotope and habitat, with which I have taken great liberty in the foregoing section of this paper, Frank Fraser Darling suggested that I might "set the broad theme of what the habitats of North America are and their nature," and that I might "indicate something of their stability or sensitiveness to change and the type of change to which they are severally being subjected."

For a part of this, fortunately, Dr. A. W. Küchler has just published his map entitled "Potential Natural Vegeta-

---

[15] See note 9.

[16] See Hutchinson (1957). Small niche space, or narrow ecological amplitude, is illustrated by a bird feeding only on one species of plant, a butterfly laying its eggs always on the same species of plant, and by the koala eating only eucalyptus. See also, Klopfer (1962).

tion of the Coterminous United States."[17] This magnificent new map is accompanied by a manual with photographic illustrations and capsule diagnoses of the 116 types of phytocenoses which he recognizes. In the text there is also a sensible and penetrating discussion, not only of the problems of vegetation mapping, but of vegetation itself. One illustration of Küchler's handling of these complicated matters will suffice for present purposes. Of tne ecotone which occurs in two forms, he calls one kind *transition.* This is where "the life forms and taxa of the two types are mixed; they share the available biotopes more or less. . . . In a transition, the species of one plant community disappear gradually, i.e. first one, then another, to be replaced little by little by the species of the other community." The other type is called a *mosaic.* He says, "Mosaics are so arranged that each of the two vegetation types involved retains its discrete character. The species of one type are not mixed with those of the other. Usually, 'islands' of one type are embedded in a matrix of the other type. . . ."

I leave the broad theme of what the habitats of North America are and their nature to Küchler and others who have undertaken to describe and map natural areas. What remains of Darling's "charge" will be commented on variously.

Quality of the environment

It is, I think, a good omen that a concern with the influence of human impacts on the future status of wildlife in North America has been directed in this Conference more broadly toward the human habitat. I do not need to defend the conclusion that the quality of the environment, in human terms, is diminished

[17] This beautiful map and accompanying manual are published by the American Geographical Society, New York, 1964, as Special Publication 36.

by every needless loss of a species of animal or plant, by every heedless degradation of natural beauty of the landscape, and by the pollution of water, air, and soil. Every long-term economic loss for shortsighted benefit, that is caused by diminishing the productivity of nature, should be anathema to an enlightened society; but to the tangible must be added the intangible. What price beauty?

"Man's Nature and Nature's Man" poses the intimate interrelations of the two. We of the North American continent are fortunate. The concept of the great national parks is nearly a century old; the states and provinces, local government and private groups have a growing dedication to parks and the preservation of natural areas and vanishing species; and there are important efforts to conserve wildlife, especially that which interests the sportsman or has economic value for tourism. Perhaps in time a rare minnow will not be sacrified to rainbow trout, a rare violet to the road grader, much less a grove of redwoods, or the last large predator (owl, hawk, eagle, coyote, wolf, cougar) to the stockman.

Quality of environment does not start at the edge of the wilderness. It starts at home, in our cities, and along the roads. Fortunately, again, there is a growing wonder whether human happiness and health, including mental health, may not have environmental parameters, in open space, living space scaled to man, quiet, order, variety, and beauty.

This Conference is one effort to estimate choices of ways we may go and consequences of choices we may make. Some hints can be found in the following paragraphs.

Habitat preservation

Habitat preservation is the key to species preservation, whether it be a microscopic flatworm on the underside of a water-lily leaf or a thousand-pound moose browsing water lilies at the edge of a wilderness lake. Actually it is the ecosystem that is the key—the biocoenosis and its habitat. The vegetative mantle of the earth is a patterned mosaic of biocoenoses, and each biocoenosis when undisturbed has its normal full range of biotopes and species adapted to occupy them. When ecosystems are drastically disturbed and disarranged, there are two quite different consequences: some species have their populations diminished and may even be extirpated; other species develop exploding populations.

It is said that nature abhors a vacuum. Empty niches do get filled. Clearing the forests for agriculture (which is not being decried) spelled the doom of the passenger pigeon and made opportunity for the English sparrow and starling.

On Isle Royale in the absence of predators the moose population exploded, ate itself "out of house and home" (a fine ecological expression), and crashed to a small fraction of its former superabundant population. With a reduced population and a better relationship to its food sources, the moose population commenced again to build up. Fortunately a vacant niche got filled; wolves crossed the ice from Canada and began to prey on the aged, infirm, and young moose. For several years now the studies of Durward Allen and his students show a predator-prey relationship in a balance of about thirty wolves to 600 moose; but this will not last for long. The balsam trees and other preferred browse species are gradually growing up and out of reach of the moose. The balance can be maintained only should an extensive wildfire (an act of God!) reduce the forest and allow again for young growth the moose can browse; or a controlled burn (an act of man! and a difficult decision for the National Park Service) can accomplish the same end. One sees the same dramatic problem in deer herds in many places and in the surplus destructive numbers of elk in Yellowstone National Park, now drastically cut down in numbers through direct reduction by Park Service personnel. Michigan in December of 1964 held its first elk hunt in nearly a century. Never numerous in the region, eight elk were reintroduced in 1918–19; today the number is estimated at 3500 animals spread over four counties, and eating their browse faster than it grows. Unlike the Isle Royale moose, man and his gun in sport hunting will fill the empty niche of the natural predator and, the Michigan Department of Conservation hopes, will bring the herd under control.

La Mont Cole[18] makes the point in a less familiar vein: "When once we accept the proposition that natural selection will operate in the direction of filling vacant ecological niches, we must logically begin to wonder whether total eradication of destructive forms is desirable. I have been fascinated to note that some leaders in medical research have recently arrived independently at the sound ecological conclusion that it might be more desirable to replace harmful viruses and bacteria with innocuous types than to leave niches open by trying to keep our bodies free of these forms. By the same principle, the broad-spectrum antibiotic or pesticide is likely to empty not just one niche but several. Ever since antibiotics came into use, physicians have been plagued by secondary infections resulting from the destruction of an innocuous intestinal flora thus leaving ecological niches available for drug-resistant and pathogenic staphylococci. The same applies to biotic communities, and we have a wealth of examples of such secondary infections in which, for example, orchard mites replace the codling moth as the pest of apples and spider mites replace the spruce budworm as the defoliator of fir trees following the application of insecticides."

18 See note 14.

Part of the problem of species preservation through habitat and biocoenosis preservation lies in the differences among endangered species. Some species have small territories and others are very wide-ranging. A hunting wolf pack may range thirty miles or more in one night. Migratory caribou cover hundreds of miles. Migratory waterfowl may require habitat preservation in northern Canada during the summer and the Gulf of Mexico in the winter with resting and feeding places in between. The principal problem, however, generally resides in whether a species is a "narrow" or a "wide." These expressions refer to whether the species population on a genetic basis has only a limited tolerance for environmental diversity or whether it has a wide ecological amplitude. The fewer biotopes and phytocoenoses a species finds it possible to occupy, the greater the hazards to it from natural or human interference. Species with exceptionally broad tolerances have a better chance to survive and even flourish in the face of environmental changes.

However, breadth of ecological amplitude of a species is not necessarily a matter of wide tolerances of individuals. When a species population is genetically heterogeneous, when among its members there is a large number of different genotypes (based on richness in alleles), there is a concomitant wide array of adaptations. Some forms will not succeed in the face of changing environment, but other forms with more appropriate adaptations will survive and prosper, and the species will prosper. In general, then, an endangered species is more likely than not to be one of genetic poverty and limited adaptability, and a successful one is apt to be a "wide."[19]

These biological phenomena have several suggestions for human choices. Large tracts of mature, stable, and climax bio-

[19] This point is discussed in Cain (1940).

coenoses are sometimes referred to as "biological deserts" because of the seemingly limited number of species present. This is not really true if one considers the community per se, because every niche is likely filled. A redwood forest or a tract of primeval tropical rain forest has a great many more species than meet the eye. A pure, even-aged secondary stand of pine, however, does have very few niches and as a consequence is relatively poor in species. An equal area of land covered by a mosaic of successional communities will have a much greater variety of species per unit area than a homogeneous stand of climax vegetation—or of one successional community, for that matter. This is because the mosaic consists of several different biocoenoses, each with its own array of niches providing differences in foods, shelter, and nest and den sites. Physiognomy is variable and there is a lot of "edge." Wildlife managers dearly love what they call "edge effect," because the transitions between biocoenoses produce increased variety of niches.

Solution of the preservation problem must be geared to that which is to be preserved. Some species of animals require vast areas over which to roam. This is especially true of the top predators which form the ends of food chains. Other species require much smaller habitat areas, but in order to maintain a sizable population, the necessary areas must exist in large scattered numbers. Successional vegetation, by definition, is transient in a given place. Weed stages of abandoned fields may last only a few years; shrub and intolerant tree stages (intolerant of shading) may last only a few decades; and complex later stages may take centuries to be replaced, but the trend is toward the climax, and it can be set back only by disturbance. Disturbance is provided in nature by disease, physiographic activity, wind throw, and fire. Man is the principal disturbing agent, and this is a lesson for wildlife managers and nature preservationists. Leaving nature to take her course may result in the loss of environmental qualities, and plants, animals, and communities which are cherished. With most parts of the world already disarranged by man, and with most remaining areas that are nearly natural relatively small, man seems to have no alternative but to employ management practices to encourage the formation of desired habitats and communities. Vanishing species can be preserved only by preserving the necessary biotopes.

Students of vegetation have long been interested in what they call *minimal area*.[20] This is the least area on which a given community can develop its "typical" composition and structure. Such an area (in botanical terms only) may be as small as a few square feet or as large as several acres. Studies to determine minimal area have usually done so in terms of the common, prevalent plant species. All such studies show a rapid increase of species as an area is first enlarged, and a slower rate of increase in number of species as an area is further enlarged, but always some additional species will be encountered as new area is added to the examined territory. The lesson in this seems to be that rare species are very finicky about the biotopes which they occupy and such special kinds of habitats are themselves rare. The preservation of large areas would meet the needs of most of nature. But in much of the world this is impractical and undesirable. In an agricultural region one ungrazed forty-acre wood lot is enough to preserve dozens of species of spring-flowering plants, but only by chance one or more of the rarer species. A scattering of such wood lots, as islands in the sea of corn, would have a

better chance of preserving a considerable number of rarer species of plants and animals than would all of the acreage in one tract. The same thing applies to ponds and marshes and other kinds of habitats. It is on a basis of this principle of many small areas that Massachusetts, Connecticut, and counties around the District of Columbia are endeavoring to improve the quality of the environment —quality for man in terms of quality of nature.

The fragility of ecosystems

The National Park Service has discovered that montane and subalpine meadows and alpine tundra are fragile ecosystems, and they have had to take measures to disperse the wear and tear by pack trains of trail riders. Wildfire in the drier arctic tundra can set it back for decades, perhaps centuries. A boy-scout jamboree in one weekend on the sand dunes of Michigan can disarrange the vegetation and start blowouts which can later destroy more stable vegetation beyond the capacity even of youthful vigor. A comparatively few scuba divers can upset the entire ecosystem of a coral reef. Overgrazing by cattle, sheep, and goats is known around the world. Not only natural grasslands and savanna but mature forest (as in the case of midwestern farm wood lots) can be destroyed by superabundant grazing and browsing animals, wild as well as domestic. Nothing in nature can long resist man with a gun, ax, fire, and bulldozer.

Fragility of communities, then, is a matter of degree. Communities with low productivity—communities containing important species of plants with low growth rates and animals with low reproduction rates—are generally fragile and, if to be preserved, need special protection from heavy use. Communities with high productivity can generally recover rapidly. It is said, however, that sufficiently knowledgeable persons can tell whether

[20] Minimal area has long intrigued the author of this paper. See Cain (1938, 1944).

a high, tropical rain forest has had pre-Columbian disturbance by Indians after, perhaps, three to four centuries or more have elapsed. In other cases fragility may be due to instability of the substratum or to key roles of certain species of plants or animals in the ecological action system.

One kind of problem in maintaining quality of environment arises from disturbances that may originate more or less remotely from the biocoenoses being disarranged and deteriorated. The Everglades of southern Florida are a good example of this situation. The biocoenoses of the glades are dependent on the sheet flow of fresh water that originates far to the north. This flow, now cut off by engineering structures developed for flood control and drainage, is rapidly eliminating the biotopes for roseate spoonbills, flamingos, egrets, anhingas, alligators, crocodiles, and other interesting and beautiful subtropical creatures. Municipal and industrial water pollution may have its effects many miles downstream. Radioactive isotopes blasted into the upper atmosphere in the United States or the USSR affect the entire biosphere.

Problems of the quality of the environment range from the back yard to the globe—from the smallest biotope to the biosphere.

BIBLIOGRAPHY

Cain, Stanley A. 1938. The Species-area Curve. Amer. Midl. Nat. 19:573–81.
———— 1939. The Climax and Its Complexities. Amer. Midl. Nat. 21:146–81.
———— 1940. Some Observations on the Concept of Species Senescence. Ecol. 21:213–15.
———— 1944. Foundations of Plant Geography. New York.
———— 1947. Characteristics of Natural Areas and Factors in Their Development. Ecol. Mono. 17:185–200.
———— and Oliveira Castro, G. M. de. 1959. Manual of Vegetation Analysis. New York.
Clarke, George L. 1954. Elements of Ecology. New York.
Clements, F. E., and Shelford, V. E. 1939. Bio-ecology. New York.
Cole, La Mont C. 1964. The Impending Emergence of Ecological Thought. Bio Sci. (July): 30–32.
Curtis, John T., and McIntosh, Robert P. 1951. Ecol. 32:476–96.
Dansereau, Pierre. 1957. Biogeography: An Ecological Perspective. New York.
Dice, Lee R. 1952. Natural Communities. Ann Arbor, Mich.
Dubos, René. 1964. Environmental Biology. Bio Sci. (Jan.): 11–14.
Elton, Charles. 1927. Animal Ecology. New York.
Gleason, Henry Allan. 1939. Amer. Midl. Nat. 21:92–108.
Grinnell, Joseph. 1917. Field Tests of the Theories Concerning the Distribution Control. Amer. Nat. 51:115–28.
———— 1924. Geography and Evolution. Ecol. 5:225–29.
———— 1928. Presence and Absence of Animals. Univ. Calif. Chron. 30:429–50.
Hutchinson, Evelyn G. 1957. Cold Spring Harbor Symposia on Quantitative Biology. 22:415–27.
Kendeigh, S. Charles. 1961. Animal Ecology. Englewood, N.J.
Klopfer, Peter H. 1962. Behavioral Aspects of Ecology. Englewood, N.J.
Lindeman, R. L. 1941. Seasonal Food Cycle Dynamics in a Senescent Lake. Amer. Midl. Nat. 26:636–73.
Platt, Robert B. 1960. Environment. McGraw-Hill Enc. Sci. and Tech. New York.
———— 1964. The Importance of Environment to Life. Bio Sci. (July): 25–29.
Tansley, A. G. 1935. The Use and Abuse of Vegetational Concepts and Terms. Ecol. 16:284–307.
Thomas, W. L., Jr., ed. 1956. Man's Role in Changing the Face of the Earth: 103–12. Chicago.

MANAGEMENT, RESPONSE, AND VARIETY

Ian McTaggart Cowan*

The idea of caring for small groups of wild animals has been part of the operating equipment of man since before the beginning of recorded history. The earliest purpose was doubtless to domesticate. However, a millennium ago the concept of improving the habitat to provide for a better crop of game was already established in the Orient (Marco Polo). Food, cover, and predation were the aspects of the environment manipulated.

It is significant to note that even the earliest concepts of management developed only where the evolution of human culture had led to an educated segment of society that had established land tenure. In the old world, wildlife management was a practice developed by the aristocrats in temperate and subarctic climates where a few species of wildlife dominated the scene and where there were obvious seasonal changes in the environment. These changes had their impact on man also and thus almost certainly focused his attention on the lives of the creatures around him, leading by logical process to the developing concept of ameliorating the most destructive circumstances.

The origin of the idea of altering the natural circumstances that were controlling the lives of creatures other than ourselves is a major landmark in the flowering of human ideas. It marked a

point at which man had gained such mastery of the principles of his own survival that he had developed a confidence in his ability to alter the environment, and to extend this umbrella of understanding and competence beyond the immediate area of self and family.

Once the original concept had been added to our vision of the natural world it was inevitable that it should evolve, becoming at once more complex in its detail and more simplified in its synthesis. The expansion of natural history into ecology, during the scientific revolution on the American continent, saw the principles on which the idea of wildlife management rests added to abundantly, both at the operating level and in concept. The community as a vital entity operating in accord with discernible laws that could yield prediction, the ideas of the limiting factor and of density-dependent feedback between organism and environment were among those hypotheses that provided important new conceptual equipment.

At the same time, the human objective gradually evolved from those of the native predator, through the phases of animal culture for consumption and animal culture for recreation, to the sophistication of a broad and diverse pattern of human interest in the creatures with which he shares the world. Aldo Leopold crystallized the new idea in his definition of the "ecological conscience." Man is seen not as the outright owner of the world or any part of it, but rather the holder of a life rent, and bearing the

* Prof. Cowan, who presided over Session I, is identified in a note on page 9.

responsibility to so order his activities that he turns over to his successors the biological capital with which the world is endowed in at least as good condition as when he got it. This is a powerful and attractive view and one that immediately demands further definition of our precise purpose and of our vision of the ideal human environment.

Evolution is never uniform in rate nor in coverage either in the objectives or in the abstract. It would be unlikely, therefore, that large parts of humanity would arrive at the same point in their ideas simultaneously. Always, however, the high point is an important landmark. The Leopoldian thesis is widely accepted in principle on this continent and in Europe as the operating base of the ecological conservator. There are, however, great diversities in the interpretation that can be and are placed upon the vision of the desirable human environment. These run the gamut from the sordid monoculture of cement and pollution where it profits, to the idealistic, almost escapist "good old world" with some modern conveniences. Ideas and ideals, however, have never changed with greater tempo, and our burgeoning capacity to alter and regulate our environment on a massive scale makes ever more urgent an improved understanding of the ecology of man as the dominant influence in the world's terrestrial ecosystems.

Management is an activity of man. For our purposes I will define it as any planned and purposeful action directed toward altering the environmental impact on an ecotype or on an animal population. It will include the regulation of the direct or indirect impact of man himself on the ecotype or on a wild species, as well as all attempts to influence such other features of the environment as nesting sites, shelter, food, parasites, disease, predation, competition, or distribution. Inherent in the management approach to the occurrence and numbers

of a species is the belief that it is within our competence to determine numbers of the species, to detect the critical features of the environment that are influencing the species population, and to alter these in a planned direction.

Our view of ourselves as possessing these capacities finds reflection in a broad spectrum of judgments and attitudes with reference to wild species. One of the most elementary is found in the question heard so often "What good is it?" The implication is that the biological world can be divided into the useful and the useless with obvious corollaries of attitude and action. The objective today, however, is directed toward the provision and maintenance of the maximum of variety. Each living organism is the repository of a unique assortment of biological information gained through the eras via the interplay of opportunity and response. Each offers a potential enrichment of human knowledge, experience, and enjoyment that is limited only by our capacity to appreciate. This capacity will certainly expand to levels yet unimagined and the loss of any single element in the world's store of varied life is an erosion of our potential.

This view of the objective of management in conservation finds general support among ecologists and has already penetrated to the action level in some areas of governmental administrative responsibility. No species, however, lives alone; the majority occur in a variety of different environments, each calling for a different set of responses. Each biotope, therefore, is as unique as the species that compose it and is possessed of a variety of yet another order of magnitude. Today our management abilities are effective where the simple manipulation of one factor influencing a single species is pertinent. Under the more complex circumstances of the biotope, in very few instances do we possess the information upon which management practices can be designed.

A review of present areas of management and of the responses elicited will orient us in our attempt at projection. In general terms our management efforts are directed to encourage those species we desire to assist, to reduce populations of creatures we consider damaging to our interests, or to maintain the integrity of an entire assembly of plants and animals—that is, to maintain an ecotype for its riches of species and associations. In order to accomplish these ends we concern ourselves with the manipulation of forces that influence mortality, with other conditions that govern distribution, and finally with attempts to increase or decrease the fecundity of the species. It is useful to consider examples of the application of these approaches in three main categories: (1) the management of survival, (2) the management of distribution, (3) the management of numbers.

The management of survival

Here and there throughout the world are species of animals whose numbers and population trends leave them vulnerable to extinction. The disappearance of any one of them is regarded as contributing to the progressive deprivation of our long-term opportunities. Wherever possible, active steps are being taken to circumvent the extinction.

In some instances the population has reached a vulnerable position through the direct action of man. Under these conditions the obvious management action has been to restrict or eliminate human predation. The outcome of this will depend upon whether or not the remaining population is viable in terms of numbers, distribution, and biological structure. The short-tailed albatross has responded, as has the bowhead whale, and both are gradually climbing back from the brink. Great effort is presently directed toward the attempt to manage the whooping crane into a position of safety, but success is far from certain.

In general, management directed toward the survival of an endangered species has greatest likelihood of success with a form of limited migration that confines its movements within a politically stable and sophisticated area, and aggregates during its period of greatest vulnerability. Ease of identification is an additional favorable attribute while highly specific environmental requirements have a negative influence.

Species that are in trouble because of the secondary consequences of human activity have proven more difficult to assist. The ivory-billed woodpecker appears to have vanished with its chosen habitat of mature cypress forest despite efforts at management. The widespread disappearance of the native avifauna of the Hawaiian islands has most probably arisen as an outcome of the combined introduction of avian malaria and a mosquito vector. These conditions resist management correction.

A reasonably recent approach to assisting the survival of wild populations of endangered species is the application of captive-rearing techniques to part of the population, with the objective of later release into the wild. The nene (native goose) of Hawaii is apparently responding to the combined application of this method and field techniques designed to improve the environment and to distribute the population more favorably.

There are several international programs in the planning or early implementation phases that will bring captive rearing to the emergency assistance of endangered species of mammals. It can not be regarded as a panacea because some species are not susceptible to confined rearing and others have been shown to possess a heritable factor for wildness that may be selected against in captive rearing (Spurway, Leopold). It is possible that this is a major factor in the failure of programs of introduction and reintroduction.

Island populations of bird and mammal endemics have proven particularly difficult to manage in the interests of survival. In general, long periods of evolution out of contact with the specialized competitors, predators, and diseases of the continents leave the insular species most vulnerable. Restoration management has been successful in the few instances in which it was possible to remove the new destructive factor.

A dramatic instance is the rebuilding of the biota of Laysan Island. The island was almost completely devastated by domestic rabbits and guinea pigs introduced in 1903. By 1923 only four species of plants remained of a flora of twenty-six species; of the five species of indigenous birds three were gone, the other two were in danger (Bryan, 1942). The last surviving rabbits were destroyed about 1925, and over the succeeding forty years the flora has largely returned and the two surviving species of land birds have increased, probably to the capacity of the habitat.

In this, as in many other island problems, the destructive element was a single man-made influence and the task of management for survival is simple in principle even if frequently difficult to achieve.

The recognition of the elemental importance of preserving the integrity of the genotype has presented management with a new and important yardstick. The culture of preferred species can easily lead to the unwitting extermination of another species or local form. The widespread transplanting of such species as bobwhite quail and cottontail rabbits may have changed the genotype of local adapted stocks and thus destroyed the peculiar genetic distinction of certain forms. Similarly, it was feared for many years that the liberation of plains bison

into the last habitat of the wood bison had eliminated the latter. A relatively uncontaminated herd of the latter discovered recently has provided the source for an important attempt to establish a genetically unaltered herd.

In this connection the campaign by Needham to maintain the genetic integrity of the unique assortment of species and subspecies of California mountain trout offers an important example of this kind of management situation. With hatchery programs burgeoning and becoming steadily more important in the management of game species for large harvests, only the most dedicated appreciation of the principles I have outlined could have preserved these very local and confined endemics from elimination by competition, genetic inundation, or hybrid sterility.

A very special program in management for survival is the European attempt to re-create the lost genotype of the European aurochs by recombining the features isolated by selective breeding to provide the modern breeds of domestic livestock (Street, 1964). It is unlikely that this kind of program can ever be completely successful. Indeed we have no criteria against which to judge the reassembly. However, certain attributes of the re-created stock strongly suggest that it at least closely approximates the original. Of special importance are attributes of hardiness that have appeared in the recombined stock. Such an attempt to reassemble a vanished species would be possible as an endeavor only where several captive derived stocks are available.

It is impossible to foresee the direction that our interests in the biota will take as human tenure of the earth lengthens, as our populations increase, our demands upon the resources expand, and our understanding of the environment becomes ever more sophisticated. Today our orientation and concern is toward the trees, certain more obvious elements in the flora, and to the birds, mammals, and fishes. Our knowledge of the ecological facts pertinent to the management of most of these species is most inadequate; we are totally innocent of the information that would permit us to manage the populations of most of the living creatures of the world.

It is probable that this situation will continue. This being so, the only tenable approach to the maintenance of the largest part of the biota is the management of ecotypes rather than species.

Where management is to be directed toward the perpetuation of a climax situation, the task, in theory, is relatively simple and would be categorized in the general area of protection. However, the restoration and maintenance of any of the host of complicated evanescent seral stages is a task of the greatest complexity.

We have experimented extensively with the development and manipulation of wet ground for the primary purpose of improving the environment for waterfowl. Many of these aquatic and marsh habitats are biologically rich and the host of associated species prosper along with the waterfowl. The management of such wet-ground areas revolves primarily around the control of water in sufficient amounts and in desirable patterns. This may be supplemented by the introduction of appropriate plants. In general, however, success depends upon the development and maintenance of emergent vegetation. This has proven to be a difficult task in some of the larger impoundments in the Canadian prairie provinces. Here gradual deterioration of the plant-supporting capacity of the shallows occurs unless the water levels are caused to fluctuate appropriately. Marsh management has also encountered the hazard of western duck sickness epizootics. Again the most satisfactory control involves the capacity to change water levels and to regulate water temperatures.

More limited experiments have been devoted to the maintenance of prairie areas in Wiconsin and Minnesota. In general, however, it can be said that greatly expanded research programs in ecology are urgently needed to supply the information upon which successful management of ecotypes must depend.

We are presently relatively powerless to plan successful ecological management of even the smaller of the national parks of this continent. This lack alone is likely to severely hamper the successful implementation of the recommendations of the Leopold Committee (1963) that call for the restoration of the primitive ecology of the park areas.

The usual approach to the management of vanishing habitats has been to create a refuge or park to include it. Here again, though the end result may be the survival of a vanishing biotope, the initial concern is largely with a simple species.

Special reserved areas have been established to maintain stands of climax redwood forests, Douglas fir forests, Monterey cypresses, organ-pipe cactuses or similar species. The preservation of these has necessitated the maintenance of the ecosystem of which they are a part. The truly ecological view of the objective is only beginning to enter into planning and administration. Among the best examples of advanced thinking in this context is to be found in the attitude toward the unique crater flora and fauna in Mount Haleakala National Park, Maui Island, Hawaii.

In general the attitude has been that all requisite action has been taken with the exclusion of fire and the protection from direct attack upon the area or species by man. Gradually the greater complexities of the task are becoming manifest as the problems of the alteration of the environment by human trampling or through the increase of plant-eating mammals are met. These frequently present the necessity for objective judgments that we resent being forced to act upon and consequently postpone long after the critical point is passed.

There are many examples in the national parks and elsewhere where the basic ideal of the maintenance of maximum variety is being destroyed rapidly by rigidly held dogmas transferred from other areas of land management. We are rapidly losing the early successional stages of the plant communities that culminate in the well-known climax conditions, such as spruce forests, where the terminal stages support relatively sparse biota.

The recent study of changes in the forest cover of Yosemite Park over a century of our stewardship offers an important example (Gibbens and Heady, 1964). Fire has become anathema to the manager of forest areas who consciously or unconsciously harbors as his objective the ideal of a uniform stand of well-shaped trees unmarred by fire, disease, insects, deformity, or senility. But fire has been the great reinitiator of forest areas, the creator of variety of cover type on the large scale, while insects, disease, and senility have instigated diversity of habitat on the smaller scale.

Management of distribution

In general a species becomes less vulnerable as its occurrence becomes distributed more widely. Of special importance is the discontinuity of distribution as this protects against the inadvertent catastrophe that can overwhelm a single small population. This fact poses one of the most difficult decisions faced by those engaged in captive rearing to support the survival of very rare species. A current project sponsored by the World Wildlife Fund offers a pertinent example. An attempt is being made to use a captive-rearing project to save the Arabian oryx from imminent extinction. Wild capture produced two males and a pregnant female. There were others already in captivity in zoos in various parts of the world. Their distribution provided the safety inherent in dispersal, but the isolated pairs offered little likelihood of the establishment of a successful breeding nucleus. The decision requires weighing the dangers inherent in transporting the creatures to a common site, plus the dangers of epizootic disease or some other catastrophe striking the entire group, against the improved chances of successful captive rearing that will arise from the larger group.

A somewhat similar alternative was considered as part of the program to save the California condor. In this instance a proposal by San Diego Zoo to capture some wild birds for confined breeding was rejected on the basis of the minimum viable wild populations (now down to forty birds). Such decisions often involve selecting between the principle of the safety of dispersion and the principle of the minimum viable population. Each instance becomes a special case.

The ideal outcome is to be seen in the handling of the nene project in which the captive birds were divided up into dispersed breeding nuclei as stocks became adequate.

The management of distribution has involved introductions and reintroductions. The distinction between the two is based upon whether the species introduced was in earlier time an indigenous inhabitant of the region. By introduction we can create variety beyond what existed previously and we can theoretically give the introduced species the benefit of the advantage of dispersement. However, we seldom use scarce species for transplant, and this factor is therefore of little consequence.

Large numbers of species have been moved around the world in programs of introduction. In North America such game birds as pheasants, gray partridge, and chukar partridge are well known. In many areas they occupied hitherto untenanted ecological niches and contributed to the enrichment of variety. Among the nongame species the European sparrow, European starling, rock dove, whitewinged dove, English skylark, and a number of others have entered the North American fauna in this way. Certain of them have entered niches either created by man or unexploited by native species. Others have competed with, or displaced, natives and have thus not been of support to our over-all objective.

It is probable, for example, that the introduction of the black-tailed deer to the Queen Charlotte Islands of British Columbia contributed directly to the extirpation of the unique indigenous caribou of the islands.

An examination of the New Zealand fauna provides probably the greatest concentration of ill-advised introductions of any area in the world. These were made without appropriate forethought and in the absence of the necessary biological information on the probable impact of the introductions upon the native biota.

Introductions in North America are frequently difficult; attempts have failed many more times than succeeded. Even after most careful comparative studies of donor and host environments have led to the selection of the most suitable genotype for the transplant, the odds against success have been high. Frequently the liberation of large numbers over a period of several years has led to success. The implication is that a new genotype, developed by local selection, provided the unique adaptive capacity required for success in the new domain.

Reintroduction is a special case that has often directly contributed to desirable objectives. The California bighorn is being reintroduced to parts of its former range in Washington and Oregon from surviving herds in British Columbia. Wapiti have been taken from Yellowstone Park to re-establish vanished populations in British Columbia and Alberta. Other examples could be cited.

Most of the successful reintroductions have been achieved with small numbers of individuals, sometimes by open release, sometimes by a period of captive rearing followed by soft release that provided the animals an opportunity to adapt gradually to the new environment.

Both in introductions and reintroductions too little attention has been paid to the possibility of transporting disease organisms with the host.

A dramatic example of ill-considered transplanting is to be seen in the movement of the Wainright, Alberta, herd of plains bison into the last remaining habitat of the wood bison. The transplanted herd was tuberculous and carried at least this disease into the wildlife on its new range with unfortunate sequelae.

Any such movement of organisms into an environment unoccupied by the species provides an opportunity for the establishment of a disease-free nucleus that should be taken advantage of. Natural extinction has been an active process throughout all of existence. We have few clues to the cause of extinction but a ready possibility is epizootic disease. Thus the existence of disease-free discontinuous populations should have added survival value to the species and will provide additional surety to our objective of management for variety.

Management of numbers

The greatest management effort on this continent has been devoted to maintaining a large population of the varieties of animals that contribute to commerce or to recreation. Millions have been spent managing populations of salmon, trout, grouse, pheasant, quail, turkey, deer, moose, elk, and other species. In general, management activities have fallen into three categories: fact finding, restrictive regulation, and positive management. The fundamental difference between the last two is that restrictive regulation is oriented toward regulating man as a predator upon the wildlife species, while positive management is oriented toward increasing the production and survival of young and lengthening the life of adults of the managed species. Obviously it is not possible to place all our management practices clearly in one or other of these categories but for most this is appropriate.

It is not necessary to comment at any length upon the various restrictive regulations that have been used with varying success on different species. Open and closed seasons, sex restrictions, bag limits, and weapon specifications are widely used. It has become obvious that the restrictions can be effectively varied from species to species, from place to place, and from time to time if they are to achieve their objective. There is no one tried and true set of rules that will lead to successful management of a species throughout its range and over an extended period of years.

The positive approach has included the destruction of animals known to prey upon the managed species. The biological situation is much more complicated than it was earlier imagined to be. In general, predatory animals are now known to play a role that differs greatly depending upon the relative sizes of the predator and prey populations, the availability of alternative food sources, and the presence in the environment of special features that facilitate the escape of the prey. Predators are now known to serve seldom as the limiting factor. They may, however, serve as the intermediate host of undesirable parasitic organisms or they may compete with man for use of the prey species.

The management of predators has so far consisted, for the most part, of direct killing of the undesirable species by gun, trap, or poison. Recently some control programs have used artificial limita-

tion of input to reduce the population of unwanted species. The chemical treatment of the eggs of gulls and some other sea birds so as to prevent their hatching is an example of the effective use of such a technique.

Disease control has the potential to contribute greatly to the population available for human use; however, it has proven extremely difficult to influence the incidence of disease in wild populations. An outbreak of hoof and mouth disease in deer in California was attacked by an attempt to remove all deer from the affected area. The disease did not become enzootic in the deer, but whether or not the containment program was contributory is not known. Western duck sickness can now be controlled by techniques that are practical upon large and small waterfowl management areas.

The screwworm (a blowfly larva) has been shown to be an important parasitic organism of deer in the southeastern United States. Ingenious biological methods appear to have brought it under control.

Necrotic stomatitis was at one time a disease of local importance among mule-deer populations in California. Improvement of water supplies has done much to reduce losses to this disease.

It is safe to say that we know relatively little yet about the impact of disease upon wild populations. Our capacity to manage the impact cannot even be explored until much more research has been done.

Animal species that have special requirements can often be increased both in numbers and in distribution by practicable measures. The provision of suitably isolated nest sites on artificial islands, or mounds, or in washtubs can increase populations of Canada geese. The hole-nesting species of ducks, such as wood ducks, goldeneye, and bufflehead, frequently respond to the provision of suitable nest boxes.

In the Florida Everglades fluctuation of water levels from year to year can have strong influence upon the population of alligators. The creation by blasting of "alligator holes," in which the animals can survive drouth periods, can extend the distribution, increase the minimum numbers, and accelerate the rate of recovery of the population following a drouth.

There have been many attempts to manipulate the environment so as to improve its capacity to support wildlife species. Cover planting to provide shelter and food during periods of severe weather or to provide safe nesting sites in the early spring has influenced the size of breeding populations and rendered their reproduction more effective.

Management for numbers, inasmuch as it is generally related to some direct form of human use, can be in collision with the broader objective of the maintenance of the greatest variety of species, and the preservation of all existing identifiable genotypes. The fisheries manager is now equipped with chemical means of removing all competitor fishes from waters managed for "sporting" species of fish. South of the glaciated areas of North America there are many species of fish with extremely limited distribution. Unless the facts are known, the rare species and their distribution understood, and the danger recognized, there is an ever-present possibility of the unintentional extermination of a species in the course of management activities devoted to the improvement of stocks of another kind of fish. As a case in point, recent use of piscicides in the Green River exposed to the threat of extirpation several species confined to this river system.

The future of management

It has been shown that we have developed some facility in manipulation of populations where we can identify a single limiting factor that it is within our power to alter. Thus we have been able to maintain some threatened species long after they would have been lost left to their own resources.

We are still struggling to develop our concepts and practices to the level that we can direct our efforts to the maintenance of intact biotopes. The promise of this approach is so great that much new ecological research should be directed toward acquiring the understanding necessary for successful management.

We have been able to diversify either by transplanting species into environments not previously occupied by them or by reintroducing them to areas from which they had vanished.

We have very limited capacity to apply positive management methods designed to improve on unaided productivity or survival. We can, however, contribute to our ideal by controlling human activity on habitats where directly or inadvertently species and communities of species might be destroyed. We can also attempt to assure the survival of a large part of this continent's biota by maintaining enough discrete populations of viable size to protect against the possibility of accidental elimination.

It seems certain that as our populations increase on this continent they will not expand as rapidly as our technological competence. This will soon force a complete reappraisal of the objectives of human living. It is safe to say that the pattern that will emerge on this continent may differ remarkably from the present one. More people with less time spent by each in making a living and more time for nonessential activities of life will change our attitudes toward the living environment.

Transportation patterns for some time to come will be increasingly destructive of the integrity of wild land. Air travel will increase and diversify and impose further problems of conflict between wildlife and machines on airports. We will develop techniques for altering the habitat on airports so that large species of birds or those smaller species that aggregate into large flocks will be discouraged. Other species that skulk rather than fly and do not flock will probably expand their distribution and numbers.

Intensive agriculture may reduce the area available for the raising of farm wildlife and will produce even larger areas of uniform culture. This again will encourage the seasonal aggregation of species that favor man-made steppe conditions or extensive vegetable and orchard acreage. Demands for control will be met.

At the control level I feel certain that more use will be made of chemical management. The important need is for target-specific chemicals that will avoid secondary effects. These will certainly be developed and used. It is to be hoped that chemicals will be discovered that will act by restricting fecundity so that these can be applied to baits where control is necessary but large-scale slaughter is undesirable.

We can, I think, foresee an increased development of apartment dwellings of large capacity spaced widely apart in landscaped surroundings. With adequate planning these will encourage the close association of urban dwellers with a variety of wildlife species. Here again the plant species used by the landscaper and the plantation forms used will tend toward uniformity and the encouragement of a restricted variety of species.

There will continue to be vast areas of undeveloped land within which most of our species of wildlife will survive. Those that migrate will have a more difficult time than resident species because they will meet a series of changed habitats as they move.

Many waterfowl species will probably decrease to the point that their shooting will be greatly curtailed or terminated; a few highly adaptable and successful species, that respond readily to simple management techniques, will bear the brunt of the harvest. Opportunities for waterfowl shooting will pass more into private hands, and the task and approaches of management will have to change accordingly. The Anseriformes will probably suffer more than any other group from the problems imposed by migrating over a greatly altered land. The demand for publicly controlled refuges will increase and will probably be directed more precisely toward the needs of given species.

In general, one of our most urgent management tasks is to identify biotypes for preservation and to devise successful patterns for managing both the seral and climax ecotypes. If the suggested conceptual change in the management of national parks toward the renewal of primitive states prevails, this will provide the impetus for progressive thinking. It will also stimulate the development of many improved techniques of cover manipulation and animal-population management. Again I see induced temporary sterility as a more desirable management technique than today's unfortunate necessity of killing surplus individuals.

Winter range for the large wild ungulates will become an ever-increasing problem. I see no alternative but reduced populations of some of them, especially wapiti, and along with this, public control over ranges selected and designated to preserve several herds of each of the ungulates. They will probably come to be regarded as state treasures, and states will vie for the privilege of responsibility for such a management unit. Special care will have to be taken to preserve the wild quality of both the herds and the habitat.

Public grazing of sheep and livestock on mountainous pastures will be greatly curtailed so that the wildlife can take more of their annual energy budget from the summer range and demand less from the winter range.

In some areas it may be found that

the mule deer and the moose in their respective habitats are the most effective way of producing edible material from wild-land acres, and these species may be intensively encouraged for that purpose.

Our conservation departments will make much more use of ecologists than they now do, and they will be entirely staffed with men and women educated in the biological and social sciences. The orientation of these departments will no longer be toward a few species of interest to those that hunt. They will be expected to guard and manage the ecology of the wild lands and reserved areas, the suburban conservation regions, and the scientific reserves that will have come into existence as our interest in the variety of wild species and communities of this continent reaches higher levels of sophistication.

As we attempt to look forward and to discern the general outline of problems and the attitudes and understanding that will guide our reactions to them, it would be wrong to ignore one of the deep-seated weaknesses in our basic pattern of social orientation. Many of the most vexing problems of conservation today and in the foreseeable future stem from the disparity between the concept of long-term public benefit as I have dealt with it and the privilege of the individual to convert natural resources for immediate private gain. The relationship between the two values has been evolving rapidly but very unevenly and with frequent violent oscillations. This social conflict remains as one of the most challenging before us and is already emerging as a major frustration to the attainment of our ideals.

Where large resident human populations have developed within public reserved areas and national parks they inevitably view the area as almost solely for their private gain. Because their geographic entity gives them organization and dedication to their purpose, such small groups of individuals have exerted undue influence upon national conservation policy. Searching studies of the social position and political impact of such small towns as Banff and Jasper in the great Canadian Rocky Mountain park system would provide important guidelines for our future reaction to private vested interest within national parks or similar areas. It is not the objective of this discourse to explore the impact of our social organization and principles upon the management of our living wild resources. However, the policy within which our successes and failures will emerge evolves from the interplay of groups with different ideals and objectives. It is acknowledged, therefore, that those who in special knowledge, unique capacity, or accepted responsibility guide the evolution of policy will continue as most important contributors to our success.

BIBLIOGRAPHY

Bryan, E. H., Jr. 1942. American Polynesia and the Hawaiian Chain. Tongy, Honolulu.
Gibbens, R. P., and Heady, H. F. 1964. The Influence of Modern Man on the Vegetation of Yosemite Valley. Calif. Agric. Exp. Sta. Manual 36.
Komroff, M. 1926. Travels of Marco Polo. Boni & Liveright, New York.
Leopold, A. S. 1944. The Nature of Heritable Wildness in Turkeys. Condor, 46(4):133–97.
——— 1963. Study of Wildlife Problems in National Parks. Trans. 28th N. Amer. Wildl. Conf.: 28–45.
Needham, P. R., and Gard, R. 1959. Rainbow Trout in Mexico and California with Notes on the Cutthroat Series. Univ. Calif. Pubs. Zool. 67(1).
Spurway, H. 1952. Can Wild Animals Be Kept in Captivity? New Biol. 13:11–30.
Street, P. 1964. Re-creating the Aurochs and Tarpan. Animals 5(9):251–53.

ADAPTABILITY OF ANIMALS TO HABITAT CHANGE

A. Starker Leopold*

All organisms possess in some measure the ability to adapt or adjust to changing environmental conditions. But the degree to which different species are capable of adjusting varies enormously. This chapter concerns the nature and extent of adaptability and demonstrates the truism that in a world undergoing constant and massive modification by man, the animals with the highest capacity for adjustment are those that persist in abundance. Specialized animals with narrow limits of adjustment are those that have become scarce or in some instances extinct.

Relation of ungulate populations to plant successions

In any given ecosystem, there are animals that thrive best in the climax stages of plant succession and others that do better when the climax has been destroyed in some way and the vegetation is undergoing seral or subclimax stages of succession, working back toward restoration of the climax. This can be interpreted to mean that the climax animals are more specialized in their environ-

* Dr. Leopold is Professor of Zoology and Associate Director of the Museum of Vertebrate Zoology at the University of California, Berkeley. Co-author of *Wildlife in Alaska* (1953, with F. Fraser Darling), he has since written a perceptive study of *Wildlife in Mexico* (1959). He was Chairman of the Advisory Board whose report to Secretary Udall (1963) on "Wildlife Management in the National Parks" served to reorient the management of the parks along ecological lines.

mental needs, while the seral or successional species are more adaptable and able to take advantage of transitory and unstable situations. The principle can be well illustrated by considering the status of various native ungulates in North America.

The mass of data accumulated in studies of North American deer permits us to draw some general deductions about population dynamics in these animals, particularly in relation to food supplies. The following remarks apply equally to the white-tailed deer (*Odocoileus virginianus*) and the mule deer or blacktail (*O. hemionus*). The quality and quantity of forage available to a deer population during the most critical season of the year has proven repeatedly to be the basic regulator of population level. Usually this means winter forage, but not always. In desert areas or regions of Mediterranean climate, like coastal California, summer may be the critical season. In any event, the nutritive intake of the individual deer during the critical season determines both productivity of the herd (Cheatum and Severinghaus, 1950; Taber, 1953) and mortality in the herd, whether death be caused by starvation, disease, parasites, or even to some extent by predation or accidents (Longhurst et al., 1952, and others). Average population level is a dynamic function of these two opposing variables—rate of productivity and rate of mortality. Hunting is a source of mortality artificially interposed in the formula, and although it is intercompensatory with other forms of loss (that is, hunting kill will reduce starvation losses, etc.) it is not regulated by nutrition, but by legislative fiat. However, since hunting is generally controlled in North America to remove no more than annual increment, and usually less, it cannot be construed as a primary determinant of population level in most areas. Putting all this in much simpler form, good forage ranges generally have many deer; poor ranges have few. All other influences are secondary.

Good deer ranges characteristically include stands of nutritious and palatable browse which as a rule are produced in secondary stages of plant succession (Leopold, 1950). Burned or cutover for-

est lands support most of the deer in the continent; some brush-invaded former grasslands are of local importance. In a few special cases, as for example that of the burro deer (*O. h. eremicus*) on the desert, sparse populations live in climax floras. But on the whole the association between deer and secondary brushlands (the connecting link being nutritional) is so general as to permit classification of deer as seral or successional species.

Assuming that range relationships are equally dominant in determining populations of other North American ungulates, and much evidence indicates that this is so, a general characterization can be made of each species, permitting classification along lines of range affinities, as has been done in Table 1.

TABLE 1. General association of North American ungulates with climax or subclimax successional stages

	Boreal	Temperate	Tropical
		Biotic zone	
1. Associated primarily with climax forage types:			
Caribou (*Rangifer arcticus*)	x		
Bighorn (*Ovis canadensis* and allied species)	x		
Mountain goat (*Oreamnos americanus*)	x		
Musk ox (*Ovibos moschatus*)	x		
Bison (*Bison bison*)		x	
Collared peccary (*Pecari tajacu*)		x	x
White-lipped peccary (*Tayassu pecari*)			x
Tapir (*Tapirella bairdii*)			x
Brocket (*Mazama americana*)			x
2. Associated primarily with subclimax forage types:			
Moose (*Alces americana*)	x	x	
Elk (*Cervus canadensis*)		x	
White-tailed deer (*Odocoileus virginianus*)		x	
Mule deer (*Odocoileus hemionus*)		x	
Pronghorn antelope (*Antilocapra americana*)		x	

This rather subjective classification requires some explanation.

Climax species. The northern caribou is a classic example of an animal that depends heavily in winter on undisturbed climax vegetation of the subarctic zone. The lichens which supply much of the caribou's winter food grow either as an

understory to the spruce forest or suspended from the spruce limbs. Any disturbance such as fire or grazing that depletes this particular vegetative complex lowers the carrying capacity for caribou.

Similarly bighorn sheep and mountain goats in their alpine retreats, bison on the great prairies, and musk ox on the arctic plains are adapted to feed on climax species of forbs, sedges, grasses, and a few shrubs.

In the southern reaches of the continent the two species of peccaries are generalized in their food habits, like other pigs, but the mast of oak and of many tropical fruit trees contributes heavily to their diet. Besides mast, the bulbous roots, palmettos, cacti, forbs, and grasses on which these pigs feed are on the whole characteristic of climax associations. The tapir and brocket are even more typical of climax rain forest (Leopold, 1959).

It is notable that of nine species of North American ungulates associated with climax vegetation, four are of boreal or arctic affinities, four are tropical, and only the bison and the collared peccary in part of its range occur in temperate latitudes.

Subclimax species. Nearly all of the ungulates that thrive best on kinds of weeds and brush that characterize disturbed vegetative situations are native in the temperate zone. This includes the two common deer, elk, and the moose, which extends northward through the boreal zones as well. The pronghorn antelope is predominantly a weedeater (Buechner, 1950), although it may consume much sage and other browse at times. On the Great Plains, the weeds and forbs that supported antelope originally may have resulted from local overgrazing by the native bison. On the deserts of Mexico, however, the antelope almost certainly depended on climax vegetation, but this is the fringe of its continental range.

Whereas most boreal and tropical ungulates have climax affinities, the temperate-zone species thrive largely on successional vegetation. In an evolutionary sense this would suggest that these adaptive species, all highly successful today, developed in an environment subject to frequent disturbance, presumably fire.

Even the bison, here classed as a climax species, would fall in this category if one accepts the prairie as a subclimax, maintained by fire (Sauer, 1950).

Recognition of successional affinities of big-game species is basic to determination of sound management policy. The subclimax species (two deer, antelope, elk, moose) fit nicely into multiple-use land programs, including logging, grazing, and controlled burning. The climax species do not. Preservation of wilderness areas, without competing or disturbing uses, is particularly important in sustaining remnants of the climax forms designated in Table 1.

Plant successions and other wildlife

The principle illustrated above with ungulates applies generally to wild animals. In areas heavily modified by human action, the abundant species are those adapted to take advantage of disturbed ecologic situations. Over much of the United States, the upland game species that supply most of today's recreational hunting are the bobwhite quail, cottontail rabbit, ruffed grouse, mourning dove, and the introduced ring-necked pheasant—all typical subclimax or successional species.

Game species once abundant on the continent, but now localized and scarce because of shrinkage of particular climax vegetational types on which they depended, are the prairie chicken, sharp-tailed grouse, sage hen, upland plover, and wild turkey. Extinct are the heath hen and passenger pigeon.

The case of the passenger pigeon illustrates particularly well the dilemma facing an unadaptive species. The fabled legions that "darkened the sky" were supported in large part by mast crops produced in climax stands of mature timber, especially oak, beech, and chestnut. The flocks were highly mobile and searched the eastern half of the continent for favorable feeding grounds. When a good food supply was found, millions of birds would congregate to establish one of the massive colonial nestings so well documented by Schorger (1955). With the settlement of the country, two things happened concurrently that contributed to the swift collapse of the pigeon population: uncounted millions of the birds were slaughtered in the nesting areas, and the mature timber stands that produced the mast crops were felled to make way for farms. The demise of the pigeon is traditionally blamed on the market hunters; but had there been no hunting, it is doubtful that the pigeon would have survived the depletion of its food supply. So specialized was this bird that it seemingly had no capacity to adjust to the modest, scattered food source that certainly continued after the main hardwood forests were felled. When the big pigeon flocks were reduced, the survivors simply perished without a single pair exhibiting the ability to feed and reproduce under changed conditions. Its close relative, the mourning dove, on the other hand, adjusted very well indeed to the conversion from forest to farm, and today is undoubtedly much more numerous than in primitive times, despite heavy and persistent shooting.

The nature of adaptation

Precisely what is this character of "adaptability" that some animals have and others do not? What are the mechanisms by which animals adapt?

The paleontological record tells us that over the eons of time there have been enormous changes in climate and hence in habitat. With each major shift many animal species became extinct; these presumably were the unadaptable ones. Other animals persisted but evolved and were modified to meet the new conditions. One component of adaptability, therefore, is the capacity for genetic change.

At the same time, current experience offers many examples of individual animals learning new tricks of survival that contribute to longevity and hence to persistence of the population. A coyote can learn to be trap-shy; a raccoon learns to search for eggs in wood-duck boxes; mallards learn the precise hour when legal shooting ceases, which signals the exodus from a refuge to go in search of food. Some species are quick to pick up new behaviorisms; others are not. Adaptability, therefore, may include the capacity to learn.

Genetic and learned adaptations will be discussed in that order.

Morphologic adaptation

One manifestation of genetic adaptation to local environment is the demonstrable evidence of subspeciation in animals. Many widely distributed species are segmented into local populations that show marked and persistent differences in morphology. Some of the characters that vary and are easily observed and measured are body size, proportion of body parts, and color of plumage or pelage. The bobwhite quail (*Colinus virginianus*) is an example of a resident (nonmigratory) game bird that varies greatly from place to place. This bird occurs throughout the eastern half of North America, from New England and South Dakota south to Chiapas in southern Mexico. Within this range, twenty-one well-differentiated races or subspecies are recognized (Aldrich, 1955). In size, the bobwhite decreases from over 200 grams in the north to slightly over 100 grams in Chiapas. Likewise there is a general north-south gradient in plumage color, the palest birds occurring in the open or arid ranges, such as the Great Plains, the darkest forms being found in the wet tropics or subtropics of southern Florida, the coast of Veracruz, and the interior valleys of Chiapas. It is presumed that each population is particularly adapted to the local habitat in which it exists. The capacity to be molded genetically by local environment doubtless underlies the bobwhite's success in occupying such an extensive range in North America.

Commenting on this general question of genetic plasticity, Grant (1963, p. 434) states: "The great role of natural selection in the formation of races [subspecies] can be inferred from the observation that racial characteristics are often adaptive. The adaptiveness of the racial characters in many plants and animals is demonstrated by two sets of correlations. First, the different races of a species have morphological and physiological characters that are related to the distinctive features of the environment in their respective areas. Second, the same general patterns of racial variation frequently recur in a parallel form in separate species inhabiting the same range of environments." He goes on to comment on some of the generally accepted "rules" of morphologic adaptation that have been summarized and analyzed by many other authors, including Mayr (1942, p. 90). These are:

1. *Bergmann's rule:* The smaller races of a species are found in the warmer parts of a species range, the larger races in cooler parts.
2. *Allen's rule:* Protruding body parts, such as ears, tails, bills, and other extremities, are relatively shorter in the cooler parts of the range of a species than in the warmer parts.
3. *Golger's rule:* Dark pigments (eumelanins) increase in the warm and humid parts of a range, paler phaeomelanins prevail in arid climates.

The bobwhite illustrates all of these rules of local adaptation. The same may be said of white-tailed and mule deer, the raccoon, the bobcat, hares of the genus *Lepus,* cottontails of the genus *Sylvilagus,* and many other widely distributed birds and mammals. In the case of the white-tailed deer, the size gradient is extreme; in Wisconsin an adult buck weighs well over 200 pounds, in parts of Mexico scarcely seventy pounds. The larger size and smaller ears of northern animals presumably gives an advantageous ratio of body mass to exposed surface, for heat conservation. The opposite is true in warmer climates.

Physiologic adaptation

More difficult to measure, but perhaps even more important in fitting local populations to their environments, are the physiologic adaptations. To be successful, a population must breed at the right time of year, produce only as many young as can be cared for, be able to digest and assimilate the foods locally available, and otherwise adjust its life processes to the local scene. Migratory birds lay on fat (fuel) for their travels and require elaborate navigational machinery. Research to date has scarcely scratched the surface of this enormously complicated area of animal adaptation.

A species that has been studied in some detail and that well illustrates several facets of physiologic adaptation is the common white-crowned sparrow of the Pacific coast (*Zonotrichia leucophrys*). There are two races of this bird, very similar in appearance, that winter together in central California; but in spring one race migrates to British Columbia to breed while the other breeds locally, on the winter range. Blanchard (1941) showed a number of differences in the life cycles of these two populations. Though living together all winter, the migrants laid on fat in spring and departed for the north; the residents did not accumulate fat but went leisurely about the business of nesting. The migrants, having less time on the breeding grounds, compressed the reproductive cycle into approximately two thirds of the time used by resident birds. Subsequent investigation by a number of workers has demonstrated that the mechanism triggering these events is changing length of day in spring, but the important differences in response reflect inherent, physiologic adaptations peculiar to the two populations.

Differences in timing of breeding are demonstrable in many other species. Black-tailed deer along the California coast fawn in May, mule deer in the Sierra Nevada in July, whitetails in northwestern Mexico in August. In each case fawning corresponds to the period of optimum plant growth—spring in California, summer rains in Mexico. Time of mating (seven months before fawning) is presumably timed by changing day length—in this case by shortening days, since the breeding occurs in fall or early winter. Ian McTaggart Cowan has kept a number of races of black-tailed deer in pens in Vancouver, and notes that the southern Alaskan and British Columbian stocks breed at almost the same time, whereas the Californian stocks have retained a response that induces antler growth, shedding of velvet, breeding, antler drop, and pelage molt a month or more in advance of the northern races kept in the same pens.

The number of young produced by a breeding population is regulated by physiologic controls. Lack (1954) presents examples of clutch size in birds varying apparently with food availability. He cites the work of Swanberg on the thick-billed nutcrackers, in which it was shown that in years when the autumn crop of nuts was below average, the birds laid only three eggs. In years of good or excellent nut crops, clutches of four eggs were normal. When the experimenter supplied nuts in winter for certain wild nutcrackers, those particular individuals had clutches of four eggs, even in years of poor mast crop. The change in number of eggs was therefore apparently a physiologic adjustment to the amount of food available. But in all cases the birds laid no fewer than three eggs, nor more

than five, the limits presumably set by hereditary factors.

Clutch or litter size likewise may be a function of predator populations and the likelihood of losses of eggs or young due to predation. The mallard of continental North America lays eight to twelve eggs and predictable losses are high. The closely related Laysan duck, on isolated Laysan Island where there are no predators, lays only three to four eggs.

Certain deep-seated physiologic differences have been detected between wild and domestic turkeys which shed some light on how the wild birds are adapted to live successfully in the woods (Leopold, 1944). In the Missouri Ozarks the native turkey persists even under highly adverse circumstances and populations respond readily to protection and management. Domestic turkeys cannot exist away from farmyards. Hybrids between the two barely hold their own in refuges under intensive management. Differential reproductive success seemed to underlie the disparities in population behavior. Time of breeding is earlier in domestic and hybrid turkeys, leading to loss of eggs and chicks in late-spring storms. Behavioral differences between hens and chicks suggested other reasons why wild birds raised more young. These differential reactions were related to size of brain and relative development of some of the endocrine organs that control behavior, suggesting a few of the components that may be involved in "local adaptations."

Danger of transplanting local races

If indeed some kinds of animals are delicately attuned to life in specific local environments, one may question the advisability of trapping and shifting these populations about in an effort to restock underpopulated ranges.

During the era 1920–40 there was a very large trade in Mexican bobwhites, imported into various midwestern states for release to augment local populations. Actual measurements of the results of this endeavor are lacking, but there seemed to be a consensus among observers that such releases never led to sustained increase in bobwhite numbers, and in fact some thought that in years following a liberation, local populations were depressed. This may well have been the case, since birds from the tropical coast of Tamaulipas (the main source of stock), and their progeny if crossed with northern birds, would not likely have been winter-hardy. In any event this program was abandoned, attesting to its failure.

Dahlbeck (1951) reported a similar failure when gray partridges from southern Europe were imported to Sweden and mixed with the hardy northern populations. A catastrophic drop in number followed. He also relates a case of shipping in Carpathian red deer stags to "improve" the stock on an island off the Scandinavian coast. The resulting hybrids apparently were unable to stand the rigors of the northern climate, and the population on the island fell to near extinction. Following these experiences Sweden adopted regulations to prohibit import of game birds and mammals from outside the country.

Individual adaptability

Certain adaptive responses to a changing environment appear to be nongenetic. Some animals seem capable of internal physiological and behavioral adjustments and as a consequence can tolerate wide fluctuations in weather and other environmental factors. A classic example would be the mourning dove (*Zenaidura macroura*).

There is no more widely distributed or successful game bird in the North American continent than the dove. Its breeding range extends from the Atlantic to the Pacific and from the prairie provinces of southern Canada to Oaxaca in southern Mexico. Two weakly differentiated subspecies are recognized—an eastern and a western race. But each of these races successfully occupies a great variety of habitats. The western mourning dove, for example, breeds in the pine zone of the mountains, in the bleakest southwestern deserts, and along the tropical Mexican coast with equal success. If there are local physiologic adaptations, no one has detected them. In our present state of knowledge we must assume that the individual birds are capable of this range of adjustment.

The same can be said for some migratory birds like the mallard, which breeds from the arctic tundra to northern Baja California and from coast to coast. There are no detectable morphologic differences among North American mallards, nor is there any hint of local physiologic variation. Not only is the mallard adaptable in the sense of occupying a variety of breeding situations, but it has shown a remarkable capacity to adjust to the changes wrought in its wintering habitat. In primitive North America the mallard wintered in the natural marshes, sloughs, and backwaters and ate aquatic foods along with other ducks. Today most of these waterways are drained or otherwise made unattractive, and during the autumn much of the remaining habitat bristles with the guns of eager duck hunters. The mallard copes successfully with this situation by several adjustments in its habits. First, it feeds at night, spending the day in safety of a waterfowl refuge or on some open bay or sandbar. Secondly, it has learned to feed on the waste grain of stubble fields—wheat and corn in the midwest, rice and kafir in Texas and California. Each day with cessation of legal shooting the birds rise in great masses and fly to the stubbles for the evening repast. For a period in the 1940s shooting closed at 4 P.M. and the flight began at 4:15. When the law was changed to permit shooting till sunset, the birds adjusted their exodus to fifteen minutes after sunset, attesting to their capacity for quick reaction to circumstances. As a result, the mallard today is by far the most abundant duck in North America.

Some other species of waterfowl have learned the same tricks. The pintail and widgeon in the west, and various geese, feed on crop residues and avoid guns during the day by flocking in safe refuges. But many of the ducks have not adjusted and are steadily decreasing in number. The redhead, canvasback, wood duck, and shoveler continue to feed in the marshes and along shorelines where they are exposed to heavy shooting. These nonadaptive species require special protection and their situation will not likely improve in the future.

Another example of an adaptable species is the coyote. Originally it occurred in modest numbers through western North America, something of a hanger-on in the range of the wolf, scavenging scraps left by this lordly predator and catching such rodents as were available. In the remaining climax forests of the Mexican highlands, where wolves still occur, coyotes are scarce or absent (Leopold, 1959). But over most of the continent where the virgin flora and fauna (including wolves) has been eliminated, conditions for the coyote have been vastly improved. The scourge of rodents that came with agriculture and with overgrazing of the western ranges, plus the carcasses of domestic stock, offered a food supply much superior to that originally available. As a result, the coyote has thrived and extended its range far to the north and east. It invaded Alaska in the 1930s and currently has moved as far east as New York State. The coyote, in other words, is an example of a successional or subclimax predator that has profited from alteration in the climax biota, as much so as the deer. Because it occasionally preys on sheep and poultry, it has been the object of intensive control efforts, more so perhaps than any other carnivore in the world. Yet so adept is the coyote at learning the tricks of avoiding guns, traps, poisons, dogs, and even airplanes (from which it sometimes is shot) that it persists over nearly all of its original and adopted range, at least in modest numbers. The coyote will be among the surviving wild species long into the future.

Evolution of behavior

When species like the mallard and the coyote show adaptive behavior, as described above, it is difficult to say what part of this adaptation may be genetic and what part is learned. Many mallards are shot and many coyotes are trapped or poisoned. Are these the slow-witted ones? Is man, acting as a predator himself, applying a strong selective force to hunted species that may be bringing genetic changes in the survivors? If so, nothing is known of this force, but there is room for speculation.

Consider first the mallard. Much of a duck's behavior we know to be learned. The quick adjustment of the birds to a change in legal shooting hours could hardly be based on anything but experience. This quickly could become a tradition, transmitted from older experienced birds to young ones as some migratory habits are transmitted (Hochbaum, 1955). Yet over the years many individual mallards depart from this tradition and decoy into small ponds during shooting hours. They are among the missing when the breeders migrate northward in spring. Shooting, then, may be creating a new strain of mallard that tends to conform to mass behavior patterns and is less prone to make mistaken individual judgments.

In the southeastern United States, where the bobwhite has been heavily hunted for a century or more, it is generally reported that the birds have changed their habits. Old hunters claim to remember the day when a covey, flushed before a dog, would fly 100 to 200 yards and scatter in the broom-sedge or weed fields where they could be taken easily over points. Today covies tend to fly 300 to 400 yards and to seek shelter not in open fields but in dense oak thickets. Often such coveys put a "hook" on the end of their flight, turning to the right or left after entering the woods, thus being much harder to relocate. Is this change in behavior, if true, strictly learned and transmitted from adults to young? Or is there a genetic change involved as well, favoring the birds that fly far, seek woody cover, and change directions after entering the cover?

Much of the coyote's skill in avoiding peril is clearly learned. Individuals known to have escaped from a trap or to have survived a dose of strychnine become wary and are much more difficult to capture than young, inexperienced individuals. But the innate capacity for wariness may be strengthened and bolstered over the years by constant removal of the least wary individuals.

Thus, it may be that the hunted animals are evolving under a new selective force not affecting those animals that are permitted to live without persecution. In this sense, the adaptability which may be expressed as a genetic trait—or put in other words, as the ability to learn—is not a biological constant but a shifting attribute of a species.

Summary

There are notable differences in the response of wild animals to the sweeping changes in environment brought on by man. Some species are clearly associated with and dependent upon undisturbed climax situations, and these suffer the most from environmental change. They are here designated as nonadaptive species. The list includes all the rare or endangered species and some that have become extinct.

On the other hand, other animals adjust very well to changes in vegetation and in land use, and these on the whole persist or may even increase in abundance. Included in this group are many of the common game birds and mammals that supply the bulk of the recreational hunting in North America today. There appears to be a direct correlation between the affinity with seral or subclimax biotas and adaptability in the sense of the capacity to adjust to change.

The ability to adapt seems to involve two distinct components: (1) genetic plasticity, or the capacity for segments of a population to evolve rapidly to fit local conditions; and (2) the capacity for individuals to learn new habits of survival under altered circumstances. These cannot readily be separated, since the capacity to learn is itself a genetic trait.

BIBLIOGRAPHY

Aldrich, J. W. 1955. Distribution of American Gallinaceous Game Birds. U.S. Fish and Wildl. Serv., Wash., D.C. Circ. 34.
Blanchard, B. D. 1941. The White-crowned Sparrows (*Zonotrichia leucophrys*) of the Pacific Seaboard: Environment and Annual Cycle. Univ. Calif. Pub. Zool. 46:1–178.
Buechner, H. K. 1950. Life History, Ecology, and Range Use of the Pronghorn Antelope in Trans-Pecos Texas. Amer. Midl. Nat. 43:257–354.
Cheatum, E. L., and Severinghaus, C. W. 1950. Variations in Fertility of White-tailed Deer Related to Range Conditions. Trans. N. Amer. Wildl. Conf. 15:170–90.
Dahlbeck, N. 1951. [Commentary During U.N. Conf., Fish and Wildl. Res.] Proc. U.N.

Sci. Conf. on Conserv. and Utiliz. of Res. Lake Success, N.Y. Aug. 17–Sept. 6, 1949. 7:210.

Grant, V. 1963. The Origin of Adaptations. Columbia Univ. Press, New York and London.

Hochbaum, H. A. 1955. Travels and Traditions of Waterfowl. Univ. Minn. Press, Minneapolis.

Lack, D. 1954. The Natural Regulation of Animal Numbers. Oxford Univ. Press.

Leopold, A. S. 1944. The Nature of Heritable Wildness in Turkeys. Condor 46:133–97.

———— 1950. Deer in Relation to Plant Succession. Trans. N. Amer. Wildl. Conf. 15:571–80.

———— 1959. Wildlife of Mexico: the Game Birds and Mammals. Univ. Calif. Press, Berkeley.

Longhurst, W. M., Leopold, A. S., and Dasmann, R. F. 1952. A Survey of California Deer Herds, Their Ranges and Management Problems. Calif. Fish and Game, Game Bul. 6.

Mayr, E. 1942. Systematics and the Origin of Species. Columbia Univ. Press, New York.

Sauer, C. O. 1950. Grassland Climax, Fire, and Man. J. Range Mgt. 3:16–21.

Schorger, A. W. 1955. The Passenger Pigeon: Its Natural History and Extinction. Univ. Wisc. Press, Madison.

Taber, R. D. 1953. Studies of Black-tailed Deer Reproduction on Three Chaparral Cover Types. Calif. Fish and Game Bul. 39(2):177–86.

EXPERIMENTAL ECOLOGY AND HABITAT CONSERVATION

J. D. Ovington*

INTRODUCTION

The growing interest throughout the world in the conservation of natural resources can be attributed to various causes. In particular, the greater mobility of man, coupled with more leisure time for outdoor recreation and a desire to relax in natural surroundings, has increased public use and appreciation of relatively undisturbed land. This land is of high conservation value because it contains the main reserves of wildlife surviving in fairly natural conditions. Already, human influence is so pervasive that few natural communities remain which do not bear the stamp of man's activities. Man's capacity to change and pollute natural environments is being enhanced rapidly; within the last quarter of a century there have been far-reaching developments in earth-moving equipment, the release of radioactive materials, the aerial application of fertilizers, and the manufacture of nonselective poisonous chemicals which have been used widespread over the countryside.

The greater demands placed on natural resources by a multiplying and more prosperous human population create an ever-increasing sense of urgency to set aside natural areas to preserve species or

* Dr. Ovington is Chairman of the Forestry Department at the Australian National University at Canberra. A close student of energy flow through the woodland ecosystem, he was formerly associated with The Nature Conservancy's Monks Wood Research Station at St. Ives, Huntingdonshire, England.

natural communities threatened with extinction or modification. Paradoxically, some degree of management may be needed to protect natural areas if they become subject to external influences or if it is desired to maintain a particular ecological situation. Conservation, expressed through the preservation of natural or seminatural areas, has been justified emotionally as safeguarding national heritages for posterity. Materialistically, justification can be found in terms of the needs of biological research, of keeping amenity attractions, to obtain revenue from tourists, and of the maintenance of supposedly irreplaceable stocks of genes and population assemblages for possible future use by man.

At the same time, conservation has much to contribute to human welfare in locations where the needs of forestry, agriculture, or industry are uppermost. Dramatic examples of unwise land use, as when extensive flooding and soil erosion occur or when dust bowls are created, plus the obvious advantages gained from successful applied land-use projects, such as that of the Tennessee Valley Authority, have demonstrated the many potential applications of conservation principles to land-use planning in general.

With recognition of the advantages to be gained from sound conservation projects, both from the preservation and applied land-use viewpoints, official organizations are being established to serve conservation interests and academic courses are being orientated more in this direction. The principle that there is a biological limit to the world's natural resources and their renewal rates is being recognized more generally and viewed against the background of the requirements of an increasing world population.

In this affluent technological era, in which scarcities and surpluses are largely the product of political divisions, sympathetic support for conservation is still possible. Conservationists are fortunate in having both the opportunity and the responsibility to place conservation on a sound scientific basis so that it can make its full contribution to human welfare. A fuller understanding of ecological processes and the interrelationships between living organisms and their environments can be provided by critical research in experimental ecology designed for application to conservation projects. Careful consideration needs to be given to the nature and organization of this research. Clearly, it should be of a multidisciplinary nature and be concerned with whole ecosystems, recognizing them as dynamic situations liable to change, both naturally and as a result of management.

ECOSYSTEMS AS PRODUCTIVE UNITS

Studies of ecosystems must center largely on the living organisms and how they affect or are affected by their environments. Living organisms are produced by two main kinds of organic production, namely primary and secondary.

Primary production involves the formation of organic matter from inorganic substances by photosynthesis and chemosynthesis. In photosynthesis, terrestrial plants utilize solar energy to produce carbohydrates by combining carbon dioxide from the air with water from the soil in the presence of chlorophyll pigments. Recent research shows photosynthesis to be an ancient process which began in the extreme environmental conditions prevailing during the first half of the earth's life. It is also remarkably inefficient, since only a small part (less than 5 per cent) of the incident light energy is held as chemical energy in the primary products. Chemosynthesis occurs to a lesser extent than photosynthesis and differs from it in that the energy for synthesis is derived by oxidation of inorganic compounds. Of the assimilate produced by photosynthesis and chemosynthesis (i.e. gross production), part is used up by the respiration of the producer organisms and the rest (i.e. net production) either constitutes new growth or is stored within existing plant organs. For synthesis to take place, adequate amounts of such nutrient chemicals as nitrogen, phosphorous, and calcium are essential. The form and chemical composition of the different kinds of plant material comprising primary products vary greatly but include the flowers, seeds, leaves, stems, and roots of plants of different species.

Secondary production involves the breakdown and use of primary organic material or its derivatives by nonphotosynthetic plants and animals. Progressively, plant and animal residues are transferred through successive organisms until complete disintegration and energy release are achieved. The breakdown of primary material begins on the living plants with the attacks of disease, pest, and grazing organisms and usually ends on or in the soil. The complicated systems of organic transfer and breakdown associated with secondary production form an intricate pattern and at all trophic levels involve numerous organisms whose activities are interconnected in diverse ways. At present, complete studies of the secondary production system are impossible for most terrestrial ecosystems because of ecosystem complexity and the inadequacy of ecological technique. However, the more obvious pathways of organic breakdown can be identified and their proportionate magnitude assessed, since, over a specified time period, the size of the secondary system as a whole is given by the balance between net primary production and biomass change after making allowance for the removal of material by harvesting.

While primary and secondary production can be considered as two distinct processes, in practice they modify each other in several ways. The regular cropping of grasses by herbivores, for example, can stimulate or diminish primary production, depending upon the ecological conditions and the timing, selectivity, and intensity of grazing. Primary producers also depend upon the secondary producers to release for reuse the mineral nutrients taken up from the soil by previous plants. On the other hand, differences in the structure of plant communities, as for instance between grassland and forest, result in characteristic adaptive differences in the fauna.

Great variation occurs in the amount of annual net primary production over the earth and presumably also in the amount of secondary production, since the two types of production must balance, where organic change and harvesting are negligible. Primary production tends to increase with distance from the poles. Thus the approximate average annual net production of dry matter, as 10^3 kg per hectare for plant communities dominated by woody plants, is for ecosystems within the willow shrub communities of the arctic tundra 2, the taiga pine forests 6, the temperate forests 25, and the equatorial tropical rain forests 50. This latitudinal gradient results largely from climatic differences, the general increase in production toward the equator being associated with longer, more favorable growing periods and greater amounts of incoming solar radiation. Dendrochronological studies have also shown climate to be a major determinant of production, close correlations being obtained for corresponding years between the widths of the annual rings

in the stems of woody perennial plants and climatic factors, notably temperature and rainfall.

At a given latitude, net primary production may vary greatly, partly because of local climatic variations caused by altitudinal or geographic differences but also because of differences in pedology, vegetation structure, and human influence. For temperate forests, for instance, annual net primary production (as 10^3 kg per hectare) ranges from about 10 to 30 and possibly higher if only the more productive period of a forest rotation is considered. Whittaker (in press) has found that the net primary production of above-ground plant material by climax forest and shrub communities in the Smoky Mountains varies from about 6 to 14×10^3 kg per hectare; production decreasing toward higher elevations at a mean rate of 4×10^3 kg per hectare per 100 m elevation rise. In this case, the local effect of increasing altitude is closely associated with a moisture gradient, the upper slopes being the drier. For high, mountain snowbank environments Billings and Bliss (1959) report a low annual net production by American alpine meadow communities of 0.2×10^3 kg per hectare. The silvicultural-site index, which is based on the rate of height growth of trees, has also been used as a measure of production. Cruttwell (1952) found that for plantations of Monterey pine the production index increased by about 8 m for each 100-m-decrease in altitude. The effects of geographical situation are to be seen in the marked contrasts in production along a latitudinal transect across a continent such as Australia or by comparing production in Labrador with that of Britain, both of which occupy similar northern latitudes but with Britain benefiting from the warming effects of marine currents.

Since soil development is influenced by climatic factors, the effects of climate and soil on production are closely interwoven.

The importance of soil has been demonstrated by ecological surveys where correlations have been obtained between soil properties and production values in regions of homogeneous climate. In the United States Coile (1952) and his coworkers found the production of southern forests to be related closely to soil type. Physical soil conditions, particularly those affecting moisture supply, have been stressed but undoubtedly nutrient availability is important also and in some instances critical, as when trace deficiencies occur such as of cobalt and zinc in Australia. The development of methods to measure the availability of nutrients from the soil for plant growth is urgently required by ecologists and it seems essential to express the results in terms of the volume of soil utilized by the plants rather than as mg per 100 g of soil sampled without reference to over-all rooting depth. Further evidence of the importance of soil is provided by the many agricultural and silvicultural experiments in which crop production has been changed greatly by soil modification.

Ecosystems may differ widely in their floristic and faunistic composition and yet exhibit general similarities of structure, biomass, and production. Similarity of physiognomy is associated usually with likeness of environmental conditions but situations can be found where seminatural plant communities of different structures are present side by side with no great differences in climate and soil. On the Anoka sand plain in Minnesota, for instance, a vast complex of prairie, savanna, and woodland communities exists, possibly reflecting the past effects of burning by Indians and of abandoned agricultural operations by European pioneers (Pierce, 1954). Ovington, Heitkamp, and Lawrence (1963) found primary production there to be greater in the more structurally complex communities where shrubs and trees replace the forbs and grasses as the main production agents. Annual net primary production of above-ground plant material as 10^3 kg per hectare for the prairie, savanna, and oakwood ecosystems was 0.9, 5.3, and 8.2 respectively. The greatest annual production of 9.5×10^3 kg per hectare was recorded for a field of maize nearby but depended upon the application of large amounts of fertilizer and regular farming operations so that soil conditions were greatly different in the maize field.

High rates of primary production are often associated with large biomass, although exceptions occur. Peat bogs contain much organic matter but have a small rate of primary production because a large part of the plant material is dead and nonproductive. More meaningful production relationships are likely to be obtained by relating production to the amount of living plant material or of plant components such as roots and leaves rather than over-all biomass.

Unfortunately, few data are available of root weight and surface area, but it is evident that root mass is considerable in certain ecosystems. Tropical woodlands, for example, have about 90×10^3 kg per hectare of roots, equal to about a fifth of the biomass.

The leaf mass in such woodlands amounts to approximately 25×10^3 kg per hectare and has a surface area about eight times that of the underlying ground surface. Agriculturalists have devoted much attention to the determination of the weight and area of foliar material per unit area of land surface and have emphasized that for high production rates in field crops it is essential to have a leaf system capable of intercepting a large proportion of the incoming light energy throughout the year. Leaves vary in thickness, shape, orientation, and photosynthetic efficiency, and a more precise indication of production by plant communities may be provided by the amount of chlorophyll present over a unit area of ground surface. Brougham (1960) considers that the maximum growth rate of pure stands of crop and pasture species is closely related to the amount of chlorophyll above the 95 per cent light-interception level within the community.

The full importance of vegetation structure has not always been recognized by conservationists. Natural plant communities composed of many plant species form complex multistoried associations in which different strata overshadow one another so that the vegetation microclimate is modified progressively downward. The vertical strata sequence is best seen in woodlands, where the strata are thicker because of the tallness of the trees. Within each stratum the photosynthetic organs are adapted for plant production in the environmental conditions characteristic of their level so that in entity plant communities constitute highly integrated photosynthetic mechanisms. For instance, the uppermost leaves, which normally receive full insolation, are able to maintain greater rates of photosynthesis at high light intensities than the lower leaves, which live in the shade; the reverse is true at low light intensities. In deciduous temperate forests, the early-spring flush of growth by the field layer, before the tree leaves develop, permits fuller utilization of the site for organic production as do the complementary rooting depths of plants of different species. Consequently, it is not surprising that some natural plant communities are highly productive, equaling or surpassing cultivated vegetation in the same region even though they are not subjected to cultural operations such as fertilizer application or soil working.

While the relatively good photosynthetic efficiency of some mixed natural stands can be attributed in part to the variety of plant species present, diversity as such is not prerequisite to high levels of production. Some of the most productive temperate plant communities are monoculture plantations of conifers whose crowns are so dense that no understory vegetation can survive in the poor light conditions. Silviculturalists are attempting to increase production by such stands even further through tree selection and plant breeding.

However, a distinction should be made between short- and long-term production. If monoculture stands prove to be more susceptible than mixed stands to hazards such as fire, soil degradation, wind blow, or the attacks of pests and disease, then their short-term high production rates could be misleading. Experience with Norway spruce (*Picea abies*) in Germany and with Monterey pine (*Pinus radiata*) in Australia suggests that high production is difficult to maintain over several generations of pure spruce stands, although the reasons for this are not clearly understood. This has led silviculturalists to emphasize more the advantages of mixed forests, particularly if the mixture includes soil-enriching species such as alder, whose roots bear nodules for nitrogen fixation. The beneficial effect of alder has been demonstrated by Tarrant (1961), who found that pure stands of Douglas fir in the northwest United States were much less productive than mixed fir and alder stands.

The relevance of the structure of plant communities to conservation considerations does not lie solely in its effects on the amount of organic matter produced, but also on the variety and distribution of primary production. If the Minnesota prairie, savanna, and woodland ecosystems are compared (Table 1), it can be seen that over 90 per cent of the production of above-ground plant material takes place close to the ground in the prairie and high above ground in the tree crowns in the oakwood. The savanna represents an interesting compromise between these two extremes, having an intermediate amount of primary production with both herbaceous and tree material well represented. Moreover, in the savanna the pri-

TABLE 1. The distribution and amount of primary production in
neighboring plant communities in Minnesota

Ecosystem	Strata	Number of species of higher plants	Average upper limit to strata m	Annual net primary production kg per ha
Prairie	Herbaceous	40	0.2	920
	Shrub	2	0.4	10
	Tree	0	Absent	0
Savanna	Herbaceous	32	0.2	1886
	Shrub	6	0.7	41
	Tree	2	10.0	2833
Oakwood	Herbaceous	17	0.2	182
	Shrub	6	1.2	389
	Tree	2	17.0	4046

mary production is more evenly distributed down the vegetation profile so that
the grazing and decomposer systems of
plant breakdown are both well represented. The same wide range of environmental conditions occurring from tree
top to ground level in the wood are present in the savanna, but the variety of
environments in the savanna is further
enhanced by the comparatively large
horizontal heterogeneity. The savanna
trees are unevenly scattered and often
have a clumped distribution with the intervening treeless spaces of varied size,
shape, and orientation. These open spaces
act as sun traps and have a characteristic
climate not found in the prairie or woodland. Despite competition with trees and
shrubs, the herbaceous layer is best developed and most productive in the savanna ecosystem, which might therefore
be expected to be capable of supporting
a larger population of grazing mammals.
Furthermore, the savanna herbaceous
layer is also relatively rich in minerals,
since it benefits annually from the mineral nutrients added to the soil by leaves
falling from trees and being blown into
open spaces.

It is not without significance that many
man-made communities which are recognized as being biologically rich, such as
the Swedish meadow-forest complex or
Western European coppice with standard woodlands, have many of the structural attributes of savanna vegetation. In
densely populated regions with small nature reserves from which the maximum
yield of biological interest must be produced, management is often aimed at
developing a vegetation complex with
varied woodland and open places represented by pathways, roads, glades, or
fields (Fig. I-2). The conservation value
of otherwise monotonous woodland can
be enhanced and the number and variety
of kinds of living organisms present increased with relatively little loss of timber
yield by the creation and careful management of open spaces. Forest pathways
and roads can be made more favorable
to wildlife if a border of herbaceous
plants and shrubs is developed and the
width and direction of the roads are varied to provide shelter and a variety of
aspects. Normally, forage plants beneath
tree crowns are of poor feeding quality,
being poor in carbohydrates because of
shading, so that the wildlife-carrying capacity of a forest is greatly enhanced if
open-grown forage is available. Where,
as in national parks of East Africa, the

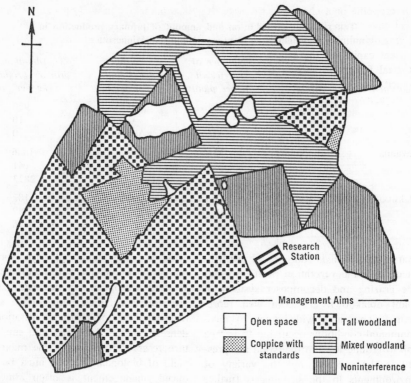

N

FIG. I-2. Management map for Monks Wood Nature Reserve. Prepared by R. Steele.

Research Station

Management Aims

Open space   Tall woodland

Coppice with
standards   Mixed woodland

Noninterference

tree component of the savanna is being destroyed, it is essential for conservation purposes to appreciate the significance of this change in terms of its lasting effects on the fundamental structure of the productive system.

Ecologists pay too little attention to root ecology, and this can lead to misunderstandings of the structural nature of the plant community. Woodland trees are often joined below ground by root unions so that the tree components of a woodland should not be visualized as a collection of individual trees but rather as separate shoots arising from a more or less common root system. In this way it is possible to interpret better the spread of root-infecting diseases, the competitive vigor of woody plants, and their role in soil stabilization.

ECOSYSTEM PROCESSES AND
HABITAT MANAGEMENT

In order to understand better the functioning of ecosystems, ecologists are attempting to make detailed balance sheets of organic production and turnover and two other closely associated processes, namely energy flow and mineral cycling. Knowledge of these processes permits reliable forecasts to be made of the consequences of general trends in ecosystem dynamics and of management operations. Such information is invaluable in formulating plans of habitat management since conservationists normally need to adopt a long-term viewpoint. For instance, the maintenance of the soil must be a vital consideration in habitat preservation.

Overcropping or a change in the type of plant cover caused by too high a density of grazing animals may slowly reduce the nutrient capital of the soil or affect soil physical factors in such a way that the capacity of the soil to support a variety of organisms or to sustain a required level of production is diminished gradually. In extreme conditions of instability, the loss of the protective plant cover under certain climatic conditions can lead eventually to extensive soil erosion.

The biomass of a terrestrial ecosystem may increase, decrease, or remain constant from year to year depending upon the balance among primary production, organic breakdown, and the harvesting of organic material. The balance changes greatly according to the stage of community development. Thus, where a woodland becomes successfully established there is an initial phase of rapid biomass accumulation; annual values of about 8×10^3 kg per hectare are common in temperate woodlands. This is followed in middle age by a period of relatively stable biomass, and finally toward the end of the rotation the biomass begins to decrease—since primary production is small and harvesting large. Depending upon the type of plant cover, the rate and direction of change for individual components of the biomass may differ from that of the biomass as a whole. During the initial phase of rapid biomass accretion in European temperate woodlands, for example, little annual change in litter accumulation over the forest floor occurs under most broad-leaved tree species while under conifers litter builds up quickly.

Some organic matter may persist for centuries relatively unchanged if perennial plants are present or waterlogging occurs, but generally the primary organic products disappear from ecosystems within a few years of their formation. In some circumstances much of this depletion can be attributed to harvesting or grazing, but usually decomposition is the main cause. The natural loss of organic matter by decomposition from commercial forest plantations, for example, is often double that removed by the harvesting of tree trunks. Decomposition occurs largely through the activities of living organisms, but the annual rate of organic turnover is influenced also by environmental conditions and the different resistances to decay of different kinds of plant material. Consequently, different amounts of dead organic matter accumulate over the soil in different ecosystems. Litter accumulation on the soil has sometimes been mistakenly considered to indicate a small annual turnover of organic matter, but, in fact, shows only that litter fall has exceeded decomposition at some previous time. Some of the most productive ecosystems with a large annual turnover of organic matter have a thick litter layer over the soil. Records of organic turnover rarely take into account root breakdown, even though Russian scientists (Remezov, 1959) have pointed out that root turnover may be about half that of above-ground material.

The energy going into ecosystems is dissipated in various ways, most being expended by reflection, net long wave loss to the atmosphere, heating the ecosystem, and evaporating water. Only a small part of the incident energy is converted to chemical energy and held within the primary products; annual values of energy capture of over 600×10^8 calories per hectare have been recorded for some highly productive woodlands (Ovington and Heitkamp, 1960). Because the calorific values for organic matter do not vary greatly and energy cannot be recycled within an ecosystem, the pattern of energy flow broadly parallels that of the organic system.

The movement of chemicals through ecosystems is very different from that of energy. Chemical elements are continuously being recycled within ecosystems; and the concentrations of chemicals within organic matter vary greatly, since elements are taken up differentially by plants and are distributed unevenly through plant bodies (Ovington, 1962). The general character of plant and animal communities is influenced greatly by nutrient status, expressed in terms of the capital of available nutrients and the rate of their cycling in ecosystems. Specht (1963) has pointed out that sclerophyllous heath and herbaceous swards in southern Australia occur within a few meters of each other and the only consistent difference in environment is the fertility level of the soil, heath being present on soils low in phosphorus and nitrogen. When the nutrient status of the heath areas was changed by adding fertilizers, plant production almost trebled, the individual heath plant species varying in growth response according to the amount of fertilizer added. At the same time, the species composition of the heath vegetation changed more toward a herbaceous sward with annual grasses, herbs, and a moss appearing and surviving on fertilized plots. This dramatic response to fertilizers was rapid, changes being obvious within a year of applying the fertilizers. Clearly, conservationists need to know something of nutrient status and balance of the ecosystems with which they are concerned.

Investigations of nutrient cycling have to take into account various external factors. Nutrients are added to ecosystems in precipitation, in fertilizers, by nitrogen fixation, as a result of soil and rock weathering, and by deposition of airborne material carried from industrial installations, roads, and fields. Loss of nutrients from ecosystems occurs when materials are harvested, water drains from the soil, and organic matter is consumed by fire. Animal movement can also cause loss or gain of nutrients from ecosystems depending upon the over-all direction of movement.

The accretion of organic matter in eco-systems normally results in a build-up of nutrients within the biomass, and this may be associated with significant changes in the level of soil fertility. Movement of nutrient chemicals between plants and soil occurs in various ways. Both major and minor inorganic nutrients are washed out of plants by rain, dew, and mist. The leached nutrients are subsequently reabsorbed from the soil, and this recycling can be very rapid, taking only a matter of weeks. Tukey and Mecklenburg (1961) have suggested that foliar leaching is an important ecological factor affecting plant distribution, since in maritime climates with much precipitation some plants seem adapted to nutrient loss through leaching and sometimes to the utilization of leachates from plants of other species. In addition to rapid cycles such as these, longer cycles occur as in the annual transfer of nutrients in plant litter falling to the ground or when nutrients are held for many years in perennial plants. Since the movement of mineral nutrients is of a polycyclic nature, the nutrient capital of an ecosystem varies both quantitatively and in distribution, according to the balance among all the internal cycles and the diverse external factors affecting nutrient input and output.

CONCLUSIONS

Much of the early ecological work related to conservation was rightly concerned with recording the species and numbers of organisms present in ecosystems. With the application of conservation principles to land use in general and a growing appreciation of the need to manage seminatural areas, some attention is being paid now to ecosystem processes, particularly organic production and turnover, energy flow, and the cycling of mineral nutrients. The two kinds of approach are complementary and by providing a more comprehensive insight into ecosystem dynamics permit conservationists to place habitat management on a sounder basis.

Nevertheless, there is some danger that conservationists may be daunted by the growing number and complexity of factors they need to consider. This problem is more apparent than real, because with more knowledge it becomes possible to have a better perspective from which to judge the significance of individual ecological factors. Projects such as the International Biological Program should contribute much to the available fund of relevant knowledge. At the same time, powerful new ecological tools are being developed and it is imperative that they be utilized fully. For instance, high-speed computers now permit ecologists to assess the effects of many environmental factors which may be interrelated in diverse ways. Analogue computers enable ecosystems to be simulated artifically so that hypotheses relating to management can be tested quickly without endangering natural ecosystems. Recently it has been demonstrated that radioactive materials can be introduced safely on a large scale into ecosystems so as to follow more pre-cisely the polycyclic movement of materials.

Within the last decade experimental ecology has provided new information on techniques of habitat management such as burning, the regulation of the water table, and manipulation of the vegetation by cutting and chemicals. Nevertheless, the application of experimental ecology to conservation has not been fully exploited. Some indication of the potentialities of this approach is provided by the work of the Russians Bazilevitch and Rodin (1964), who have shown how the magnitudes and detailed patterns of ecosystem processes can be used for ecosystem classification in a similar way to the more traditional method based on the numbers and types of organisms present. While the practical applications of experimental ecology to conservation are both varied and numerous, perhaps the greatest and most challenging contribution that ecologists can make is to provide the necessary perspective by which to evaluate the intricacies of ecosystems and to develop a conservation philosophy based on a more sensitive and scientific understanding of man and his environment.

BIBLIOGRAPHY

Bazilevitch, N. I., and Rodin, L. E. 1964. Types of Biological Cycles of Ash Elements and Nitrogen Turnover for the Main Natural Zones of the Northern Hemisphere. Genesis, Classification and Geography of Soils in the USSR: 134–46. Moscow.

Billings, W. D., and Bliss, L. C. 1959. An Alpine Snowbank Environment and Its Effects on Vegetation, Plant Development, and Productivity. Ecol. 40:388–97.

Brougham, R. W. 1960. The Relationship Between the Critical Leaf Area, Total Chlorophyll Content and Maximum Growth-rate of Some Pasture and Crop Plants. Ann. Bot. (N.S.) 24:463–74.

Coile, T. S. 1952. Soil and the Growth of Forests. Adv. Agron. 4:329–98.

Cruttwell, C. R. 1952. The Influence of Altitude, Density of Stocking and Exposure on the Height Growth of *Pinus radiata* in Beaumont Forest. N.Z. J. Forestry 6:330–33.

Ovington, J. D. 1962. Quantitative Ecology and the Woodland Ecosystem Concept. Adv. Ecol. Res. 1:103–92.

——— and Heitkamp, D. 1960. The Accumulation of Energy in Forest Plantations in Britain. J. Ecol. 48:639–46.

——— Heitkamp, D., and Lawrence, D. B. 1963. Plant Biomass and Productivity of Prairie, Savannah, Oakwood and Maize Field Ecosystems in Central Minnesota. Ecol. 44:52–63.

Pierce, R. L. 1954. Vegetation Cover Types and Land Use History of the Cedar Creek Natural History Reservation, Anoka and Isanti Counties, Minnesota. M. Sc. thesis, Univ. Minn., Minneapolis.

Remezov, N. P. 1959. Methods of Studying the Biological Cycle of Elements in the Forest. Pochvovedenie 6:71–79.

Specht, R. L. 1963. Dark Island Heath (Ninety Mile Plain, S. Australia) VII. The Effect of Fertilizers on Composition and Growth: 159–60. Aust. J. Bot. 11:67–94.

Tarrant, R. F. 1961. Stand Development and Soil Fertility in a Douglas Fir–Red Alder Plantation. Forest Sci. 7:238–46.

Tukey, H. B., Jr., and Mecklenburg, R. A. 1964. Leaching of Metabolites from Foliage and Subsequent Reabsorption and Redistribution of the Leachate in Plants. Amer. J. Bot. 737–42.

Whittaker, R. L. Estimated Net Production of Forests in the Great Smoky Mountains (in press).

WEATHER MODIFICATION AND THE LIVING ENVIRONMENT

Paul E. Waggoner*

Although our influence over the weather is distinctly less than might suit a parched farmer stirring in the dust of his yard or a flood fugitive perched upon a ridge pole, our devices have at least become more logical and worthy of test. This possibility of changing the weather immediately awakens the ecologist's interest, for it is an axiom of his science that no change will have only the simple, expected consequence. Thus, manufactured rain will gouge gullies while it waters the cornfield; and the hurricane will not flood the marshes with salt water if it does not inundate the city. In this paper, I examine the work of the weathermakers, suggest some changes in our plant-clad environment that weathermaking might cause, and finally investigate how man feels after the surrounding plants are changed, whether indirectly by weather control or directly by an ax. This course, on the one hand, carries us from the grand but still questionable scheme of remaking the climate to its consequences in plant and then human ecology. And on the other hand, it shows the small and certain changes in outdoor man's personal energy budget that follow putting in or taking out plants in his neighborhood.

* Dr. Waggoner, a bioclimatologist who received his Ph.D. from Iowa State College in 1951, is Chief of the Department of Soils and Climatology at The Connecticut Agricultural Experiment Station, New Haven.

CHANGING THE WEATHER

The limits of settlement and cultivation are perennially pushed across the boundaries of secure climate. We therefore perennially grasp for a tool to change the weather, to improve it according to our current lights. Small wonder, therefore, that Schaefer and Langmuir's experimental verification in 1946 that super-cooled clouds could be transformed into ice clouds as the Bergeron-Findeisen theory predicted triggered an outpouring of weather modification. The events that followed are related by Huschke (1963) in an article that "must be placed among the 'nonproductive' items of the *late* retrenchment era." The *experimental era*, 1946–50, revealed that "the artificial modification of cumuliform clouds is of doubtful economic importance for the production of rain." Meanwhile, in the Southwest and later in the Midwest and South a drouth began. The simultaneous appearance of desperation for rain and presumed means of getting it touched off the *bandwagon era*, 1949–54. In 1952 fully one tenth of the land of the United States, 300 million acres, was a target for cloud seeders. Although the commercial seeders continued optimistic, by the end of the era others were "mired in the statistical no man's land of inconclusiveness."

The collision of human hopes and scientific skepticism caused Congress to put the Advisory Committee on Weather Control (1957) to work during the *evaluation era*, 1952–57. When they concluded statistically that 10 to 15 per cent increases in rain had been made by seeding winter-type storm clouds in mountainous areas in the West but that no increases could be detected elsewhere, they were attacked by both sides. The Advisory Committee also, and this was less sensational, encouraged important physical analyses that began the *retrenchment era*, 1957–.

The peak of published work on weather modification passed in 1956. But the variety of means investigated and of phenomena attacked has increased. This continuing research is annually reviewed (e.g. NSF, 1963), and bibliographies are occasionally compiled (e.g. Thuronyi, 1964).

Further, this research was thoroughly evaluated during 1964 by a panel of the National Academy of Sciences-National Research Council (NAS, 1964):

"The striking development during the past ten years of a number of new tools that produce intensely interesting effects, often involving the triggering of large releases of energy in clouds, in the atmosphere near the surface, and in the upper atmosphere, provides a basis for future efforts in weather modification. In the activities that have possible economic importance, our findings are as follows: It is possible to disperse stable clouds, such as super-cooled fog and stratus, by seeding; it has not been demonstrated that precipitation from winter orographic storms can be increased significantly by seeding; it has not been demonstrated that hurricanes can be 'steered' or diminished by seeding; it has not been demonstrated that asphalt coverings, black dust, or any other surface modifications increase precipitation. On the basis of these findings, we conclude that the initiation of large-scale operational weather-modifi-

cation programs would be premature. Many fundamental problems must be answered first." Now the research behind the conclusions will be reviewed in somewhat more detail and an optimistic, even overoptimistic upper limit set upon effectiveness. The conservative nature of society that may want its hurricanes slowed but not its average climate changed will also work to keep any actual weather modification well within the upper limits that will be assumed here. My considering very high upper limits will help guarantee against oversight, but biological effects, in the process, will far more likely be overestimated than otherwise.

Dissipation of clouds of super-cooled water and of fog is in the "engineering" stage. United Airlines has already demonstrated the feasibility of airport clearing (NAS, 1964), apparently by cloud seeding. In Operation Pea Soup the dusting of sixty pounds of carbon black per mile of stratus top caused the stratus to part, and the sea could be seen below. The amount of precipitation that reaches the ground from these stratiform clouds is minute, however, and calculated to be no more than one millimeter of rain. Later, the ecological effect of occasional extra sunshine will be examined.

Rainmaking has been a generally discouraging affair, but enough straws of hope can be grasped to permit us reasonably to conceive some increased rain and then consider the ecological consequences. Most discouraging is the general failure to get more rain from seeded skies. In addition, however, the very theoretical foundation is insecure, for precipitation in convective clouds may not be initiated by the ice-crystal process (Battan, 1961). The straws of hope, on the other hand, are two. First, orographic clouds are naturally colloidally unstable (Bergeron, 1949), and the Advisory Committee (1957) did state that seeding in mountains increased rain 10 to 15 per cent. Second, the dynamics of tropical cumulus clouds can be affected by seeding (Howell, 1960; Malkus and Simpson, 1964), and in the tropics Howell (1960) did demonstrate 20 per cent increases in rain where he had seeded. Later, therefore, the ecological effect of moving 20 per cent more precipitation to a target region will be examined.

The renewal of stratus will obviously warm the soil beneath and the air nearby. In fact, that region of the earth and its atmosphere will be darker and reflect less radiation back to space. But when we consider temperature changes, grand changes come to mind. Modifying the energy balance of a region by carrying in warm water or by changing the reflectivity of the earth through cloudiness or opaque gases aloft is the usual device considered. Kraus predicts that decreasing the radiation reaching the earth will cool the lower atmosphere, increase precipitation, and cause a new ice age; the deserts would flower and the northern United States, Canada, and Russia would be buried in snow. Wexler, however, concluded that warming, not cooling, would increase precipitation. So far no one has settled this paradox (NSF, 1963). Nevertheless, the ecological consequences of a 1° C warming will be examined. This is the magnitude of the winter warming from 1880 to 1940 in the zone 40° to 70° N (Mitchell, 1961) and was the greatest warming that could be found in several combinations of periods and zones.

Project Storm Fury has awakened hope that hurricanes may be steered or dissipated. "Esther" and "Beulah" have been seeded and the results have agreed with the hypothesis: seeding would cause super-cooled water to freeze in the towering clouds near the eye, and the released heat of fusion would decrease the pressure gradient and the maximum wind speed. No "check" hurricane exists, however, and the 10 per cent decrease of the wind and ten-mile migration of the eye wall that followed seeding is not an uncommon fluctuation of an unmodified storm (Malkus and Simpson, 1964). Nevertheless, ecological consequences of no hurricanes will be examined.

Lightning is a sufficiently frequent cause of forest fires that the U.S. Forest Service undertook Project Skyfire, hoping to modify thunderstorms in ways that would decrease cloud-to-ground lightning. In eighteen pairs of storms, cloud-to-ground lightning was a statistically insignificant, 38 per cent less in the treated storms than in the untreated (NSF, 1963). In Arizona, however, Battan failed to obtain the same result (NAS, 1964). Despite these variable results, the ecological consequences of fewer fires through decreased lightning and fire control by rain-on-order will be examined.

People who are concerned with "habitats" certainly fear reckless tampering with the climate and want to know whether the weathermakers are likely to exceed or are bent upon exceeding the ranges written in preceding paragraphs.

Several influences are at work. First, if the consequences of weathermaking are known, politics will smother and suppress it to harmlessness. Even if weathermakers were omnipotent in physics, the pulling and hauling of society would likely limit them to blunting extremes universally regarded as bad. For example, few would object to relieving a drouth that was already many months old, but many would object to making a climate rainier, month after month.

The greatest concern, however, is whether the weathermakers might unpremeditatedly and innocently set off a disaster that was nonetheless irretrievable and irreparable. Several things hinder them, and reassure the fearful. First, the "balance of nature" opposes the weathermaker as it does, say, the jungle clearer. The natural climate is the balance among forces whose immensity boggles human schemes. Hence, even those man-made perturbations involving the energy of atomic explosions are soon damped out.

As a further restriction, the weather-makers share the caution of conservationists: "In his search for the understanding which he hopes will lead to control over weather, man is severely limited. He is limited by his knowledge and by his resources. In addition, he is limited by the fear that his experiments may engender unforeseen consequences." (NSF, 1963)

The greatest hope, however, is that meteorologists may learn to anticipate consequences of changes in the weather. The most promising model that will permit these harmless tests seems the mathematical one, the simulation of the atmosphere in an electronic computer. A notable attempt at simulation is described by Smagorinsky (1963): in some ways the model behaved as the atmosphere, in some ways it did not, and even more realistic models must be developed. Eventually the consequences of diverted ocean currents, altered albedo, and felled forests may be understood or predicted by manipulating mathematical models rather than by debates or tampering. In the meantime the ecological consequences of much greater changes in weather than we can now make need examination. This will reveal that biologists, like meteorologists, know much less than they need.

EFFECT OF WEATHER CHANGES
UPON PLANTS

A change in weather would surely affect man and other animals directly. But, and this is the way I shall view the matter, it will also affect their habitat by changing the plants about them.

The removal of clouds, in addition to its effect upon temperature, will admit more sunlight to drive photosynthesis. In the short term, increasing insolation from 0.4 to 1.2 cal cm^{-2} min^{-1} will not speed photosynthesis in a tobacco or dogwood leaf, but it will about double the speed in leaves of productive species like corn, sunflower, or sugar cane (Waggoner, et al., 1963). In the long term, Stanhill (1958) has found that increasing the net radiation received by English turnips from 17 to 18 thousand cal cm^{-2} during their ten weeks of growth increased their fresh weight from 100 to 230 g. If the difference in net radiation between a clear and cloudy day is 100 or 200 cal cm^{-2}, the difference between 100 and 230 g plants could be produced by changing five or ten of the seventy growing days from cloudy to clear. Conceivably, these changes might enhance the advantage that the fast-growing, light-requiring species have over their shade-tolerant but slower-growing competitors and thus create the qualitative changes that would interest the student of plant sociology.

An even distribution over the growing season of adequate rain to replenish the moisture transpired from the soil is an advantage to most plants, and much of the compulsion behind hopeless cloud seeding comes from this need in farm crops. Grain sorghum in the southern Great Plains provides an example of that need. In two years, adding two inches of water or about 20 per cent to storage and rainfall added about 800 pounds per acre to the grain yield. This increase can be compared to the range of observed yields, 208 to 2650 (Bond, et al., 1964). Thus a 20 per cent increase in rainfall would surely raise substantially the average yield and sometimes prevent catastrophic losses from drouth in this region. Such an amelioration of this arid climate would almost certainly change the quality as well as quantity of plant growth, because the new profitability and security of grain growing would encourage expansion of the area of cultivation. Also, the more regular rainfall would likely encourage more vegetation that would shield the soil from erosion by wind and water.

In the natural populations of plants the effect not only upon growth but upon species composition can be seen as one moves from the arid ridge top to the moist glen or the soggy marsh. Conceivably, increasing rainfall could move the communities uphill, and even decrease the depredations of the gypsy moth that prospers in oak foliage on some New England ridges.

A more explicit estimate can be attempted through Thornthwaite's (1948) climatic index I_m. If the potential evapotranspiration or need is 50 to 80 cm, as it is over much of the United States, each 1 cm of surplus rainfall added or 1.7 cm of deficiency relieved will add 2 to the index in humid places and 1.2 in dry places. If weather modification added one fifth to the rainfall of places receiving 50 and 100 cm of rain, the corresponding indices would increase 20 and 24 units. This would change the classification one category, e.g. from B_1 to B_2 or from B_3 to B_4.

In the northern zone of the United States this change corresponds to oak-hickory becoming beech-maple or birch-beech-maple-hemlock becoming spruce-fir (Thornthwaite and Hare, 1955). Thus setting a very optimistic view indeed of the efficacy of rainmaking and translating this view into ecology by means of Thornthwaite's criterion, we conclude that a significant change in plant community—and hence habitat—follows.

In the Rocky Mountains, climographs show that the difference in environment between the *Artemisia* and *Pinus* belt is rainfall during the cool and warmth during the warm season (Daubenmire, 1956). An increase in rainfall of 1 cm per month, about one fifth, during the cool season would move most of the *warming,* but less than half the *cooling* curves for stations in the *Artemisia* belt within the range of stations in the *Pinus* belt. A similar outcome can be seen in examining the climographs for *Pseudo-*

tsuga and *Thuja-Tsuga* belts in the Rockies. Thus, this criterion provides a less clear conclusion concerning the effect of increased rain upon plant communities than did the Thornthwaite index, and the final conclusion must be "maybe."

The indirect consequences of $1°C$ warming would likely be considerable. But speaking of these generalities is generally fruitless, and direct consequences will be examined. In the case of the climographs for the Rocky Mountain vegetation belts that were mentioned above, winter temperature did not discriminate between the pairs, but $1°C$ warming throughout the year would nearly transpose the climographs for *Festuca* stations into the temperature region of the *Agropyron* stations. Between the belts the differences in precipitation, of course, would still remain together with other unknown and possibly restraining factors.

In an alpine tundra in Wyoming, temperature—in this case soil temperature—was only occasionally a significant factor in determining standing crop (Scott and Billings, 1964). On the other hand, $1°$ C warming during the growing season would increase the annual PE (potential evapotranspiration) 3 to 4 cm. This could be associated with a change from tundra to forest tundra, for the entire range of PE within the forest-tundra subzone is only 31 to 35 cm (Thornthwaite and Hare, 1955). Thus we must conclude, as we did concerning rainmaking, that a warming of $1°C$ would change the communities of plants near the present boundaries between vegetation belts—maybe.

Hurricanes, unlike small temperature changes, have such dramatic results that the consequences of extinguishing this factor in the environment should be predictable. The eastward reach of the New England shore makes the woodlands of this region an excellent laboratory for learning the effect of hurricanes. And the most devastating treatment was applied in 1938. Eighteen years later Spurr (1956) reported the outcome:

"Where ample advance growth was present and no logging was carried out, the new stand is essentially a late-successional association composed of the released understory trees. Where advance growth is present but where the timber has been logged, the released understory trees are intermingled with pioneer species that have seeded in on disturbed areas. Where little or no advance growth is present, pioneer associations exist.

"In practically every case, the character of the new stand was apparent within only two growing seasons of the hurricane. The absence of later successful invasion of seedlings is attributable in part to competition from growth already established and in part to unfavorable environment in the blow-down area."

Hurricane winds do not, of course, damage everywhere equally. Exposed stands may be leveled and sheltered ones escape. Because of the variable consequences of blow-down and the irregular blow, hurricanes advance succession in some places, start it again elsewhere, and leave it an orderly procession in still other places. If variety in the habitat is desirable, hurricane removal may be "bad"; but if uniformity is desired, it may be "good."

Hurricanes also affect the soil in the forest. As the giants topple, their roots plow up the forest floor and leave mounds. This variety of microrelief then favors variety in the vegetation. When the forest is visited years later, the porous soil of nearly every mound is occupied by young seedlings or, later, by mature trees. Further, water filters into the porous mounds at a rate several times as rapid as it does into the undisturbed soil (Lutz, 1940).

Another violent storm, the thunderstorm, may disturb plant succession by fire. In some areas 6 per cent, in others

only 0.5 per cent of the discharges of lightning to ground cause reported fires (NSF, 1963). Anywhere, great fires could be arrested if rain could be driven in like a fire engine. Thus, successful weather modification could nearly extinguish the effects of fire upon the landscape. For example in the Pitch Pine Plains of southern New Jersey, groups or individuals are found larger than their neighbors; they are larger because they grow along old roads where they have been protected from fire. Thus if fire were controlled, the Plains likely would support a taller forest like the Pine Barrens (Lutz, 1934).

In other places, fire may be the maintainer of Douglas fir, paper birch, and several pines (Little and Moore, 1949). Both longleaf pine in the South and prairie in the Midwest are maintained by occasional fires. Thus, if fire could be controlled through weather control, competitors would likely march in from the boundaries of many coniferous forests and of many grasslands, slowly converting the habitat.

If weather could be managed—and except for stratus removal we can't yet manage it—the examples of changes I have given would likely be seen. A new backdrop would appear, slowly and only subtly different from the old one that we are accustomed to act before. The game of conjecture, even with the rules of weather changes no greater than our tamer dreams and with plant changes factually related to the postulated weather changes, can be played on and on. If the zoologist were to play the game, he could undoubtedly predict at least as many direct effects of the postulated weather changes. And if he considered the indirect effects, e.g. the fish that would not be born because reservoirs would no longer be built, the game would be endless.

My course, however, is to end conjecture with the foregoing predictions concerning plants. Now I will turn to some measurable influences that plants in our habitat have upon us. Changes in these influences are then a predictable outcome of postulated weather modifications.

Alternatively, changes in these influences are a predictable outcome of reforestation, clearing, or paving that, unlike weather modifications, we can surely do.

EFFECT OF PLANTS UPON HABITAT

Two among many ways that plants in our habitat influence us will be considered here. First, they change the quantity of water that remains in the soil or seeps into streams. Finally, they directly change our energy budget and hence comfort when we are outdoors. Clearly, changes in water supply or our energy budget will also mean changes for other creatures. In this case we are the guinea pigs.

Once upon a time the forest was a bad place, I suppose. A dark and mysterious dwelling of witches or dragons, highwaymen or deposed kings. By 1799, however, tastes had changed, and the Connecticut Academy of Arts and Sciences received a paper from Noah Webster, who attributed the inconstancy of winters of his day to the clearing of the forest. Later, in the era Kittredge (1948) calls the "period of propaganda," 1877 to 1912, most attention turned to water. Increased rain and decreased evaporation were accredited to the forest. The increased rain would have mattered but was impossible to prove. The decreased evaporation was easy to prove in the forest shade but turned out unimportant. The important phenomenon that can be demonstrated is the consumption of water by the forest.

Plants, especially trees, intercept a great deal of precipitation. If the trees are bare of foliage, or if stomatal resistance to transpiration (resistance of the leaf pores to evaporation from inside the leaves) is considerable, the intercepted water is evaporated and lost to the atmosphere more rapidly than if it had percolated into the soil.

"There seems no doubt that the evaporation of intercepted water proceeds much more rapidly than transpiration." (Rutter, 1959) Further, during the winter the disappearance of water from a pine plantation in England was 40 per cent greater than even the evaporation predicted for open-water evaporation by the well-known Penman equation (Rutter, 1963).

Once the precipitation strikes the surface, it is available to runoff, flooding valleys or filling reservoirs for us to drink or for fish to swim in. If the surface is not paved, however, some rain will percolate into the soil. Then plants will determine how much of this is returned to the air and how much eventually reaches streams.

The effect of plants versus no plants upon the amount of water that remains in the soil or leaches from it is clear. The distribution of rainfall will, of course, affect the proportion leached: much will leach if rains are few and heavy, and little will leach if rains are frequent and light. In the climate of Connecticut, 32 per cent of the growing-season rain leached through bare soil, but only 18 per cent leached through grass and sod after the transpiration of the grass had taken its toll. From late November to late May, however, half the rain leached through the soil, whether it grew grass or not (Morgan, et al., 1942). The effect of plants versus no plants upon the schedule of runoff and upon the silt content of streams is also clear.

The effect of one sort of plant versus another, however, is not so clear. The population of plants upon the land might be changed so that more sunlight was intercepted and less reflected by foliage. Or a rougher surface might be presented to the wind, or foliage might be thoroughly hydrated because some kinds of roots gathered more water. Then more water would undoubtedly be sent from soil to air. Whether these differences are practically significant and whether other factors are even operative between, say, a lawn and a pine forest, however, are questions that ensure debate.

Some facts, nevertheless, seem available. The experience of a score of years of studies of water yield at Coweeta has been summarized:

"There can be little doubt that in most well-watered lands conversion of mature forest to low-growing vegetation will increase supply of water to streams. First-year increases in the order of five to sixteen inches may be expected at Coweeta after complete clear-cutting of a mature hardwood forest. The average increases are perhaps less than formerly expected, but are nonetheless real; and, fortunately perhaps for future management efforts, tend to occur during late summer and fall when water supplies are lowest. Evidence from various types of experiments in the temperate regions of the world indicate that Coweeta's seventeen-inch increase in one treatment may be the largest return to be expected from reducing vegetative cover."

Further, the increase is proportional to the fraction of the canopy removed and is much less on slopes that face south than on slopes that face north (Hewlett and Hibbert, 1961). These facts, these increases, might be attributed to the interception and reflection of sunlight by fallen trees and exposed soil, by the smoothing of the surface, and by appearance of shallow-rooted and presumably often drier plants as well as to less obvious effects of a changed kind of population.

In the Harz mountains the stream flow from the forest of Wintertal has been compared to the flow from the grassland of Lange Bramke. The differ-

ence between five-year rainfall and runoff, which is the presumed consumption by the plants plus the presumably small evaporation, was only 10 per cent less for the grassland than the forest (Penman, 1961). An extensive review from a physical point of view of vegetation and hydrology has also been prepared by Penman (1963), and his conclusion is as in the examination of the German watersheds: differences may exist, but all well-watered vegetation transpires about the same.

A botanist, however, may continue hoping that his plants may matter. Perhaps the closure of stomata following a chemical spray may sufficiently increase resistance to the flow of water from soil through a stand of plants that transpiration may be trammeled (Zelitch and Waggoner, 1962). In fact, artificial stomatal closure in a barley field did decrease evapotranspiration by one eighth to one third (Waggoner, et al., 1964). When attempted in a forest, however, the aerial spray did not reach the stomatous undersides of the leaves, stomata did not close, and stream flow was not significantly increased (Waggoner and Hewlett, 1965).

If, therefore, weather modification or our husbandry makes our habitat plant-clad rather than bare, floods will be fewer and reservoirs will receive less water. If these forces merely change the plants from trees to grass, the yield to reservoirs may reflect a mere one-tenth change in evapotranspiration. Perhaps stomata-closing sprays may change the yield this much without changing the plants in the backdrop. The plants in our habitat, however, will surely change the way we feel, our comfort, when we are outdoors.

If we stand beneath trees rather than above a lawn or a paving, we are in a different microclimate, and if the climatic differences are great enough, we shall feel different. Our habitat will be more or less comfortable. Students of forest influences, e.g. Geiger (1950) or Kittredge (1948), have already found that relative to grassland the forest interior receives much less insolation, is much less ventilated, has somewhat more moderate air-temperature fluctuations, and contains little, if any, more water vapor. Our task is integrating these diverse effects of the plants in our surroundings into a measure of their impact upon us.

If our flesh is actually to be frozen or burned, then air temperature alone may be the significant measurement. Otherwise—and perhaps even in these extreme cases—we feel mainly the defense measures that our body takes to maintain its core at an even temperature. Therefore, the influence of plants in our environment has been summarized in the energy budget of a lightly clad man. From meteorological measurements, the gains and losses via radiation, convection, and evaporation are calculated for a man. The net loss must, of course, be compensated by metabolism if the man is not to become warmer or colder than normal. Thus a microclimate in which loss is great will be comfortable if the weather is hot or the work heavy. Alternatively a microclimate in which loss is slight will be comfortable if the weather is cool or the man rests. Energy budgets for man are explained by Buettner (1951), and the following examples have been presented by Waggoner (1963).

Meteorological measurements taken under clear autumn skies but before leaf fall are presented in Table 1 for a pas-

TABLE 1. The environment and estimated heat losses from a lightly clad man in a pasture (P), beneath an apple tree (A), in a clearing (C), or in a thicket (T), September, 1962

| Date and hour | Place | Radiation, cal cm^{-2} min^{-1} | | | | Wind cm sec^{-1} | Energy loss, kg cal m^{-2} hr^{-1} | |
| | | Upper hemisphere | | Lower hemisphere | | | Dry | Wet |
		Insolation	Long-wave	Insolation	Long-wave			
20 1324	P	1.10	.38	.19	.60	2.4	8	139
1337	A	.09	.58	.03	.56	6.1	121	336
1227	C	1.10[a]	.61[a]	.10	.55	3.6	−24	135
1247	T	.07	.59	.03	.58	0.6	77	137
21 1154	P	1.19	.45	.24	.58	225	256	1526
1203	A	.09	.47	.03	.53	194	399	1572
1138	C	1.27	.43	.17	.58	82	154	960
1130	T	.09	.54	.02	.54	20	189	583
21 1810	P		.34		.45	91	474	1267
1846	A		.48		.48	64	381	1045
1752	C		.41		.48	17	281	623
1743	T		.47		.49	0	211	418

[a] R_u measured, S_u estimated.

ture, the shade of an isolated apple tree, a clearing, and a thicket. About nine tenths of the insolation from above is a direct beam and is assumed to be 65 per cent absorbed over a quarter of our square meter of surface. The remaining tenth is scattered and absorbed over half our surface. The insolation reflected upward is absorbed over half our surface. Long-wave radiation is emitted by ourselves (414 kg cal m^{-2} hr^{-1}) and 96 per cent of both that from above and that from below is absorbed over half our surface. Finally, convection and evaporation are proportional to the square root of ventilation and the difference in temperature or vapor pressure between the air and our skins.

As it turned out, the differences in temperature and humidity were slight among the four environments and are not shown in the Table. The radiation received on a horizontal surface and wind speed were, of course, markedly changed by the plants and are shown. Finally, the effects of the plants upon man are shown in the last columns as the energy losses that must be compensated by metabolic heat if the man is to become neither chilled nor feverish. Similar observations were made on a beach and an asphalt paving.

"Trees may shade and shrubs may shelter a man, making him more comfortable. Or he may find the plants make a place less pleasant. They change temperature and humidity little, however, and these two common indicators of climate alone won't measure comfort.

"Instead of temperature and humidity alone, we observed the streams of calories in shade and shelter and then summarized them as loss of heat energy from a dry or from a sweating man. If he is comfortable, the temperature of his body becoming neither chilled nor hot, he has nicely balanced many streams of energy that enter and leave him. Against losses, he must balance the gains of visible sunlight, invisible long-wave radiation from warm things around him, and his metabolism. His losses leave via invisible long-wave radiation from himself, via convection and via evaporation, for all consume calories from his body. If these caloric accounts are not easily balanced, the uncomfortable man must shiver or sweat. Thus in several sites on clear days and nights, we measured radiation and ventilation in addition to air temperature and humidity. From these observations we calculated the net gains and losses, the heat a standard man could eliminate in each environment. Obviously an environment that permits great losses will be comfortable on a hot day and uncomfortable on a cool one.

"A clearing in the woods is a sheltered place where heat is lost slowly, for the sun shines there as brightly as on the pasture or lawn, long-wave radiation is greater, and ventilation, especially, is less. The shade of a tree that stands in the pasture, where breezes can blow freely, subtracts most of the radiation of the sun and is an unmixed benefit on a hot day. The shade and shelter of a thicket, however, subtract ventilation with sunlight, and heat may be even more slowly lost in the shade of the thicket than in the sunlight of the pasture.

"Heat was lost more rapidly by a man standing on a lawn than on a parking lot and—surprisingly—than on the beach.

"In hot weather, when the air is nearly as warm as the skin, convection is relatively unimportant. Blowing warm air over a warm, dry body cools little, and the shelter of clearing and thicket matters little. In hot weather, therefore, even the shade of the thicket increases the loss of heat from the dry man. To lose heat created by himself, however, requires perspiration, and it is evaporated slowly in the shelter of a clearing and thicket.

"Thus air temperature and humidity are scarcely changed by plants, but within their shade and shelter they greatly alter the heat a man can eliminate and, hence, greatly change his comfort. They can both shade the traveler in the desert of the parking lot and smother the dweller in the thicket of the second-growth suburban forest." (Waggoner, 1963)

This completes our course. Weather modification can certainly so far only clear stratus. But if it could also bring rain, warm air, still winds and arrest lightning and fire, the plants in our habitat would change. Some of the changes can be anticipated. The conclusions will disappoint those who might view weather modification as a means of building a whole new world and relieve most of those who fear it might.

Finally, whether the plants about us were changed by weather modification or husbandry, the amount of water in our reservoirs might change, and our energy budget or comfort would change when we were outdoors.

BIBLIOGRAPHY

Advisory Committee on Weather Control. 1957. Final rep. Vol. 1. U.S. Govt. Print. Off., Wash., D.C.

Battan, L. J. 1961. Some Factors Governing the Formation of Precipitation in Convective Clouds in Arizona. (Abstr.) Bul. Amer. Meteorol. Soc. 42:832.

Bergeron, T. 1949. Problem of Artificial Control of Rainfall on the Globe. Tellus 1:32–43.

Bond, J. J., Army, T. J., and Lehman, O. R. 1964. Row Spacing, Plant Populations and Moisture Supply as Factors in Dryland Grain Sorghum Production. Agron. J. 56:3–6.

Buettner, K. J. K. 1951. Physical Aspects of Human Bioclimatology: 1112–14. In: Malone, T. F., ed., Compendium of Meteorology. Amer. Meteorol. Soc., Boston.

Daubenmire, R. F. 1956. Climate as a Determinant of Vegetation Distribution in Eastern Washington and Northern Idaho. Ecol. Monog. 26:131–54.

Geiger, R. 1950. Climate Near the Ground. Trans. 2d Germ. ed. Harvard Univ. Press, Cambridge.

Hewlett, J. D., and Hibbert, A. R. 1961. Increases in Water Yield after Several Types of Forest Cutting. Q. J. Assn. Intern. Hydrol. (Sept.): 5–17.

Howell, W. E. 1960. Cloud Seeding in the American Tropics: In: Weickmann, H. K., ed., Physics of Precipitation: 412–23. Amer. Geophys. Union, Wash., D.C.

Huschke, R. E. 1963. Brief History of Weather Modification since 1946. Bul. Amer. Meteorol. Soc. 44:425–29.

Kittredge, J. 1948. Forest Influences. McGraw-Hill, New York.

Little, S., and Moore, E. B. 1949. Ecological Role of Prescribed Burns in the Pine-oak Forests of Southern New Jersey. Ecol. 30:223–33.

Lutz, H. J. 1934. Ecological Relations in the Pitch Pine Plains of Southern New Jersey. Yale Univ. Sch. Forestry Bul. 38.

———— 1940. Disturbance of Forest Soil Resulting from the Uprooting of Trees. Yale Univ. Sch. Forestry Bul. 45.

Malkus, J. S., and Simpson, R. H. 1964. Note on Potentialities of Cumulonimbus and Hurricane Seeding Experiments. J. Appl. Meteorol. 3:470–75.

Mitchell, J. M., Jr. 1961. Recent Secular Changes of Global Temperature. Ann. N. Y. Acad. Sci. 95:235–50.

Morgan, M. F., Jacobson, H. G. M., and LeCompte, S. B., Jr. 1942. Drainage Water Losses from a Sandy Soil as Affected by Cropping and Cover Crops. Conn. Agr. Exp. Sta. Bul. 466:731–59.

National Academy of Science-National Research Council. 1964. Scientific Problems of Weather Modification. Pub. 1236.

National Science Foundation. 1963. Weather Modification. Fourth annual report, 1962. U.S. Govt. Print. Off., Wash., D.C.

Penman, H. L. 1961. Weather, Plant and Soil Factors in Hydrology. Weather 16:207–19.

———— 1963. Vegetation and Hydrology. Comm. Bur. Soils Tech. Commun. 53.

Rutter, A. J. 1959. Evaporation from a Plantation of Pinus sylvestris in Relation to Meteorological and Soil Conditions. Compt. Rend. Assoc. Intern. Hydrol. Sci. Hannover Symp. 1:101–10.

———— 1963. Studies in the Water Relations of Pinus sylvestris. I. Measurement of Rainfall and Interception. J. Ecol. 51:191–203.

Scott, D., and Billings, W. D. 1964. Effects of Environmental Factors on Standing Crop and Productivity of an Alpine Tundra. Ecol. Monog. 34:243–70.

Smagorinsky, J. 1963. General Circulation Experiments with the Primitive Equations. I. The Basic Experiment. Mon. Weather Rev. 91:99–164.

Spurr, S. H. 1956. Natural Restocking of Forests Following the 1938 Hurricane in Central New England. Ecol. 37:443–51.

Stanhill, G. 1958. Effects of Soil Moisture on the Yield and Quality of Turnips. II. Response at Different Growth Stages. J. Hort. Sci. 33:264–74.

Thornthwaite, C. W. 1948. An Approach Toward a Rational Classification of Climate. Geog. Rev. 38:55–94.

————— and Hare, F. K. 1955. Climatic Classification in Forestry. Unasylva 9:51–59.

Thuronyi, G. 1964. Recent Literature on Weather and Climate Modification. Meteorol. and Geoastrophys. Abstr. 15:1518–53.

Waggoner, P. E. 1963. Plants, Shade, and Shelter. Conn. Agr. Exp. Sta. Bul. 656.

————— and Hewlett, J. D. Test of a Transpiration Inhibitor on a Forestal Watershed. Water Resources Res. 1:391–96.

————— Monteith, J. L., and Szeicz, G. 1964. Decreasing Transpiration of Field Plants by Chemical Closure of Stomata. Nature 201:97–98.

————— Moss, D. N., and Hesketh, J. D. 1963. Radiation in the Plant Environment and Photosynthesis. Agron. J. 55:36–39.

Zelitch, I., and Waggoner, P. E. 1962. Effect of Chemical Control of Stomata on Transpiration and Photosynthesis. Proc. Nat. Acad. Sci. U.S. 48:1101–08.

General Discussion

COWAN: Now, ladies and gentlemen, I would like to open this forum for critical examination of the six papers that have been presented to you.

OVINGTON: I would like to comment on Dr. Waggoner's paper. It does seem to me that there is a possibility of looking at the effect of climatic change on a small scale in certain situations. I am thinking primarily of the atomic-power stations with a surplus of energy which could be dissipated locally, for example in warming up a lake. Where this results in an increase in temperature of perhaps one or two degrees, an interesting field experiment would be to try to evaluate what the effect of this kind of change is in these situations.

STEERS: Would you enlarge on that particular point—how far can the change go if it takes place? What sort of area? What sort of degree of temperature, rainfall, and so on? What kind of change do you think is possible?

WAGGONER: At the present time?

STEERS: Yes.

WAGGONER: At the present time the only thing that we can do with certainty is to clear stratus. If we did decide to do this, we would presumably increase the amount of sunlight by a tenth.

There are species of plants that will certainly benefit in this environment and in many others by a little more sunlight. They will grow more rapidly and productivity will go up. At the same time the shade-tolerant species would probably suffer, so there would probably be a small net gain of productivity and a change in its quality.

A 10 per cent increase in rainfall would undoubtedly move some boundaries. The red maple would probably move up the hill a little in Connecticut, and the oak would shrink back.

Lightning arresting, say, by anticipation of thunderstorms, would in many cases reduce the amount of fire. To some people this would be a good thing; to others it would be bad. Just as with the removal of hurricanes from our environment: to some people this would be a wonderful thing—to the shippers and to the insurance companies, but not to people interested in a variety of environments.

NICHOLSON: Of course, there has been a good deal of work done on the natural experiments formed by the climatic amelioration in Scandinavia, on the changes in the range of various birds and mammals. For example, the

European chaffinch and the brambling—related species—evidently are very sensitive in the course of climatic changes.

As the climate ameliorates, the chaffinch goes north in its breeding range. And there was at one time a fear that the brambling would be squeezed up against the north edge of the taiga, north of which the breeding habitat is no longer suitable. There has been some reversal of that recently.

There is a good deal of literature on this complicated phenomenon. For instance, climatic amelioration led to a big increase in oystercatchers in the Faeroes and Iceland, a bird that had nowhere to winter there. They came down and wintered on Morecambe Bay and practically wiped out the cockle fishing there. You have to think not only of local effects, but of effects many hundreds or perhaps thousands of miles away, especially where birds are involved.

FOSBERG: In connection with the next to the last question, I wonder if Dr. Waggoner or anyone else has considered the matter of increase in water loss by evaporation resulting from fog dispersal, presuming that such fog dispersal could take place over a large area. Would this possibly increase the drouth incidence, or is this a negligible thing?

WAGGONER: The rapid evaporation of water would increase exactly as you increase the sunlight. Of that we can be sure, for the Penman equation has proven practical.

FARBER: With realization of the complexity of air pollution, I would like to hear comments on the role of air pollution—considering it widespread, increasing, perhaps to stretch hundreds of miles, influencing weather.

WAGGONER: The accumulation of undesirable pollution in the air in our immediate neighborhood is of course a weather problem. If there is a stable airmass over us, then we go about our normal activities in polluted air. The presence of pollution in the air does decrease the amount of light reaching the earth and does conserve water. This is a pretty tough way to conserve water.

FARBER: There have been identified in the air some 3000 particulate matters—chemicals—of which perhaps 300 have been studied carefully. What are their effects?

WAGGONER: Could I say a word? Yes, I presume many people here know that one of these chemicals, ozone, is deleterious to plants of many kinds, all the way from grass to pine trees. It is a major agricultural problem in Connecticut: ozone will cause lesions on tobacco leaves that unhappily make them unfit for wrapping cigars.

COWAN: Where does this ozone originate?

WAGGONER: I suspect Dr. Leopold of California knows better than I do. It was discovered ten years or so ago that when nitrogenous compounds from the exhaust of automobiles are freed into sunlit stable air, an oxidation process ensues which produces ozone and other oxidizers. First we see cracked automobile tires, but we soon also see severely damaged vegetation and feel burning eyes.

DARLING: It just struck me that we are getting some weather modifications already in the increasing carbon-dioxide content of the air. In a place like Los Angeles, weather is a smog problem which may be referable to petroleum refineries, and in Britain we have even considered whether the new refinery at Grangemouth on the Firth of Forth was having an effect on the weather at Edinburgh in the condensation of moisture on particles in the atmosphere. I wonder if you have any comment. This has to do with our future.

WAGGONER: So far the increase in carbon dioxide with time in the open country is still so small that there are people who don't believe there has been one. This is reassuring.

The release into the air of condensation nuclei is—happily, I think, in many cases—not significant because there are so many there already that a little addition doesn't matter.

I don't think that an oil refinery would add noticeably to the condensation over Auld Reekie (Old Smoky). Isn't that what Edinburgh is called?

CLAWSON: It seems to me that if you can talk about possible weather modifications in the future, one of the things you have to think about is what changes man is going to make in the use of the environment.

Fifteen years ago, when there was a first flush of enthusiasm, I did some speculating about what would happen if the average precipitation in the whole western half of the United States were raised by 10 per cent. There would be some considerable shifts in land use. At least first round. A lot of the Great Plains that are now submarginal for wheat would be above the margin, and we would have still more magnificent wheat-surplus problems than we have today.

But we would also open up a whole new cycle of stream-flow exploitation for irrigation and so on with all kinds of secondary and tertiary effects back upon the environment and some of the things we have been talking about here. That is admittedly a speculative line. You started in your paper to talk about the effects of some as yet unrealized or unrealizable changes in weather modification upon the oaks and the maples. I am suggesting that we ought to talk a little bit now about what man would then do with the land and water and vegetation and other resources as the result of these shifts.

These might very well lead to secondary or, as I say, still further rounds of changes which might be much greater in their effect than the first round.

WAGGONER: Yes. I introduced this section in my paper with an agricultural example. I thought probably this would tire the ecologists, so I didn't pursue it further. For example, there would be a great increase in the productivity of land for sorghum in the marginal region if the rainfall increased 10 per cent. Removing variability might affect land use more than increasing the amount.

SEARS: I think we do have some evidence of what is likely to happen from these long, protracted drouths and equally long moist periods in the grassland country. We have been shown just what tends to happen with vegetation. Human behavior and bank credit are also affected. For example, after a succession of wet years everybody wants to buy land and is willing to pay more than it is worth. After a succession of dry years there are foreclosures and the boom collapses.

CALDWELL: Referring back to the comments of Marion Clawson, when you get secondary effects, particularly in agricultural land and water use, growing out of ability to manipulate weather, it follows inevitably that there will be economic and hence political questions. The structures of government in Canada and in the United States do not take into account the ability of man to manipulate the weather. Weather modification, if successfully undertaken on a substantial scale, implies changes in governmental institutions. While I suggest that this is a topic that is more appropriate for the sixth session, it seems to me that it ought to be mentioned as a significant by-product of this sort of manipulative potential.

TUNNARD: One thing I didn't pick up in Dr. Waggoner's paper but that may very well be there is the possibility of large engineering constructions effecting climatic change. I have in mind the suggestion for a barrage across the English Channel which would allow, with tidal flow, cold water to flow out and the warmer waters of the Gulf Stream to flow in—which might change the climate over a large portion of northern Europe.

WAGGONER: There could be two answers to this. One is that I would accept that this would warm up the climates; then we would go to the task of deciding what sort of changes in the landscape would follow, as I attempted earlier to evaluate the consequences of cloud seeding. The other view that I could take is that we probably don't really know that it would warm up the climate.

MILTON: I wonder if it is possible to identify ecosystems within North America which are likely to be more directly affected by weather modifications. It seems to me there are certain types of habitat which the people who are interested in increasing agricultural production are going to be concerned with, specifically the semiarid and desert ecosystems. And at the same time this suggests to me that we should be thinking about setting up centers for ecosystem research of the type that Dr. Ovington has been concerned with—within these areas that are going to be affected and in which the economists, engineers, and other people concerned with land use are pressing for changes.

I think we can probably pick out certain types of habitats where we have to be ready to accurately predict the effects of climatic and other types of environmental modifications, such as desalinization. Weather control poses particularly difficult problems. If, for example, we have a primeval park area in the Southwest that we want to maintain intact for wilderness recreation or for scientific study, and at the same time we have a weather modification program to assist agricultural development a few miles away, can we control the climatic change so specifically that it does not affect the primitive area? I would doubt it very much at our present level of technology.

WAGGONER: The answer to that is a flat no. The answer to the question "Can you control the weather in one place only" is no for two reasons. First of all, you probably can't control the weather; second, if we could, we probably couldn't hit a target.

You also spoke of the need for centers for experimental ecology where you actually test some ideas as well as observe things, and then hypothesize cause-and-effect relationship. Dr. Ovington has already supported this need, and I would second it. This experimenting might in many cases cause a very trying wrench in traditional ecological philosophy and thinking, however.

DANSEREAU: Wouldn't you say that an ecosystem which shows maximum of buffering of climate, maximum differential between microclimate and macroclimate, would show the greatest resistance to weather modification? For example, in New England forest types would change very slowly. In fact, some forest types in eastern North America are relics as matters stand now, in the normal course of change, at both ends of the range in the North and South.

BRANDWEIN: May I now ask for clarification, particularly of Dr. Cowan's remarks.

You gave the analogy of the amoeba. Do you see what we euphemistically call natural areas as food vacuoles in the amoeba, or do you foresee man building concentration camps of animals and plants, which he tastefully calls natural areas?

COWAN: You are applying terminology that one might well have used. The two concepts are probably equally true to the extent that as these are areas surrounded by changed conditions, they would be concentration camps. To the extent that we are going to use them for human enjoyment somehow or other, they would be food vacuoles.

BRANDWEIN: Then do you see the term "preservation of natural environments" or future environments as one that would follow us into a hopeful point of view—that we are really pressing for concentration camps of animals and plants? We can call them large ecosystems if we wish. But is this a hopeless point of view for the future?

LEOPOLD: I would like to take one facet of the question, the concept that an ecosystem has evolved in a given area, let's say the Great Prairie, and produced a soil that today we depend on to produce our surpluses of wheat and corn. We don't know a hundred years from now that those soils are still going to be as productive as they are today. Soil scientists keep learning more about productivity of the land all the time. Within the natural system that formed the soil, there may be elements which in the long run are going to have extremely practical application in better management of these resources. The German forestry that shifted from a mixed hardwood conifer forest into sprucewood ran into such problems after generations with spruce. Now they are trying to see what went wrong with the ecosystem.

I think just as good insurance we can make a good case for developing these natural areas as places to constantly study the processes by which energy from the sun is reduced to a point where we can use it.

The sort of work that Dr. Ovington is doing is crucial and may have a great deal to do with our practical interpretation of agricultural problems in the future. This takes us far beyond the concentration camp idea, for these natural areas are themselves going to produce for us knowledge, knowledge which has application outside the natural area.

Dr. Cowan touched on this in speaking of their scientific value. I think this could be emphasized a great deal more.

STRONG: I question why Dr. Cowan wishes to save all the species now in existence. Even if man hadn't been here to destroy some of them, some species would have ceased to exist and would have been replaced by other species.

Are you suggesting that we attempt to control and, to some extent, to halt what would be a natural succession of species? Do you differentiate between destruction of species caused through man's action or through natural change apart from man's action?

COWAN: The adventure of trying to thwart the natural conditions of change is one of the great adventures mankind has been engaged in. It is one of the things that have been taxing our ingenuity, that have led to the development of our technology. When we lock horns with what we regard as the inevitable conditions of mutative change in the world around us, we gain competence on a far wider scene.

You might argue that most of the species—I don't know which ones you would like to pick, say the North American condor—now in serious trouble or which have become recently extinct are in this state because of man's activity.

LEOPOLD: The condor is a good example. In terms of the history of North America the condor obviously is straight on its way out. But it isn't out yet.

Had it not been for the white man, the question is, would it have lasted another thousand years or ten thousand years? The fact is it is here today. I for one feel an enormous responsibility to maintain it, even though it was a species that was on the decline in the geologic sense.

OSBORN: Would you express again why we should protect the species? What are the basic motivations?

COWAN: I expressed several points of view. The first was that in the past we have found very great value from availability of genotypes. We have taken a small wild strawberry of California and by recombining and selecting have built it into a cultivated crop which is of value to us.

At the moment the plant breeders of Canada, and I am sure of the Soviet Union also, are carefully selecting certain genetic components of wild grasses and combing them into the cereal-crop gene patterns to attempt to increase the capacity of our plants to survive farther north. We do have this very real reason for trying to arrange for the survival of genetic variety in all its complexity. We never know what we are going to need in the future. We can be quite certain that our needs are going to be more complicated and our capacity to use opportunities is going to be much greater.

A second one is the question of a moral value itself. Playing God is risky business. Are we going, off the cuff, to condemn certain species to extinction?

A third one is that man is a very different creature from other animals and he gains something from pitting himself against certain difficult adventures. I would regard one of the most interesting and inspiring adventures as locking horns with what appears to be inevitable mortality of a species.

The extent of the interest that is aroused in the people of North America today is quite heartening and interesting to behold. People get centered on the survival of the eagle or the survival of the whooping crane. It does something to them and to their lives. It makes their lives completely different, more vital, more interesting. This is what we are striving at, the enrichment of the human environment.

FOSBERG: I think that anything that preserves or augments the variety in our world ecosystem is worth doing.

BRINSER: I am in a minority position. This may be the consequence of my inability to comprehend the position you are taking. I find it hard to understand the validity of the argument that we should preserve all possible opportunities.

It seems to me that the issue is not between preservation and destruction. I think the question is: what is it we want to produce? What is destruction to one person is production to another. Therefore we must have some choice of deciding whose concept of production should be valid.

The second point—if we are going to try to preserve all variety on the assumption that sometime this may be useful: preservation isn't achieved without cost. We have a problem of allocating the cost so it produces the highest return. Therefore it is important to decide where we should concentrate our efforts on preserving variety, and not just preserve for its own sake.

These are not necessarily research issues. I think in the area of research everybody obviously has to be free to move as he chooses. The things that we are talking about, setting in motion weather modifications, control of species, are things that interpenetrate the whole economy, up to the decision making of an individual to produce. These activities affect the whole chain of activity: economic, social, and political activity.

I think the problems of choice of what is to be done are great and the criteria of choice, at the level of the ecologist, are extremely poor. One of the reasons that the economist and ecologist have great difficulty in communicating with each other is that they are using different terms and that they haven't defined the problem so that it can be mediated.

If out of ecological research could come the basis of choice decisions—choices that are ecologically valid, and that could then be translated into political, economic, and social terms—then I think we would be moving in a direction where the whole society could benefit.

FOSBERG: I would like to make one suggestion on this matter of communications between economists and ecologists and others.

Maybe the trouble is that the economist considers only what you can do with or do to something. That is his criterion, expressed in money values. Many people are convinced that there is value—maybe not money value, but value—in having things as they are and in enjoying them, whether or not you can *do* anything with them, whether or not you can *use* them.

The economist perhaps by the nature of his profession must deal with tangible things that therefore can be expressed in money or some other system, while some of the rest of us at least like to think that we can set values that are not tangible.

COWAN: At the same time, the economist as a social scientist is in his way striving to do what we are trying to do. All of us here are striving to develop the criteria for measuring and expressing values quantitatively. From conversations with my own resource-economist friends, I know that they are deeply interested in trying to attach some sort of measurable basis to the values that you are referring to.

BRINSER: I would like to comment briefly on what you said, that the economist has worried about the problem of value. He has never been able to define it satisfactorily from his own point of view. The basic concern of economics as a decision-making science at the level of social decision is how to distinguish more from less. More of what is an open question, and it is to be defined within the society itself.

Really, I don't think the failure of communications is on that point. I think it is rather in the way in which the people approaching the phenomena of their science organize it and structure their attack. If these structures do not have correspondence, or points at which they can correspond, then they cannot provide integrated comprehension.

MUMFORD: It seems to me that in this whole discussion there is an unstated premise, a very important one, that we should be conscious of. It is related to the historic fact that civilized man has been an exterminator. We are concerned with this problem because over 5000 years he, in the course of achieving an enormous amount of power and an enormous amount of social control, has devastated the landscape from China right to the other side of Europe—destroyed the forest vegetation, left barren lands wherever civilization has flourished.

COWAN: The first word, and so the last word. Dr. Darling?

DARLING: As we destroy and change in this continent of North America we should remember, I think, that loss isn't all loss, because you get recombination and readaptation. You get the creation of new environments entirely with very beautiful ecological reactions within them.

This continent, in our knowledge of it, is a new continent in many ways. But take Africa, which is such a very old continent in its relation to man. I don't think that there is very much in Africa that has not been influenced by man, wherever you go.

You get recombinations of habitat. The savanna habitat, with its tremendously rich fauna, how much of it is man-made? The savanna fauna adapted itself to the savanna which we believe is not natural, whatever we mean by natural. It has been created by lightning fire to some extent, but very largely by man.

Coming to a place like England, we have the English downland which is possibly the oldest man-made environment in England. We think of it as the very roots of our being, those bare chalk hills. The point is that there are very definite downland associations of plants and animals. They don't exist in that combination anywhere else. It is within the power of habitats to re-create, to readapt. I think in this continent there is immense room yet for the creation of new biological communities, and that we should remember this when we are playing the Devil.

Afternoon Session
(2 P.M.)

OVINGTON: Our Deputy Chairman said this morning if someone could find an animal that ate spruce leaves, he would be creating a new ecosystem. There are animals that eat spruce leaves or at least parts of spruce leaves and if these didn't exist we might in spruce forests be knee deep in spruce needles. There must be something utilizing the leaves since decomposition is taking place.

LEOPOLD: It can be bacteria.

OVINGTON: Some organisms are making use of the leaves. They may not be of particular interest to most ecologists, but in the long run the activity of the secondary producers must be equivalent to the activity of the primary producers, otherwise you will have a surplus.

LEOPOLD: Let's narrow it down to what interests me, namely the primary animals, many of the large and medium-sized animals that exist in highest density, certainly, in the temperate zones, and feather out both ways toward the pole and toward the equator in terms of total number of these larger animals. There must be some fundamental reason for this. As I say, I would certainly assume it to be a qualitative rather than a quantitative element of plant activity.

OVINGTON: I tried to draw attention to the fundamental differences between a prairie, savanna, and woodland. If you are dealing with woodland, your primary production is taking place largely at maybe fifty to a hundred feet above ground level, and animals are going to feed on it there or as it drops as dead leaf material on the ground. This is obviously not the kind of community which would necessarily support large mammals, whereas in a prairie system you have narrowed down your primary production to a relatively low level above ground.

In a savanna system, which seems to me to have a lot of advantages and is of great value to conservationists, you have a great variety of production over a wide vertical range and therefore you can support a wide diversity of animals.

I think also that the savanna ecosystem is remarkably efficient. It has remarkably high rates of production compared with some prairie systems and some woodlands.

FOSBERG: I was worried by the same question and was going to ask it in a different way. It seemed to me that the discrepancy between the animal biomass and the productivity that you brought out was perhaps the result of interest only in large conspicuous portions of this biomass. I remember when I was a kid being tremendously impressed by a statement that was made, and I have no reason to doubt this statement, that the progeny of a single gravid rose aphid during a year, if unchecked by all environmental factors, would equal the bulk of the earth. The insect populations, as well as those of other invertebrates, are truly enormous in some of these tropical areas. The animal biomass is divided in many little pieces instead of concentrated in rhinoceroses, giraffes, and the like. Animal populations are there nevertheless.

I would like to add one more thing to this. Probably there is a lot of destruction of material produced that could scarcely be termed secondary production, which I think is a misleading expression. Since you people use it, I will also. I would say that much of the primary production may be dissipated as oxidation products of many of the microorganisms which utilize this without producing great masses of tissue as a result.

So perhaps you have two things to consider. One is failure to observe the actual animal biomass, and the other is that some of the enormous productive capacity of the tropics is dissipated in other forms of biological activity than simply producing more tissue.

DASMANN: I believe it was at the last conference of this kind that Albrecht advanced the idea of a gradient in protein production running from low in the tropical forest to another low in the desert, and reaching a peak in intermediate-rainfall regions. He felt that this coincided with the greatest production of animal biomass. I wonder if you might comment on that, Dr. Ovington.

OVINGTON: I think this could well be so; I would like to see the figures to work this out. There is some confusion in biologists' minds between biomass

that is to consider the factors individually and yet systematically. Any preconceived subjective classification, of course, differs with every school of thought. We try to take all the main factors which are relevant, to check those site by site, and then to relate like site with like site irrespective of whether one of the same type is described as savanna and another as steppe.

What we are trying to do here, I think, has relevance to the point made as to the economic angle. We are trying to show what are the site factors which are correlated with presence or absence of different ecological features, and with the conservation status. Theoretically we should be able to produce returns from sites—world-wide—which enable us to correlate a site which is still in its natural state and another site which has been heavily modified by grazing or burning—and another site which is of the same type but now is completely an artifact one under crop. We should then be able to link all these together by their basic features—geographical, soil, rainfall, climate generally, geology, and so on.

I have discussed this in FAO with the forestry side and the plant-production side, and it does look as if this *pro forma* we are working on does promise to yield for the first time an objective basis for the description of sites in such a way that we can evaluate which sites have a known economic use—therefore which ones should be reserved for conservation merely because it is an economic waste to use them for anything else— and which ones present a conflict between conservation and one, more, or a dozen economic uses that can then be fought out on merits.

I think in this way we do have the possibility also of meeting the demands which are put in Dr. McHarg's paper. We have something here, which I have shown to Dr. McHarg, on which we can get away from the subjective ecological classifications—not that we have anything against them once the data have been obtained. Then they can be related to whatever classification may be preferred. It may well be that there are several different ecological classifications which are valuable for different purposes. One may be suitable for one purpose, one for another.

Then, of course, there is vegetation mapping, which explicitly excludes all the environmental factors. We, in this case, are bringing in the environmental framework—placing the whole ecological problem within the setting of the environmental.

I would very much like to hear from anybody who is interested in this because it seems to me that in the light of this discussion what we must not do is to produce a basic source of information which is comprehensible and valid merely in terms of ecology or conservation. We must produce one which is capable of being used for any purpose—any land-use purpose—agriculture, forestry, recreation, or any other. We must have an objective world site classification so that any site can be related objectively in terms of its measurable factors to other sites—whether that site happens to be natural and of special interest to conservation, or whether it is an exploited site.

COWAN: Do you consider the limiting factors on the environment as well as the basic factors in your classification?

OVINGTON: The main aim is to look at a wide range of factors which we believe from past biological observations to be significant.

FOSBERG: It seems to me, and I may be wrong here, that you are worrying about eliminating subjective factors in classification but you are doing it simply by substituting subjective factors in the selection of the questions to be asked.

I don't object to subjective things. I think the subjective approach is simply the use of your mind. This has a very bad reputation. Still, our minds are the best things we have to reason with.

I don't like the idea of saying this is objective and that is subjective; therefore, this is good and that is bad. We should have a better criterion for distinguishing between the good and bad.

NICHOLSON: What you say obviously makes sense. We have, of course, not just the one *pro forma*, we have a set of these which are broken up for ecological purposes, land use, and conservation. If anybody thinks of any other item that ought to be put in, it is the easiest thing in the world to put it in here. It will come out in the wash when we run through it on the computers. I quite agree there is some subjective element. It may be that we will put in certain factors that are not relevant. That is a risk we have to run.

COWAN: I think there is one other area that we brought out this morning that has not been discussed so far, and that is the question of the preservation of examples of ecotypes, the preservation of ecosystems. A number of subsidiary questions can arise out of this.

If we opt for the preservations that we have been suggesting—that is, the preservation of ecosystems for future study—we then come face to face with a variety of decisions.

For instance, where, how many, how distributed, of what size? These questions immediately enter the field of economics, which we can probably reserve for more detailed discussion later on.

I know that there are some strong views about this. I would like to see some discussion in this area now. Would you like to lead off on this, Dr. Waggoner?

WAGGONER: In reading the papers presented this morning, it struck me, as the one farm boy here, I guess, that we were living in an ivory tower. I think in any rational society—by that I mean the society that isn't going to extinguish itself—the human needs are always going to get first priority. This priority is especially true for land.

Agriculture has temporarily reduced the land it requires in North America and in Western Europe. One of the ways this has been done is to reclaim some very fertile land—or land that is made fertile. For each acre reclaimed, somebody gets back two acres that can again grow perennial plants and wildlife. I think you may have to accept that you can't have abandoned farms without reclamation elsewhere.

This morning at times I thought it almost sounded as if we thought we could have both. This one acre of fertile reclaimed land may be the price that you pay for the restoration of two acres of New England, let's say, to perennial plants.

Another thing that disturbed me a great deal was that at times we were speaking in opposition to fertility of the land. It was understood that if a landscape could be kept infertile, nonproductive, this would be a good thing because it would keep the people out. Brazil is a beautiful example of this. They have certainly kept the people out of the interior of Brazil by keeping it infertile, and even the investment in Brasilia is not going to change this.

I doubt if in Brazil they would have the leisure and the wealth to hold this meeting we are holding here today and develop this higher morality, in the first place. And, even worse, I think, if they did hold it, it would be a mere exercise in words which they could not afford to do anything about because they don't have the fertile lands.

I think that the condition of Latin America, Africa, and Asia does press in on us. The population explosion there makes this affluent period that we are experiencing in North America a brief one.

I don't think that the people of Connecticut would long live on the produce of their rocky acres alone while the people in Iowa grew fat. And I don't think that in the period of, say, the rest of this century that North America is going to be permitted the luxury of great quantities of idle fertile land while two or three billion people starve elsewhere.

This has already happened. In 1940, Africa, Asia, and Latin America exported eleven million tons of grain. In 1950 they imported four million tons. In 1960 they imported sixteen million tons. In 1964 they imported twenty-five million tons of grain. Already our agriculture is being used to support those people.

Since the population will increase by a billion people in the next fifteen years, and I don't know how any significant birth-control measures can be effected before that, it is going to take 300 million tons of grain to feed these people, and 300 million tons of grain are approximately the present production of North America and Western Europe together. I think we are indeed living in a very brief period of affluence for land.

All this is a very long introduction to my point, which is this: the solution to the wildlife problem that has been presented frequently here today is land, lots more land. To preserve this species we have to have more land. To preserve that species we have to have more land set aside without men on it.

I submit to you that the chore for the people interested in wildlife is to start work to economize acreage and not be so extravagant with land.

Agriculture has done this for a while. But agriculture can't do it forever. You must carry part of the load. I put it to the wildlife people as a fine challenge to learn how to increase the array of wildlife per acre. That is your chore as increasing bushels per acre is the agronomist's chore.

COWAN: Durward?

ALLEN: While fresh in my mind, I would like to take the last point. The wildlife biologists that you heard talking this morning were considering the problem of endangered species, endangered ecotypes, ecosystems. And obviously if you are going to preserve an ecosystem you have to give it space somewhere. That is why we are concerned with devoting a reasonable amount, not unreasonable, to wilderness types that have been here a long time and which will be worthy of study for a long time yet.

In regard to improving habitats, wildlife biologists have been working on this since back in the 1920s and it has been one of their principal preoccupations for the reason that sportsmen commonly pay the bill. Of course sportsmen want game to shoot. So in rather crude fashion we have been trying to produce game crops to be harvested with the gun.

This has been somewhat successful but not nearly so successful as it ought to be. We would be more successful if we were better ecologists, objective ecologists. It seems that by definition ecology should be the basis for these operations, because ecology presumably includes all of the factors in the environments. Populations are part of an ecosystem. It is only by understanding its relationships, and the synergism of various factors affecting it, that we can come out with a specific result on the land that someone wants and is willing to pay for.

TUNNARD: These excellent remarks point to the possible eventual domestication of the biosphere—not necessarily in the sense of farming. We know that more and more can be produced on less and less land, but we are now getting villages in the arctic, and living in the tropics is being made easier with the conquest of disease, and will not all of these habitats—including, say, that of the gorilla—be eventually in some way controlled by man?

NICHOLSON: What goes on in North America goes in other continents as well. A high percentage of the damage done to conservation interests, say in Latin America, at the moment—in the Andes—is this terrible tragedy that land is being burned, cut over, and so on, not in aid of improving food production, but with the result of completely spoiling that land. You get loss of timber, loss of water yield, loss of top soil, blockage of navigation.

I am astonished that we should still hear in this room people saying that one acre is as good as another acre for agriculture. The question is the shaking out: which are the right grades of land, which should on no account be exploited because you are going to lose your money on them?

All over the world the most respectable bodies, the World Bank and such, support acquisition of reclaimed lands which are going out of agricultural production, but only when they have been irretrievably ruined from the conservation point of view. That includes not only conservation of wildlife but soil and so on.

We must look at this qualitatively as to the grade of the land. There are certain types of land which ought to be set aside for conservation if only in the interests of economics, because a great deal of investment which can ill be afforded is still being diverted to the low grades of land where it cannot be productive.

I think when we get down to a qualitative basis for establishing priorities it will be much easier to find some sort of *modus vivendi* between conservation and sound developers on the higher grades of land where admittedly there is a choice.

BRANDWEIN: In the light of what has been said, I am forced to conclude that, in view of the great population increase and man's inability to be dispassionate about his future for children's sake, what he will do is to blanket the earth with his species, encroach upon the habitats and biotopes now existing, segregate them, and modify them through his change in the environment so they will exist in islands, if you will, at his sufferance. Is that the model of the earth that I see being developed here? Perhaps this is an irrelevant question and an irreverent one. This is, is it not, a Conference on future environments?

If I draw correctly from what you have been saying, particularly from what Mr. Allen has been saying, and Mr. Waggoner, and Mr. Tunnard, and others here, we cannot in due time ask man to cease and desist. He will in the future when the crises are upon him. But at the moment he seems not to be doing so. And add a billion more in fifteen more years, and geometrically a billion and a half more fifteen years later, then we see the larger animals being sequestered in islands, natural areas—unnatural areas.

I call them concentration camps. We will concentrate them there. Is that the model?

If it is not a model, what is a model that we can describe?

DARLING: Models of what is the shape of things to come. The land needs urgently this reclassification which Max [Nicholson] has spoken of and which Ed Graham could elaborate on, which has been done so much in the United States already.

Land classification should lead us toward proper use of land as we see it at this moment. I think we should realize that the plant breeder, the animal breeder, the soil chemist have within the last twenty years altered the agricultural situation so greatly that the intensive use of land for agriculture is producing crops such as we never knew before, and it has lightened the load on what in Britain they foolishly call marginal land.

In Britain we are still in the position of giving 50 per cent grants for clearing of marginal land, and for making it into agricultural land, at the very same time that Britain has become the most intensive agricultural producer of any nation in its mechanization of agriculture, its production per man.

I think with proper use of land at any one time, as we see it at the moment, and the population situation not getting up on top of us, that we reach the stage where the intensification of agriculture is actually liberating land, giving us a pattern and a model for a much freer expression of the wildlife of the continent. We are not going to go dry farming into ridiculous places any more because we can get much bigger yields on good wheat and corn land. I would say the intensification of agriculture on good land is one of our best hopes for the future.

COWAN: I think that many of us would agree that ecosystems will be to a degree certainly sequestered—will be isolated, if you like. But the concept that is contained in the words "concentration camp" implies the building up of unstable and unusual populations on these, with the consequent destruction of the basic habitat upon it. This is not the necessary consequence of sequestration of populations. I think that you could find considerable argument here.

DASMANN: I would like to believe what Frank Darling predicts is the shape of the future, and I think that both Ian Cowan and Starker Leopold used the same reasoning in looking at the future of the planet. And yet I wonder if this is not just a phase in which we have temporarily gotten ahead of the food supply by intensification and use of our good lands. Perhaps, if our populations continue to increase at the present phenomenal rate, we will be forced out into the marginal lands, which are unsafe to use under the technologies we have employed on them in the past, but which we will have to use in the future simply because we will have to have every available inch of space producing necessities, absolute necessities—food to keep alive.

Unless someone can produce a somewhat more optimistic picture of population control in the future, I don't see how we can sit back and say that we are going to intensify production on fewer acres and we are going to give land back to wildlife and natural areas. I think we are in just a temporary phase.

COWAN: If I could make one more remark. Looking at it from the Canadian situation, where we have vast areas and small population and very large land areas that will not be of agricultural use no matter what you do with them, it is very unlikely that we can divise techniques to produce food on huge areas of Canada.

In the sort of area that we are talking about at the moment—my own province, for example, British Columbia—the park areas amount to 9000 square miles out of a provincial area of 360,000 square miles. If these 9000 square miles were used to produce food—and virtually none of them can be because they are not that kind of land—the food production would be inconsequential in the kinds of population increases we are talking about.

It would be like trying to support the poor of Calcutta out of your own pocketbook. For this reason alone it seems to offer me some hope for the kind of situation we envision.

Dr. Graham?

GRAHAM: I would like to make two or three comments. I remember seeing a map by Dudley Stamp, showing the area of cropland in Britain in 1650, and another map showing the area of land in crops in about, I think, 1914, when the land-use survey was made.

I can't quote the figures, but the area in crops had been reduced tremendously.

I don't know what the situation is today. I think that there is still a great deal less land in cultivation in Britain (and the British can check this) than there was 250 years ago.

Another point of interest is that a country like Japan can at present have 6 per cent of its land area in national parks, and expects to have 10 per cent of its land area in national parks. And you know what the population pressure has been there.

The business of a model bothers me because I don't think we can look ahead so far. It seems to me that as planners you have a set of alternatives before you and you must make a decision with respect to the alternatives available. You make that decision and you go on to the next one.

I think it is not practical nor reasonable to try to design a model here, in four days, for the future environments of North America. All you can do is use the available information, hoping that the next time you meet you will have more information than you have today, and make a decision with respect to the knowledge you have and the alternatives open to you. But I do believe that a lot depends upon the faith you have in human intellect; whether we are all going down, as Bill Vogt said, like Gadarene swine, or whether we are going to be smart enough to handle the population issue along with the rest of the issues that we discuss here.

I think we can do this. I think today, more than at any time that I can remember, there is evidence that we are employing more ingenuity to solve these problems than the human species has ever employed.

We may wait until the last minute. This is typical human behavior. But in many cases the last minute is soon enough. We have tackled many of our conservation problems in this country in this way. We certainly did with soil erosion and we did with a lot of other things. But look where we are today with soil conservation compared with where we were only a quarter of a century ago. I just can't feel as pessimistic as I sense the group feels about the future. It bothers me just a little.

BRINSER: I do think that it will be useful to clarify what is meant by good land. The most productive agricultural land in the United States today, I believe, is in Florida, which is practically sand.

Another area that is very productive is the Caribou silt loam in Maine, which has very little natural fertility. In other words, it is good enough to absorb inputs to make it productive. These inputs consist of a variety of things. It is not a question of soil itself.

So that if you are talking about good land, and the distribution of good land and its classification, you should think of classifying all of the factors that make land productive. There is a tendency to regard good land as naturally fertile land, whereas most of the areas in the United States of highest productivity today are those in which land is capable of absorbing capital inputs. This is what makes the classification problem much more interesting than simply one of looking at a soils map and saying this is good and this is bad.

ORDWAY: I feel uncomfortable with the thought that some land will be used for crops and some of it will be used for wildlife.

I am also disturbed by the relation of that to Max Nicholson's reference to the classification of land. I am not an ecologist. But consider the best, most highly classified land that I know of, which is being used for crop production—in this case alfalfa—and the rangeland which is not good for production and is classified in Class VII and VIII, where the deer are supposed to roam. Now, as soon as we create a nice oasis with a lot of alfalfa on the high-class land, immediately the deer come down and join the cattle. So you are handling both. You can't separate them.

STRONG: Presumably you will favor one over the other in these areas. You will have a conflict that you will have to resolve. You may want to shoot the deer.

ORDWAY: No, I would like to keep the deer and the cattle. I don't want to resolve it.

CALDWELL: As a tentative answer to Paul Brandwein's question about whether we must live in a totally managed environment: it seems to me that indeed we must—and, in fact, we do, although the management is often by inadvertence. Any natural areas—and I use "natural" here in quotation marks, assuming that man and his artifacts are also in a sense natural—that we have existed by sufferance. It isn't really, I think, a matter of "concentration camps" for wild nature in these set-aside areas of national parks. One must realize that the pressures of the technology itself, meaning the demands upon the environment by the human population, equipped with the instruments of the technology and with the perceptions and desires that technology makes possible, involve diverse demands upon the natural environment that must somehow be reckoned with if any part of this natural world is to survive.

We simply can't let alone any part of this environment and do nothing about it. Somebody will have designs on it. Somebody will intrude upon it. So I would suggest that even though we were to stabilize the population of North America today, we would nevertheless still face the problem of management of the environment, due in very considerable part to the consequences of this rapidly proliferating technology.

VOGT: I should like to say a word against the human intellect, if I may, reacting to Dr. Brandwein's comments.

Paul Waggoner exhorted us to learn how to raise twice as many animals per acre or per square mile as are now produced, but the animals have built into their nervous systems in one way or another self-limiting mechanisms, territories in many birds, pecking orders.

Wynne-Edwards just published a very interesting book on this, *Animal Dispersion*. It seems to me virtually impossible to build species of wild animals above a certain population limit under natural conditions. They have predators.

If you get rid of predators you can feed them and build up elk populations in the parks, for example. But under natural conditions—that is, before they have been interfered with by the unnatural creature—man—and I don't know at which point man becomes unnatural; I wish this meeting could solve that—they take care of this problem.

William Morton Wheeler quotes M. Roberts as having suggested that the human forebrain originated as a malignant overgrowth. It gives him, of course, a great deal of control over his environment.

We shipped something over six million tons of grain to India last year—which simply compounds the difficulties in India. As long as we continue to do this kind of thing we are going to double the population in these underdeveloped countries every eighteen or twenty years, and these countries themselves are much more effective in death control than they are in birth control. India, for example, appropriated 100 million dollars under the third five-year plan for birth control—a sizable amount of money for a country like India—but she also appropriated 600 million dollars for health measures and also a great deal more for agriculture, water, and so on. If she had appropriated 600 million dollars for birth control and 100 million dollars for death control, it might have made a lot more sense.

It is going to take—under the most happy circumstances—quite a while to change people's habits enough to bring down birth rates. I would think there would be little chance of avoiding famine.

One of the most serious areas for us is in Latin America, where there are now about 220 million people who, at the current rate of increase, will hit well over 600 million people before the end of this century—with about 100 million to 125 million in Mexico across that very small stream, the Rio Grande.

We shall have to put heavier and heavier burdens on our land unless we want to face rising death rates in these other countries, and in some cases it simply may not be politically possible for us to do, if we can avoid it.

I don't think that we are really being as wise as the cardinals we hear here at Airlie—one cardinal on that ridge and one 200 yards away. You are not going to get another cardinal in between; they are self-limiting in their population.

ALLEN: I think that our only possible attitude must be that this population problem is going to be solved. If we give up on it and say we are going to have unlimited demands, it means that we are going to write off a great many things that ought to be a part of our future in North America. That is why I have called the preservation of these things a somewhat arbitrary action because it is providing more for the future perhaps than it is for right now.

I don't think there is any ecologist or any combination of ecologists who can draw a model of the future or even define the human living standard. It has been my observation that ecologists deal more in terms of trends and influences than they do in finite quantities, and that we can, many times, tell when we are headed in the wrong direction, even though we can't be quite sure of where we are going to end up.

HUBBERT: Mr. Chairman, perhaps the thing that impresses me most about these discussions is their shortsightedness, backward and forward.

I am not impressed with time in terms of two or three decades when we are trying to solve problems of these kinds. However, to come back to the ecological side of the picture, if there is such a thing as a normal state, it is a fluctuating steady state, or else a state which changes very slowly with time. An abnormal situation in ecology is one in which populations go up or down spectacularly.

During recent years I have taken a look at the human population from a geological viewpoint. I don't know how many people there may have been a million years ago, but I venture that a thousand is too small a number. During this million years the average length of time per doubling has been the order of 50,000 years. At the present time this doubling period has been reduced to about thirty-five years.

This shortening of the doubling time has happened within the last couple of centuries. Specifically stated, the entire face of the earth during the last few centuries—we are probably in the middle of it right now—has undergone one of the most drastic ecological upsets in terms of magnitude and speed that has occurred during geological time. Our premise seems to be that this is more or less a normal state of affairs, whereas actually it is one of the most abnormal in either human or geologic history. Furthermore, it is based on the exploitation of such nonreplaceable, nonreplinishable things as coal, oil, and minerals—things whose magnitudes of consumption within this century exceed that of all preceding human history.

What about the future? I regard it as inevitable, that after the present upset we shall approach another ecological steady state. It will have to be a steady state not only of the human population but of other biological populations as well. And to the extent that we can bring intelligence to bear upon it, we can perhaps adjust it to such a level that it will be moderately comfortable for the human species.

With regard to the nonreplaceable resources such as coal and oil, they will be gone. Metals—we shall be forced to go to lower-grade metallic ores.

Energy—for a long time to come we shall have nuclear energy sufficient to carry us along. And there will also be sunshine.

But I particularly wish to emphasize that we are squarely in the middle of the most profound ecological upset in history. To look forward for twenty years, or fifty years, we shall still be in the midst of the transition. Ultimately—and not too far away—we simply have to look forward to a state of nongrowth as an ecological necessity. I would venture that our intellectual adjustment to this state will probably be the next major intellectual revolution.

FOSBERG: I wonder if the findings of paleontology support the idea that there ever has been a steady state.

HUBBERT: After all, the human population during most of its existence has had an average doubling period of 50,000 years. No census could detect such a rate of change during one man's lifetime. Paleontology is a very slow science, so to speak, and even drastic things in geology have taken a million years.

SEARS: I have a few general comments. In nature when you get a relative equilibrium, it is an *open* steady state, one which continues to receive energy but which recycles the material that keeps the system going.

Here is a thermodynamic model which we should strive to approximate if we can in our own use of land. I don't think it is impossible. Certainly there is nothing in nature today that compares with what we see in a great city which siphons in material from a wide range of territory and then dumps the wastes into the air or water. At best, these wastes are a nuisance; at worst, they are toxic. In nature there is recycling, continuous reuse.

Concerning another matter, I am not sure that the use of land for production and for preservation of ecosystems involves quite the incompatibilities we have been assuming. I was struck not long ago in reading [George Perkins] Marsh to see that he estimated a hundred years ago that most areas would be in much healthier condition if 20 to 25 per cent of them were back in native vegetation. I had previously arrived at that judgment just on the basis of my own observation, so I was quite encouraged.

The point is that this isn't wasteland, even though it is not producing food, because the processes that go on in well-integrated communities are constructive so far as soil formation and regulation of the water cycle and things like that are concerned. So it isn't a net loss, a luxury, to set these areas apart to keep them going, nor need they be forever excluded in the production of food. If you have a long enough cycle, they can go back into it, and other areas can be retired.

BOULDING: I think the thing we are missing out here is the biological revolution that is going on at the moment. We don't know where this will lead us. From what I hear, not being a biologist, I get the impression that in biology we are almost where we were in nuclear energy, say, in 1910—that is, we have the code of life almost in our grasp. The consequences of this could be enormous.

I suspect that agriculture is a dying industry. It has gone from 90 per cent of the labor force to 9 per cent. Even with existing techniques it will go to 3 per cent. It could go out altogether. That is, it is a rather crude method of food production, after all, cows and pigs and all these primitive obsolete objects.

(*Laughter*)

Obviously what we are going to have is coffee-flavored algae, bread-flavored algae, produced in tanks, not even in sunlight, perhaps even synthesized all together. These are certainly on the horizon. We are already getting pretty good protein from petroleum, I understand. Of course that won't last very long.

The thing I think we have to recognize is that this transition that you are talking about is still going on, and we are still very much in the middle of this. It is essentially a transition of knowledge, and there are no signs of this slowing down as yet. Of course it will slow down.

One thing we know is that we will never get exponential growth forever. If we ever had, it would be only one thing. All the growth curves follow the ogival pattern and presumably the growth of knowledge will do the same.

I think the important thing is that we are not really in the middle of this curve yet. We still don't know where technology is taking us. There are perhaps even grounds for modest optimism—though I hate to sound optimistic among conservationists.

(*Laughter*)

I think there is reason for modest optimism about population. We may have as radical a change in birth rates in the next twenty years as we saw in the death rate in the last twenty years, which would make the situation enormously different.

DARLING: I wanted to ask, before Kenneth Boulding spoke, what will happen to this organic environment which we are dealing with today if somebody comes up with an efficient form of artificial photosynthesis? Where are we then?

BOULDING: We are off.

DARLING: It seems to me it is only just around the corner. I think we would really be in some trouble then.

ALLEN: Wouldn't we have the same thing, Frank, if someone suddenly discovered how to take the salt out of sea water very cheaply?

DARLING: That is going on. The artificial photosynthesis would be such an upsetting thing to so much that I think we ought not completely to neglect it in our thoughts of the organic environment of North America in the future—or of anywhere else in the world, for that matter.

Is that a discovery which could be controlled at the beginning? Would the nations be able to handle such a situation which somebody could produce overnight?

DANSEREAU: I think Dr. Brandwein earlier gave us a very objective statement of the way we are going. He developed an image of what you might call the hamburger stage, where we would do to the steers what we have already done to the Leghorn hens and park them in pens and continue to exploit an essentially agricultural world. Dr. Boulding confronts us with the post-hamburger world where agriculture is passé. However, there is a painful adolescent stage in between, even between now and the complete hamburgerization of our civilization. It seems to me that the future environments of North America have to be organized in some way, hopefully not a blueprint to be published on Saturday of this week. But what we might contribute from our various points of view are the criteria of both values and implementation.

As an ecologist I would pose the question, looking at the map of vegetation patterns, and I would say here is a picture of the major divisions of environment in the United States. Do we have, within each one of these areas, a well-preserved sample for study, a reasonable representation of the range of ecosystems that can exist, having in mind the so far poorly known relationship between the relative importance of control by climate, by soil, or site factors, and of course by evolutionary and geologic history? These four things are associated in every ecological situation that we consider in a completely different and more or less unpredictable way.

There is a great deal to be found out which is absolutely essential to any future plan of modifying the climate, modifying the water table, all of which is happening with or without us.

This is the kind of thing that it seems to me we should try to be stating, not a complete blueprint, but a contribution of what we think should be preserved, how it should be managed, and, if possible, why. The technique will not be enough. It carries in itself no measure of conviction because it is not we but the people who will make the decisions.

WOODBURY: I was going to say, on the question of the farmer disappearing from agriculture, that one of the things we haven't taken into account here is the automation of other industrial productive processes.

I should think I would be more worried about what man is going to do to the face of North America when he has more leisure time on his hands than I am with the possibility that the population of this continent is going to get completely out of hand.

I think it is not. As far as the United States is concerned, the birth rate has turned down. It has been down for the past several years. That is not long enough to indicate any major trend. Our death rate has been going down some, but is now leveling off.

The prospect is that very substantial portions of our people are going to have an amount of leisure or, at least, nonwork time on their hands greater than anything they have ever known before. How is it going to be distributed? How is it going to be used? What the impact and influence is going to be upon our habitats seems to me to be perhaps the greatest pending question.

This, of course, is not simply a question of people having more time on their hands, and maybe this gets us outside of the realm of this Conference, but what standard of living is going to be maintained in an economy of this kind of abundance. Are we simply going to develop an economy with a substantial portion of the population at a more or less subsistence level and another rather small portion of highly skilled technicians and executives who are going to profit from this increased productivity? This seems to me a part of the ecological problem we are facing in the country. Maybe I anticipate later discussions.

STRONG: Doesn't this take us back to the same question that Dr. Waggoner raised, that we can't assume that we in the United States are in a vacuum? We still have the population of the rest of the world to consider in terms of the food supply. We have it also to consider in our use of leisure time. How can we assume that we will continue to have luxury of choice with a totally different pressure and level of affluence in the rest of the world?

OVINGTON: I feel that conservationists have temporary luxury available to them. They have time to put their house in order before these pressures build up, whether they are pressures occasioned by a shortage of feeding materials or by a shortage of recreation space.

I think what is the greatest urgency of conservation is to understand ecological systems much more than we do at present. This is what we really need to get clear in our minds—what we are aiming at and how we are going to tackle it so that we have the answer when the pressures become really serious. I am very worried that we are not doing this in the right way.

OSBORN: Mr. Chairman, to what degree should we consider, if at all, the marine and wildlife along our shores? Is this involved in our considerations?

DARLING: There is every indication that the exploration of the ocean is going to be one of the great features of the next twenty years, and of course it will relieve the terrestrial situation to some extent, if some leveling out in the population takes place. I think the marine resource is immense, and will become utilized with improving techniques.

I was hoping I might have a chance to be a bit destructive about our deliberations today. We are just on the close of our work, and yet I am rather disappointed. We haven't got our guidelines on the future of the organic environments of North America. Possibly we have been talking about the most intangible things today. How can we make any guidelines? Yet I think this is part of what we are here for, to note trends.

I feel with Ovington, and Durwood Allen, that we could make some sites available which would fit in with Nicholson's International Biological Programme if these sites were there; if they were proclaimed and kept together, they could be used for research and as conservation areas.

As the Conference works along we should get more notion of where human activities of transport and planning, population movement, and so on will affect the loci we have available. Possibly ultimately we could even produce a map with a set of transparent overlays on it of the way things were likely to happen in several fields of technology and so on. We could perhaps get a few planning areas we should go for as soon as possible as being places where ecosystems would persist, where logically research could carry on for a considerable number of years yet, which would ultimately redound to the survival of the organic environments of North America we cherish, leaving us something other than rubble and a bit of mountaintop somewhere.

FISHER: I would like to follow that by asking our paper writer or panel a specific question, to get us off this grand theme of population and land and resources to which I suppose we will be returning from time to time.

I don't think they should be allowed to go to their cocktails without answering a question like this: will you list for us, 1, 2, 3, 4, 5, what you think should be the criteria or guidelines for deciding what we North Americans should preserve in animal and plant species, in ecosystems, or what we will?

What are the guidelines that you offer to us from science, from the point of view of users or any other point of view? What are the guidelines, 1, 2, 3, 4, for what we should preserve? And give us a few comments on the relative importance of the different ones.

COWAN: If I could answer, I think the guidelines are already set down in the papers that we have produced and that we have been considering. The guidelines, I think, will be clearly drawn. But they can't be set down 1, 2, 3, 4.

FISHER: Give me the top four.

COWAN: I think we might differ on these, but in general I think my panelists would agree that we would seek the preservation of suitable sample areas for future studies, for future human use, using the term "use" in the largest sense, of those areas which will be most quickly and most thoroughly modified by the day-to-day activities of man. These are of the first order of priority.

LEOPOLD: I think that the ultimate end, Joe, is certainly a working sample— preferably several—of each major ecological type in the continent. I am not willing to accept yet that agriculture is obsolete. This may happen in the future. But at the moment it is areas such as a block of prairie that constitute in my mind the most critical immediate need for conservation; perhaps the Rocky Mountains are the least critical because everyone is willing to give us the Rocky Mountains to preserve as wilderness or as national parks.

There is involved a great deal more of an investment for society to set aside a piece of potentially productive country for an analytical study. The block can be fairly small. You don't need to have half of Iowa to study the ecology of a prairie, but certainly some thousands of acres.

As I tried to bring up this morning, out of the studies of basic ecosystems and how they worked originally—the sort of work Dr. Ovington is doing—comes a better understanding of that particular type of soil and its possible exploitation and use. In other words, I would bend our preservation of ecosystems around to being of an immediate and direct concern and interest in production, in maintenance of the human population. The moral issues, the esthetic values, the love of recreation in wild country— all enter into this, and all are important. But as an ecologist I am at the moment concerned with understanding these ecosystems so that we will know, A, how to preserve them and, B, how to use them.

FISHER: Can you give some idea of a cutoff point, how far society should go in preserving different identified types of ecosystems or their vanishing species?

LEOPOLD: In acres?

FISHER: Any way, numbers, any kind of units that lend themselves to this. Even dollars.

LEOPOLD: That is almost impossible to answer. I can't.

FISHER: How do we come up on that problem?

DANSEREAU: I think the answer is very simple. You come up with a conflict of interest. That is as far as you can go.

I think each in our sphere of competence can say this is desirable, knowing full well that all that we want, would like to realize, is not possible.

I think it is a perfectly wise general decision to make to go to those areas that are under immediate menace. We have a pretty good idea of which ecosystems are presently most endangered, certainly. Not the tundra, but certainly the grassland. We can't fence off half of Iowa. We know we can't do that. But to get a good representation of the primeval or reconstructed prairie, that is just about what it would take. We can't do it.

GRAHAM: Don't we have the tendency to put the ecosystem here and man over there? I think that if we conceive a cornfield to be just as much an ecosystem as an undisturbed prairie, we may get a different slant on what we are driving at.

I am not saying we don't need protected areas, but I am saying that we are going to have to include man as a part of this ecosystem everywhere, and I come back to what Frank Darling said the first thing this morning when he made comments along this line. The mere fact that you establish an area for study brings man into the picture. I believe we may throw ourselves off if we don't take a very broad concept of what we mean by ecosystems.

I suppose that in a sense, the city region is an ecosystem of a sort within which you may have other types of ecosystems. It is conceivable that you may have more than one ecosystem on one site.

With respect to Joe's question, I would think, Starker, that as areas which ought to be high on the list of ecosystems to be studied, we should certainly add the coastal marshes of the Atlantic and Gulf coasts. They are going very fast. They are highly productive areas, as Odum has proven with his studies. Perhaps they are going as fast as any general type of area on the continent. But even there, too, I think that we have the same opportunity for study when we take a marshland where man is an important factor as we do in one where he is not. We don't want to separate man from these ecosystems we want to study, and I think we have had the tendency in this meeting to do just that.

FOSBERG: I would like to point out one thing in relation to what Ed just said. I don't think we want to separate man from these ecosystems, but at the same time, man is the most effective agent of instability and change. If we can—as nearly as possible—exclude man from a few examples, we will have a better chance of understanding the rest of them which man is changing.

The other thing I want to say is that I detect a considerable discrepancy or difference of opinion between what Frank said in his last comment and what the two of you said immediately afterward. Frank's suggestion was that we superimpose all the different probable land uses on transparent overlays over our map of ecosystem types and then pick out what is left. In other words, use the scraps for our studies.

I must say I favor the former point of view, that we had better get busy and pick out some of the pieces that are, shall we say, subject to conflicting interests and preserve them before it is too late. They are the ones that we need to know about more than anything else, not just the scraps.

I will go further and say that we should perhaps pay very good attention to a paper written by Luna Leopold a few years ago in which he said society has to make up its mind that we want certain things, even though we can't justify them or express them in terms of dollars, and then set them aside for whatever purpose we want. But we had better do it.

MC HARG: Somebody speculated that the world will someday be so covered with people that we will be extinguished by our own metabolism and that the oxygen will be consumed and that the only thing to do will be to climb into a volcano or mohole. This kind of speculation is really morbid.

Yet I can't live in Richard Meier's world of 150 billion people, and I can't envisage it, either, although in fact it may be quite humane.

I can easily understand six billion people and 300 million Americans, and this causes me no consternation at all. If 25 per cent of the land area is in agriculture and about 5 per cent is in urban uses, we still have 70 per cent left. These aren't scraps.

More and more people are going into less and less space. Seventy per cent is left, either nonurban or nonfarm use. Given this situation—and I am neither an economist nor an ecologist, but a working man—I want simple rules so that a man with good will, small intelligence and small influence, can act wisely. That is: of all choices, which choice is the best?

To what extent are habitats permissive? What limitations should we have for numbers of people in habitats? To what degree are natural processes permissive to man? Where should he select to build, where should he intervene, and how?

If you can speak of physical and natural processes, the degree to which these represent value and the degree to which man may or may not interpose, given a choice, then I think you can persuade a simple man of good will to follow your injunctions. But with Dr. Fisher I say you have to tell simple men where and how to intervene.

NICHOLSON: May I stretch my neck out to provide something? If we look at the vegetation map of the United States, we see 116 different habitats. Taking the major variants, possibly nearly 150.

I would like to put out the hypothesis that there should be reservations for scientific work, as living museums, of an average of approximately three per habitat on that map, and that the median size of these would be not less than 10,000 acres. Some of them could be very small; some of them, in the case of prairies and so on, as has been said, would have to be perhaps up to 100,000 acres, or even more. But the median might be, perhaps, 10,000.

So you would have roughly on the order of 450 reserves covered, of which quite a number already exist.

That is simply for living-museum purposes. You would also have a pretty big demand for expendable scientific-research areas. It might even be of the same order if you were far enough ahead. At the present time it could be put at a good deal less, but it might be prudent to put it of the same order.

Third, there would be a requirement for educational reserves which in acreage would probably be considerably less because they would have to be within reasonable distance from urban areas. From a land-use standpoint this might raise problems. On that basis you might have on the order of 1500 reserves of all types, of which, as I say, some hundreds, possibly— I don't know how many hundreds—already exist, or partly exist.

I am just trying to give Joe Fisher something, so he doesn't go away entirely empty-handed. I suppose I will get torn to pieces by the ecologists on this, but it seems to me this is something somebody has to decide at some stage when we stop talking and get down to planning a reserve system.

BUDOWSKI: While the scraps look encouraging for the United States, the picture is very different for tropical America. I should remind you that there are countries with over 60 per cent of their population engaged in agriculture.

This is largely a destructive agriculture. It does not leave scraps at all. It destroys everything.

Time is running out. While we may have such optimistic statements as artificial photosynthesis being around the corner, I beg you to find alternative new ways. Don't reckon on artificial photosynthesis in the next twenty, thirty, or forty years. We will just be left without anything else.

(Darling looked upon artificial photosynthesis as a pending disaster, not a matter for optimism.)

I am afraid I have no choice—no one has a choice when he travels to tropical America but to get this very pessimistic view that time is running out.

WAGGONER: Mr. Chairman, I will offer a single priority: to learn how to preserve as much as possible on the smallest possible acreage—and the ecologists shouldn't give up until they have tried.

BEAR: I have much interest in the prairie. I would like to ask a few questions about this prairie preserve that you set aside. Let's suppose it is 100,000 acres, if that is the size you want. Are you going to set this aside and put a fence around it? Or are you going to allow egress on it for any animal or man who wants to go in there? Are you going to allow the weeds to grow up just as they would under nature's conditions? How are you going to deal with this problem?

LEOPOLD: Last year, or two years ago, I was a member of a small board advising the Secretary of Interior on this problem of the management of national parks. Assuming that this prairie might be a national park, the principles that we recommended then, I think, would apply to this area—namely, as ecologists we should be able to do a pretty fair job of reconstructing in our own minds what was that prairie at the time the white man arrived, when Lewis and Clark crossed that country, and rebuild it and manage it in such a way to maintain it in this primeval condition.

BEAR: Are you going to let a prairie fire go across it?

LEOPOLD: Yes. Not only let it; set it. If fire was part of the prairie, this is indeed part of the management program, and within many of the national parks this is going to be mandatory, to maintain anything like naturalness.

Therefore, although it is artificial in the sense that there is no 100,000-acre prairie left right now, you would have to rebuild it from whatever scraps do remain; it could become almost natural if managed, using the same basic influences that created prairie in the first place. Then you could have comparative studies between an area with natural stratified native grasses and adjoining areas of cereals and forage under cultivation and intensive management for cropping.

This is a scientific value that I think such areas should serve.

BEAR: How long do you think it will take you to build this prairie back up again?

LEOPOLD: Not long. The University of Wisconsin started from scratch and built up a little prairie. It is not as big as the grounds of this Airlie House. But obtaining the species from railroad rights of way, graveyards, places where species have persisted, and bringing them together and re-creating this same association of plants that constituted the prairie, they have a little prairie.

BEAR: What will you do with all these people who want to go in there and look it over?

LEOPOLD: Just as in any other national park, I think such a place should be zoned; there should be places where people can see it, and big blocks that are kept in semiwild condition and not overrun with people. I think this zoning concept should apply to all these big reserves, national parks and others.

OVINGTON: Mr. Chairman, there is something here I disagree with strongly, namely the idea that it is possible to re-create a natural ecosystem as it was at some specified time in the past. This is impossible in this day and age when the environment is modified and polluted with toxic chemicals, etc. Furthermore, I doubt that we know sufficient of the nature of past ecosystems to re-create them accurately.

In the prairie example, a sample of prairie ecosystem has been developed artificially using native plant species and presumably is being maintained by a prescribed system of burning. Obviously this is more similar to the past prairie than an agricultural crop but it is nevertheless an artificial product of management. Plant and animal species important to the ecology of the past prairie may be missing and the effects of the new management regime may differ in subtle ways from the effects of previous management. Nevertheless, the new prairie is valuable both culturally and scientifically.

TUNNARD: The analogy of historic preservation might be helpful. At a meeting of ICOMOS[1] held in Venice last year, two resolutions were passed. One was that buildings should be preserved with the additions that had been made through time, kept intact, rather than putting them back to an earlier arbitrary state; and the second was that no ruins should be reconstructed unless the parts could be found lying on the ground.

COWAN (*closing the session*): I have suggested to our Chairman that this panel will try to come up with a succinct statement of where we think we are, at the end of today. This we will deliver to you tomorrow without expecting debate. We hope this will set a pattern that subsequent panels may follow. We will try to stick to the strongly held views, whether or not they were strongly supported, and to come to some stage in our evolutionary process here these four or five days.

1 International Commission of Monuments and Sites.

II REGIONS: THEIR DEVELOP-MENTAL HISTORY AND FUTURE

---

* Dr. Graham, who died while these pages were in proof, was a consultant to the International Biological Programme, which has been described as "hoping to do for ecology what the IGY did for geology." Known as a specialist who had brought ecology into land management, he was the Director of the Plant Technology Division of the U.S. Department of Agriculture from 1953 to 1963. His *Natural Principles of Land Use* of 1944 (*Uso racional del suelo*, 1947) has been of far-reaching influence.

Introductory Statement

GRAHAM: Mr. Chairman, my lady, and gentlemen, we now open a session which I think grows naturally out of the one we had yesterday. It is called "Regions: Their Developmental History and Future."

We talked a great deal yesterday about ecosystems, but I had the feeling that we were talking about them pretty largely in terms of species and natural areas. Perhaps today we can begin to look at ecosystems, albeit through a regional approach, as something more dynamic than we really got to in our previous session.

In relation to the interests of the economists and the planners, it seems to me that what might be of greatest value to them is an understanding of ecosystems in terms of the dynamic qualities and the processes that are involved in nature, whether we identify these by ecosystems, by site condition, or what not.

Certainly the preservation of a given ecosystem today may turn out to be the preservation of something quite different over a period of time—ecosystems are affected not only by man, but by natural cataclysm, as we all know.

The idea of productivity in ecosystems was suggested yesterday. In the International Biological Programme, which is probably going to provide biologists and particularly ecologists with one of the greatest opportunities they have had for world-wide coordinated research, we find that the theme is the biological basis of productivity and of human welfare. So there must be something in ecosystem analysis that will be of real value to those in economics, urban regional development, environmental planning, and so on. I'm inclined to think that the value lies more in examination of environmental processes and dynamics and potential productivity than it does in some of the things we discussed yesterday.

What is a region? I have had trouble enough with ecosystems, and I must admit I can't find much of a definition of regions, either. I went back to Richard Hartshorn, and he tells me that a region is essentially what you want it to be. You can have regions of all kinds, and for all purposes. Here again, it seems to me, we engage an abstract rather than a reality.

I thought I would like to comment briefly on our four papers. Our panel thought we would not have a five-minute summary by each of the panelists, but would abide by my general introduction and then would go directly into discussion. So perhaps I am at liberty to comment on each of these papers and to highlight what I think are some of the significant points made in each.

I would like to comment first on Mackay's paper and his consideration of northern regions, of tundra and closely related coniferous forests.

He has pointed to limiting factors as being important in a consideration of those regions, and has described a fragile and delicate kind of environment. For example, he talks about the Hudson Bay Company's Fort Anderson, which was established in 1861 and was abandoned only five years later. During the past century, revegetation has been minimal. Most of the vegetation is still composed of grasses, with a few willows. Forest clearings still define the original outlines of the stockade.

Inevitably such disturbances will increase as man's activities spread. Whether or not they will be harmful in the aggregate is quite another issue. Mackay admits that only local modifications are likely to be important in the immediate future in these regions. But the significance of limiting factors in an extreme environment of this sort, as compared to that which we have dealt with in temperate latitudes, seems to me to be one of his important points.

Next, I would like to point to Gilbert White's paper in which he makes the statement: ". . . water as a limiting factor seems to be declining in importance . . . in the southeastern United States." This sounds like just the opposite of what you might have expected to read. He points to broader choices of use appearing, such as use of arid areas for residence and recreation as opposed to the traditional use for grazing and mining.

Here, I think, he is pointing to human innovation in dealing with a natural system. He says, "A major aspect of the decision process is perception by the resources manager, whether he be a farmer, a government administrator, or a legislator. His views set the conditions of choice as surely as natural features impose certain constraints on his action." He seems to me to be saying that man's innovation and ingenuity are as important—if not more important—as the natural environment with which he is dealing.

Next, let me point to Dr. Bear's paper in which he says a number of provocative things. One of them is that "The productivity of a given area of land is not a property that is inherent in the soil." He is telling us that human ingenuity is the key to land use, that technological improvements, which are the result of the creative mind and the contriving hand, are the important factors in environmental use.

He says a lot of other things, which no doubt will come out in discussion, with respect to the number of people we can support in the United States, given a certain change in custom, diet, and so on. But his central point seems to be, again, that human creativity and ingenuity are the important factors. He makes the point that all land is not alike. In its potential use and productivity land should be considered on its terms and be accounted for through an interpretive classification system.

Finally, we come to Budowski's paper, which takes us into the tropics, particularly the humid tropics, and in which I think he has crystallized the environmental problem in terms of social concern and welfare.

Frank Darling referred to his sense of pain in reading this paper. I didn't put it in those words, but I certainly was disturbed by the very difficult situations in which people find themselves in Central America. Budowski quotes Lee as saying, "They are too poor to learn, too ignorant to improve, too frightened to try. The large mass of the tropical peasantry is seemingly doomed to an endless round of inadequacy."

How do we account for the difference between the land north of the Mexican border and the land south? There isn't a sharp line; the natural regions melt into each other gradually from north to south. But you only have to cross the border to see the difference.

The European came to what is now the United States, dominated the native population, and introduced his own religion, culture, and background. Perhaps he was bound to develop a different environment from that of the settler who was absorbed by the native population and came from a different type of culture, religion, and historical background.

It seems to me, in summary, that these papers begin to pose some questions, particularly for the ecologist, and these questions are certainly as obvious to you as they are to me.

My interest is in natural history and I was trained as an ecologist, although I suppose of the old classical school. But I can't help wondering what place the traditional ecologist has in this acquisitive, exploitative society in which we live; and whether or not he is going to remain an incurable environmentalist, and treat the world's ecosystems as apart from man as a dominant element. It seems to me that he himself has got to become part economist and planner and constructionist, and he has got to admit that man is a part of nature.

We said yesterday that we didn't want to play God. Well, in many ways I think we are God. At least if I can understand my philosopher friends who say that first man had many gods, then he had one God and he became opposed to the forces of nature and nature was outside of him. There is evidence today, I think, to indicate that man is beginning to think of himself as a part of nature. In doing this, I think the ecologist is going to have to give full consideration not only to environment, but to ideas and inventions and attitudes as parts of ecosystems.

HIGHLY PRODUCTIVE LANDS OF NORTH AMERICA
Firman E. Bear*

This paper deals with the whole of Canada and continental United States. Our primary interest, however, is in the wide expanse of rolling lands, prairies, and plains extending from the Appalachians on the east to the Cordilleras on the west and from Hudson Bay on the north to the Gulf of Mexico on the south.

The soils with which we are dealing in this vast agricultural complex can be broadly classified as chernozemic in the central part of the continent, podzolic to the near north and east, latosolic to the south and east, and chestnut-brown to the near west. Farther north the tundras come into play and farther west the desertic soils.

The chernozemic soils, which constitute the core of the continent, are black-brown soils developed under mostly grassland vegetation, hot summers, and moderate rainfall. They were neutral to slightly alkaline in reaction in their virgin state. They contain a deposit of calcium carbonate near the surface to the west but at an ever-increasing depth to the east, until it finally disappears altogether. These are the corn-belt soils of

* Dr. Bear, who has made it his professional concern to look at the future from the ground up, is a member of the Advisory Council of the Conservation Foundation. During the 1930s he directed agricultural research for American Cyanamid; from 1940 to 1954 he was Professor of Agricultural Chemistry and Chairman of the Soils Department at Rutgers University, New Brunswick, New Jersey.

the United States and the wheat-belt soils of Canada.

The podzolic soils to the near north and east are gray-brown soils developed under forest vegetation, cooler temperatures, and greater rainfall. They are mostly acid in reaction, having been subjected to extensive leaching by rains that carried the basic constituents, including the calcium carbonate, out to sea. These are the grass-hay and pastureland soils that are the mainstay of the dairy industry.

The latosolic soils to the near south and east are red-yellow soils developed under heavier forest vegetation, longer summers, and higher rainfall, with resulting more complete disintegration of the silicate minerals. With further extension toward the tropics these soils contain higher and higher percentages of iron and aluminum oxides. At what might be considered the halfway point in the southern United States, they can be termed the cotton-belt soils.

The chestnut-brown soils to the near west developed under short-grass vegetation, hot summers, and limited rainfall. They are alkaline in reaction, being liberally endowed with the basic constituents that would have been carried off in the drainage in regions of higher rainfall. These are important wheat and grain-sorghum soils in the United States.

The tundras, into which the podzolic soils eventually grade to the north, are frozen soils. They support only such dwarf types of vegetation as can survive the cold climate and develop sufficiently during each successive short summer, while the surface of the soil is thawed out, to permit their living through the next winter. They provide forage for reindeer.

The desertic soils, into which the chestnut-brown soils gradually merge to the west, are alkaline soils. They bear greater resemblance to the parent rock, having been subjected to less and less rainfall westward until they finally are bare of all vegetation except for short grasses and desert shrubs. These are the beef-cattle and sheep lands, requiring up to fifty acres or more to support each steer, or its equivalent weight in lambs.

In addition to the vast central agricultural region of the North American continent there is a large coastal plain beginning in New Jersey, broadening out to cover the whole of Florida, extending across southern Georgia, Alabama, and Mississippi, and including the Mississippi River delta and a large area in eastern Texas. The soils in this large area consist of outwash from higher areas to the north and west and, for the most part, tend to be sandy, often to the point where they become almost pure quartz. When adequately supplied with water and mineral nutrients, however, they are generally highly productive, being particularly valued for the production of winter vegetables, citrus fruits, and pecans, although widely used for cotton and general agriculture as well.

In their natural state, soil, climate, and vegetation are so intimately related that if one knows the details in a given region about any one of these three, he can predict the nature of the other two. The factor of time, however, is also involved. Soils may be young, middle-aged, mature, or in a state of old age, depending on the amount of time that has elapsed since the soil-forming process began to operate in their formation. Thus

the soils in the region most recently covered by the glaciers of North America, the terminal moraines of which are found as far south as the Ohio River, are relatively very young in comparison with those farther south. The younger the soil in humid regions the greater its reserve of mineral nutrients required by plants.

In terms of crop production the most important features of this vast interior land mass of the North American continent are its topography and climate. The soil may or may not be naturally highly productive locally, but if the lay of the land is such that the soil can readily be worked with modern machinery and if the temperature and rainfall are favorable, acre yields on all but the most extreme soil types within this region can be raised to high levels by the means and measures that science and technology have placed at the farmer's disposal.

The factors affecting plant growth can be conveniently divided into climatic, biotic, and edaphic groups. The most important climatic factors are sunshine, length of day and season, temperature, and precipitation. The composition and movement of the atmosphere are also involved. The carbon-dioxide content of the air is gradually increasing, with important possibilities for making plants grow more luxuriantly. And atmospheric contributions of soluble sulfur and nitrogen compounds have materially increased, often to marked advantage to crops but sometimes to their disadvantage.

A crop grows best under a complex of climatic factors that are comparable to those in which it originally evolved or has become adapted to, either on its own or through the assistance of man. The farther removed an area is from the climatic center of adaptation of any given crop the more difficult it is to grow that crop successfully, until a point is reached at which it may no longer be advisable to make the attempt. Thus cotton is not grown north of the Ohio River and relatively little corn is grown in Canada or west of central Kansas and Nebraska.

The biotic factors affecting crop growth include man, animals, other plants, and the crop itself in relation to its environment. Man is by far the most important biotic factor since, in addition to his ability to change, in part, the properties of the soil, to regulate the processes that take place in it, and to modify the climate, he is able to control such other biotic factors as the insects, diseases, and weeds that interfere with the growth of crops. This may be accomplished by the use of chemicals or by breeding and selecting to develop new varieties and strains of crop plants having greater resistance to insects and diseases or higher capacities to withstand drouth, wetness, heat, or cold.

From this it is apparent that the productivity of any given area of land is not a property that is inherent in the soil but one that must be considered in relation to the environment of that soil, the crops to be grown, and the capacity of the farmer to control any biotic and climatic factors negatively affecting their growth. The success of the farmer in growing crops is determined by the extent to which he is able to choose varieties or strains of crops to fit the soil and climatic conditions with which he has to deal, or to modify the effects of these factors to meet the needs of the crops he has decided to grow.

The 1959 Census estimated that of the 1902 million acres of land constituting the United States mainland (forty-eight states), about 458 million were being used for the production of man-harvested crops, 630 million for grazing, 640 million for forestry, and 124 million for special purposes, with fifty million acres in unclassified use.

The Soil Conservation Service of the United States Department of Agriculture has divided this total land area into eight classes that are based on its suitability for farming purposes. An estimated thirty-six million acres is Class I land with few or no conditions that limit its use in crop production. Some 290 million acres fall into Class II, with some limitations on the kind of crops it is adapted to and requiring some easily applied conservation measures. Some 311 million acres are placed in Class III, with more serious limitations because of the slope of the land or the depth or wetness of the soil. These three classes of land, covering only one third of the entire mainland, constitute the land area on which the primary dependence of the United States is placed for crop production. To this may be added 169 million acres of Class IV land that is suitable for occasional use for the production of man-harvested crops if followed immediately by several years of soil-conserving crops. The remaining Class V to VIII lands include noncrop federal, state, and local government holdings, western grazing lands, reservations, recreation and wildlife preserves, urban and other built-up lands, and waste.

Although most of this Class I–III land lies within the wide region between the Appalachians and the Rocky Mountains and on the Coastal Plain, other acreages of it are to be found scattered about over the country within the hilly to mountainous regions and to the east and west of them, including the river valleys in the humid regions and about thirty-one million acres of irrigated land in the seventeen western states.

Of the estimated 637 million acres of land that is best suited to continuous production of man-harvested crops, some 240 million are still in pasture and woodland where they serve as a reserve against the time of need for increased acreages for crop production. Our population, estimated at 194,200,000 as of April 1, 1965, is growing at a rate of around three million people per year.

The needed increases in food and fiber reproduction, however, are currently being more than met by improved farming practices based on continuous agricultural and industrial research. Against this must be placed the annual loss of around one million acres of cropped land to other uses. Also, man-harvested crops are being grown on some fifty million acres of Class V–VIII land that should not be used for this purpose.

The agricultural output of the United States mainland can be greatly increased by bringing more of the Class I–III land into production, using better methods of soil manipulation, increasing the rate of application of chemical fertilizers, breeding and selecting plants with higher yielding capacities, and making more effective use of pesticides. The numbers to which the population of the United States can grow and be adequately fed depend not only on the degree to which these measures are put into operation but on the extent to which soil and water conservation measures are effected. The accomplishments of the federal Soil Conservation Service, by way of some 3000 Soil Conservation Districts and their farmer supervisors, have been outstanding in this connection.

If it should happen that the population of the United States is not brought under control at what might be thought of as a reasonable level, other highly important possibilities for meeting their food needs could be brought into play. Carleton P. Barnes and F. J. Marchner, in the 1958 Yearbook of the United States Department of Agriculture, wrote: "If we took 500 million acres of our best cropland and used it as intensively as the Japanese use their cropland, we could feed almost two billion people—assuming that these acres are as productive as the Japanese acres and that we consumed cropland produce directly rather than as animal products."

This estimate of the federal economists includes a highly important principle. To feed grains to livestock and then consume their meat or milk, as is done in a very large way in North America, is a highly wasteful practice in terms of food economy. Some 80 per cent of the energy and protein values of grains is lost by this procedure. Livestock, however, do provide a means of harvesting large acreages of rangeland produce that could not be made usable by any other means.

If the need arises, the people of the United States can shift to a diet of more grain, potatoes, and legume seeds and much less meat and milk. Even though a great deal of grumbling would be heard for some years, this would gradually disappear as succeeding generations that had never had the privilege of a luxuriant diet of animal foods came into being. Long before this had come to pass, however, production of synthetic foods, supplemented by increased food supplies from the surrounding oceans, might well have come into operation on a large scale.

Every acre of land in the United States has value for several purposes but, insofar as feasible, it should be put to its best possible use. This means that the land especially well adapted to crop production should be reserved for that purpose until some other more pressing need for it develops. There is a widespread tendency to shove farmers off the best farming land onto nearby land that is less well suited to agriculture and is often subject to serious erosion when farmed. Such indiscriminant use of good agricultural land is a matter of great and growing concern to federal, state, and local governmental agencies that see the need for planning for the future.

Because of the similarity of the climatic conditions in Canada and Alaska, the land resources of these two will be considered together. Canada has a total land area of 2272 million acres and Alaska 365 million acres. Two thirds of Canada is too cold for commercial agriculture. A large part of the land in the remaining southern third is too rough, rocky, or swampy to permit its use for farming purposes. Of the total Canadian land area only 103 million acres, or less than 5 per cent, were classified as improved farmland in 1961. Of this, twenty-four million acres were devoted to forage crops, twenty-five million to wheat, eleven million to oats, eight million to other small grains, soybeans, and corn, three million to flax, rape, and mustard for seed, and one million to vegetables, fruits, potatoes, tobacco, and sugar beets. Of the remaining area some twenty-eight million acres, mostly in Manitoba, Saskatchewan, and Alberta, were in fallow, a moisture-accumulating measure.

Canada's reserves of potentially arable land are estimated at around forty-three million acres. Of this five million are located in the Appalachian region, ten million in the interior Canadian shield, six million in the prairies, eighteen million in the forested portion of the interior plains, three million in the Cordilleran region, and one million in the permafrost region. Most of this reserve land requires clearing, much of it must be drained, and some of it must be irrigated before it can be put into production.

The soils in the Appalachian region, embracing all of eastern Canada up to and including the larger part of Quebec, are podzolic, naturally acid, and low in natural fertility. Much of this region is unsuited to arable agriculture. Some 72 per cent of the land in farms is devoted to forage crops. Climatic conditions are favorable for grass hay and pasture crops and for oats, potatoes, and fruits.

The Great Lakes region, covering the southern part of Ontario and Quebec, is one of the two most important agricultural areas of Canada. About sixteen of the twenty-nine million acres contained in this region were improved farmland in 1956. The climate and soil are favorable for oats, hay, and pastures and, nearer the lakes, for vegetables, tobacco, tree fruits, small fruits, and grapes. Virtually none of the remaining land is suitable for agriculture because it is stony, rough, or drouthy with shallow soils overlying bedrock. Some of the land once farmed has been abandoned and is growing up to trees. Since some 60 per cent of the Canadians live in this region, considerable acreages of land, including some that was arable, have been required for urban, industrial, airport, and highway purposes. Relatively little has been done with the million and a half acres of peat soil in this region.

The Canadian shield region, an extended land mass covering the vast interior of Canada north of the Great Lakes region, and between the Appalachian and Cordilleran mountains, is largely a wilderness of rock outcrops, stony soils, lakes, and forests, with very cold winters and short cool summers not generally suitable for agriculture. This region rests on Pre-Cambrian rocks that are exposed over a broad area. Farther west, on the interior plains, these rocks are overlain by horizontally bedded limestones, shales and sandstones that thicken from east to west. Grass for hay and pasture and oats occupy 70 per cent of the shield's improved land. Agricultural developments are largely of a pioneering nature, and it appears likely that the area of land now being farmed in this region will decrease with time.

The prairie region of the western interior plains, lying between Winnipeg and the Rocky Mountains and bounded by forests to the east, north, and west, is covered with chernozemic soils. Some 90 per cent of the 110 million acres in this region is now occupied. In 1956 over half of this area was classified as improved farmland, the remainder being natural grazing lands not suited to arable agriculture. Wheat is the most important crop.

The forested region of the western interior plains south of the permafrost region, extending from northwestern Manitoba across north-central Saskatchewan to the Rocky Mountains of Alberta and British Columbia, has an area of about 200 million acres. Of this about eleven million acres are improved farmland devoted largely to oats and barley. Considerable agricultural expansion may occur in this region in due time.

Less than one million acres of land in the Cordilleran region is classified as improved, and most of this is in grass. Some 170,000 acres are under irrigation. A much larger acreage of land in this region can be put to agricultural use when economic conditions become favorable.

Only about 1000 acres of land in the permafrost region are being farmed, but possibly one million acres, notably in the valleys of the Yukon and Mackenzie rivers, will ultimately be used for farming purposes.

The National Soil Survey Committee of Canada has developed a system of land-capability classification similar to that employed by the Soil Conservation Service of the United States. Of the seven classes of land recognized, the first three are capable of sustained production of crops. Those in Class 1 have no important limitations. Those in Class 2 have moderate limitations in climate, topography, wetness, erodibility, or structure. Those in Class 3 have such additional limitations as shallowness, stoniness, or salinity. Soils of Class 4 are suited to only a few crops, those of Class 5 have serious climatic or other limitations, those of Class 6 can be used only for natural grazing, and those of Class 7 are not useful for either agriculture or grazing. Organic soils are placed in Classes 2 to 5.

With such a vast land area to explore it is not surprising that considerably more information will be required before a truly satisfactory picture of the agricultural potential of Canada will be at hand. From the facts currently available, one might hazard the guess that 30 per cent of the presently improved mineral soils falls into Classes 1 and 2 and 50 per cent in Class 3, Classes 4 to 6 making up the remaining 20 per cent. Of the potentially arable mineral soils, possibly 5 per cent would be placed in Classes 1 and 2 and 50 per cent in Class 3, with 45 per cent in Classes 4 to 6. Altogether one might estimate that Canada possesses 100 million acres of currently and potentially arable mineral soils that fall into Classes 1–3.

The cold climate of much of Canada and the limited rainfall in part of the prairie region are seriously limiting factors in crop production. No doubt many things will be done in time to overcome these handicaps. But even so, over 90 per cent of the land area of Canada will probably never be used for the production of the common food crops and livestock.

The word "Alaska" is said to mean "the great land." It is great in area but not in agricultural potential. Present estimates indicate that some ten million acres, or about 3 per cent of the total land area, are suitable for cropping purposes, and for hay and grazing that are associated therewith. This is mostly in the Tanana and Matanuska valleys in south-central Alaska.

The soils of Alaska consist mostly of podzolics and tundras. The podzolic soils are extremely acid when first cleared from the brush, but become neutral to alkaline after some years of cultivation. In the permafrost regions of the tundras the soils thaw more deeply after clearing, with the result that the ice lenses melt irregularly and holes develop that make farming difficult, sometimes to the point where the land has to be abandoned.

To date, farming in Alaska has been of the in-and-out type. Men pioneer, give farming a trial, find themselves not suited for it under the conditions that obtain, and leave. In 1957 the total area of cropped land was estimated at 20,000 acres. The most important crops are small grains, potatoes, vegetables, and such wild fruits as low-bush cranberries and blueberries. It is estimated that about 80,-000 acres of land would meet the local needs of some 200,000 people, more than now live in Alaska. Exports of food products other than fish, and possibly berries, is not economically possible. Forestry is important in southeastern Alaska along the Pacific Coast.

This is not to say that Alaska and the corresponding regions of Canada are without agricultural potential. Population is clustered and social costs of isolated settlements are high. If productive soils ever become in short supply in relation to the food needs of the people of North America, large additional acreages of land could be developed for agricultural use, first in the more favorable climatic zones, and later in the less favored regions to the north. Meanwhile these more northern regions are extremely valuable as space to be explored and developed in accordance with the capabilities of the land under the climatic and economic conditions that prevail. Great value can be attached to the recreational and wild-life resources of the vast area of land contained in the upper two thirds of Canada and most of Alaska. But that is beyond the scope of this paper, which deals primarily with the highly productive lands of North America.

Considering, therefore, only the southern third of Canada and the whole of the United States mainland, we find an estimated total of 737 million acres of Class I, II, and III land on which our primary dependence for food production will have to be placed. Of this, some 283 million acres are being held in reserve. In case of serious need, however, many more millions of acres of land in Class

IV could be brought into crop production by careful attention to the conservation measures required in its agricultural use.

For some years past it has been found necessary to retire large acreages of formerly farmed land on the North American continent from crop production, and this notwithstanding the very rapid growth in population. This is in part related to world trade in agricultural commodities. In larger part, however, it is due to more efficient farming made possible by the development of greatly improved agricultural machinery, larger tonnages of chemical fertilizers, more effective pesticides, and much higher-yielding varieties of crops developed by breeding and selection. Acre yields of the staple crops have been raised to much higher levels than had ever been anticipated. One Mississippi farm boy harvested over 300 bushels of corn from one acre by official measurement. A farmer in the State of Washington harvested 156 bushels of wheat from an officially measured acre. The ten-ton-per-acre tomato club in New Jersey had to be raised to a twenty-ton club, and one farmer produced thirty-eight tons of tomatoes per acre by official measurement. Similarly high acre yields of cotton, potatoes, and other crops have been authenticated in various places. The average acre yield of corn in the United States is a little over fifty bushels, that of wheat around twenty-five bushels, and that of tomatoes about six tons.

This is not to say that farms occupying even the best of land and using the best possible systems of soil and crop management have production under complete control. Many very troublesome new diseases and insects appear from time to time, and a great deal of damage is done before means of control have been found. The weather is a much more difficult problem to deal with, since there are only partial controls. Local drouths and freezes are usually compensated for by especially favorable weather in other competing areas. But occasionally a greatly expanded drouth area develops and may continue for several years. One such drouth cycle was experienced over most of the area west of the Mississippi River during the four-year period 1933–36. Total wheat production in the United States during that period fell to about three fourths of the average for the years just preceding and following the drouth, and total corn production to about two thirds.

Grazing lands do not generally fall into Classes I to III, but they are highly important, notwithstanding. Meat will be the first food item in deficiency on the North American continent if our population continues to grow until it reaches the point where it taxes the capacity of the land to grow foodstuffs. A great deal has been and can be done to make grazing lands more dependably productive. Since they can be kept largely covered with browse, no insurmountable troubles with soil erosion need arise on most of them.

It is quite apparent that soil is of no agricultural value without water. A good many more million acres of land in the arid regions of North America could be added to that now in crop production, if water was available for use on them. The productivity of cropped land in the semi-humid region west of central Kansas would be greatly increased by irrigation. Supplemental irrigation is being practiced on a very large and rapidly growing scale in the humid regions.

Desalinization of ocean water, rain-making operations, reservoir storages of water in regions of high rainfall, and means of increasing water infiltration into the soil in regions of lesser rainfall are being examined with ever greater seriousness. The productive capacity of the land now being farmed and of that yet to be brought into production depends in greatest measure on our capacity to effect control of water, whether in deficiency or excess.

BIBLIOGRAPHY

Barnes, Carlton P., and Marchner, F. J. 1958. Our Wealth of Land. In :Yearbook of Agriculture: 2–18. U.S. Dept. Agric., Wash., D.C.

Freeman, Orville L. 1962. Agricultural Land Resources, Capabilities, Uses, and Conservation Needs. Agric. Inf. Bul., U.S. Dept. Agric., Wash., D.C.

Hurley, Ray. 1959. United States Census of Agriculture. U.S. Dept. Agric., Wash., D.C.

Johnson, Hugh A. 1958. Seward's Folly Can Be a Great Land. In: Yearbook of Agriculture: 424–39. U.S. Dept. Agric., Wash., D.C.

Leahey, A. 1961. Appraisal of Canada's Land Base for Agriculture. Pap. prepared for Resources for Tomorrow Conf. Dept. Northern Affairs and Nat. Res., Ottawa.

———— 1964. Outline of the Canadian Soil Capability Classification for Agriculture. Can. Dept. Agric., Ottawa.

McCannel, J. E., ed. 1960. A Look at Canadian Soils. Agric. Inst. Rev. (Mar.-Apr.). Agric. Ins. Can., Ottawa.

MIDDLE AMERICA: THE HUMAN FACTOR

Gerardo Budowski*

The land and the people

Middle America is a conglomerate of many countries, most of them cited in

Table 1 in alphabetical order together with other demographic characteristics.[1] Other islands in the Caribbean and

TABLE 1. Population and other demographic characteristics of Middle America

Country	Population est. mid-1963 (millions)	Annual rate of increase since 1958 (per cent)	Population under 15 (per cent)	Life expectancy at birth (years)	Population literate 15 years and over (per cent)
Costa Rica	1.3	4.4	46.4	50–60	75–80
Cuba	7.2	2.1	36.4	45–55	75–80
Dominican Republic	3.3	3.4	44.5	40–50	40–45
El Salvador	2.7	3.6	41.2	35–45	35–40
Guatemala	4.1	3.1	42.3	35–45	25–30
Haiti	4.4	2.2	37.9	30–35	10–15
Honduras	2.1	3.0	48.1	40–50	35–40
Jamaica	1.7	1.6	41.2	60–65	70–75
Mexico	38.3	3.1	44.4	45–55	65–70
Nicaragua	1.6	3.5	44.5	40–50	35–40
Panama	1.1	2.7	43.4	40–50	65–70
Puerto Rico	2.5	1.6	42.6	65–70	80–85
Trinidad and Tobago	0.9	2.9	42.4	60–65	70–75
Total	72.2				

British Honduras would add another 1.8 million, bringing the total population to about 74 million. In the table, the low

* Dr. Budowski heads the Forestry and Conservation Department of the Tropical Center for Graduate Studies of the Inter-American Institute, located in Costa Rica. He received his Ph.D. from Yale in forest ecology, and has done an immense amount of field work in the forest ecology of Middle America. He has served as an adviser to E. M. Nicholson's International Biological Programme for the Conservation of Terrestrial Biological Communities.

annual rate of increase of Jamaica and Puerto Rico since 1958 can be explained by the immigration to the U.S. rather than a low birth rate.

Variation from country to country is the rule and should always be understood when looking at the whole region. This refers to the sizes of the countries and

[1] According to chart published by the Information Service, Population Reference Bureau, 1755 Massachusetts Ave., N.W., Washington, D.C.; October, 1963.

their resources, the racial and cultural background, the political and economic patterns, and many other aspects.

It must also be borne in mind that changes are coming fast to the regions. Some are of the same nature as in the United States or Canada, but many are different. It is the dynamics of these changes, their motivations and results, which need to be carefully evaluated.

Our concern in the study Conference will then be necessarily restricted. As a subject matter I have chosen an ecological outlook in relation to man and his environment, with an underlying quest for the fate of this area in years to come and a series of suggestions toward an approach more in line with ecological principles.

This is a legitimate concern, as it affects everyone whether living within or outside the area.

A balance is upset

An ecologist's dream is to see man in balance, or rather in harmony, with nature. Naturally it is not a static balance but dynamic, involving, if possible, gradual improvements of the physical, spiritual, economic, and social values. This balance has been violently upset for a large part of Middle America, especially for the last thirty years when technological advances and increases in population have resulted in land-use patterns that have taken a tremendous toll in the use and abuse of natural resources. It should be borne in mind that a large percentage of the active population depends on agriculture varying from 37 per cent for Puerto Rico to as high as 83 per cent for Haiti and Honduras (CIDA, 1963). Farming over most of the area is carried out under very primitive conditions quite often at the level of subsistence. The process has been well described by Bartlett (1955) for tropical areas. Annual income is very low, usually below a hundred dollars, for the very large major-

ity of the farmers. Illiteracy is high among the sector connected with agriculture and animal husbandry.

There are many other often linked factors which can be judged as unfavorable for the improvement of man and his habitat, such as food and health conditions, the prevailing political and social structure, and the general lack of knowledge of the physical environment in which man is living.

With few exceptions, the interaction of all these factors has resulted in poverty for a large sector of the population. True, such poverty is only relative, and for many the present situation can be judged as an improvement on conditions existing in the past over the same area. But there is a great fallacy in such reasoning when it comes to people who have received the benefit of some education. The present array of better communication media has tended to have man compare himself not with former generations as in past centuries but with others of his kind who have a better life which he sees in the movies, reads about in newspapers and magazines, or hears about on the radio or from neighbors. The result is what many have called a revolution of expectations, of which we are witnessing violent outbreaks in the forms of revolutions, general discontent, and other manifestations of disconformity. What is worse, it appears that what many believe to be a violent upset due to present conditions is possibly very mild in comparison with what may come. The result may lead to more and more violent situations unless awareness of the problem by the people who could do something about it and proper solutions understood by a large majority are the next immediate steps. Presently this does not appear to be the case for the great majority of the region.

The impact on resources

From the physical and biological angle the most destructive effects have been the tremendous impact on soils, natural vegetation, water regime, and wild animals. Productive areas are being depleted at fast rates and converted to sterile lands. Water resources are being mismanaged so as to make them unusable for the future. Immense genetic reservoirs of valuable plants and animals have been or are being destroyed. Even worse, this loss of biologically indispensable material is often irreparable, since it involves an irreversible trend.

The destructive impact is apparently geometric in its progression, as are so many of the other changes, especially population increase.

For centuries, use of resources of man has been in a geographical area where conditions have been relatively favorable for human occupation and the impact on the resources has been relatively mild. It is a region where precipitation is not excessive or, as it has been outlined by Holdridge (1959), where the ratio of precipitation over actual evapotranspiration is close to 1.

Some of these areas are some of the densest, most heavily settled of the world —such countries as El Salvador, Haiti, Puerto Rico, some of the Lesser Antilles, or some selected areas of other countries, especially the central valley of Mexico, the highlands of Guatemala, and the Meseta Central of Costa Rica. Curiously even in these heavily settled areas natural development schemes have left untouched, at least until recently, what were typically submarginal areas such as those with very steep topography, poor soils, very heavy rainfall or absence of it. In overpopulated countries such as Haiti, the Forêt des Pins, south of Port-au-Prince, an area of very poor soils covered with beautiful pine stands, or in El Salvador the flat and often alkaline *Crescentia alata* savannas, are typically depopulated, as are some of the steep slopes in most other countries—at least until recently.

Many other areas were left untouched because they were inaccessible.

The great change in this pattern witnessed in this century, a change presently in full swing, is the impact on those marginal areas, or on what are becoming accessible areas, through the opening of new roads. Sometimes such a change appears justified and the opening of new lands to produce food for the increasing population can be done without detriment to the natural resources. Examples are well-conceived irrigation schemes such as those witnessed in Mexico. Most of the time, however, such "planned" or unplanned encroachment leads to a rapid and often irreversible destruction of the present land cover with incalculable losses in material, esthetic, and scientific values.

In this connection it should be borne in mind that marginal areas are much more sensitive to the effects of disturbance through standard methods of farming. Large areas of fresh volcanic soils have been farmed in Mexico and Central America for centuries without adding fertilizers or using refined conservation techniques. But it takes only a few years, usually less than five, to produce a great deterioration or complete loss of the topsoil when it comes to the marginal lands not favored by natural fertility or inherent favorable soil structure.

This destruction of areas not suitable for settlement, at least with our present methods or knowledge, confers an alarming character to this upset in the natural balance. It engenders further destruction, like a chain reaction, leading ultimately not only to an unproductive environment but to an equally negative force affecting adjoining productive areas. No one connected with natural resources can escape the feeling that it is his obligation to help in stopping this process while there is still time.

The population explosion and its repercussions

Population explosion is possibly the most significant single factor responsible for this change. Annual population increases have recently reached such numbers as 4.4 per cent for Costa Rica, 3.6 per cent for El Salvador, and so on (see Table 1). It implies a tremendous stress on the land so as to produce more food and hampers economic development. It does not take much training in economics to realize that for a country with such a large part of its population below the working age, the economic growth rate must be of such magnitude that it remains outside of the present potential of most of them. The fact is that this dramatic situation is not understood, or not mentioned for several reasons, by the majority of people who influence policy. A single number such as, for instance, an annual net population increase of 3.5 per cent does not tell the whole story. The average life expectancy still remains much below that of the United States. Although infant mortality is below what it was some twenty years ago, it is still much higher than in the United States and Canada. A sad factor is that the number of births per woman is very high, and so is the number of abortions and deaths, still leaving a relatively high margin of living children. Many of the children who survive are further weakened by malnutrition, parasites, and other diseases. One could go on and on showing the contrast and the waste of energies and resources.

It is of course obvious that there is room for more people and that under planned conditions a much larger population than the present would eventually be able to live in good conditions, at least in many of the countries. This reasoning has often been advocated in favor of a policy of *laissez-faire* in relation to birth rate. The trouble of course is not the ultimate population number to be reached but the rate of increase which should be expected yearly. With an annual high population increase, the strain to achieve economic improvement is so great that it cannot be matched through the growth of productivity as expressed by the gross national income of the countries. Hence stagnation or even a worsening of the human condition may be the unavoidable outcome of a very fast population growth.

Attitude towards natural resources

Indians, when organized in communities with a certain degree of self-government, often had a good knowledge of ecological balance. This was well described by Cook (1909) and more recently by Sears, using historical data (1953). It can still be witnessed today by the elaborate system of terraces for conserving soils and productivity. Good examples can be found north of the steep Cuchumatanes Mountains in Guatemala, or in that same country the preservation of natural forested areas very close to population centers where cuttings or encroachments are regulated by a special council chosen among elderly people. For instance, in the highlands of that country, where a heavy Indian population prevails, one can still find beautiful forests on the Maria Tecum range in central Guatemala, covered with beautiful pine and fir trees, in spite of the vicinity of the rather large Indian town of Totonicapán and the passage of several roads and numerous trails, all with heavy traffic. This area has been densely settled for centuries, even before the arrival of the first Spaniards. The mountain range is of utmost importance for water conservation and for the supply of timber products and fuel to several of the nearby Indian communities.

The above picture is sharply in contrast with other areas where opening of new roads leads invariably to the clearing of the prevailing forest in a relatively short time and often subsequent destruction of the productivity of the land. Some authors dealing with the impact of Indian agriculture on the soil resources have forwarded the hypothesis that the decline of the Mayan culture may be connected to their population increase, leading to exhaustion of soils by the shortening of the rotation of the *milpa* system (Gourou, 1953). Although this assumption has been challenged, it can be concluded that there are reasons to believe that with the smaller population in Pre-Columbian years, impact on nature was relatively small. Moreover, it is uncertain that marginal areas such as those on poor soils or high rainfall were ever densely populated. Most of the areas of dense Indian population were dry or moderately wet. The wet habitat of many of today's small nuclei of Indians should not be interpreted as their most favorable niches for the past centuries. Rather, they have been driven to them because of pressure from other population groups.

In contrast to the controversy on the impact of Indian groups on land resources in the past, there is no doubt that presently they are definitely the cause of much of the destruction, but then they are also exposed to a completely different set of values.

On the whole, however, it can be stated that on the basis of present attitude and past available evidence Indians had and still have a better comprehension of natural ecological balance than their European masters and descendants.

The arrival of Spaniards and their introduction of cattle meant a very large change in the environment. A characteristic attitude of the new landlords was a generally adverse feeling toward the forest. A man who had cleared the forest or literally had "opened the land" was doing good. The Spaniards, of course, used fire even more liberally than the Indians, mainly because it was indispensable to maintaining grasses and avoiding forest encroachment. Forest products were thought to be plentiful, and for a long time it was unthinkable that the immense reservoirs of forests would ever be threatened.

This feeling still prevails today in those countries where forests presently occupy a large portion of the country. Characteristically only the wet forests have escaped this massive destruction, mainly because they would not burn. A recent survey of natural habitats in need of conservation, derived from the published ecological life-zone maps based on the Holdridge system and covering Panama, Costa Rica, Nicaragua, Honduras, El Salvador, and Guatemala, shows that there is very little left of the original lowland dry forest —although this life zone occupies about 100,000 square kilometers or 22 per cent of Central America while the wetter lowland forest areas, which occupy about 181,000 square kilometers or 38 per cent, have been largely untouched (Budowski, 1964). This tendency is also true for the highlands, where the dry forests have practically disappeared because of higher density of population. Here the encroachments on wet forest areas have been much more severe in recent years. The wet forest areas are then the last frontiers of wilderness in most of Middle America but for how long?

Any programs of preservation today must take into account that feelings toward forest protection are practically absent in rural areas. The case for forests as regulators of watercourses is not generally understood. And to demand feelings for esthetic and scientific values or preservation of wildlife is to be completely unrealistic *vis-à-vis* the small farmers or cattlemen.

This may be the reason why in almost every country in Middle America there is so much emphasis on legal aspects to achieve conservation aims. Such emphasis derives its origins from well-educated urban groups that have good intentions but are quite ineffectual on the whole. As a result, many countries have had several forest or conservation laws succeeding one another over short intervals. Even foreign experts, dealing with technical assistance, are often requested to participate in the making of a new law to remedy the situation. It usually does not take long to realize that ignorance, resulting in deeply entrenched adverse feelings toward the forests and the strong motivations for clearing or misusing more land for food production mainly as a result of population increase and poor farming systems, makes those laws completely ineffective.

Altogether rural sociology, which is a relatively young science, has a very long way to go to bridge the gap of understanding between the policy makers and the poor farmers of Middle America, who are presently ignorant of what goes on beyond the immediate surroundings of their dwellings. Lee (1955) has forcefully summarized the situation when he wrote: "Too poor to learn, too ignorant to improve, and too frightened to try, a large mass of the tropical peasantry is seemingly doomed to an endless round of inadequacy. Here and there, a spark may be kindled, now and then an improvement made; but in spite of a growing awareness of the outside world, such people may still present a considerable drag to any progressive force."

HOW IMPROVEMENTS MAY BE
ACHIEVED

The question has often been raised as to how much different political, economic, and social factors interplay to influence advances, progress, declines, etc., of communities, countries, or regions. This leads, of course, to suggesting possible solutions and plans of actions which have filled books and reports. From an ecologist's view, there are several basic items which will be stressed here so that they can serve as a basis for discussion.

The need to emphasize family planning

Scientific studies to ascertain the attitudes of different sectors of the population toward the size of the family, sexual practices, and other factors connected with birth rates are generally lacking. Puerto Rico is a notable exception.

There are good reasons to believe that a large percentage of the children who are born every year are the result of unwanted pregnancies. One cannot escape the conclusion that in order to remedy such a situation a change in the system of values and morals appears to be in order.

Moreover, the general attitude of many influential sectors in connection with this formerly very controversial factor is swiftly moving in a direction where the dangers of a policy of ignorance of the problems are stressed.

What is needed now is a kind of mass education in this respect. Such education needs a policy understood by and acceptable to a large majority of the population and enforcements by the necessary agencies. Such objectives as "a plea that every child born is wanted by its parents" and similar well-understood slogans would undoubtedly help to change the attitude of large, less educated sectors of the population.

The publications distributed by different international and national agencies, written in a language accessible to everyone, are important instruments for achieving this purpose. A recent booklet published by the Center for International Economic Growth and translated into Spanish is an excellent example (Jones, 1962).

At any rate, ecologists or scientists in general, connected with natural resources, should understand that it is their duty to raise this question. An era of tabu in writing or speaking about this theme is nearing its end and scientists and other persons connected with natural resources should play a much more important role in promoting a sound policy toward family planning. A great majority of those people know the problem and privately will explain their views, almost always favoring family planning. It is the channeling of these opinions in a way that they can be heard and used by governments, and other agencies influencing and promoting programs of action and public opinion, which is the greatest need at present.

A new approach toward land use

In most of Middle America, man, through a process of trial and error leading to selection, has selected many of the soils and crops and sometimes even the methods of cultivation which were most suitable for the different life zones. Certainly there is still room for plenty of improvement such as the use of irrigation, fertilizers, improved varieties, weed control, and so on. But there are also limitations for these improvements due to social, economic, and ecological factors. In relation to the latter it can be said, as a generalization, that in marginal areas, especially those of heavy rainfall, these improvements if used in a conventional fashion are less effective.

Since man has the tendency to stick to his methods of cultivation when moving from a dry area to a wet one, his expansion into the wet environment is often doomed to failure unless he is willing to change to new crops better adapted to the different environment.

The effects of high temperatures and abundant rainfall hasten such processes as decomposition of organic matter and leaching of nutrients. On the other hand, plant growth is extremely fast, especially that of weeds. There are many detailed studies on these matters (see, for example, Lee, 1957) showing that it is necessary to make the necessary adjustments

to meet the environmental factors if the latter are to be used for the best benefit of man.

A pathetic example is the attempt to establish pastures. In areas where a long dry season prevails, maintenance of pastures, while still a problem, is definitely easier than for areas of high rainfall and high temperature. At present, the clearing of natural forests in most of the hot tropical wet lowland areas to make room for pastures is a process which leads to extensive animal husbandry with a very low production per unit of surface. What is worse, most of these artificial grasslands are not permanent and the increased presence of aggressive shrubs and other woody species usually leads to the abandonment of the land after a few years. Notwithstanding the costly destruction of the original forest, of which very little is being utilized, this process is very wasteful when the production is compared to the large labor input.

Consequently a new approach for wet areas must be found and promoted as has been suggested by Holdridge (1959) and more recently by Tosi and Voertman (1964). Essentially a plea is made for a combination of crops that involves the use of tree crops either alone or in combination with annual crops of short duration. Holdridge indicates that this would best simulate the forest environment and its high biomass productivity. It is commonly found in many of the yards or orchards of peasant families, where fruit trees, vines with useful food products, and animals grow together. This would imply intense use of the area while protecting the soil and environment as opposed to pure cultivation of the same annuals or perennials over a long period of time.

Plantations of bananas, cocoa, or African oil palms under scientific management systems has been practiced notably by the United Fruit Company in many Central American countries. Although praised by Sears (1953) this is only a limited solution because here, too, good soils with level topography are essential. Besides the economic limitations such as capital investment and ready export markets, there are numerous social limitations which make the plantation system unpalatable to the bulk of the peasant community and politically unstable under the present trends of nationalism and demands for agrarian reform.

Combination of tree crops producing food is a distinct possibility which deserves further exploring. Some pejibaye-palm plantations (*Guilielma gasipaes*) have recently been established in the wet lowlands of northern Costa Rica, where the mean annual temperature is about 25° C and the mean annual rainfall about 160 inches or 4000 millimeters, with apparent great success. The fruits have a very high nutritive value for human consumption and they can also be fed to hogs. The pejibaye palm is a well-known food plant and cultivated by many lowland Indian communities from Costa Rica to Peru, and feeding hogs is a common practice in some areas—for instance, among the Indians of northwestern Panama, equally a very wet area.

Altogether, however, it should be clearly understood that with our present knowledge, the possibilities of using the wet lowlands of the tropics for food production are very limited, in spite of the assumption widely held by many sectors (see, for instance, CIDA, 1963) that unpopulated areas could easily be "colonized" by farmers. The few exceptions, such as rice cultivation in Southeast Asia, demand a series of special factors linked with cultural backgrounds (Gourou, 1953) which cannot be duplicated in Middle America, at least within the next decades. Hence, taking again a good look at nature it seems obvious that the most promising use of the wet tropics for the benefit of man is forestry.

The role of forestry in the development of the wet tropics

Anyone who is aware of the high biomass production potential of the tropical forests, or simply looking over the vegetation maps of tropical countries and finding out that many countries with a large percentage of their land under forests have to import wood or its derivates, faces one of the greatest paradoxes of our present land-use patterns.

We know that, generally speaking, trees grow much faster in tropical than in temperate countries. True enough, climax species of the tropical forest grow slowly in their environment, but secondary species, including many of the most valuable, have amazing growth rates. Some pines introduced in tropical wet areas and properly inoculated with mycorhiza have done remarkably. Some simple managing practices can achieve very much when markets are nearby, even if most of the species are of limited value. A few years of research can pay off handsome dividends—as has been shown, for instance, in Malaya. In the lowlands of Middle America there is presently very limited forest research except in Trinidad, where the oldest continuous programs are to be found; Puerto Rico, where forestry has a rather limited future; and Costa Rica, where it has been practiced on a small scale. In other countries, research is either very recent or practically absent. Forest-harvesting practices in most countries imply the cutting of a few valuable species out of the virgin forest when the latter becomes accessible, and hence the development of forestry has often been linked with communication. But this of course is not forestry but high-grading and the end result is the gradual impoverishment or disappearance of the forest altogether, since logging roads are later used by farmers practicing shifting agriculture. Silviculture has been mostly planting of native or introduced species, often without sufficient knowledge of their ecological requirements. Many of these trials have shown to be failures, but there have been some notable achievements and this may lead to promising developments.

1. *The combination of agriculture with forestry (taungya system).* The use of shifting cultivation to the purpose of establishing plantations of valuable tree crops has long been practiced in India and other Asian countries, but has scarcely been given a test in Middle America, except in Trinidad (Cater, 1941) and most recently in Costa Rica (Aguirre, 1963). It appears a logical way to direct natural land-use systems, notably shifting agriculture toward much more intensive production of the land. Species like teak (*Tectona grandis*), Caribbean pine (*Pinus caribaea*), some eucalyptus species (*E. deglupta, E. saligna*), and laurel (*Cordia alliodora*) appear very promising in areas of suitably drained soils and hot temperatures and heavy rainfall, although teak still needs a dry season. Laurel, native to tropical America, is a typical example of such a promising tree. It is an aggressive secondary species of fast growth and unusually good stem form, of easy propagation. In some wet areas of heavy encroachment by man this species has become a dominant feature of the landscape of Central America. When clearing the land for crops or when weeding the grass from shrubs and undesirable trees, farmers and cattlemen of many Central American countries are prone to leave the valuable laurel trees. An economic rotation of less than thirty years can be achieved for timber production, and there can be several intermediate crops in the form of thinnings, when plantations are established.

The taungya system then appears to be very promising under certain conditions where ecological conditions, patterns of shifting cultivation, pressure on land, and suitable markets combine favorably. It

could well play a decisive role in future controlled colonization schemes. If successfully applied, it would gradually transform inefficient farmers into efficient forest workers while the establishment of industries using the products of the plantations would also absorb a good part of the population. As can already be witnessed by the increased importance of newly founded "colonization institutes" or "agrarian reform" programs, it is appropriate to think that for wet areas, successful colonization can be achieved through the application of forestry practices and schemes based on proper research. Taungya is one possibility; there is still another.

2. *The large-scale forest industry as a land-use scheme.* The industrial complex with a variety of different products derived from the forests is not new for the United States, Europe, or Australia, but has witnessed few examples in Latin America, where the problem is complicated by the larger number of tree species. One successful example is located on the Yucatan peninsula and appropriately called Colonia Yucatan. It covers an extensive area on soils not suitable for permanent agriculture. At least six industries producing plywood, veneers, saw boards, fiberboard, compressed boards, frames for windows and doors, as well as other products, have been installed here. The Mexican government supports the industries through the system of *unidades forestales* (forest units) by which provisions are made to manage the forest and to ensure sufficient supply of raw materials for this large industry. A well-planned village, with living conditions much above Mexican rural standards and a sense of dignity and security for the inhabitants, is linked with the industrial complex. Colonia Yucatan is an excellent example of what can be done elsewhere to make the forest land produce. Here again, provided that capital, markets, and technical skills are available, such forest

colonization schemes offer much better promise for development and improvement of human condition than uncontrolled cutting of the forest for wasteful high-grading of timber, or simply clear-cutting for shifting agriculture.

It is time to stress scientific, recreational and esthetic values

Clearing large areas of primeval forests to produce only subsistence crops is obviously a tremendous waste of scientific, recreational, and esthetic values. At first it appears that preservation has not a chance when confronted by the demands of an increasing rural population. But the examples of the preserved areas in Puerto Rico and around Mexico City, as well as other national parks throughout the world, offer a clear mentis. With an increasing number of scientists being trained—this curve, too, fortunately appears to be geometric in most countries —as well as more leisure time for city workers and growing pains of city life, pressure toward preservation of natural areas is increasing. A more comprehensive attitude toward wildlife is slowly developing among educated people. Since urban sectors hold the political power, what is mostly needed is to bridge the gap so that urban and rural sectors can achieve a program ultimately benefiting both.

Such action would require an intense program of enlightening of public opinion, leading to the establishment of national parks and other protected areas. In many countries it is true that the desire for having and enjoying national parks must first be created, but working toward improving such desire seems an excellent investment. Because there are at present few leaders and practically no resources available, there is right now a pressing need for external support. These two factors, the lack of leaders and the proper channeling of external support, are of paramount importance if national parks,

wildlife sanctuaries, and other preserved areas are to be successfully established.

Training of leaders

It is quite clear from the previous discussion that changes are imperative if a deteriorating situation is to be stopped. They involve policies, attitudes, public enlightenment, etc. One of the saddest aspects of the countries of Middle America is possibly the lack of sufficient politically powerful leaders with a sound scientific training to deal with conservation programs. On the other hand, one may speculate that even such potential leaders will not appear until a sizable sector of the population is willing to follow them. Whatever the reason, and until the number and the quality of those leaders reach a certain minimum, it is difficult if not impossible to expect changes within a country. As many scientists or scientifically minded people have experienced, it is frustrating to try to convince the political leaders to bring about the necessary changes until these leaders either have sufficient training themselves or are being submitted to pressure from what we can call subjectively the "proper sources" (Beltran, 1962). The same can be said, of course, if these changes are to be forced. It is the top which needs to be strengthened first, later the lower ramifications.

Under present circumstances, education in all its forms is certainly one of the best investments. But education, too, must be carefully channeled. For example, it is a mistake to build a school for forest rangers, as has been done in one Central American country, if no provisions are made to provide for the "cadres" in the form of foresters of high-quality university training.

On the other side, it is just as impractical for a country with limited possibilities to build up several second-class faculties to train the needed leaders. Successful training at a higher level in the field of natural resources is very much dependent on high-quality staff, research, and proper facilities. If these are not provided, university graduates will acquire a false feeling of confidence in their abilities to deal with the numerous and often complicated problems. But the same mistakes are being done over and over.

Technical aid

It is not the purpose of this short appraisal to criticize technical aid as presently offered by friendly nations or international organizations to so many of the countries of Middle America. Technical aid in the form of missions, advisers, easy loans, or plain grants is a mark of our time. Everyone is aware that political, economic, and social factors are involved to a larger or smaller degree. But in the light of past evidence and working myself in a kind of technical assistance program dedicated mainly to training and research, I cannot help feeling that in order to create an impact, it is not enough to intend to solve some of the immediate problems of the country. It is absolutely indispensable to adopt a long-term policy involving an integral approach to the different problems. To leave one of the facets of these problems out because it is politically or economically risky or dangerous is to ultimately lose the possibility of achieving any result at all. To neglect, for instance, the training of local leaders or to ignore the wild population-growth figures is to doom the whole program to failure.

The implications are obvious. Too often, help is merely prolonging the agony of a country in need of drastic reforms which, on the other hand, can only be achieved through pressure from inside. In fact, external help often creates a false feeling of confidence because it is assumed that a new crisis will be solved by a new apport. And intervals for the appearance of a new and often more violent crisis may become shorter.

Until such aid is used to deal with some of the most fundamental problems such as birth rate, development plans based on sound ecological principles, and education, its long-term effects will be wholly insufficient to help the countries to stand on their own much less to meet the aspirations of the people of Middle America.

BIBLIOGRAPHY

Aguirre, A. 1963. Estudio Silvicultural y Económico del Sistema Taungya en las Condiciones de Turrialba. Turrialba 13(3):168–71.

Bartlett, H. H. 1955. Fire, Primitive Agriculture and Grazing in the Tropics. In: Thomas, William L., Jr., ed., Man's Role in Changing the Face of the Earth: 692–720. Univ. Chicago Press.

Beltran, E. 1962. Educación de Dirigentes Políticos e Industriales. In: Proceedings, Fifth World Forestry Cong., Seattle, Aug. 29–Sept. 10, 1960: 1248–51.

Budowski, G. 1965. The Classification of Natural Habitats in Need of Preservation in Central America. Presented to the Symp. on Conserva. along the Pacific Coast, Mexico City, Feb., 1964. Turrialba 15(3):238–46.

Cater, John. 1941. The Formation of Teak Plantations in Trinidad with the Assistance of Peasant Contractors. Carib. Forester 2(4):144–53.

CIDA. 1963. Inventario de la Información Básica para la Programación del Desarrollo Agrícola en la América Latina. Informe Regional. Pan-Amer. Union, Wash., D.C.

Cook, O. F. 1909. Vegetation Affected by Agriculture in Central America. U.S. Dept. Agric., Bur. Plant Industry, Bul. 145.

Gourou, Pierre. 1953. The Tropical World. Its Social and Economic Conditions and Its Future Status, trans. by E. D. Laborde, Longmans, Green, London.

Holdridge, L. R. 1959. Ecological Indications of the Need for a New Approach to Tropical Land Use. In: Symposia Interamericana No. 1:1–58. Instituto Interamericano de Ciencias Agricolas, Turrialba, Costa Rica.

Jones, Joseph Marion. 1962. La Sobrepoblación Significa Pobreza? Ctr. for Inter. Econ. Growth, Wash., D.C.

Lee, Douglas H. K. 1957. Climate and Economic Development. Harper, New York.

Sears, Paul B. 1953. An Ecological View of Land Use in Middle America. Ceiba 3:157–65.

Tosi, Joseph A., Jr., and Voertman, Robert F. 1964. Some Environment Factors in the Economic Development of the Tropics. Econ. Geog. 40(3):189–205.

TUNDRA AND TAIGA

J. Ross Mackay*

The sparsely inhabited cold regions of northern North America are variously designated as polar and subpolar, arctic and subarctic, or tundra and taiga. Perhaps the terms "tundra" and "taiga" are most appropriate for the North American Habitats Study Conference, because of the biotic connotations of the Russian words from which they are derived. "Tundra" is now used in a sense not far different from the original meaning of a level or undulating, treeless plain of northern arctic regions. "Taiga," however, is employed in a more restrictive sense than that of the Siberian swampy, coniferous forests which lie between the tundra and the steppe or boreal forest.

The topical emphasis in this paper is on the environmental factors in the tundra and taiga, with particular stress on physical processes. The regional emphasis is on the western arctic, because it has a greater potentiality for settlement in Canada, and is best known to the writer. Discussion of plant and animal communities, economic development, and man are covered in other sessions of the Conference and so are only cursorily touched upon here. The specific purposes of this paper are: (1) to examine the

* Professor Mackay teaches geomorphology (permafrost) and cartography at the University of British Columbia. He received his Ph.D. at Montreal in 1949 and is a Fellow of the Royal Society of Canada and a Fellow and part Board Chairman of the Arctic Institute of North America. His specialty has been arctic geomorphology.

combination of physical elements which give character to the tundra and taiga; (2) to discuss the physical processes which are of major importance in an understanding of habitats; and (3) to suggest possible future pressures on habitats and changes which might result. Focus will be directed more toward the tundra than toward the taiga, because it offers a sharper contrast to the more familiar middle-latitude environments.

Little is gained from the interesting intellectual exercise of debating the precise method of delimiting the tundra-taiga boundary, because the subject has been exhaustively argued in the literature. In many theoretical and practical respects, the problem is akin to defining the arid-semiarid or desert-steppe boundary. Something is to be gained, however, in reviewing the characteristics of the boundary zone, because it helps in understanding the environmental factors involved.

Traditionally, the tundra has been defined as treeless; the taiga as the transitional open woodland (forest-tundra) belt between the tundra and the boreal forest. The definition of tundra therefore hinges on what is a tree, or collectively, a forest. Is the tree line the economic limit of forestry; the last upright tree of a given species in tree form; a combination of the most northerly of all treelike species; or the limit of species, irrespective of being prostrate or treelike (Hustich, 1953)? Should the limit be confined to conifers, or should tree birch and poplar be included? For the purpose of this paper, the tundra-taiga boundary is placed approximately at the present limit of trees which rise roughly ten or more feet in height.

The difficulty in delimiting the tundra-taiga boundary fades by comparison with the problems of specifying the southern boundary of the taiga. In this paper, following Polunin (1959, p. 483), the taiga is described as "sparsely timbered country, especially near the northern limit of arborescent growth." The approximate position of the tundra-taiga boundary is shown in Fig. II-1. The limit in Canada

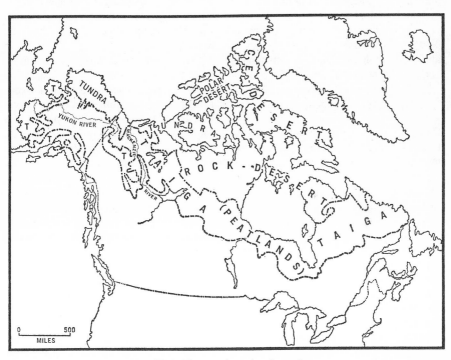

Fɪɢ. II-1. The tundra-taiga boundary.

has been compiled mainly from Halliday (1937) and Rowe (1959) and that in Alaska from Sigafoos (1958). It is obvious that many details, particularly in mountainous Alaska and Yukon Territory, have been generalized on such a small-scale map. No southern limit for the taiga is shown; the southern boundary in Canada is that given by Rowe (1959) for "forest and grassland" and "forest and barren." The complexity of the terrain in relation to map scale makes it impossible to extend the pattern into Alaska and to alpine areas of Can-

ada. Perhaps few would object if the southern boundary, just discussed, was arbitrarily assumed to be that of the southern taiga. For convenience in subsequent discussions: the tundra is inferred to lie "north" of the taiga and boreal forest, although, of course, the tundra may lie to the south, as in southern Alaska; tundra is considered as synonymous areally with arctic, taiga with subarctic; and cordilleran areas of tundra and taiga are generally ignored.

It might be relevant, at this juncture, to stress the futility of a homologous transference of latitude by latitude or climatic region by climatic region comparisons between the North American and Eurasian subarctics and arctics. The two arctics are quite different (Marsden, 1958–59) and even in North America, there is not just one arctic, but several. To cite but one example, there is the influence of glaciation on soil. The last major glaciation in North America covered by far the greater part of the mainland and the arctic islands of Canada and much of Alaska, but a much smaller area of the northern part of Eurasia.

CLIMATE AND VEGETATION

Climate, particularly summer temperature, is usually considered to be the major environmental factor responsible for a treeless tundra. This explains the numerous attempts which have been made to relate temperature to the tundra-taiga boundary. Especially well known has been Köppen's boundary line of the 50° F (10° C) isotherm for the warmest month (usually July) of the year. Throughout the north, sizable tundra areas lie south of the 50° F isotherm. Nordenskjöld (1928, p. 73) took into account both summer and winter temperatures by proposing the formula $v = 51.4 - 0.1k$ where v and k represent the mean temperatures of the warmest and coldest months, respectively, in Fahrenheit degrees. In the Nordenskjöld line, the mean monthly temperature of the warmest month required to support tree growth should be at least equal to v or higher. The Nordenskjöld line mostly lies slightly south of Köppen's line and gives a better fit to the tundra limit. In Alaska, a good correspondence has been established among vegetation, the number of degree-days above 50° F, and the mean temperature of the coldest month (Hopkins, 1959). Nearly all weather stations beyond or above the limit of forest had fewer than 130 degree-days above

50° F. Hare (1950) has included temperature and precipitation effects by showing that in Labrador-Ungava the tundra-forest boundary is approximated by Thornthwaite's (1948) potential evapotranspiration index of 12.0 to 12.5 inches. A similar value may apply in northwestern Canada (Mackay, 1958, p. 100). The preceding climatically determined boundaries agree reasonably well with the tundra-taiga limit, but they do not explain it.

During the year as a whole, the tundra is the coldest region with vegetation (vascular plants) in the Northern Hemisphere, simply because most of it receives less solar radiation than areas to the south. Most weather stations experience a large annual mean monthly temperature range of about 50° to 70° F (Thomas, 1960). In areas proximate to the sea, maritime effects may be notable. February, rather than January, is often the coldest month of the year. July is normally the warmest month with mean daily temperatures below 50° F. Coastal temperatures are noticeably affected by ice conditions, the nearby presence of sea ice being conducive to low summer temperatures.

The mean annual precipitation of the tundra is usually less than fifteen inches, the maximum occurring in summer. Parts of the Queen Elizabeth Islands may receive less than five inches per annum; consequently the snowfall is extremely light. The popular image of a deep, snow-covered arctic landscape is false, because the mean annual maximum depth of snow is mostly less than twenty-five inches, except for restricted localities, such as in parts of Ungava.

The presence or absence of snowfall is a most important factor influencing plant cover, ice thickness, and ground temperatures. Once the depth of snow reaches about six inches, a further increase greatly dampens the fluctuations of the ambient air temperature at the ground surface

(Krinsley, 1963). For example, when one foot of packed, drifted snow overlies sandy gravel for six months, the shift in mean annual temperature from the air-solid interface to the ground surface would be expected to be about 8° or 9° F, using Barrow, Alaska, as an illustration (Lachenbruch, 1959, p. 29).

Thus, a deep snow cover, such as occurs in parts of the taiga, makes for a sharp vertical environmental gradient (Pruitt, 1957, p. 138). In lakes which are the natural habitat of furbearing animals such as muskrat, mink, and beaver in the Mackenzie delta the role of snow depth and ice conditions is most important. A heavy autumn snowfall helps to reduce the ice thickness. In places where there is an unusually deep and persistent snow cover, as in a gully, ground temperatures tend to be above normal; but if the snow cover persists far into the warming period, subnormal temperatures may result. Snow also has many other effects, both advantageous and deleterious, besides those on temperature. Certain combinations of snow load, compaction, and basal snowcreep (Mathews and Mackay, 1963), accentuated by steep slopes, mechanically damage plants. The nature of snow cover is also of importance to wildlife, particularly with grazing animals such as caribou, reindeer, and musk oxen.

The mean wind speed in northern areas differs little from that in more southern latitudes. However, the absence of trees in the tundra reduces the drag force at the earth's surface because the roughness parameter for most tundra vegetation is low, and the velocity profile near to the ground relatively steep. Plants may be subjected to excessive water depletion by exposure to drying winds, especially while the roots are encased in frozen soil and cannot absorb water (Benninghoff, 1952, p. 36). Snow crystals may severely abrade exposed rocks, when driven by high velocities at below-zero temperatures, because the hardness of ice increases markedly with a decrease in temperature (Blackwelder, 1940). Rocks such as granite may be strongly snow-blasted, and it would be surprising, therefore, if unprotected plants escaped injury. Deflation and deposition by wind contribute to changes in the soil. Gravelly pavements (lag gravels) frequently result from the winnowing action of wind. Along bare beaches, lake shores, and stream beds, swirling clouds of fine dust may be lifted up and dropped, as if from a flour sifter, onto vegetated areas. Some of the fines may lodge around the stems and leaves of plants or even smother them. In winter the fines may darken snow and ice and thus contribute to a more rapid melting by absorbing radiation. The "black ice" of the Mackenzie River is an excellent illustration of the preceding.

In the tundra and taiga the interrelated effects of low temperature, snowfall, and wind on vegetation are everywhere apparent, although not fully understood. Despite the long summer days, the annual growth rate is relatively minute, and regrowth of disturbed vegetation may be extremely slow. Climate is also responsible for the widespread occurrence of perennially frozen ground and frost action. An understanding of these climatically induced environmental factors is critical to an appreciation of the distinctive aspects of land utilization in the tundra and taiga.

PERENNIALLY FROZEN GROUND

Continuous permafrost (perennially frozen ground) underlies nearly all of the tundra and discontinuous permafrost is below the taiga (Figs. II-1 and II-3). Because the thickness of permafrost is, in general, a function of the secular mean annual ground-surface temperature, depths decrease southward. At Winter Harbour, Melville Island, the depth

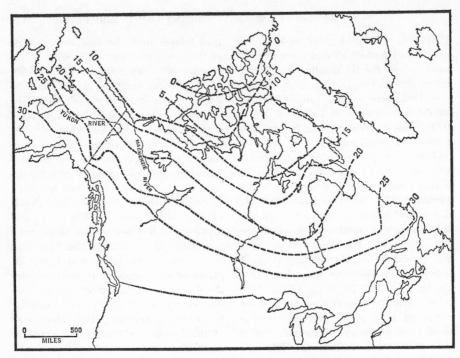

FIG. II-2. Mean annual isotherms in degrees Fahrenheit. Mainly after Thomas (1953).

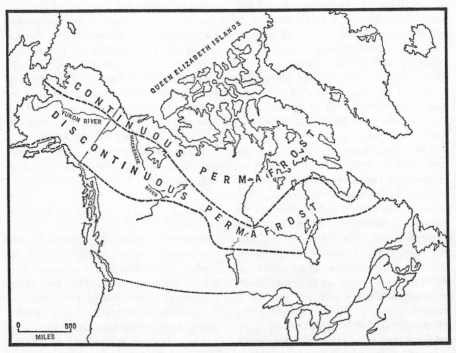

FIG. II-3. Permafrost boundaries, mainly after Brown (1960).

probably exceeds 1700 feet; at Barrow, Alaska, and Resolute, Cornwallis Island, the depths are about 1300 feet; at Norman Wells, NWT, about 150 feet; and at Hay River, NWT, permafrost may range from zero to 40 feet thick. Permafrost exerts direct and indirect effects on plant and animal life in numerous ways, such as inhibiting subsurface drainage, contributing to soil instability, and maintaining a steep thermal gradient in the active layer (the layer which freezes and thaws seasonally).

Permafrost tends to form, and persist, where the "long period" mean annual ground-surface temperature is below 32° F. The mean annual ground temperature is usually a few degrees warmer than the mean annual air temperature, because of the insulation provided by snow and a complexity of other factors. Therefore the 32° F mean annual isotherm, recorded for air temperature in a standard weather screen, lies well south of the southern limit of discontinuous permafrost (Figs. II-2 and II-3). Mean annual air temperatures of about 15° to 20° F are required in order to have continuous permafrost.

The active layer varies in thickness from a few inches to several feet, not just on a regional scale, but also on a microscale involving horizontal distances commonly of only several feet (Mackay, 1963, pp. 57–60). Commencing about September–October, freezing of the active layer progresses downward, at times aided by slight upward freezing from the frost table. Thawing of the active layer starts in May–June, likewise from the surface downward. In most of the tundra, air temperatures may drop below 32° F during any summer month, but the ground itself may not experience a freeze-thaw cycle. For example, at Resolute, NWT, only one annual cycle was recorded at a depth of one inch in 1960 (Cook and Raiche, 1962, p. 68). The annual range at the ground surface was

127° F, at one inch 100° F, at eight inches 82° F; the air (Stevenson screen) range was only 102° F. Thus, roots a few inches below the ground may undergo only one annual freeze-thaw cycle, in contrast to multiple cycles for the exposed parts of plants. As the thickness of the unfrozen ground in the summer months rarely exceeds several feet, the vertical temperature gradient between the frost table at 32° F and the ground surface, possibly at 50° F or above, is steep. Thus, separate parts of a plant may experience a wide temperature range both diurnally and simultaneously.

Frozen ground, whether of bedrock or composed of unconsolidated material, tends to be quite impermeable. Therefore, ground-water flow—especially in areas of continuous permafrost—is lateral rather than vertical and is confined to the active layer, a fact of considerable consequence from the viewpoint of human utilization. Flat terrain is nearly always ill drained. Even on slopes, local undulations of the frost table are often sufficiently pronounced to form closed depressions, like the bottom of an egg carton, so that saturated soils are close to the surface. As a result, ponds, lakes, and soggy ground are common. A concomitant feature, however, is the large amount of moisture available to roots in spite of the low precipitation.

The root systems of plants are normally considered as being restricted to the thickness of the active layer, below which is the thermal hardpan of the permafrost surface. Lateral growth of roots is frequently observed above the thermal hardpan. On floodplains and alluvial fans, where sedimentation adds accretions to the ground surface, the upper permafrost table tends to rise concurrently, thereby maintaining a constant thickness of the active layer. Thus, if the rate of aggradation is rapid in terms of the life span of a plant, the deepest roots become embalmed in the upward-rising permafrost as exposed parts are buried in the active layer. Some plants, such as the white spruce, balsam poplar, and willow, may send out adventitious roots and continue growing even after the permafrost surface has risen above the initial level of the ground when growth commenced. On some Mackenzie River floodplains, the permafrost surface has been elevated more than six feet during the lifetime of spruce trees growing there. On the other hand, degradation of permafrost by a thickening of the active layer —often the result of clearing and removal of shrubs, trees, and organic matter—may cause a depression of the permafrost table, thus giving a thicker active layer, reduced thermal gradient, and permitting a longer growing season.

Although it is generally assumed that the permafrost surface forms an impenetrable thermal hardpan to roots, this may not be the case. Dadykin (1950) has reported roots of cloudberry, sedge, and horsetail penetrating into frozen ground to a depth of three feet while still remaining viable. Root penetration of oats and potatoes into frozen ground was also observed. Inasmuch as fine-grained soils, such as clays, may have a high unfrozen-water content at subfreezing temperatures while still retaining plasticity, the role of permafrost in root development presents intriguing questions.

SOILS, PATTERNED GROUND,
AND MICRORELIEF

Despite the extreme variations between soils of the southern taiga and northern tundra, most localities share one or more of the following features: parent material reflecting late Wisconsin glaciation; soil instability resulting in the formation of patterned ground; and impeded drainage caused by an impermeable frozen substratum.

Most of the tundra-taiga bears the imprint of recent glaciation. In Alaska, glaciation was centered in the montane areas of the Brooks and Alaska ranges, with the lower terrain remaining unglaciated. In Canada, glaciers covered all of the taiga and most of the tundra, with the major exceptions of parts of the Queen Elizabeth Islands and the northwestern cordillera. The scouring action of glaciers is still reflected in the large bare expanses of bedrock concentrated primarily in the Canadian shield (Glacial Map of Canada, 1958), the rock deserts of Figure II-1. Other areas were veneered with drift of varying thickness. The relative shortness of postglacial time has limited soil development. After all, the Hudson Bay and northern Ontario region had glacier ice only 7000 to 8000 years ago (Lee, 1960). Weathering has been so slow that numerous rocky outcrops still preserve the minutiae of glacial striae. Another facet of glaciation has been the postglacial elevation of coastal strips which range in width from several miles to over a hundred miles. The coastal areas include the shores of Ungava Bay, Hudson Bay, Foxe Basin, Gulf of Boothia, Queen Maud Gulf, Coronation Gulf, Dolphin and Union Strait, and Amundsen Gulf. On these recently emergent coasts are sited most of the settlements, harbors, and airstrips. Fortunately, the soils tend to be gravelly, well drained, and less susceptible to "damage" than those of more elevated inland regions.

The tundra, and to a lesser extent the taiga, is characterized by soil instability. The soil may be cracked, churned, and overturned; soil material may be differentially sorted into coarse and fine particles; and all soil moves downslope by slow creep or rapid flow. These processes of soil displacement form patterned ground and distinctive microrelief features (Britton, 1957; Washburn, 1956). The link between specific genetic soils and patterned ground in northern Alaska has been so close, in fact, that two pedologists (Drew and Tedrow, 1962) have suggested a scheme for the classification of soils based upon the association with patterned ground. Many distinct and diverse processes are operative in the development of patterned ground and microrelief features, but alternate freezing and thawing, with gravity-induced downslope displacement, are the most important. In fine-grained soils, ice segregation tends to occur so that the soil in the frozen state contains more water (ice) than it can in the unfrozen (liquid) state; i.e. the frozen soils are supersaturated. The growth of ice layers normal to the thermal gradient tends to produce frost heaving, at times accompanied by stretching or breakage of roots. The growth of ice layers helps to impart a structure to the soil. Lateral expansion from vertical ice veining may exceed 10 per cent and also damage roots. The migration of the freezing plane, whether from the surface downward or laterally from the side of a hummock, may size-sort the soil (Corte, 1963). Alternate freeze-thaw cycles do much, therefore, to change the microhabitat of plants and animals. These cycles are confined to the active layer; consequently, most features of patterned ground and microrelief are only "skin deep." On slopes, any soil disturbance tends to cause a net downslope movement (solifluction), and where rapid, the pattern resembles frosting flowing down a cake. The overrunning of lower slopes and flats by solifluction debris frequently causes an increase in the organic content of the soil, by burial, and the blockage of drainage leading to soggy flats and elongated lakes.

Patterned ground and microrelief features in the tundra and taiga are usually in quasi-equilibrium with the environment; inactive or fossil arctic patterns do occur, however, mainly in the taiga. Consequently, a disturbance to the surface may set off a train of geomorphic and biotic events. A natural or artificial disturbance which tends to accentuate the instability might be locally disastrous. In the tundra and polar desert regions, where frost boils, mud circles, stone rings, etc., are common, regeneration ranges from slow to rapid, depending upon conditions. Mud circles have been known to begin reforming within a few years of artificial surface grading. If, however, the disturbed patterned ground does not soon reassert itself, then a habitat change may quickly result. To be specific, let us examine some results of common disturbances to terrain with ice wedges and ground ice masses. Such terrain is widely distributed in the arctic.

A characteristic feature of tundra underlain by continuous permafrost is a type of patterned ground usually referred to as an ice wedge or tundra polygon. Ice-wedge growth in these areas is active, in the sense that vertical fissures opened annually by thermal contraction in winter tend to become ice-filled. The ice wedges form a boxlike network, like the unfinished walls of a single-story house. Tens of thousands of square miles of low-lying terrain have very conspicuous ice-wedge polygons; upland areas usually have less distinct patterns. The ice wedges are particularly subject to thermal erosion and upon melting, conical hillocks—the *baidzharakhi* of Yakutia—are left protruding. Streams which follow an ice-wedge network may become beaded; coasts cut into ice-wedge terrain may have long gullies which work headward by thermal erosion along the wedges; and so forth. Thus, ice-wedge terrain is peculiarly susceptible to change, whether naturally or artificially induced. Disturbances are also critical in thick sections of fine-grained soils with horizontal or irregularly shaped ice masses. The ice content (percentage of ice to dry soil on a weight basis) may average 100 to 300 per cent for the upper few tens of feet of permafrost in fine-grained sediments. A natural or artificial rupture of the surface cover may therefore initiate ground ice slumps which retreat headward, mainly by melting. Coastal recession and gullying are rapid in such areas. A break in the vegetation cover or a blockage in drainage may be sufficient to create a thaw (thermokarst) topography with depressions and cave-in lakes (Hopkins, 1949; Wallace, 1948). There seems little doubt that further study of thermokarst features in North America will show that they are extremely important in causing habitat changes, as has been recognized in Russia.

In the taiga, Raup (1951) has pointed out that forests on actively moving slopes are more or less unstable, root systems may be torn loose from their intimate soil contacts, and mortality is high. Such forests are prone to disturbances, both natural and artificial. The frequent sight of tilted or drunken trees is nearly a sure sign of such a disturbance.

As stressed in the discussion of permafrost, much of the arctic and subarctic terrain is ill drained, and soil development is impeded. Some areas are well drained, however, and there mature soils may develop (Tedrow, Drew, Hill, and Douglas, 1958). Interestingly enough, where well-drained soils occur in the arctic islands, some are dry desertlike in appearance, at times with salts accumulated at the surface, giving the polar desert of Figure II–1 (Tedrow and Douglas, 1964).

Man's activities can and do alter the interrelated elements of soil–patterned ground–microrelief. The establishment of a summer campsite for one or more seasons leaves its mark by disturbed vegetation, which in abandoned Eskimo sites is usually recognizable by a more luxuriant growth than in nearby tundra areas (Wiggins and Thomas, 1962, p. 27). Frequent vehicular traffic, if unconfined to a road, may slice up the tundra with remarkable rapidity, especially where track

or wheel furrows concentrate drainage into flow channels. A footpath, used for only one season, may persist virtually unchanged for decades. Regrowth of vegetation is so gradual that a disturbance, such as forest cutting, may be perpetuated nearly unchanged for a century. For instance, the Hudson's Bay Company established Fort Anderson (on the Anderson River, 150 miles east of Inuvik, NWT) in 1861 and abandoned it only five years later in 1866. In the intervening century, revegetation has been minimal. Most of the vegetation is still composed of grasses with a few willows. The forest clearing still preserves the original outlines of the stockade. Inevitably such disturbances will increase as man's activities spread; whether they will be harmful in the aggregate is quite another issue.

THE YEARS AHEAD

Nearly everyone who has viewed the tundra and taiga from the air or the ground is more likely to ponder on how these arctic and subarctic lands can assure adequate economic support for the existing population, rather than to question why it isn't measurably larger. In our speculating on future habitat changes —the years ahead—for man and other living creatures, numerous questions arise. Some questions are answerable, but most are not. The foremost question is undoubtedly climatic amelioration, because it is the hostile climate which inhibits much development. If the climate cannot be ameliorated, can the pioneer fringe of settlement be moved northward appreciably? If settlement does push farther into the taiga, and small communities (e. g. mining) become established in the tundra, what impacts will there be from land clearing, forest fires, road construction, dam building, hunting, fishing, and tourism?

Should an effort be made to supplant

caribou with reindeer and musk oxen? Can the southern part of the treeless tundra be treed (Tikhomirov, 1962)? If it can, would there be an advantage in trying to extend the taiga northward, if even only for a few miles? Can improved long-range weather forecasts, satellite photography, and remote sensors make it possible to predict and follow ice and open-water conditions and thus aid in transportation and the utilization of land, marine, and ocean-floor resources?

Climatic amelioration

Climatic changes of first magnitude have taken place in the past 10,000± 2000 years since the glaciers receded from most of the tundra and taiga. Following the climatic optimum (hypsithermal) of about 5000 years ago, there have been many minor climatic fluctuations, such as the little climatic optimum, 1000–1300 A.D., and little ice age, 1550–1850 A.D. (Bryson and Julian, 1963; Dansereau, 1953). Instrumental records of temperatures in the tundra and taiga are of only short duration, but climatic trends may be inferred by other means, such as freeze-up and breakup records for lakes and rivers. For example, ice records for the Hayes and Churchill rivers, which empty into Hudson Bay, show marked fluctuations since the early 1700s. For the arctic, commencing in about 1920, instrumental records show a noticeable temperature rise until the 1940s, the difference in five-year annual mean temperatures between 1880 and 1940 being roughly 4° F (Callendar, 1961; Mitchell, 1963). However, there is no evidence of trends from historic records (e.g. Wing, 1951) to suggest that the climate in fifty or a hundred years will be warmer or colder than at present, and by how much.

In spite of no positive evidence to favor either a warming or cooling trend, biotic boundaries are not static. Because the tundra-taiga environments are in a youthful stage, there may be a considerable lag in response to past climatic changes. In many places in Alaska at present the forest boundaries are mobile migration fronts rather than static boundaries (Griggs, 1934, p. 92; Raup, 1941, p. 224). On the east coast of Hudson Bay, "Trees are invading tundra areas as soil develops . . . given sufficient time, with climate held constant, forest will occupy the entire area as soils of organic and inorganic nature develop. . . ." (Maar, 1948, pp. 143–44). Tikhomirov (1960) reports a northward and vertical expansion into the Russian tundra. Even some species of birds, whose mobility seems unlimited, are still immigrating northward (Tuck, 1964). Thus, if present climatic conditions remain constant, a slow northward encroachment of the taiga into the tundra may continue. If there were a warming trend, the shift should be both accentuated and accelerated. Locally, however, the tundra may replace the taiga along the tree line (personal communication, V. J. Krajina) through the establishment of a sphagnum-moss ground cover, a resulting shallowing of the active layer, and an eventual favoring of a tundra succession.

If there is no evidence suggestive of climatic warming, the question naturally arises as to whether climate can be modified artificially on a macro (regional) or micro (local) scale. Although numerous field experiments have been carried out on weather modification, these have primarily involved rainmaking over a relatively small area, unfortunately with disappointing results (Workman, 1962). The outlook for large-scale weather modification is not, at present, encouraging. The issue can, however, be approached by other means. For example, the unusual appearance of capelin and Atlantic cod in the Ungava Bay area in the 1950s was probably due to a change in the marine climate (Dunbar, 1962). Might it then be possible to alter hydrographic patterns in the arctic to achieve similar desirable ends?

Newspapers have, at times, devoted attention to a "scheme" for a Bering Strait dam to warm the arctic. Is it feasible from an engineering viewpoint? Would it be economical? What effects would such a dam have on arctic circulation either with or without pumping of water? Would there be an amelioration of the Arctic Ocean climate? Dunbar (1962, p. 134) has partially answered these questions: "At all events, the main issue is clear: the damming of Bering Strait, without any pumping of water in either direction, would alter the marine climate of the coastal eastern arctic quite significantly, to an extent which at present can be estimated only within wide limits." Dunbar also points out that to pump the cold arctic layer off the Arctic Ocean, with the purpose of bringing warmer water to the surface, would probably take several tens of *thousands* of years! And if there were an ice-free open Arctic Ocean, would this, in turn, bring about an ice age again (Ewing and Donn, 1961)? Would a smaller hydrographic change, such as the proposed Rampart Dam on the Yukon River, with its 10,-850-square-mile lake (Cooke, 1964), affect the local climate? An answer might be suggested by examining the areas adjacent to Great Bear and Great Slave lakes. On balance, the weight of evidence is now against any regional amelioration of climate by artificial means.

The local microclimate can easily be altered, but whether it would be desirable and economical is another matter. Snowmelt may be accelerated by appropriate artificial dusting (Arnold, 1961) or inhibited by artificial insulation. Snow fences, the use of trees as snow breaks, and other means similar to dune control in arid areas can increase or decrease the snow cover. Powdered coal, sprinkled over the ground, may increase soil temperatures by tapping solar energy

(Black, 1963). Clearing, cultivation, and drainage may profoundly modify the energy exchange at the ground surface. Methods such as the above may be suitable for changing the local microclimate but are impractical, at present, for any large area.

Any pronounced local climatic warming, if sustained for many decades, would have major consequences on the southern distribution of discontinuous permafrost. As an approximation, under equilibrium conditions the thickness of permafrost is equal to the product of the geothermal gradient and the number of degrees that the mean annual ground-surface temperature is below freezing. Thus, if the geothermal gradient is 1° F per 100 feet, and the mean ground-surface temperature is 31° F, the expected thickness of permafrost is 100 feet. Therefore, if the mean annual ground-surface temperature rises over several decades from slightly below 32° F to slightly above, the discontinuous permafrost, which is already thin, will degrade and may disappear. Even if a zone of relic permafrost still remains at depth, so that winter freezing fails to reach it, drainage conditions should normally improve. In certain marginal areas, there is no reason why complete degradation of permafrost could not be achieved artificially by altering the thermal balance at the ground surface. In areas underlain by continuous permafrost, sustained secular climatic changes of great magnitude would be required to cause appreciable degradation. Thus, the critical areas of permafrost aggradation and degradation are in the southern taiga, not the tundra.

Fires

Forest fires, whether ignited by lightning or by man, have devastated thousands of square miles. Even the treeless tundra has not escaped from fires; some peaty terrain has burnt or smoldered for months. In forested parts of Yukon Territory and Alaska, Hansen (1953) estimates that fire has been more destructive in the past half century than during the rest of postglacial or even Pleistocene times. Sufficiently large areas have been burnt over in the Mackenzie Valley that they are mapped on the hydrographic charts. To cite a specific example, in 1954 an area of 820 square miles of the reindeer winter range area, east of the Mackenzie delta, was 70 to 80 per cent burned and rendered useless for grazing (Cody, 1964, p. 9; Mackay, 1963, p. 168). Ten years later, the lichen flora had not recovered sufficiently to allow reindeer to graze. In Labrador-Ungava, Hare (1959) has mapped burned areas as one of the main cover types. In the "taiga" part of Labrador-Ungava, over 10,000 square miles are shown as burned areas.

The direct consequences of fires are several. There is, of course, the destruction of standing vegetation, and thus the immediate loss of a resource which may not be renewable for generations; in the Mackenzie delta area, 500-year-old spruce grow to the tree line. Frequently, a forest fire consumes organic matter in the upper part of the soil, rendering it sterile for revegetation. A thickening of the active layer is usual as an aftermath to a fire, and if the ice content of the ground is high, thawing tends to produce hummocks, drunken trees, miniature thermokarst features, local ponding, and gullying. It is abundantly clear that control and prevention of fires is necessary in the taiga, and to a much lesser degree, in the tundra. As northern areas become more accessible to hunters, fishermen, tourists, and others, the risk of fire increases.

Soil productivity

Barring an unforeseen breakthrough in agricultural technology, it is most unlikely that outdoor agriculture, beyond the local vegetable garden, will be of consequence in the tundra. Even in the taiga, the future of agriculture is circum-scribed both in Alaska and Canada (Underhill, 1959; Bladen, 1962; *Resources for Tomorrow; Science in Alaska*). "When land needs become critical in North America, it is possible that considerably more than a million acres may be farmed in Alaska" (Mick, 1957, p. 107), the number of farms being estimated at about 5000 or 6000 only. In Canada, "it appears that any future agricultural development will be largely limited to the valleys of the Yukon and Mackenzie river systems in the northwest. Here more than a million acres of suitable soil for agriculture may be found." (Nowosad and Leahey, 1960, p. 50) But the occurrence of arable soils does not necessarily mean that the climate is suitable for crops or that they will ripen. Restrictions on agriculture are imposed by the physical environment compounded by a low demand for agricultural produce, excessive costs of production, and continually tightening competition from the southern areas as transportation facilities improve.

The long photoperiod of the subarctic partially explains some of the surprising productivity observed at a few favorable sites, even in areas of continuous permafrost. When land is cleared, the removal of the natural vegetation cover and later cultivation alter the energy exchange at the ground surface, usually toward a net heat gain. For example, in June, 1956, an experimental garden of the Department of Agriculture was started at Inuvik, NWT, at the taiga limit. The active layer, which was about eighteen to twenty-four inches thick in 1956 prior to clearing, has thickened to six feet. Good vegetable crops have been obtained. At nearby Aklavik, vegetables have been raised successfully for several decades. Vegetables have been grown near Fort Chimo, Quebec, in a permafrost area, in both greenhouses and in the open garden.

Problems may arise, however, in the artificial depression of the active layer by cultivation, especially where the ground-ice content is high. Thawing and pitting may result as has been observed in farm-lands near Fairbanks, Alaska (Rockie, 1942). In the Yukon Territory and Mackenzie Valley of Canada, much of the potentially arable land has fine-grained soils which probably have a high ice content. Particular caution is required in the utilization of such thermokarst-susceptible soils.

Future developments in agriculture are likely to be in the taiga (subarctic) and will conform to historic patterns. The long hours of summer insolation, advances in agricultural technology, and the demand of local urban communities may stimulate agriculture on a small scale. However, even the most optimistic northern protagonist can hardly envisage the taiga, much less the tundra, as a granary for the future.

Wildlife and man

Although the human population of the tundra and taiga was sparse in prehistory, is still sparse, and is likely to remain so except for special community developments (e.g. mining), man has not played a passive role in affecting the biotic environment. The killing of game to supply whaling ships of the late nineteenth and early twentieth centuries, the introduction of firearms, and the growth of a trapping economy greatly reduced the caribou population and nearly decimated the musk oxen. The caribou population of northern Canada has declined from an estimated 1,750,000 for 1900 to 250,-000 at present (Banfield, 1951, 1964). Only stringent protective measures since 1917 have allowed the musk oxen to multiply to the present 10,000 and of these few, most are in the arctic islands.

The exigency for wise use of the wildlife resource will intensify as arctic and subarctic lands become more accessible. The supply of wildlife, whether migratory fowl, barren-ground caribou, musk oxen, polar bear, grizzly bear, or even fish, is not inexhaustible and easily renewable, as experience has shown. Some uses are competitive. Is it preferable to kill game animals for dog food to support a trapping economy or to support a tourist industry? Some uses might be improvements, such as the domestication of reindeer and musk oxen. These are research problems requiring further investigation.

CONCLUSIONS

On the regional scale, low summer temperatures, glaciation, and the short span of postglacial time are three major factors which contribute toward the treelessness of the tundra and the harshness of the taiga. Although significant climatic fluctuations have occurred in the past few centuries, there is no evidence favoring either a warming or a cooling trend in the years ahead. If there is no likelihood of a long-term warming trend, can it be induced economically on a regional scale by artificial means? The present answer is no. However, the local microclimate in which plants live—both above and below the ground—is capable of considerable amelioration through modification of the snow cover, clearing, burning, drainage, use of additives and mulches, etc. Here lies the best possibility for microhabitat amelioration.

The widespread distribution of perennially frozen ground (permafrost) is reflected in soil types, patterned ground, microrelief, and ice segregation. Seasonal freezing and thawing of the active layer above the impermeable permafrost leads to soil instability, gravity-induced downslope movement, and impeded drainage. Because the ice content tends to be low in coarse-textured soils and high in fine-textured ones, coarse-grained soils are best for construction purposes, whereas fine-grained soils texturally ideal for agriculture are also frost-susceptible and therefore potentially damaging to plants. There is no present prospect for agriculture in the tundra and a poor outlook for it in the taiga. However, local farms and vegetable gardens may be established adjacent to new mining, transport, and other settlements. With improving accessibility, the total effects of forest fire and local soil disturbance will be magnified, thus leading to large-scale habitat changes in sparsely settled areas. The resource uses of wildlife in the tundra and taiga are posing the problem of alternative choices. Caribou or reindeer? A trapping or tourist economy? In brief, despite the sparseness of human population in the tundra and taiga, and the questionable likelihood of appreciable augmentation, the habitats are still under the influence of man.

ACKNOWLEDGMENTS

The writer would like to thank Dr. V. J. Krajina and Dr. J. L. Robinson for reading the manuscript and offering helpful comments.

BIBLIOGRAPHY

Arnold, K. C. 1961. An Investigation into Methods of Accelerating the Melting of Ice and Snow by Artificial Dusting. In: Raasch, G. O., ed., Geology of the Arctic, vol. 2:989–1013. Univ. Toronto Press, Toronto.

Banfield, A. W. F. 1954. The Barren-Ground Caribou. Dept. Res. and Develop.

———— 1964. Specially the Caribou. In: Smith, I. N., ed., The Unbelievable Land: 25–28. Dept. Northern Affairs and Nat. Res., Ottawa.

Benninghoff, W. S. 1952. Interaction of Vegetation and Soil Frost Phenomena. Arctic 5:34–44.

Black, J. F. 1963. Weather Control: Use of Asphalt Coatings to Tap Solar Energy. Sci. 139:226–27.

Blackwelder, E. 1940. The Hardness of Ice. Amer. J. Sci. 238:61–62.

Bladen, V. W., ed. 1962. Canadian Population and Northern Colonization. Univ. Toronto Press, Toronto.

Britton, M. E. 1957. Vegetation of the Arctic Tundra. Arctic Biol.:26–61. 18th Ann. Biol. Colloquium, Oreg. State Col., Corvallis, Oreg.

Brown, R. J. E. 1960. The Distribution of Permafrost and Its Relation to Air Temperature in Canada and the USSR. Arctic 13:163–77.

Bryson, R. A., and Julian, P. R., eds. 1963. Proceedings of the Conference on the Climate of the Eleventh and Sixteenth Centuries, Aspen, Colo., June 16–24, 1962: Notes 63–1. Nat. Ctr. for Atmos. Res., Boulder, Colo., NCAR Tech.

Callendar, G. S. 1961. Temperature Fluctuations and Trends over the Earth. Q. J. Royal Meteorol. Soc. 87:1–12.

Cody, W. J. 1964. Reindeer Range Survey, 1957 and 1963. Plant Research Inst., Can. Dept. Agric., Ctr. Exper. Farm, Ottawa, March 23.

Cook, F. A., and Raiche, V. G. 1962. Freeze-thaw Cycles at Resolute, N.W.T. Geog. Bul. 18:64–78.

Cooke, A. 1964. The Rampart Dam Proposal for Yukon River. Polar Rec. 12:277–80.

Corte, A. W. 1963. Vertical Migration of Particles in Front of a Moving Freezing Plane. U.S. Army Cold Regs. Res. and Eng. Lab., Res. Rep. 105.

Dadykin, V. P. 1955. On the Biological Peculiarities of the Plants of Cold Soils. In Russian (1950), Priroda 5:21–29. Abstr. in Arctic Bibl. 5:182–83.

Dansereau, P. 1953. The Postglacial Pine Period. Trans. Royal Soc. Can., 3rd Ser., Sec. 5, 47:23–38.

Drew, J. W., and Tedrow, J. C. G. 1962. Arctic Soil Classification and Patterned Ground. Arctic 15:109–16.

Dunbar, M. J. 1962. The Living Resources of Northern Canada. In: Bladen, V. W., ed., Canadian Population and Northern Colonization: 125–35. Univ. Toronto Press, Toronto.

Ewing, M., and Donn, W. L. 1961. Pleistocene Climatic Changes. In Raasch, G. O., ed., Geology of the Arctic, vol. 2:931–41. Univ. Toronto Press, Toronto.

Gates, D. M. 1962. Energy Exchange in the Biosphere. Harper, New York.

Glacial Map of Canada. 1958. Geol. Assn. Can.

Griggs, R. 1934. The Edge of the Forest in Alaska and the Reason for Its Position. Ecol. 15:80–96.

Halliday, W. E. D. 1937. A Forest Classification for Canada. Dept. Mines and Res., Ottawa, Dom. Forest Serv., Bul. 89.

Hansen, H. P. 1953. Postglacial Forests in the Yukon Territory and Alaska. Amer. J. Sci. 251:505–42.

Hare, F. K. 1950. Climate and Zonal Divisions of the Boreal Forest Formation in Eastern Canada. Geog. Rev. 40:615–35.

——— 1959. A Photo-reconnaissance Survey of Labrador-Ungava. Geog. Br., Ottawa, Mem. 6.

Hopkins, D. M. 1949. Thaw Lakes and Thaw Sinks in the Imuruk Lakes Area, Seward Peninsula, Alaska. J. Geol. 57:119–31.

——— 1959. Some Characteristics of the Climate in Forest and Tundra Regions in Alaska. Arctic 12:215–20.

Hustich, I. 1953. The Boreal Limits of Conifers. Arctic 6:149–62.

Krinsley, D. B. 1963. Influence of Snow Cover on Frost Penetration. U.S. Geol. Surv. Prof. Pap. 475-B, Art. 38, B144–B147.

Lachenbruch, A. H. 1959. Periodic Heat Flow in a Stratified Medium with Application to Permafrost Problems. U.S. Geol. Surv. Bul. 1083-A.

Lee, H. A. 1960. Late Glacial and Postglacial Hudson Bay Sea Episode. Sci. 131:1609–10.

Mackay, J. R. 1958. The Anderson River Map-area, N.W.T. Geog. Br., Ottawa, Mem. 5.

——— 1963. The Mackenzie Delta Area, N.W.T. Geog. Br., Ottawa, Mem. 8.

Marr, J. W. 1948. Ecology of the Forest-tundra Ecotone on the East Coast of Hudson Bay. Ecol. Monogs. 18:117–44.

Marsden, M. 1958. Arctic Contrasts: Canada and Russia in the Far North. Intern. J. 14:33–41. Toronto.

Mathews, W. H., and Mackay, J. R. 1963. Snowcreep Studies, Mount Seymour, B.C.: A Preliminary Field Investigation. Geog. Bul. 20:58–75.

Mick, A. 1957. Arctic and Subarctic Alaska. Arctic Biol.:100–9. 18th Ann. Biol. Colloquium, Oreg. State Col., Corvallis, Oreg.

Mitchell, Fr., J. M. 1963. On the World-wide Pattern of Secular Temperature Change. In: Changes of Climate, Proc. Rome Symp., UNESCO and World Meteorol. Org.:161–81.

Nordenskjöld, O., and Mecking, L. 1928. The Geography of the Polar Regions. Am. Geog. Soc. Sp. Pub. 8.

Nowosad, F. S., and Leahey, A. 1960. Soils of the Arctic and Sub-arctic Regions of Canada. Agric. Inst. Rev. 15 (Mar.–Apr.):48–50.

Polunin, N. 1959. Circumpolar Arctic Flora. Oxford Univ. Press, Oxford.

Pruitt, W. O., Jr. 1957. Observations on the Bioclimate of Some Taiga Mammals. Arctic 10:131–38.

Raup, H. M. 1941. Botanical Problems in Boreal America. Bot. Rev. 7:147–248.

——— 1951. Vegetation and Cryoplanation. Ohio J. Sci. 51:105–16.

Resources for Tomorrow, vols. 1 and 2. 1961. Dept. Northern Affairs and Nat. Res., Ottawa.

Rockie, W. A. 1942. Pitting on Alaska Farm Lands a New Erosion Problem. Geog. Rev. 32:128–34.

Rowe, J. S. 1959. Forest Regions of Canada. Forest Br. Bul. 123. Dept. Northern Affairs and Nat. Res., Ottawa.

Science in Alaska, Alaska Div., Amer. Assn. Adv. Sci. Annual Proceedings.

Sigafoos, R. S. 1958. Vegetation of Northwestern North America, as an Aid in Interpretation of Geologic Data. U.S. Geol. Surv. Bul. 1061E:165–85.

Sjörs, H. 1963. Amphi-Atlantic Zonation, Nemoral to Arctic. In: Love, A., and Love, D., eds., North Atlantic Biota and Their History: 109–25. Pergamon, Oxford.

Tedrow, J. C. F., Drew, J. V., Hill, D. E., and Douglas, L. A. 1958. Major Soils of the Arctic Slope of Alaska. J. Soil Sci. 9:33–45.

Thomas, M. K. 1953. Climatological Atlas of Canada. Nat. Res. Council, Ottawa.

————— 1960. Canadian Arctic Temperatures. Dept. Transp., Canada, Meteorol. Br., CIR-334, CLI-24 (May 9).

Thornthwaite, C. W. 1943. An Approach Toward a Rational Classification of Climate. Geog. Rev. 38:55–94.

Tikhomirov, B. A. 1960. Phytogeographical Investigations of the Tundra Vegetation in the Soviet Union. Can. J. Bot. 38:815–32.

————— 1962. The Treelessness of the Tundra. Polar Rec. 11:24–30.

Tuck, L. M. 1964. Birds in the Arctic. In: Smith, I. N., ed., The Unbelievable Land: 29–33. Dept. Northern Affairs and Nat. Res., Ottawa.

Underhill, F. H., ed. 1959. The Canadian Northwest: Its Potentialities. Univ. Toronto Press, Toronto.

Wallace, R. E. 1948. Cave-in Lakes in the Nebesna, Chisana, and Tanana River Valleys, Eastern Alaska. J. Geol. 56:171–81.

Washburn, A. L. 1956. Classification of Patterned Ground and a Review of Suggested Origins. Bul. Geol. Soc. Amer. 67:823–66.

Wiggins, I. L., and Thomas, J. H. 1962. A Flora of the Alaskan Arctic Slope. Univ. Toronto Press, Toronto.

Wing, L. W. 1951. Cyclic Trends in Arctic Seasons. J. Cycle Res. 1:20–25.

ARID LANDS

Gilbert F. White*

The rapidly spreading invasion of dry sectors of North America during recent years reveals that new factors are shaping man's view and use of this diversified territory of thin soils, sparse vegetation, and highly variable climate. Habitat changes are widely evident. Their consequences and the conditions which bear on decisions as to new uses are less apparent.

Arid lands are taken as areas with substantial mean moisture deficiency, including the semiarid lands, according to the Thornthwaite classification (Meigs, 1953). Displaying great variation in altitude, land form, and length of day, they have in common the three characteristics of mean deficiency in moisture, large variability in rainfall from year to year, and uncertainty as to the character of next season's weather. Closely associated with high risk and persistent uncertainty is a delicate equilibrium of climate, soil, vegetation, and water which makes the physical environment especially susceptible to drastic changes in the path of minor modifications by man in vegetal cover or water flow.

Several avenues of approach offer themselves to efforts to review current

* Dr. White is Professor of Geography at the University of Chicago, a post he has held since 1956. Before that, he had been President of Haverford College. A former President of the Association of American Geographers, he has been particularly concerned with the conservation of water resources and the problems of arid lands.

trends in the state of these lands and to inquire into what the future may hold for them as habitat. One approach is by regional investigation of trends in the entire complex of surface characteristics, including the works of man. A second approach is through inventory of major changes now in progress on the land surface. A third is through appraisal of factors which seem to play a role in human decisions as to management of these resources of water, land, air, plants, animals, and minerals. The most convenient avenue often is the inventory of current trends and their projection into the future on various assumptions. While readily projected, estimates of water use, irrigation extension, grazing-land deterioration, or city sprawl may obscure understanding of the basic natural processes which are at work. It is these rather than the ephemeral trends that challenge long-term appraisal.

This paper comments briefly on the current trends and examines in a little more detail the factors likely to affect future decisions. It does not attempt to summarize the regional studies which are available for scattered sectors of the arid lands.

The importance of regional studies is great, and their extension is urgently needed as the pace of landscape alteration accelerates. The kinds of investigation which have been made in the Sonoran Desert (Scheffey, 1958) or Lower California (Aschmann, 1959), or the broader reviews of sequence of occupance in southern California (Thomas, 1959), or in arid sectors of California (Gregor, 1959), or in southern Arizona (Wilson, 1962), differing considerably in their orientation and method, but sharing an interest in landscape and its changes, gradually will give a more incisive picture of the complex forces at work throughout the arid lands. There is an immense body of government reports describing conditions and opportunities for water or grazing use in dry sectors of the United States.[1] Drawing from such studies, it may be useful to ask what appear to be those factors distinctive to arid lands showing promise of shaping the choices man exercises in his management of areas of dry risk and ragged balance.

Five attempts have been made in recent years to assess major questions associated with occupance of arid lands. The two symposia sponsored in the United States by the AAAS (White, 1956; Hodge, 1963), the Mexican round table (Instituto Mexicano . . . , 1955), and the chapter in the UNESCO volume on history of arid lands by Logan (Logan, 1962) offer broad-brush reviews of the subject. At the 1960 UNESCO symposium an effort was made to canvass on a global scale the chief research problems associated with continued use and preservation of arid lands (UNESCO, 1962). Clawson's chapter in the AAAS symposium on "Aridity and Man" is especially comprehensive and thoughtful in dealing with problems in the United States. All of what is said in this paper must be viewed against that background. The regional investigations show a tremendous range in character of local conditions and in the nature of landscape change: flourishing mining of limited ground-

[1] Among the numerous reports are those on projects by the Bureau of Reclamation, Corps of Engineers, and Soil Conservation Service, and on range conditions by the Forest Service, and Bureau of Land Management.

water supplies in southern Arizona, slow rebuilding of degraded range vegetation in Utah, progressive destruction of commercial plants in Sonora, rapid invasion by city workers of waterless California desert. Government reports reveal gradual control of range deterioration, quickened interest in protection of places of natural beauty, and persistent investigation of ways of getting more water to dry lands. The scientific symposia repeatedly emphasize man's ignorance of critical links in the natural processes; the means of assessing evapotranspiration, the movement of water in unsaturated soils, the mechanism of precipitation.

It is significant that all four efforts in North America were stimulated by international concern with problems of arid-land use and development, a concern which in turn led to fresh and integrated attack upon them in the United States and Mexico. Unified assessment on a national scale thus owed its organization to the confrontation of American scientists with scientists from other countries who faced similar but distinctive problems of arid-land use. Perhaps there is a lesson here for any who seek a genuinely thoughtful assessment of future habitat: the underlying problems and basic issues seem more likely to be recognized if the range of choice for land and water use is first defined in a context which cuts across national lines and cultural barriers than if defined within a national and relatively homogeneous cultural community. Unconventional ideas and fresh approaches seem to flow from the broader approach.

CURRENT CHANGES IN LANDSCAPE

At least five great instruments of change are at work in arid lands today. In terms of extent, probably the management of the sparse grazing lands is the more pervasive. Closely related to it is development of transportation networks by construction of roads and airstrips. A third significant instrument is construction of residential dwellings in the desert and its margins. A fourth is the exploitation of mineral deposits. Fifth is the extension of irrigation lands and of water points into dry areas. All five of these are in varying degrees interrelated. Thus, road building into mesquite lands is associated with possible intensification of both grazing and seasonal residential land uses and may stimulate mineral development and demand for additional water.

All five are not likely to be of major significance in the same area but they occur in distinctive combinations. We have only begun to recognize the full impact of one upon any other. For example, the effect of irrigation expansion upon the use of grazing lands, while once considered to be highly salutory in terms of stabilization of grazing and, indeed, one of the aims which Powell had in view in seeking integrated use of the arid lands, has been found in some instances, in fact, to disrupt the grazing economy and to render irrigation agriculture itself less stable than had been anticipated (Beyer, 1957). There still is much to be learned of the interrelation of vegetation and soil with surface and underground water regimes. The consequences of extensions of residential areas in dry lands are only vaguely described, and before wide generalizations can be made it is necessary to measure the degree to which water is first retarded and then speeded by city asphalt and roofing and to which urban structures and land use affect or might assist the recharge of aquifers (Harris and Rantz, 1964).

While certain of the direct linkages among grazing, irrigation, roads, urban sprawl, and other aspects of the habitat are recognized, some are not yet measured, and others still are speculative. Certain of them, such as those involving water regimen, soil salinity, and vegetation, are extremely delicate. Little is

known as to how quickly and surely deterioration can be reversed once started. A deepening range arroyo or a paved mesa or a waterlogged valley soil therefore must be viewed as having largely unpredictable consequences for both biological communities and the expanding network of urban society.

A few gross figures can be given as to the magnitude of the changes currently in progress in the United States. The largest single owner of arid lands in the United States is the federal government. In the 179 million acres of federal lands under the management of the Bureau of Land Management the range is subject to various kinds of manipulation, the most important of which is setting annually, with the active participation of associations of ranchers, the carrying capacity and season of livestock use. There is no clear basis for judging the extent to which the range is deteriorating or improving under the management practices which now are followed. Only about 16 per cent is considered to be in good or better condition, 31 per cent in bad or poor condition, and 53 per cent in fair condition according to the Bureau's rough appraisal.[2] The Bureau has reported that the rate of deterioration appears to be radically smaller than in the first two decades of the century, and a modest program of improvement is under way. It estimates that trends are upward on about 15 per cent of the land, downward on 14 per cent, and static on the remaining 71 per cent. While specific improvements can be measured readily, their long-term effects are less evident, and the significance of changes in the permitted grazing load are undoubtedly greater but more difficult to assess.

When we take the last four years of record, it appears that in ten western

2 Unpublished estimates from U.S. Department of the Interior, Bureau of Land Management.

states weed and brush control is proceeding in the federal grazing lands at a rate of about 200,000 acres a year, representing in considerable measure a clearing of sagebrush, creosote bush, and mesquite for grazing purposes. In some instances this is an effort to counteract changes in brush resulting from control of fire over a long period of time; in controlling fire in recent decades, range managers have encountered trouble in maintaining grass cover. Furrowing and deep tillage of grazing lands is occurring on about 25,-000 acres per year. Pests and rodents were a subject of control operations on about 400,000 acres per year, chiefly in the New Mexico and Utah areas, until public controversy over the use of pesticides and its biological consequences halted the work in 1963. About 800 small water reservoirs are thrown up each year across dry watercourses, and somewhere in the neighborhood of 250 springs are developed or improved. The chief BLM improvements are summarized in Table 1. Similar data are not readily

TABLE 1. Federally owned land in ten western states: conservation and improvement programs—1960–63

State	Water management Reservoirs (No.)	Springs (No.)	Wells (No.)	Weed and brush control (Acres)	Furrowing and deep tillage (Acres)	Pest control (Acres)
Arizona	447	101	84	59,537	500	–
California	93	43	15	83,925	–	–
Colorado	421	231	18	62,555	15,909	66,775
Idaho	239	195	22	100,712	752	–
Montana	359	34	50	14,490	3073	114,806
Nevada	86	157	63	48,168	2507	200,000
New Mexico	499	15	128	140,351	58,823	817,868
Oregon	495	128	608	206,530	4414	6000
Utah	352	80	25	28,507	3533	116,070
Washington	No data					
Wyoming	340	37	102	31,718	8659	–
Total Ten states	3511	1045	1115	776,494	98,170	1,141,519

Source: Public Land Statistics, 1963, U.S. Department of the Interior, Bureau of Land Management

available for dry land under Forest Service management.

In the total acreage under federal ownership in the western states, it is not a large proportion which is directly affected by these programs, but at current rates of investment it is an amount which might be expected to exercise a major effect upon the character of the landscape over a period of several decades. Evidence is least satisfactory concerning the relation of range management practices to plant and animal communities. In many arid lands the rate of natural succession of plants is at best very slow, and the records are sparse. The data on animal populations over large areas, except for deer and other game animals, are meager. Because of the high local diversity in landscape types, generalization from the few detailed studies is likely to be speculative. The statistics on public improvements, therefore, are only one partial index to the magnitude of alteration in progress.

In twelve western states about 557 million acres are not owned by the federal government and are in some type of private management. About 70 per cent is in pasture, most but not all of it semi-arid. We have a partial record of changes which have taken place in the physical characteristics of lands under the agricultural conservation programs since 1936. These are summarized in Table 2. Almost four million acres were affected by contour tillage on range or pastureland. The control of competitive plants was attempted on forty-three million acres, chiefly in Texas. Altogether, efforts at improvement of the vegetal cover and control of erosion and measures for water conservation, including artificial seeding of rangeland, were carried on over twenty-one million acres during this period. In addition, more than half a million storage-type reservoirs were constructed, 92,000 new wells were built, and at least 50,000 springs and seeps were improved.

Out of the 381 million acres of pastureland in farms in twelve western states it seems reasonable to estimate that at least a third of the area has been directly affected by one or more of the agricultural conservation programs. These have changed in some degree the vegetable cover, the surface flow of water, and the storage of water in watercourses and shallow aquifers. The reservoirs alone would represent one storage area for every 700 acres of pastureland, if evenly distributed, and an evaporation loss of more than four million acre feet annually, an amount exceeding the mean yearly flow of the Colorado River in Texas. In the aggregate this is a massive alteration of surface-drainage pattern.

From figures on highway construction (Table 3), it is clear that the total expansion of highway networks in arid lands has been proceeding at a rapid rate

TABLE 2. Agricultural conservation practices in twelve western states (1936-1963)

Western states	Improvement of established cover to control erosion and conserve water	Summary of all new storage-type reservoirs	Livestock water development		Control of competitive plants	Contour tillage on range or pastureland
			New wells	Springs, seeps		
	1,000 acres	*Number*	*Number*	*Number*	*1,000 acres*	*Acres*
Arizona	54	17,336	1,767*	855	1,307	128,082
California	1,648	17,656	3,024	12,616	709	23,875
Colorado	1,675	33,227	11,475	5,662	469	1,332,588
Idaho	802	4,368*	421*	4,047*	276	706
Montana	2,023	53,273*	12,156*	11,657*	130	20,397
Nevada	197	4,327	630*	682	84	7
New Mexico	240	50,744	10,068	1,197	1,936	926,851*
Oregon	1,603	11,252*	1,017*	7,843*	258	1,229
Texas	9,578	312,963	40,095	842	37,687	1,330,303*
Utah	732	18,426*	968	2,074	351	12,786
Washington	1,644	3,193	412	3,538	109	719
Wyoming	1,148	44,707*	10,432*	5,013*	293	54,530
Total	21,344	571,472	92,465	56,026	43,609	3,832,073

* Includes data with respect to Emergency Conservation Measures (supplemental) in applicable years.

Source: *Agricultural Conservation Program, Summary by State, 1963,* U.S. Department of Agriculture, Washington, D.C. September, 1964.

TABLE 3. Changes in highway and street mileage for eleven western states, 1946–1961

State	Municipal mileage			Rural: Classified by type of surface								
				Non-surfaced mileage			Surfaced mileage			Total rural and municipal mileage		
	1961	1946	Percent change	1961	1946	Percent change	1961	1946	Percent change	1961	1946	Percent change
Arizona	5,119	1,324	287	21,303	22,105	−4	12,714	7,103	79	39,136	30,532	28
California	33,333	17,218	94	44,916	45,068	−0.3	71,949	52,853	36	150,198	115,149	30
Colorado	5,429	3,537	53	36,398	59,487	−39	37,010	16,280	127	78,837	79,304	−1
Idaho	2,424	1,536	58	15,411	19,493	−21	24,519	16,598	48	42,354	37,627	13
Montana	1,763	2,200	−20	44,937	52,298	−14	28,609	17,322	65	75,309	71,820	5
Nevada	1,045	418	150	30,561	19,485	57	12,997	4,280	204	44,603	24,183	84
New Mexico	3,055	1,266	141	46,275	53,546	−14	14,180	8,313	71	63,510	63,125	1
Oregon	5,638	4,467	26	28,102	31,586	−11	40,877	22,468	82	74,617	58,521	28
Texas	38,694	21,425	81	74,414	124,964	−40	119,901	71,651	67	233,009	218,040	7
Utah	3,950	3,151	25	15,217	15,794	−4	15,353	8,621	78	34,520	27,536	25
Wyoming	1,109	875	27	47,052	21,252	121	11,978	5,714	110	60,139	27,841	116
Total, 11 states	101,559	57,417	77	404,586	465,096	−13	390,096	231,203	69	896,232	753,678	19
U.S. Total*	444,837	316,536	41	945,199	1,505,212	−37	2,174,961	1,503,846	45	3,573,046	3,325,594	7
Percentage, 11 states of total U.S.	23	18		43	31		18	15		25	23	

* Not including Alaska and Hawaii.
Sources: U.S. Department of Commerce, Bureau of Public Roads, *Highway Statistics*, 1961, 1947.

in recent years by comparison with the density of the network in the 1930s, when it was conspicuously low. Between 1946 and 1961, the total highway mileage for eleven western states increased by one fifth, with the largest percentage gains in Nevada and Wyoming. This has been enhanced by road-access building programs in the national forests, and by road improvements in Bureau of Land Management areas in addition to the construction of state highway and county feeder roads. All of these involve an interruption of drainage channels and concentration of feeder flows at the infrequent times when rain causes surface runoff. All increase the accessibility of lands previously difficult to reach by auto.

The expansion of residential land use in the arid lands has been a prominent aspect of the pattern of American population growth in recent decades. Well recognized is the rapid rate of growth of population in southern California and Arizona, where rates of 130 per cent to 160 per cent were attained in the decades between 1940 and 1960. Between 1950 and 1960 the area in urban places in the arid zone appears to have doubled. The chief enlargement took place in Arizona, California, and Texas, and the major gains percentage-wise were in Arizona, Nevada, California, and Texas.[3]

Total expansion in mineral operations in the arid lands during recent years is modest by comparison with earlier activities and, with the exception of a few of the notable open-pit operations in Utah and Arizona, does not mark a conspicuous new aspect of use of these lands. Although the destructive placer opera-

tions have been reduced under public regulation, the total annual value of federal mineral leases has enlarged, indicating a growth of the operations with their accompanying transport and service improvements.

Approximately thirteen million acres of new land has been brought under irrigation since 1940, largely the result of federal programs. The net effect of the storage and regulatory activities associated with irrigation extension—hydroelectric development, flood control, and, in a few instances, navigation improvements—has been to regularize greatly the flow of the western streams and in some instances to bring the total consumption and withdrawal of water close to the amount of water available, although in many areas there has remained a significant margin of water available at high cost. The recent irrigation enterprises have been better planned than the earlier ones, are less destructive in inducing channel erosion, and are less likely to cause soil deterioration through salt accumulation and waterlogging. It has been estimated that as much as one quarter of the irrigated land may be adversely affected by salt (Dregne, 1963, p. 222). The effects of new irrigation upon prevailing agricultural patterns are still uncertain, as witness the experience with the Columbia Basin Project (Macinko, 1963). And their effectiveness in promoting a healthy quality of life on family-sized farms has been brought into doubt by the record of settlement in the face of economies of scale in larger units.

In noting these changes, no attempt has been made to suggest the social and natural consequences of any one of them. As already indicated, to do so would be an exceedingly complex task and one for which at best it would only be possible to offer partial explanations. We do not understand the full implications of the pasture management programs, or the effects upon downstream channels and

---

[3] This estimate was compiled from the area of incorporated and unincorporated places in the arid zone of the United States (defined by Meigs) as recorded in the U.S. Bureau of the Census (1962) and U.S. Bureau of the Census (1963). It includes areas that have not been built up, but is probably a rough measure of urban expansion into the arid lands.

aquifers of engineering regulation of stream flow, or of extension of urban occupance into previously wild desert areas such as the Antelope Valley in California.

One of the developments especially difficult to assess is the growth of a new kind of nomadism which finds a peculiar cultural expression in the North American landscape in contrast to the traditional nomadism of North Africa and Southwest Asia. A combination of road construction, mounting income, enlarged leisure time, and improvement of road and trail transport has led to easy and ephemeral access to large sectors of the arid lands which previously were touched only rarely by humans. This was shown most dramatically in the uranium explorations of the four-corners area in the 1940s and it continues not only in the interest of mineral exploration but, more important, in connection with recreational demands of the growing adjacent urban populations.

FACTORS AFFECTING ARID LAND
DECISIONS

It may be helpful to think of man's decision to manage arid land as an intricate process in which he considers a range of possible uses, assesses the resources with which he has to deal, applies some parts of the technology and organization at his command, winnows out the measures which seem inefficient in meeting his economic aims, readjusts his institutions to serve the desired uses, and confronts the effects of his action on other areas. These six aspects of decision making are closely related to one another in the course of arriving at a final choice of resource use.

For example, a farmer on a semiarid alluvial fan may have the choice of planting any one of several dry farming crops or of putting down a well for irrigation. His decision will rest in part upon his judgment of the range of uses which are available to him given these resources, his appraisal of the resources available, the kind of technology he thinks he can employ, his estimate of the economic returns in prospect, and his judgment of the effects of his works on users of the available water and soil nearby or downstream. All of this takes place not only in a cultural system of customary behavior but in a social system of education, economic exchange, and property control that restrains certain actions and encourages others. One farmer may consciously review a few aspects of his choice, while others may act entirely according to the custom of their group, and still others make careful economic calculations of the probable consequences. To recognize the factors which affect these decisions in handling resources of grass, soil, and water is a basic step toward understanding the conditions in which the habitat may be altered in future.

When governments make the decisions —as they do in launching new irrigation programs or regulating the grazing on open grasslands—the process of choice may be more evident but the same elements are present.

A major aspect of the decision process is perception by the resource manager, whether he be a farmer, a government administrator, or a legislator. His views set the conditions of choice as surely as natural features impose certain constraints on his action. If a farmer does not recognize the possibility of plowing up his land to convert range to wheatland, as is so common in southeastern Utah today, he cannot canvass the technical or economic aspects of doing so. If an urban industrialist does not recognize that he has access to significant shallow aquifers, he will continue to depend upon municipal surface sources. Thus, perception becomes an important and primary aspect of analysis of the factors entering into decisions.

A prominent feature of perception of range of choice of arid lands in North America is the progressively widening view of the number of choices open for the use of any piece of arid land. This broadened view is a product, in part, of the lengthening experience of native sons who have had opportunity to compare their environment with similar arid environments in other parts of the world. It is compounded by the increasing admixture of migrants from radically different environments in the East who bring the experience of travel and work in overseas arid lands to situations where secondary and tertiary production overshadows the wresting of a livelihood from the soil. Added to this, and an expression of it, is the increasing emphasis by state and federal agencies upon multiple-purpose management of forests, land, and water in arid as well as nonarid zones. We still are far from the kind of sophisticated integration of land use within areas which Powell called for in his classic report, but we have in fact brought to bear technologies and techniques of land use which permit a degree of diversity and complexity in arid land management which was hardly dreamed of in Powell's time (Powell, 1879). The important point is that the dry terrain is no longer considered as subject only to one or two exploitive uses such as grazing and mining. It has become a colorful land of diverse opportunity.

Residential use no longer is regarded as limited to a few favored urban sites. Potential recreational use ranges as far as road and jeep permit. The net effect of these new views, growing from lengthening time and area of experience, and from public support of multiple use, is to expand the number of possible uses to which the arid landscape may be subjected.

Perception of environment also is

changing to a remarkable degree, and with the extension of current scientific assessment and public information techniques the human view of natural features may be expected to evolve even more rapidly in future. Although topographic mapping still is far from complete, and soil, biota, and cover surveys are few and spotty, the main aspects of the landscape are being charted. Public information and education are making the results known. Recreational travel and mobile employees are spreading the direct experience with nuances of environment.

The climatic risks now are more clearly identified than when the Great Plains rashly were dismissed as desert or embraced as sites for a new forest belt. Experience with a variety of risks and uncertainty has enlarged and seems to be differently related to perception of aridity. The recognition of drouth hazard appears to shift from extremely arid to semiarid regions (Saarinen, 1965). In large measure, the increasing refinement of perception of environment has led to greater and more intensive encroachments upon arid lands. The progressive plowing of semiarid lands is one example; notwithstanding searing drouths in the thirties and fifties, farmers have become more adept at gambling on the chances of wheat loss in an upcoming year. The encroachment by residential users on floodplains and of irrigation farmers upon inadequate aquifers is another example. Some of these ventures spring from ignorance or faulty perception, but in each case there apparently has been more detailed recognition of risk associated with willingness to accept this risk by either bearing the loss from floods and exhausted water supplies or by looking to government agencies for remedial works.

In this regard, confidence in new technology is playing an increasing role. Curiously enough, water as a limiting factor seems to be declining in importance, although it is common to speak of an impending hydrologic curb upon economic growth in the southwestern United States. The shift has taken place in part because the practicability of conveying water over long distances has been enhanced and in part because the technical possibilities of carrying on intensive land uses without large amounts of water are increasing For example, it is not quite fanciful to suggest that situations are approaching in which urban land use for residential purposes can operate with a closed system of water for most household purposes, drawing on outside and limited ground water sources only for drinking water. Industrial plants are progressively reducing the amount of water required for cooling and other transportation purposes, and, indeed, the practicability of air as a substitute for water in the cooling process appears in more and more industries. To be sure, the gap between these new technological advances and their direct adoption in the field also continues to be large. It is especially so in the agricultural sector, and least in urban sectors. The social problem of how to reduce the gap between knowledge and its earthy application probably is the most significant one facing the development of low-income areas, and even in the United States it is apparent in continued heavy use of irrigation water and continued degradation of arid soils.

In general, increasing technical capacity for nomadism and for rapid and quick transitions from one type of arid-land occupancy to another renders the future more subject to drastic and rapid shift. Confidence grows in those technological prospects whether they be yet undiscovered means to curb Colorado River reservoir silting or newly emerging devices to link cheap nuclear power with desalting. Paradoxically, as scientists in the United States become more acutely aware of their ignorance of the sensitivities in the ecosystems which would be affected by water management, there is growing public interest in massive engineering measures which would promise a kind of sweeping solution to looming water shortages. The lively attention to desalting research and to schemes for interbasin transfers from Pacific Northwest to western Gulf is symptomatic. Directing confident support to such dramatic technological ventures may, in fact, stimulate rather than reduce the very shortages they are intended to forestall, for they divert attention from other less appealing but practical technologies.

One of the momentous advances in economic analysis of resource management in arid lands has been recognition of the changing value of water and of the higher productivity of water when used for recreational and industrial purposes than for agriculture (Wollman, 1962). Notwithstanding this recognition, the existing and large continuing commitments for water management lie in the direction of expanding and solidifying irrigation.

The recent set of contracts for development research for design of a nuclear power plant combined with desalting in the southern California area may be a turning point in federal policy in the United States with respect to arid lands. In undertaking these contracts the Department of the Interior, in effect, declared its primary concern with the production of water at modest cost for use in a metropolitan area without subjugating that aim to agricultural development, flood control, or navigation. Although the earlier irrigation investments by the federal government were a major form of regional income redistribution, this new form of investment extends the former broad policy of support of infrastructure in the Southwest by taking explicit account of water supply for urban areas.

A more sophisticated economic analysis combined with greater range of technology is decreasing the capitalization period for investment planning in dealing with water and soil, and thereby encouraging attention to smaller, flexible works. When the full financial cost of construction and maintenance is tallied up, there is incentive to favor the projects which are used to capacity quickly and may be replaced as rendered obsolete by new technology. These considerations work against the massive projects in future.

Recognition of intimate linkages among the several uses of resources in arid lands is being sharpened. The horizon of areal planning has been broadened while time horizon tends to be reduced. We are beginning to see the full implications of Colorado River water management upon land use not only in southern California and Arizona but in Mexico, and we are seeing, after three decades of studies and interstate negotiations, the full complexity of relationship between land and water management in the upper Rio Grande. Thinking about unified water plans for the Southwest or the entire group of western states has begun to take form, although, unfortunately, in the context of political maneuvers for water allocations following the Supreme Court decision in the Colorado River case. Appraisal of the economies of irrigation, power, and municipal water supply continues to obscure the assessment of less tangible effects upon habitat.

In the United States, institutional framework and policy seem ill adjusted to the needs on a regional scale and especially so in the context of expanding metropolitan areas. Management of rural grazing lands under the Bureau of Land Management and management of peripheral urban lands by private operators, within the loose constraints established by county and city agencies, no longer serve the requirements of rapid growth and changing uses. Even where a single purpose is dominant, federal management devices are slow to adjust to the new conditions and perceptions, as witness the

difficulties of organizing suitable research, tenure, pricing, and control for the grazing lands (Caleif, 1960). Metropolitan organizations are confronted with an intricacy and magnitude of problems that were rarely imagined a decade ago. These institutional obstacles become acute when the selection of alternative measures for handling arid-land resources, such as drouth insurance as a substitute for additional irrigation or floodplain regulation as a substitute for additional dams, are arrayed along with traditional engineering works. The integration of one engineering program with another, as in the Central Valley of California, in itself encounters strong obstacles of organization and policy, and the extension of the machinery to cope with nonengineering measures calls for reorganization that will be a long time in coming.

These are broad generalizations about the character of decisions affecting management of arid-land resources. To some extent they may apply to any western society with high levels of income and technology. However, they have a special significance in relation to an area which more than any other portion of the North American continent is subject to risk of annual resource deficiency, high annual variability, and dramatic uncertainty.

In dealing with regions where the short history of industrial man already has provoked accelerated gouging of gullies, and wholesale conversion of plant cover in the interest of grazing and mining, and has spread a scabrous net of shabby dwellings in the desert, it is important to recognize that man's view of the number and combination of possible resource uses is expanding while his perception of the diversity of landscape and of spatial linkages among his works is growing in accuracy. Technical advances increasingly make possible rapid and massive means of husbanding or destroying the thin veneer of soil and vegetation and of controlling movement of scanty water supplies, but they also enlarge the number of tools at man's disposal. Some of these are small and flexible. Because the equilibrium of the elements in the landscape is so sensitive to interference, the human capacity for both improvement and degradation enlarges in a setting in which regional integration of management measures from watershed to delta, and from wilderness upland to city plain is unquestionably essential to the attainment of new equilibria. Urban growth and economic efficiency criteria foster the adoption of short-term measures selected among a wide range of opportunities. The possible actions of man on the arid landscape thus multiply and become further flung but possibly easier to reverse from a technical standpoint. Any thoughtful effort to predict the future course of human decisions to advance or retreat in the arid lands must take account of these factors which promise to affect the choices lying ahead.

BIBLIOGRAPHY

Aschmann, Homer. 1959. The Central Desert of Baja California: Demography, Ecology. Berkeley, Calif.

Beyer, Jacquelyn. 1957. Integration of Grazing and Crop Agriculture: Resource Management Problems in the Uncompahgre Valley Irrigation Project. Univ. Chicago, Dept. Geog. Res. Pap. 52.

Caleif, Wesley. 1960. Private Grazing and Public Lands. Chicago.

Dregne, Harold E. 1963. Soils of the Arid West. In: Hodge, Carle, ed. Aridity and Man.

Gregor, Howard F. 1959. Push to the Desert. Sci. 129:1329–39.

Harris, E. E., and Rantz, S. E. 1964. Effect of Urban Growth on Streamflow Regimen of Permanente Creek, Santa Clara County, California. U.S.G.S. Water Supply Pap. 1591-B. U.S. Govt. Print. Off., Wash., D.C.

Hodge, Carle, ed. 1963. Aridity and Man. Wash., D.C.

Institute Mexicano de Recursos Naturales Removables. 1955. Mesa Redondas Sobre Problemas de las Zonas Aridas de Mexico. Mexico City.

Logan, Richard F. 1962. Post-Columbian Developments in the Arid Regions of the United States of America. A History of Land Use in Arid Regions. UNESCO, Paris.

Macinko, George. 1963. The Columbia Basin Project: Expectations, Realizations, Implications. Geog. Rev. LIII (2):185–99.

Meigs, Peveril. 1953. World Distribution of Arid and Semi-arid Homoclimates. Reviews of Research on Arid Zone Hydrology. UNESCO, Paris.

Powell, J. W. Report on the Lands of the Arid Regions of the United States: 1879.

Saarinen, Thomas F. Perception of Drought Hazard in the Great Plains. Univ. of Chicago, Dept. Geog. Res. Pap. (in press).

Savini, John, and Kammerer, J. C. 1961. Urban Growth and the Water Regimen. U.S.G.S. Water Supply Pap. 1591-A. U.S. Govt. Print. Off., Wash., D.C.

Scheffey, Andrew J. W. 1958. Natural Resources and Government Policy in Coahuila, Mexico. Ann Arbor, Mich.

Thomas, William L., Jr., ed. 1959. Man, Time and Space in Southern California. Annals of the Assn. of Amer. Geographers (suppl.), vol. 49, no. 3, pt. 2.

UNESCO. 1962. The Problems of the Arid Zone. Proc. of Paris Symp., Arid Zone Res., XVIII. UNESCO, Paris.

U.S. Bureau of the Census. 1962. City and County Data Book.

———— 1963. Land Area and Population of Incorporated Places of 2500 or More, April 1, 1950. U.S. Census Ser. 5.

White, Gilbert F., ed. 1956. The Future of Arid Lands. Amer. Assn. for the Adv. of Sci., Wash., D.C.

Wilson, Andrew W. 1962. The Impact of an Exploding Population on a Semi-developed State: the Case of Arizona. Ariz. Rev. of Bus. and Pub. Admin. II:5–9.

Wollman, Nathaniel, ed. 1962. The Value of Water in Alternative Uses. Albuquerque, N.M.

General Discussion

GRAHAM: Let us now open the discussion. The panelists will stand ready to answer questions relating to their papers. Or there may be other questions which you would like to discuss among yourselves.

FOSBERG: Perhaps Dr. Bear could explain why it is not important that all lands are not alike—granting his point that human ingenuity is the important thing in the productivity of land rather than the character of the land itself.

BEAR: What I meant was that with modern machinery at our disposal, and man working to improve plants and fertilizers that can be used and so on, you can take any piece of land that is level and make it fairly productive. It is just a matter of mechanics. Some acres would be more productive than others as they come out of nature, but productivity can be evened up materially by the actions of man.

SEARS: There is a difference in energy and capital input. I suppose that was what you had in mind, Dr. Bear.

BEAR: Yes, there is a tremendous difference there. We have these things at our disposal. If we are prepared to use them, we can overcome the disadvantages the soil might have in the beginning. Not necessarily all the disadvantages, but many of them.

HUBBERT: An interesting example of variation in agricultural productivity occurs in central Illinois. A few tens of miles south of Urbana the terminal moraine of the last, or Wisconsin, glaciation crosses the state. At least up until a few years ago this line was a boundary between agricultural prosperity and poverty. North of the line, where plant nutrients had not been leached from the soil, one saw rich farms and prosperous-looking farm buildings. South of that line, poverty was visibly evident. This is a region of uniform topography and climate; the difference is due solely to the leaching of plant nutrients from the older Illinoian glacial drift.

I am not sure whether this handicap has since been overcome, but I doubt it.

BEAR: I would say today that line isn't quite as sharp as it used to be now that modern agriculture has been put to work there. What you are dealing with there is, of course, the more recent the glaciation, the newer and more fertile the soil. The older the soil, the farther south you get in the United States, the greater your problem of adding the necessary nutrients. You have to build up organic material because you are dealing with an older soil. Any line of glaciation will show a difference of that type immediately when the soil is put into production. But that line can be redrawn after a while.

FOSBERG: I could give a simple and categorial answer to the question about the Illinois and Wisconsin glaciation. I drove over that land less than eight months ago. The line is just as sharp as it ever was. You are in a different landscape when you cross it, economically.

NICHOLSON: I wonder if Dr. Bear could comment on the very important matter we touched on yesterday, in his paper, that it had been found necessary to retire large acreages, that formerly were farmland, from crop production because you can get greater production from smaller acreages. This statement as it stands is related to the past. Is it possible to see the prospects for the continuance of that trend? Is it going to intensify, or is there reason to think it may be leveling off? This is important for land use, whether one can foresee a continuance of the trend toward withdrawal of farmland.

BEAR: At the moment we see this trend continuing for the withdrawal of land from agriculture because of the increased efficiency of the farmer with machinery and fertilizers at his disposal; putting farms together in the larger units also increases their efficiency of operation. At the moment, I think we can say more land can be withdrawn from agriculture and still meet our needs.

NICHOLSON: Does it follow from that that there would be a qualitative concentration, that the economics would dictate a concentration on the better land? Here is a statement, from Bear's paper, referred to yesterday: ". . . man-harvested crops are being grown on some fifty million acres of Class V–VIII land that should not be used for this purpose."

Does this imply that these technological possibilities forbid such good to be continued in agricultural production without incurring economic penalty?

BEAR: There is an economic penalty. After an area has been put into agricultural production, the people cling to the area, whether it is the most economic one or not. Once you get them established in an area producing crops, with farm lines drawn, and so on, it is pretty hard to displace them —they are likely to stay there indefinitely.

What we should probably have done originally was never allow them to get in there; nevertheless, they did get in there and started farming. They will be there for a long time and their competitive position is not very good.

CLAWSON: With the tremendous decrease in numbers of farms, and yet the total acreage in farms remaining essentially constant, we are getting larger and larger farms in this country. The average size has more than doubled in the last thirty years. Some of us think it would quadruple in the next thirty years. This is opening up enormous possibilities for land-use changes within the same farm. These may be more important over the next generation than the shifts between farming regions. There will be plenty of the latter. When you get this substantial enlargement in farm size, then it is within the decision-making power of the farmer to make the land-use shifts within it.

Whereas the average size of farms for many years was around 150 acres and it is now somewhat in excess of 300 acres for the whole United States, we may well get up to 1000 to 1200 acres national average. The way you use 1200 acres in one farm may be quite different than the way you used it when it was in eight different farms. I think this offers interesting possibilities for change over the next generation.

BEAR: In Pennsylvania the average-size farm in the early days was eighty to 160 acres. That was adequate for the early pioneers to make a living. As time went on, and the second and third generations came into being on these farms, the younger folks tended to disappear and the old folks remained with the farm until they got so old they couldn't take care of it any more, and then it was sold to someone who would put farms together in a larger unit.

Whereas these original farms were used for growing a variety of crops for market purposes, one large unit that was developed was used for three purposes. One use was to grow heifers, which meant that the land suited to it would be put into grazing. These heifers were grown for use someplace else to replace dairy cows as they grew older. The second use was the growing of Christmas trees. The third use was growing regular forest trees. In other words, instead of having twelve small farms, each with a diversified system of farming, you had one big farm with a definite program.

FISHER: I would like to challenge Dr. Bear and other ecologists and economists to develop a new system of land classification on grounds that the traditional eight classes really are not very useful.

Mr. Brinser yesterday noted that the most valuable farmland wouldn't probably rate very high: the potato land of Maine and the tobacco land of Maryland and the sandy soil of New Jersey, and so forth. What we really need is a different system on the basis of which to make these broad generalizations that are being tried.

It is a little like taking a group of boys and classifying them very carefully according to height. This has very limited usefulness. I suppose it is useful for determining which ones would be good basketball players, but it doesn't have any very general usefulness.

I would like to challenge people to come up with a different basic system because I don't think this traditional eightfold classification will carry the load that we are trying to put on it.

GRAHAM: I quite agree with you. The eight-class system was developed for a specific purpose—namely, to indicate the susceptibility of the land to deterioration through use—and it does not satisfy the kinds of demands we are talking about here.

DARLING: I felt that from Dr. Bear's paper that we were up against a fundamental philosophical point here as to whether we wish to make land produce anything anywhere. You could grow bananas on an ice island in the arctic; but why? Do we really want to make good farms on areas of the Laurentian shield? I don't think so.

We can use rather poor ground in Florida and farm it hydroponically, as it is being farmed. You are really not buying good land there, but space and climate where, by a certain kind of fertilizer treatment, you can produce enormous crops.

What are we trying to do? To produce anything anywhere? Or are we using our heightened perception of using the best for what it can do, and of acknowledging the social calls upon large areas that do not produce? The Laurentian shield and many, many places within Central America and in the United States are obviously headed for social purposes of recreation areas and national parks and that kind of thing. I don't think we need bother—at this stage in history, anyway—with the possible productive powers of what we usually call poor land. There is so much else we can do with it in shaping the future environment of North America. The ultimate criterion of population density will not be food, anyway, but space.

GLACKEN: I think Dr. Fisher brought up an interesting point, and Dr. Graham as well. If I interpret correctly, you seem to feel this old system of land classification was more centered on the early history of soil erosion in the early days of the Roosevelt Administration; what sort of things do you think should be done to divide the new system?

GRAHAM: This isn't easy to answer. I will say that the old system was primarily directed at the management of soil, and therefore at the management of crop and tame pastureland. It was actually never very applicable either to forest or to open-range management.

The difference being, it seems to me, that when you are dealing with the conventional crops and the tame pastures which require rotation and soil management, you are in fact dealing with soil which can be amended, which can be fertilized, which can be turned over, its tilth and composition changed. You are actually manipulating the soil.

When you move from these annual cultivated crops to native perennial vegetation, as on range and forestland, you are no longer dealing with direct manipulation of soil; you are dealing with the manipulation of vegetation. The eight-class system was never really adapted to the management of native perennial vegetation.

If we want a land-use classification which will consider not only those basic traditional uses and changes in the use of land, but also recreation, open space, suburban residential development, industrial siting, and all the rest of it, we do indeed need a new kind of land classification. Formulating this is going to require the close collaboration of ecologists, economists, and planners.

This could well be a job to be done as a result of this Conference if at the end of it we agree that this is what we want to do.

FOSBERG: A classification to satisfy a dozen different purposes may not be the best thing to satisfy any of them. Perhaps it might be a good idea to decide which purposes we consider important, and devise a classification individually to satisfy each of these purposes, rather than to try to make something that fits the whole gamut of land-use fields.

GRAHAM: Maybe there is an analogy to the soil survey which is a classification of soils and their potentialities. These can be interpreted for greatly different kinds of use, and are so interpreted. If the ecologist has anything to contribute as a base which can then be used for interpretation for various purposes, I would say that a classification is a possibility. It would give a common ground from which to depart. So far the ecologist has not suggested this.

FOSBERG: Some of the Australian ones have.

GRAHAM: In terms of land form, yes.

CLAWSON: Two points, one of which Mr. Fosberg has partially made. The classifications we have today are probably more useful for the elements, which we can read and examine in other ways, than they are for the final classification.

The land classification, as you say, was designed really to measure erosion hazard and management practices necessary to control. It isn't the same, for instance, as a productivity classification—although, if you made a productivity classification in different areas, there would frequently be considerable conformity.

The sort of thing Richard Meier was referring to yesterday is to classify lands in relationship to their capacity to respond to certain kinds of inputs—which is a different kind of thing.

I quite agree with Mr. Fosberg that it would be difficult indeed to come up with a single classification for all purposes. I should add further that some of us in Washington have been working on a book—now in press—trying to outline a much more comprehensive system of land-use information than has ever been available in the past. And this is one of the very points that we make—that it is impossible to classify land according to its natural qualities without some idea of the uses to be made of it.

The combinations of natural qualities are so great, the range of qualities is so wide, and the importance of different combinations for different purposes is so varied that a universal classification of natural qualities of land is an impossibility, or at least it would be so extraordinarily complex as not to be useful.

HALL: I am not an economist and I really want to make a plea for economics in this study. It seems to me that we are dealing with a problem of competing land uses, of very many different uses—not many types of agriculture perhaps, but other land uses besides agriculture. And that because of this, *no* system of classification—based on one set of criteria—could ever be really useful.

You have to find a way of comparing the value of land for all these different uses by means of one factor. The only factor we have been able to discover, in this case, is dollars. The question is, really, what would be the value of Manhattan Island for agriculture? We might be able to have a soil classification of Manhattan Island, but it wouldn't be very useful.

If you could develop the concept of land use based on the rent which it pays, in different uses, this, it seems to me, would be a more useful approach than a simple physical approach in the terms of land-use classification.

WHITE: One of the striking aspects of the sorts of land classification to which we have been referring—the old soil-erosion reconnaissance survey, or the Department of Agriculture land-use productivity classification, or the soil survey—is that each has built into it a whole series of assumptions of a social character as to what technology will be applied: as to the conditions of farm organization, as to the conditions of markets—assumptions that for the most part go unstated.

Perhaps the most important aspect of these classifications is the nature of these assumptions. If we could begin to think of classifications which confronted the assumptions and dealt explicitly and honestly with the implications of varying the assumptions slightly, we might then come out with a whole series of subsets of classifications which would be useful for particular land uses.

I think we see this mainly in the kind of classification that has been made of water resources. Assumptions were made, for example, in predicting the future capacity for water use in the United States that certain price systems would apply, that certain technologies would apply, that certain quite inefficient public controls would apply.

But the estimates then are taken without any serious examination of these assumptions.

DANSEREAU: We need a system much more than a classification. In fact, a classification is not possible without a system. What we need to put into a classification are the relevant features. What do we need to know about climate, about topography, about soil, about potential and actual vegetation, and about history, human occupancy, and the regional economy?

What we can't seem to accept in existing classifications—the IGU classification or others—is the fact that they are weighted toward a certain economy such as the agricultural economy. The Australian land survey, for instance, for quite obvious reasons is geared to the pastoral and agricultural economy.

The only way of freeing ourselves from that is establishing an empirical system such as Köppen originally devised. Köppen's original idea was a system, not a classification. A classification has been built upon the system. Küchler never built a true classification on his system. He continues to apply it in a sliding-scale fashion. Maybe this is the sort of thing we need.

SEARS: I think this relates to something you brought up earlier, the problem of defining a region. In other words, the region is not merely a natural phenomenon; it is a cultural phenomenon, too.

DURDEN: As more North American environments are brought into urban spheres I think that most broad regional classifications and much regional planning are meaningless in relation to the real things that happen on the landscape. Specific site evaluations—particularly those of entrepreneurs—seem to be more important. We have tried to regionalize, but our concepts of regions really may not be germane. Questions of site classifications seem much more pressing issues than regional classifications, at least if we are to better understand the actions of entrepreneurs who are leading urbanization and the resort colonization of remote habitats.

BRANDWEIN: I want now to question Dr. Budowski, but I can't avoid making a comment, that the chemical industry has not been accounted for in this classification, nor the physicist. I think you had a different classification when horses drew the plow than when you had bulldozers, and I think evolution of technology is not over yet.

I was going to ask Dr. Budowski what assumptions he was making in his suggestions for improvement of the Middle American situation. I refer particularly to your suggestion of training of leaders. Leaders for what? To what end? I think you were making vast assumptions there which I would benefit from having clarified.

BUDOWSKI: Maybe I could begin from the other end—that is, what kind are the present leaders?—and conclude there is room for improvement. We might improve essentially by looking at past examples from more advanced countries.

I would suggest we replace the people now in leadership positions dealing with technical matters with people who attain that leadership position because of—at least in part—their technical merits. Mere political leadership is not good enough and it lacks continuity.

This situation should be amended by an adequate provision of people with high technical background and who still will have a good enough grasp of the political situation to take over.

Right now these people do not exist. There is a vacuum. And this vacuum of course is neatly filled by politicians.

BRANDWEIN: You are implying that a scientist-politician, socioeconomist, is the type you want to get at?

BUDOWSKI: Yes. Maybe I shouldn't go too far. Very seldom has a good scientist also been a good politician. I would say, at least, politicians need some basic knowledge of important ecological problems, and a knowledge of how to use scientific findings. This would be certainly a better compromise than just dealing with political pressures from certain groups which are not scientifically minded and are not even planning-minded.

DANSEREAU: It seems to me this is a civil-service problem more than anything else; the situation you describe is identical in Europe and in North America.

Ministers come and go. But the makers of policy are the civil servants. Some countries have produced a high grade of civil servant, and have been able to attract the right men in the right jobs.

It seems to me that Latin America could well operate in that way. I don't doubt that it has in some cases.

BUDOWSKI: Yes, only it should proceed not only by security of tenure, but also by merit. In other words, people should not keep their position just because there is a civil-service security and no one can remove them. This is the other extreme.

CALDWELL: I have seen a good deal in the past fifteen years of effort to improve and develop civil-service and administrative systems in the so-called underdeveloped countries. This is what I have been primarily involved in before becoming interested more directly in the kind of thing we are discussing here.

If I read Dr. Budowski's paper correctly, and understand some of the things that Dr. Vogt and others have been saying, and if I also draw conclusions from what I have seen, I think it might not be getting too far out to say that some of the smaller countries in Central America—and perhaps some other places in the world—are headed for what we might call economic receivership. These countries are not large enough or rich enough to postpone the day of reckoning through military adventures. I think the situation in El Salvador, Costa Rica, or Guatemala is quite different from that of the government of Indonesia which could stave off intervention, internal or external by a series of political and military adventures.

I suspect that we may be faced within the latter part of this century with the necessity for international intervention—either through the United Nations or through the Organization of American States—in countries that have reached the point where they cannot help themselves.

It is a difficult problem to develop a wise and effective indigenous leadership in a country like Guatemala or Honduras. The historical and cultural bases of politics in these countries offers a poor prognosis for ability to cope with the real social and environmental problems that now confront them.

Someone ought to be addressing himself to the ways in which international assistance can be more effectively used in smaller countries.

One of the elements in this, it seems to me, was implicit in something that Dr. Fisher said yesterday. When we move into a country with international economic development programs, we so often move in with a series of discrete resources development programs—power, agriculture, elementary education—with comparatively little coordination among them. Such coordination as is effected through the American-aid program with its country team and country plan usually reflects *our* notions of the proper basis of coordination, not necessarily the prevailing viewpoint in the aided country.

I don't think that the United States is going to be able to move in unilaterally in many of these countries that go into receivership. In fact, there may be rather strong anti-United States feeling in many of them. It will be more likely a job of international collective intervention.

If we do not have some kind of guidelines, if the colleges and the economists have not been able to converse and find their common points of understanding, as Kenneth Boulding suggests that they should, we will be poorly prepared to apply what we now know in these countries. There are at least two parts to this particular challenge of receivership.

One of them—certainly the fundamental one—is to develop the kinds of guidelines that would assist an integrated approach in some manner to the reconstruction of the economies. This obviously means the involvement of people in the country; it means that through some kind of educational program, and technical assistance to people who already have some background in national planning, we can carry on work that is now underway through the Alliance for Progress and the Organization of American States, to conceptualize what the future environments and economies of these countries may be.

Our second challenge is to do some thinking, perhaps speculative at this stage, about the nature of institutional arrangements which will be feasible for this kind of undertaking.

I think Dr. Budowski's paper is a very depressing one from the point of view of the immediate prospect. But if we proceed as I think we have in these sessions—on the assumption that our job is to find some solutions or to explore solutions rather than to simply resign ourselves to a view of hopelessness in the situation—then we face a tremendous challenge.

VOGT: I would agree somewhat with what Dr. Caldwell has said, except that I doubt that many of these countries will accept intervention, even if they recognize the fact that they are bankrupt, as indeed some of them already are. In most of these countries there is a reserve of skilled agronomists, foresters, engineers, and so on, although these skills are in many cases drawing well over half of their gross national product from the land, and perhaps over 90 per cent of their foreign exchange, none of the Central American countries spends as much as 4 per cent of its governmental budget on agriculture.

Land management in these countries is far more difficult than it is here in the United States. They are using up—they are living on the capital rather than developing their agriculture. They are losing the soil, forests, and so on. Perhaps what Dr. Budowski has in mind is the education of the oligarchies that essentially run these countries, so that they will make use of the brains and the technology that are available to them—and that are not being used now.

MEIER: I have been looking around for new growth, new sources of dynamism in the international zone; so far government has been mentioned, and government does seem to introduce some of this willingness to intervene or at least to interact.

One idea has been left out completely, and it is probably closer to academics than government: that of the international corporation. There has probably been a growth rate of between 5 and 10 per cent a year in international corporations—and a much stronger growth rate in those that are more technically inclined, operating on the international scene, than the average during this particular period. They are also creating a kind of international civil service which is technically oriented. It is coming directly out of the universities.

If you make any projection into the future, you will see that we will need a far more educated and sensitive group of international corporate servants—they aren't quite civil servants—than we can find at the moment.

BUDOWSKI: I would like to comment on what Mr. Caldwell has said. My point was to say that political leaders should take more notice of potential scientific advisors.

Even now, as Mr. Vogt said, these people exist in the countries but they are discouraged from participating in government on planning activities for many reasons. One of them—maybe the underlying reason—is that there is in each country a tremendous mass of illiterate peasants, which causes instability and does not encourage programs directed by scientists.

As a result, these scientists stay away. They are good scientists—they can get good jobs somewhere else. It is not promising for them to become involved in political affairs.

This is a very different situation from the United States, for instance, where we see people with good jobs in science who are willing to go into government for much lower pay because they feel they can be effective. It is almost the reverse, I would say, in Middle America. They just don't think they can do a good job. Sometimes that means a vacuum is left and this vacuum is occupied by people of much lower capacity.

If some pressure could be exerted on present political leaders—and I don't mean that these political leaders have to be scientifically trained; I only request that they listen to scientific people—then this would probably change the situation because at that time scientists would feel it was time to come in and advise on programs, particularly through national planning boards.

NICHOLSON: I would like to ask a question on Budowski's table of increase of population. The two countries that have the lowest rates are Jamaica and Puerto Rico, which are down to 1.6. Suppose we could get the other countries down to something of that order in five or seven years, which I take it would be a very optimistic assumption. What sort of problem would there then be? You have an enormous peak of younger population here coming up to employable age.

Are you going to get into problems of the peaking of this population which will last over twenty years, fifty years, or seventy years? Has anyone done a tabulation on what would happen if you got these rates of natural increase under control fairly quickly? How long would it continue to have an unmanageable effect on the economy?

BUDOWSKI: I don't know about that.

VOGT: I don't think anyone has assumed that there is any chance of getting this under control quickly—anyone who knows the situation.

BOULDING: The real problem here is the nature of the knowledge process in these societies. There are two kinds of knowledge, one of which might be called folk knowledge, which is the kind of knowledge you acquire in face-to-face contact in the ordinary business life, a lot of which is perfectly true. There is nothing untrue, necessarily, about folk knowledge.

The other kind is what might be called sophisticated knowledge which you acquire in the scientific culture. One of the problems we face here is that the links between the folk knowledge and the scientific knowledge are tenuous. The scientific subculture is propagated by means which actually destroy the folk knowledge and do not link into it.

This is the trouble with the education system. This is why formal education in almost every country is actually destructive of the knowledge structure. The main problem we have to grapple with here is the almost total inadequacy of formal education to deal with this. This is particularly so, I think, in Latin America, in the developing countries generally.

The trouble with the international corporations is that they are tied in with sophisticated knowledge; they are not tied in with the folk-knowledge structure—and because of this, they have an extraordinarily shaky base of legitimacy. There is no way of legitimizing international corporations. This is their great problem. They are all prostitutes; they are all fundamentally illegitimate; and no matter how useful they are and how valuable they are, their whole future is insecure.

Unless you develop political institutions which legitimatize them, the advantage the Communists have is that Marxism is folk science. It is very bad science, really. But it has a peculiar intermediate quality in being the folk knowledge and the scientific knowledge. This is the thing we in the West haven't developed. Our great problem is that we react to Marxism defensively, not creatively. And hence, we haven't developed, as it were, a folk science which is really appropriate to the needs of the day.

I would put this as really the main problem that we have to face: the absence of what I call the developmental philosophy which can really capture the imagination of the folk. How do you get into the folk culture, as it were, penetrate with bold, sophisticated ideas, and develop a general level of energies of the world which are capable of a developmental process?

Up to now we haven't done this.

BUDOWSKI: I was very pleased with Mr. Boulding's remarks. It is certainly a fact that right now, in most Middle American countries—in fact all except one notable exception—the farmers and, to go a little further, the Indians are being pretty much snubbed and looked down upon. It is often a disgrace to be a farmer or Indian.

The one notable exception is Mexico. Mexico is perhaps the only country which has returned dignity to the Indians. And significantly, Mexico is one of the countries making good progress in their gross national income and also in raising the level of their farmers. In other countries the situation is quite different. Also I should say Mexico is one of the countries which does not accept AID money.

What I want to emphasize is Boulding's idea of the link between folk history and the more educated masses; if you want to have success you must stress education, not education coming from outside but education coming from within. This is basically the point of my paper, that you have to stress education, in using—and I use your suggestion—the whole capital of people within the country and to build up on that, rather than to transpose cultures and values from outside within your own country.

Education in that case also includes education in family planning. I still insist on that as one of the basic needs. If these points are stressed, I believe we will eventually make progress. This is where foreign investment can help, in stressing education from inside.

LOWENTHAL: I have a brief correction of Dr. Budowski's paper. The two populations on his table which are shown as having lower rates of increase do not in fact have lower rates of natural increase. Their apparent rates of increase result from emigration in the case of both Puerto Rico and Jamaica. Consequently, one could say that in the form of Mr. Caldwell's diagnosis they are already countries which have been taken into receivership to some extent by the United States and by Britain.

GRAHAM: Mrs. Strong?

STRONG: I am curious as to whether Dr. Budowski has concluded that we must relocate portions of the population in Latin American countries because the land will be unable to support them.

BUDOWSKI: A great process of relocation goes on right now in all Latin America, especially Middle America. And the planners had little to do with this—it is, unfortunately, a great natural expansion.

The point I tried to make in the paper is that often this extension goes into what have been traditionally marginal areas, those which are extremely sensitive to clearing. I still believe that the present land use of potentially good agricultural soils is so ineffective in relation to its potential that much more can be achieved by just teaching better methods of land use and industrialization and so on.

Progress can be had with a minimum of relocation and with a maximum of better land-use methods.

STRONG: You were speaking about relocation within the countries?

BUDOWSKI: Yes.

STRONG: I was speaking about relocation to other places that would support larger populations. You do feel, then, that by better land management the present and prospective populations can be supported in each country?

BUDOWSKI: I would say generally yes, excepting one country, Haiti, which is pretty hopeless. I don't know any solution. I don't think that immigration is the solution, either, taking into account the present political situation.

Today, immigration—mass immigration from one country to another—is bound to face too many difficulties. From Haiti it will be even more difficult. Personally I don't know what can be done in Haiti. In other countries I think that if you could only stop the present population where it is right now, and by a sharp program of relocation of land use and improvement you might get away with it—but I don't see how you can stop it right now.

GRAHAM: We might ask Dr. White about the changes he has described in the utilization of arid lands, whether these areas might absorb some of this excess population with proper technology applied.

WHITE: I wouldn't see this as a very promising prospect except in terms of industrial growth. I think in the United States sector, the arid zone, there has been emphasis on the development of resources of water for agricultural purposes which we are now coming to see has been quite illusory, and although public policy has in a monumental and massive way been oriented in that direction, it is probably changing very rapidly now. Only as we see very high-value production of agriculture can we anticipate what would seem to be efficient investments in development of further lands for agricultural purposes.

BEAR: That impressed me, the thought that, in some areas, it may be time to discontinue increasing the use of water for agricultural purposes because it has a higher value for industrial and urban purposes. In the State of Arizona, for example, the tendency might be to discourage the use of any more water for agricultural purposes—or to reduce it.

WHITE: This isn't to say that this is what the State of Arizona is now trying to do. Quite the contrary. Its policy is to get as much from the Federal Treasury for further water development as it can, while the policy still permits this.

ALLEN: These points I think all tie together on a basic question that perhaps is worth facing, even though it may seem a little overecological and over-abstract. I think most of us are agreed that there is a world demographic trend and that it is desirable to reduce the rate at which populations are increasing.

The question applies to arid lands in particular, and it is this: Do we have an incentive as a people, and as a whole population of this continent, to spend very large amounts of capital to develop new areas for occupancy by people?

The question was raised here about transferring people. You don't just transfer people. You transfer something that is highly dynamic—as when we introduced the Chinese peasant to the Willamette Valley of Oregon.

We really started something. When you transfer any number of people to an area that has been an open space on our map and spend enough money to make it habitable, those people will build up to X level in that area and you will have in total a larger continental population than you had before. Ultimately we are going to have more people and a greater demand on all of our resources.

I think this whole process of reclamation and filling in the open space, and making the land productive beyond a certain point, is about like bull-dozing the Rocky Mountains into the Pacific Ocean and setting up another state.

BOULDING: I think it is about time that somebody came out and said abolish the Bureau of Reclamation. This is a leftover from what you might call Teddy Roosevelt socialism. It should have been abolished twenty years ago. We put far too much investment in this. We also ought to abolish the subsidization of agriculture and water. This is nonsense. Somewhere somebody ought to come up and do some real cost-benefit analysis of all this imaginary stuff. Gilbert and I were on a committee supposed to be advising California on water some time ago. When they found out what the committee was going to say, they abolished it.

The only way you could explain the water policy in this country was the religious explanation that we worship the water goddess, and hence had to build all these pyramids—all these dams and temples. There is no other conceivable rational explanation.

I think we will go down in history as the age of the dam builders. The domination of almost all our resources policy by engineers and people of this kind is utterly disastrous.

VOGT: It seems to me that, in the absence of any homeostatic mechanism to distribute benefits over the landscape, these economic investments are having a sort of thalidomide effect. You are having excessive growth of an arm here, or a withered growth there; we are going to find that we have a monster on our hands.

BRINSER: I have probably as much reason as anybody to be chary of the Bureau of Reclamation. I have tangled with them in Colorado. But I would not be prepared to abolish them quite so quickly.

The issue is not simply building dams or finding cost-benefit ratios for further investment. The issue in the arid lands is one of institutional creativity and innovation as well.

This is something on which we usually turn our backs. We need to try to find an answer from the physical sciences—we like to think people are also looking for answers from cost-benefit ratios. And behind this lies the problem of institutional innovation. Institutions need to be created to deal with new situations.

I don't feel the ecologists have given us the kinds of answers they could give us on the impact of populations on arid areas. I don't think the economists have given us all the answers we need about the allocations of resources. I don't think we have done anything to explore what sort of institutional innovation and adjustment is appropriate for a future greater benefit from arid lands.

CLAWSON: It seems to me that the ecologists have a wonderful opportunity right now to talk about what may happen in the arid lands *before* it happens. In that wisdom of hindsight that we all engage in, everybody can say that much of the grazing use of the dry lands was irrational and destroyed things and so on and so forth. It wasn't so, apparently, at the time. To grazing you can add irrigation and drainage ditches and placer mining.

It is fairly obvious we are beginning to move out on the desert for residential purposes, for recreation, and probably for manufacture and quite possibly for waste disposal. What are some of the ecological hazards that these land uses will create? What are the ecological opportunities? What are our limits?

This is something on which relatively little has been said by the ecologists. It seems to me that they ought to have something to say. Now they have a prime opportunity to say it in advance of some of the difficulties. I suspect the opportunity won't be taken. But if we were back here forty years from now people would be saying, "I told you so."

Let's now try. My own suspicion is that many of the arid lands are very sensitive to recreation. They don't have a high carrying capacity. Now we move out into the arid areas and I strongly suspect that recreation will quickly destroy the very resources that attract people. The resources that are attracting a lot of people for residential purposes are space and clear air. We seem to be rapidly destroying these.

What are the capacities and the opportunities? What are the conditions under which this sort of development should take place? This is a prime opportunity for ecologists to give some guidance to all sorts of economists, planners, administrators, and investors.

HUBBERT: I should like to call attention to a well-known semiarid area which exemplifies most of the facets, except metal mining, which have been discussed. This is the Llano Estacado, or the high plains, of the Texas Panhandle—a region extending about 300 miles north and south and 150 miles east and west, with an elevation of about 3500 to 3700 feet, and twenty inches per year of rainfall. When I first knew this area forty years ago, it was principally a single large cow pasture with occasional small towns. Earlier it had been a buffalo range. At present it is one big cotton field, irrigated, with a dense agricultural population.

The irrigation is by means of water pumped from the Ogallala sand which underlies the whole region at depths of about 200–400 feet. The rate of water recharge into this sand is negligible compared to the rate of withdrawal. The water in the sand is consequently being mined. Its amount is known, and it is estimated it will be about half exhausted by 1970, and that the pumpage rate will have declined to about half the peak rate by 1980, with only about one fifth of the water initially present still remaining.

The question raised a minute ago regarding large-scale transfers of population appears to be particularly pertinent to this area. In response to the exploitation of this limited water supply, the population density increased from that of a sparsely settled grazing area, to that of a region of intensive agriculture. When the water is gone—about twenty years from now—we shall be faced with a very real problem of what to do with this surplus population.

I am aware of no ground-water basin in the world that can sustain heavy withdrawals for agricultural purposes, without a continuous diminution of the supply.

GRAHAM: What happens when desalinization gets to the point where limitless water is available to arid lands?

SEARS: That is fine for Tucson if you can afford to desalt it, pump it 2000 feet in the air and 200 miles inland.

BOULDING: Desalinization is a will-of-the-wisp. Let's face it. It is nonsense. The energy requirements are enormous; the transport costs are enormous. The whole trouble with the oceans is that they are terribly low. (*Laughter*) It is all right for Kuwait, it is all right for high industrial purposes. But this idea of desalinization giving us unlimited quantities of water everywhere in the world is bunk.

WHITE: It is an important lesson for us. Why is it that desalting the ocean and the brackish waters has such appeal to man? Why is it so easy for our scientists and technicians and government to sell these extravagant research programs for desalting to legislators and intelligent administrators? Why does it catch the imagination of the popular press and of our Chairman here? (*Laughter*) I wonder if it doesn't reflect perhaps the last glorious demonstration of reliance on technology, massive technology as a means of solving any problem that we have presented by nature.

BOULDING: It is the wrong technology. You can teach vegetables to like salt much more easily than you can take salt out of the water. The Japanese have the idea. Seaweed is delicious.

(*Laughter*)

WHITE: I think this is just the point, Kenneth: that we tended to rely on a massive engineering measure, a single-purpose kind of measure. If it weren't going to be a big dam, then it would be a big desalting plant.

What we are moving toward, and I think in scientific circles it is well recognized, is the importance of regarding all the opportunities there are in the system to manipulate and adjust, and in that, desalting might take its proper place—probably in those rare locations where you need large generation of nuclear energy at sea level.

SEARS: Men love a witch doctor, whatever they call him—politician, engineer or scientist.

DASMANN: I would like to say one thing on the subject of the appeal of desalinization. It has a tremendous appeal to those wilderness advocates who are being so overpowered by the big dam-building problem in the West that they see little hope for further wilderness preservation unless some alternate means of getting water is found.

One of the things that bothers me is that we don't have Harrison Brown or Bonner from Cal Tech here to defend desalinization, to look at the future of energy resources, and the potential of virtually unlimited energy in the near future—within the next hundred years—which will make possible desalinization on a broad scale, the transport of water up and over mountain ranges into the interior basins.

Apparently, if Bonner is correct, we are going to be basing our mineral technology on the exploitation of granite and other rocks for many of our minerals, and upon the exploitation of the salts of the ocean for other minerals.

I think we are taking a very short-term point of view in this Conference. We are looking at the next ten or twenty years. We are not extending the view out over the centuries to come. If we do that, we may have a different picture on some of these problems than we currently are exhibiting.

FOSBERG: Given unlimited energy supplies you could have unlimited desalinization. The obvious prediction would be that you are going to make the desert just like everywhere else, so you have eliminated all possibilities of using the desert for recreation. You can use it to build skyscrapers and to live on, or you can use it to make another Illinois to produce corn. If you are interested in other types of land utilization, such as outdoor recreation, then I would say you have to write the desert off.

Once we admit or produce the possibility of changing it, we will change it. We seem to have the urge toward uniformity. We hate uniformity, yet everything we do pushes us in that direction.

I would get back to Mr. Leopold's suggestion that we decide what we want and then make what we do take us in that direction, rather than abandon ourselves to this helpless drifting along with the current of the results of technological progress.

FISHER: I think we have fallen into a trap and maybe subsequent sessions will get us out of it. As economists we look at the Bureau of Reclamation and the land irrigation of the West and say, "How stupid can you get?"

As ecologists we look at some of the western cities wandering off into the desert with their subdivisions and say, "What craziness is this?"

Or we look at ocean desalinization and we say, "What madness goes on here?"

From each of these particular points of view probably it is madness. But I think we have to have a different framework which incorporates history and social and political factors in order to understand what is going on and have an appreciation for the motivations which drive Congress and subdividers and engineers and so forth to do these things.

I think when put in that framework it can be understood—which is the first step toward exerting any changes.

You can make quite a nice theory of development—and people have—about badly unbalancing a system, or seizing upon crises or some other thing, in order to put dynamism into things.

Then, of course, people like economists or ecologists who have elaborate equilibrium systems come along and try to tidy up and redress the balance and even out the situation on the landscape or among people.

I insert this note before we conclude that so many of our brothers in other fields are cockeyed.

BRANDWEIN: I think we have been hampered by notions that the institutions that exist now are valid. If I thought so I would resign from the human race. Assuming that we will not spend twenty million dollars for a small part of a submarine, and that we will turn our attention to peace-evoking mechanisms, then while I realize that desalinization is expensive, I would say that it is not as expensive as war or going to the moon, or the Mohole Project.

In time I think the ecological dream may be realized and if this Conference is going to deal only with short aims, I would be very resistant to putting them into print.

I think men will come after us. This world is not at an end. And we ought then to picture why it is that desalinization is inadequate at this moment and to consider whether there are other means of getting water—or changing the whole educational system so that youngsters in the first grade have as their midtime snack sukiyaki, and change it that way.

I think we must deal with the cultural evolution, which is the transmission and transformation of values. I don't think too much has been said here on the nature of cultural evolution—which is, I think, the next business of man.

FOSBERG: Could we ask Dr. Brandwein to explain what the ecological dream is?

BRANDWEIN: It is not very difficult. It is a good dream. It says that man is manuring the soil of a future harmony, when he will live in concord with plants and animals, and take the responsibility of his effects upon land.

It is not very difficult to state. And I think we may even succeed in it if we change the direction of the evolution we have been talking about from a biologically determinant evolution to a cultural evolution. And so we may even control smog. Who knows?

CALDWELL: There is a danger, I think, that technological innovation may retard cultural evolution and industrial change in some respects.

For example (a sequel to the enthusiasm for technological innovation that Dr. White observes): one of the motive forces behind the transformation of the desert is the reprieve that the idea of desalinization of water gives to our traditional pro-unlimited-growth attitudes.

That is, legislators, government administrators and others seize upon desalinization avidly because it postpones the disagreeable day of reckoning with respect to the pressures of the population, particularly pressures for food and for industrial development.

So we have to take cognizance of the differential nature of technological innovation as it affects attitudes and values. Simply left to an essentially technological evolution, without some inputs here with respect to other values, the effects may be as retarding as they may be creative.

STEERS: Can we talk about arid lands? We seem to have gone a long way from them. What—if I may put it as a stranger in the States—what do you do with your arid lands? Do you wish to conserve some as arid, or do you wish to change them all?

Do we wish to preserve some of these lands as natural features?

WHITE: This perhaps refers to the earlier statement of what we want or what are our long-term aims. I would like to think our record of experience in arid lands—an environment in which one can discern a delicate response in the whole complex of relationships to relatively minor changes in one of them—points out that perhaps the most effective way of taking the long-range view is following an immediate strategy in which the criterion is: What position maintains the greatest flexibility in the near future? This flexibility recognizes the rapid march of technological innovation, recognizes the slight knowledge we have of the complex forces that affect the decisions that both individuals and public agencies make about managing resources. We should not try to take the long view in which we set the long goals—as, for example, Powell did for the West in 1878—but we should remember that the effective long-time goal is one which tries to preserve the situation over the next twenty years in such fashion that we have not cut off to ourselves any major avenue of action which we could now anticipate.

This becomes more sharply focused in the arid lands than in some other areas, because they have a narrow margin of safety.

CLAWSON: I am quite aware of the fact that the deserts can't take much more, but I am also fairly sure they are going to get a lot more.

It seems to me that—I don't expect to be here fifty years from now—the probability is that fifty years from now, looking back, we will see this as a time when some very considerable changes in arid areas were just beginning. How far can they be guided? Joe Fisher made the point that we shouldn't assume that everybody but us is irrational, that we are the only rational people.

How far can groups such as ours, or the professional community, bring to bear knowledge, or ideas, or processes, and what is our responsibility in this? By what means do we move?

MC HARG: I would like to speak of one prospective use of arid lands. There may be 190 million more Americans by the end of the century. I don't think there is any reason to believe that if they had the choice they would like to add themselves to the annular rings which accrete around Boston, Philadelphia, New York, San Francisco, Los Angeles, and so on.

Everybody assumes that metropolitan areas will get larger and the countryside will get smaller. It seems to me natural to start from the assumption that in a country of this sort, with great wealth and greater prospective wealth, and limitless technology, and a modicum of artists, it is conceivable that the distribution of population will be related to the best of all possible choices.

For some portion of these 340 million Americans there might very well be splendid cities in arid lands. Given a superabundance of arid lands I am not concerned about the spoliation that may occur.

There are many good examples of triumphant cities. Generally they are all evidence of people who were able to sustain hydraulic civilizations, which produced great gardens and great cities. Arid lands might very well be a splendid physical environment for an allergy-prone America.

LEOPOLD: Early this morning we were talking about the process of planning and the criteria to be brought to bear on land use. One possible set of criteria that could be activated here by ecologists is evaluation of land in terms of its durability, meaning its ability to absorb punishment and remain productive or stable.

I think Mackay's excellent article on the tundra emphasized what was my belief already, that perhaps the most friable of all the ecosystems are in the Far North, but not far behind it is the dry West.

Parts of the West, in California or Arizona, can absorb cities very well. And with moderation I think a certain amount of irrigation can be continued indefinitely on some of those soils. But it is particularly in these friable types that planning has to be the most carefully laid out.

You can get away with murder in the glaciated northern United States, and go back fifty years later and revise the whole system of land use and the country will still absorb it. But you make one bad mistake in the arid West and it is semipermanent. You make one bad mistake in the Far North and it is permanent for all practical purposes.

Here, then, I think is a point where ecologists and their knowledge of these ecosystems can be extremely helpful in the planning process, in defining these various grades of durability—or, conversely, of friability—and in pointing where the greatest dangers lie in excessive development.

GRAHAM: I think these remarks of Dr. Leopold lead us into the final subject we have for this morning—namely, the northern lands.

He has touched on the fragile nature of this environment. We all know there are going to be pressures there as well as in the arid areas. I think we might ask Dr. Mackay to comment on this point of how delicate a balance there is in the tundra and taiga, how easily it can be damaged, whether he agrees with this point of fragility, and so forth.

MACKAY: I think the main thing we should remember is that the tundra and taiga is very large—and there are many, many different types in the tundra. In some of the areas of bare rock and no soil development we could set off an atomic bomb and the area wouldn't look appreciably different afterward from the way it did before.

On the other hand, where the soils are fine-grained and where the ice content is very, very high, I think the fragility of the environment is of critical importance; any slight disturbance to the thermal regime of the ground causes then a change in the superficial features which trigger a series of reactions.

GRAHAM: Will soil classification be of much use in guiding development in the arctic?

MACKAY: I think it would be, yes.

DARLING: Wouldn't regeneration of vegetational growth be a prime criterion? I am thinking of western and northern Alaska, where you had reindeer grazing. They were eaten out, and they have not yet revegetated.

If you get up 20,000 feet, you still can clearly see these great areas where reindeer were. I was just wondering—apart from actual attempts at agricultural use in the fine-grained areas, for example, the loess land round Fairbanks—isn't the first criterion the regeneration of vegetational growth?

The other point I want to make, as a start about the tundra and taiga, is the place of the Eskimo and the Indian who are living there. These men are still living a subsistence culture for the most part off that country.

We are tending to lift them out of that subsistence culture without proper thought about whether they can stay outside it.

I am thinking particularly of a place like Barrow, where you have employed the Eskimo to do all manner of things and he is being relieved of his subsistence culture and skills—the traditional skills which have enabled him to live in that environment. It takes only one generation to lose those skills and you can't get them back. They are gone.

That tundra and taiga can only be inhabited subsistence-wise by a continuance of the repository of these traditional skills. I think we are being a little lighthearted in our treatment of these small groups of people—for example, in Barrow. They are working there for government at the present time. They are buying Rice Krispies. Then suddenly the government says, "We have no need for Barrow as a naval base any more"—and they pull out.

If those people are left, the new generation hasn't the skills that enable them to live there, and they have to pull out. I am wondering what this really means for that environment of the tundra and taiga.

LEOPOLD: In the process of social planning for a continent, certainly one of the alternatives that is always before us is the chance to do nothing at all. I think in the arctic—above all other places—this might be the best choice.

The possibilities of superimposing our productive type of industrial-agricultural community on the arctic are extremely limited. So why even attempt it? Why can't we leave that component part of the continent exactly as it is, as a basis for planning. This is precisely what Frank was saying in another way.

COWAN: I would like to comment on Dr. Leopold's remark. Would that it were possible to leave the arctic alone. It isn't.

A recent study by a sociologist working for the Canadian government has produced an interesting document on the Eskimo who live west of Hudson Bay. Twenty or twenty-five years ago there were 386 inhabitants supporting themselves, more or less naturally, on 100,000 square miles of tundra. Twenty years later there are 368 inhabitants occupying the same 100,000 square miles. The ecosystem is full. This is the carrying capacity for native man living wild on this system.

A catalog of the mortality that these people have experienced over this period shows that their births per thousand run about forty-two. Deaths per thousand run about forty-three. The decline in population has been by emigration. It is a small drain.

When you study the catalog of mortality, the cause is known for 186 out of the 209 inhabitants who have died in this community during that period. It shows a third of them died of pulmonary disease, and a third in infancy. Of the other third, a majority died of starvation—and this is in the last twenty years. Most of the rest died of accident.

The mortality rate in this community was 256 per thousand live births, while mortality rate in Canada at large has been twenty-eight per thousand live births in the last twenty-eight years.

This is not going to be tolerated by the Canadian people. We cannot tolerate any elements in our Canadian society that have a mortality rate of roughly nine times the standard mortality rate.

This means that we introduce the mortality-controlling forces that we are so good at. Western man has exported them all over the world. This environment under wild circumstances and under any type of culture that is not dollar-based will not support any more people.

As soon as you impose the dollar-based culture—which we did when we came in with fur resources—we gave the Eskimo the opportunity of making money which he could convert into goods. In order to get furs he had to travel a great deal more than he had to before, which meant he had to have three times the size of dog teams, three times the number of dogs —which required three times the amount of food and immediately reduced the carrying capacity of the environment by this amount.

We can't leave the Eskimo alone. We have already wrecked the primeval community. We are into it up to our necks.

The Eskimo is involved in twentieth-century culture just as surely as the rest of us are. He is going to be absorbed into twentieth-century culture. A small proportion of his people may remain as wild-living peoples in the North by choice—but it should be *their* choice. Indeed, some of them are opting out of the twentieth century, though we have had to establish radio-telephone posts, strategically located throughout the arctic where they could call for help when they get into serious trouble. Starvation is still an ever-present specter to the individual in the family living wild in the barren lands of northern Canada.

BEAR: I would like to ask Dr. Mackay about such matters as recreation, hunting, and tourists for these areas.

MACKAY: This is being pushed a great deal. I think there are several different aspects.

First, in the region of the taiga, if we plot the burned areas on maps we find that these tend to occur along rivers where either Indians travel or tourists travel.

The Mackenzie River system has extensive burned areas. If tourism ever did expand into the taiga, the problem of fire would be severe—already 20,000 or 30,000 square miles have been burned over in the last fifty years.

Again there is the problem of wildlife supply, on which I am not competent to comment. But I gather that the polar bear, for example—or even the fish in some of the rivers like the Copper Mine River—can be depleted very rapidly by tourists.

I would like to, if I could, return very briefly to Dr. Cowan's remarks and add my own; the most recent study of Canadian Eskimos has been carried out by Canada's leading ethnologist, Dr. Guy Jennes. He stresses the very fact Dr. Cowan has stressed. The area is overpopulated. He feels a solution is immediately to start moving them south.

DARLING: This is the point, I think, that they must choose the one way or the other. But we cannot muck about in that country and leave them to it, or half bake them, as we are doing.

I felt when I was at Barrow that when everybody stopped work suddenly one day and went duck shooting, however much it upset the running of the Barrow base, it was nevertheless a native reaction to retain their skills of getting duck when the duck were flying, and that this was more important than Barrow base—and indeed it was.

I think this human problem in the arctic is a very sharp one, that we have to decide. Are these people to be encouraged to move out, and do we stop sentimental attitudes about this being an awful pity? You must either leave them wild or take them out.

Even the Nunamiut, in the Brooks Range, rely on the wolf bounty, receiving fifty dollars for each wolf killed, when actually Alaska has given up the idea of the wolf bounty. They have got the idea that it doesn't work, that it is undesirable. But those 250 people are now dependent on such a figment.

STEERS: I would like to ask Dr. Mackay if he could enlarge on the hydrographic patterns relating to climate. It is of considerable importance.

MACKAY: One suggestion is the Bering Strait Dam; this was analyzed in detail by Dr. Dunbar, of McGill University. His conclusion was that it would alter the arctic climate somewhat. But if we took the largest pumps in existence and ran them for 10,000 years, this is about the length of time it would take to appreciably alter the climate—and that doesn't seem feasible.

There have been suggestions as to the implications of a very large dam like the Rampart Dam which would flood 10,000 square miles. Quite aside from the biologic aspects—what influence would this have on the climate? I think it would have very little because we do have present large lakes like Great Bear Lake and Great Slave Lake, and there are no homesteads around those.

LEOPOLD: Everything is relative. I didn't mean to be absolute, that nobody should ever go into the arctic, and just leave the place alone. You can't say that certainly about the desert. But in terms of long-term planning, instead of trying to convert the northern Indians and Eskimos to an industrial type of culture of our own, we should look upon theirs as having great values inherent in their culture, and whatever aid and help we give them should be of a sort to maintain their culture. Certainly it has to be humane; we have to utilize such skills as we have to help them over periods of starvation and so on. And each one should have a choice. If he wants to work for the U.S. Navy or the Canadian government, he should have the choice to do so.

This is a different thing from forcing people into a mold based on something that we have derived elsewhere in the world. I think this still applies in the arctic, that the help should be of the sort that they want and need to maintain their own culture. This is a very limited sort of help, rather than a conversion to our way of living.

COWAN: I certainly agree with that. Of course, with the development of mines in the north, which will continue, there will be moving sources of employment and economic input into Eskimo society.

Recently some interesting and reasonably successful experiments have been done in export of luxury fish products—arctic char being air-freighted to the luxury markets all the way down the Atlantic Coast of Canada and the United States, from fishing communities manned exclusively by natives on Baffin Island, Southampton Island, and so on. There are possibilities of having a surviving culture up there with many of the ingredients of the native culture which are fascinating and worth preserving.

But these people, many of them, do not want to be museum specimens of the Stone Age culture. I agree with you that we should permit them the option of making this choice.

VOGT: I want to raise the question as to whether or not the Eskimo culture isn't a function of the relationship between the birth and the death rate. And if you increase the longevity—cut the death rate by sanitary measures, medicines, and so on—you are almost inevitably going to have a population increase unless you cut your birth rate. And that is bound to change the culture.

BUDOWSKI: The discussion on the Eskimo is quite similar to a great controversy which goes on with what to do with Indians living in some of the wild areas in the Amazon and in Central America.

One assumption is that because in our civilization we have a death rate —an average death rate—of, say, sixty or seventy years, that we should automatically, because of our common human nature, transpose this to the Indians.

One good reason to challenge that is that if the Indians were asked, right at the beginning when the first interference is made, if they would like people to come up and give medicine, the answer would often be no— they don't want that interference. Sure enough, after a time of contact with our civilization this attitude changes. But it is a cultural change brought about by the interference of white men.

I think if finally white men decide to bring this about, then they must deal with all the consequences. They are guilty of having changed the cultural pattern and the death rate. And they have to deal with it. Just to decrease the death rate and not do anything else is really to bring about ultimate destruction of much more than the culture. It usually leads to the destruction of the whole area itself. Man must deal with this problem.

WOODBURY: Even in the relatively simpler shifts within our urban and metropolitan areas, we certainly have still a crude, a brutal process of inducting people into a new environment, into a new way of life. And if you apply this experience to the Eskimos who can't be maintained in their original economy if we cut down the death rate from pulmonary disease, maybe here is an area in which innovation and institutional change should no longer be respected.

HUBBERT: The growth of human population is an essential part of this whole ecological upset. The upset includes men as well as animals and plants, and it is at present irreversible.

For the Eskimos, from the statistics which have just been given—a birth rate of forty-two per thousand, and a death rate of forty-three per thousand, I believe—there would be a life expectancy of just under twenty-five years. This is about the same as that for the Massachusetts Bay Colony, according to colonial statistics; and also about the average figure for the human race during all of history before that time. If we adopt the view that we have to reduce this terrible death rate, then we must also adopt the view that we have to reduce this terrible birth rate in order to maintain a stable population—unless we propose to provide some other form of sustenance.

Once an indigenous culture has been disturbed, these people, as has been remarked before, frequently become dependent. They have lost their old culture; their biological support has been undermined; and it becomes necessary that they be taken into the culture of the twentieth century.

In this connection, I am reminded of an account which I read a few years ago in a local newspaper in Santa Fe, New Mexico. According to this account, a local lady of means, Mrs. X, who lived in a large mansion near

Santa Fe, was one of the leaders of a group who were bemoaning the gradual deterioration of the pueblo culture of the Indians in that neighborhood. The rejoinder of one of the young Indians, who lived in the nearby Taos Pueblo, was a contemptuous remark that "those people who wish to preserve the pueblo culture have never lived in a pueblo." He added that, in view of her interest in preserving the pueblo way of life, he would gladly exchange places of residence with Mrs. X.

(*Laughter*)

DANSEREAU: It seems to me that the Eskimo culture has a very short span ahead of it. The Canadian conscience has been aroused, as Dr. Cowan has said, by the statistically readable evidence, and the Canadian government is trying to do well by the Eskimo. I think they won't have to find out what goes on in Nigeria, Ghana, or other parts of the world. All they have to do is to look at the efforts that have been made to preserve some subcultures within the Canadian culture. All of this dreadful artificial artisanship—the Quebec and Maritime artisans have been brought back to life and they produce absolutely dreadful stuff that is not worth conserving.

FOSBERG: I am rather surprised to hear that it is the ecologists who have this defense reaction—of moving people. So far all the ecologists whom I have ever heard comment on it were appalled by it. I think it is the administrators who usually take this as the solution to all problems. People aren't getting along well, so move them—without consulting the ecologists at all. They might not do these things if they took ecological considerations into account.

GRAHAM: Dr. Darling?

DARLING: There is an ecological analogy about the contact of peoples with small primitive cultures. I thought of this one in Africa first, but it applies equally in the north: that is, that in our penetration of lands, we have used a form of easy exploitation, usually by means of pastoralism. That is our first attack on an ecological climax or association of plants and animals. We penetrate it with the mouths of pastoral animals, and we have usually ruined an area before we have really started to think of it as a living place.

In applying this to human situations, we go into Central Africa and we are touching those peoples very, very slightly—but badly, not ecologically. They finish up neither one thing nor the other.

Were it possible for us to start again, we would leave peoples strictly alone until we could change them completely and integrate them. It is the halfway stage in which trouble comes.

Just the same with land. Much land has been ruined because we didn't change it quickly. To change a complete ecological situation and make it into arable ground is often a good thing. You get a rise in productivity. It can hold up that productivity. Fine, but it needs to be done quickly and completely, instead of half doing it.

The same in the arctic. These people, I feel, should either be left alone or quickly integrated.

And if I may say so, in Alaska, where there has been a good class of education of the Eskimo, they have been integrated very quickly with the society. There is a good deal of intermarriage. From what I have seen of it, it is successful. This is quick integration and an enrichment of the incoming culture by the existing culture.

GRAHAM: We are thinking about North American environments. I think we have made it quite clear that there are certainly regional differences which must be recognized. And we come around to talking finally about people as part of these environmental systems.

Yet we still have not answered the questions brought up by Fisher and Clawson. I wonder if any generalizations or summary points occur to any of you in relating our discussion to what you can visualize as the future in these four major regions we have discussed.

DICKINSON: I suppose as a geographer I probably have something of a one-track mind. But I am still bothered by your opening remarks about this regional concept.

As a geographer I just can't really begin to operate on this question until I know precisely what I have got to regionalize. I am still bewildered by this.

I think it was Dr. Fisher who raised this question, and I am still with it, as to what kind of meaningful ecological criteria we can use in breaking down any of these major areas into their component environmental complexes.

We have also heard a great deal here about the population explosion and all the rest of it. That undoubtedly is a tremendously important aspect of this whole problem of the future environments in North America and this hemisphere. I want to couple that with what to me as a geographer is of more fundamental importance, concerning what are now called space indexes, space indices. What are the spatial requirements in terms of per head of population or per family? We have had no mention of automobiles yet, but this is going to come along. This is another kind of space index.

We have heard a great deal about recreational impact. We all know what this means in general terms. But there is another kind of space about which we know very, very little. Until we do get some sort of a yardstick in terms of space index, I don't think we can get very far in coming even to a general grouping of the environments of America in terms of what should and what should not be conserved.

MUMFORD: It seems to me one of the difficulties we have in defining a region—in getting the region into focus—is that we are proceeding really in a very old-fashioned way, as if time and space could be separated.

A geographic region isn't purely a geographic problem. It is a historical problem. It changes whenever there is change in the culture—the people who are looking at the region, who are utilizing the region, who are making something of it.

I think one of the real difficulties of the discussion this morning is that we are operating within a very narrow time band. We seem to be talking about the future but we are actually talking about the problem immediately under our noses. Whereas we should think of it in terms of the enormous changes that have taken place from the very beginning of man's origin.

Nothing has stayed put. The geologic processes have changed. Just think: only 5000 years ago there was no North Sea—there was a land bridge between Britain and the Continent. If we think of that we see that even the most stable environment is involved in the flux of history. And man has been intervening at every point in this change. Sometimes very mildly, because his means were modest. Today his means are immodest and his desires, his plans, his projects are sometimes exorbitant. They have all the authority of the state behind them; they have the authority of a kind of secret religion, a priesthood of scientists, some of them around this table. We are in danger of being overpowered by a single aspect of our culture.

III ECONOMIC PATTERNS AND PROCESSES

* Dr. Fisher is President of Resources for the Future, a private foundation devoted to the economic aspects of natural resource development. After receiving his Ph.D. in economics from Harvard University in 1947 he served on the Council of Economic Advisors to 1953. He was co-author with Hans H. Landsberg and Leonard L. Fischman of *Resources in America's Future*, which appeared in 1963.

Introductory Statement and Summary Remarks

FISHER: This session is to be devoted to economic patterns and processes. I think quite likely we will keep coming back to the differences and similarities and interplay between economists and ecologists in the course of our discussion.

Frequently, in gatherings like this, economists feel somewhat short-sighted, narrow, a bit greedy and grubby, pecunious, man-centered, and lacking in total perspective. It is probably very good for us to have a chance to exchange ideas with ecologists, conservationists, geographers, and so forth.

However, I do think that economic theory, methodology, and thinking generally do adapt slowly to changes in the way we perceive economic problems. More and more we are concerned with the indirect, the remote, the side effects of economic decisions and actions.

I think we are becoming increasingly concerned with the long-time horizon, although it is a bit of a stretch for us because when the rate of discount on future benefits gets to zero we tend to lose interest, and that usually happens about a generation from now.

But I think to a greater degree we are trying to look beyond the zero rate-of-interest dimension. I think we are becoming more concerned with regional planning, with the carrying capacity of natural areas, with renewal of various kinds in country and city, and all of these I take to be promising signs for economists.

Also, I believe our analytical tools are being sharpened. We have had quite a following in welfare economics, as we call it. Ken Boulding has been one of the leaders among economists in systems analysis.

We have, I think, learned quite a bit about the use and misuse of the famous benefit-cost ratio. We are more and more concerned with the design of institutions that may affect economic behavior. So I am not so sure we are a hopeless lot.

Some words were spoken earlier in the sessions about playing God. I wonder, is it playing God to kill off a species, as people are sometimes accused of doing, or perhaps it is equally playing God to preserve the species when otherwise it would die off.

I can't help but make a little diversion here. I was attracted yesterday by Waggoner's proposal to force the conservationist to become more productive in the use of acres. This was a rather frightening thought. He was in a way suggesting a miniaturization of natural areas so that you could get the benefits of science, education and museum and everything else on tiny areas, rather than vast tracts of land.

This led some of us to speculate a little bit. A matching proposal would be the miniaturization of animals and especially people. If we could breed small people they would take up less space, eat less, they would ride around in smaller cars. All in all, they would cause a great deal less trouble. So we can imagine the miniaturization of natural areas along with breeding for smaller people—somebody said what we need is a miniman.

This serves, however, to bring up one of the main contributions economists can make, I think, and that is to look at all of the alternatives across the board. If we have anything to offer, perhaps it is this. In fact, as you know, economists are inclined to measure the cost of anything simply by noting what would be the value of some alternative thing that we might have done with the money or the resources. So it is built into our way of thinking always to look over the scene to find the possible alternatives in solving a problem. We have some advantages, I think. In addition to having our hand on the pursestrings, we have a practical device for measuring values—namely, money. It is not a perfect device, but it is pretty hard to find a better one that will allow you to compare a large number of alternative ways of doing things. We are concerned, therefore, always with choice and with criteria for choice in trying to rack one course of action up against another, and in some sense find an efficient or least cost.

I should think ecologists would therefore welcome economists who can sometimes put the viewpoints of the ecologists into a framework which permits comparisons, on the basis of which people can make decisions about budgets and appropriations and laws.

By the same token, I think economists would welcome the greater substance and content that ecologists can put into the economic decision frameworks that we try to erect.

I feel, myself, somewhat a split personality—by training an economist, by inclination and instinct a conservationist. So I have a particular interest in any way we can draw these two disciplines together.

I was intrigued yesterday by the discussion of the purpose for which people in North America might want to protect a vanishing species or preserve a unique ecosystem. It seems to me that as the discussion went on various reasons for doing this came up, all of them quite legitimate.

These areas can be museums, they can be classrooms, they can afford outdoor recreation, they may be beautiful, they may preserve genetic stock, they may have sentimental values for old times' sake. All of these, it seems to me, are legitimate reasons for wanting to have a program of preservation and protection of species and areas.

It is my belief that the economic framing of decisions that may involve preservation of areas can include all of these values or purposes. Of course they can't all be measured by dollars in a marketplace. That is obvious.

When you stop to think of it very little can be measured accurately by the market price. When I am hungry, a loaf of bread is worth a lot more than the twenty-five cents that the market makes me pay for it, and this is not substantially different from the situation in which we would all say that a preserved species or a piece of natural scenery is priceless or it is worth way beyond what anyone could conceivably pay for it. But all these values, I think, can be entered into an economist's scale of reckoning if you will accept certain loose indicators of value other than market price. When we would make a budget decision or an appropriation decision we are saying—in dollars, so to speak—what is it worth to preserve the area or build the school or build the battleship or whatever it is we are doing? But in none of these cases are we saying that the amount of appropriation is somehow an exact measure of the value of this thing.

I am intrigued by the different ways of getting indicators of value—say, of natural areas—that don't involve prices or markets or dollars at all. One way you can do it is go around and ask people to rate values on some kind of a comparative scale. This is a kind of indicator of evidence.

I think the main thing I want to do in these opening remarks is to talk long enough—which I have now done—to draw the group toward the wavelength of the economist, and to indicate that we are not such narrow-minded fellows as we are sometimes thought to be.

I am going to ask each of my colleagues here to speak very briefly and bring out what he regards as the highlights of his paper.

To begin the discussion, I am going to ask Kenneth Boulding, whose paper I suspect is more in the center of our discussion than the others, to bring out what he regards as the highlights of your paper.

BOULDING: What I have tried to do here, really, is perhaps create a unification of economics and ecology, to point out that there are profound similarities in the method of the two; and I have outlined five of these similarities.

We both deal with populations of species, and I have argued that automobiles are just as much a species as the whooping crane.

I have argued also that we are both interested in the general equilibrium of population and that this goes for the population of commodities as well as to the population of natural species. The basic equilibrium concept is that everything depends on everything else. If everything depends on everything else, you have n equations and n unknowns. It is as simple as that. If they are reasonably well behaved, they may have a solution. If they don't have a solution, something will drop out until you do have a solution. That seems to be ecological succession, involving the theory of evolution essentially.

I have argued also that we are both interested in exchange, which is of course central to economics. On the whole, economics, I would say, is the science which builds itself around the abstract concept of exchange. But ecology is also very much interested in community metabolism and in what the Russians call material balances, such as the circulation of nitrogen.

We are also interested, I suggest, in development. This is a complex problem. It isn't only ecological succession and evolution, it is also the matter of how we use energy—inputs of energy—in order to create information.

You create order here by creating chaos somewhere else. This is a very fundamental principle of social systems as it is of biological systems. I suggest we are both interested in policy, which is essentially how you distort the equilibrium in favor of some kind of system of values. It may be our system of values is a little different. At any rate, we each have the problem of the distortion of the ecosystem, of the economic system, in favor of something, as in agriculture. I suggest that economic policy may be called social agriculture, essentially. It is a matter of distorting the "natural" system in favor of some sort of values. I don't know whether my colleagues will be shocked at this but I am profoundly against anything that is natural.

I think the whole business of policy is to create the unnatural—the artificial, in other words. This is what we are interested in. I suggest there are some interesting ethical differences between economists and ecologists. I suggest that economists are Christians and ecologists are Buddhists when it comes to fundamental ethical systems.

Economists are very much man-centered, whereas ecologists tend to be earth-centered or system-centered. We probably both learn from each other on this point.

Then, in the course of my paper, I issue some warnings, I put up what I call a Dead End sign for ecologists, for conservationists especially.

The dead end is a blind conservatism that simply has the state of the world as of 1862 or something as the ideal and fails to recognize that development goes on all the time, and that whatever nature is, she isn't a conservationist. She doesn't conserve anything, really. Nothing is sacred. Absolutely nothing. And that means more species were destroyed before man arrived on the scene than after. In a sense you can say that the main impact of man has certainly been to speed up the evolutionary processes which were going on before him.

Then I put up a Thin Ice sign for economists. That is, we have had a tendency in our economic thinking, I think, to regard man as if he operated in an infinite environment; the most valuable thing that the ecologist has to say is that the environment isn't infinite and that we have to face the problem of what I am calling the earth system; that is, we have to think of the earth as a closed system, essentially—apart from the intake of solar energy and a certain amount of information that comes in from the astronomical universe.

The earth has a biosphere, an econosphere, a sociosphere, whatever you want to call it. It is an essentially integrated system, and these divisions into the biosphere and the econosphere and so on are just academic conveniences. They don't represent anything—anything real or fundamental.

BRINSER: Perhaps I can summarize what I have to say in my paper briefly, in part because the topic to which I was assigned left me out on a limb with the idea that the ecologists could saw me off at their opportunity. It was a uniquely narrow economic base. However, I do think that it would be significant to consider how economics approaches the problem of the environmental resources.

We are concerned not only with distinguishing between more or less as the basis for choice, but also with how much more and how much less— and of what. This causes me to respond to the summary of yesterday's papers with somewhat less than full enthusiasm because I still believe that variety itself is no criterion for making decisions about how to proceed; that diversity does involve the matter of making choices. The really important thing is, how do you choose variety?

In more specific terms, as Joe Fisher has indicated, what we really are concerned with as economists is a concept for selecting alternative investment opportunities. I would say that in making such choices in this area of environmental resource development, we should emphasize growth and development aspects of the investment processes; our criteria should not be aimed at measuring or dealing with static situations. They should not be aimed at preservation. They should not be aimed at restoration of the past. But they should be aimed at improving the quality of choices that will come in the future. This is the essence of welfare.

The choices you will make in the future are obviously a function of the choices you make today. However, there are a great many uncertainties in the measurement of such choices and that being the case I find myself among the growing minority in believing that we should use incremental planning in such designs rather than comprehensive planning.

In order to distinguish the issues as I see them, we can't have comprehensive designs, designs that comprise the total range of alternatives. The plans for achieving these designs—that is, the action programs with which we implement the design—should be incremental rather than comprehensive in order to avoid limiting ourselves, in part because of the inadequacy of our data and in part because of the changing situation in which we find ourselves.

We are projecting ourselves into an uncertain future, and increments, I think, would improve the range of choice rather than comprehensive planning, which would limit it.

Finally, to take a sort of negative criterion, I suppose, I think that if you are dealing with the quality of the human environment the choice should not be confined to concern with scarcity. I do not think scarcity puts the problem in the right frame of reference. I think if development means anything it means creating a better environment, and we need to use natural resources in this development.

It seems to me that the value natural resources can give depends on conceiving of them as instruments for change and growth, instruments by which we can improve the situation as distinguished from instruments by which we can prevent the situation from deteriorating.

This leads me to the final point—which has been brought up by other people at various times—that the fundamental resource, and the one I don't believe is scarce at all, nor likely to become scarce, is the quality and wealth of the human mind. I think if we are prepared to invest in the improvement of the human mind and its capacity for imagination, we are dealing with a resource that is limited only by human will and understanding.

CLAWSON: By and large, social scientists and, even more, ecologists and other physical scientists have neglected the use of human time. We economists have been tremendously concerned with money—national income and measured money, gross national products, prices of different commodities, flow of funds, and all this sort of thing, but we have never really given much attention, nor have the sociologists, to the use of human time.

I set out in the paper (taking them from another article which I once helped to inspire) some very rough guesses as to how the total time of the American public was used in 1950, and as to how it might be used in the year 2000. Leisure is not uniquely inversely related to work but it depends in part upon the whole age composition and work force and so on of the population, and comes, as pointed out here, in three or four major kinds: daily leisure hours, weekend leisure hours, vacation time, and retired time. The latter, for instance, has increased very largely and will continue to increase; paid vacations have also increased. My own conviction is that over the next generation or more the competition for time of people is going to become enormously more acute than the competition for income.

The estimates which I make here—and I might say, to anticipate any critics, I have been roundly attacked on each side that I was very much too high, and very much too low on my estimates of future leisure—include an approximate 12 per cent increase in per capita leisure between 1950 and 2000.

Since a great deal of leisure is taken up with mere routine daily activities, the usable part of that leisure for outdoor recreation and other fairly large undertakings might rise a good bit more than 12 per cent, but still there are very real limits, and it will vary enormously according to your age and occupation and sex and so on.

In contrast, it seems highly probable that over this same period of time the per capita real income will double or more and therefore I think we will see increasingly stiff competition for time of people. I suspect most of you in this room are finding time more of a limiting factor on your activities than you do income. I frequently have said that I am broke as to money, but bankrupt as to time, and that may apply to others as well. The good share of this paper is taken up with the exploration of outdoor recreation as within use of leisure time. To the best of my ability to estimate it, it is a minor use of leisure time, using something like less than 5 per cent of the total leisure.

This may seem awfully small, but curiously enough a great many people do not engage in outdoor recreation and have no intention of doing it. Most of us do not engage in any outdoor recreation in our daily leisure time. We do more on weekend leisure, but still it is by no means dominant. And we are outdoors still more on vacation time. I think outdoor recreation could well rise as a percentage use of leisure in the future, although this is speculative.

FISHER: Thank you. The last of our group is Dick Meier. I introduced him as an economist and I did that quite well, without strain. He could have been introduced as a scientist or an engineer or planner equally well. He is a phenomenon, also a person.

I remember once before I commented, I guess, on a paper of yours and said something to the effect that if you didn't exist, we should have to invent you.

I won't predict what Dick will say.

MEIER: Actually, my challenge was to figure out, as far as I was concerned, what kind of surprises are being hatched in the very recent literature. This was a challenge to me because up until about three years ago the literature had been very thoroughly researched by Joe Fisher and his colleagues at RFF. It was with some interest then that I was looking around for new developments within the area of science or anything else that had these surprises that would be relevant to this Conference.

I was quite conscious of these nonmonetary types of accounts, and I actually started thinking in terms of where the bind was likely to come, or the bankruptcies, in time accounts, in energy accounts, in space accounts, and in entropy accounts, entropy being the knowledge system that Boulding has been describing. Out of those I found a few that are of interest that begin to suggest that if this Conference were held ten years from now there would be quite a bit of talk in different areas from those we are discussing today; I am in effect trying to bring your attention to the kind of areas about which such talk might proceed ten years hence.

One of these areas derives from the balances within the energy accounts. When we begin to see the kinds of fossil fuels that are likely to be developed and that the demand for fossil fuels, despite somewhat improving efficiencies in their use, will be quite substantial, we see that it is likely the economy will be directed toward the more western side of the Great Lakes than before because of the tar sands and of the large coal deposits in the mid-continent next to the Rocky Mountain area.

That has many interesting applications, much more for pollution than for people, because as one projects jobs there are probably enough people already in the area to handle the jobs. It takes about half a million to a million dollars' worth of equipment in those areas in refining petrol chemicals, etc., to create a job. Although the investment would be very large, and the threats to the environment would be very considerable, the shifts in population probably would not be very great. In most instances I think we know enough, if it were only to be organized, so that they can be accommodated.

Another major problem area concerns the growth of knowledge. I did not put any numbers to the rate of the growth of knowledge or some of the implications of a growth of knowledge, mainly because I was myself disconcerted in the last year or so. I thought I had fairly good measures of the rate of growth in knowledge, in physics and chemistry, logic, law, and some of the social sciences and was disconcerted by some of the recent studies in Washington which indicated that the so-called growth of knowledge was based upon indices which are much more dependent upon the finances made available to the respective professional societies than upon the actual growth of knowledge. The chemists, therefore, being the richest and the oldest in the field, had a growth of chemical knowledge of 7 per cent per year in their abstracting systems; but what had been happening is that they had been invading all the neighboring areas of knowledge. So you just see the imperialism of the chemists spreading over the seat of knowledge. And the physicists are doing the same thing these days.

If you are adding these basic nouns, let us say, to the system, actually more relationships than that are being added and there may be a 3 per cent growth rate per year. That is still an explosion.

The way in which new knowledge will be needed for application to future problems can be illustrated by a past experience of mine. I was invited three years ago to Athens, on a Ford Foundation venture. We were trying to find out how the cities of the twenty-first century would be constructed and where they would be, how they might be organized, and what resources they would use. We set up a model that was supposed to be worked in our absence, as to how to move the people from where they are now multiplying to those places where they can ultimately reside.

The name of the city was given already. It was called the Ecumenopolis. This is Doxiadis' invention. When I came back the second year, they greeted me somewhat diffidently. There was some trouble, I could see. They said, "It now looks as if we will have to accommodate a few more people than we had anticipated before."

I said, "How many?"

They said, "Due to political disturbances, we had to plan for twenty million people or so for the Ecumenopolis, at least, and we must be able to handle a range of fifteen million to thirty-five million."

Then the next problem was that there wasn't enough room upstream, that the water supplies were limiting over the long run, and that they would have to move people around the earth—they would have to resettle them. It looked like fresh water supplies in the interior of the continents would be one of the limiting factors, there not being enough room on the fringe of continents where they could desalinate sea water.

They said, curiously enough, there wasn't enough reservoir capacity in Asia or in Africa. Africa was the best of the large continents. South America had very little, given its land reforms.

I could see what was coming. I said, "How many do you want to move to the Great Lakes?"

They said, "At least three million."

My reaction was, "Where are the rest going?"

They said, "According to the model, we can't place them anywhere, so we have left them at sea."

I said, "Why don't we leave them there?"

(*Laughter*)

So that the question was, was it technically feasible to leave them at sea if the world population expanded to those dimensions?

To our surprise, as a kind of offshoot of missiles and aerospace programs, it does look now as if we can build technical systems that will stand up under typhoons, etc., and the cost level is only 50 per cent higher than middle-class suburbs and is declining; there is then a possibility of thinking through the processes of starting from the fringe of the land and handling the invasion of the sea.

It will probably start with North America, rather than with Asia, because we here can afford it, and then it will move, in a cheap dime-store version, very likely to Asia and Egypt and a few other places.

Here we have a chance to synthesize a human ecosystem in equilibrium or steady state with cities all over again, at a higher state of knowledge than we had in the past.

FISHER: Thank you very much, Dick.

My own paper carries the title "Natural Resources and Economic Development: The Web of Events, Policies, and Policy Objectives." What I do in this is to play these three things against one another, more or less in this manner: that we may begin, we will say, with a policy objective of economic growth, national development, resource conservation, or something like that, and these are factored out into more tangible policies having to do with sustained-yield forestry, or soil conservation, or something like this, and these in turn lead into programs and activities and events. Things happen.

A lot of things happen that weren't intended, or things happen that were conceived of in other connections that get in the way. Yet in the end the events themselves positively reflect the policies and objectives.

You can find many examples of this.

In the thirties we conceived a number of farm programs in the United States aimed primarily to lift incomes of farm people. These led to certain events, most of them not intended or intended exactly the way they turned out, which in turn have caused us to readjust not only the policies but the very objectives of the policies. Then I say in my paper that understanding the interplay of these events, policies, and policy objectives is necessary as a basis for speculating about the economic future of resources and resource activities.

I end my paper with a few speculations which are not particularly strange to any of you, relating primarily to the United States and Canada. One speculation that I think is a good one is that there will be no sheer quantitative problem, no lack of resources in any major sense in these two countries for a good many decades to come. There may be spot problems such as not enough water at a certain place or not enough outdoor recreation land near New York City, but no very massive problem.

There will be enough to eat, enough shelter, enough transport, enough energy.

The second speculation is that I do, however, see severe qualitative problems all along the line if you will allow the abstraction of separating the quantity from the quality. We have had a good deal of talk about this already, and the word "pollution" conjures the whole thing up—water pollution, air pollution, etc. In my community of Arlington, Virginia, the thing that irritates people most under this heading is not the water pollution or air pollution, or the disfigurement of the landscape, or the dumping of beer cans beside the road, but the sheer noise—principally of airplanes going into and taking off from the National Airport, which is in Arlington.

There is a very high level of emotion and concern about this throughout the country.

A third speculation I worked over a little bit is concerned with some of the problems that seem to stem from the growth of cities and metropolitan areas which I think most of us as conservationists are aware of and thoroughly prepared to accept, but we haven't really thought about them long enough and hard enough to see their full dimensions.

I wind up by saying that so far as I can see it, the prescription for the United States and Canada for a planning horizon over the rest of this century is to be found in keeping up a pretty full head of steam on science, technology, planning, resource conservation, management, administration, and most of all education, which is the fuel and the support under all of these things.

ECONOMICS AND ECOLOGY
Kenneth E. Boulding*

The two sciences whose names are derived from the same Greek root, economics and ecology, have had surprisingly little contact, no doubt because of our deplorably compartmentalized systems of education. For some reason the sociologists and the ecologists seem to have had much more in common, for human ecology, at least, has long been a recognized branch of sociology. This is perhaps because sociology and ecology, as recognized departments of science, are about the same age, whereas economics is much older, dating back as a systematic body of theory at least to Adam Smith's *Wealth of Nations* in 1776. Even though, as we shall see, there are striking parallels between the concepts of ecology and economics—and I believe the two sciences can learn a good deal from each other— up to this point, there has been little interaction between them. From the Greek root one would suspect that each science is devoted to the study of households, one to the household of nature, the other to the household of man, and in a broad,

though very broad, sense this is true. One of the central concerns of ecology is the way in which all natural species earn their living—that is, attain the input which is necessary for their survival. Economics likewise is concerned very largely with how man earns his living. Nevertheless, both ecology and economics go far beyond this initial concept and devote themselves essentially to the study of how the interaction of individuals and species constitutes a total system.

I have detected at least five basic similarities between ecology and economics, and there are probably more. In the first place, they both study not only individuals as such, but individuals as members of species. The concept of a population of like individuals constituting a species is indeed fundamental to ecology. The corresponding concept in economics is that of the commodity, and it is easy to see the population of commodities as a simple extension of natural species. The automobile, the pair of shoes, and the loaf of bread are just as much members of species as the whooping crane and the horse, or indeed man himself. A somewhat casual observer from outer space indeed might well deduce that the course of evolution in this planet had produced a species of large four-wheeled bugs with detachable brains; peculiar animals which rested when they sent their brains away from them but performed in rather predictable manners when their brains were recalled.

* Professor Boulding is an economist active in general-systems theory who has also broken new ground in integrating the concerns and techniques of economics and ecology. A Professor of Economics at the University of Michigan, he holds the John B. Clark medal from the American Economic Association and is a member of the American Philosophical Society. It was while working at the Center for Advanced Study in Behavioral Sciences at Stanford, California, that he finished his book *The Image*, which appeared in 1956.

Commodities, of course, are not the only social species. We also have organizations, such as farms, steel firms, PTAs, schools, churches, and so on. It is just as reasonable to talk about the distribution and habitat of the Kingdom Halls of Jehovah's Witnesses or the supermarkets of the A&P as it is to discuss the distribution and habitats of field mice. Each of these species is equally part of an ecological system. In this sense we see economics as a subspecies of ecology, studying that restricted group of species and individuals which enter into exchange—that is, commodities, and studying particularly those kinds of organizations, such as firms or even households, whose activities center around exchange.

Like all populations, populations of commodities consist of individuals which are born, which age, and which even die. The analysis of a population of automobiles differs in no respect from the analysis of a population of horses, as long as we stick to the birth, aging, and death phenomena alone. I have indeed (1955) analyzed the population of automobiles from the point of view of finding out the results of some distortions in the age distribution,[1] exactly as one might analyze a similar population of natural species. The principal difference between populations of commodities and natural populations lies in the genetic apparatus by which births are made. The death or survival functions are highly similar in both cases, though there may be more infant mortality in the case of natural populations. When it comes down to the birth functions, however, striking differences occur. It only takes the cooperation of a horse and a mare to produce a colt, whereas the cooperation of two automobiles has never produced another. Sex and sexual reproduction are vir-

tually unknown in the world of man-made commodities, although, of course, insofar as natural species become commodities, such as domestic animals, the natural processes of sexual reproduction are significant. Even here, however, the effective birth rate depends much more on the decisions of man than on chances of nature, and there is really more similarity in principle between the reproductive processes of the domestic animal and the domestic automobile than there is between the domestic and the wild animal.

A second similarity between economics and ecology is that both have an important concept of general equilibrium. In the case of ecology this is a concept of general equilibrium of population, depending on a proposition that the birth and death rate of each species is a function of the numbers of all species, and that an equilibrium system can be postulated in which the birth rate and the death rate are equated for all species in the long run. The struggle for existence, indeed, can be regarded as a rather elaborate computer for solving these equations. If there is no solution to a particular set of equations, one or more of the species must disappear, and this will go on until a solution is found. Frequently when a solution is found, it is surprisingly stable in what might be called the medium run. The equilibrium of species in a lake or a pond, for instance, seems to be stable for quite large disturbances. If we take 25 or even 50 per cent of the individuals of a particular species out of the system, in a year or two the old numbers are restored. Any ecological system, of course, is likely to exhibit what are sometimes called watershed points, beyond which the old system will not be restored but a new process will be set up leading to a new equilibrium. In economics we do not usually postulate a simple system of ecological equilibrium of populations of different commodities,

[1] Boulding, K. E., "An Application of Population Analysis to the Automobile Population of the United States," *Kylos* 2(1955): pp. 109–24.

even though there is no fundamental reason why this could not be done. The general equilibrium of the price system, however, as developed, for instance, by Walras or by Hicks, or even as implied by Adam Smith and Alfred Marshall, has many basic similarities to a system of ecological equilibrium. It implies, for instance, that the birth rate, which is the rate of production, and the death rate, which is the rate of consumption, of all commodities should be equal, so that the stocks of commodities should remain unchanged. In the case of economic equilibrium, we generally postulate that production and consumption are functions of the set of prices rather than of the set of stocks of commodities. Nevertheless, as the set of prices is itself functionally related to the set of stocks, it is clear that the price set is in a sense an intermediary or an additional set of variables in the system, and its introduction does not alter the basically ecological framework of economic equilibrium. Indeed, it is quite easy to extend the concepts which are analogous to the price system.

This, indeed, is the third basic similarity. Both ecological and economic systems involve a system of exchange among their various individuals and species as an essential element in determining their final equilibrium. In the case of economics, this system of exchange is symbolized in the price system, which is the set of rates of exchange of different commodities with each other. In the case of ecological systems, the exchange consists of the metabolic system—that is, the ratios of inputs to outputs of different individuals, organisms, or species. In both cases there has to be a system of balances of payments. That is, for any segment of the system and for any particular input or output, input must equal output in the long run, otherwise there will be accumulations or decumulations of something in different parts of the system which will destroy the equilibrium. Thus in ecological systems we have a subtle balance of payments in, for instance, the nitrogen cycle and all the various nutritive cycles, by which the various elements which comprise the organisms are circulated through the system. The one important difference between ecological and economic systems is that there seems to be no parallel in ecological systems for the economic concept of money, perhaps because in ecological systems there is no overriding species in the interests of which the value of the system is gauged. Man needs a medium of exchange and a measure of value in the form of money, because he needs to refer the whole system of commodities to his own welfare. In ecology no single species has the temerity to arrogate to itself the character of judge of everything that goes on, and hence no general and uniform measure of value is needed.

A fourth similarity between economics and ecology is that both imply some concept of development. Neither of them is content with the concept of equilibrium as such. In the case of ecology, this involves the concept of ecological succession—that is, the process by which the underlying determinants of the system of ecological equilibrium change in the course of the operations of the system. A famous example, of course, is the gradual filling up of the lake bed by the operations of the ecological system which comprises the lake. The plants and animals gradually absorb carbon from the air, more is washed into the lake than is washed out, and in the course of time the lake shrinks and eventually becomes a swamp, a prairie, or perhaps a forest. In the search for sources of development we have to look for irreversible processes. In the case of ecological systems, we find these not only in certain cumulative processes which violate the principle of equilibrium of balance of payments—that is, balance of inputs and outputs—but we find it also in the phenomenon of genetic mutation. Genetic mutation, by creating individuals of a new species or a potential new species, introduces new parameters into the equations of ecological equilibrium. In the great majority of cases, the old equilibrium is stable enough so that the new species are rejected and perish. In a few cases, however, the mutation is favorable enough so that it survives and then a new equilibrium has to be found for the ecological equations. The whole process of evolution can then be written in terms of successive solutions of the ecological equations under the impact of genetic mutation.

Social evolution exhibits many parallels to the process of natural evolution, and we have ecological succession in society just as we do in the pond or the forest. Here again there seem to be two major processes at work which correspond to the processes of simple accumulation on the one hand and processes of genuine mutation on the other. It is harder to tell these apart in social systems because of the extreme complexity of the genetic process of social species, but the distinction seems to be an interesting one. The cumulative growth of population and the accumulation of capital in the form of larger numbers of the same kind of good represents the sort of thing which seems to go on in the filling up of a pond, and as both population and capital accumulate, certain changes take place in the social system simply as a result of the greater densities of people and things. This, however, is quite inadequate to explain the great processes of social evolution, and again we have to introduce something that looks like mutation in the form of new ideas, new ideology, and new inventions, both mechanical, biological, and social. As in systems of natural evolution, a great many mutations do not survive, but enough survive to introduce what seems to be a constant irreversible succession of social and economic equilibria.

A critical problem in social evolution which also has important implications for natural evolution is that of the growth of knowledge. This is the principal source of the irreversibility of the process of social evolution, and once mankind got past the paleolithic and entered the age of agriculture and metals, this process seems to have been virtually irreversible and constantly cumulative. In the paleolithic period, there seem to have been many times when the slow growth of knowledge was interrupted by an epidemic or a natural disaster which simply carried off the few people in whose heads the accumulated knowledge resided. With mankind living in small clusters and without the aids of writing or records, the "wisdom of the tribe" must have been in constant danger of loss by death, simply because it was contained in so few heads. With the advent of agriculture and especially of writing, the chance of loss of knowledge was much less, and it seems to have entered into its irreversible cumulative phase. There were, of course, periods of retrogression, especially in particular localities, but if we look at the whole world as a single system it seems pretty clear that in the last 8000 years there has been practically no period in which the "quantity of science," as Adam Smith calls it, has diminished. Furthermore, the growth of knowledge seems to be not only cumulative but it seems also to accumulate at an increasing rate. The more knowledge there is, the easier it seems to be to find still more, for one of the items of knowledge which grows is the knowledge of how to find more knowledge.

If we think of knowledge as a species, we see that this also grows, in part, by simple accumulation—that is, the addition of more items than are subtracted in a given period, as, for instance, the simple growth of vocabulary in a language. There is also, however, a phenomenon that looks very much like mutation. This is the reorganization of knowledge into a new system, a new theory, a new way of looking at things, or even a new ideology. This happens usually in a single mind, from which, however, it can be propagated rapidly through a whole society if it happens to fit the particular ecological system of ideas which is prevailing at the moment. The spread of the growth of knowledge therefore seems to follow many of the principles of ecology, and the various kinds of knowledge flourish or decline according to the competition of other kinds of knowledge and according to the general habitat in which they are found.

We may note parenthetically that while there are some elements in this process of socioecological succession which might be called dialectical; in fact, the dialectical scheme adds very little to our understanding of this process, and most of the great processes of ecological succession are in fact nondialectical, in the sense that they do not operate through a process of thesis, antithesis, and synthesis, but rather through the introduction of small parametric changes into the equations of equilibrium. There is competition and conflict, of course, in the processes of ecological succession, but the conflict is among a particular species, not among systems as a whole. Even the phenomenon of ecological revolution, in which a small change in some parameter of the system leads to a total transformation in the habitat of the numbers and kinds of species in equilibrium, there is nothing that really looks like a dialectical process. When, for instance, a slight change in rainfall or perhaps in temperature destroys the equilibrium of the forest and eventually produces the prairie, this is not because the prairie as antithesis challenges and conquers the forest as a thesis, but simply because of the fact that under some circumstances a relatively small change in the parameters of the habitat controls large changes in

final position of equilibrium. For this reason it seems to me the ecological point of view is profoundly unfriendly to the Hegelian-Marxist view of the nature of the world, and leads into what I have elsewhere called a developmental rather than a dialectical philosophy of history, in which emphasis is placed not on the Hegelian-Marxist type of revolution in which one system is overthrown by another but on the long, slow, quiet nondialectical processes by which equilibrium positions change.

A fifth important parallel between economics and ecological systems falls under the general head of policy. That is the distortion of the equilibrium of the system by man in his own favor. In the case of ecological systems, we see this most clearly exemplified in agriculture. Here man deliberately interferes with the "natural" ecosystem of a piece of land, producing corn and hogs instead of prairie grass and gophers, or trees and squirrels. This distortion of the natural ecosystem requires constant intervention in the shape of plowing, harrowing, sowing, harvesting, and so on, and indeed many domesticated species of both plants and animals have now got to the point where they would be quite incapable of surviving without a symbiotic relationship with man. Corn, for instance, in its present form could not possibly survive in a wild state, and the same is probably true of many domestic animals, although there is some possibility that these might retreat toward a state in which they were capable of surviving in the absence of man, were his hand to be removed. Corresponding to agriculture in the natural ecosystem we have policy at all levels in the social system. The law, for instance, is supposed to discourage criminals in much the same manner that harrowing or weed killer discourages weeds. Similarly, the institutions of education and religion are supposed to promote intelligent citizens and happy families. I recall once walking in the jungles of Brazil with a distinguished British economist and remarking as we contemplated the tangled growth that this at least showed that anarchy was possible. He came back immediately with, "Yes, but it also shows that it is not desirable." Without some form of policy as expressed primarily through political organization, the social ecosystem tends to degenerate into a jungle, and the well-ordered society seems to require a "farmer" in the shape of government to distort the natural social ecosystem in favor of some ideals or values.

Both in the case of agriculture and in the case of social policy, however, the fact that we distort the ecosystem in favor of man does not mean that we destroy the principles of general equilibrium of populations. Unless, indeed, we know something about the laws which govern this general equilibrium, we shall not be very successful in distorting it toward our heart's desire. If man is to achieve a distribution of populations of all kinds which conforms to his own values, he must at least learn to cooperate with the great ecological forces which determine the equilibrium of coexisting populations, otherwise he is likely to be grievously disappointed. His crops will fail, his irrigated acres will turn saline, his animals will fail to produce or will die, and his social policies will turn out to have unintended and undesirable consequences. It is hardly too much to say that the failure to appreciate the ecological point of view and to see society as an enormous interacting network of coexisting populations is behind the failure of most social policies.

Up to now we have looked at the similarities between economics and ecology, and indeed these are striking. For the rest of the paper I intend to look more closely at the differences, for these also are important and without proper appreciation of these differences, false analogies may be drawn and the two disciplines will fail to learn the appropriate lessons from each other. The differences arise, I think, not out of any fundamental principle except insofar, as already noted, that the genetic apparatus of social species and populations is very different from that of biological species. The differences arise out of different sets of values, particularly as applied to the whole system. Economists are irretrievably and irredeemably man-centered. Economics is the theory of the household of man, not the household of nature. Ecologists, by contrast, tend to have a value system which encompasses all species. In their underlying value systems, ecologists often tend more toward Hindu or Buddhist values, in which man is seen as only part and perhaps not even a very important part of a vast natural order. Economics, however, emerged out of a civilization, part of Western Europe, that was created largely by Christianity and which regarded man as the measure of all things and the universe as existing mainly for his pleasure and salvation. Ecologists, therefore, have a strong tendency to look with affection on the whooping crane, to regard the disappearance of any species as a major tragedy, and to regard man on the whole as a nuisance, upsetting the balance of nature, destroying the ancient equilibria of the world, and generally behaving like an outrageous and irresponsible caretaker of his delightful planet. The economist, by contrast, is much more apt to look at things from a strictly human view and while he would no doubt regret the passing of the whooping crane, when the chips are really down, the question he asks himself is, what would it cost to preserve it?—cost in terms of strictly human values.

The contrast is seen very clearly when we reflect that ecology has really no concept corresponding to the enonomists' gross national product. It never occurs to the ecologist to try to evaluate the ecological system in terms of a single measure. One sees occasional references to the total mass of living matter which a given habitat will support, but I have never seen ecologists pay much attention to this, and they certainly would not judge the desirability or interest of a habitat by this measure. I have never heard any mention of the gross carbo-hydrate product or the gross protein product of a habitat, and indeed concepts of this kind are quite foreign to the multidimensional, structural, interaction-ist point of view of the ecologist. The economist, on the other hand, has seized upon the concept of the national product with the avidity of the dog seizing a bone. The sophisticated economist, of course, knows that the concept involves a great many dubious assumptions and that it has to be interpreted pretty care-fully. Nevertheless, he is not at all dis-pleased to find this concept becoming important in political discourse and used in measuring the over-all progress of the society or the comparative position of different economies. The absence of any gross-product concept in ecology and its presence in economics stem directly from the human orientation of economics and the tendency of economists to reduce large complex systems to some single-value parameter descriptive of their value to man, whereas ecologists have no such interest.

There is, indeed, a deep ethical prob-lem involved in this difference, and one which is by no means easy to resolve. It is a problem which becomes more acute all the time as the power of man over nature increases. The problem has be-come particularly acute because of the pressure on the resources of the earth which comes from man's exploding popu-lation. In a world of a few hundred million human beings, most other spe-cies can survive fairly easily. The growth of the human population may, perhaps,

threaten a few highly localized species, but does not threaten to upset the gen-eral constitution and distribution of liv-ing populations. When the human popu-lation grows to three billion, even more when it grows to ten billion, as it soon will, the pressure on all other populations becomes acute. In the next hundred years, indeed, if things go on the way they are going, we face the extinction of very large numbers of species of both animals and plants, as man in his in-satiable pressure for food supplies gob-bles up all the wilderness and turns it into agriculture or something like it for his own use. The lion, the elephant, the tiger, the hippopotamus, the rhinoceros, the ostrich may soon go the way of the passenger pigeon or the dodo, and very little can be done about it. If the price of not extinguishing the lion population, for instance, is the survival of a few thou-sand humans, who would pay the price? It is one thing when a little care and conservation will preserve a nonhuman population, such as the whooping crane. It is quite another thing when the sur-vival of another species must be paid for in human life. The question, therefore, becomes one almost of theological im-port. Is man going to conceive of himself as a steward of the planet, conserving a priceless heritage of germ plasm and ge-netic code material which, once lost, can never be replaced, so that like a good steward he is willing to sacrifice himself in order to preserve his charge; or is man in himself literally the only thing that matters, in which case we face the brutal fact of the future (and the not really very distant future, at that), that in the absence of very stringent control of the human population, any species which cannot in some sense be domesti-cated is doomed.

The ultimate resolution of this ques-tion is clearly far beyond the scope of this paper. All one can hope to do is to put up a few warning signs, such as

Dead End Road for the ecologist or Thin Ice for the economist. The Dead End Road is a blind conservatism which simply takes the existing distribution of populations, particularly of natural populations, as given, sacred, and sacrosanct. It digs in its heels and regards any departure from the existing world ecosystem as undesirable. The economist, I think, can run rings around this position, and the cause of conservation has been substantially weakened because it has been associated in some cases with this blind and obstinate conservatism which regards all dynamic movements as bad. The logical outcome of this position would be the conclusion that the invention of man himself was deplorable and the only decent thing the human race could do would be to feed itself collectively to the lions and hope the evolutionary process would not make the mistake of creating intelligence of this kind again.

Whatever kind of sense we try to make out of the evolutionary process, it is clear that nature abhors a stationary equilibrium. Nature, in other words, is not a conservative. The evolutionary process destroyed more species than it created long before man appeared on the scene, and it is absurd to suppose that the existing distribution of genetic material in the shape of phenotypes represents the *summum bonum* of this part of the universe. Whether we like it or not and even whether man is here or not, the evolutionary process will continue, and to its blank and random stare nothing is sacred, not even the whooping crane. We have to face the fact, therefore, that since the advent of man the evolutionary process has been enormously speeded up, and that man, for good or ill, now has some kind of control over it, a control which is likely to increase even more dramatically in the future as the practical consequences of the recent revolution in biology are

worked out. Suppose, for instance, that in the next hundred years, as is by no means impossible, man is able to modify directly the gene pool of the earth and produce new species quite unheard of before, cranes with louder whoops, more ferocious lions, more absurd hippopotamuses, and even perhaps to re-create the dodo. One feels somehow that the ecologist will look with a kindlier eye on the creation of new species than on the destruction of old ones, but the ethical problem is much the same. The right, or the absence of right, to be born is just as much a moral problem as the right or the absence of right to survive. If the moral impact of the ecological point of view is to be felt, as it should be, it will have to develop a dynamic ethic which will accept the role of man as an evolutionary agent and seek to develop standards and criteria for evaluating this role, rather than taking refuge in a hopeless and obscurantist conservatism.

If, therefore, one wants to put up a few Dead End signs for the ecologist, one also wants to put up some Thin Ice signs for the economist. In his pursuit of purely human values, the economist may easily be running mankind itself into grave dangers. The Greeks were perhaps all too aware of the dangers of *hubris,* that pride and overweening self-confidence in the power or good fortunes of man which so easily leads to his downfall. The extraordinary achievements of the last 200 years have given us certain delusions of grandeur and a certain feeling that man can accomplish anything if he only puts his mind to it. We see this in its extreme form among the Communists, where a belief in the infallibility, omnipotence, and immortality of man and his societies reaches absurdities beyond the most extreme religious dogmas. Even Western economists, however, are by no means exempt from the belief that there are really no limits on man's capacity to manipulate the world to his own advantage. It is highly necessary, therefore, for the ecologist to take these flights of omnipotent fancy and bring them down solidly to earth, and to a highly limited earth at that. Man is beginning to inhabit a pretty small and overcrowded space ship, destination unknown, and the possibility that he may ruin it and himself in the process is by no means negligible. Here the conservatism of the ecologist is badly needed. The technical achievements of the last 200 years have been achieved largely with the aid of the spending of a long accumulation of geological capital in the shape of fossil fuels and ores. A very few hundred years, a mere tick of the clock even on a human time scale, will see these exhausted. One of the most critical questions before us is whether man can achieve a stable high-level economy with high energy and information input and high product output which is not dependent on fossil fuels and ores and exhaustible resources. There are certain indications that such an anti-entropic economy, as I have called it, is possible, and indeed may be just around the corner, but that particular corner has not yet been turned.

Economists, and indeed mankind generally, have tended to treat the economic system as if it could enter into continuous exchange with an infinite reservoir of nature. Thus we have regarded the atmosphere and the oceans as if they were infinite reservoirs which we could pollute indefinitely and from which we could draw indefinite supplies of what they had to offer. Similarly in regard to mines and fossil fuels, we have tended to treat the earth as if it were an infinite reservoir of these substances. This attitude has been less noticeable in the case of land, where, perhaps because of the relative smallness of the habitat, man in many of his societies has developed soil conserving practices which make him and the land together virtually a closed system, in which land is regarded not as an infinite reservoir but as a scarce resource which constantly has to be replenished. Even in the case of land, there has been a good deal of soil mining, often with disastrous results.

It is the peculiar virtue of the ecologist that he does look upon his system as essentially a closed system, in the sense that there are no imports from or exports to the outside apart from those which bring about the processes of ecological succession. In economics, this is what might be called the "space ship" point of view. If man is ever to make long voyages in space, he will have to develop a self-sustaining economy on a small scale, in which the very small capital stock which he is able to take with him will have to be circulated constantly through the system in such a way as to maintain his life and, in some degree, his comfort. We are now beginning to see the earth as a space ship, not only politically but also in economic terms. Even today it is clear that the oceans and the atmosphere are by no means inexhaustible reservoirs. It may be fatally easy, for instance, for man to change the composition of either of them in such a way that the earth will pass some watershed point—for instance, through something like the greenhouse effect of the accumulating carbon dioxide in the atmosphere —which will destroy the existing equilibrium and move us to a new equilibrium which may be much less desirable for man. As the human population increases, the chance of man's activities seriously interfering with the whole balance of the planet becomes greater and greater. One of the greatest contributions of the ecologist, therefore, is to point out that the earth is in fact a total ecosystem of which man's activities are only a part, and that he can no longer regard himself as operating with infinite reservoirs.

This does not mean, I think, that the

problem of operating the earth as a high-level space ship without any inexhaustible reservoirs is insoluble. In what might be called traditional agriculture, indeed, man has already largely solved the problem of a self-sustaining economy on a permanent basis. Even though our existing economy is essentially suicidal, depending as it is on past accumulations of natural capital in the shape of ores and fuels but also in the shape of the atmosphere and the oceans, it is not unreasonable to look upon the present era as a chance which man has (and probably a unique chance at that, which will never be repeated) of translating his natural capital into enough knowledge that will enable him to do without it. We can certainly imagine a world economy at a high level in which man's life and comfort depend on a self-sustaining process in which the input of energy and knowledge is enough to counteract the otherwise inevitable increase of entropy. Either the energy input will have to come from the sun, which from the point of view of mankind has to be regarded as inexhaustible, or of course it may be supplemented with energy from nuclear fusion, which is, in a sense, the same thing. We do not know how large the knowledge input has to be. I think this is a problem which is theoretically capable of some kind of answer. At the moment, however, we do not really know whether the knowledge input is just a little more than what we have today or whether it requires knowledge of another order of magnitude than what we now have, in which case man's long-run situation is probably hopeless. There is no point, however, in acting upon hopeless assumptions. We might as well assume that there is hope, and get on with the business of trying to realize it.

A critical question on which, as far as I know, very little work has been done is: What is the optimum total population of the world under this space-ship type of self-sustaining economy? It may very well be that out of the space research of the next generation an answer to the question will emerge, and I know of no question of greater import for the long-run future of mankind. If it turns out, say, that only something like a hundred million people can live in real comfort on this particular space ship, a terrible agony is in front of man, for he has never succeeded in reducing his population without enormous disaster. If the earth can support three billion, we still have time to catch the population increase, though not much. If it can support ten billion, we have a fair amount of time, at least a couple of generations. The problem, however, is urgent, and it would be quite easy for the current population expansion to carry the load of this planet beyond a point and the world would, in an almost literal sense, sink. Ecologists have sometimes compared the present growth of population rather gruesomely to the explosive expansion of the first occupants of new or changed habitats, like the fireweed after a forest fire. These first occupants, however, are rarely the last occupants, and the climactic ecosystem is usually very different from the initial one. This is a grim note to sound, but it is, I think, the peculiar business of ecologists to be pessimistic. In these days ecology may well take the mantle of doom and the name of "the dismal science" from economics.

BIBLIOGRAPHY

Boulding, K. E. 1955. An Application of Population Analysis to the Automobile Population of the United States. Kylos 2:109–24.

STANDARDS AND TECHNIQUES OF EVALUATING ECONOMIC CHOICES IN ENVIRONMENTAL RESOURCE DEVELOPMENT

Ayers Brinser*

"Environmental resource development," if it means anything, probably means a great many different things to a wide variety of people. Economic choice is reasonably specific. It is essentially an attempt to state as clearly as possible the question: Who should pay how much for what? The problem at hand is to attempt to join these badly matched terms to produce a definition of criteria that would be useful in guiding decisions about the kind of world in which we hope to live.

If this mésalliance is to produce viable offspring, environmental resource development has to be translated into terms that can be weighed on an economic scale. At the same time, it must be assumed that the term means something more than resource allocation and investment, otherwise "environmental" would be an irrelevant adjective. At the risk of losing some important and unique quality, for the purposes of this discussion, environmental resource development will be considered an equivalent to economic welfare defined to include as a major objective the enhancement of the quality of living. Furthermore, the aspects of welfare under consideration will be restricted to those goods, services, and sat-

isfactions flowing from the development of the natural landscape. It must be admitted that in any final analysis this last restriction is meaningless. To be valid, economic criteria must ultimately mediate the whole range of economic decisions that affect the level of living now and in the predictable future. It is useful to begin with a limited range, but in the end whether one starts with forests, wildlife, or iron ore the value produced is measured in terms of a net result to the whole economy.

It is by no means clear that economics as defined by many practicing economists is a proper instrument for evaluating decisions about investment in environmental development. One distinguished student of these problems came to the melancholy conclusion that "economic welfare is a subject in which rigor and refinement are probably worse than useless."[1] For a practitioner of the academic arts to approach a subject by first casting out

* Professor Brinser teaches resource economics and public policy at the School of Natural Resources of the University of Michigan. He has taken an active interest in community planning, watershed development, and natural resources policy.

[1] I. M. D. Little, A Critique of Welfare Economics, Oxford University Press, 1957, p. 279. It should be added that Mr. Little did not stop with this counsel of despair. He continues: "Rough theory, or good common sense, is, in practice, what we require. It is satisfying, and impressive, that a rigorous logical system, with some apparent reality, should have been set up in the field of the social sciences; but we must not let ourselves be so impressed that we forget that its reality is obviously limited; and that the degree of such reality is a matter of judgement and opinion."

the opportunity for "rigor" and "refinement" is tantamount to saying that it is irrelevant. Yet, in spite of the low estate of welfare in the canon of academic economics, the problems it poses are becoming more obviously significant as more and more government programs are set up to produce a growing array of social goods and what Musgrave called "merit wants." Economists cannot avoid making prescriptions about how and why the quality of the environment should be managed, but they do this largely by implication. By this device, environmental resource development is subsumed under the aegis of economic development. Development becomes expanding the gross national product and the rate of growth. Rigor and refinement are restored by quantifying the measurable inputs and outputs as a workable index of welfare.

A consideration of the validity of such an index has the virtue at least of carrying the argument beyond a discussion about words. While gross national product may be an index of the direction of welfare, and that is by no means certain, practically no one today would accept it as a measure of welfare. The real issues are, rather: Must we be satisfied with it as the best possible yardstick? Should we abandon economic measures altogether because they are more than a little imperfect? Or is it possible to adapt economic criteria to the kinds of decisions that determine the quality of the environment?

Nothing would be gained by continuing this discussion if it were not assumed that economic criteria can be adapted to the decisions that determine environmental resource development. Therefore, a way must be found to reconcile measures of economic value with the physical, social, and esthetic values that are created by the organic processes of the environment. The conventional standard for economic performance has long been efficiency. In a world in which both absolute and relative scarcity has been the dominant condition, the primary emphasis has naturally been on efficiency of production. If by environmental resources we mean space and the natural features of the landscape, they are already produced. Their further development is largely a problem of resource allocation and the quality of consumption. The criterion for development is quantity weighted by quality of satisfactions made available.

Economics can provide tests of the internal consistency of the criteria that may be used to measure the factors that influence the quality of the environment. Economic models can measure most of the direct costs of environmental development. Concepts such as opportunity costs and shadow pricing can provide an indication of what the value of the goods produced should be when it is impossible to use direct market prices as a measure. In the past decade we have developed increasingly sophisticated techniques for distinguishing more from less on an ordinal if not a cardinal scale. All of these are necessary aids to rational choice among alternative ways to develop the resources of the environment. But as the method of measurement becomes more precise we become less certain that the significant variables are being measured.[2]

[2] "There does seem to have been, at least until recently, something fundamentally circle-squaring in the alleged primary purpose of welfare economics of 'trying to set standards of judgement by which events and policies can be judged as economically desirable,' or to 'formulate propositions by which we may rank, on the scale of better or worse, alternative economic situations open to society,' and to do this within the confines, apparently, of only such value judgements, if any, as are universally or generally acceptable, or as part of 'a positive science of what is and tends to be, not a normative science of what ought to be.' It is from this basic claim, or attempt of welfare economics, or the attitude it represents or fosters, that so much confusion has resulted for the discussion of policies, in that choice is rather eliminated than elucidated."

This becomes a very complex issue when, as in the present instance, the data to be evaluated for a program of development cannot be quantified in economic terms. For example, the earth sciences and the life sciences have established bodies of data and analytical systems that are tested by criteria quite different from those available to the social sciences. The political scientist and the sociologist are concerned with processes of decision making in which economic criteria are only a small proportion of the variables. The economist attempts to confine himself to determining which choices will yield more satisfaction with less expenditure of resources over a determined time period. But the more and less with which he is concerned involve both physical properties that are in the province of the natural scientist and the value systems with which the political scientist and the sociologist work. An attempt to synthesize all of these is not without peril, as the fate of Herbert Spencer and Social Darwinism attests.[3]

The growing body of literature on this subject leads to two conclusions. There is now no readily available way out of this dilemma, and the problem is sufficiently relevant to our well-being and growth that we must seek to find one.[4]

Rather than postulate a grand design for an economic solution to the problem and then be met with the necessity of using the *ceteris paribus* principle to avoid facing the real issues, it may be more useful to attempt to approach the solution in short steps knowing that you will never really get there but that you have a chance of moving in the right direction and possibly of getting closer.

As a point of departure it is useful to identify the economic concepts that are relevant to evaluating man's place in his environment. It must be assumed that man is the center of interest in the environment. The measure of success in managing the interaction of man and his environment is the quality of real choices open to him over time.[5] The means for achieving objectives involving economic decisions shall be consistent with the goals and within this constraint greater satisfactions achieved at less cost are more desirable. Up to this point and in this system, economics is neutral. It merely indicates in very general terms how a decision to consume, preserve, or develop might be made if a system for valuing the quality of the environment were given.

Environmental resources have many of the characteristics of common property. Many are owned by units of government. Their protection and development depend on public investment. A large proportion of the important services they provide, such as scenery, are not consumed when they are used. The quality of the environment is imperfectly measured by the market. When the objective is preservation for future generations, those who bear the costs are denied the benefits. In general, these are some of the reasons why the management of en-

T. W. Hutchinson, *"Positive" Economics and Policy Objectives*, London, George Allen & Unwin Ltd., pp. 159–60.

[3] This is not to say that attempts to achieve a synthesis have not continued since Spencer. Cf. Walter Firey, *Man, Mind and Land*, in which an effort is made to bring economics and sociology to bear on problems of resource use. Walter Firey, *Man, Mind and Land*, The Free Press, Glencoe, Illinois, 1960.

[4] This brief list of titles may at least suggest the range of the inquiry: R. A. Dahl and C. E. Lindblom, *Politics, Economics and Welfare*; J. K. Galbraith, *The Affluent Society*; J. Tinbergen, *Economic Policy: Principles and Design*; Gunnar Myrdal, *Values in Social Theory*; G. L. S. Shackle, *Decision, Order and Time in Human Affairs*; M. Oakeshott, *Rationalism in Politics*; K. R. Popper, *Conjectures and Refutations*.

[5] This follows in a general sense the formulation of I. M. D. Little, *A Critique of Welfare Economics*, second edition, Oxford University Press, 1957, especially Chapters VI, VII, and XIV.

vironmental resources depends on public intervention. Therefore, the economic criteria relevant to decisions about how they shall be used and developed include both private-market choices and tests of public policy.

Most economists once did believe, and some now do believe, that the private market if left to its own self-equilibrating devices creates an optimum allocation of resources and distribution of income and consequently an optimum rate of growth and development. The problem of economics in these terms is to avoid imperfections and frictions in the system. With a growing concern for the quality of what is produced and its availability over time, most people have accepted the idea that some kind of intervention in the market process is necessary if the right values are to be expressed and realized. There is general agreement that the purpose of such intervention is to enhance the opportunities for choice among individuals. The real questions are choices about how much to do, of what, by whom, and when.

If decisions are to be made in the framework of those choices, there must be some measure of a change from the present to a better situation. Moses Abramovitz has pointed out the weaknesses of using the gross national product for that purpose.[6] He gives three reasons for this weakness. "First, changes in output [are] accompanied by changes in work and life." The manner in which income is earned and used becomes as important as the amount of disposable income. Second, we have inadequate information about "the relation between increments of output and increments to utility," which is critical if the issue is growth and development. It is important to know not only that there has been an increase, but also how much of an increase. Finally, "In the course of economic development . . . want systems must be supposed to change, partly because wants and needs differ among social and economic classes and the relative importance of such classes changes in the course of economic development, partly because changes in the organization of society produce changes in personality which control the significance of income to people."

The factors Abramovitz has identified as significant elements of growth are essentially elements that contribute to the quality of life. They may be included as a major proportion of those things that determine the quality of the environment. Finally, they are in large measure supplied by public investment or are affected by the influence of public agencies on private firms. This is not to argue that the criteria relevant for measuring factors determining the quality of the environment should apply only to the public sector of the economy. The public sector is, however, a starting point for an analysis of the factors critical to the enhancement of the landscape. The substantive reason for making such a beginning is to recognize that the control of the quality of environment depends on public initiative.

In dealing with this problem the issues are frequently stated in terms of external economies and diseconomies. As Mason has pointed out, "the examination of external economies and diseconomies and the means appropriate to the capture of the one and the elimination of the other is a part of the political economy of natural resource use."[7] When the environment is the area of observation, these externalities have a particular significance.

---

[6] Moses Abramovitz, "Welfare Interpretation of Secular Trends" in The Allocation of Economic Resources, Stanford, California, 1959, pp. 20–21.

[7] Edward S. Mason, "The Political Economy of Natural Resource Use" in Perspectives on Conservation, edited by Henry Jarrett, The Johns Hopkins Press, Baltimore, 1958, p. 173.

This follows from the fact that the management of environmental resources falls largely in the public sector where policy on externalities is centered. As long as one is considering the private economy, the only significant problem is to develop programs that will meet Mason's criteria: to capture external economies that are the consequence of public investment, and to prevent external diseconomies.

There are, however, a growing number of opportunities for public investment to avoid external diseconomies or to create new external economies, many of which will produce social goods or values which cannot be priced.[8] Some aspects of water and air pollution fit this case. The proper investment policy prescriptions would seem to go beyond mere capture and avoidance, which is essentially a negative policy, and require positive programs for creating additional external economies and for assimilating external diseconomies.

That we do not have precise criteria for making such decisions is no excuse for doing nothing. Systems analysis can lead the decision in the right direction and if one were to use McKean's "proximate" criteria along with a workable combination of short-run social time preference and social opportunity cost, reasonably good investment decisions could be made that would certainly be better than waiting until the criteria may be perfected.[9]

From the point of view of public investment the two conventional applications of externality are to the allocation of resources and the distribution of income. These concepts are essentially specific formulations of certain aspects of static marginal analysis. They help predict consequences of investment if all or most of the related factors are unchanged or change at particular rates in given directions. By adding externality it is possible to explain why income distribution and resource allocation moved in directions that were not predicted by an analysis of internal forces. Because theoretically this makes it possible to explain more, it is a useful addition. But just how useful is limited by the fact that externalities are very difficult to measure. Furthermore, many of them are associated with public investment, which responds to other than market signals and embraces values and patterns of time distribution significantly different from those of the private economy.

This immediately raises the problem of combining public and private values in the same set of criteria. Is there a rate of discount which will really equate the values of public and private investment? As Feldstein points out, "Although economists have long accepted propositions that rest on diminishing marginal utility of consumption by an individual, there is no reason to assert that increasing *total* consumption would have diminishing marginal utility, even if *per capita* consumption were constant."[10]

This suggests that a primary objective of criteria for guiding investment in environmental resource development should be to establish a set of rules for dealing with uncertainty. These uncertainties include, first, not only ambiguity about the relation between social and personal time preferences but also differences in the values that are assigned both to what is produced and to the processes by which it is produced. Secondly, these uncertain-

---

[8] On this point, for example, Allen V. Kneese, *The Economics of Regional Water Quality Management*, Resources for the Future, Inc., 1964.

[9] On these points cf., Roland F. McKean, *Efficiency in Government Through Systems Analysis*, John Wiley & Sons, New York, 1958, especially Chapters 4, 5, and 6, and M. S. Feldstein, "The Social Time Preference Discount Rate in Cost-Benefit Analysis," *The Economic Journal*, Vol. LXXIV, No. 294, June, 1964, pp. 360–79.

[10] Feldstein, loc. cit.

ties imply something less than full agreement about the role of environmental resources and consequently no consensus about the proper tests for choosing between alternative policies and objectives.

These difficulties are compounded by the fact that the development of environmental resources depends increasingly on public investment and political action. As Julius Margolis pointed out in his well-known article reviewing the current literature on water resource development, "Economic analysis does not have a model of the government as a behavioral unit. Instead, analysis has tended to abstract from its unique characteristics and has treated it as a passive intermediary for private households and producers. This lifeless image has inhibited the development in these studies of optimizing behavior rules for the government."[11]

In its pure form the *laissez-faire* model endorsed this passivity as a necessary condition of an optimum. The realization that this model is inadequate cannot be taken as a sign of significant progress. Before we can make substantial improvement in choosing between alternative programs for the development of environmental resources we need a model to describe the interaction of the public and private economy in situations in which the public unblushingly accepts the role of innovator. In the light of our present inadequate knowledge of the interaction of definition of forces in such a model it is necessary to settle for what McKean has called "proximate" solutions which proceed in steps that begin with the immediate and relatively certain criteria and move forward toward larger problems as the tests of the validity of the criteria warrant.[12]

Many people have been at pains to point out what McKean himself fully realized: that this approach opened the possibility of overlooking major gains from complementarity and economies of scale. In the case of environmental resource development where size of the investment, the wide distribution of those who benefit and those who should bear the cost, the geographic interdependencies and potential complementarity are very great, the comprehensive planners have argued that the incremental planners would miss the great opportunities. This is not an answer to the incrementalists' fear that imprecision of the data and the difficulty of prediction would not only lead to major inefficiencies, but would probably preclude better choices in the future.

A possible solution to this dilemma may be comprehensive design to be implemented by incremental plans. Under this formulation a general design pattern for a river basin could be drawn up to represent the range of possibilities. This would not require a precise calculation of the relationships among the various parts of the design. The general pattern would, however, have to be taken into account once a schedule of priority for work to be done is established and plans are drawn for the first steps to be implemented. For example, if recreation possibilities were indicated in a basin design, a small watershed project could not be planned, if that were a first-priority project, without taking into account its relationship to recreation in the basin. However, until a method of this kind can be tested by at least a well-documented simulation model, it is merely a potential hypothesis.[13]

Stephen Marglin has made proposals for resource-investment decisions that would support incremental planning, al-

[11] Julius Margolis, "The Economic Evaluation of Federal Water Resources Development," *The American Economic Review*, Vol. XLIX, Number 1, March, 1959, p. 107.

[12] Roland N. McKean, *Efficiency in Government Through Systems Analysis*, New York, John Wiley & Sons, 1958, pp. 29–34.

[13] This proposal grows out of a suggestion by Eugene Weber of the U.S. Corps of Army Engineers.

though that was not his specific objective. He concluded that approximate information would lead to better decisions than data that were used as if they were certainties. From his point of view, "all we really want to find out is the marginal time preference in the neighborhood of the optimal rate of investment."[14]

In this context, whether benefit-cost analysis, rate of return, or some other measurement device is a useful guide to choice depends on the kind of project selected. The critical issues from the point of view of environmental resources would seem to be these: (1) A significant proportion of the values to be produced are what Musgrave has called social and merit wants. They require public investment and the product is usually a collective good. (2) The planning horizon extends well into the future. During the life of the investment there will be important technological development and changes in tastes, some of which will be the result and possibly the intention of the investment itself. (3) The objective is social as well as economic development. This requires criteria that will guide change influenced by developing normative values in contrast to the conventional development model, which is primarily concerned with resource allocation and product distribution in terms of present fixed values. (4) The budget of investment funds may not be fixed or may involve budgets from several units of government. Cost benefit is inoperable without a fixed-budget constraint. These conditions would dictate that benefit cost and similar types of analysis would contribute to ranking specific projects within a given budget but could do little to distinguish choices among an array of investment opportunities where the only possibility would be to work toward some partial and shifting equilibrium.[15]

Where direct measurement is impossible or at best difficult, opportunity cost and shadow prices may be used as indirect measures. In the case of environmental resources it is important that proper weight be given to social opportunity costs in relating the interactions of the public and private sectors of the economy.[16] Steiner has attempted to deal rigorously with this problem of the allocation of investment funds between the public and the private sectors of the economy.[17] An admitted limitation of his model in its present form is that it rests on an assumption of full employment of resources. Thus it is concerned with allocation within a stable pattern while the major problem of investment in environmental development is to find criteria to guide changes in a pattern where either there are unemployed resources or resources now employed must be shifted to future uses with predictably higher net marginal productivity.

A more specific measurement problem has to do with the proper definition of benefits. Whether consumer surplus should be included in the benefits de-

---

[14] Stephen A. Marglin, "The Social Rate of Discount and the Optimal Rate of Investment," *The Quarterly Journal of Economics*, Vol. LXXVII, No. 306, February, 1963. See also his article, "The Opportunity Cost of Public Investment," the same *Journal*, Vol. LXXVII, No. 307, May, 1963.

[15] John Krutilla, *Welfare Aspects of Benefit Cost Analysis*, Washington, Resources for the Future, Reprint 29, 1961.

[16] On this point see the article by Feldstein, op. cit., and Gordon Winston, "Taxes, Leisure and Public Goods," *Economica*, Vol. XXXII, No. 25, February, 1965. Winston makes the point that "the collective nature of the consumption of public goods and services makes them qualitatively quite distinct from those *marketed* goods and services that an individual's personal income can provide." He takes the position that the consumption of public goods does not affect the income available for private goods, but it does affect the consumer's preference pattern.

[17] Peter O. Steiner, "Choosing Among Alternative Public Investments in the Water Resource Field," *The American Economic Review*, Vol. XLIX, No. 5, December, 1959, pp. 893–916.

pends in large measure on who the perfectly discriminating monopolist may be who would capture the surplus. In the case of environmental resources developed by public investment it seems to be clear that such a surplus is indeed a net benefit to society and therefore should be weighed in the balancing of benefits and costs.[18]

These questions of the techniques of measurement of costs and returns to be anticipated from investment in resource development have quite naturally received most of the attention economists have devoted to the field of natural resources. In addition to the general issues of measurement concepts, more specific problems have also been examined. Some, such as the matter of cost allocation and cost sharing, have a decisive impact on the types of projects selected under various kinds of budget constraints. Other formulations, such as Clawson's studies of demand for recreation, have a direct relevance to selecting criteria for evaluating environmental resource development.[19] If a general set of concepts for establishing such criteria does evolve at some future date, the findings of these specific studies will have to be accommodated in the evaluating framework.

There is, however, another set of criteria of a somewhat different order but which is equally important to rational decisions in resource investment. These have to do with the concept of scarcity. For many people the primary reason for

concern with environmental resources is that they are rapidly disappearing. What Morris Miller has written is an example of this position: "The truth or fallacy of the assumption of a fixed or relatively limited supply of natural resources in its economic role is very difficult to check against the evidence—while in terms of environment it is a blatantly obvious fact and poses critical problems."[20] Landsberg, Fischman, and Fisher in *Resources in America's Future* take a somewhat more sanguine view.[21] If they are concerned about the scarcity of environmental resources it is for a time beyond the reach of their projections. Barnett and Mores using the criterion of net cost as an index of resource scarcity concluded that there is no evidence of such a scarcity.[22] Galbraith goes even further and takes the position that the essential problem of western society at least is to achieve a rational distribution of abundance rather than to ration against scarcity.[23]

[20] Morris Miller, "The Scope and Content of Resource Policy in Relation to Economic Development," *Land Economics*, Vol. XXXVII, No. 4, November, 1961, p. 298. Miller adds: "The danger and problem of shortage in a physical and in an economic sense may be much greater for these environmental resources since the process of substitution is ruled out or very severely limited. In fact, technology can have only an indirect effect and its influence on the end-product to be enjoyed is likely to increase the pressures of demand and need for the resources."

[21] Hans H. Landsberg, Leonard L. Fischman, and Joseph L. Fisher, Washington, D.C., *Resources in America's Future*, Resources for the Future, Inc., 1962.

[22] Harold H. Barnett and Chandler Mores, *Scarcity and Growth*, Baltimore, Johns Hopkins Press, 1962.

[23] John Kenneth Galbraith, *The Affluent Society*, Boston, Houghton Mifflin Company, 1958. Gunnar Myrdal takes issue with Galbraith's conclusions, not on the grounds of scarcity but rather on our failure to use the means at our command to erase the effects of the poverty of our institutions. Cf. his *Challenge to Affluence*, New York, Pantheon Books, 1963.

[18] On consumer surplus see Stephen A. Marglin, "Economic Factors Affecting System Design," in Arthur Maass, et al., *Design of Water Resource Systems*, Cambridge, Harvard University Press, 1962, and Jack L. Knetsch, "Outdoor Recreation Demands and Benefits," *Land Economics*, Vol. XXXIX, No. 4, November, 1963, pp. 392–93.

[19] Cf. Marion Clawson, "Methods of Measuring the Demand for and Value of Outdoor Recreation," Washington, D.C., Reprint 10, Resources for the Future, Inc., February, 1959.

The critical issue is not whether there is scarcity, but rather what is scarce. In the case of a limited number of natural resources there may be instances of irreversible destruction, but in most instances expanding technology, investment in research and development, and institutional innovation could increase the supply and, what is more important, achieve better distribution, which would overcome the present appearances of scarcity.

This position should at least be tested in those areas in which environmental resource development is significant. The principal threats to the quality of the environment presently seem to fall in the following categories: the pollution of air and water and the destructive effects of noise; shrinking space in both the urban and rural environment; deterioration of landscape quality in both the city and the countryside (in the United States particularly this last is due in part to our failure to accept the city as a major work of art); growing need for recreation and natural areas; the waste of mineral land and water resources; wildlife; the waste or destruction of, or the failure to develop, esthetic and historic values.[24] The significant issue in dealing with these problems is not one of overcoming scarcity, which is essentially a negative approach. It is, rather, the issue of designing programs of investment to overcome the present constraints on distribution and productivity and to realize the potential development of beneficial uses. The critical resources are human ingenuity, the quality of taste and of human value systems, and the institutions that can be improved to ensure a more satisfactory environment. These are abundant resources and their supply in the future is deter-

[24] A manuscript in preparation entitled *Problems and Opportunities in Managing the Quality of the Environment,* by Orris C. Herfindahl and Allen V. Kneese, deals effectively with these issues and their possible solution.

mined almost entirely by what we are prepared to invest in them today.

CONCLUSION

To summarize the criteria that are now available to evaluate economic choices in environmental resources is not a wholly satisfying experience. One is at once struck by the repetitive references to ideas that were available almost a decade ago. It is striking how the bibliographies on this subject are made up mostly of the same basic texts with a scattering of a few new commentaries on what has been said, largely to refine those statements rather than to extend them. It is perhaps inescapable that in this area we are still in the period of trying to create methodologies, certainly something less than an exhilarating process. The concepts on which those methods are based have been inherited from the conventional past, although we are becoming aware that the issues to be resolved do not yield to those concepts. A summary thus is in some measure an apology for seeming to run while standing still.

The essential and constant problem of evaluating economic choices remains in very general terms to find measurements that will show not only the difference between more and less, but how much more and less. It is unlikely that with present techniques such criteria could be embodied in a comprehensive plan. We lack the necessary tools for discovering either individual and social time preferences or for finding their proper relationship. The same problem of relationship holds for private and public funds invested in improving the quality of the environment. Private and social opportunity costs, shadow prices, rates of return are approximations and the data used to construct them are at best unstable. Comprehensive design with incremental planning may, if it is carefully tested, provide a means for more effective development.

The criteria that are selected for alternative investment opportunities should be designed to promote growth and development. They should not be static and aimed at preserving what is or restoring the past, but rather they should be concerned with improving the quality of choices that will come in the future. With all uncertainties about present information and the difficulty of making projections, incremental planning would seem to be a necessity.

It should be recognized that a major purpose of such criteria is to measure social investment. The problem is not merely to capture the returns from external economies and prevent external diseconomies, it is also to increase the opportunities for external economies flowing from public as well as private development.

Finally, in dealing with the quality of the human environment, the choice of criteria should not be confined by an overwhelming concern for scarcity. If development means anything it means creating a better environment. Natural resources must be used in this development, but the value they can yield depends on the critical active input, the quality of human mind and skill. There are limits on that resource but they are self-imposed by the failure of will or the poverty of imagination.

BIBLIOGRAPHY

Abramovitz, Moses. 1959. Welfare Interpretation of Secular Trends. In: The Allocation of Economic Resources. Stanford, Calif.

Barnett, Harold H., and Mores, Chandler. 1962. Scarcity and Growth. Baltimore.

Clawson, Marion. 1959. Methods of Measuring the Demand for and Value of Outdoor Recreation. Resources for the Future. Reprint 10. Wash., D.C.

Dahl, R. A., and Lindblom, C. E. 1953. Politics, Economics and Welfare. New York.

Feldstein, M. S. 1964. The Social Time Preference Discount Rate in Cost-Benefit Analysis. Econ. J. 74:360–79.

Firey, Walter. 1960. Man, Mind and Land. Glencoe, Ill.

Galbraith, John Kenneth. 1958. The Affluent Society. Boston.

Herfindahl, Orris C., and Kneese, Allen V. Problems and Opportunities in Managing the Quality of the Environment. MS. in preparation.

Hutchinson, T. W. "Positive" Economic and Policy Objectives. London.

Kneese, Allen V. 1964. The Economics of Regional Water Quality Management. Resources for the Future. Wash., D.C.

Knetsch, Jack L. 1963. Outdoor Recreation Demands and Benefits. Land Econ. 39:392–93.

Krutilla, John. 1961. Welfare Aspects of Benefit Cost Analysis. Resources for the Future. Reprint 29. Wash., D.C.

Landsberg, Hans H., et al. 1962. Resources in America's Future. Resources for the Future, Wash., D.C.

Little, I. M. D. 1957. A Critique of Welfare Economics. Oxford.

Maass, Arthur, et al. 1962. Design of Water-Resource Systems. Cambridge, Mass.

Marglin, Stephen A. 1963a. The Social Rate of Discount and the Optimal Rate of Investment. Q. J. Econ. 77. 1963b. The Opportunity Cost of Public Investment. Q. J. Econ. 77.

Margolis, Julius. 1959. The Economic Evaluation of Federal Water Resources Development. Amer. Econ. Rev. 49:107.

Mason, Edward S. 1958. The Political Economy of Natural Resource Use. In: Jarret, Henry, ed., Perspectives on Conservation. Baltimore.

McKean, Roland F. 1958. Efficiency in Government Through Systems Analysis. New York.

Miller, Morris. 1961. The Scope and Content of Resource Policy in Relation to Economic Development. Land Econ. 37.

Myrdal, Gunnar. 1958. Values in Social Theory. New York.

———— 1963. Challenge to Affluence. New York.

Oakeshott, M. 1962. Rationalism in Politics, and other Essays. London.

Popper, K. R. 1963. Conjectures and Refutations. London.

Shackle, G. L. S. 1961. Decision, Order and Time in Human Affairs. Cambridge, Eng.

Steiner, Peter O. 1959. Choosing Among Alternative Public Investments in the Water Resource Field. Amer. Rev. 49:893–916.

Tinbergen, Jan. Economic Policy: Principles and Design.

Winston, Gordon. 1965. Taxes, Leisure and Public Goods. Economica 32.

ECONOMICS AND ENVIRONMENTAL IMPACTS OF INCREASING LEISURE ACTIVITIES*

Marion Clawson†

The real wealth of a nation or a people is the time of its members. That time may be used to produce a wealth of goods, or to produce but a minimum quantity barely sufficient for existence; it may be used in highly productive ways, or inefficiently; it may be complemented with relatively large volumes of capital (stored past labor) and of natural resources, or it may operate with a paucity of each. Technological and other changes may, in effect, create new natural resources or seriously impair the value of those now existing; economic change may well increase greatly the stock of capital goods, or stagnation may hold it steady. The quality of the human resource itself can be modified in numerous ways—by better health, by more education, and so on. In the event of nuclear holocaust, the decisive factor for the future would be the extent to which people, especially productive people, survived, rather than the extent to which capital goods were destroyed.

In view of the great importance of human time, it is surprising that so few studies have been made of it. Economists have compiled increasingly sophisticated "national income" estimates, but these deal entirely with goods and services measurable in monetary terms. A few sociologists have studied the use of time by selected groups of people, but few efforts have been made to estimate the total national use of time. It may be objected that an hour of time by one person is not comparable with an hour of time by another; but the same argument can be applied equally to money, yet has not prevented calculations comparing money incomes of the whole population. Ecologists have given virtually no attention to human time; they seem to feel that they have taken man sufficiently into account when they merely notice his actions and his numbers.

Leisure, as it will be defined for the purposes of this paper, is discretionary time above that needed for the basic existence and subsistence requirements of man. In order to maintain life, man must sleep, ingest food, and attend to minimum personal hygiene; each of these takes some time. In order to subsist, he

* This paper draws upon my article "How Much Leisure, Now and in the Future?" in *Leisure in America: Blessing or Curse?*, edited by James C. Charlesworth, Monograph 4, American Academy of Political and Social Science, Philadelphia, April, 1964; and upon an as yet unpublished book manuscript on outdoor recreation, now under preparation in Resources for the Future.

† Dr. Clawson has, since 1955, been Director of the Land-Use and Management Program for Resources for the Future, Inc., in Washington, D.C. He had formerly been Director of the Bureau of Land Management of the U.S. Department of the Interior. A specialist in the economics of land use, he has played a leading role in the conceptual development of the recreation field.

must work, ordinarily at a rather well-defined job; and this takes further time. For better lifetime subsistence, he must be trained for higher productivity, which means going to school for many years, and this takes time also. But, beyond these categories, there remains a great deal of time where greater choice is possible; this, in my terminology, is leisure. These categories are not, and no categories can be made, completely watertight. Some people make fun out of eating; some men find more pleasure in their job than in any other activity and willingly devote longer hours to it than are required of them; and some discretionary time activities produce some income. Yet the central core of meaning is, I think, fairly clear.

To me, leisure connotes a large degree of purposefulness or choice; mere idleness, doing nothing because the person concerned does not know or is otherwise unable to do anything he wants to do, is not really leisure. This does not preclude a purposeful decision to do nothing, to relax idly. This distinction is not sharp and clear, but a significant difference in central meaning seems to exist. The amount of leisure is obviously conditioned by the nature of the general society in which the individual lives; but so is the content, and even the meaning, of leisure. In many low-income countries today, the bulk of the population has a great deal of idle time, yet little true leisure in the sense of the word as we use it. Or, to take an illustration closer to home, many elderly indigent persons today, especially if in poor health, are in complete idleness yet they have no real leisure.

Leisure is primarily a time-oriented concept; recreation, which we shall discuss later in this paper, is an activity or personal experience concept. One may engage in recreation during leisure time, and thus the two ideas are closely related; but leisure may be used for other purposes, and there is a major difference in the orientation of the two ideas.

The concept of discretionary income has become widely employed by economists, marketing specialists, and others. Sociologists and anthropologists may point out that one may not have much true freedom to spend money when many aspects of life are socially determined; "keeping up with the Joneses" may be almost as compelling a need for expenditure as hunger itself. Leisure is for time almost what discretionary income is for money. In each, the emphasis is upon ability to choose, upon something over and above the basic necessities, upon personal freedom. Some writers have made much of this aspect of leisure, and regard it as a necessary antidote to the orderedness of modern industrial society.[1]

Both leisure and discretionary income can be overcommitted by their owners, until, for the moment, little or none is left of either. The person who undertakes to meet installment payments for house, car, TV, other appliances, vacation travel, or other expenditures until his paycheck leaves little or nothing for food has his counterpart in the man who undertakes to write several professional papers, engage in numerous professional and community enterprises, carry out major hobbies, and of course hold down a job for its necessary income. Sociologists and others have distinguished between level of living, or what one has, and standard of living, or what one aspires to; perhaps these concepts are applicable also to leisure. One may long for leisure while at the same time busily bargain away such leisure as he has. It is altogether possible that sheer idleness or even leisurely performance of activity is less common in our modern society than was the case a generation or more ago.

[1] See references cited in my article on leisure.

Yet, over the longer run, one can plan and readjust his use of leisure, just as one can plan and readjust his use of discretionary income. The installment payments do come to an end, hopefully before the car is worn out; and, if one has the stamina to resist the next salesman, no new installment commitments need be entered into. Likewise, if one truly wishes to reduce his time commitments, this is wholly possible over a period of time— a month, a year, or several years, depending upon the particular commitments. It is fashionable among professional and business people of middle-high income or higher social classes to brag about how busy they are, how little real leisure they have, how leisure is a myth for them even if it exists for others, etc. While they are often responding to general social pressures of real magnitude, it remains true that they do have a major degree of freedom in use of their time, have they but the sense and courage to use it.

The total amount of leisure, the timing and size of its pieces, and its uses depend largely upon the phases of the individual life cycle. Children have a good deal of leisure, in spite of the existence time demands of sleeping, eating, and personal chores; this decreases as school requires more and more time. The young adult in a job or engaged in homemaking has modest amounts of leisure; the older adult has more demands of some kinds, but the rearing of children is likely to take less time. Retirement brings wholly new amounts and forms of leisure. Over the past several decades, the age at which young people enter the labor force has gradually risen; whereas once boys and girls were likely to get their first job at thirteen or fourteen, now it is more likely to be at eighteen or older. As school requirements increase, and as employers increasingly want mature and full-time workers, the age of entry into the labor force is likely to rise further. Young

women have always typically given up their jobs as marriage and children brought new demands on their time; but a more recent trend has been the re-entry of women into the labor force, usually after thirty-five, as the time demands of their families decrease and as their need for additional income or for more stimulating activity rise. Retirement has always brought more leisure for some workers, but the proportion is rising as various retirement income plans make retirement economically more feasible, and as longer life expectancies give more years, on the average, to the older worker. The average years in retirement have increased from about three in 1900 to about six today, and in another generation may well rise to nine.

Children use their leisure for active play, for reading, watching TV or movies, and in many other ways. Adolescents and young people have other patterns, so do young married adults, and so do older adults. The retired persons are likely to have still other programs. Age is one major determinant of leisure activities, but far from the only one.

Using available data as to numbers of persons by age classes, which are rather complete and accurate, and other data on typical time uses of individuals by various age classes and activity groupings, which are less complete and less accurate, Holman has calculated a national time budget for 1900 and for 1950, and projected one ahead for 2000 (Table 1 and Fig. III-1). At each time period, sleep took the largest single amount of time— roughly 40 per cent at each period, or about nine and a half hours per day. If the latter seems large, one must recall that a substantial proportion of the total population is children whose hours of sleep often exceed this. Personal care took about 5½ per cent of the total, or about one and a quarter hours per day on the average—more for some age groups, less for others. Work, school, and house-

TABLE 1. National time-budget and time-division of leisure, 1900, 1950, and 2000

Use of time	1900			1950			2000		
	Billion hours	Per cent of total time	Per cent of leisure time	Billion hours	Per cent of total time	Per cent of leisure time	Billion hours	Per cent of total time	Per cent of leisure time
Total time for entire population	667	100		1329	100		2907	100	
Sleep	265	40		514	39		1131	39	
Work	86	13		132	10		206	7	
School	11	2		32	2		90	3	
Housekeeping	61	9		68	5		93	3	
Preschool population, nonsleeping hours	30	4		56	4		110	4	
Personal care	37	6		74	6		164	6	
Total, accounted for above	490	73		876	66		1794	62	
Remaining hours, largely leisure	177	27	100	453	34	100	1113	38	100
Daily leisure hours	72		41	189		42	375		34
Weekend leisure hours	50		28	179		39	483		44
Vacation	17		10	35		8	182		16
Retired	6		3	24		5	56		5
Other, including unaccounted	32		18	26		6	16		1

Adapted from "A National Time-Budget for the Year 2000," by Mary A. Holman in *Sociology and Social Research*, Vol. 46, No. 1, October, 1961.

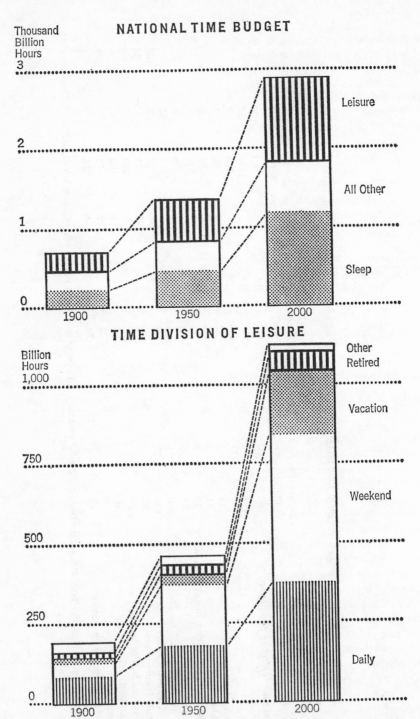

FIG. III-1. National time budget and the time division of leisure in 1900, 1950, and 2000.

keeping were important users of time, but not everyone used time for these purposes at any given date. Their share of the total has come down from more than 23 per cent in 1900 to slightly more than 17 per cent in 1950, and may well be reduced to less than 14 per cent by 2000. Work has come down far more than this, but has been offset in part by the relative rise in school time.

Leisure has increased as a proportion of total time, and seems likely to increase much further. Particularly noteworthy has been the increase in vacation and in retired leisure. In 1900, leisure as we define it was roughly twice as large as work; by 1950, more than three times as large; and by 2000, may be more than five times as large. These increases in leisure have been possible only because far more people have shared in it. This is the meaning of "mass leisure," as the term is often used.

Perhaps equally important with the total amount of leisure is its timing and the size of its pieces. The typical adult employed male rises between six and eight, showers and shaves, eats breakfast, and departs for work, usually with no leisure except possibly a look at the morning paper or hearing the radio. His journey to work may provide a little leisure for reading or visiting; the coffee break, lunch, and just plain time-killing at the office or factory or construction job may provide a little more. From three to six hours are likely to remain after his return home, for eating, necessary personal chores, and leisure, before bedtime. Over the weekend, larger personal chores, including often maintenance of home, car, and yard, will occupy some time; but as much as four to twelve hours can be found for leisure pursuits on each of the two typical weekend days. Once a year, or oftener with increasing frequency, this man and his family will go for a vacation, with a wholly different leisure pattern.

There are many variations on this pattern, even for adult employed males. Housewives and school children have somewhat different daily and annual patterns of activity, and yet considerable similarity exists for them also. As we have noted, the retired person has still a different pattern. It is not possible nor necessary to consider all the variations in leisure patterns, but four major kinds of leisure seem evident:

(1) Daily, for the approximately 180 school days for school children or for the approximately 240 workdays for most employed persons, in amounts of three to six hours each day, not in one continuous piece but divided into smaller parts.

(2) On weekends, for about 100 days per year, when school and work are typically absent, and when the leisure may run as high as twelve hours per day.

(3) Annually, for vacations as long as seventy-five to ninety days for school children and to as long as twenty to thirty days for many workers, when the whole pattern of daily living is different.

(4) In retirement, for the last several years of life, when leisure may be relatively very high.

One can obviously do very different things with these different sizes or pieces of leisure. One can go to Yellowstone National Park on annual vacation but most people cannot go on the weekend and almost no one can go after work on a working day; at the other extreme, one can read the daily paper in the evening, after dinner and before bed, but few people would be content to read the daily paper during their whole vacation time. Innumerable other illustrations could be given.

One may accept the present pattern of leisure as a fact, an established relationship which it would be very difficult to change even if this seemed desirable. But there is good reason to believe that total leisure will increase over the next generation. One way of dividing an increased future total leisure has been shown in Table 1. The potentialities can be illustrated by a rather simple example. Suppose that we, as a nation, should decide to reduce the average work week by 20 per cent, from its approximate average of forty hours now. Total leisure might increase in various other ways than reducing the length of the work week— by increasing the years of compulsory schooling, by lowering the retirement age, etc.—but we use this one method to illustrate our point. The average daily hours of work could be reduced from eight to six and a half; this is approximately 20 per cent. Or the working days per week could be reduced from five to four; this is exactly 20 per cent. Or the eight-hour day and the five-day week could be left intact, but vacations lengthened to one week during each of three quarters of the year, plus one month during the fourth quarter, plus six months' paid vacation once in five years; and this works out to approximately a 20 per cent reduction in work time. The uses that could be made of these different forms of increased leisure are so obviously different as not to need further discussion.

This issue is not "academic" or fanciful; union and other employment contracts are constantly being changed, and the length of working hours and the amount of paid vacation are prime bargaining items. It is unlikely that total working time will be reduced by 20 per cent in any single action or at one time; changes are likely to be more incremental, but they may be cumulative. There is some danger in incremental adjustments, because each seems small and not to present a major issue, yet over a period of years their total effect may be different from what anyone would have chosen at the beginning of the period.

OUTDOOR RECREATION AS ONE USE
OF LEISURE

The close interrelation between leisure and recreation has been noted above. Recreation, as we use the term, means an activity (or a chosen inactivity) undertaken because one wants to do it. The activity, including the process of choice, involves a major human experience of intellectual, emotional, and sensory kinds; to some writers, recreation means the experience, but we choose to consider it as the activity to which is associated various kinds of experiences. The distinguishing characteristic of recreation is the attitude with which it is undertaken; the same activity, if chosen freely and on a "want to" basis, may be recreation, while if undertaken primarily for income or from sense of duty or social obligation may be work. Leisure is the time, recreation is the activity; and each has the same element of freedom of choice.

Outdoor recreation is simply those kinds of recreation typically carried on outdoors. There are some borderline activities, that may be either indoors or outdoors, of course. Outdoor recreation includes a great many specific activities; a full and detailed list would run literally into the hundreds, and is unnecessary for our purposes. Persons of different ages, tastes, income, and other characteristics will choose different outdoor recreation activities. All require some area of land or water, often relatively large areas of land and water. Some outdoor recreation is highly demanding in terms of the resources it requires. One cannot go spelunking unless there are caves, to use an extreme case; or one cannot enjoy a true wilderness experience unless there exists a real wilderness. Other activities are less demanding in terms of natural features or qualities required. In nearly all activities, but especially so for some, man may alter the natural environment by constructing roads, erecting buildings, or in one of many other ways. Within some limits, capital, labor, and management capability can be substituted for natural resources in providing opportunity for outdoor recreation. All forms of outdoor recreation leave their mark upon the environment, as well as perhaps affect the person who experiences them.

The numerous kinds of outdoor recreation activity and the many kinds of outdoor recreation areas can be grouped or classified in various ways. The Outdoor Recreation Resources Review Commission employed a sixfold classification, on essentially management criteria.[2] I prefer a threefold classification, based primarily on the relationship between the location of users and the location of the recreation areas, as being more significant for economic inquiry.[3] At one extreme are the user-oriented areas: close to where people live, suitable for use after school and after work, individually often rather small and not too demanding as to physical characteristics, ready location is their prime requirement. Farther out lie the intermediate use areas, designed primarily for day-long recreation use, generally within an hour's travel time of most users, on the best sites available, they present much more flexibility in location and in resource qualities required. At the other extreme are the resource-based areas, whose superb and unusual physical or historical characteristics make them desirable in spite of a frequently inconvenient location for most users. The first require or are best suited to daily leisure, the second to weekend leisure, and the third to vacation time.

But, no matter what terminology is used or what basis used for classification, there is in fact a continuum of kinds of areas, locations, and kinds of uses. As with any continuous variable, there may be advantages in establishing divisions or groups, but there are not discrete differences between one kind of area and another, or between one kind of experience and another. More importantly, the various kinds of outdoor recreation areas have a strong *systems* aspect, roughly analogous to an ecosystem or to an electric-power system. There are competitive relationships between units of similar type; if a person goes to one, he cannot go to another at the same time. But there may be complementary relationships even here; some people will buy a motorboat and all the accessory equipment if there are several lakes or reservoirs when they would not do so if there were but one. Likewise, there are competitive and complementary relationships between units of different types. If there are plenty of attractive and conveniently located state parks providing intermediate-type outdoor recreation, fewer people will decide to undertake long and expensive trips to distant national parks of the resource-based type, for instance. But outdoor recreation experience on one type of area seems also to whet the appetite for more experiences of other types on other areas, at least for some people.

If a new outdoor recreation area of any kind becomes available, then the use of other areas in the system of which it is a part changes, sometimes in complex and not easily measured ways. In this way, a system of outdoor recreation areas is like an ecosystem reacting to the shock of a new introduced species, or to an electric-power system reacting to the installation of a new generator or a new major-load factor. Shocks or changes may come either from the supply side, by the addition of new recreation areas or the improvement of old ones, or from the demand side as population increases, new roads make previously inaccessible

[2] "Outdoor Recreation for America—A Report to the President and to the Congress," by the Outdoor Recreation Resources Review Commission, Washington, 1962.
[3] Marion Clawson, R. Burnell Held, and C. H. Stoddard. *Land for the Future,* Johns Hopkins Press, Baltimore, 1960.

areas available, or in other ways. In any case, there is an immediate and direct, or primary adjustment; the new area attracts visitors, or the new people go to some established area, etc. But this primary adjustment will almost certainly lead to further changes; the new added load on one area leads people to go to other areas, some of which may be relatively far away; or the new facility draws some of the pressure off some presently overloaded area, thus making it more attractive, and this in turn induces some people to use it who previously had rejected it. Outdoor recreation areas have not been, but could be, subjected to systems analysis, if the necessary basic data are available, and the full consequences of a change in one part could be traced through the whole system.

In considering outdoor recreation, one useful basic concept is that of the whole recreation experience (Figure III-2). This has five rather distinct phases:

(1) Anticipation or planning, when the family or other unit decides when and where to go, what to do at the area, what equipment to take, how much to spend, and the like. This takes place primarily in the user's home, or at least in his home town; as nearly as we can estimate, more than half of all the expenditures for outdoor recreation take place in this stage. Most equipment is bought here, but so are many supplies, including food and gasoline. Recreationists probably could use and would welcome expert advice more during this stage than later. This phase may be careful, conscious, and informed, or casual, offhand, and ill advised. It may long anticipate the summer vacation but occur only a few minutes before the local experience.

(2) Travel to the actual site of the recreation is necessary in nearly all cases. For the more distant areas, more time and money are spent traveling to the site than are later spent there. Some people find the travel experience itself pleasurable, while others regard it as a necessary psychic cost to reach the target area. It might well be made more pleasurable.

(3) On-site experiences are those most often thought of in connection with outdoor recreation. They can run a wide gamut, as we have noted. Since the unit of participation in outdoor recreation is often the family, an area which offers a variety of recreation opportunities is likely to be most useful. Even users of a single age and sex group are likely to want to do more than one specific activity —camping and fishing, for instance. It is the on-site experiences which often give purpose and point to the whole experience, but they are not the whole of it, and should not be so treated. They are the part which makes the most direct demand upon natural environment.

(4) Travel back home is obviously necessary. Though beginning and end points are the same as travel to the area, the specific route may vary. More importantly, the attitude of the travelers may now be different. We can only speculate on this point, for little specific study has been given to it. But it is altogether probable that travelers will respond to different stimuli in the one case than in the other.

(5) Recollection is the last, and possibly the most important, phase of the total experience. It is altogether possible that more total satisfactions or values arise here than in all the other phases combined. Recollection need bear only a loose relation to reality—the fish caught, or that got away, are larger in the living room or office than on the lake or at the stream. Many people get great pleasure in relating their experiences to others, perhaps reinforced with color slides or other artifacts. The recollections of the past trip are often decisive for the next one, and recollection gradually merges with planning.

The whole experience must be treated

ANTICIPATION

In anticipation of an outdoor recreation experience, a family plans where it will go and what it will do, and buys equipment and supplies

This in turn leads to planning for next trip.

RECOLLECTION

Back home again, the family recalls its recreation experience, often with great pleasure. Memories may be an important part of the whole experience

TRAVEL TO

In order to reach the outdoor recreation area of its choice, a family must travel. Considerable expense is involved in such travel, and often as much time is consumed in travel as later on the site. Travel is often not as pleasurable as experience on the site

TRAVEL BACK

When the activities at the site are through, the family must travel back to its home. Often tired, frequently in a hurry, sometimes broke, the family is in a different mood than when it traveled in the opposite direction

ON SITE

When it arrives at the recreation site, the family may engage in many activities. Bodies of water are especially valued for outdoor recreation. The activities at the site generally provide the basic purpose for the whole experience, even when they occupy less than half the time and require less than half the total expense

FIG. III-2. The five phases of the recreation experience.

as a package deal, for many purposes. We have found that demand for outdoor recreation can be studied meaningfully only in terms of the whole experience. The recreationist will balance up his total satisfactions from the whole experience against its total costs; the dirty restroom will loom as large for some persons as the fine new park museum. Improvement should be possible in each phase, and have its effect upon all other phases. Unfortunately, government organization and professional specialization have each tended to divide the whole experience into parts—the highway engineer and the park manager, for instance, each taking a part of what is a whole for the participant.

All available statistical evidence documents a rapidly rising total demand for outdoor recreation. This is true, whether one uses demand to mean attendance at parks or whether one uses demand in the economist's sense of a schedule of prices and volumes. Attendance has been rising steadily and rapidly at nearly every park and recreation area for which we have data. In the case of the national parks, this has been true since 1910; data are available for shorter periods for other areas. The rate of rise has been remarkably close to 10 per cent annually; as total attendance has risen, the absolute increases from year to year have also risen, to preserve a nearly constant percentage growth rate. The severe depression years of the early 1930s flattened out the rate of growth, while the gasoline and tire rationing of the war years resulted in a two-thirds decline in recreation use of national parks and national forests. With these exceptions, the rate of growth has been remarkably steady. It has been possible only because the different kinds of areas have expanded in number or acreage or have been opened up for use by more roads, or some combination of these changes. The past rate of growth cannot continue indefinitely, for it would

in time lead to people spending more time at various kinds of recreation areas than existed in a year; much short of this, past growth rates would lead to time usages which seem improbable. But there is yet no clear evidence of a slowing down in rate of increase, much less an actual leveling off.

The larger attendance at various areas has been caused in some part, perhaps in large part, by people living at greater distances coming to the specific facility. It is thus highly probable that average cost per visit has risen over the years, in spite of improvements in transportation facilities; we lack specific information on this point. But average costs per visit could hardly have fallen. A sharply rising total quantity with a constant or rising price per unit can only mean a shifted demand curve.

Although outdoor recreation is one highly important use of leisure, my best (unpublished) estimates indicate that it accounts for only a very small fraction of total leisure (as we have defined the latter). Using all outdoor activities for which we could get reasonably good information, we could account for only about 3½ per cent of all leisure in 1960. This may seem small, but one should recall that much or most leisure is in seasons, at times, and in pieces which are not suitable for outdoor recreation, and that many people lack either the desire or the ability to enjoy much if any outdoor recreation. These estimates necessarily excluded activities in the yards or around the homes of families, because of lack of data, and the inclusion of this factor would raise participation considerably. Including all forms of outdoor recreation could hardly raise its proportion of total leisure to as high as 10 per cent, however. Still less adequate information suggests that this proportion has risen greatly in the past; and it may well increase much further in the future, but a more or less definite ceiling surely exists even if we cannot now locate it.

One major characteristic of outdoor recreation is its extreme seasonality or its extreme unevenness through time. The local playground may be nearly idle, not only during the night hours but during much of the day, while at the same time overcrowded after school; or the national park which can scarcely accommodate its visitors in July and August may be closed to visitors all winter; or the state park which is full to overflowing on Saturday and Sunday may be only a third full on Tuesday; and so on. This problem afflicts private areas as well as public ones. Area of land or water, capacity of buildings, and other features must be geared to meet extreme peak needs or some means must be devised for deflecting part of the peak demand. But costs on an annual basis are largely a function of maximum peak capacity; if use is very low, in proportion to total annual capacity, then cost per unit of use must be relatively high. The private resort with a ten-week season must charge enough per day during the season to earn a minimum annual income, for instance. With public areas, the extra costs of meeting peaks may be less obvious, but nonetheless real. If the cost for the last units of capacity were to be charged against the few days or hours when those last units of capacity were in use, the cost per unit of time would be very high indeed in many instances. The only redeeming feature of this extreme time-peaking of use is that it does give many areas a much needed recuperation period; but perhaps longer use at a more modest intensity would meet this objective equally well and at the same time keep costs per unit of service much lower.

In the typical outdoor recreation area, there exists a space-peaking of use as extreme as the time-peaking of use. The flood of visitors may overtrample the popular spots while only an occasional visitor will reach the more remote ones. It has been estimated that over 95 per cent of all visits to national parks occur on 5 per cent or less of their total area, although precise measurements on this point are lacking. In the summer of 1964, the present author observed a steady stream of closely spaced autos on the highway leading into Yellowstone National Park from the south, while a few miles to the east on trails through the Teton National Forest Wilderness Area there was no evidence that human foot had touched there since the elk-hunting season nine months earlier. This space-peaking of use seems to afflict all kinds of areas, including popular city parks.

The outdoor recreation made possible by increased leisure has both direct and indirect impacts upon the natural environment. The direct effects are mostly adverse, as people crowd onto popular areas. Enough human feet can be as destructive of vegetation, wildlife, and even of soil as a bulldozer. One need only visit the popular parts of any national park, national forest, state park, or city park to see vividly the physical damage done to the original environment by the hordes of visitors. We have obviously been exploiting original natural conditions as ruthlessly as did any timber baron or rancher; in many cases, the very existence of the area as a physically attractive recreation area may be in jeopardy. Certainly we have not yet learned how to practice sustained-yield management of popular outdoor recreation areas; original and present vegetation cannot reproduce under the kinds of use situations that have grown up. The day of reckoning will arrive for many areas within a few years or decades, unless drastically different methods of management and of use intensities can be devised.

The impact upon the psychic environment may be as great or greater. A substantial portion of all present outdoor recreation areas was established because those areas offered a certain type of privacy, solitude, or naturalness. This has been lost in all too many cases; the popularity of the area destroyed the qualities that led originally to its establishment. One may argue that the original objective was unrealistic, or that society cannot afford very extensive use of natural resources merely to provide a certain kind of recreation, or on other grounds one may defend heavy use of available outdoor recreation areas. But one should not be under any illusion that this has been costless.

The indirect effects upon environment of the heavy recreational use of natural resources in general may be more favorable. Preservation or improvement of environmental situations often depends upon public—that is to say, governmental —action, either for investment or current outlays or in terms of institutions restraining socially undesirable private action or providing incentives for private action in desired directions. In a democracy such as the United States, such public action cannot go far beyond that which a substantial majority of the citizens considers reasonable. As the general public becomes familiar with and knowledgeable about natural resources, through personal recreation experiences, its attitude toward such public action may change. This is a point which we shall consider in more detail later in this paper, but we raise it now to suggest that not all impact of people upon natural environment is adverse.

OTHER ASPECTS AND
POTENTIALITIES OF LEISURE

A complete analysis of the economic and social implications of more leisure in the future is a larger task than this author feels able to undertake. The ramifications of more leisure, on a mass basis, are many and complex. But a few

probable consequences may be noted.

First of all, increased future leisure is likely to mean a relatively greater emphasis upon consumption, and relatively less upon production, than has been the case in the past. Most uses of time will involve some use of income, sometimes of a good bit of income. People may take their role as consumers more seriously than they have in the past. Production would, of course, be greatly influenced by market possibilities, and thus more leisure would indirectly affect production. But the emphasis might well shift from production of raw materials, basic goods, and production machinery to the production of consumer goods, especially those in which style, fashion, and the like are particularly important. One should not labor this point, for people have always been both consumers and producers, but there might be some shift in emphasis of their relative roles.

When it comes to consumption, the availability of time and the use of free time may come to be as important as the availability of income. If the latter rises for the average man, so that direct wants are taken care of and a considerable amount of discretionary spending is possible, additional amounts of income might be less highly prized than at times in the past. On the other hand, if the past is a good criterion, the demands for time may well rise faster than additional amounts of it are made available. Competition on TV, among movies, and in the amusement world generally now seems to be as much or more for time than for money, although both are involved. The same may well be true for outdoor recreation. We have suggested a considerable rise in total leisure by the year 2000; if we can put this on an average per capita basis—recognizing that perhaps no one exactly fits the average, and that some deviate a long way from it—this will amount to a 12 per cent rise in leisure, as we have defined it, over the next generation or longer. In contrast, the consensus of economists is that real income per capita will about double over the same time period. Income is thus far more flexible than time. There will be many ways in which more income can substitute for scarce time; but it still remains true that time is likely to be more frequently a greater limiting factor than income in the future, compared with the past.

The future U.S. society, with its increased total leisure, will be an urban-dominated society. There are today many fewer people with direct personal ties to the soil, even through parents and grandparents, than there were a generation ago; and in the next generation there will be still fewer in absolute numbers and many fewer relative to the total population. These people will surely not have the agricultural fundamentalism that was so characteristic a generation ago and that is still strong in many quarters. Neither will they naturally have a strong resource or conservation bias. But there is little reason to think that urban-reared people will be anticonservation. The young people are often getting more sciences, physical and social, in their basic education than did their forefathers, and they may well be more informed about nature. They are likely to be friendly but critical, interested but not inherently dedicated, and willing to be shown but less willing to accept conservation on faith or as dogma.

The probable greater future leisure will be primarily urban leisure, and the immediate environment of most people will be an urban one. They will travel in increasing numbers to parks and other open-country areas. But there may well be need for much more social guidance to the use of recreation, including outdoor recreation. People may need some form of formal education for the use of leisure, and for enjoyment of the outdoors generally. At the same time, more thought must be given to the management of the immediate urban physical environment. While open space will continue to have its attractiveness, in many instances we must make do with more intensive and better-planned use of small spaces. We may have to shift more toward the carefully tended pocket-sized garden of the Japanese and less toward the great rolling lawns of a bygone day. Foresters may have increasingly to practice forestry for suburban open areas, and wildlife specialists increasingly to work with wildlife in the same general areas. Many people, of course, have been concerned with the use of leisure and with urban environment. Our present purpose is primarily to reinforce this concern and to relate it to increased leisure.

The increased leisure for urban people and their difficulty of direct contact with open environment suggests some possible lines of action. There might be more deliberately planned resource education, not only for young people in school, but for older people as well. Two or three generations ago the agricultural extension idea was new and novel: to take practical adult education to the farmer, on his farm and in his home. Might there be an urban resource educational service? This same increased leisure could be used, by some urban people, to promote political action on matters affecting natural environment. The League of Women Voters is a present example of mobilization of essentially urban persons for public action on many fronts, including that of resources. The retired persons and the unemployed women will have large amounts of time, and often would welcome the excitement and activity of political action. It may not be out of the question to have direct work projects on resource matters, based upon donated leisure time. Many people take up hobbies of various kinds, in order to have something interesting to do in leisure hours. Some would welcome working together with others, for the sociability this would permit. The resource manager would usually prefer to build a dam or plant young forest trees with hired labor, but if the work was done by volunteer workers they would then have a personal participation which might have great indirect effects.

The foregoing is meant only to be suggestive. But one should not think that all social invention has come to an end, or that all increases in income and leisure will have adverse effects upon environment. There are or will be many resources, financial, technological, and human, which could be mobilized to help improve natural resources and environment.

MAN AND HIS ENVIRONMENT IN A HIGH INCOME, URBAN, AND MASS-LEISURE SOCIETY

A few more general comments can be added to the foregoing, that are not limited strictly to leisure but include various other aspects of the future likely to be associated with mass leisure.

The old simple direct dependency upon environment, which characterized our society up to nearly a hundred years ago and which today typifies much of the world, is gone in the United States today, and will be still less evident in the future. We ourselves do not grow the food we eat, nor raise the sheep for wool for our own clothes, nor cut firewood from our own woods, nor do any one of numerous acts common only a few generations ago.

In the place of this kind of dependency upon environment has grown up a new and more complex dependency. In the long run and in total, we are still strongly influenced by environment; but science and technology have enabled us to fashion many new materials and products, to produce in highly specialized areas and ways, by specialized workers, and with a much more indirect relation to our environment. At the same time, other features have become more important than before—the capacity of streams to absorb wastes, of the air to carry off its pollutants, and so on. Perhaps more basically, man as an emotional as well as an intellectual animal is influenced by his environment, natural and as he has altered it. It is at least arguable that the great natural scenes such as our national parks are more highly appreciated and more needed today than ever in the past, and likely to be still more so in the future.

Perhaps urban man of the future, with more total leisure than today but with still greater demands on his time, could be induced to take more interest in his natural environment. Men and women will have time and money; some, in spite of other demands, might like to spend some of each on nature, conservation, environment, and all the rest. Their interests are hardly likely to become effective without stimulation and without help. The specialists in these various nature fields might ponder the possibility that mass conservation or mass ecology is possible, too.

BIBLIOGRAPHY

Clawson, Marion, et al. 1960. Land for the Future. Baltimore.

Holman, Mary A. 1961. A National Time-Budget for the Year 2000. Sociol. and Soc. Res. vol. 46 (Oct.).

Outdoor Recreation Resources Review Commission. 1962. Outdoor Recreation for America —A Report to the President and to Congress. Wash., D.C.

NATURAL RESOURCES AND ECONOMIC DEVELOPMENT: THE WEB OF EVENTS, POLICIES, AND POLICY OBJECTIVES

Joseph L. Fisher

In this symposium on "The Future Environments of North America" economic patterns and processes must be accorded a significant place. Even in the relatively affluent society of United States and Canada, at least as measured in averages, economic factors loom large in the everyday preoccupations of people; in earlier years of frontier settlements such factors were more clearly dominant. My purpose here is to present, not in detail but in more general outlines, some thoughts on the interaction of events, policies, and policy objectives in the economic development and use of natural resources. For the most part, I shall be thinking of the United States, although Canadian experience is similar.

Future trends and possibilities for resources and economic development unfold out of the past. There is a web of events, policies, and policy objectives, each simultaneously a cause of and result of the others, which, taken together, make up the resource situation at any given time. Broadly conceived policy objectives can give birth to more consistent and purposeful policies, which in turn can influence the flow of events. The reverse is also true: events spawn policies which aim to mold and rationalize future events which in turn may lead to the restatement of policy objectives. Thus, for example, in the 1920s and 1930s relatively depressed conditions in American agricul-

ture led to the formulation of policy objectives to raise farm incomes and stabilize this segment of the economy. Specific policies, such as government support of crop prices and limitations on acreage planted, were devised to give expression to the broad objectives. Among the events which flowed from these policies some were intended and some were not. The unintended events included overproduction, excess stocks, storage problems, higher prices in the domestic market, the temptation to dump crops on foreign markets, and relatively little benefit to the poorer segment of American agriculture. These results have led to some redefinition of policies and to proposals for rather sharp changes in policies.

The word "policy" means different things to different people. Here policies are regarded as those underlying principles which give form and direction to the more specific programs and actions intended to carry them out. Thus, sustained yield in forestry, multiple-purpose development of water, and least-cost production of metals or fuels may be regarded as policies. A hierarchy is involved in which what is policy to those down the line in a government agency or a business firm may be program to those higher up. The process for formulating policy typically is a two-way one, with much of policy resulting from an upward flow of ideas and analysis. Policy in resources as in other fields has two faces; it responds to the flow and pressures of events, and it also frames and guides that flow. Both are important. Many resource-policy issues arise directly from problems of demand and supply; others are related to matters of ownership and equity, to conflicts in use or over monetary or psychic returns from resources. Still others are traditional with their reason for being lost in the shadows of history.

Policy objectives are those broader, less tangible goals regarding which a wide consensus exists or is sought, and toward which policies deliberately try to move events. Economic growth, national security, international cooperation, and wise use of resources are among the important policy objectives. One finds these and other goals expressed in the preambles of legislation and in State of the Union addresses. They give form and direction to policies, as policies do to more specific programs.

In this paper I shall first review some highlights in recent U.S. history relating to natural resources to bring out this interplay of events, policies, and policy objectives. Second, I shall list some of the major social, economic, and technical forces with which natural resource policies and developments must be reconciled. Third, I shall consider separately what I regard as the main policy objectives, stated in general terms, which can give consistency and direction to the future course of resource development and use. Finally, I shall offer some speculations regarding future resources and economic development in the North American environment.

I. RESOURCE HIGHLIGHTS IN
RECENT HISTORY

It would be fair to say that the United States had little or no natural resource

policy as such until near the end of the nineteenth century. Even since that time, despite the attention given to conservation in the Theodore Roosevelt-Gifford Pinchot period and in the New Deal period, much of what could be called resource policy has derived from a concern for other matters such as curbing the power of large business monopolies or near-monopolies and combating unemployment and depression.

Throughout our history many governmental policies have had important effects on natural resources, but in the main the major objectives of such policies have concentrated on other things.[1] In land, for example, the large extensions of U.S. national sovereignty westward to the Pacific which ended with the Gadsden (1853) and Alaska (1867) purchases had their roots in national aggrandizement and national security objectives. Land-disposal programs beginning shortly after the American Revolution but not reaching flood tide until after the passage of the Homestead Act in 1862, followed from an overriding concern that the land westward to the Pacific be occupied rapidly. Thus, the objective was land settlement on family-size farms owned and worked by sturdy, independent, democratic-minded farmers. To some extent the raising of public revenues through land sale was an objective, although successive land-disposal acts probably fell far short of raising as much revenue as would have been possible. Water policy in these earlier years was concerned primarily with transportation. Channel improvements on the Mississippi, Ohio, and other major rivers along with canal building absorbed much

[1] The following discussion follows rather closely that contained in: Joseph L. Fisher and Donald J. Patton, "Natural Resource Policies in American Economic Development" in Seymour E. Harris, ed., *American Economic History*. McGraw-Hill, New York, 1961.

attention from state governments, the federal government, and a variety of private ventures. The development of water transportation routes in the agricultural West was one of the main features of Henry Clay's "American System" which combined an emphasis on western development with tariff protection for the growing industries of the Northeast.

The long and vigorous period of expansion through the 1800s was characterized down to its closing years by a relative abundance of natural resources—of land, water, coal, and other necessary raw materials. The chief problems were the adequacy of manpower and capital to exploit the rich and varied resource base.

By the end of the century a number of factors combined to draw attention more dramatically and directly to resource policies as such. Frederick Jackson Turner and others had announced the passing of the geographic frontier. Explorers and trappers, and then settlers, had penetrated most parts of what became the forty-eight contiguous states. Free, unchecked exploitation of forests and minerals, in some ways promoted by early legislation, had led to large monopolistic trusts—for example, in the developing oil industry. Against these, sharp criticisms were leveled and legal actions were undertaken.

Scientific and technical advances had proceeded to a point where policy makers were becoming conscious of the web of interrelations among resources—for example, among the land and water resources of the Mississippi Valley. The obvious good sense of more comprehensive resource-development policies and management was becoming evident. By the turn of the century the essential concepts of multiple-purpose resource development had been stated for water and related land resources. Flood control, navigation, watershed protection, irrigation, and even electric power were being viewed as interlocking purposes whose development should be sought on an integrated basis. The insights into ecology of George Perkins Marsh plus the broadening geological perspectives of W. J. McGee and the comprehensive view of irrigation potentials in the west of Powell, Newell, and others all contributed to the evolution of the multiple-purpose idea.[2] The ecological and economic benefits of sustained yield in forestry had been clearly established in principle and buttressed by experimental field work in the Biltmore Forest in North Carolina through the efforts of Gifford Pinchot. Finally, the leadership of Theodore Roosevelt with Gifford Pinchot and his colleagues in dramatizing resource conservation and in legislative and administrative accomplishment, especially in forestry, has to be noted.

The so-called first conservation movement emerged from all of these events and situations in the first decade of the twentieth century. The famous Governors' Conference of 1908, called by President Theodore Roosevelt to consider resource programs, marked the apex of this period. Out of the conference came purposeful statements about the need for viewing resources as a whole and in relation to human welfare over the long run. A stamp of general approval was placed on Pinchot's attractive definition of the objective of conservation which was to do "the greatest good for the greatest number for the longest time." President Taft, with his well-honed legal mind, shortly afterward struck a quizzical and slightly sour note when he observed that everyone seemed to be for conservation

[2] See Ernest S. Griffith, "Main Lines of Thought and Action" in Henry Jarrett, ed., *Perspectives on Conservation*, Johns Hopkins Press for Resources for the Future, Inc., Baltimore, 1958. Also Samuel P. Hays, *Conservation and the Gospel of Efficiency: The Progressive Conservation Movement*, 1890–1920 Harvard University Press, Cambridge, 1959.

"whatever it means." In any case, the ideas enunciated and the policies begun during these vintage years in conservation history continue to dominate much of the thinking and action on the subject down to the present time. For example, both the National Forest and the National Park programs have evolved along directions laid out during this period. Similarly the Land Reclamation Program has continued along the lines stated in the Reclamation Act of 1902 and predecessor enactments.

During the next twenty to twenty-five years conservation and resource questions were not at or even near the center of attention. The country was concerned with the First World War and the long period of business prosperity of the 1920s. But even during these years a number of the ideas set forth earlier were translated into legislation in important though unspectacular ways. The Federal Power Act (1920) established federal licensing for private development of water-power sites, the Minerals Leasing Act (1920) tightened and organized the leasing of mineral lands in the public interest. The National Park Service was created in 1916, and in 1924 the Clark-McNary Act extended federal technical cooperation to private forest owners. The Texas Railroad Commission was authorized in 1917 to regulate and conserve oil and natural gas in that state. In these and other ways ideas generated earlier were put into action.

The onset of the great Depression of the 1930s saw the second major period of creative thinking in the resource and conservation field. There was a broadening and deepening of public policy relating to land and water resources particularly, although resource matters were largely subordinated to general economic and social policy aimed at solving problems of unemployment, low income, and depression.

Soil conservation on a broad scale, the Civilian Conservation Corps program in forests and parks, land resettlement, the Tennessee Valley Authority, the shelter belt and other measures to prevent dust bowls, and public works for land reclamation, flood control, and other purposes were launched in this period with varying degrees of permanence and success. Public policy in energy and minerals, largely dormant through the 1920s except for tariff legislation, began a period of rapid extension which has continued to the present time. Efforts were made to stabilize the coal industry, severely hit by depression, through establishment of minimum prices. Conservation regulation of oil and gas gained momentum, especially after the price collapse which followed the discovery of the fabulous eastern Texas field in the early 1930s.

Attempting to articulate, guide, and provide research underpinning for these multifarious activities was the National Resources Planning Board and its predecessor agencies (1933–43) under whose auspices planning studies were made of the major resources of the country, the principal river basins and regions, public works programs, and a long list of related subjects. State resource and planning agencies were established during these years with the support of the national agency with similar objectives for their respective states. Under state enabling acts and with national government encouragement, the agricultural areas of the country were organized into soil conservation districts for the purpose of promulgating that program. The conservation payments program of the Triple A (Agricultural Adjustment Administration) and successor agencies operated through selected local committees. Grazing districts also were organized through which the federal program for rehabilitating much of the western rangeland was carried forward.

Before this rash of new resource policies and activities could properly be digested, the country was plunged into the Second World War and its aftermath, extending to the present, of cold war, limited war, high-level defense, economic prosperity with only minor interruptions, persistent inflation, and a growing sense of responsibility for the peace of the world and the economic welfare of non-Communist countries. During the war the national objective necessarily was to mobilize men and resources rapidly and efficiently to achieve victory. After the war and once the fear of postwar depression had been dispelled, resources and to a large extent resource policies were enlisted in the service of maximum employment, production, and purchasing power which had become a national objective in the Employment Act of 1946. The use of resource policy to promote economic stability remained in the background during much of the postwar period, awaiting a protracted recession while the makers of high economic policy tried to combat inflation indirectly by restrictive monetary measures and the so-called automatic stabilizers embodied in graduated income-tax rates, unemployment insurance, and farm-price supports. Occasionally when inflation threatened, efforts were made to cut back resource programs, along with others, but political pressures and real needs have worked in the opposite direction. Contrariwise, when the economy was in recession, efforts were made to accelerate public works which included resource projects. Usually these efforts were too late and too small to produce the intended effects. More flexibility and executive discretion in the timing of such programs has been sought by recent Presidents, but without success.

The long period of war and postwar economic prosperity placed very great demand on raw materials, especially fuels and metals, and led to strenuous efforts, successful to a considerable degree, to find new sources of supply and develop substitutes for those items increasing in scarcity and cost. An entirely new industry, synthetic rubber, was established. Stockpiling of a long list of critical metals and other items became a large undertaking. During the Korean war, it was found necessary to reinstall government control on the use of basic materials, notably steel, copper, and aluminum, and to encourage industrial capacity in certain lines.

Shortly after the Second World War the United States for the first time became a net importer of such basic commodities as oil and iron ore. The non-competitive imports such as coffee, tea, cocoa, tin, manganese, and natural rubber continued, but the dramatic increases were in the more basic mineral products. During the early 1960s the United States was importing 15 to 20 per cent of its crude oil, and around one quarter of its iron ore. These facts drove home to most people the importance of a rich flow of raw materials and new technology if economic growth and a strong defense were to be maintained.

These developments called for major policy responses consistent with a new role in world affairs, enlarged responsibility for aiding underdeveloped areas, an increasing net import position for important raw materials, new and uncertain defense requirements, and an urgent need to maintain a stable and growing domestic economy. A number of notable studies, such as that of the President's Materials Policy Commission (Paley Commission), were made of the impact of these changes, each in its field attempting to state the problems and recommend more comprehensive and consistent public policies. Despite their cogency most of these recommendations have not thus far found great response from the policy makers, perhaps until 1964, when the Congress enacted several far-reaching laws relative to water resources research, a land and water conservation fund, wilderness areas, private access to fissionable materials, and other matters.

But in the main, agricultural policies continue to be characterized by price supports and surplus stocks, acreage controls and fertilizer payments, and soil banks and subsidized irrigation—all underscoring stubborn inconsistencies. Demand for outdoor recreation continues to outrun the modest expansion of areas and facilities, although the passage in 1964 of the Land and Water Conservation Act promises to check this tendency. Water resource policies and administration continue in a tangled condition with rival claimants, purposes, and agencies competing for position. Mineral industries clamor for protection and favored tax treatment, to be sure with some justification, while comparative cost trends viewed on a world-wide scale and the need of less developed countries to export raw materials inexorably lead this country to more and more imports. The stockpiling program, both its goals and procedures, is assaulted annually in the Congress.

These inadequacies and dilemmas point to the need for recasting resource policies in a new mold of greater internal consistency and of greater harmony with the broader policies of foreign relations and defense. In any such new mold these kinds of resource policies should find a place: multiple-purpose management frequently on a regional basis, sustained and increased production and use of land and water resources, minimum economic waste of the stock resources, wide diffusion of benefits from resource development projects with equitable sharing of costs, adequate consideration for the qualitative, more or less nonmonetary aspects of resources such as clean air and unspoiled scenery, enhancement of both national defense and world peace, and sustained contribution to economic growth and stability in this country and elsewhere.[3]

II. MAJOR SOCIAL, ECONOMIC, AND TECHNICAL FORCES

Underlying the movement of events and policies sketched in the last section have been a number of significant social, economic, and technological forces which will continue to exert much influence on future resource and economic developments. Indeed, most of what can be done through resource policy will be severely conditioned by these forces.

Population growth can be mentioned first since it underlies everything else. Although the birth rate in the United States has been falling slightly in the past several years, the rate of growth of population still exceeds 1½ per cent per year. By the year 2000 there could well be in the neighborhood of 330 million persons in the United States compared to 180 million in 1960. The rate of growth of population in Canada can be expected to be similar to that in the United States. In most Latin American countries, for comparison, the rate of growth has been in the 3 to 4 per cent range. This prospect for many more people, combined with considerable increases in income and mobility, obviously will have important effects on the natural environment. Other papers in this symposium will identify particular effects and consider them.

Within the United States the geographical center of population is expected to continue its slow meander west and south. Within the next decade or two it may well go west of the Mississippi and south of the Missouri rivers for the first time. The Pacific Coast states and the

[3] A story broadly similar to that told in this section regarding the United States could be told about Canada, although with many adjustments for differences in institutions, geography, and timing. See, for example, the *Canadian Frontiers of Settlement* series.

southwestern states have been growing relatively rapidly.

The principal feature of internal shifts of population has been and probably will continue to be into metropolitan areas. Historically, three phases of urban population growth can be delineated: first, into the central cities; second, into the suburbs; and third, into the outer reaches of large metropolitan regions and into the less developed areas now separating existing metropolitan centers such as Boston, New York, Philadelphia, Baltimore, and Washington. A countervailing though weaker tendency for certain racial, age, and other groups to move into the central cities may also accelerate in future years. The shifting character of urbanization reveals where the greatest pressures for changing land uses will occur. It also tells something about the amount and location of land and water needed for domestic consumption, industry, and outdoor recreation.

The growth in outdoor recreation itself can be thought of as a major force, buttressed as it is by increasing leisure, income, and mobility. Already large amounts of land and water are devoted to outdoor recreation, hundreds of thousands of persons are employed in this industry, and some twenty or more billion dollars a year are spent on it. Outdoor recreation is moving into the category of an industry which can be studied and planned much like any other industry. Not only outdoor recreation, but the service component of the economy generally, what Colin Clark calls the "tertiary activities," are still on the increase relatively.

Looking ahead for the balance of this century, one sees as the principal changes in land use a doubling of urban land and perhaps an even larger increase in the amount of land devoted to outdoor recreation. On the other hand, the amount of land devoted to crops will probably increase only slightly, while that used for

grazing and commercial forestry may remain about the same. The increase in urban land will have to come out of farms, pasture, and forestlands now surrounding existing cities. The increase for outdoor recreation to a considerable extent may not have to be subtracted from existing forest or other land but can be obtained by multiple use of land already in some other category.

Undoubtedly, demand for water will increase considerably in the years ahead as it has in past decades. Here again improvements in management of water supply, such as treatment and reuse, can make it possible for fairly large increases in demand for specific purposes to be met without a severe general problem of shortage. In the eastern part of the United States plentiful rainfall fairly evenly distributed indicates that the chief problem will not be one of sheer supply, but rather one of maintaining or improving water quality. In the West the chief problem will probably remain that of assuring sufficient supplies, but even in quite arid places, some shift in use away from irrigation toward municipal and industrial uses would make possible a continued population increase and industrial development. In the West more than 90 per cent of water withdrawn from streams and underground sources, and actually depleted or used up, goes for irrigation of crops many of which are in surplus supply.

The spread of environmental pollution in many forms is one of the more noticeable and objectionable trends of our times. In addition to water pollution, the atmosphere in many metropolitan areas at certain times is heavily polluted, thereby imposing costs and irritations for large numbers of people. Much has been written recently about what may be called the pollution of agricultural land, lakes and streams, and the ground and foliage generally as a result of the way in which certain pesticides are used.

Various solid waste materials, especially in cities but also in the rural countryside, constitute another kind of environmental pollution, as does noise from automobiles and trucks, airplanes, and certain industrial operations. Both the urban and rural landscape have in many respects been disfigured as a result of poor planning, shoddy construction, or other unesthetic manifestations of our type of civilization. Many roadsides have been made ugly by refuse, auto graveyards, garish signs and emporiums of various kinds, and lack of landscaping. In short, pollution in general, as well as in many specific forms, has become pandemic and calls for increasing attention of policy, investment, and other corrective activities. These various kinds of pollution are characterized by the phenomenon of indirect or side effects, which are costs placed on persons, groups, or activities outside the range of normal responsibility, or even calculation, of those who cause the pollution. In this situation public policies and actions are usually called for of a regulatory, incentive, or more direct nature.

No list of social and economic forces powerfully at work in modern society would be complete without mentioning science and technology. These have their own inner momentum and become of particular concern when they find economic application in transportation, industrial production, the provision of social services, and in other ways. The impact of the automobile, for example, on the natural environment has been most profound and far-reaching. The impact of still newer forms of transportation, of synthetics and other new products, of new means of communication, of new tools and machines for making use of the natural environment, of automation and what it implies for the use of natural and human resources—all of these have to be examined closely and with much insight if trends in the future use of

the natural environment are to be discerned.

New sources for conventional materials are being discovered and put to use with increasing frequency. For example, commitments have recently been made for a plant to produce oil from Alberta tar sands. Experimental work on Colorado oil shale indicates that liquid oil could be produced commercially from shale at only slightly above current market price for oil. Fairly low-grade iron ore is now being beneficiated to give a high-grade product which is competitive with richer imported ore. Crop yields continue to rise as the agricultural labor force falls and total farm production goes up. Efficiency in the use of fertilizer, irrigation water, and farm practices generally increases with the spread of improved technology. Fast-growing hybrid trees are already a reality; plantations of them on a large scale may not be far off. Nuclear reactors can already produce competitive electric power in many places and uses. By 1980 as much as 20 per cent of new generating capacity might be nuclear. In addition, we are crossing a historic technological threshold in that by molecular engineering we can design and produce new materials altogether to meet anticipated uses; the various synthetic plastics are a notable example.

Over some years there has been a tendency toward homogenization of certain economic and perhaps social characteristics. For example, per capita incomes, rising generally, are tending slowly in the direction of equalization among regions and income classes. To some extent this is accompanied by a homogenization of culture generally, as schooling tends to become more standardized, modern means of transportation and communication come within the reach of nearly everyone, and more and more people, in Riesman's phrase, become "other directed"—taking their cues in behavior from what seems to be done generally

tain classes of users be given preference —for example, municipal and cooperative consumers of public power? To what extent should farmers, especially larger-scale operators, be subsidized in the interests of reduction of output, maintenance of prices and hopefully incomes, or conserving soil and moisture? To what extent should special tax advantages be accorded producers of fuels and minerals?

One of the most thorny problems here is to arrive at acceptable compromises in aid of groups suffering disadvantage as a result of progress or change: for example, how much and what kind of aid should be provided for the declining agricultural segment of the labor force or for chronically depressed mining or cutover forest areas. These policies which ease and promote adjustment to other, hopefully more productive forms of employment in the same areas if possible, otherwise in other places, will be most helpful, but care should be taken that they do not result in locking unemployed persons and resources into hopeless situations in which there can be no end of special subsidies.

Two further objectives of resource policy have become of great significance in recent years. They intertwine with the objective already discussed, that of increasing the welfare of people, but deserve special mention. The first relates to the *development of other countries,* especially those in an earlier stage of economic growth. Many of these countries have long and culturally rich histories, large populations, and good resource potentialities. But they lack an advanced technology, enough professional and skilled workers, sufficient capital or capacity to acquire it, and in most instances an efficiently functioning set of business and governmental institutions for economic growth. Incomes are generally low over most of Asia, Africa, and Latin America; in many countries less

than 10 per cent, or even 5 per cent, of that in the United States in terms of per capita income. Characteristically they are in the demographic stage of rapidly falling death rates and stationary or slowly falling birth rates. With populations increasing at sometimes 2, 3, or more per cent a year it remains exceedingly difficult for such countries to increase investment by much more than enough to provide for the larger numbers at the same living levels. In the face of the strong desire on the part of these people to raise these levels, the situation in many places has become explosive. The temptation is strong to turn in whatever direction seems to promise immediate assistance.

Since the Second World War especially, the United States has found itself inescapably caught up in the hopes and problems of the less developed countries. Many of the problems have to do with natural resources—with agriculture, water and irrigation, electric power, minerals of all sorts—and how these can be developed and can contribute to economic growth. A substantial part of the fifty or so billion dollars that the United States has provided since the Second World War in net grants and credits for rehabilitation and development of such areas has rather directly involved natural resources. An objective of resource policy for the future must be to continue assistance in resource matters to less developed countries in timely and carefully selected ways so that their very low levels of living can be raised.

A final objective has to do with the *promotion of national* security by means of resource policies. This, too, is closely connected with the other objectives set out here. To a large extent, resource policies good for other purposes will be good for security. But from time to time additional measures may be necessary, such as stockpiling of strategic and critical materials, maintenance of investment in resource discovery and technologic development, special purchasing arrangements, or encouragement to overseas suppliers. In a few instances the scale of public effort, directly or through support of private activity, may have to be very large, as for example in atomic energy. In many instances military requirements can be met through the normal economic channels without special policies. This objective is not narrowly nationalistic because the security of the free world depends importantly on security.

A number of broad objectives for resource development have been identified. These include a rising level of welfare which is thought of as made up of economic, ecologic, technologic, and esthetic parts; aid to poorer countries striving for resource and economic development; and national security. Testing of specific policies in the major resource fields of land use, water, and energy and minerals against these general and interrelated objectives can give a greater degree of direction and consistency to what traditionally has been a confused assortment of special and limited purpose actions.

IV. SPECULATIONS REGARDING THE FUTURE

What future patterns of public policy can be discerned which will relate natural resources and economic development? Granted that there is a web of events, policies, and policy objectives—this has been noted in the preceding sections—what are some of the principal elements of this pattern? Several only will be identified here.

First, in sheer quantitative terms it appears highly probable that for the next few decades there will be no general running out of raw materials or the natural resources from which they are derived in this country or in Canada for that mat-

ter.[4] For the year 2000 the U.S. population has been projected to increase to 330 million, gross national product to $2200 billion, and annual output per worker to nearly $16,000. Accompanying these over-all economic growth projections, requirements for a number of important resource materials can be noted in the table on the following page.

A rather careful checking of these requirements against the supplies that can be forthcoming would indicate that there is little danger of any general running out of resources before the end of this century, and probably for some time thereafter. This is not to say there will not be shortages of particular items at particular times and in particular places; for example, water may be short in the arid West, recreation land near large cities may be inadequate, and there could be supply and price difficulties from time to time for certain metals. But in the main, the possibilities for using lower grades of raw materials, new discoveries, imports of certain materials, substitution of plentiful for scarce materials, increases in efficiency by means of which more use can be obtained from given amounts of raw materials, multiple use of land and water resources—these and other possibilities can be called on to hold in check any tendency toward scarcity. All of this implies that new and improved resource technology will be available for the discovery, production, transportation, and use of resource materials. It also means that this country must be in a position to draw upon other parts of the world for a portion of its requirements for oil, iron ore, lead, zinc, and many other necessary items. It also means continuing attention to the conservation of resources all along the line from the basic land, water, and

[4] Landsberg, et al., op. cit. Regarding the outlook for resources in Canada see: *Resources for Tomorrow*, conference background papers, issued under authority of the Minister of Northern Affairs and National Resources, Ottawa, 1961.

U.S. *Requirements of Selected Natural Resources and Resource Products,*
1960 and Projected 2000

	1960	2000
Cropland including pasture (million acres)	447	476
Wheat (million bushels)	1110	1385
Cotton (billion pounds)	7.0	16
Timber (billion cubic feet)	11	32
Fresh-water withdrawal depletions (billion gal. per day)	84	149
East	13.7	37.4
West	59.7	91.7
Pacific Northwest	11.1	20.2
Oil (billion barrels)	3.2	10.0
Natural gas (trillion cubic feet)	13.3	34.9
Coal (million short tons)	436	718
Nuclear power (billion kilowatt-hours)	—	2400
Iron ore (million short tons)	131	341
Aluminum, primary (million short tons)	2.1	13.3
Copper, primary (million short tons)	1.7	4.5

Source: Landsberg, Fischman and Fisher, *Resources in America's Future.* The Johns Hopkins Press for Resources for the Future, Inc., Baltimore, 1963.

minerals themselves through the stages of extraction and processing and finally in end uses.

A second discernible element in future patterns is indicated by the increasing importance of the quality of the resource environment itself, as against the sheer quantity of goods and services which can be extracted from it and used. Examples of quality deterioration abound: polluted streams, smog hanging over our cities, damage to fish and wildlife from unwise use of pesticides, radioactive fallout, noise from trucks and airplanes, unsightly highways, and squalid areas in our cities.

Although there is a natural tendency for many to think that economics has no part to play in the analysis of environmental quality problems or in the prescription of policy, this is far from the truth. If the full social and esthetic benefits of clean water or clean air cannot truly be measured in monetary terms, the costs of programs which will achieve stipulated levels of water or atmospheric purity nevertheless can be indicated fairly closely. Control, treatment, and management schemes can be worked out through modern systems analysis employing the talents of engineers, management specialists, and economists. Indeed, whenever a resource quality program is funded, or whenever an appropriation is made, a kind of judgment regarding the social worth of the program is made. Much hard work needs to be done to bridge the gap between those who want a cleaner, more beautiful natural environment and those who have to make the hard decisions as to what precisely to do, what level of quality is to be strived for, and how much money should be spent.

A third element of great significance for the future pattern of resources and economic development is the continued growth and elaboration of metropolitan regions. Urban land planning, the development of clean water for city people, the provision of electric power, clean air—all these and many more resource matters are now entwined in the whole process of urban growth. Natural resources are no longer a matter of concern only, or even primarily, out in the country. Those who are planning for parks and other outdoor recreation facilities must have in mind principally the needs and wishes of city people. Forest policies increasingly will have to recognize that outdoor recreation is likely to surpass timber supply as the most valuable aspect of many of our forests. Adequate and clean water for urban uses is becoming paramount in water development.

Each metropolitan area can be thought of as having a number of resource sheds: for outdoor recreation, water supply, electric power, and so on, in the same way that each such area has a milk shed. For given stages and forms of development each of these sheds has a carrying capacity which will define the number of users or intensity of use that can be tolerated. For example, the park and outdoor recreation system available for use of persons in a particular metropolitan area should be considered from the viewpoint of how many and what kind of use can be made of the elements of the system without endangering essential characteristics of the system itself. These characteristics can be defined in terms of ecology, scenic effects, and the like. Much more investigation needs to go into determining the way in which carrying capacity varies with the level and type of development of park areas. Here, design and location of facilities become critical, since a given area may be able to carry twice as many users with one kind of design as with another. And all of these factors need to be related to cost if optimum recreation systems are to be determined.

A fourth element in the evolving pattern of resource and economic development is the continuing concern with resource development in other countries, especially the less developed countries. The U.S. economy, and the Canadian as well, has always been closely linked with the economies of the mother countries in Europe. Ties with Latin America and with other parts of the world, though always somewhat smaller in magnitude,

have been important and sustained over a long period. Since the war the two North American countries have played a major part in aiding in the re-establishment of the West European economies after the dislocations of the war, and continue to provide economic aid to developing countries in Latin America, Asia, and Africa. In turn, other countries have been exporting large amounts of raw materials, especially to the United States, so that North American dependence on the rest of the world remains high. Dependence carries a special meaning: for most commodities, the United States could be self-sufficient, although frequently at considerable increase in cost. However, the scale and structure of many of our export and import industries would change drastically if foreign trade were severely reduced. In addition, and probably more serious, repercussions on the economics and politics of other countries could be severe.

In any case, resource policies here will have to take account of the interconnections of world trade and investment. Among the questions that arise are these: Should production of basic agricultural crops in this country be planned deliberately so as to produce a surplus for shipment overseas through government channels? Should this country continue by means of tariffs and quotas to protect investments and employment in local areas which depend on the production of domestic products which have a hard time to compete with imports? What further changes in the program for stockpiling strategic and critical materials are now indicated by changes in military strategy, the world political situation, and the possibilities for domestic production and substitutions?

Other elements in the pattern of resource and economic development can be discerned in the lines of scientific and technological development that are now being opened up. New sources of oil, such as oil shale and tar sands, nuclear energy, new plastic materials, genetic improvements in plants, trees, and livestock, new ways of improving management of water systems, new techniques of mineral exploration—these and many other possibilities, as they are applied, can have large impact on resource patterns in the future.

How can all of these fit together in a future pattern of resource and economic development? Population growth, especially in the urban regions; adequacy of resource supply to meet the demands of a larger economy in general but with specific areas of difficulty; increase in environmental pollution and disfigurement; rapid scientific and technological development accompanied by lags and problems of social adaption through laws, institutions, and policies—can one discern new patterns emerging from these tendencies? Several points seem to be worth mentioning by way of conclusion.

(1) The age-old concern for resource shortage seems to have boiled away to a scientific-technological-economic-management problem, at least in the countries that have more highly developed economies, such as Canada and the United States. The essential thing is to enlarge our capacity in science, engineering, and management. This, in return, depends on the quality of the educational system.

(2) In the United States and Canada, both relatively affluent, matters of resource quality are becoming more and more important. Policy and management of resources will be giving more attention in the future to pollution, landscape and wildlife preservation, and related questions. These factors will have to be brought within plans and decisions across a wide range of concerns for land and water conservation, urban development, even international policy.

(3) Efforts to peer systematically into the future for several decades ahead at the interrelations between resources and the whole economy of both countries and regions should be encouraged. Long-range, comprehensive projections of demand and supply, updated periodically, can provide the necessary framework for resource planning and investments, and thereby impart greater consistency to what is done.

(4) The growth of population in the United States and Canada, though rapid, does not as yet signal any Malthusian disaster. Long before these countries might become "overpopulated," behavioral and institutional changes could take place to contain the problem. One already sees the beginnings as birth control becomes more widely accepted and practiced. Nevertheless, a wary eye should be kept on the relationships between demographic and economic trends, especially as these affect basic land, water, and mineral resources.

(5) More comprehensive programs for resource conservation and development will have to be worked out for the future. Multiple-purpose, multiple-resource approaches will no doubt become more common as the range of possibilities to be served by various programs widens and as techniques of management permit. Increasingly, resource programs will be taking account of side effects that are important from the broad, long-range, social viewpoint. These frequently will take the form of regional programs as in Appalachia or the Columbia River Basin. In the future other U.S.-Canadian regions may be developed as integral regions: for example, the Great Lakes-St. Lawrence region, or the Alaska-Yukon-northern British Columbia region.

Other concluding points could be mentioned, but these are enough to indicate some elements of the future resource and economic patterns. The challenge for economic and social science research will be to perceive the emerging patterns. The challenge for policy and policy makers will be to react to the events and possibilities inherent in the ongoing scheme of things in constructive ways so that people will be able to live in and use the natural environment for the fulfillment of their own desires without diminishing future possibilities. They will call for the weaving of new patterns from both new strands and old ones.

BIBLIOGRAPHY

Harris, Seymour E., ed. 1961. American Economic History. New York.

Hays, Samuel P. 1959. Conservation and the Gospel of Efficiency: The Progressive Conservation Movement. Cambridge, Mass.

Jarrett, Henry, ed. 1958. Perspectives on Conservation. Baltimore.

Landsberg, Hans H., et al. 1963. Resources in America's Future. Baltimore.

(Minister of Northern Affairs and Natural Resources). 1961. Resources for Tomorrow. Ottawa.

TECHNOLOGY, RESOURCES, AND URBANISM—
THE LONG VIEW

Richard L. Meier*

My role in this assessment is that of the forecaster-planner. As such I must take a long look at the future and identify those components in it surprising to policy makers. It is my task to see that they are not ill prepared when new problems arise. If they are to believe me, I must first describe my intellectual position—the heights from which this long view is to be sketched. Then a series of portrayals of the more surprising vistas can be reeled off, and finally recommendations can be outlined for more thorough investigation prior to actual choice of development path. The program is quite simple but the argument gets a bit intricate in spots, due to some recent altercations in the scholarly literature. My principal aim is to avoid the disputes, treading lightly over the minefields of controversy, in order to get from here to a collection of interesting conclusions.

First, it is necessary to assert that a new set of insights will reconstruct the outlook for natural resources. The classic stance of the nature-interpreting scientist, whether ecologist, geologist, geographer, or meteorologist, whether field worker or

theorist, is already in eclipse. Nature-centered adaptive policies of the kind which have been repeatedly advanced in the past (at this point I should cite instances, but that would invite mortar fire from entrenched positions, so the reader is invited to choose his own examples) are being philosophically undermined, statistically outflanked, and economically overwhelmed. Urban interests, in particular, are finding amplifiers for their activities with increasing potency. Always before a strong factor in determining how a natural resource was to be treated, the cities henceforth will dominate.

The insights are derived from a process of amalgamation. Systems of thought created by behavioral scientists, operations researchers, and organization theorists are beginning to coalesce. Consequently, ideas that were once qualitative and elusive are susceptible to measurement. Much finer differences in value can be distinguished. Our knowledge base is being reorganized in such a manner that it promises to maintain steady growth in most directions for decades to come; much of this research output can and will be applied to the control and direction of the natural environment. Boulding has eloquently summed up the major movements in the over-all transition to the twenty-first century and has highlighted the emergence of postcivilization.[1] I ac-

* Dr. Meier teaches at the University of Michigan School of Natural Resources. His main interests have lain in demography and regional planning and in the implications of technological innovation for environmental change. Among his recent books are *Modern Science and the Human Fertility Problem* (1959) and *A Communications Theory of Urban Growth* (1962).

cept his broad strokes as an appropriate backdrop, and shall pencil in some of the more specific features.

In order to gain the greatest possible resolution in the picture to be presented it is necessary at the start that some bench marks be established. Definitions of terms and a standardization of expectations from analysis are certainly needed, but they must be extended by a recounting of new, as-yet-undigested findings:

Technology, according to this new view, is a means for applying communicable knowledge to the environment (physical, biological, social) so as to produce valuable goods and services. It is different from the art of the artisan, who is also engaged in the production of goods and services, since an indescribable element of personal skill is incorporated in the art. Many desirable features of an artistic product cannot be replicated elsewhere. In technology, however, the rules for synthesis are put into blueprints and an operating manual, the components produced are interchangeable, and virtually all the knowledge is accessible to the public.[2] The artisan carries his instructions in his head and his hands.

Technological processes are invariant with respect to location and culture; although shifts in environment may cause the efficiency to vary, so that adjustments in procedure aimed at local optimization are normal. Modern technology steadily improves upon itself as relevant knowledge continues to accumulate. Older ap-

Twentieth Century. Harper & Row, New York, 1964.

[2] However, the closer one gets to technology, even the most modern, the more he is struck with the realization that much still depends on artistic flair founded upon a body of intensive experience acquired by a creative person unable to explain the bases for his success. Perhaps the factory should be regarded as a more completely planned and programed *atelier*, the survival of which as a going concern depends upon the development of a few individuals with supernormal talent.

plications of knowledge are repeatedly superseded by those which provide better-quality outputs, require less labor, or make fewer demands upon the natural environment. Even if it were desired, there is no known way at the moment for halting the knowledge accretion process in modern technology short of destroying civilization itself.

The emphasis upon "communicable knowledge" in this definition provides a foundation for all the arguments and forecasts that follow. In whatever human activity systematic knowledge is already well established and uncontested, and wherever essential supplies are available, the technical knowledge for resource exploitation is purchasable.

The most common method for forecasting the volume of use of a given technology starts from the observation that the early exponential growth gradually tapers off as the unsatisfied world demand approaches saturation, and thereafter growth depends upon the level of prosperity.[3] These recognized methods for projecting over-all economic growth into the future are helpful for establishing normal expectations; they provide a framework for analyzing the implications of changing demand for product mix and thus yield a standard forecast for the use for the technologies that process the various natural resources. This mode of analysis, when conducted at the national level, provides policy makers with a set of assessments of the future; it presents a picture which may be readjusted incrementally as new knowledge is acquired. Such a sober, prudent approach was adopted by Landsberg, Fischman, and Fisher of Resources for the

[3] This method has been in use for decades, but the most recent application that has come to my attention reviews the patterns for commodities depending on tropical soil resources. G. L. F. Beckford, "The Growth of Major Tropical Export-Crop Industries," *Social & Economic Studies* 13, pp. 413–29, 1964.

Future, Inc. in their comprehensive review[4] and extended by Fisher in a contribution to this symposium.

Accordingly, a balanced forecast of the impact of known characteristics of technological development upon resources in the leading political unit on the North American continent already exists. Most of my assignment has already been accomplished. Moreover, the diffusion of the most modern technology to the other nations on the continent is accelerating, so the resource-use patterns of the others are quite predictable. *It is important to note that the Landsberg, Fischman, and Fisher study did not discover any resource scarcity so critical that it threatened to retard the development of the continental economy during the twentieth century. By implication, no habitat is in danger due to crises of scarcity.* If the value of any habitat in the path of change is at all significant in the minds of many people, the land (or water, soil, forest, etc.) use can be converted so as to fit the best nondestructive utilization scheme, and no deprivation need result. This is a most unusual conclusion, since equally thorough studies of other continents would almost certainly result in much less favorable outlooks, except perhaps in the cases of underpopulated Antarctica and Australia. It should be emphasized that these projects depend upon resource use technologies that have already been tested in practice but in most instances are not yet in universal use.

The aforementioned emphasis upon *communicable* knowledge also enables one to forecast the innovations in technology likely to be adopted in the next few decades. I undertook such a forecast about a decade ago,[5] and it is now pos-

sible to review its dependability. For this method of long-range forecasting the investigator must first identify the particular kinds of *scientific* studies which are presently expanding rapidly, comparing the prospective opportunities introduced by the new findings with the expectations for rising costs that are encountered with a few critical commodities when using the known technologies. New knowledge might well offer the potentiality of a technology producing economical *substitutes* for these critical commodities. A careful evaluation of the details in the scientific and technological literature uncovers the most promising exceptions to the trend-line projections of the economic forecasters for the respective industries and commodities. The Resources for the Future scholars were also aware of this means for assessing the long-range future, and used it for making adjustments in their forecasts. Therefore, the only features which could very easily be added to their view of the future are those which are most affected by additions to scientific knowledge, fundamental and applied, *over the past three years* and further interpretation of the data available to them which, for reasons of space limitations and a shortage of time, they were unable to consider.

The discussion that follows has been subdivided into resource-oriented categories convenient for the appraisal of long-range shifts. The argument covers the commonly anticipated changes, such as the establishment of a route to the moon from some point in North America, either very lightly or not at all, because such ideas have been worn down to clichés. These oft-repeated forecasts have a strong self-fulfilling property, but they are no longer informative. Instead, some of the rather surprising and unexpected features of large-scale interaction be-

[4] H. H. Landsberg, L. L. Fischman, and J. L. Fisher, *Resources in America's Future.* Johns Hopkins Press, Baltimore, 1963.

[5] R. L. Meier, *Science and Economic Development: New Patterns of Living.* M. I. T. Press and John Wiley & Sons, Cambridge and New York, 1956. The second edition (in press, 1965) discusses the reliability of this kind of forecasting.

tween technology and ecosystem are emphasized. For each case where surprising futures are introduced as either probable or quite likely, a quantitative projection based upon foreseeable changes in the cost of production and the growth in effective demand could be used to justify the specific generalizations made. Obviously all the evidence cannot be presented in an overview of this sort, but some clues are provided for the specialists in technology who may wish to undertake independent appraisals. Natural resources are grouped into a materials-and-energy classification, followed by land and water, and then a newly recognized feature, that of human resources and knowledge.

MATERIALS AND ENERGY

The central portion of the North American continent seems destined to become the metallurgical and petrochemical workshop of the world. All the resource locations, the transport potentials, together with the economic and cultural factors, enable it to produce large volumes of fabricated materials at the lowest costs.

The opportunity is easily described. World prospects for petroleum supplies promise greater production, by far, than ever before, but in the 1970s or 1980s the fantastic growth in demand in Europe, Japan, and in the developing countries is likely to encounter production limits. Oil is not as plentiful as coal, tar sands, or even oil shale. When oil becomes more difficult to find and produce, its price should rise to that of competitive fuels. These scarcities will open up a magnificent opportunity to produce petroleum products from the Athabascan tar sands at market prices.[6] By the 1980s it is likely that tens of billions of dollars

will be spent in equipment for the extraction and utilization of tar sands. Shale-oil development has been highly publicized in the United States, but the costs of production presently look less favorable, so the scale of development is expected to be much less. Attention should also be drawn to the huge deposits of low-grade coal that underlie the western Great Plains from Canada to Texas. As the natural-gas fields run out, known technologies can be applied to the gasification of these coals, and the present pipelines can be used for gas transmission. Simultaneously, electric power plants can be located on these coal fields to supply the new continental grid system.[7]

The network of pipelines and the high-voltage grid both converge upon the Great Lakes. Along the way is a huge reserve of medium-grade iron ore, in the Mesabi Range, the Iron Range, and on the eastern edge of the Ozarks. High-grade ore from Labrador, or anywhere else in the world, can come up the St. Lawrence Seaway. Heavy manufacturing is best supported on the lake shores where these independent flows can meet. Although light metals and plastics will make further inroads into the materials of construction, formerly almost monopolized by concrete, ceramics, and steel, the advantages still rest with the ferrous alloys, stressed concrete, glass, and the sintered products—due not so much to their economy as to the fact that a very wide range of properties is available. They fit the requirements of an age when quality standards, especially performance specifications, will be far more rigorous than at present.

The synthetic-chemicals industries, including plastics, paints, and synthetic rubber, are likely to re-establish themselves increasingly in this same region. Automotive fuels should be relatively plentiful, if

[6] *Oil and Gas Journal*, March 2, 1964, pp. 84–86; May 18, 1964, pp. 122–24.

[7] Federal Power Commission, *National Power Survey*, Washington, D.C., 1964.

only because the refineries in this region will specialize in the production of unsaturated hydrocarbon gases for the high-volume polymers, and the motor fuels are by-products of this gas production. Heavy machine tools, railway equipment, trucks, and large construction equipment should find most of their growth located in the same region. Much energy-intensive light metals (e.g. aluminum, titanium, magnesium, beryllium, etc.) fabrication is likely to be integrated into the industrial complexes. In general, the trends for industrial location in the mid-continent seem likely to continue in the same direction they have been moving over the last decade, but the concentration of heavy industry may well accelerate when the richest gas and oil resources in Texas and the West have been utilized.

Most heavy industry is dependent upon steady supplies of cooling water, so the Great Lakes and the Mississippi Valley provide a considerable attraction. That side of the Great Lakes, presently depressed as an aftermath of clear-cut lumbering, can therefore be expected to serve as the locale for increasingly heavy investments. The number of jobs produced by industrial growth is not likely to be very great, however, because most of the processes and transport technologies are easily automated and will, perhaps in less than a decade, be operated through DDC (direct digital control, with closed cybernetic loop). The pay scales should be raised to quite high levels, however, so that an increasing number of service workers can be supported by the relatively constant number of production and construction workers. Most of these service workers need not reside within sight or smell of the heavy industry.

No reason can be found for reversing the locational trend of consumer-oriented industries—fibers, fabric, synthetic leather, garments, furniture, appliances, etc. They prosper in the South. The paper industry may halt its hitherto steady growth, however, because increasing amounts of information will be transmitted through electronic channels. It will be printed on newsprint or book paper only when it needs to be carefully studied. Tough plastic films are already beginning to take over a share of the container field formerly served by paper and foil.

Coincident with this further industrial intensification of the mid-continent is the full mechanization of agriculture. Food for 400 million persons is easily obtainable from the soil resources of the Mississippi-Missouri Valley with half the present farm-labor force. The most expensive input, synthetic fertilizer, should be cheaper in the mid-continent than elsewhere in the world due to savings in both transportation and the cost of energy. The lowest-quality soils now in cultivation (those that do not respond well to fertilizer) will very likely continue to be abandoned and be allowed to revert to forestland and prairie.

On the eastern seaboard energy-using industry should be less dynamic but highly competitive with the world at large. The underground stocks of coal in Appalachia should last well beyond the twenty-first century with minor prospective increases in relative costs. Nonferrous metals and imported commodities can therefore be fabricated economically at various estuarine industrial complexes. These activities may process double the present quantity of minerals by the end of the century, but only moderate amounts of extra space will be required. The highly instrumented, continuous-flow technologies use space more efficiently than their labor-intensive predecessors. I conclude by observing that it is impossible to find any point where new locations for industry and the reconstructed harbors will conflict seriously with the principal functions of the northeast coast of North America. The megalopolis there serves now as the political, financial, and cultural capital of the world. The massive urban aggregates in the East have already well established themselves in these roles and are favored to retain them indefinitely because potential competitors face still graver air pollution and congestion problems than those anticipated for the Atlantic Coastal areas.

The future of the West Coast has little to do with materials processing, mining, or the export of energy-rich products. Innovations in all these directions may very likely be triggered by organizations working in the West, but the chief exports will be designs, films, television tapes, recordings, instruments, sophisticated aerospace equipment, research, education, etc. California has established itself as the research-and-development capital of the world in all major technical fields except medicine; its future lies in exploiting its organizational successes in the use of new knowledge and of artistic creations.

WATER AND LAND

It is already recognized that water for industry and air-conditioning, to mention two expanding demands, is due to become scarce in North America.[8] Thus population will cluster around the Great Lakes and the principal rivers as the rural expanses are emptied. Seaside areas should also increase heavily in numbers, even in areas presently experiencing water-supply crises, because large quantities of desalinated water are obtainable at a price that is not too exorbitant. Since mean family incomes in excess of $10,-000 per year are expected, while the water cost for family requirements should reach a plateau at no more than $100 per year greater than at present, even the driest shore lines are inhabitable.

The extra hundred million people that the censuses have forecast will arrive by the turn of the century will prefer to live in urban areas. They will occupy, it is believed, twenty or thirty million acres now in pasture, fields, orchard, and scrub forest, not to mention some mud flats, desert, and steep slopes that were hitherto too expensive or unattractive for settlement. The amount of territory they need (30,000 to 50,000 square miles) is very modest as compared to the supply. The greatest task associated with the doubling in population of the urban areas, and a multiplication by three or four of the space they occupy, is the orderly distribution of metropolitan services despite the political fragmentation of the metropolitan regions.

Certainly the most striking transition to be anticipated is one that is presently still in its gestation period. It involves the settlement of the nearest wilderness to the megalopolis, the sea. The technological foundations for this invasion have come into existence since 1960.[9] Only in 1964 did oceanographers and marine scientists begin to talk publicly about the possibilities.[10] Nevertheless inventors and many small innovating enterprises have been working for some time on the thousands of separate problems that are encountered as people begin to think about living permanently at sea.

At present the greatest single hazard to life on the sea is that of weather. In Florida, the insurance on a vessel equal in value to a house is roughly ten times as great. If better weather prediction were available, and if protection from the most violent storms could be devised, some of the ocean surfaces would become as convenient and desirable as the

[8] Abel Wolman, *Water Resources*, Report to the Committee on Natural Resources, National Academy of Sciences-National Research Council, Washington, D.C., 1962.

[9] Proceedings of the International Conference on Buoy Technology, Marine Technology Society, Washington, D.C.; April, 1964.
[10] Roger Revelle, "Oceans in 1984: A Long View from the Beach," *New Scientist*, 21, 1964, pp. 485–87; also Athelstan Spilhaus in various addresses during 1964.

land remaining at the margins of large cities. The new weather satellites, combined with the computerized, continent-wide systems for the digestion and interpretation of meteorological data, ought to produce better predictions in the not-too-distant future. There is even some experimentation on the control and modification of storms.[11]

The only weatherproof solution available at present is a cylindrical spar buoy drawing 300 feet of water with thirty to fifty feet exposed. Its motion in a high sea is less than that of a boat in a mild swell. Thus far only seagoing laboratories have been built to these specifications.[12] Their design is well suited to development as elevator apartments with thirty to a hundred dwelling units per buoy.

Much larger investments are now being made in seagoing barges which house workers and supply a platform for well-drilling, mostly oil, gas, and sulfur. Under the most adverse weather conditions they will take refuge in a nearby harbor.[13] Barges of the future may be designed to provide the arrangements and conveniences of garden apartments, perhaps ten to thirty per barge. Small vessels would be tied alongside for convenient transportation.

Houseboats are already being built. They are becoming increasingly popular and seem likely to attract a large population because many features of this mode of life are well understood. Well over 10 per cent of all dwelling units produced in the United States are mobile homes, and the proportion is increasing. With the steady improvement of marina services, the living conditions available to houseboat dwellers are becoming competitive with the mobile-home courts. Hundreds of thousands of people in the middle-income range are likely to try houseboats in the next decade or so. The rising price of shorelands makes it already economic, if the family unit does not need schools or other community-type services.[14] In severe storms the residents may be advised to flee to public refuges, but it is anticipated that this should happen only once or twice in ten years. It occurs with that frequency in a few low-lying land settlements, and the dangers of flood and wind have not deterred the residents in those locations.

The greatest demand for living space exists not in North America, but in Asia and nearby territories. Thus it is in Tokyo, Hong Kong, Singapore, Shanghai, Java, Bengal, and Egypt that we expect to see the greatest overspill into marine settlements in the long run. Nevertheless a large share of the early pioneers will most likely be North Americans, primarily from Los Angeles, Florida, New York City, and the Chesapeake Bay area, because a few key individuals there have the initiative, independence, technical competence, and wealth needed to occupy this wilderness. Almost all attempts will be undertaken in the name of sport, or research—it is often difficult to discover which motive is dominant when a frontier is being penetrated. The other enterprising metropolitan seaside settlements in the world (e.g. Melbourne, Sydney, Athens, Buenos Aires, Lima, Tel Aviv, etc.) will be quick to imitate. The overpopulated regions exposed to severe shortages of fresh water, electric power, and space for free movement would need to develop a low-cost version for their

[11] National Academy of Sciences-National Research Council, *Scientific Problems of Weather Modification*, Publication 1236, Washington, D.C., 1964.

[12] Philip Rudnick, "FLIP (Floating Instrument Platform)," *Science* 146, 1964, pp. 1268–73.

[13] *Fortune* 71, February, 1965, pp. 132–35.

[14] Such a settlement has even begun in the Hudson River off Seventy-ninth Street. It was made possible by the installation of an air-bubbling device which prevents freeze-up. *The New York Times*, Feb. 25, 1965, p. 29.

needs. On the basis of journey-to-work time or simple accessibility to central business districts, the real estate value of the presently unoccupied water surfaces amounts to many billions of dollars. Tokyo and Hong Kong, for example, have already generated downtown-land values per unit area in excess of those reported for New York City, and there are water surfaces available for settlement only five to fifteen minutes away from the metro-center.

The population pressures in Asian cities could seriously affect North American urbanization. If the technological advances permitting settlement of the seas evolve too slowly, we Americans will be accommodating a new wave of immigrants. An inspection of the maps of urbanizable areas around the world will reveal insufficient space for the ten billions or so of population that are expected to crowd into the world's cities in the next century (there are likely to be many more than ten billion if birth control is not accepted with unprecedented rapidity).

The choice of location for settlement depends most heavily in the long run upon climatic variability and transport costs. The refugees from the supersaturated rural areas must push on to the less densely settled territories that have fresh water to spare and uncongested access to raw materials. If they do not move out onto the high seas in free-floating cities, the targets for migration will be Australia and North America. If these continents were overrun militarily, the nondesert fringes of Australia could support hundreds of millions and North America several billions of Asiatics at living standards their middle classes hope to reach. The Great Lakes region and the humid South would be particularly attractive territories for such population transfers.

Thus the solution of the fascinating technical problems of the settlement of the seas, when put into perspective with

long-term world-wide demographic pressures, can be viewed as a means of deferring, perhaps preventing, a concentration of population in North America up to Asiatic densities. The empty areas, the seas, seem to offer the most convenient reserve living space for the long run.

HUMAN RESOURCES AND INFORMATION

Why do rural people continue to move into the cities? It is because the city offers the prime source of opportunity to improve one's position in life. Cities provide the best locus for human resources development.

At this point it is necessary to be quite clear regarding what is meant by human resources. The resource itself, a "potential for enrichment" analogous to other natural resources, is the aptitude to learn, acquire skill, and use information. This potential is found in almost all human beings. The resource is developed primarily through education and training; it is conserved by medical practice and accident prevention. Higher levels of useful learning and skill quite consistently command a higher price in the labor market. The "capital" that economists isolate and measure is fabricated from commodities derived from nature. Human capital is formed through the education process. In an individual the development of the potentials can be estimated through the administration of a comprehensive achievement test, but short of that it is judged by the educational accomplishments, professional recognition, and experience accumulated.[15]

Some human capital also resides in each social aggregation such as the community and the corporate organization. Personal knowledge is fitted into a social role, and the roles interact to produce extra wealth in most instances. (Organi-

[15] B. S. Bloom, *Stability and Change in Human Characteristics*. John Wiley & Sons, New York, 1964.

zations and communities in violent conflict may, however, use almost any of these roles to destroy the opponent's wealth so that organization does not necessarily result in the creation of surplus value). These social institutions are capable of learning and of reorganizing their own internal structures. Most of their knowledge is recorded in their files and it is applied through a series of decision rules used by the members. In a profit-making economy institutions can be created which capture part of this wealth and distribute it as dividends.[16]

Scientific knowledge, since it is accessible to anyone who wishes to take the trouble to read and understand it, is best categorized as social capital.[17] It belongs to mankind. It can introduce increased efficiency in the use of natural resources and other factors of production, and therefore has economic value, but not very often does it have a scarcity which permits us to establish a value in the marketplace.

Cities that develop and grow, generating wealth and attracting the energetic individuals, are built and organized so

[16] Over the last several years, for example, organizations in the knowledge technology business have changed hands at prices which are equivalent to $150,000 for each responsible position. Thus the present value of a firm with 1000 professionals and highly qualified technicians, aided by several thousand standard clerks and secretaries, with a growing business and a good reputation but no physical equipment and an insignificant inventory, would be about $150 million. This value has been created despite the fact that such a firm is committed to paying higher-than-average salaries. Virtually all of the $150 million is capital created by the organization of specialized knowledge into an institution with a life of its own.

[17] The clearest distinction that can be made here is between *human* capital in the narrow sense, where the returns are to households; *community* or *organizational* capital, where returns are distributed to members according to agreements registered in a charter; and *social* capital, the returns from which are enjoyed by a large part of society.

that human capital is conserved and expanded. They provide a reasonable, healthy environment, they sponsor education, and they maintain institutions like libraries and museums for the storage of information. Equally important, they offer a milieu in which experiments in organization can be initiated at comparatively little cost in time and effort. Some of these innovations will survive and prosper. The accumulated wealth will be spent upon high-quality services more than ever before.

Of these services to urban regions the most resource-intensive is that of outdoor recreation. Land requirements for recreation are very extensive, and the energy costs for transport may well exceed any other category of passenger movement. Contact with nature increases proportionately with the build-up of human and social capital; it appears to be used as contrasting experience to the communications-intensive mode of life in the city, enabling a person to gain greater salience out of both experiences.[18] We need to know much more about the life styles adopted by educated persons engaged in urban pursuits who have the means to get to whatever part of the world that attracts them. Occasions have already arisen where access to certain subtropical shore lines has been bid up to high prices.

THE CONSERVATION EFFECTS OF
TECHNOLOGICAL KNOWLEDGE

It is only quite recently that scholars have begun to comprehend the extent of the effects of knowledge accumulation processes upon resource use. True, conservation principles were incorporated into the school curriculum more than a generation ago as part of the policy for preventing waste, and the adult education among rural populations emphasized soil conser-

[18] R. L. Meier, *A Communications Theory of Urban Growth*, p. 137. M. I. T. Press, Cambridge, 1962.

vation and fertilizer usage. Nevertheless it was research (i.e. knowledge creation), by piling up the evidence and translating it into technological practices, that proved to be most effective for obtaining returns from the resources. Printed media from the urban centers were responsible for its diffusion; then the educational system undertook persuasion and indoctrination.

The concepts of *energy* and of *chemical-element requirements* are instances of the level of theorizing that could only have come into being in a society which supported extensive knowledge-accumulating institutions—archives, libraries, guilds, colleges, scientific societies, publishers, laboratories, corporations, etc. Conservation today is a relatively sophisticated set of ideas that are transmitted through urban media and are founded upon urban viewpoints.

The evolutionary process by which this came about is now quite clear. A careful observation of aborigines does not reveal any advanced conception of resource utilization, since some quite correct assessments of nature are muddled by many superstitions. Those bands and tribes survived that learned a few crucial resource-saving customs, while others vanished. Later, as populations settled into agrarian life, many more conservatory practices were adopted. The higher population densities could not accumulate until a good many of these custodial rules were incorporated into the culture. Nevertheless, Malthusian pressures eventually push a population to dimensions where the best customary treatment of forest, soil, and water resources results in an exhaustion of the natural capital. Catastrophe is a natural consequence of such unbalanced relationships with the environment; in history the fall of agrarian empires was speeded up by the rigidification of government and by the diffusion of techniques of military technology to

the barbarians. The agrarian populations usually contrived to absorb the invaders, develop a hybrid culture with a few extra characteristics added that went significantly beyond prior cultural forms, and then mobilize the enhanced potential of the territory. Cities helped in this cyclical process of development because they encouraged the division of labor and the specialization of crop type by sponsoring commerce between regions.[19]

Although cities have been repeatedly castigated for their profligate waste, also for the pollution both of streams and the atmosphere, it has rarely been recognized that they are also the primary source of concern about resources. Some city people become wise as a result of examining the record, and through agitation they create new attitudes toward resource use. Thus there emanates from urban culture both an enhanced demand for resource-based commodities and an increased capacity for producing them. In the past several decades the technology based upon urban potentials for production and consumption has created a network of reserves and capacities sufficient to meet the increasing demand.

In the autonomous or self-transforming society that seems to be taking shape, the appearance of a serious instability in nature leads to investigation. The sources are identified, and projects employing known technologies are formulated which seem likely to restore the balance. But occasionally the expected loss is not worth the effort to re-establish prior environmental conditions. The social values of the politically and economically effective strata in the population, including their valuation of the future state of the

[19] There are many variants in the exposition of this theme. The most recent contributors have been Lewis Mumford in his *The City and History*, Harcourt, Brace & World, New York, 1961, and W. H. McNeill, *The Rise of the West*, University of Chicago Press, Chicago, 1963.

natural environment, will then determine what irreversible action should be taken.

CONCLUSIONS

The over-all outcome is predictable. About 99 per cent of the area of North America, and the surrounding seas, will be open space redeveloped with the know-how of city dwellers. Gradually conditions in this environment will be adjusted to meet the demands of the visitors, sojourners, and refugees from the urban areas. The present residents of the more open spaces have too little knowledge or political power to resist for very long. Most are being urbanized *in situ* through television, schools, and the availability of automobiles. A majority of rural and small-town families will migrate to the urban fringe in search of economic and social opportunity. In the future the proper habitat for man in America is the modern city.

As American cities complete the acculturation of the rural immigrant, fewer problems involving known resource deficiencies can be inferred from our present state of knowledge. Lacking dependable local evidence to the contrary, it is possible to argue from first principles: as knowledge continues to accumulate, the control over unwanted changes in the natural environment will increase.

Nevertheless, pressures external to North America, particularly the unconstrained population growth in South Asia, could boil over and threaten these prospects. Presently each small-scale failure in foreign policy (ranging from Hungary to Cuba and Hong Kong in the past decade) has resulted in the influx of tens or hundreds of thousands of educated refugees. If millions upon millions should arrive, the most serious foreseeable problems are those of maintaining public order decades later when the almost inevitable injustices are felt most keenly.

The recommendation that follows from recognition of this threat is that mutual efforts should be encouraged toward penetrating the marine frontier leading to eventual settlement of the aquatic wilderness. The sea offers the most promising escape from overcrowding.

For urban Americans the greatest challenge is to redesign the environment, land and sea. Increased income, knowledge, and cultural sophistication will induce them to extract a greater *variety* of direct rewarding contacts with natural phenomena. An extension of the *range* of those experiences should be the next measure of success on the part of government.

BIBLIOGRAPHY

Anonymous. 1964. Federal Power Commission. National Power Survey. Wash., D.C.
Anonymous. 1965. Fortune 71:132–35.
Anonymous. 1964. National Academy of Sciences-National Research Council. Scientific Problems of Weather Modification, Pub. 1236. Wash., D.C.
Anonymous. 1964. Oil and Gas J., March 2:84–86; May 18:122–24.
Anonymous. 1964. Proc. of the Inter. Conf. on Buoy Technol. Marine Technol. Soc. Wash., D.C.
Beckford, G. L. F. 1964. The Growth of Major Tropical Export–Crop Industries. Soc. & Econ. Studies 13:413–29.
Bloom, B. S. 1964. Stability and Change in Human Characteristics. Wiley, New York.
Boulding, K. E. 1964. The Meaning of the Twentieth Century. New York.
Landsberg, Hans H., et al. 1963. Resources in America's Future. Baltimore.
Meier, R. L. 1956. Science and Economic Development: New Patterns of Living. Cambridge and New York.
———— 1962. A Communications Theory of Urban Growth. Cambridge, Mass.

McNeill, W. H. 1963. The Rise of the West. Chicago.

Mumford, Lewis. 1961. The City and History. Harcourt, New York.

Revelle, Roger. 1964. Oceans in 1984: A Long View from the Beach. New Scientist 21: 485-87.

Rudnick, Philip. 1964. FLIP (Floating Instrument Platform). Sci. 146:1268-73.

Wolman, Abel. 1962. Water Resources. Rep. to the Com. on Nat. Res., Nat. Acad. of Sci.-Nat. Res. Council. Wash., D.C.

General Discussion

FISHER: We now turn to you, Kenneth, as was promised.

BOULDING: Let me say a few things that weren't in the paper. I think your model, Joe, is resources for the not-too-distant future. We all take great satisfaction, we say we are all right today, and our kids are all right. And after that, the deluge.

The fact is that if you look to the twenty-second century, things look pretty rough, particularly if things go on as they are now.

It is an interesting exercise to ask oneself what is the implication of present movements, even though this is no more than an exercise. I did this recently with the aid of some log paper. I charted the per capita gross national products of the nations of the world as of 1957, projected at the rate of growth of the fifties, to calculate when does the United States become the second richest country, the third richest country, the tenth richest country, and so on. In the fifties there were forty-five countries which had higher rates of growth and per capita income than the United States. And their overtake dates are quite close: 1977 for Germany, 1984 for Switzerland, 1992 for Japan, 2000 for France and Italy, 2020 for practically everybody.

This is already obsolete, of course; these were the rates of growth for the great Eisenhower stagnation. We have already exceeded these substantially, and the rates of growth of the socialist countries have declined. But it is an illustration of how very rapidly the whole world situation is changing under the impact of differential rates of growth.

One of the things that worries me today is that these differentials have increased enormously over what they were before the Second World War. Before the Second World War the world's record was held by Japan and Sweden for sustained economic growth—2.3 per cent per annum from about 1880 to 1930. The United States was close behind, about 2.2.

Since 1945 the Japanese have made 8 per cent, the Germans made 7 per cent, the Italians and the French and the Jamaicans and South Africans and all sorts of implausible people have made 6 per cent. The United States made 1.8. And Syria made minus 2.

The gap between the 8 per cent of Japan and the minus 2 per cent of Syria is very large. This means whereas before the war it might take fifty or a hundred years to develop a reversal of the world power structure, today this can happen in fifteen or twenty years. That is, with these kinds of differentials.

Another thing which I was talking about last night—and they still don't believe me: In spite of the fact we had a pretty good rate of growth last year, the United States is in very serious trouble technologically because of the absorption of our growth resource in the war-space complex.

Even though only 10 per cent of the GNP goes into the war industry, Melman estimates 60 per cent of research and development goes into it. This has meant now that the war-space complex is a whole generation or two generations ahead of the civilian economy, and there is practically no feedback from it any more. When you look at our machine-tool industry, shipbuilding, textiles, railroads, even construction, you see we are falling behind the Japanese and the Europeans very rapidly.

It is quite probable that, for instance, Western Europe will be a much more important power in the world than the United States in 2020. This isn't just arithmetic. This is quite plausible projection.

Here we are all assuming it is the law of God that North America is the real center of the world. It isn't true at all. Especially in these days the advantages of acreage get less and less all the time. You don't really need acres to produce GNP any more.

It may be that the mineral resources are the really more fundamental limitation at the moment and we are fairly well off on this basis. This is an interesting question. Nevertheless, I can see some danger of the United States becoming another Spain. We are so obsessed with our position as a great power, we are so determined we are going to dominate the world and throw our weight around everywhere, that we simply fall behind everybody who doesn't think as we do technologically.

You wanted me to be shocking.

FISHER: I will swallow my own tonic and ask for reactions to this.

MEIER: Of course he is dead wrong.

(*Laughter*)

Because he didn't apply his own economic system principles to this whole problem of the question of growthmanship, and as soon as these imbalances of rapid growth and slow growth become still more evident, he is quite aware of the fact that frictions and pressures begin to develop within the system which bring about equilibration of various sorts.

In fact, in the last two to three years you can begin to see some of this going on rather rapidly. The most peculiar kinds of equilibrations occur such as methods of trying to pull out of the aerospace industries and the missile systems approach, and the whole basis for training the Job Corps personnel.

In other words, you get into the antipoverty act directly from aerospace. This is partly because of the bankruptcy of vocational education. It was the one place we had to turn to and more and more often we are trying to figure out how to grab hold of the special know-how that was created one to two generations ahead of the rest of the economy. Boulding is right there.

But it is being first trickled out in small amounts, and we hope to open the spigots a little bit more.

HUBBERT: I should like to comment on the last few remarks of Mr. Boulding. When one speaks of the rate of growth of the GNP, I haven't the faintest idea what this means when I try to translate it into coal and oil and iron, and the other physical quantities which are required to run an industry. So far as I have been able to find out, the quantity, GNP, is a monetary bookkeeping entity. It obeys the laws of money: it can be expanded or diminished, created or destroyed; but it does not obey the laws of physics.

On the other hand, physical growth involves growth in the consumption of energy, of metals and other minerals, and of biological products, all of which are subject to the conservation laws of matter and energy. Because of these physical restrictions, it is accordingly impossible to maintain a physical growth at a constant exponential rate for longer than a brief period of time. I doubt if any such restriction applies to the growth of the GNP. Consequently, I am not impressed by arguments based on the GNP unless these can be translated into physical quantities whose properties are known.

BOULDING: As I say, these exercises are arithmetic, and I am not putting these forward as predictions in any sense of the word.

These are simply implications of, shall we say, the fifties, and they are already obsolete. If I may say something else, it does seem to me that when we come to look at the world system—this earth machine, whatever you want to call it—knowledge is fantastically deficient, particularly in the physical sciences. The things we do not know about the earth are simply fantastic.

HUBBERT: I should like to challenge that statement, as a basic proposition. We are not ignorant of physics, nor of the earth. Our knowledge of both of these subjects is comprehensive and immense.

BOULDING: Our knowledge of the physical sciences is backward. They lag hopelessly behind the social sciences in sophistication, they do not make use of the mathematical developments or the conceptual developments of the last twenty-five years, and you ask any physical scientist any sensible question and he cannot answer you.

(*Laughter*)

We just don't know. We haven't done enough work on it. We don't know anything about such things as elementary as the CO_2 level. Are things warming up or cooling down? Nobody knows.

Meteorology is worse than economics. Its predictions are worse. Its information system is worse. You don't have any sophisticated knowledge in ecology. Ecology as far as I can see has been one of the most unsophisticated of the sciences.

You are a bunch of bird watchers.

(*Laughter*)

You really are. The National Academy of Sciences, if I may say so, is still living in the eighteenth century. It could practically be presided over by Benjamin Franklin.

(*Laughter*)

FISHER: I have engaged in this business of economic projections and so on quite a bit. I am always very careful to tell what time period I am talking about. And I think this is essential.

I don't think it is much use for economists to try to look more than a few decades ahead. When we do, we are trying to see further than our eyes will carry.

The main reason is that, frankly, so many things can happen that you can speculate about. Anybody can write about what it is going to be like 100, 200, 500 years from now. But this is prophecy. You can't handle it in a scientific way at all. The reason is perfectly simple: you don't know what is going to happen.

I can easily imagine that by the time 2000 rolls around, the whole business of family planning and birth control—the world over—will be so different from what now appears to be possible that it would be idle to make precise calculations of how many people there would be.

On the technological side I think it is equally difficult. You simply don't know what kinds of combinations and breakthroughs and new sources will be spawned by the enormous increase, communication, and storage of knowledge and its capability of retrieval.

It isn't that I can't, or any economist can't, look way down the pike and prophesy. He can. But he doesn't think it is worth the candle, for the reasons that I have given.

ALLEN: Ecologists are bird watchers. But so help me, when we get into the realm of human ecology we are not dealing with birds entirely any more. We are dealing with the relationship of the whole human race to its earthly environment.

This is a pretty broad subject. It includes a realm of study in the human species that we call sociology. In the broader context of ecology we feel we are dealing with the ultimate welfare of man. I think this means a human living standard that is respectable and comfortable, and one that we all could properly aspire to.

That is our motive in managing resources through the concept that we call conservation. Conservation isn't something you set aside areas for. Conservation is a way of life and it is the application of ecology in preserving and managing resources for their maximum and ultimate usefulness. This is the objective of the ecologist and the conservationist.

I think our concept must be that we are dealing with a fund of resources acted upon at a given cultural level. And that cultural level is changing all the way from the primitive culture of the Eskimo to our atomic-age science and the one we will have 1000 years from now if there is any human culture left.

The basic fund of resources that is converted to human use is divided up among x number of people and you can't ignore this part of the equation. The population is going to be lower or higher, and that is all going to factor out into a living standard. This is the way the ecologist thinks of the human race in relation to its earthly environment, and he brings time into it—a long time.

I contend that this is a respectable viewpoint; it is the context in which a lot of things have to be considered, and it is not just the permutations of a bunch of visionary dicky-birders.

(*Laughter*)

BRANDWEIN: I wasn't going to rise to Kenneth Boulding's bait, which was cast very neatly. But I would ask whether we have transcended the origins of knowledge and assumed that knowledge proceeds much faster than it does.

After all, the Newtonian doctrines or concepts are now being used in Cape Kennedy. That doesn't mean that it has taken such a long time. It simply means that concepts change very slowly, and remain fairly permanent.

For instance, I imagine that a chicken is an egg's way of making another egg. I imagine that this is going to last for quite some time, and I don't need to upset this kind of knowledge.

And if you are now more sophisticated in the graduate-school level and say it is deoxyribonucleic acid in the chromosomes that produce the chicken eggs, I think that is merely sophistication.

I think earlier you were much wiser when you indicated that there are really two cultures, and you have to come to the fulcrum level to get the umbilical cord to the sophisticated knowledge, and in the same way scientific knowledge changes very, very slowly.

Let me proceed on this basis. First by defining science, and therefore defining economics in the same way.

Science is an exploration of the material universe—note the adjective—in order to seek explanations of objects and events, orderly explanations, if you will, and if this can develop into art, into music and sociology.

And another aspect of it becomes highly relevant; scientists need to know when their theories tell them what is wrong, not what is right, so that their theories are somewhat testable.

Economics, if it is to be a science, will have to state its theories so that they are testable. All I find is Gresham's law.

OVINGTON: I would like to say that I disagree violently with some of the things that Boulding says in his paper about ecologists. But I agree wholeheartedly with him in what he said this afternoon about the limitations of ecologists.

I find it disturbing that at this meeting you are looking to the ecologist to give answers, and the ecologist is sometimes pretending he knows the answers or has the data to give those answers; the fact is that in the present state of ecology we don't have a lot of the basic information. And there is still very little likelihood of getting it in a reasonable time.

For example, we are being questioned about what numbers of people the earth can support in different areas. But we don't yet know what is the basic, primary production of these areas, the total production of the earth, and how this varies. We don't know where there is gross underproduction due to some critical limiting factor. In parts of Australia, if you put down zinc or boron, you can increase production enormously.

I think ecologists must be perfectly honest in this, and have to make their needs felt, because man's future depends upon this ecological knowledge. We are now beginning to look at the functioning of ecosystems and this is the sort of material which will give the answers that are required.

Just as there is an explosion of chemical and physical research, there is a need for a great expansion of the right kind of ecological work. But I don't think you can get around this by pretending to know the answers; we just haven't got the basic data at present to give these answers.

SEARS: Granted that all this is true—imperfection of our knowledge, and so forth—I would like to ask whether there isn't a good deal that is already known that we should use, but do not. I am thinking for example of what happens in the absence of material recycling, inefficient use of energy, poor disposal of wastes, things of that kind. With the knowledge we already have don't you think we do have some basis for a critique?

OVINGTON: There are enormous gaps. We don't know what is really the maximum efficiency which one could get.

SEARS: There is more research being done today on primary production, I think.

OVINGTON: Yes, but it is quite inadequate, and not being undertaken sufficiently rapidly for the nature of the problems which the ecologists are being asked to answer.

NICHOLSON: I would like to support what Ovington has just said. I think we need a program, like that of the Nature Conservancy in Britain, which is one of the largest comprehensive concerted programs in this field—I reckon we have a total put into it so far of about 2000 man-years of work.

This is tiny in comparison with most of the other things we are talking about. We cannot really expect—if ecology is as important as it has been said from many quarters—to get adequate information to work out principles and so on without very much greater inputs of scientific effort into many branches of ecology.

We are really being asked to make bricks without straw.

Just to illustrate, if I may, and to put some questions to the ecologist, there seem to be three areas just touched on in these papers, but not developed—ecology and conservation are penalized in many of these discussions.

Take first of all pollution. There are many cases of development where the income is being gained at the expense of a rundown of capital. You are wasting a capital resource by creating erosion or by some permanent rundown in the capital resource.

We have no economic means by which that cost can be shown, and by which the charges inherent in that cost can be credited to research.

SEARS: We concede it is happening.

NICHOLSON: We concede it is happening.

FISHER: Give an example of a resource capital that is run-down that is really dangerous in this country or in Canada.

MEIER: Or in the world.

NICHOLSON: Take extractive industries. Take strip mining. In the course of getting minerals out—unless there is social provision for restoring topsoil and so on, as there is in some countries—you are getting a certain amount of ore or water, it may be, at the expense of a permanent product.

FISHER: That is a problem, we will grant that. But suppose you don't take strip-mined coal but all energy, which is quite substitutable, one source for another, and you can transport many kinds of energy commodities rather easily, and there are new things that are coming into the picture.

On any time horizon of plan, social, economic, political, engineering planning, where is the problem?

NICHOLSON: Many of these industries are making an apparent profit at the expense of doing damage by pollution. This is the point which comes out in your paper.

FISHER: Granted.

NICHOLSON: This pollution is handed out to somebody. It is not costed in relation to the industry which produces the pollution. That is one area.

If I may mention the other two—I think it is important to look at them together—there is the question of the capital rundown.

There is also the question of these phony costings that you get in relation to, say, agriculture, land reclamation, and so on, where you get subsidies or you get some kind of lower rates of interest drawn.

Take hydroelectric power, for instance. In the case of hydroelectric power in Scotland we had a committee on costs, which set up new criteria by which they absorbed a share of the real figures in terms of the market rates of interest and so on. Having tried to prove that hydroelectric was highly economic, when the new criteria were set up they found that there wasn't a single hydroelectric project that could be put forward which would match these perfectly objective criteria. Yet the schemes had been going forward as if they were an addition to the national wealth.

A third angle on this I think is in relation to the intangibles, the invisibles. If you take re-creation of time, economics, there are backward economics for measuring additions to wealth other than the output of crops or skiing or whatever it is. This penalizes conservation.

Many of these values—one sees it in tourism particularly—are very real in the balance of payments, yet they are constantly slipped through the net of economic techniques, especially if you look at it in relation to one reason.

You may have an apparently poor reason which is a good income earner in terms of tourism. It never gets credit for that. You can't get this taken into account where you are in a conflict for land use, say with some development which is tangible. The thing is always loaded against you because you are arguing for something intangible.

While I tried to agree with Dr. Ovington, I also tried to state the case in conservation terms, but it is difficult to put in concrete form, yet we must make an effort.

I think in economics we are very backward in seeing that the scales are held truly as between certain types of development which get far more resources for research and development, and which are often able to make a phony case, particularly with the citizens, as against conservation because these things are blended through the particular blind spots of economic techniques.

DARLING: I was interested in the remarks on sophistication of the social sciences and the lack of sophistication in ecology. I once knew a fellow who said his wife helped him a great deal in decision making. She was always wrong. (*Laughter*)

He referred everything to her. Social sciences are rather like this. I cannot think of any economist over the years who has been right for terribly long, but he carries you through until the next stage. John Stuart Mill, Keynes, and the rest of them had to go down eventually.

BOULDING: You are talking nonsense.

FISHER: Malthus?

DARLING: He was hammered to pieces by the social sciences in the 1930s, but has raised his head out of the grave since then with a ghoulish grin on his face.

The social sciences have let us down terribly badly all the way along the line, I feel—such things as the economy of open mining and so on; eastern Kentucky can ruin its hills to get out coal at two dollars a ton. The Ohio Valley is being made a swamp by the silt and muck that is going down from there. Just over the hill from eastern Kentucky is this model of conservation economics, the Tennessee Valley Authority. They are buying that two-dollar-a-ton coal and they will not pay two twenty-five for the coal to help in some kind of rehabilitation of the affected watershed.

I had spoken, when I opened this Conference, about the National Coal Board. This is exactly what they are spending, about one ninth or one tenth of their income, to do some rehabilitation.

FISHER: Frank, why do you seem to lay this—or blame this—on the economists?

DARLING: Because this is called an economic price of coal. (*Laughter*)

It is economic because it is used for something at a money price.

FISHER: I would agree with you we are not including enough of the costs here in the price, and we have to find ways not only of measuring the social costs or the side effects, as we now tend to call them, but we have to find legislative or market means, or other instruments for getting that into the price, if we can. Otherwise we have to resort to prohibitions and other things of that sort.

I am on your wavelength here entirely.

DARLING: In ecology, however far behind we are, we are trying—I believe—in a scientific spirit to find out, as it were, a code, a system on which we can go for causes and consequences.

We are dealing with process, with time. Some of us are trying to work back through history with an ecological slant of mind, so that we can look into a future that isn't just a kind of projectionism, but something which will last as an approach.

If I may say so, I complained yesterday afternoon of being a little disappointed with the way the day had gone, that we weren't moving to the future at all. But I am proud of my fellow ecologists this afternoon. They have really done everything today which they didn't yesterday.

CLAWSON: It seems to me there are plenty of deficiencies in each field, whether you want to look at my field and I at yours, or whether we each want to look at our own.

It seems to me as an economist that ecology is an extraordinarily difficult field. More so really than the social sciences. And I base this on one point, and I may be completely wrong. As I understand the whole concept of an ecosystem, and the interrelationships of its parts, one point seems to me to be the essence of it: all you have to do is leave out one part and you are wrong about the whole structure.

On the other hand, in economics, certainly comprehensive changes and comprehensive economic planning have much to be said for them. Yet in a highly developed country like these two countries that we are primarily concerned with here, we can do enormously well with marginal adjustments and even piecemeal attack if we can show that certain parts of the economy can be made to function better without being too explicit or thorough in consideration of the remainder of the economy. We can frequently bring about considerable improvements.

As an economist who is far too old to be translated into an ecologist, even if I were welcome, it seems to me that you fellows have an enormously more difficult field to work in and do it well.

Retrospectively you can frequently say, "Aha, they"—whoever "they" are—"overlooked this and that factor." Prospectively looking ahead, it is never so easy to see what all of these relevant factors are going to be.

Heaven knows we economists have made our share of errors about projections. I am not so sure you ecologists have made many projections. This is of course one way of not having many errors in your projections.

(*Laughter*)

There are, quite seriously, some fairly considerable differences here between the two fields of knowledge. I don't know the answer.

COWAN: Mr. Chairman, I think there are some parallels that have appeared. While we ecologists are searching for the root processes that work their way completely through ecosystems, we come to the management level at which economists are frequently forced to operate in terms of day-to-day decision making. The ecologist also operates at that level, and he does it by the device of searching for what he calls limiting factors.

At any given time point one thing is likely to be the major limiting factor on a population, just as one thing may be chiefly limiting in economic development in one direction or another. The skilled ecologist can spot these factors. This is not the kind of ecology that Dr. Ovington has been talking about, but it arises from the kind of basic ecology that his group is working on. It is the working-level ecology that most of us who are in the business have to apply on the day-to-day basis, the same way as Dr. Clawson and his associates apply their working knowledge at the day-to-day decision-making level.

This is applicable, it does work, it is being used daily. We can't always predict what will happen, but it proves up. Therefore I do feel that there are many parallels of considerable interest between the two fields.

FOSBERG: I would like to ask the economists a question. Maybe it is not one that they properly should deal with. I wonder if it is a matter that is too difficult or if it hasn't occurred to anyone to try to assess and assign the cost of most economic development in terms of the increasing ugliness of the resulting countryside. Is this something that can't be assessed, or is it somebody else's job, or hasn't it occurred to anyone to do it?

MEIER: May I reply to that? I have seen some papers that have not yet been published. The people who have been responding to this question are the mathematical geographers.

Landscape architects are yet quite a ways behind the mathematical geographers. In general they are trying to take images on the surface, and assess how do people interpret those images and are they valued images, or disvalued images.

I had some of my students applying such techniques trying to discover, given the belief that the taste-makers of the 1980s exist in their midst, what were the tastes with respect to the images of dwellings and the spaces around the dwellings for living when, let us say, they were able to own their own house, they had a considerable income, and they had reasonable expectations of income.

The answer seems to be that about 5 per cent of them will want to live in urban areas, that somewhere around 10 or 20 per cent will accept suburban, and a different group of mathematical geographers have already distinguished another category beyond the suburban, which they called dispersed urban. It appears that about 70 per cent or so would prefer the kind of images on the land and on the environment that are equivalent to the dispersed urban, which in the Middle West would be about 1000 persons per square mile, or about one fourth the density of the surburban and one fifth the density of the urban.

Right there the tidiness of the environment, the wildness, some kind of esthetic combination, is what is preferred. They will have the income to expect it. They dislike the disarray which is caused by the untidy urban fringe, and these valued images in part are a response to what they see.

In other words, they don't like what they see in suburbs, in the central city, etc., where the environment seems to be out of visual control. But they don't want the urbane architecture, either. And the architects, who submit their designs—we had twenty architectural, landscape-architecture students in this sample—they submit urban designs to get their grades in class, and privately they choose, 70 per cent of them, to live in the opposite kind of environment.

FOSBERG: I was thinking less in terms of architecture and more in terms of the type of depressing landscape that you see when you drive from Buffalo to Niagara Falls, or from Philadelphia to Wilmington, that just seems— maybe this is a purely subjective reaction, but I have heard other people say the same thing, so it isn't unique to me—that it is so appalling that if this is what the world is to look like fifty years hence, I am glad that I am almost sixty years old.

FISHER: I think there are probably several approaches that come to mind on this. Let's take water pollution, stream pollution. One way is to get from the public-health people some kind of a standard of cleanliness of the water, expressed in the way that they would express it—"dissolved-oxygen content" or some other way—and then pass a law which would permit you to restrain anybody from dumping stuff into the water that would cause it to slip below the standard. This is kind of inflexible and difficult.

Another way that one of my colleagues has studied is to try to rig up a system of charges on individual industrial plants or municipalities that put effluent into a stream according to the best indicator you can get of the damage that that causes other people, and rig up the charges so that the individual polluter has a choice, either he dumps the effluent in the stream and pays the charge, in which case the public body has to clean it up, or he cleans it up himself and dumps fairly clean effluent in and doesn't pay the charge.

This is the kind of thing that usually appeals to social scientists because it has many benefits to it. It sets the cost on the guy who causes the trouble, and it allows him some discretion in the matter.

FOSBERG: Of course the man who builds an ugly factory or sets up something that is hideous does it on his own property. He doesn't dump it into the environment. He just does it right there.

FISHER: I would like to have discussion of Ray Fosberg's question, which I think goes to the heart of this whole Conference. What can we say now after our discussions as to how to go about reducing ugliness? Is that the way you would put it, Ray?

FOSBERG: Reducing the loss of beauty.

FISHER: Reducing the loss of beauty not only in connection with stream and air pollution, but also in the whole configuration of the landscape. Since most people live in cities, and this trend will probably increase in the future, it seems to me that a big piece of this question has to do with city landscape.

WOODBURY: The recognition of the need for attractiveness or beauty in the urban landscape certainly has grown substantially in recent years. It wasn't very many years ago when the courts of this country refused to countenance or accept this as a justification for the regulation of land use.

There are some amusing cases on this point. Ordinances—zoning ordinances that were very obviously meant to exclude billboards from certain areas for reasons of visual quality and so forth—were in some cases held to be capricious and unreasonable. But they were sometimes upheld under the most strained interpretations.

For example, in a high-court case a learned justice said that billboards could be excluded from an area because they might fall over on people; they might accumulate rubbish at the rear and start fires; immoral acts might be performed behind them.

(*Laughter*)

This is literally true. Therefore, the restrictions in this area came within the proper exercise of the police powers, protection of the health, safety and general welfare.

In more recent years the learned gentlemen of the courts have taken a more head-on view of this issue, and there are cases now in which substantial visual or esthetic controls have been upheld on their own merits.

This didn't just happen. This is the result of some agitation, in which planners had some small part. The most extreme pronouncement of a court on this I suppose was in the Supreme Court of the United States in an urban-renewal case a few years ago, Berman-Parker, in which the issue was whether it was proper for the redevelopment agency of the District of Columbia to take certain properties in southeast Washington in connection with the redevelopment project.

These properties, by stipulation, were not necessarily substandard themselves, but they were in an area of predominantly substandard property. The argument for taking them was that condemnation was essential to bring about the type of redevelopment that was thought to be appropriate there, and that if they were left and the project had to be designed around them, it would be less satisfactory in many ways, including visually.

The Supreme Court of the United States in a sweeping decision, much of which our lawyer friends will recognize as dictum, did say that if a community wished to have a redevelopment project which was beautiful as well as sanitary and attractive as well as well controlled and regulated, there was nothing in the Constitution of the United States that stood in the way.

This again represents some advance. No one dissented; it was a unanimous decision.

I think it is worth some recognition that attempts have been made and are still being made to bring this dimension of the environment into the planning and regulatory process.

Having said this, I think the difficulty again is the one that Dr. Brinser raised earlier. The concept of beauty, of visual attractiveness, which is to some of us appealing, is awfully hard to give content as a criterion.

And Brinser said he found variety not a very useful criterion for an environment or a specification of a desirable environment because it is all together too loose. Variety is vague. What is in it? What is the mix? What are the proportions?

It is a mix. But we don't seem to have the ways of getting beyond that rather obvious statement about it. This is the part of the economists' counteroffensive that we might now discuss. With the obvious merits of inclusiveness that an ecologist has, is variety a concept sufficiently definite, sufficiently analyzable, so that we can say of it we want more of this and less of that—and we exclude x, y, and z, and include a, b, and c?

STRONG: I agree with Dr. Brinser for the most part. As an example of the problems we face in this variety question, there are ordinances saying that all houses in an area must look alike and other ordinances saying no houses in an area may look alike. Both have been upheld. We are at a dead loss at present for criteria for amenities. We have all types of ordinances which we can draft if people want them: for example, we can require trees over a certain diameter to be preserved, but what kind of trees, located where, for what reasons? We badly need some standards as to what to preserve.

McHarg and I, along with a few others, have been engaged in an open-space project for the last several years in the Philadelphia metropolitan area. We set out to try to design a prototype system of open space for the metropolitan area, hoping that this would help others across the country. I think Ian, more than any of the rest of us to start with, had a strong feeling that it was the amenity we were after, but we also had a sense that we couldn't set forth sufficient standards for amenity to design the system. Therefore Ian proposed, and we have proceeded, to develop our system on the basis of water-resource preservation.

In fact, while our system may preserve water resources, it doesn't give nearly as much open space as we would like. We find that we would choose to impose development limitations on two thirds of the metropolitan area, but in many cases, these limitations would be no more restrictive than the kind of development we are getting anyway.

We may say that you can permit 15 per cent site coverage, or 10 per cent site coverage, which in fact works out to one house per acre, including the road service. This is not really what we had in mind, for amenity purposes.

I don't know what Ian will say. My conclusion is that the water resource requirements on which we tried to peg our open-space system have
proven not to be sufficient. We have got to add amenity, and our next step
must be to find some definitions for amenity that we can use.

MC HARG: The reason I am in this group at all is because my objectives are
perfectly simple, I think.

Americans and Europeans certainly should be able to make ennobling
cities. If they want to make them, of course they would have to use landscape architects.

Having been a landscape architect for twenty years, and having found
very few people who want to employ me, I have found two things were
necessary: I had to be a propagandist to change their values—which involved contesting the first chapter of Genesis, among other things, and
also involved using a tougher coinage than simple and vulnerable things
like beauty and delight. And so I became the poor man's ecologist, in
order to say that natural processes, in fact, constituted values: air, water,
and land resources. And with superabundant land presumably we didn't
have to simply lay about brutally everywhere with matted hair and glazed
eyes, unable to differentiate the beautiful from the useful, and covering
the land remorselessly and without discrimination with hot-dog stands,
billboards, asphalt, concrete, chewing gum, Kleenex, beer cans: these
splendid testimonials to mid-twentieth-century civilization.

On our open-space study we chose eight parameters—surface water, riparian lands, marshes, fifty-foot floodplain, aquifers and aquifer recharge
areas, steep slopes, forest and woodlands, and prime agricultural lands.
We found that even after doubling the population of the Philadelphia
metropolitan area, we still had 70 per cent open, which gave us some
freedom. We suggested then that each of these areas in fact did perform
work and had inherent constraints. We found marshes shouldn't support
any development at all on the grounds they were important for flood control and drouth control and water equalization, and riparian lands
shouldn't have any development save those things which are dissociable
from waters like ports, harbors, and water-related industries.

Floodplains by and large should be exempted from development because
it would be tedious to have the federal government bail people out physically and metaphorically; reasonable men should not insist on development
of the floodplains.

Unfortunately, these approaches don't produce all of our objectives.
This is just a policy of prudence, and prudence doesn't necessarily produce
art at all.

I would be glad to work toward a simple objective; that is, stopping
simple, stupid-minded, bloody bestiality, rapacity, despoliation for no
value—because much of the destruction is just this—and developing a simple discrimination which allows development not to be remorseless and
unthinking.

So we then have pockets of development which may be handsome, may be attractive—or may not. But that then is another problem. That is one which I think cannot be as easily legislated.

ORDWAY: The discussion we were on just now deals with the subject the planners are going to take up at length later and to some extent the education and legal problems. The question that this session really has to wrestle with is what the economic approach to the valuation of both beauty and amenity may be.

FISHER: Yes. These sessions, of course, interrelate. One of the difficulties of the economist and one of his shortcomings—one of my shortcomings—is a failure to go halfway with the city planner or the ecologist and understand what kinds of standards he is working with.

I think if I do that, and try hard at it, I will be able to translate even such standards as diameters of trees and these things that McHarg was talking about into cost. While this isn't the whole story, it greatly helps the decision maker who has to put up the money or conceive the administrative device, if he knows what it will cost to achieve this standard or that standard.

I think Sam Ordway is correct—maybe we shouldn't try to run this vein out in this session, but let it rest with that: that it is important to the economist to try to understand these standards that you ecologists and planners work with, so that we can get properly into the act at that point and wrap these factors up in terms of what they cost in money, in people, in alternatives foregone, or however you wish to look at it.

BRINSER: May I stop you for a second?

Economists are constantly saying we can solve these problems if you tell us what they cost. This isn't true. We must also ask what are they worth, what do they yield?

We are going to get closer to this idea if we get through our heads that cities are one of the great works of art, and that we should approach the city in these terms and not as a problem. It is a creative opportunity.

ORDWAY: I think this is all correct. The ecologists certainly have as much to learn about all of your parameters and your definitions in order to pursue their efforts, too.

FOSBERG: May I put in one correction to two things that have been said? I think the economists have interpreted our reference to the value of variety as variety for variety's sake; the ecologists, on the other hand, are emphasizing variety from the standpoint of the system, the stability and flexibility of the system that they are dealing with, rather than for any purely mystical virtue of variety itself.

Variety gives us more flexibility, more self-correcting properties in the system.

FISHER: I am a little sensitive to Sam Ordway's point that the main address to this kind of problem probably comes at a later session. I am going to be a bit arbitrary and turn to Bill Vogt, who I think was going to turn the discussion into some new channel.

VOGT: I wanted to come back to Ken Boulding's point on the strictures on the ecologist, which I think are quite justified.

I am rather surprised that nobody has brought up economics as an ecological phenomenon, really a branch of ecology. Man is part of the ecosystem in most parts of the world today and economics is something that originates in the human nervous system.

It develops, as so many human activities do, largely on a symbolic level. We have been called a symbolic class of beings: using words to some extent and other symbols, at times gold, wampum, pieces of money. But the symbols become more abstract as time goes on. A symbol always gives a partial representation. You never can have a map which shows everything and a symbol may be regarded as a map.

I think one of the reasons why we run into a good deal of confusion is that we don't recognize the limitations of economic symbols as we don't recognize the limitations of words as symbols. That brings us into situations where we talk about gross national products, leaving out of consideration a great many very important factors.

Dick Meier talked about rate of economic growth. Mexico has had a rate of economic growth nearly twice that of the United States for the last few years. But in its increasing gross national product, there is no recognition of a loss of capital that has been mentioned, and this is a very concrete and destructive thing in Mexico: well over 50,000 square miles have lost all their topsoil.

There are places in Mexico where people are being settled for want of good land where land is going out of cultivation at the rate of about 3 per cent a year. That is, they will take people into a tropical forest, cut down the forest, farm it, and in about thirty years it is abandoned. That has happened over and over again.

When we talk about the growth rates and the gross national product in Mexico, it is a very misleading language. It is a misleading map.

It even misleads a good many of the Mexicans. Only about a third of the people in Mexico have really shared in this so-called economic growth in the increase of the gross national product, which has resulted in a tremendous amount of dissatisfaction. If we feel content with the gross national product in Mexico, it misleads us about both the people and the environment they live in.

The reason I am bringing this out is that while economics is an indispensable tool, I think that we tend to depend on it too much and overvalue it.

I think if we can get economics into perspective, seeing it as a measurement of symbols largely, whereas ecology is a measurement of processes, energy exchange, ion exchanges, nutrients, and that sort of thing, it will give us a better basis for weighing the two sciences or the two disciplines in using them to evaluate what we are doing or what may be happening in the future.

BRANDWEIN: I was trying to say earlier that knowledge proceeds very slowly in terms of concepts, but fast in terms of images and data.

While I respect Dr. Ovington's notion that we don't know very much about the environment, and the economists' strictures that we really can't predict far ahead, as a teacher at the university or in elementary school I used to go in to teach every day, even though I didn't know how children learned, because I was faced with a situation of classes coming in, and I had to teach them.

Is there anything that the economists can now lend reason to and give basis to? While we don't have all the necessary environmental information, we still must make decisions affecting the environment—because they are forced on us right now.

Dr. Brinser has pointed out very well that we may not have all of the information but we do need to make the choices somehow on available information.

With this state of our ignorance, and this state of our competence and compassion, is there anything that economists can say to illuminate this problem and give us room for decision at this point?

FISHER: I think so. Maybe one of the economists on the panel should speak of that, before we turn to the next question.

BOULDING: You have to look at the whole process of social decision making, really. Economics is only one of the social sciences. We are, I think, moving toward an integrated social science. This is an interesting development of a highly integrated body of theory, and actually the process by which decisions are made in government isn't terribly different from the way they are made in businesses or in churches, for that matter. Look at this whole process as a decision interaction process. Where do you impinge on it if you have certain values which you want to propagate?

BRANDWEIN: Ian McHarg made certain decisions.

BOULDING: Nobody carried them out. This is the difficulty here—that almost all planning is conducted in a total vacuum.

Town planning is one of the most fatuous occupations anybody indulges in, because either it results in nothing or it results in imposition of middle-class esthetic standards on a situation to which they are completely inappropriate.

I would like to say on the whole up to now town planners have done much more harm than good almost anywhere because of their lack of an ecological point of view and of any sense of the nature of community, and because of the imposition of these esthetic standards.

You say, "Here is a slum—get rid of it." All right, you get rid of the slum, and you do more harm than good, usually, because this is an integral community. All you do is look at the shell and you don't care a damn for the oyster. And the physical environment is just the oystershell—that is all—of a living community.

The thing I am pleading for here is an ecological point of view in the social system as a whole.

TUNNARD: It looks as if the economists are trying to get off the hook by blaming the planners for this.

I believe there is something economists can do, and it hasn't been mentioned yet. I think the American public is woefully ignorant of its resources and natural features. They drive by parks and they don't think that they cost money or are worth anything. Why can't economists develop a method of benefit-cost analysis for facilities like parks and maybe historic preservation areas? They have done it for highways.

CLAWSON: I think an economist can measure and put values on anything where you can find a reaction of people. For instance, as far as parks are concerned, some of us have begun to do this.

I would certainly be the first to say that what we have done is far from perfect. I do think, though, that there are serious problems here. It is easy for the economist to follow after something has been initiated and has had some effect on people, or people have had some effect on situations.

But if the physical scientists can give us reasonable—reliable or not—estimates of what will happen, and how people will react to them, I think we can put value figures on them. I would certainly agree that we have lagged in doing it, but I think we can try. I do think, though, to take the idea of beauty, if people do recognize it in social actions, in purchase prices, in ordinances—goodness knows what—then I think we can put some value estimates on it.

But if it is only a small group of us who talk about it, and there is not observable action, then it is pretty difficult to put a value on it.

TUNNARD: I think that is an encouraging answer. Thank you.

MC HARG: I am sure Kenneth Boulding doesn't really execrate ancient Athens and Rome and Venice, Siena and Edinburgh.

I spent a good deal of time trying to talk social planners into learning a little about ecology. So I feel I can look them straight in the eye.

I think the illuminating thing for me, the unity of economics and ecology, from what understandings I have of ecology, is that the system is expressive.

As a natural scientist, an ecologist views the prairie and sand dunes, for example, and one begins to understand the processes that are revealed in the plants and composition and distribution of the plants themselves.

One understands that there is, Mr. Boulding, coinage in the system, which is light and water and nutrients, and these are husbanded really very cleverly in the ecosystem, made up of that conjunction of organisms, which can utilize materials and energy and recycle them through the system in a stable way. And their complexity is in fact, I understand, some compromise between the maximum efficiency which a monoculture might achieve and the maximum stability which complexity provides. This seems to correspond closely to the circulation of money in the economic system.

What also interests me is the concept that morphology leads us into some basis for understanding esthetics. If this is true, then the nautilus, the chambered nautilus, reveals its process to that man who knows something about it by the form of the shell.

The coral reef does the same thing, and the mites, millions of them, reveal themselves as an expressive process. And so does a beehive, and so then do the pueblo villages and the Dogon on the escarpment of the Sahara, or even Japanese architecture, and Japanese village-making. And perhaps with a little more understanding we can see a larger symbolic content but still this kind of morphology in the architecture of the New England villages or Charleston or Savannah.

It is true that one sees with some sort of understanding a landscape where man intervenes; one can say it is good because in fact the process does operate well, and the harmony one sees is in fact the harmony which is achieved.

It seems to me there is a unity of ecology and economics in terms of energy utilization and the adaptation of organisms to the environment, including each other, and man.

In fact, esthetics is in some sense a perception of an appropriateness and an expressiveness which is particularly powerful.

DASMANN: The economist grows impatient with the ecologist and conservationist when the conservationist proves to be blindly conservative.

I believe it is the duty of the ecologist or conservationist to be flexible and willing to bargain on most points; for example, in regard to the care of 75 per cent of the country that is going to be used most intensively by man. But there are areas where we simply cannot bargain, and the whooping crane that Boulding has mentioned is one of these. We must preserve it. If it is gone, it is gone forever. It cannot be replaced by anything else.

There is a whole list of endangered species and endangered habitats that are in this category.

What the ecologist-conservationist must ask of the economist is that he understand this problem and seek some way of rating it in the economic scale so that it is given proper consideration.

We simply cannot afford to lose this irreducible minimum in order to produce more of some product or crop that is already here on the landscape in abundance.

COWAN: I was interested by the economist's statement that he takes a look at the choices that are made by the community and uses these choices to rate the values that are applied.

I would like to suggest that those of us who are ecologists have quite a lot of influence on the nature of these choices. We are scientists, but we are also persuaders. Some of us have been reasonably successful in persuading our fellows to make certain choices. Once these choices have been made, the economist comes in and sees how successful we were in persuading our fellows to make this, that, or the other choice.

So that in the gentle art of decision making we play a part which is quite different from the part we play as scientists. I would like to suggest that this is something we must recognize and actively utilize.

HALL: All afternoon I have been sitting here feeling somehow as though I were on the north face of the Eiger waiting for a foothold, and that the economists haven't quite given it to us.

A few minutes ago we seemed to be coming near this when it was said economists essentially seek objective criteria for decision making in that they seek a basis for how people actually behave. They seek a money value of what people would pay if they could somehow be made to pay the price.

In the particular case of decisions about using land for conservation or not, then you have to consider in some way the alternative rents that the different uses would pay.

There are considerable problems here because conservation uses really come into a bundle of categories rather like hospitals, prisons, and the universities and perhaps the Statue of Liberty that don't really seem to yield a rent in normal terms. One can't find out what the money value of conservation is.

It might be possible to try to work this out through possible recreation uses of conservation, very small parts of the total value.

It might be possible, although this is even more tenuous, to work it out through the educative value of conservation. As I think the economists would be the first to admit, the economics of education is still in the very early stages of development. The values of any educational resource are still difficult to give a money value to.

Therefore, it might seem best really to ignore these complex problems of the money value of conservation lands and to concentrate the attention on the other side of the argument—to say, given that there are certain amounts of money to be spent, what are the rents of the land in alternative uses? Are these rents really a true reflection of value? Are the rents in some way distorted because they are not reflecting the total costs or the total means involved in the use of this land for the other purposes?

Here I think there are some interesting technical questions which have been touched on in the course of the afternoon. For instance: How, precisely, do you calculate the spoliation cost by the Kentucky coal industry, or how do you calculate the wreckage along the highways, and how do these modify in fact the rents which this land is at present yielding?

BOULDING: One point isn't understood here, really. There are two segments of the economy. One I call the exchange economy. This is where you get a quid for a quo. Then there is the grants economy, where you don't get a quid for a quo. You shovel it out; you make unilateral transfers.

The grants economy is from about 3 to 7 per cent of the GNP in this country, depending on what you put into it. It is obscure. It grows all the time. If you want to save the whooping crane—and I have nothing against whooping cranes; they haunt me; I dream about them—and I would give anything to have a dodo—in a sense the whooping crane has to be a part of the exchange economy or part of the grants economy.

It doesn't seem to be a part of the exchange economy. In the first place, the whooping crane doesn't have any money. It has no income. They aren't owned by anybody, as a matter of fact. So that the whooping crane in a sense has to come out of the grants economy. This is partly public, partly private. If it is public, this is political science, not economics.

Why do you always expect an answer to all these questions? This is political science. You have to persuade somebody to shovel it out for the whooping crane. That is all right. This shouldn't be too difficult.

Then you want to hire somebody in Madison Avenue. This isn't economics. This is persuasion. This is how you persuade people to shovel it out for the whooping crane. This may not be very expensive. I imagine a few thousand dollars. Or even the Ford Foundation can do it. The Ford Foundation is an unresponsible private government. It is responsible to nobody. This is also part of the grants economy. So are the other foundations.

But we don't blame economics for this. You have to look at this in a wider setting.

BEAR: I would like to get back to something Dr. Brinser said a while ago. He talked about a city being a work of art. Did you say that?

BRINSER: Yes.

BEAR: You believe, if it isn't a work of art, at least it could be made a work of art.

I was interested in what Dr. Meier had to say about these people who are not satisfied with the city, or with the suburbs, but want to get farther out in the country to satisfy some sort of need.

I think the city of Newark, New Jersey, is interesting in that connection. It has a population of about a million people in the daytime, and a population of 500,000 at night. In other words, half of those people who are there in the daytime spread out around the surrounding country in suburbs and beyond the suburbs and come back every morning. That seems a very illogical system of waste of time and effort in driving back and forth. And here is a man who says the city is a work of art.

Do you anticipate that we can make the city so attractive that all this dispersal that occurs every night doesn't need to take place and they will be attracted to stay in the city?

BRINSER: I don't mean to be wholly captious. Newark rather stretches my definition.

(*Laughter*)

I don't trust any survey, and in this I perhaps differ considerably from my colleague Meier in asking people what it is they would want.

One thing we must recognize is that values are created by values—that this is a process, too, and that value creation is a consequence of experience.

I worked on a project in Boston of rehabilitating a district, a small district in a very downtrodden area of the city. We were astonished to discover that once we got this conservation process going, we were bringing in a lot of people from out beyond Route 128 in the Concord-Lexington area; that there were advantages to living in the city which had not been available before—amenities, if you wish to call them that. I think this is a shifting process.

I would suggest that if you look at some of the very old cities such as Paris and London, where people associate themselves with the life of the city, the community becomes a conscious work of art.

Cities will survive and grow. We must make conscious efforts to create this community, this style—this sense of life—that a city can give. I think we happen to be in a phase in our development where we have neglected this. A great many people who look at the landscape think that the landscape doesn't begin until you get out among the grubs, grass, birds, and bees—whereas as a matter of fact the landscape is everywhere.

I don't think we have devoted enough serious attention—outside of the city planners—to creating man's landscape and man's creation of the landscape.

It is ridiculous the way we handle transportation in the city. This is the classic example of sheer idiocy. Any economist would be rather helpful in overcoming such idiocy. I think that we can do this—we probably shall. The question of waste disposal, and so on and so forth—technology, other things that are coming into play—can play an enormous part.

I think the economist is extremely helpful here in providing a better definition of the relevant questions, a definition of the relevant criteria for answering the questions, and for establishing the proper terms of the comparisons necessary to calculate the alternative costs and returns.

With esthetic values this cannot be done. I think economics dealing with esthetics can only deal with it as a cost. I do not think economics is very good in dealing with esthetics as a return.

BOULDING: Nonsense.

BRINSER: What returns do you trust—?

BOULDING: Look at a well-planned suburban development, the land values in it. This is what you pay for esthetics. You have an immense variety here. This is really a question of entrepreneurship and leadership. This is the real question, that is, that the man who designs a well-laid-out subdivision, such as I live in, is the artist. And this is as good.

Ann Arbor Hills is as good as the town of Edinburgh, and much nicer to live in. And most of the European cities depend on a class society, on slaves carrying buckets of coal from the kitchen up to these beautiful houses. I would raze them.

I think we are deluded at the moment because the cities are in a profound transition, wanting to turn inside out.

We are moving into a period where the rich are going to live in the central cities. This is perfectly clear. They are going to be able to do without cars. A really rich person is a man who doesn't have to have a car. The poor will have three cars—Cadillacs—and live in the suburbs.

(*Laughter*)

The really poor will be exurbanites and live on the waves or in the rural slums. We just haven't got ourselves adjusted to this upset in the structure of the city which the automobile has created.

NICHOLSON: I think it is time somebody came back on Boulding. May I say I am shocked to hear that he is so backward about making people pay for the whooping cranes, when the nearest thing we have in Scotland is the osprey? In that case, we put up signs leading to the osprey and had a collecting box there.

We got $7.50 per young osprey per day. So we are ahead on this economic endeavor.

(*Laughter*)

This does suggest park space in relation to where the menagerie is. I wonder if anyone has done a study of the Cook County preserves where you have a costly but well-planned leisure facility, park facility, just on the doorstep of the city, as compared with the cities which have no facility within fifty or a hundred miles.

Is it possible to assess what are the relative advantages and costs of a facility of that sort in Chicago as compared to making people go long distances to the nearest park?

MEIER: We find a very large number going to strip mines, right past the parks.

BOULDING: I think strip mines are fun. They are lovely. What is the matter with strip mines? It is the most interesting country.

You can have canoes on the lakes. People go 2000 miles to Arizona to see a natural strip mine.

(*Laughter*)

CLAWSON: We have begun to make some estimates in a few places about the values of parks close in as against farther out.

I think it is entirely possible to demonstrate, on purely economic grounds, that relatively expensive land, or reservoir sites close in, may be a good bargain as compared to cheaper stuff far out.

I will admit the number of such studies made to date is relatively small. As far as I know the Cook County one has not been studied.

For instance, there was one quite detailed study made of the St. Louis area about the values of reservoirs not yet built at different sites. It indicated that the closest in site, though it was much the more expensive, would be of higher net value to it than the one more distant.

Many of our states in this country—the federal government has been pretty bad—have attempted to buy recreation land where it was cheapest.

As one state park director said, "We finally woke up to the fact that there weren't any people living near it, and that we may have to come in now and buy land at very much higher prices where it is much more accessible to people."

You can't generalize too sweepingly. But frequently this will be good economics.

MC HARG: A metropolitan open-space study which we have worked on had Dr. Tomazinas, who did a recreation demand model. He found a straight-line relationship between distance and use. That is, the greater the distance to facilities, the less they were used.

DARLING: I want to ask about the economics of the growth of subdivisions, town planning, or the lack of town planning.

I always feel about Spenard, near Anchorage, Alaska, that it is the lowest ebb of real estate merchandising going mad. There is no check on what you do with that land.

You buy a quarter-acre lot for a home and the next quarter-acre lot may come to be a hamburger stall, and a used-car lot on the other side.

There must be economic value or disvalue in such goings on.

CLAWSON: I have been saying recently that the value of every tract of land is more a function of what happens off of that tract than it is of what happens on it. It is the externalities in land use which are governing value. The prime illustration is one much like what you just used.

I said that if I should live—which fortunately I do not—in a seriously declining residential neighborhood, there is not a damned thing I can do on my piece of property to keep up its value. Down she goes, with others.

If, on the other hand, I live—as I think I do—in a good, well-sustained neighborhood, I could let my property deteriorate seriously in a physical sense and still watch it maintain its value, or most of it.

This gets enormously more complex as between different kinds of uses. The values of a commercial area, a shopping center, depend upon the kind of residential area that is around it, and upon the competition from the next shopping center. It is the externalities in land use that have grown up out of the enormously specialized uses of man and enormously specialized kind of society and economy in which we live.

I argue then that one of the functions of the planner is to try to bring these externalities into relationship one to another so that the value of a total area is at the highest level and the economic justification, at any rate, for controls over land, is to prevent the kinds of uses that tend to diminish the values not of the tract involved but of the surrounding tracts.

This is obviously a great deal easier to say than to measure and to put into legal language. I do think that we need to develop some new concepts of where value and property come from, and new ways of measuring.

I think economists have lagged rather seriously in this, but I think we can do it.

FISHER: This will make you sad. But the Lake Spenard he refers to is on the outskirts of Anchorage. When I was younger I lived in Anchorage and used to go out of town on a Sunday afternoon in winter and fish through the ice there. I think there were two little cabins on the margin of that lake, and that was all.

DARLING: Alaska is very dear to my heart. I have seen the decline in thirteen years. Spenard . . . It makes me wonder—how did it happen that such degradation can result in a matter of fifteen years? How can it happen when surely from the very economic point of view it would have been better to do it another way?

Up at Palmer, Alaska, which is a mess—believe me—in one of the most beautiful settings in the world, we went to a resort on a lake where people were water-skiing at enormous speed. I said to the lady, "I suppose one day there was a loon here," and she said, "Well, there was, as a matter of fact." She remembered the loon.

There is no loon there now.

I said, "Look at this landscape in Palmer. Who could possibly live here happily?" She said, "Now listen, for seven months of the year it is under snow. You don't see all that. And for the other five months," she said, "lift up your eyes to the hills and just look."

That was her answer.

I do feel this placement and assortment of activities has real economic value. As we are thinking of the future, we must think perhaps tomorrow about how far prevention of malassortment can get into economic terms and control terms by law and voluntary control.

FISHER: I think perhaps we have struck a good note here for the end. It has been quite an interesting session. We have been up the hill and down again with the ecologists and the economists. We are indebted to you especially for putting things in sharp focus, shall I say?

(*Laughter*)

Economists are sometimes aggressive and sometimes defensive. Frequently they go back and forth between the two rather rapidly.

It does seem to me, however, that economists have a responsibility in the matter of what we are going to do with this continent. As I see how the great decisions seem to be made in government and corporations and elsewhere, it becomes clear to me that the economists, more than any other professionals, stand athwart the decision process, although they are very close to the people who make the decisions.

We can be quite a useful funnel, if nothing else, for framing and organizing a variety of information in such a fashion that the man who makes the decision can make comparisons. He can't be an expert in anything. So the comparisons which he must look at and among which he must choose have got to be clear and reasonably simple. I think the economist has an advantage of position here.

I was reminded of this last fall when President Johnson appointed a number of task forces in different subjects, from natural resources to education, public health, and foreign affairs. These were groups that were to bring in ideas for his first full-fledged administration to work with.

I was quite pleased but a little alarmed to see that well over half of the chairmen leaders of these groups were economists. As I say, I was pleased because I am an economist. But a bit alarmed by it all.

This was a reminder to me of what I am convinced is a rather strategic position we have as professional people who think we have got a science or the elements of a science so close to the points of great decision.

Therefore I am extremely interested and concerned that we operate responsibly and understand and make intelligent use through the particular funnel that we have our hands on of ecological, biological, engineering, and many other kinds of information.

We are adjourned.

IV SOCIAL AND CULTURAL PURPOSES

* D. R. Glacken is Professor of Geography at the University of California at Berkeley. He
received his Ph.D. in Geography from Johns Hopkins in 1951; in 1957–58 he was a Ful-
bright research scholar in Norway. His main interest has been in tracing the development of
man's image of himself in relation to nature.

Introductory Statement and Summary Remarks

GLACKEN: Mr. Chairman and fellow members of the Conference. This session is devoted to a discussion of the papers relating to social and cultural processes. It is a difficult one to be involved in, especially in an administrative capacity, because it is a field like politics in which everyone has an opinion and everyone is his own authority.

I would like to begin by telling you about my adventures in flying from Berkeley to Washington because I think they might have a bearing on this meeting. The trip may be divided into three laps: from the heliport in Berkeley to the San Francisco airport; from the San Francisco airport to the Dulles International Airport; from there to the Albert Pick Motel at Twelfth and K Streets in Washington. First, I will tell you about laps one and three and then about lap two.

Lap one took us immediately over San Francisco Bay, and we saw all the familiar sights—cars paying their tolls at the Bay Bridge, the Oakland estuary, the freeways, the skyline. It took about twelve minutes. Lap three lasted about forty minutes; we traveled through the lovely Virginia countryside, crossed the river, continued down Constitution Avenue to Twelfth and then up to K Street.

The middle lap was the longest. It took a little over four hours. The day was exceptionally clear. I had an aisle seat and couldn't see out; the young sailor who had the window seat was asleep. Soon the stewardesses, with commendable solicitude for the comfort of their passengers, announced that they were going to show a movie. And with a typically intense American preoccupation with sterilized products, they passed out earphones to us in plastic bags, with assurances that after each use they were dismantled and resterilized so that there was no danger of any infections of the ear. Then they showed a travel film.

(*Laughter*)

It was about a group of Swedish students who left on a sailing vessel from Göteborg to the Mediterranean and adjacent lands. The narration was in a "Come with me through Belgium" style. I had the pleasure of seeing Princess Grace of Monaco start the annual automobile race along the dangerous mountain roads of the Mediterranean shore. We went to Mykonos; we went to some wonderful old ports on the Adriatic and wherever we went all of the village dancers were awaiting us. We went up the

Nile. We went all the way up to Thebes. We were in Port Said, we were in Old Cairo, we went to the Golden Horn.

I have told you only a few of our adventures. And I have been trying ever since to discover what conclusions would be drawn from this tale. (*Laughter*) I came to the obvious conclusion that it is possible to travel by air across the United States on a clear day without seeing anything of the country and to receive at the same time instruction on the Mediterranean. I saw more of the United States on laps one and three than I did on two. Those of us profiting from the technological marvels which annihilate space clearly felt a picture about foreign lands was worth seeing, but that what we saw below was merely space intervening between the two terminals. In any event, the experience suggests the significance of attitudes and the social and cultural milieu in which they flourish and develop.

Are attitudes necessary, are they important, do they exist? I do not believe these are easy questions to answer. If we have nothing else in common, we are united in having opinions and attitudes. Many people who have lived in the past and written about them would agree about their importance, but they probably were people like you and me—people with opinions. Many have been curious about the relationship of their daily lives to their environments, what kinds of feelings their surroundings evoked in them. Many, too, have thought about the environmental contrasts in different ways of living. One of the early statements about the artificiality of the city and the naturalness of the country is in Varro's (116–27 B.C.) book on farming. There is a pleasant Latin poem which tells of the environmental preferences of religious orders. The Cistercians liked the valleys, the Benedictines the mountains, the Franciscans the towns, and the Jesuits the cities. One could give countless illustrations from many cultures showing that men have had strong reactions to their environment. These associations are of great antiquity—and for good reason because the man-nature relationship, like man's relation to man, to society and culture, to his God or gods, has been one of the great themes in human belief and thought.

These attitudes, therefore, exist and have existed through time and in many civilizations, but we have little idea how representative they were or how large a proportion of people shared them. It is easy to associate them with educated, religious, or esthetic people but we do not know. It is possible perhaps for a society to have a large number of people who might have no particular attitudes or only ones of the vaguest sort. A young man who took a trip along the redwood highway was asked how he liked the scenery, and he said it was O.K.

Attitudes or their absence are intimately related to purpose, or lack of it, and to social and cultural processes. Two of our participants, Bill Vogt and Ray Dasmann, have commented on the bulldozer mentality, a phrase that is coming into fairly frequent use. The word "mentality" implies purpose and the word "bulldozer" great brute power, but in my own view the term narrows the responsibility too much. I can remember some years ago reading in the paper that the Plasterers' Union was protesting the use of the term "plastered" to describe a certain common human condition as being a completely uncalled for reflection on the profession. (*Laughter*) The bulldozer mentality might be quite foreign to the bulldozer operator; it might have closer affiliations with practical utilitarian points of view, or with aspirations of mayors who like to see their towns grow because growth is progress and progress is undefined.

In the original title of our session, the expression "social and cultural" purpose was used and it may be worthwhile to say a bit too about this expression. Teleological explanation has not been popular in recent decades in either the sciences or the social sciences, but we know from reading the cogent critiques, especially of Hume and Kant, that the teleological interpretation of nature and the idea of design have been extremely important in Western thought. Teleology survived in a secular fashion in the idea of evolution and of progress. But these teleologies are no longer available; we must create our own values, purposes, and attitudes. Whatever criticisms one might make of the existentialist philosophers (to my knowledge they have not discussed to any degree the man-nature theme in the sense we use the term here; they have been preoccupied with human existence and have had little time for nonhuman existence) they have stimulating questions to ask about purpose, values, norms, the existence of order in human affairs against the cosmic background.

I thought we might conduct the discussion which follows first by asking each of the panel members to summarize the points he would especially like to make. Before proceeding, however, I would like to say a few words about each of the papers.

Dr. Dasmann's paper stresses the contrast between environmental changes made by men of European descent and those made by indigenous peoples in pre-Columbian times. He is also interested in the variety in American attitudes toward nature. An example is his discussion of the role of leisure and the relation of the affluent society to conservation questions.

The second paper by Mr. Eichhorn is interesting because it illustrates the force of the posterity argument that I talk about in my paper; Mr. Tunnard has used the similar expression "patrimony." He analyzes the role of selection and ideas of what constituted a suitable park, adding some sensitive observations about attitudes toward different kinds of scenery.

Dr. Farber's paper is on stress, and while he knows this well from a medical point of view, he is very much concerned with possible clues to relationships between stress and wilderness, touching here again on the theme of communion with nature. His paper illustrates the increasing attention being given stress in relation to urban and nonurban environments.

Dr. Vogt discusses themes based on population questions and ecosystems, adding another which is a recurrent one in his writings: a belief in the inadequacy of words and the constant scrutiny that must be given to their meanings. As we see from his definition of a niche, he emphasizes the role of man as a doer as well as a thinker.

Finally, I would like to say something about the themes in my paper. First is the all-pervasiveness and the antiquity of the man-nature theme; it goes back in time beyond civilizations, and in scope it reaches from science to religion. The theme is meaningless without our seeing it as part of a deeper preoccupation with the nature of life. Certain ideas are enduring and can be called ecumenical because they have appeared in so many cultures. I singled out three in particular. The first is the notion of a communion with nature. The second is the idea of plenitude in nature—of beauty, variety, complexity. As Ray Fosberg pointed out yesterday, the idea has a great deal of scientific validity. It also has a long history. Lastly, there is the posterity argument—the idea that we owe a debt to posterity, that we should use wisely and pass on to our descendants what has been given to us. It is a powerful argument in which a high degree of agreement might be reached.

One of the pitfalls in generalizing about the man-nature theme is the tendency toward monolithic summation. It is often said that Western civilization is characterized by a dichotomy between man and nature, but there is much evidence that Western thought has also been concerned with showing the unity of all nature including man. It is very difficult to generalize on these matters.

With these remarks, I would now like to proceed with the discussion and I will first call on Dr. Farber.

FARBER: When this group assembled for the first time the other morning, I was wondering just how much stress was present in the various disciplines and the actual people here. We had such a wide variation of people: ecologists, agriculturalists, landscape architects, regional planners, political scientists, educators, economists, geologists, a publisher, and a judge.

Putting all of this group together, how sure are we that we can accomplish the objectives set out by the Conservation Foundation and the Steering Committee? Our stress even continued, perhaps, through the evening cocktail hour.

One good definition of stress might be the rate of wear and tear in the human machinery that accompanies any vital activity and in a sense parallels the intensity of life.

In this country, the United States of America, there are nineteen million—or one out of ten of the population—who have some form of mental or emotional illness requiring psychiatric care. There are more people in hospitals with mental illness at any one time than with all other diseases combined. More than one million were treated in mental hospitals of various kinds last year.

But with this one million that were treated, and the nineteen million requiring some form of psychiatric care, there are endless other millions under various forms of stress whose stress contributes to some form of acceleration of other illnesses.

The important thing, perhaps, is an attempt to channel this stress.

Before mentioning that, I would like to describe the general stress syndrome very briefly. There are three stages that can be roughly described.

First: the alarm reaction, a defensive mechanism where the forces are mobilized.

Second: a stage of resistance which reflects full adaptation to the stressor.

Third: the state of exhaustion which inexorably follows as long as the stressor is severe enough and applied for sufficient time.

You have surely seen this stage of exhaustion in personal reactions with colleagues, friends, and people you have met, who act completely irrationally at some stage when the stressor has been overapplied.

But then we should consider the channeling of stress into creative areas. The great philosophic ideal of our time has become the development of a social structure in which you don't have to worry about anything. A certain amount of stress, it must be emphasized, is good for you. You should worry about some things.

E. M. Westcott puts it very wisely: "They say a reasonable number of fleas is good fer a dog; keeps him from broodin' over bein' a dog."

(*Laughter*)

Perhaps a common denominator among other common denominators in this Conference is stress, interpreted in its broadest sense. Selye very wisely said war can be intoxicating, the idea of the young man charging with a bayonet and finally becoming a hero.

But he continues: "Our children must learn that from now on man's great fight in peace, as in war, will be won by heroes of a different stamp, men with the strength of intellect and a more exceptional persistent kind of courage, the sober determination to dedicate their whole life to what they think is a worthwhile aim for existence. Youth will have to learn that it is much more difficult to live for a cause than to die for it."

And to conclude these remarks, there is the story of Kipling's that is so refreshing, in which he has two camels talking near a battle zone:

"Why, just why," one of the camels asked the other, "is the elephant such a coward? He won't carry loads of ammunition up to the firing line. But look at the donkey; he does."

The other camel explained, "It is not a matter of cowardice. The donkey is easily led once he gets going, and he will go up to the firing line. But the elephant has intelligence, and he knows the danger, and he doesn't want to."

"Then why is man at the firing line?" asked the first camel. "Isn't he intelligent? Can't he see ahead?"

"Ah," said the second camel, "that is what makes him a man. He understands, and yet he is anxious and he will face danger. And he understands what danger can do. But he can still make himself face up to it."

And that, I think, is perhaps one of the themes of the stress syndrome.

VOGT: One of the aspects of yesterday afternoon's discussion that I clearly saw was a lack of stress. It was a very gay discussion, spiced with a little chili pepper at times, but not expressing a great deal of concern about some of these problems we are facing.

There are fifty-three million people, probably, in North America south of the United States, doubling in twenty-three years. They need energy, which they can get only through the sun-earth and green-leaf exchange. About one third of them are deficient in both calories and proteins, living on fifteen cents a day.

Exaggerated malnutrition afflicts millions of children in Latin America between Texas and Colombia, and it leaves them mentally and physically marred for their entire lives, as was developed recently in a paper by Nevin Scrimshaw of MIT, in the *Journal of the American Public Health Association.*

They are hungry because they handle land in disregard of ecological relationships that have been evolved over millions of years. The land is as it is, its soil is as it is, and its vegetation is as it is through a long process of natural selection in these environments. They don't possess the ingenuity we heard about yesterday to exist in a high density in this environment. Perhaps such ingenuity could be developed, but it is not with us yet.

One of the reasons they live in such a distressful situation is that economists there have even more power than they have in the United States. I would say that they make up three quarters of any developmental commission. They concentrate their efforts and interests on the cities; they rarely if ever go out and look at the color of a river as it runs downhill; they pay no attention to the loss of fertility in the environment on which these people are depending, and almost nothing is being done to maintain productivity.

In a recent study by five members of the Central American Common Market they discovered that the big landowner, who did not use his land intensively, was producing thirty-nine dollars a year per hectare, whereas the small farmer who often had only two or two and a half acres was producing ninety-three dollars per hectare. The big man was neglecting his land, on the whole, with few exceptions, but the little man was just corning the life out of the land. The gross national product goes up, but the mass of the people don't profit by it, and there are actually more hungry and more miserable people in that region every year. There is very little doubt about this.

If human society could be adjusted to the ecological potentialities of the environment, many of which we still don't know, don't understand, there would be hope of a better life for them, and of course the place to begin on that is to stop overstocking the environment, trying to carry more people than the land can.

I would like to make just one comment on the United States. I was much encouraged when Mr. Tunnard injected a humanitarian note into Dick Meier's dream world yesterday. The human race has been evolving as human beings, depending on what anthropologist you follow, up to 175 million years. We can take a million years as an average, I believe. Natural selection has developed certain habits, physiology, capacity for attitudes over this million years. And if there was nonadaptive behavior existing during this period, natural selection culled it out.

It is only in less than 1 per cent of the time that man has existed as man that he has lived as maggots. If you think that word is too strong, I suggest you walk around the edges of Mexico City or the slums of Rio de Janeiro, Calcutta, or Bombay.

These are inhuman situations in terms of the kind of man who has been developing over a million years, and that man over the million years has been fitting his physiology and his behavior into an ecological structure that includes as one of its basic needs no excess of populations.

Thank you.

DASMANN: My emphasis has been on man in the United States, attempting to sketch a very broad picture with a broad brush of man's attitudes and role in the United States from the historical viewpoint and looking forward to the future.

I have taken the approach of considering a dichotomy in our attitudes toward the land. One based on the principles of a social conscience, which at times, and most recently, has been evolving toward an ecological conscience. And the other, the individual's search for material gain, for a place in the sun, for the good life in a material sense.

This has resulted in two different effects upon the land. Not that you can categorize people into the good guys and the bad guys with the bad guys being the exploiters, aided and abetted by the engineers, and the good guys, the ecologists and conservationists. But instead you have conflicting attitudes within each individual. He must earn a living and, at the same time, he has a feeling of social responsibility toward his fellow beings and toward the land that he occupies.

In the settlement of America there has been, I believe, a feeling toward the land which stems from the lack of any indigenous peasant tradition on the part of the North American settlers. There have been some peasant communities, but most of the people who have come here have not had any attitude of firm attachment to the land. Consequently, they have often engaged in what I have called transient exploitation, by which they made use of the resources of the land to earn a living without intending to settle or stay in the place in which they earned that living. They wanted to make their money and then go to some better place to settle down.

Also as a result of this there has been a strong desire which has been striking on the part of Americans, probably only exceeded by the Russians, to modify and change the land, rather than to adapt to its environmental necessities.

These attitudes lead to a grim picture if you look at the population-growth curve and do not assume, as we have been doing here over the last couple of days, that population growth in the United States is going to peak and level off, and that we will not have a severe population problem.

If you assume that population growth is going to continue as long as the means of earning a living are increased, then these attitudes toward the land will cause inevitable conflicts. Even the conservationist of today, when faced with the decisions that affect his own material welfare significantly, may vote against conservation measures. I have seen this type of development in my own area, where conservationists suddenly changed their tune when their own tax base and pocketbook were affected. This could present a gloomy outlook for conservation were we to assume that population growth will continue indefinitely to where we are not 300 million but 600 million, 900 million, or a billion people in the United States alone.

On the more positive side, we have the increasing rise of what Leopold has termed an "ecological conscience," a sense of responsibility toward land. This has most recently caused such phenomena as the President's message to Congress on natural beauty, something which would not have happened ten or twenty years ago.

The role of the ecologist-conservationist faced with the possible gloomy picture of the future is to try and save the pieces of wild North America, counting on the re-creative power of living organisms in natural communities to assist him in eventually being able to reassemble once more a beautiful living landscape. But in order to do this, the least you can do at this stage of the game is try and save these bits of the natural communities.

EICHHORN: The national parks are less than 1 per cent of the area of the continent. Yellowstone National Park represents probably the first attempt to preserve natural landscape, and the parks as they have been created since then have nearly all been natural areas.

There may have been something special within each park—a waterfall, a geyser—but it was implicit and specified by law that this thing was to be maintained in a natural setting and left unimpaired for future generations.

The areas we have kept as national parks have generally conformed to what was universally pleasing in some sense. I think there is no doubt about the appeal of a waterfall, or the appeal of a giant sequoia in California.

The first areas added to the park system were what people liked, and what was available.

Not until the 1920s was any real thought given to what composed the

National Park System. As a matter of fact it wasn't a system at all, it was a random accumulation. In the 1920s a commission was set up to study parks in the Appalachians, to recommend areas for inclusion within the National Park System. This was a deliberate attempt to find something to add to the system, rather than just adding something because people liked it and there was local support for the idea.

This has since been done elsewhere—for example, a survey in southern Arizona for areas suitable for addition. However, more recent acquisitions have been limited by what was available; what was available was not productive land and not well scattered over the country—it was concentrated on federal lands which really weren't good for much else.

If you read the language of the laws establishing the parks, you read people's accounts of what national parks are, what they think national parks are. The idea of display is implicit. I don't know whether Frank Darling shares my opinion of this, but nevertheless the parks are displayed, and they are displayed to very large numbers of people. You cannot maintain an area in natural condition if you are to display it without being very careful about where you accommodate people—how you accommodate people.

I think the Park Service has probably been reluctant to try innovations. If you have a back-country camp, for example, you supply it by pack train. This is very hard on the landscape. You could do less damage by taking supplies in by helicopter, perhaps, but this offends people. The helicopter is not natural; but, when you get down to it, the pack horse isn't either.

MAN IN NORTH AMERICA

Raymond F. Dasmann*

To discuss man in North America, it is necessary to generalize. This is always done at the risk of losing sight of the complexity of reality. No generalization on such a subject can fit all conditions. There is the danger that it will not entirely fit any. Our knowledge of those natural environments that once existed in North America is imperfect. We do not know enough about the changes that have been caused by man's activities. We have not even a clear picture of what is taking place around us today in the various processes of environmental change. Only with hesitancy, therefore, should we dare predict the future.

We do know that man found in North America a rich and varied land with a marvelously complex biota. We know that in a few centuries European man has reduced this variety and complexity. Save for the differences forced by geography, he has tended to create everywhere an environment marked by uniformity. There is a likelihood that this process will continue. The first of the Europeans found in America a wilderness, a place that frightened the timid and challenged the adventurous. The new settlers set

* Dr. Dasmann, whose *Destruction of California* was published last year, is a staff ecologist with the Conservation Foundation. To the mind of many of his colleagues, he made his mark with *The Last Horizon* (1963), an analysis of the impact of man on each of the major biomes. He has taken a leading role in relating the content of ecology to conservation policy.

forth to tame the wilds and seek their fortunes. However, for most of the span that man has been in America the wilderness has been there with him. It was always beyond the settlements, or over the far horizon, and thus a factor in life and an influence upon the outlook of men. Regardless of one's opinion of it the wilderness was a reality, a place to retreat to, a possible refuge from injustice or tyranny. It could be a home for landless men, a hiding place for outlaws or simply space for those who were tired of associating with their fellow man. Today, however, the old wilderness has forever gone and the fragments we have saved are but souvenirs of a past journey. They can bring back memories or create the atmosphere of past days, but they are not the reality. Thus the new generations of Americans are growing up in a tamed land with no wild frontiers. They may well be a different breed from those of the past. It is difficult to foresee their attitudes toward their lands or environment.

One can see in the story of man in relation to his North American environment an interplay between two contrasting social attitudes. Since these attitudes were often dominant at different times within the same individual, this was not a conflict between exploiter and the conservationist, between the good guys and the bad guys, but rather between the conflicting interests of man. One attitude is that of social responsibility involving the presence of a social conscience. With this the individual having knowledge or power assumes responsibility for those who may lack either, and for the lands and environment in which those without adequate knowledge, or power to influence their circumstances, must live. Running at times counter to this has been the individualistic tradition, so much extolled in America, in which each is considered responsible for his own welfare. In the pioneer history of America the scramble of individuals for personal wealth, power, prestige, or simply a place in the sun has been dominant, and responsible at times and in places for grave crimes against the environment. Accompanying it, however, has always been the social conscience, working to prevent, alleviate, or repair the damage. This attitude of concern for the welfare of the environment in which man must live, and consequently for human welfare, has been well exemplified in the words and deeds of such past American Presidents as Thomas Jefferson, the Roosevelts, and John F. Kennedy. It has been responsible for some of the major accomplishments in preservation of the American land as a place fit for men to dwell.

Today there is some evidence that the social conscience is becoming more active, and at times developing into the kind of ecological conscience that Aldo Leopold has called for in his *Sand County Almanac* (1949). If this is true, it gives new strength to efforts to maintain or improve our North American environments. A spread of the attitude of social responsibility is exemplified today in diverse ways such as the drive toward urban renewal and the successful attempt to preserve the remaining wilderness areas of the United States. But there is always an ambiguity in the workings of the social conscience, arising in part from failure to understand fully the consequences of one's actions, and in part from

conflict with individualistic motives. Thus its effectiveness is limited.

Action in the individualistic tradition is not always contrary to the public interest nor necessarily adverse in its effects upon the natural environment. There is nothing wrong in the individual seeking first to secure his own well-being. Indeed it has been part of our social philosophy that "enlightened self-interest" can serve the good of the whole. The important element is that of enlightenment. Too often a lack of enlightenment about nature and land has been destructive both to the natural resources of America and to man's welfare.

Actions guided by feelings of social responsibility and directed toward care for the natural environment are not always above reproach. Many who act strongly for conservation in America are most concerned with measures designed to take effect far from their own back yards. It was easy for the easterner in the period from 1870 to 1910 to vote for national parks and forests in the distant West. We can note, however, how few similar measures were put into effect in the East. This cannot entirely be explained away by pointing out that the federal lands, the public domain, were in the West. There is also reflected the desire to maintain the East as an area where economic development could be carried out without undue restraint. Today it is easier to pass a wilderness preservation act that affects areas where votes are few than it is to preserve the natural scene in lands near our urban centers where money is to be made and votes are numerous.

The ambiguity that exists in our feelings of responsibility toward preserving the natural beauty of our land is important in any consideration of the future. The individual naturally prefers those measures that add to his pleasure but cost him nothing. He hesitates when a desirable objective involves much personal expense. Consequently the Supreme Court decision calling for the apportionment of political power in our states on the basis of population rather than region will have important implications toward preservation of the natural environment. With shifting of greater political power to urban populations we can expect a fuller exercise of the social conscience by cityfolk toward distant rural areas about which they may be poorly informed. That this will bring feelings of desperation to those who seek to wring a livelihood from these rural areas can be foreseen. It is likely, however, that in the future the rural hinterlands of America will be shaped to a degree previously unknown to suit the needs and wishes of those who dwell in urban centers. Local economies and local governments may well be crippled in this process.

Those who set forth in their individual pursuits of wealth and happiness to conquer the American continent have in general lacked those attitudes toward the land that have in other countries characterized the peasantry. A sense of belonging or attachment to the land has not been characteristic of most Americans. Admittedly, the peasant tradition was carried to America by some groups of farmer-colonists, but over much of the country it has been absent. In its place has been the attitude of the transient exploiter who seeks to gain wealth by use of the land or exploitation of its resources, but feels that his true home is elsewhere and hopes to return with his wealth to some urbane and settled place. This attitude of transient exploitation was behind the activities of the hunters and trappers, miners and lumbermen, livestock producers and those farmers who planted their tobacco or cotton in the cleared forests of the South, or their wheat in the dry Great Plains. The rawness and ugliness of large areas, particularly in the West, is evidence of the passing or the presence of the transient exploiter, and of the absence of those who feel a sense of belonging to the land.

Transient exploitation was encouraged in the western United States by the manner in which the public domain was handled. Through a failure to establish any early control over its use, and through inept provisions for its disposal, the government favored the transient, nomadic use of federal lands. The public domain attracted people who had no hope of achieving any tenure, who could only try to get there first and grab the most from areas to which they had no attachment and in which they could plan no future. Those who attempted to stay and improve their surroundings found it difficult to do so. The West still carries the scars.

The attitude of the transient exploiter is with us today and is encouraged in some places by the nature of the American economy and the ecology of some of our biotic resources. Thus livestock ranching in much of the American West is an enterprise in which the margin of profit is often small and the return on an investment in land and capital equipment is less than could be expected from a similar investment in other activities. It is easier in many places to overstock, overgraze, sell when prices are high, and get out than it is to attempt to stay and build the land and its grazing resources. Similarly the prospects for long-term sustained-yield forest management are not bright in many private lands. The temptation to liquidate a forest resource quickly and use the profit for other enterprise is difficult to resist. Our inadequate knowledge of silviculture adds to the problem and to the temptation even for those who would prefer to manage forestlands for continual production. As Hugh Raup has pointed out, if the Harvard Forest could have liquidated its wood capital in the few years after it was established, and had invested the proceeds, its net return at the end of fifty years would have been ten times as great as it has been from management on a sustained-yield forestry program (Raup, 1946, pp. 19–20).

An attitude of transience and nonattachment toward the land or the social community is further encouraged by the way of life forced upon people in urban areas by the dispersed nature of the modern city and suburb. Many are forced to live in one place, work in another many miles distant, play in still a different area, and consequently feel no particular attachment or commitment toward any. Furthermore the extreme mobility, both spatial and social, of the American people makes it difficult to arouse their concern for the local problems of an area in which they may live for only a few years before advancement or transfer moves them to a different job in a different region.

The absence of that respect for the land characteristic of those regions in which cultures have grown up in place has had one further effect upon American attitudes. Americans have always shown a greater willingness to shape the land to suit their enterprise than to adapt their enterprise to the shape of the land. Of all past attitudes this is the one most conspicuously present and active today and has been referred to as our "bulldozer mentality." The engineer, not the ecologist, sets the tone for public debate. We locate our centers of population in arid lands and demand that water be brought to them. We chop out a forest or bulldoze off a hill to locate a suburb, rather than adapt our roads and buildings to the vegetation or topography. Exceptions to this rule among our suburbs are high in price. We prefer and find it cheaper in the short run to subdue nature rather than cooperate with it.

The preparation of this paper was slowed by a catastrophe that struck the region in which I live, northwestern California. The economy of the area was shattered by devastating river floods of a severity not before experienced in the history of the region. These floods and their consequent damage, however, have helped to illustrate the attitude of man toward his natural environment in America. They highlight an ineptitude in dealing with this environment, an inability to accept and come to terms with nature, a determination to impose by force a predetermined pattern upon the natural scene.

Floods are not new in the valleys of the Eel, the Klamath, the Trinity, or the Mad rivers. Yet people have built their homes, towns, railroads, and highways on the floodplains or in the river canyons and have hoped that the floods would not affect them. The pioneers may have been a little wiser, or more likely they lacked our earth-moving equipment. In either event, their roads on the ridge tops during the flood period replaced our broken superhighways in the canyons. In the winter of 1955, floods of a magnitude rated by the experts as unlikely to occur more often than once in a century hit this region and did great damage. But when the waters receded, the people believed the statistical odds and moved back into the same areas to put up more expensive buildings, lay out grander highways, and construct wider bridges. Perhaps they were lulled into feelings of security by the talk of engineers who spoke of dams and levees. Perhaps they would simply have gone to their old homes without such promises of future security. But this year the flood was of a magnitude rated as unlikely to occur more than once in a thousand years. The fine new highways were crumpled, the bridges tossed aside, the towns obliterated. I fear, however, that many of the people will still move back; indeed they are already doing so. They will build larger towns and wider freeways in the same places. Once more they hear the brave words of dams and levees spoken by the engineers. Perhaps once more also they will be hit by another statistically improbable manifestation of nature. This is not a purely American behavior pattern. People all over the world live on active volcanoes or are drowned on floodplains. But no other group of people manages such colossal mistakes with the help of advice from so highly trained a group of experts.

In a region such as northwestern California it would make sense to take great care of the watersheds. But perhaps nowhere else in America can one see more flagrant abuse of watershed cover. Debris from logged-over slopes and cut logs from the decks piled along the river bottoms contributed to much of the most spectacular flood damage. It would make sense in such a region to build permanent structures well above any expected highwater line, and to use the lowlands for purposes unlikely to be damaged by floods. But such sense is not in the American tradition. We do not believe in adapting to environmental necessities; we demand that they be removed. This outlook admittedly has contributed to our rapid material progress. But our gains are made at the risk of high personal losses and always with the destruction of much that could have enriched our lives in other ways.

Americans are impatient with the slow processes of nature, with the normal events of biotic succession and change. They prefer the simplicity of a machine to the intricacies of a biota. The day-by-day problems of watershed management seem tiresome, whereas a large dam built to stop floods "for all time" has popular appeal. Even when we wish to preserve nature we like to get the job over with, and by some spectacular act of Congress decree preservation forever. The continual small difficulties involved in the maintenance of any natural community tend to annoy the American temperament. Wildness is too unmanageable to suit the majority of the people. One of the most difficult tasks for a teacher

of wildlife biology is to get students to sit down and watch undisturbed animals. They all want to get out and *do something* with the animals, anything but leave them alone.

Although optimistic by nature, I often find it difficult to look forward with much optimism to the future of man in North America. It seems strange to me to read accounts by those who believe that the greatest problem in our future will be the question of how best to use our leisure time. In a world dominated by human misery and ignorance such an outlook seems incredible. When our greatest efforts to date have failed to raise living standards above a bare minimum in the nonindustrialized part of the world, even in those countries where the most money and effort has been expended, we can hardly afford such optimism. Our failure to cope with the problems of population increase, and our inability to understand the ecological necessities of our world do not permit great confidence in our future. America cannot live in isolation from the rest of the world. If we continue to think that leisure will be our greatest future problem, we may well spend that leisure defending our fat land against the hungry majority of mankind.

But apart from the possible effects of international developments upon our future, it is still difficult to be highly optimistic about the fate of our natural environments or about the kind of world we are building in North America. Admittedly, my outlook is influenced by my living in California. My home state, like all of North America, was unusually well endowed with natural beauty and resource wealth. But we have been busy destroying its beauty and perhaps will not desist until only fragments are left.

California is beset with a rate of population increase that is almost impossible to accommodate. Each year some 600,-000 people are added; each month some

50,000 more come into the state. We must build a large town each month and a large city each year to provide housing alone. But the newcomers demand jobs from industry, schooling, electric power, water, and highways. They want to hunt or fish, use the beaches, play in the state and national parks, ski on mountain slopes, and wander in undisturbed mountain wilderness. They want all of the elements of the good life that have been associated in the past with California, including unpolluted water and pure air. It is remarkable that the officials of state and local governments remain sane when forced to cope with these demands. It is surprising that the social structure of the state does not fold with the impact. It has been necessary to reshape the entire urban-industrial framework of the land. Each day we are forced to accomplish engineering miracles, but we do so often at the cost of the natural environment (Dasmann, 1965).

The cities of California have grown and continue to grow into sprawling, formless conurbations, and their suburbs have caused Wood and Heller to add the new word "slurb" to the English language to describe them (Wood and Heller, 1962). The highways of the state grow wider by the day and probe into previously undisturbed quarters. The search for water is endless, since people are encouraged to settle in greatest numbers in the more arid regions. Through the massive California state water plan we propose to dam and capture every river, move water any distance without much regard for cost in dollars or damage to the natural environment. We continue to pave over our best farmlands, but compensate by creating their replacements in vast, expensive irrigation projects in our driest regions. We behave as though we were in a desperate war for survival, and we are, but our only enemy is our own unwillingness to adapt our

pattern of living to the shape of our environment.

It would be possible to slow population growth in California to a tolerable rate and to regulate the degree of environmental change. Most of the growth results from immigration. Immigrants could be discouraged, or guided to areas where their presence would not create new problems. This could be done without infringing upon any human freedoms, through a process of not planning to accommodate them, through not encouraging the growth of industry or the expansion of other employment opportunities. By recognizing limitations not only to population growth, but to the size of areas to be devoted to housing, transportation, production of raw materials, or other land-consuming uses, we could slow down destructive change and eventually bring it under control (Dasmann, 1965).

It is madness to assume that population growth can be unending. It is inevitable that continued encouragement of growth will bring consequences that are undesirable. We know that eventually growth must cease, for resources all have some limits. It would be wise to limit growth while the land was still worth living in, while we could preserve the beauty and variety that originally attracted the Californians. Instead we encourage growth by promises of water and jobs, houses, schools, and all other necessities and amenities, as though determined to tax the physical facilities of the state to their utmost. Even some conservation groups fail to face this problem and continue to work only to save this piece of land or that from being ground under by the ever-expanding material culture. In the halls of government are heard mostly plans to accommodate more people and no evidence that curtailment of growth will ever be considered. If we seek for reasons for this unwillingness to act we find them within us, in the ambiguity of our own attitudes toward our environment.

We would like to preserve the beauty of the American land, but we are tied to the dynamics of an expanding economy. We are unwilling to face a future in which property will not increase in value because of increased demand, in which business or industry cannot grow and expand, in which opportunities for promotion or advancement become limited, and profits will find a plateau. We have grown accustomed to dependence on the economic horn of plenty for an unending and ever-increasing supply of material goods. So we vote for measures to preserve the environment only in those areas where our segment of the expanding economy will not be affected.

Hope for maintaining the richness and variety in life that come with open space, wild animal life, wilderness, or just slightly wild country lies in our facing the necessity for curtailment of population growth, and for slowing down the expansion of those segments of our economy that demand vital space or are destructive to scarce resources. California today presents an extreme example of this problem, but all of America is in the same predicament. It is difficult, however, to believe that we will take the necessary action. It seems more likely that we will restrict growth and expansion only at that time when lessened returns in material advantages result. We may deplore the loss of less tangible values, be sorry to see the wild places and the natural scene disappear, but we will not act to remove the basic cause of the trouble until we feel the economic pinch. By then it may well be too late to save more than token pieces of our natural environment.

I am taking this pessimistic view despite the success of the conservation movement in America. Conservation has been successful because we are still a rich country, and population growth has not done its most serious damage. We are able to set aside new parks and reserves and to some degree improve the care given to existing ones because these actions still do not involve much cost or sacrifice on the part of most people. A local economy may be affected and some local people without great political influence may be hurt by a national decision to remove some area or resource from further exploitation. Most people feel only the benefits to be derived from the action. But when space becomes more scarce the picture can change. Even today when any serious conflict develops between those who would preserve the natural scene and those who speak for the expanding economy, it is usually the former who give way. The great water-development plans in the West take precedence over attempts to preserve or maintain wild areas. It is virtually impossible to prevent the economic exploitation of areas that conceal valuable minerals. Highway commissions retain the power to shatter communities or slice apart state parks. Suburbs still spread over farmlands despite efforts to zone them out. The individual's quest for economic advancement still rides over his social conscience and smothers the development of any true ecological conscience.

It is a temptation to end this paper on this pessimistic note, but it would be unfair not to present other evidence. In answering questions about probable trends, or in making predictions of the future, it is necessary to ask the basic philosophical question regarding free will and determinism. To what extent are we actually free to make choices concerning our future? Most conservationists act on the premise that we have a high degree of freedom of choice. Many Americans, however, and perhaps the great majority, accept an economic determinism as a rule of life, and believe that the very nature of our economic and social system forces a pattern for the future upon us whether we will it or not. Rachel Carson has noted this feeling with her question in *Silent Spring:* "Have we fallen into a mesmerized state that makes us accept as inevitable that which is inferior, as though having lost the will or the vision to demand that which is good?"

My hopes for the future are based on the belief that people are free to determine the course they will follow, and that when faced with alternatives they will select the one most favorable to their survival. I do not think that we are at the mercy of economic or social forces beyond our control, and believe that the direction in which we will travel depends upon decisions by men who are free to make contrary decisions. However, to make an intelligent choice one must be aware of its implications and be able to explore fully the consequences of alternative courses of action. Because our knowledge is always imperfect, this is not always possible or ever easy. It presents a major problem to those concerned with the preservation of natural environments. Most people are not sufficiently aware of the value to their future of the environments that have in the past surrounded them. The pathways of understanding that Aldo Leopold once called for have yet to be built into the human mind. The well-known quotation from Thoreau "in wildness is the preservation of the world" is a truism only to a minority, and to them it is an article of faith not clearly demonstrable through facts and figures. It takes time to build in a majority of people that knowledge of the value of wild things that would cause them to work hard for preservation. But in the meanwhile choices must be made and losses will therefore continue to be experienced by those who seek to preserve wild America.

Yet there are reasons for some optimism. Economic considerations do not provide our only drives. The great and successful mass movements that have changed the world for better or for worse have seldom had purely materialistic goals. The religious leaders that changed the face and spirit of the Western world did not promise an additional crust of bread to their followers. As the pressure of our materialistic civilization becomes more restrictive to the human spirit there are increased stirrings against purely material progress.

One of the most effective conservation books of recent years is the novel *The Roots of Heaven,* by Romain Gary; although I doubt that the author intended it to be such. Morel, the hero or perhaps antihero, of the novel, who waged a war to save the elephants, represents a misdirected mass striving toward a more meaningful world. He and those who attempted to understand him in the novel ask the question that many of us in conservation fields have also raised: "Are we no longer capable of respecting nature, or defending a living beauty that has no earning power, no utility, no object except to let itself be seen from time to time? Liberty, too, is a natural splendor on its way to becoming extinct." Romain Gary has identified through his characterizations the slow, sometimes irrational way in which people in the Western world have been groping toward Thoreau's concept, and in the confusion of our times seeing their salvation in the preservation of wildness in both nature and man.

Today more than before leaders with an appreciation of our natural heritage and the value of wild things are appearing in America, often in fields once thought to be far removed from the traditional area of conservation. In consequence we are seeing some surprising happenings. The population problem has crept into the daily newspapers and receives serious attention at all levels of national life. In places the blighting suburban spread is being halted, the omnipotent freeway builders have been turned aside by some communities, a massive federal program for breathing new life into the dying hearts of our old central cities is underway, and books such as *Silent Spring* become national best-sellers. These are stirrings, but strong ones, and suggest that pathways of understanding are being built more rapidly today, and that the losses in the quality of our living are being noticed soon enough to be remedied. If so, then there is hope that we can save those unique environments that once composed the wild lands of America. Adding to this hope is the recreative power of living organisms and natural communities. With assistance even the most battered landscape can be brought back to life. If we can save the pieces, the whole can someday be reconstituted.

BIBLIOGRAPHY

Carson, Rachel. 1962. Silent Spring. Houghton Mifflin, Boston.

Dasmann, Raymond F. 1965. The Destruction of California. Macmillan, New York.

Gary, Romain. 1958. The Roots of Heaven. Simon & Schuster, New York.

Leopold, Aldo. 1949. A Sand County Almanac. Oxford Univ. Press, New York.

Raup, Hugh M. 1964. Some Problems in Ecological Theory and Their Relation to Conservation. J. Ecol. 52:19–28.

Wood, Samuel E., and Heller, Alfred E. 1962. California Going, Going. California Tomorrow, Sacramento, Calif.

THE SPECIAL ROLE OF NATIONAL PARKS[1]

Noel D. Eichhorn*

National parks have a much greater significance in a discussion of future environments than their relatively small area might indicate. They are managed to minimize the impact of man and to maintain, as far as possible, complete, functioning ecosystems with all their natural variety. They are required by law to be maintained "unimpaired for the enjoyment of future generations."[2]

National parks are not recreation areas

* Mr. Eichhorn, a graduate of Lehigh University, has pursued graduate studies at Cornell University, Oregon State University, and the University of Stockholm. Since 1962 he has been on the staff of the Conservation Foundation, where he has participated in a socioecologic study of the national parks of the United States.

[1] This paper is based upon a Conservation Foundation study, not yet completed, of the National Park System of the United States. Funds for the study have been provided by the Old Dominion Foundation. Credit for the ideas in this paper is very difficult to assign and I have given no specific references other than the Yellowstone Park Act of 1872 and the National Parks Act of 1916. None of the ideas is original. I am particularly in debt to my colleagues at the Conservation Foundation, especially Frank Fraser Darling, who is the director of the Foundation's national park study. Statements about "national parks" refer to the national parks in the United States. (The national parks of Canada are quite similar and much of what I have said applies equally well to them.) All large natural areas administered by the National Park Service except National Recreation Areas are considered to be national parks.
[2] The National Parks Act (64th Congress, 1st session, Stat. 39, 535).

in the usual sense of the word. They are areas which contain beautiful and unusual scenery, curiosities of nature, wild animals and plants, and historic and prehistoric artifacts of man. They are meant to be seen and enjoyed but left unaltered by man. The extent to which the parks have actually been left unaltered has depended upon many factors among which are their history, size, location, local political pressures, the ways in which they have been managed, and the uses which have been permitted.

The nature of park system

When the first national parks were created during the last half of the nineteenth century, most of North America fit our current definition of wilderness, and very few people anticipated a time when it might seem desirable to preserve an area merely because it was wild. In addition, Victorian notions on what constituted natural conditions were somewhat different from today's. A natural setting at the turn of the century could include soft beds, white tablecloths, and rocking chairs on a long veranda. Solitude and wilderness could still be found along the eastern seaboard; Walden Pond was only a few miles from Boston Common.

The Yellowstone Park Act set aside a large wild area to protect the natural wonders it contains from despoliation for private gain and to assure "their retention in their natural condition."[3] This park was to be maintained in a wild state just so that it might be enjoyed, but the focus of the enjoyment was expected to be the geysers and the waterfalls, and not just the wildness itself.

Each national park is supposed to be unique and to have some special national significance. Most of the units of the National Park System meet these qualifications. However, many kinds of habitat are completely missing. The system is hardly representative of all the kinds of scenery in the country.

The size and shape of park units seem to have been determined more by circumstance, political expediency, and desire for geometrical regularity than on a sophisticated consideration of geographical and biological factors. In many cases, it appears that care was actually taken to include as little land as possible that might be good for anything except sightseeing. The entire system amounts to about 1 per cent of the total national area but considerably more than 1 per cent of the country's mountaintops, deserts, and scrub forests.

Most of the national parks are in the West, where they could be established at little expense by setting aside land already in federal ownership. In addition, the bulk of the land in the National Park System is concentrated in a few large units. Consequently, seven states have more than three quarters of all the land in the system; and two, Alaska and California, account for nearly half the total.

Many of the parks contain privately owned lands whose owners have been able to use their property however they pleased. There are summer homes, motels, gas stations, trailer courts, and hunting lodges on these private holdings.

Many of the parks are difficult to manage properly because they are either

[3] The Yellowstone Park Act (42nd Congress, 2nd Session, Stat. 17, 32).

too small or are the wrong shape. Few, even of the large parks, come close to being self-sustaining ecological units, particularly as far as large animals are concerned. Few have adequate winter pasture for elk or deer. Fewer still are the right shape and size for wolves or mountain lions.

Most of the national parks have a variety of scenic features. Great Smoky Mountains National Park has both steep, forested mountains and nearly level, cleared farmscapes. Yosemite has the cliffs and waterfalls of the Valley and the groves of Big Trees. Wind Cave has the caverns below and herds of bison and antelope above. Olympic has snow-covered mountains, rain forest, and seacoast.

The influence of development and use

The wildness of a park is very dependent on the number of visitors it receives; and the number of visitors is a function of distance from large population centers, accessibility by highway, and the kinds of activity possible in and near the park. Because it is a national park and, therefore, a focus for tourists, an area like Mount McKinley National Park may be the most heavily used portion of a region which is otherwise nearly empty of people.

Large numbers of visitors can have a considerable impact on an area. They are noisy and many animals are frightened away. They feed the more appealing of those that remain and make beggars and pests of them. In and near campgrounds underbrush disappears. The soil becomes compacted and there is no regeneration of grass or forest. Sewage must be disposed of and streams may become polluted. Candy wrappers, Kleenex, empty beer cans, and yellow film boxes decorate the ground and the lower branches of the trees.

The most heavily used parks are within a few hours' drive of a large population center, are located along major cross-country highways, or can be conveniently visited as a part of a tour which takes in several parks or other tourist attractions. The park which is closest to the largest number of people is Great Smoky Mountains, and it has the largest number of visitors each year. A park like Big Bend which must be driven to for its own sake, which is not on the way to anywhere else, and which is a long drive from almost everywhere, receives relatively few visitors. Three parks, Katmai, Glacier Bay, and Isle Royale, cannot be driven to at all and receive the fewest visitors of all the large units of the National Park System.

A park near a large city may be very crowded on weekends even though it is lightly used during the week.

A few park entrance roads through National Forest or to park areas without many visitors are still nice scenic drives or pleasant ways through the woods. Most park entrances, however, are surrounded by motels, gas stations, and souvenir shops, whose billboard advertising hides the scenery along the highways for miles out from the park boundaries.

The nature of the highway system within a park is, for most parks, the most important determinant of how much of the area is to remain wild. Most tourists do not get far from their cars. A park like Olympic or Kings Canyon which has roads only at the edges is less modified than one like Yellowstone which has several roads crossing the park. In fact, in Yellowstone (and in several other parks) the most remote areas are found along the park boundaries.

The roads themselves as engineering works usually have a considerable influence on both surface and subsurface drainage patterns. In addition, they condition the behavior of many animals that learn to avoid automobiles and that the grass is greener on the road shoulders.

Parking areas may be several acres in extent and, particularly when blacktopped, may have a large macroclimatic

effect. They are also quite an eyesore. The sun is reflected from the shiny cars; a full parking lot can be seen for miles.

Lakes and other navigable waters, particularly where motorboats are allowed as at Yellowstone and Everglades, permit penetration of park areas which might otherwise be sufficiently inaccessible to be left unaltered.

For whatever reason they come, nearly all park visitors come by car, and most of them expect to take their cars with them wherever they go in the parks. Presumably they do this for the sake of convenience and privacy, and the experts claim that these visitors would object strenuously if anyone tried to separate them from their automobiles. However, separated they must be, and in the very near future, if the national parks are to avoid the Los Angeles syndrome in which 60 per cent of the center of things is taken up by freeways and parking lots.

Putting the tourists aboard buses would let present road systems carry several times the present number of people with fewer traffic jams and would very nearly eliminate the black-bear problem. There could be both scheduled service of the pick-'em-up-and-leave-'em variety with stops at all scenic attractions and all-day-aboard-one-bus tours.

The impact of management

Few national park areas are entirely self-regulating. Even the apparent balance of moose and wolves on Isle Royale will be upset if the moose habitat is permitted to grow back into forest.

There is some deliberate tampering with natural processes within the parks which is made necessary by their relatively small size and their vulnerability to change induced from outside the park boundaries.

One of the most important examples is fire control. Many fires, of course, are not natural, but even natural fires must be controlled in most parks since a really big fire could burn an entire park. At Everglades there has been an experimental program of deliberate burning to make up for the suppression of the natural fires which are very important ecologically. Other parks will eventually have to provide some substitute for natural fires.

In many parks the destruction of wolves and other carnivores which were factors of population control in species still numerous in the parks has already made deliberate removal of elk and deer necessary.

The interruption of the flow of fresh water south through the Everglades has made it necessary to build dikes and ditches to conserve and distribute the fresh water that is left.

Much more management of the deliberate, manipulative kind will be necessary as the lands around the parks continue to be changed.

Wilderness values

The national parks are used for wilderness recreation. So long as the number of back-country users remains very low this use is compatible with the purpose of the parks. However, the back country of the parks can never have high-density use and still remain "unmodified for the enjoyment of future generations." In some parks, wilderness recreation use is already high enough to have done serious damage. In places in Great Smoky Mountains National Park the Appalachian Trail has been worn more than six feet wide and more than one foot deep. The meadows along some of the trails in Kings Canyon National Park have been very severely overgrazed and recovery may take several years even with no more grazing.

The use of an area for wilderness recreation requires little more of the land than that it be nearly empty of people and not unpleasant to look at. Potentially, there is far more land outside the parks than inside which could be entirely suitable wilderness for purposes of solitude and retreat from civilization.

Scientific use

Because they are natural areas maintained as nearly unaltered as possible, the parks have tremendous value to science. They preserve the history and archaeology of man as well as natural history. Understanding and appreciation of an area cannot be complete without knowledge of what man has done there. They are museums which preserve processes as well as objects. Their value will increase as the lands outside the parks become more heavily utilized. They should not be thought of as laboratories or as places for experimentation, for these uses would require deliberate modification for test purposes and the parks are to be left unaltered. They are classrooms and libraries, storehouses of information, and places for learning.

The National Park Service recognizes the importance of the function of the parks as museums. They try to teach every tourist by means of visitor centers, trailside exhibits, park folders, nature guides, and lectures, both in auditoriums and out on trails. They encourage scientists to come to the parks to study. The use of the parks by scholars leads to greater enjoyment for all visitors.

The national parks as scenery

Not all the best scenery is in national parks, but many of them contain unusual or spectacular sorts of scenery which are not found elsewhere. As a result the parks attract large numbers of visitors: tourists who come for the sake of the scenery and not primarily for study, or for solitude, or for fun. The display of their unique features is the primary use for which the parks were intended.

There are two kinds of scenery. One kind can be enjoyed from a distance and from many vantage points spread over a large area. Mount Rainier and the Grand

Canyon are examples. The other kind is best seen and appreciated from a very few vantage points or from a very restricted area. Cliff Palace in Mesa Verde National Park and the General Sherman Tree in Sequoia National Park are examples.

The vantage points necessary for the kinds of scenery which can be seen from many places and from far away can be established on the basis of best view and least impact on an area. The vantage points necessary for the kinds of scenery which can be seen from a very few places and from a very limited area are usually chosen on the basis of best possible views without regard to impact on, or damage to, an area. Very often it is necessary to clear part of the forest to provide a good view.

Some scenery has actually been defaced in order to let people see it. For example, there are boardwalks around many of the geysers and hot springs at Yellowstone. Cave environments are changed drastically by illumination. Most cliff-edge view points are enclosed by substantial railings.

In most cases scenic display is a high density use of very small areas within the parks; however, some scenery cannot stand crowds. In several places within the Park System, visitor density is already too high. If there were a good measure of visitor satisfaction, it would probably be possible to demonstrate that fewer people in Yosemite Valley on a summer weekend would have a higher total satisfaction.

The use of binoculars can sometimes increase the number of good view points and decrease tourist density. Where the scenery is fragile or nervous, as with cliff dwellings and many wild animals, binoculars can provide the only really practical method of display.

Photography seems to be an appropriate activity in a national park, especially since it spreads the enjoyment of a visit over a much longer period. If you have a picture it may not be necessary to go back in person.

The pressures of people

Many uses of the parks are now tolerated which are not based on the unique characteristics of the areas. These uses include many which at present levels of visitation have little impact on the landscape. Others, however, do change the visual scene and the ecological stability.

The national parks are playgrounds. They serve as regional parks providing boating, swimming, skiing, camping, fishing, and many other outdoor activities for which a national park setting is unnecessary; these are activities done for their own sake without regard to the surroundings. Some parks contain swimming pools, golf courses, dance halls, and other urban transplants.

The national parks are places to stay overnight, to buy souvenirs, to stock up on groceries, camera supplies, and camping equipment, to eat meals, and to purchase gasoline. (In most parks these needs are served by concessionaires many of whom are so firmly implanted that they tell the Park Service what to do instead of the other way around. A new reinforced concrete warehouse was being built by the concessionaire in Yosemite Valley at the same time the Park Service was moving some of its own facilities out of the park entirely.)

Campgrounds can be enormous and still be crowded. Most national park campgrounds are of the drive-in variety. They are equipped with fireplaces and picnic tables.

It may be necessary to eat and eliminate in some national parks, but hotels and supermarkets, and so forth, could all be outside. If private cars were left at hotels, gas stations would not be necessary either.

A few visitors eat the fruits and berries which grow in the parks with the blessings of the National Park Service, which encourages them. The Service also encourages the fisherman and stocks many park lakes, some with exotic species and some which were naturally barren. Fishing can have an enormous impact. Fishermen now take as many cutthroat trout from Yellowstone Lake as the pelicans do, and the poor fish may not continue to break even very much longer.

At Everglades, channels have been dredged and canals cut, strictly for the fisherman, and these have changed the salinity of the coastal areas and some of the inland lakes. Wash from the boats and noise have also been responsible for the abandonment of some bird rookeries.

There are many other visitor activities now permitted which have adverse effects upon the parks. These include downhill skiing, swimming, and mountain climbing. Motorboats may be necessary and appropriate in a few areas like Glacier Bay and Isle Royale, but excuses for them are more difficult to invent at Grand Teton and at Glacier.

Other uses of parkland

There are housekeeping functions for which parkland is used. These include residential areas for park employees, administrative buildings, maintenance areas for trucks and other heavy equipment, sewage lagoons, garbage pits or incinerators, and in some cases, aircraft landing fields.

At Yosemite and at a few other parks the National Park Service owns land outside the park boundaries to which it is moving as many of these management structures as possible. In many other parks the headquarters and residential areas are located near the park boundaries in order to reduce their impacts on the parks.

There are a few completely intolerable uses made of national parkland which serve neither the tourist nor the park management. There are reservoirs in Yosemite National Park, in Grand Teton National Park, and in several other parks, for municipal water supply, for irrigation, and for power generation. There are federal highway rights-of-way across Wind Cave National Park and other parks. A few park areas are open to mining and grazing. Exempting the very small proportion of the national area which is within national parks from these sorts of intrusions would have little effect on the economy.

New dimensions of purpose and policy

The national parks are relatively small areas of very limited human capacity which have been set apart from a profit-producing use because each park is in some way unique and of far greater value in enriching man's mind than it could possibly be in filling his wallet.

In the past, display was the primary purpose of the parks and retention in natural condition important, but secondary. For many parks the point has been reached already where they can no longer accommodate everyone who wishes to visit them and still remain unchanged. For these parks the primary purpose from now on must be preservation, and display secondary. This is not a fundamental change in park policy but only a reorientation. The national parks have the capacity to be far more than just scenery. They are the natural heritage of a nation. They are sanctuaries for wildlife, areas where nonhuman life exists in its own right, places left as they were for the sake of leaving them that way.

This new conception of purpose of the national parks will be difficult to apply, as policy, in a democratic society in a period of rising population and incomes, increased mobility and a growing urban way of life which tends, for most individuals, to create the desire to visit the natural beauty of wild country.

In biological terms, the resource base of most national parks is no better than that of the surrounding country. What sets the parks apart is the special protection they receive as natural areas and their management to approximate what they might have been if the rest of the continent had not been changed by civilization. They are unique areas because they are national parks.

The changes which take place in the environments of national parks are an indication of the future of North American environments. What happens here will show the values each generation places on natural beauty, and the sacrifice each is willing to make in deference to the next.

What then must be the dimensions of park policy?

(1) The number of parks should be increased until the system includes representative samples of all the kinds of scenery and all the kinds of habitat in the country. The area of the National Park System would still be a very small percentage of the total national area.

(2) The boundaries of the parks should be redrawn on ecological lines, including sufficient land to allow them to be managed as biological units, and excluding land not necessary ecologically so that it can be used for less restrictive purposes.

(3) If the national parks are to continue to serve their purpose, the number of visitors to any given park must be held to no more than that park can stand without being markedly changed. If the people of the country continue to hold the philosophy that everyone must be able to see everything, ways will have to be found to display the parks, perhaps by television, without actually letting very many people inside.

(4) In nearly every existing park, visitor pressure is already causing changes, not only because of the presence of the people themselves, but because of the engineering works necessary to their presence. Rather than continue to expand the present kinds of tourist facilities the Park Service must develop new techniques which have less impact on park habitats.

(5) Ideally, no national park need be used for any purpose not directly related to the special resource base of that particular park. Wilderness users have no more inherent right to be in the parks than do water-skiers. There must be a reconsideration of the appropriateness of many uses which were tolerated in the past because the number of people involved was too small to do lasting damage. There is a lot of marginally productive land outside all existing, and potential, park areas which could be used for recreation and for other purposes, too.

QUALITY OF LIVING–STRESS AND CREATIVITY

Seymour M. Farber, M.D.*

"The happiest state of man is the middle state between the *savage* and the *refined,* or between the wild and the luxurious state. Such is the state of society in CONNECTICUT, and some others of the American provinces; where the inhabitants consist, if I am rightly informed, of an independent and hardy YEOMANRY, all nearly on a level–trained to arms . . . clothed in homespun–of simple manners –strangers to luxury–drawing plenty from the ground–and that plenty, gathered easily by the hand of industry; and giving rise to early marriages, a numerous progeny, length of days, and a rapid increase–the rich and the poor, the haughty grandee and the creeping sycophant, equally unknown–protected by laws, which (being their own will) cannot oppress. . . . O distinguished people! May you continue long thus happy! and may the happiness you enjoy spread over the face of the whole earth. . . ."

This apostrophe to the pastoral life from Richard Price's *Observations on the American Revolution,* written in 1785, expresses the extravagant expectations of the age: that the fresh green "garden" of

* Dr. Farber is Dean of Educational Services and Director of Continuing Education, Health Sciences, at the University of California San Francisco Medical Center. Known for his studies of lung cancer in the 1950s, he has also addressed himself more broadly to human responses to environmental stress and has been co-editor of the annual San Francisco symposia on "Man and Civilization."

North America would prove to be an Arcadia and Utopia combined. For some, like Jefferson and Franklin, it almost was, though the virtue resided in the man rather than in the soil of America.

Jefferson was troubled to the end of his life with misgivings about the evils of industrialism which was already reaching and encroaching on the land he loved. As a public man, he was compelled more than once to bow to these inevitable developments. As a private man, he was never able to accept them.

Although the machine, impelled by "a numerous progeny," has overrun the continent and blasted the dreams of Arcadia and Utopia, the conflict which disturbed Jefferson continues to disturb us.

It is the conflict between inwardness and outwardness. Man has always tended to choose the latter. Whether with stone ax, sword, or bulldozer, he has valued conquest and exploit more than the cultivation of the spirit. And now, curiously, as this meeting bears witness, mankind has reached a point where inwardness is being forced upon it by the sheer oppression of its own numbers. Man must look inward or perish.

Père Teilhard de Chardin believed that the stress of the population explosion would generate new levels of "psychical energy" in man; thus it was in his scheme not only essential to human evolution; it was, one might almost say, a blessing. It is difficult for some of us to view this stress with quite such cosmic equanimity, but let us try.

The word "stress" hardly seems to need defining. Originally it was "Distress," derived from Old French; later it became a Middle English word and lost its first syllable. But through the centuries its meaning remained the same: to impose strain upon, to press too tightly, to coerce or compel. It is only in the last two or three decades, however, that stress has become an important concept in medicine and biology.

Indeed it is difficult to discuss any of the problems in these sciences today without mentioning stress. Everyone knows what it means. Everyone is aware of it in his daily life.

And yet, the concept of evolution was neither new nor unknown in Darwin's youth. But it was not until he published *The Origin of Species* that the concept had a real impact on biology. Man has been taking advantage of the conditioned reflex in dogs for thousands of years, but not until Pavlov did it become a scientific principle. Even Einstein did not invent relativity. But he made a fruitful theory about it.

Similarly, while we have been aware of stress for a long time, it is only recently that it has been scrutinized to the point where it can be defined and measured with some precision. The most notable investigator of stress is Dr. Hans Selye of the University of Montreal, whose theories on the role of steroid hormones in health and disease I shall return to.

In his book *The Stress of Life,* Selye describes the circumstances under which he first glimpsed the outlines of what was to be his lifework. It began with the complete failure of an experiment which he had hoped would lead to the discovery of a new hormone.

"I became so depressed that for a few days I could not do any work at all. I just sat in my laboratory, brooding. . . ."

Yet he realized later that the "ensuing period of introverted contemplation turned out to be the decisive factor in my whole career; it pointed the way for all my subsequent work . . . which has been my delightful damnation ever since."

Another researcher, just as intelligent as the young Selye but perhaps a bit more dispassionate, would likely have told himself, "No use crying over spilt milk." He would very likely have pitched out the guinea pigs that had reacted so unobligingly and started off on another project. It has happened countless times.

But Selye had a different sort of personality. The stress of failure and depression activated the creative forces within him, forces which had been suppressed rather than cultivated during his long years of medical training, which necessarily meant absorbing facts rather than examining them.

Depression, disorganization, even temporary derangement seem to be essential to the creative process in many persons. Dr. Frank Barron, a psychologist at the University of California, says in *Creativity and Psychological Health:* "What has emerged most clearly from my own research on creativity is the fact that the creative person is able to find in the developmentally more primitive and less reasonably structured aspects of his own mental functioning the possibility of new insight, even though at first this may be only intuitively and dimly grasped. He is willing to pay heed to vague feelings and intimations which on the grounds of good sense are put hastily aside by most of us."

In a recent study of the effects of stress on coronary heart disease, two San Francisco researchers attached pulse-counters to the wrists of several hundred middle-aged, hard-working men. The men were asked to record their pulse rates and activities at frequent intervals during the first day.

One of these subjects was the editor

of a metropolitan daily paper. A newspaper editor encounters a number of rises and falls in stressful activity throughout the day, as do stockbrokers, insurance salesmen, and others subject to deadlines of various sorts. But the editor was surprised to find that his most stressful time of day was not at work.

His most stressful activity, as indicated by the peaks in his pulse rate, was commuting to and from his suburban home. His pulse rate was regularly higher while driving on the crowded highway than it was when the presses broke down or the front page had been reset just before deadline because of a new crisis in Berlin.

Like any red-blooded American, this man accepted the perils of the superhighway without much protest. It was, he felt, the price he had to pay for living in a pleasant suburb. He thought it was worth it.

But it is interesting to note that he was not aware of the degree of stress to which it subjected him. He had successfully repressed his fear, as drivers must. Nevertheless his body knew that it was in mortal danger every morning and evening. As Selye has pointed out, the pituitary gland is a more accurate indicator of stress than is the intellect.

In considering the effects of stress, it is important to remember that one experience may be more stressful than it seems, while another which appears to be very stressful to the observer may be much less than it seems. If a physician ordered the editor to give up his demanding job and take a more routine one, to give up his expensive country-club activities and live quietly in a small apartment near his office, it might be much more stressful for such a hard-driving individual than his present life.

Brain-wave patterns are another way to measure stress. Used in conjunction with computers, they can be expected to yield a great deal of knowledge on stress

in the near future. The patterns change visibly on an oscilloscope when a man opens and closes his eyes, solves a puzzle, or is angered by hostile questions. They change somewhat more subtly when he takes a hallucinatory drug like mescaline or LSD-25; when he is in a weightless state; when he experiences loud noise vibration, flashing lights, extremes of temperature.

As more and more sophisticated electronic equipment is developed, it will be possible to monitor continuously the immense amount of data emitted by biological organisms: brain waves, pulse rates, and the changing activities of hearts, intestines, skeletal muscles, and hormone-secreting glands of men under stress.

Meanwhile we can make some gross observations and feed them into the human brain, which has been described as a surprisingly efficient, cool-running, cheaply operated and maintained computer, produced in large numbers by unskilled labor.

We have exchanged the primeval stresses of cold, hunger, plagues, terror of wild beasts and wilder men for the subtler stresses and terrors of mechanization; crowding; increasing surveillance; polluted air, food, and water; an ever-rising level of noise.

We are subjected almost constantly to what the physiologist Dr. Ralph Waldo Gerard has described as "a rain of excessive and bizarre information." Even though we reject most of this information, it takes energy to sort it out.

Allied to this rain of largely useless information is what might be called the stress of social expectations. This stress has become, in our culture, much more than conforming to a set of mores. No single person or institution makes unreasonable demands upon us, but the *number* of persons and institutions urging, admonishing, and threatening us strains the sanity of every conscientious citizen.

Are you still driving without seat belts?

Are you carrying all the insurance you should? Are you physically fit? Are you keeping up with world events? How long since you had a complete physical examination? Do you check yourself periodically for lumps? What about the PTA? What are you doing about urban renewal, cerebral palsy, civil liberties? You're *not* coming to the block party? You have to come or the neighbors will think you're some kind of hermit or a snob. Leave your committee meeting a little early, don't stay too long at the cocktail party, and you'll just make it. Don't forget—tomorrow night, cub scouts!

There is no end to our social duties. Trying to meet them all, we are apt to become unhinged. If we try to limit ourselves to what seems possible, we are made continually anxious and guilty by the unanswered pleas which assault us from the telephone, the mailbox, and the idiot box.

The atmosphere of the home has been profoundly affected by all these stresses. We like to think of home as a refuge from the world and its work, a place for relaxation, intimacy, and society. In an affluent society why should it not be just that?

Just before dawn, "when the white man's courage is at its lowest ebb," the bodily tide of steroid hormones is also at its lowest ebb. These tides in human blood and urine have been monitored by physiologists who have a constant pattern in the ebb and flow. By 6 A.M. the tide of steroid hormones is rising again, reaching a peak at noon. It falls off to another low point around 4 or 5 P.M., though not so low as the predawn level. It climbs to another peak around midnight but not so high as at midday.

The cyclic flow is augmented by sudden outputs in response to life events—pain, anger, fear, passion, and other stressful experiences. Thus getting up in the morning at this physiological low point may be the most stressful act of the day. In most households it means rushing into action in order to arrive at school or work on time. After the working day is over, the family is reunited at the second physiological low point of the day. As we all know, this is not an invariably joyful reunion. Children are cranky, parents are tired and edgy. Posing as a restful retreat, home awaits us with still more calls to duty. Most quarrels begin at this time.

Since women have a longer life expectancy, it seems likely that their lives are, on the whole, less stressful than men's. Yet during the period when her children are small, an American housewife's life is intensely stressful. Volumes have been written about how many roles she has to fill. No matter how fast she runs, she never seems to catch up with her work, for no collection of laborsaving appliances can equal the services of an efficient maid and a good nanny. All machines must be watched, tended, serviced. They break down when they are needed most and every household is in thrall to half a dozen service men who seldom give good service. The housewife's work is frantic, endless, unsatisfying, and lonely.

After a few years of this existence, a young woman begins to feel that she is losing her mind. She seems never to be able to finish even the smallest task before she must drop it for another one. She has lost the power to concentrate on anything more difficult than a newspaper or a popular magazine. She feels a little bitter even toward her family, for it seems that she is there to meet their needs. But no one is there to meet hers.

She reads articles, while waiting to see the pediatrician, which tell her how to be seductive while doing the dishes, how to be chic without money, how to "reconcile coquetry, maternity, and economy," as Simone de Beauvoir put it. But these articles are written by women on the safe side of the menopause who have forgotten about the problems.

Also, despite stern admonishments from these female elders to put her husband first, always—since his ego cannot, like hers, be fulfilled by having babies—she wishes to be *someone;* someone besides her husband's wife, her children's mother, the house's keeper.

This identity, which she had begun to achieve before her marriage, is not likely to survive it. Unless her interests and talents were well developed, she will probably find it too great an effort to keep them alive or to cultivate new ones. It will only make her feel guilty about neglecting her home duties. But the frustration engendered by total self-sacrifice will be stressful, perhaps more so than if she chose to please herself. Whatever choice she makes, she usually finds it difficult to strike a balance.

In *The Second Sex,* De Beauvoir described the unhappy woman who has taken to orderly housekeeping as others take to drink: "When any living being enters her house, her eye gleams with a wicked light: 'Wipe your feet! Don't tear the place apart! Leave that alone!' She wishes those of the household would hardly breathe; everything means more thankless work for her." The woman who is able to resist this kind of madness, along with other kinds, is apt to be a victim of "psychosomatic illness." This is often interpreted to mean that she is neurotic because she won't accept her role as wife and mother. Sometimes her physician sends her to a psychiatrist, who is apt to be of the same persuasion. This does not help her much.

The desperately unhappy woman sooner or later will damage her husband and children as well as herself.

Her husband works hard, too, but in doing so he increases his grasp upon the world. He gets promotions, raises, recognition. But her work gets her nowhere. At forty or fifty, he will be at his peak, professionally, but she will find herself idle and useless, her youthfulness gone. It is very difficult for her to start a new life at this point, because she has spent twenty or thirty years doing what was expected of her, fulfilling a social image of wife and mother, while denying herself. Now her long servitude is over. She can do what she wants. But she no longer knows what she wants.

Of course this does not happen to every American woman, but it certainly happens to a great many who choose the path of conformity. It seems likely that it will happen more and more as automation continues to wipe out jobs. As during the Depression years, employers will increasingly give preference to men. There are indications already that hard-pressed colleges are going to stiffen entrance requirements for women.

What is euphemistically called a Good Time may be one of the most stressful of human activities. The weariness we feel after a weekend house party or a vacation trip can testify to this. Often it is a relief to get back to work.

Many of these Good Times are made tolerable only because of the sedative effects of ethyl alcohol. It makes bores interesting, turns clichés into *bon mots,* and transforms suspicion into something resembling love.

It suspends, for the moment, that sense of exclusion which makes us vulnerable to stress. Dr. Harold G. Wolff, in *Stress and Psychiatric Disorder,* described an experiment which illustrates this type of stress: "When male rat interlopers were introduced into established colonies of males and females they were vigorously attacked by resident males. Within hours or days after the attack, most of the interlopers died—but not of wounds. Some of them had been dominant rats in their own colonies. Autopsy revealed that the adrenal glands of the dead interlopers were much enlarged; yet adrenal secretion was depleted. The fact that the interlopers were excluded from the group seemed to make them more vulnerable."

Thus beneath the smiles and chatter, the pleasant tinkle of glasses, the spectacular buffet, the unpaid-for swimming pool, lies the deadly struggle to be "in."

But the stress of leisure holds even greater threats for us. Shorter hours and longer vacations present problems to people who are work-oriented. We are full of plans and projects for some distant day "when we have the time." But if, like the hard-pressed housewife, we defer these things too long, we find that we are not up to the challenge of leisure, which demands some degree of creativeness. We find only a sense of dislocation and boredom. What can be more stressful than this feeling of disintegration?

In almost every office or institution we can see the fanatical housekeeper's counterparts: the spinster secretary who literally gives her life to her boss because she has no other satisfactions in life; the boss himself, who has become addicted to his work as an anodyne spirit against the pain of living; the elevator operator who jumps off the skyscraper where he has worked for forty years when faced with retirement.

Every child is born with a spark of creativity. It is the capacity to delight in what his elders scarcely notice: a butterfly, a seashell, or a snowflake; the joy of building castles in wet sand or just day-dreaming. But he is soon taught to scorn such mundane things; by the age of twelve or thirteen he is already beginning to hanker after the expensive pleasures which are the reward of "getting ahead."

During the course of this long struggle he loses his capacity to enjoy himself. He feels that he is just drifting. He does not see that because he has no goals in living except the empty ones of status and security. So he drugs himself with still more work and sometimes alcohol, too.

As Selye remarks, the inspired artist or scientist never grows up in this respect; "he does not tend to get the feeling of aimlessly drifting no matter how old or poor he may be. He retains the childlike ability to enjoy the impractical by-products of his activity. . . .

". . . the most acquisitive person is so busy reinvesting that he never learns how to cash in. 'Realistic' people who pursue 'practical' aims are rarely as realistic and practical, in the long run of life, as the dreamers who pursue only their dreams."

Most of us need to aspire, to create, to give, and to belong. It is not necessary that all our yearnings be realized, only that they find some mode of expression.

In fact, it is always important to remember that coming too close to any ideal, however noble it may appear from a distance, is likely to be a disheartening experience. In contrast with other nations and other times, the social achievements of the United States, Switzerland, Sweden, Denmark, and parts of the British Commonwealth are truly wondrous. The dreams of the nineteenth-century reformers have been largely realized. Did any of the kindly Fabians ever suspect that their vision of efficient humanitarianism could lead straight to 1984?

Social planning is indispensable in a crowded world, but if our society is to remain viable, our planning must recognize our nonmaterial needs more than it has; and it must offer us worthwhile goals without exalting one at the expense of others. Security cannot make up for the loss of adventure; comfort for the lack of hard, creative work; nor togetherness for the lack of true companionship.

Even health, in the sense of freedom from any demonstrable disease, is not worth having if it means abstaining from all that makes life worthwhile. One might as well be dead. Indeed, we all have noticed that the individual preoccupied with the preservation of his body as anxiously as a medieval Christian with his soul often seems to be only technically alive.

Hippocrates observed that disease involves not only *pathes* (suffering) but also *penes* (toil or struggle). He believed that illness represented the struggle of the body to adapt to sudden changes in the environment. In his writings, he warned repeatedly against the danger of sudden violent change—in climate, season, diet or mode of life.

The concept of illness as a struggle to adapt has persisted, reappearing in various guises such as the defensive neurosis theory of Freud and the fight-or-flight reaction theory of the famous physiologist Walter Cannon.

As a medical student in Prague, Hans Selye first noticed what he has since called "the syndrome of just being sick." Patients with all kinds of infectious diseases had, at the onset, virtually the same symptoms: diffuse aches and pains, coated tongue, intestinal upset, and loss of appetite. They often had fever, mental confusion and an enlarged spleen or liver, inflamed tonsils, a skin rash. Yet Selye's professors dismissed these as "nonspecific and of no use in diagnosis." The young physician was directed to wait for a specific sign—the swollen parotid glands of mumps, the muscle paralysis of polio, the jaundice of hepatitis—before making his diagnosis. Even today, few would disagree with the Prague professors; yet in these nonspecific symptoms lay the key to a new concept of health and disease.

This did not occur to Selye until years later—after the failure of his work with ovarian hormones, which I have already referred to; as he sat in his laboratory, brooding, he wondered why it was that whether he injected rats with hormones or with formalin (a laboratory fixing agent) the response was the same: their adrenal glands became enlarged, the thymus and lymph tissues shrank, the stomach and intestines developed bleeding

ulcers. Selye subsequently "insulted" his rats with a wide variety of factors, such as cold, heat, dunking in water; he found that they always responded the same way. He found, too, that the intensity of the insult was directly related to the intensity of the response. For the first time, it occurred to him that stress might be a measurable entity rather than a vague abstraction.

From this beginning, he elaborated his theory of a General Adaptation Syndrome, activated by stress and susceptible to getting out of order. The mediating substances are hormones: it is hormones which mobilize blood sugar, overload the liver, stimulate the pituitary to oversecrete ACTH (the adrenal-stimulating hormone), alter the lining of the blood vessels, excite the stomach to produce acid, and so on.

All stress has the same general effect: It provokes the same general defensive response in the body; a response which, if the system is working properly, tends to stabilize the internal milieu and to preserve life.

But ringing the alarm too often overstrains the system and causes a breakdown. Response may be too small or too large, too soon or too late.

And always when Selye examined his stress-killed rats he found the same triad of effects: the swollen, drained adrenals; the shrunken lymphatic tissue; the gastrointestinal ulcers.

Thus has Selye reaffirmed the view of Hippocrates that illness is a loss of harmony between man and his environment; that it is the whole man who is sick and not just his mind, his heart, or his stomach.

Because he held this view, the great French physiologist Claude Bernard was skeptical of Pasteur's germ theory of disease. Bernard did not doubt that germs played a role in infectious diseases or that the destruction of germs might aid recovery. But he denied that illness is simply the result of the germs being present. "The stability of the internal milieu is an essential condition of a free life," said Bernard. The "internal milieu" is the whole man—his endocrine glands; his digestive apparatus; his heart and blood vessels and their contents, the blood; his skeleton and muscles; his mind and emotions.

In his book *The Mirage of Health*, René Dubos suggests that Pasteur's successful demonstration of the existence of microbial disease in plants, animals, and men, reinforced by the contemporary triumphs of antibiotics, has narrowed the comprehensive Hippocratic view of disease. Illness is seen as the direct effect of a known cause. Tubercle bacilli cause tuberculosis, spirochetes cause syphilis, pneumococci cause pneumonia, and so on. Medicine is thereby led after a mirage: the belief that if one just looks long enough and skillfully enough, one can find the cause of every disease and eliminate it. Men will then be healthy from birth to death.

Dubos believes that every disease arises as a result of a multiplicity of environmental circumstances.

Pasteur himself took Bernard's reservation about the germ theory quite seriously. His work with serums and vaccines showed that he appreciated the importance of the internal equilibrium. And on his deathbed, he told a friend: "Bernard is right. The germ is nothing; it is the soil which is everything."

During the Victorian era, when tuberculosis was rampant, physicians observed that it was especially frequent in young women who had suffered an emotional shock; a disappointment in love, for example. Most of us have had the experience of coming down with a severe infection of some kind after a period of prolonged strain. Just a change in drinking water can produce considerable disturbance, as most tourists sooner or later discover.

Among the stress-activated diseases are the coronary, the ulcer, the irritable colon, the erratic blood pressure, the migraine headache, a great deal of mental illness, and of course Selye's syndrome of "just being sick" which every doctor knows may *never* become specific enough to receive a diagnostic label.

"It still remains to be shown," says Selye, "to what extent maladaptation participates in each individual disease, since it seems to play a part in all of them, but a decisive part in only some. Another task for future research will be to show how far man can improve upon nature's own adaptive reactions. . . .

". . . work has progressed far enough along these lines for us to say that, like all the reactions of the human body, those concerned with adaptation are not always perfect and at least some of the resulting diseases of adaptation can be corrected . . . by the administration of hormones, the removal of endocrine glands, or by treatment with drugs which suppress endocrine activity."

Stress is essentially the rate of wear and tear caused by living. We cannot escape stress nor should we wish to, for only death can relieve us of all stress.

Selye maintains, however, that self-knowledge, aided by an understanding of what has been learned so far about stress, can help us to reduce the amount of pointless, damaging stress in our lives.

There is, for example, the state of mind in which one says: "I'm so tired. I don't know whether to take a nembutal and go to bed or a benzedrine and go to a party."

When we feel like this, according to Selye, it is because we have become intoxicated with our own stress hormones: "I venture to say that this kind of drunkenness has caused more harm to society than the other kind.

"We are on guard against external intoxicants, but . . . it takes more wisdom to recognize and overcome the foe who fights from within. In all our actions throughout the day we must consciously look for signs of being keyed up too much—and we must learn to stop in time. To watch our critical stress-level is just as important as to watch our critical quota of cocktails. More so. Intoxication by stress is sometimes unavoidable and usually insidious. You can quit alcohol and even if you do take some, at least you can count the glasses; but it is impossible to avoid stress as long as you live and your conscious thoughts cannot gauge its alarm-signals accurately. Curiously, the pituitary is a much better judge of stress than the intellect."

Paul Dudley White, the famed cardiologist, takes a dim view of tranquillizers as an antidote to stress, except as a temporary aid in getting through a serious crisis. The best antidotes to stress, he believes, are physical exercise, music, art, literature, and the cultivation of courage, patience, and optimism.

When stress does not overwhelm, when the organism rises to its challenge, health and creativity may result. The stomach ulcers of Dutch businessmen were observed to heal under the stress of German occupation, but when peace returned, so did their ulcers. We have all noted the gratifying response which can be elicited by a sharp blow when a radio won't work or a child won't behave. It seems to shake the recipient out of its groove. How is it that electric shocks, fever, bloodletting, flogging, and many other kinds of severe stress can sometimes, instead of constituting the *coup de grâce* we might expect them to, actually rouse the dying and open the withdrawn mind?

Conceivably, continued research may provide sufficient insight into the mechanism of stress so that physicians will be able to determine the correct amount of hormone required to treat every disorder. Yet how much better, Selye suggests, for man to learn to live in greater harmony—with himself and with the world:

to live in accordance with his craving for adventure, for variety, for noble ends.

The evolution of life has involved a gradual increase in intercellular altruism. The choice between egotism and altruism does not arise between the cells of a single multicellular organism except perhaps in the case of cancer; even the dense tissue of bone melts under the pressure of an invading blood vessel which brings it nourishment. It took countless generations to evolve the art of peaceful interdependence to avoid internal stress. The next step, to interpersonal altruism, is obviously far from being consummated.

But Selye believes that egotism, the most essential property of life, can be harmoniously reconciled with altruism and expressed in what he calls a philosophy of gratitude.

"Gratitude is the awakening in another person of the wish that I should prosper, because of what I have done for him. It is the most characteristically human way of assuring security (homeostasis) . . . each person can strive to inspire gratitude in others according to his own talents. . . . Neither wealth, nor force, nor any other instrument of power can ever be more reliable in assuring our security and peace of mind than that knowledge of having inspired gratitude in a great many people."

The essays of Teilhard de Chardin, in a somewhat more mystical vein, advance a parallel line of thought. Scientists from all nations, working together in research, were the beginning, as he saw it, of a more complex and altruistic social organism:

"Stronger than every obstacle and counterargument is the instinct which tells us that, to be faithful to life, we must *know;* we must know more and more and still more; we must tirelessly and unceasingly search for Something, we know not what, which will appear in the end to those who have penetrated to the very heart of reality."

Whether or not our common desire to know is strong enough to unite us on a higher plane of existence, there is no question that "not knowing," the feeling of being "in ignorance" can be stressful indeed. It can lead to rejection and prejudice as the racial strife in our country.

But ignorance can be a spur to learning; small children are burning to know everything; and it is wonderful to contemplate how much they do learn in their first five years: table manners, modes of dress and address, the pecking order in the household, the role of male and female, and so on.

Later the insecurity of ignorance gets us through our schooling and launches us into adult living; we learn to be husbands, wives, parents, voters, citizens; members of a sports team, a union, a board of directors.

Stress impels us to learn and, in learning, we resolve the stress, rising to a higher level of competence and a temporary plateau of equilibrium.

An infant coping with the meaningless influx of sound and light becomes very anxious and filled with rage unless he is periodically soothed and reassured. Yet, bit by bit, he masters his world and brings order out of chaos.

In the absence of stress or the capacity to respond to it, we say that a child is retarded. Retardation is found not only in children with organic defects, but in those who have spent their infancy in institutions where they were not only unloved but were deprived of all the beneficial stress of household turmoil.

Small, periodic doses of ionizing radiation, insufficient to alter fertility, appear to lengthen the life-span of rats and mice. This has been accounted for as a possible beneficial effect of stress: the occasional challenge mobilizes the internal communications—hormonal and chemical —that bind a mere collection of organs into an organism, just as urban communications turn a group of neighborhoods into a city. We may ask ourselves if the city or the nation would come apart in the absence of stress, that is, social problems.

While a baby quickly learns to cope with *too much* sensory input, a normal, sane adult is less able to cope with *too little* sensory input.

Men put into artificial states of sensory deprivation—floating in tepid water in dark silent tanks—soon show signs of psychosis, of hallucinations and unreasoning fears. One might suppose that such a "return to the womb" would be entirely stress-free but it turns out instead to be a kind of hell.

There is a similar kind of hell in the systematic removal of challenge and decision making from so many phases of our lives: "Automation and dial-watching," says Dubos, "eliminate the hardships of physical effort, but monotonous environments and mechanical operations have their own deleterious effects on the human brain . . . the efficiency of production is producing the pathology of boredom."

Surely it is boredom and a sense of futility which leads so many young people to seek "psychedelic" experiences in the growing number of cults centering around the use of hallucinogenic drugs. Too sophisticated to embrace a traditional faith, but not strong enough to live without one, students and suburbanites are creating a new religion to satisfy their needs.

It is boredom and a yearning for adventure which animate those who join the Peace Corps or go to Mississippi. It is boredom and despair which animate the students who foment campus rebellions.

SPEAK TO THE WORLD AND TELL THEM THAT YOU WANT TO LIVE! says a pamphlet written by a dissident university student. He perceives himself to be a rat on a treadmill. He is desperate and will do anything to get off.

Like Dostoevski's gentleman in *Notes from the Underground*, this young student is prepared to defy the whole social order, not because it is evil, not because he is a criminal, but because it is the only way left for him to assert his will.

"Well, gentlemen, what about giving all this common sense a mighty kick . . . simply to send all these logarithms to the devil so that we may again live according to our foolish will? . . . Man only exists to prove to himself that he is a man and not an organ-stop! He will prove it even if it means physical suffering, even if it means turning his back on civilization."

What are we to do about all these bright young people who do not want to be punched and fed into the system, besides sending them to Mississippi?

Some of our long-range thinkers would like to prevent this kind of problem from arising in the future by imitating the insect societies—that is, by breeding specialized types of men and women to fit their various roles in just the numbers required to keep the system going.

Specialists in space medicine, for example, hope to develop an "optiman," radiation-proof, with spare parts, and capable of thinking much faster and with greater precision than conventional man.

Man could evolve into a robot, highly resistant to stress, concedes René Dubos, but only at the cost of cherished human values. Yet there are psychologists and geneticists who seem bent on creating a world which will be as tidy, as thrifty, and as exhilarating as an anthill.

Isn't this passion for order the same madness which grips the perfect housekeeper? Or the dictator who sends both unfit and misfit to the gas chamber?

The antidote for too much reason is unreason; for too much order, disorder. Reason has lifted us beyond the impulsive life of animals; willfulness can save us from the compulsive life of robots. Reason strives toward a static equilib-

rium; willfulness ensures that it will not succeed.

This willfulness, which is so distressing to rational, orderly beings, is also the source of creative energy. It is well known that intelligence alone is no guarantee of creativity. Dreams and the determination to make them come true are the hallmarks of genius.

"Life," said Henri Bergson, "is a stone thrown uphill against the downward rush of matter."

"Creativity," speculates Frank Barron, "may be a stone thrown uphill against the downward rush of habit."

There are men of genius, like Shakespeare and Bach, whose enormous output of masterpieces proclaims their makers' essential harmony, both inward and outward. They were born at the right time and place; they did not have to struggle to have their work accepted; whatever conflicts they had, they resolved without the appearance of strain.

Yet they are not typical. Conflict within and without are the usual concomitants of genius. Beethoven, Michelangelo, Tolstoy, Van Gogh, Darwin, and Florence Nightingale are but a few examples.

It is worth noting, too, how often men and women of genius are tormented by illness, both physical and mental. Ill-health is not infrequently the reason for exchanging an active life for an introspective and creative one, as was the case with Robert Louis Stevenson. Illness may even enhance creative power. Stevenson observed that he wrote better when consumed by fever than when his tuberculosis was quiescent. Many other artists who suffered from tuberculosis noticed the same effect.

There are obvious relationships between some kinds of mental derangement and adaptive hormones, though the precise mechanisms are not understood.

Patients on steroid therapy often develop a sense of extraordinary well-being and buoyancy, with excitement and insomnia; this is sometimes followed by a depression and even, occasionally, suicidal tendencies. In a patient with hereditary predisposition to psychosis, serious derangement may result, though it is usually reversible by withdrawal of the hormone.

Dr. Peter Forsham, of San Francisco, witnessed a most unusual response to adrenocorticotrophic hormone a few years ago when he was treating a young woman for dermatomyositis (an inflammation of the skin and muscles). She had taken piano lessons as a child, but had not acquired any great proficiency. While taking large doses of ACTH, however, she suddenly found herself able to play the most difficult works of Beethoven and Chopin, to the great delight of all the children in her neighborhood, who gathered in her garden to hear her play. Unfortunately, she also became somewhat psychotic, and her dosage of ACTH had to be lowered. With each ten-unit reduction in dosage, one sonata disappeared; and in the end she reverted to her former unaccomplished state.

Certain breakdown products of adrenalin can cause hallucinations. It may be that excessive adrenalin secretion during stress plays a part in causing mental changes such as the delirium of fever.

Aldous Huxley suggested in his book *Heaven and Hell* that the heightened perception which leads to mystical or creative insight can arise in several ways; from fasting, from fever, from hallucinogenic drugs, and from the debilitating effects of prolonged illness. All of these are forms of stress which may be manifested by the same response, regardless of the stressor.

In view of all this, it is hard to think of health as an absolute good; and if it is only a mirage as Dubos maintains, then what are we to think?

The World Health Organization has defined health as "a state of complete mental, physical, and social well-being, and not merely the absence of infirmity." In other words, health is an ideal, like liberty or justice, something to be strived for but never wholly attained. For we live in a world of ceaseless change, accelerated by man's uneasy hegemony, where the very conquest of one disease sows the seeds of another.

It might be more fruitful to think of health and disease as the opposing principles of a polarity between which man seems fated to swing in eternal disequilibrium.

But the kind of health we desire is not necessarily a matter of physical vigor, longevity, or even a sense of well-being. It is—and here Selye and Dubos agree perfectly—a condition best suited for reaching the goals which each individual formulates for himself. These goals are apt to have little to do with biological necessity; they are often in direct conflict with what we suppose to be biologically useful.

"Work is more important than life," Katherine Mansfield wrote a few days before she died of tuberculosis. She, too, was trying to define health: "By health, I mean the power to live a full, adult, breathing life in close contact with what I love—the earth and the wonders thereof —the sea—the sun. . . . I want to be all that I am capable of becoming, so that I may be—there's only one phrase that will do—a child of the sun."

Men who are busy and successful in dealing with the world as it is are not likely to dream of the world as it might be. Therefore it is among the sickly, the weak, and the alienated members of society that we find the creative impulse most active; though, to be sure, most of the "unfit" and "misfit" individuals fail, either because they are overwhelmed by stress or because they lack creative resources.

Many studies of creativity have been undertaken in the hope of finding some method of latching on to a muse. Such knowledge might enable us to channel the energies of juvenile delinquents and campus rebels more constructively. So far the muses have remained as elusive as the bluebird of happiness.

As we have seen, conflict and stress are far from inimical to creativity; and every culture necessarily seeks to imprint its pattern on the growing mind. Yet we need the possibility of escaping this pattern from time to time. Even small children should be thrown on their own resources now and then. Just as we have set aside areas of wilderness as sacred, not to be used for any practical end, we need to set aside holidays in the original sense of the word, which will not be desecrated by the clamor, the trivia, and the "pathological togetherness" which make our leisure such a rat race.

The enthusiasm for wilderness trips and mountain climbing is, of course, one way of recovering some of the values we have lost: solitude, self-reliance, challenge, adventure, and genuine friendship, tested by adversity and danger.

For many, however, the "therapy of the green leaf" must be confined to a small garden or perhaps only a few potted plants.

But whether we struggle against pain and sickness or the dark nights of the mind; whether we eat the magic mushroom or fight our way to an icy mountaintop; or whether we wander, lonely in the crowd, through the asphalt jungle, we are turning inward, as finally we must, to the springs of being.

We have plundered the primeval garden which Jefferson cherished with so much hope. Even the high meadows and peaks are growing crowded, but the garden of the mind, where the spirit grows, which Jefferson also cherished, has only begun to be cultivated. The mind

. . . creates, transcending these,
Far other worlds and other seas;
Annihilating all that's made
To a green thought in a green shade.

REFLECTIONS ON THE MAN-NATURE THEME AS A SUBJECT FOR STUDY

Clarence J. Glacken

1

Wisely or not, most of my scholarly life has been spent in exploring the extraordinary history of the man-and-nature theme. Recently, after completing a long work on this subject from classical times to the end of the eighteenth century in Western thought, I came to two conclusions: first, that it is exceedingly difficult to say anything new or fresh about it; and second, that it has the characteristic of the college education which a young graduate defined as learning that everything is related to everything else. Let me elaborate a bit on these conclusions. Even if it is difficult to say anything new, such is the dispersion of ideas (an ancient characteristic of this theme), that any diligent collector may bring in specimens unknown to another. I am talking about ideas; I do not deny the importance of accumulating new facts. And if we accept the leadership of the perceptive college graduate, it is a simple truth that the theme of man's attitude toward nature (I prefer this broader term to "land") has in the present and has had in the past so many ramifications that they can produce despair even among its most unflinching students. It is closely bound up with mythology and religion; the relationship can be clearly established for all the great religions and for the conceptions of many primitive peoples as well. It has been intimately associated with Christian theol-

ogy for many reasons; if I were to single out one for special mention it is the close relationship among God, man, and nature and the consequent strong emphasis placed on the idea of creation which binds the three together. The theme's importance in the history of biology whether based on the teleological view of nature and the idea of design, the Darwinian web of life, or the most recent concept of the ecosystem is so obvious that the point need not be labored. Geographical writings from ancient times to the present (except the purely astronomical, mathematical, or physical portions of the old geography texts) are saturated with it. In art history its force and importance are seen most clearly in the history of landscape painting: Salvator Rosa, Claude Lorrain, Nicolas Poussin, John Constable of Europe, Thomas Cole and Asher Durand of the United States embody more often than not—and self-consciously—interpretations of man's attitude toward nature. Ruskin's chapters in *Modern Painters* on the pathetic fallacy and the novelty of landscape show how close this kind of art has been to the history of ideas concerning man's feeling for nature.[1] It is even easier to make a case for literature and poetry, if we content ourselves only with illustrations from the modern period. How many thousands of words have been written about Rous-

[1] Ruskin, 1873, vol. 3, pp. 149–314.

seau's *Julie ou la Nouvelle Héloïse* and the interchange of letters between Saint Preux and Julie at the castle at the foot of the Alps! And what of Chateaubriand, whose writings are filled with descriptions of nature and his reactions to it? Later, Wordsworth praised the freshness of Thomson's *The Seasons,* and Keble saw a succession of stages in the history of poetry—Homer and Pindar being characteristic of the heroic age; Aeschylus of the power of high philosophy; and Lucretius and Virgil, concerned with the things of nature and the culture of plowed fields in an age betaking itself to "the quiet haven . . . of Nature and the pleasant countryside."[2] In the history of economic thought, the theme, if less lyrically expressed, is still prominent: there are the Physiocrats and Smith, then Malthus, Carey, Marshall, and many other nineteenth-century thinkers, to say nothing of resource economics today. I have not exhausted the ramifications: These are only samples, but I give them because they are bearers of lessons. They ask the question: What is involved in such a body of thought? It is this question that I wish to try answering, not with hope of success but with some self-conscious reaching beyond my grasp.

2

Few subjects in intellectual history have greater fascination, not only because of the individual ideas themselves but because they are the visible parts of the iceberg. The theme of man and nature is meaningless without seeing it as a problem in the history of thought. Consider, for example, the ideas, frequently expressed in contemporary writings, that man is a destroyer of the balance of nature, that population growth obliterates

[2] See Daniel Mornet's introduction to his edition of Rousseau, 1925, vol. 1, pp. 67–75; Keble, 1912. Quotation in Wordsworth, 1944, vol. 2, pp. 419–21.

beauty and destroys the land, that there is evocative power in the landscape, that urbanization is a force in the nature-protection movement, that social mobility, recreation, and tourism are related to the wilderness in ways which require further exploration. Such ideas are based on values or assumed values, many of which have a long history; they are the visible parts. There is a corollary to this proposition. It is legitimate to pluck this theme out of contemporary or past thought and to discuss it, but it must be understood that this action is a tearing out of live tissue from a body of thought which is often formless and disorganized. Its historians give it the order which their educations think it should have. When one discusses attitudes of man toward nature, it is not a matter of taking them out of slots or grooves of either the past or the present. I suppose this is all self-evident, but discussions can acquire a disembodied quality, the theme often seeming too independent, too divorced from the pulls and tensions of contemporary life. Such a method also leads to compilations of examples resembling the entries under "nature" in a dictionary of quotations. The question of attitudes is part of more fundamental bodies of thought: the history of attitudes toward life, concepts of its dignity, of the natural order, and of the nature of man. From broader and deeper meditations on these themes we derive substance for more specific inquiries. The contemporary concerns in the United States, whether for wilderness preservation, for saving the redwoods, or for opposing certain freeways are illustrations, even if vaguely defined and held, of a broader philosophy toward life, whether it be human or plant and animal life and the surroundings in which they all flourish. Of necessity, this thought is rooted in anthropocentrism, a term, alas, too often used pejoratively. I do not know if there is a history of anthropocentrism; we certainly need it: in its crude forms, beginning in the ancient world and continuing with the early church fathers, the oceans were created for trade, the moon for marking the passage of time, but in its more sophisticated manifestations lay the question of the value and dignity which human existence and attention confer on nature. Historically, attitudes toward nature have been closely related to anthropocentrism and to the idea of a hierarchy in nature which itself has been devised by humans to find a place for themselves and all other phenomena.

The problem of man's attitudes toward nature is also a qualitative one; I do not say this with polemical intent, for it is clear that today there are growing commitments to quantification and quantitative methods in many kinds of research. The understanding and the richness, color, and vividness—all come from the detail. It is like studying the etiology of disease, the area in which the disease is found, the ways in which it is transmitted, the hosts, the symbiotic relationships, the range of carriers and the nature of their habitats, being the guide posts for bounding the problem. The detail required can also be likened to that needed in understanding an ecosystem. The main reason for this qualitative requirement is that polarities are involved extending from the culturally determined to the physically determined. It is not much help, for example, to know that favored remedies in a folk pharmacopoeia might lead to the extinction of certain animals, but it tells us a lot about the general and specific nature of the problem to learn about substances valued as aphrodisiacs in the traditional cultures of China, India, and Southeast Asia, to study in further detail the reasons for the supposed efficacy of rhinoceros horn and then to relate the trade in the horn over the centuries to the past and present distribution and the threatened extinction of the animal. Plant and animal extinction as a cultural phe-

nomenon is tied in with detail—desire for lifelong sexual virility, medicine, trade, animal habitats, and the effective physical environment. In speaking about qualitative study I do not, of course, advocate an either/or dichotomy, but I do say that understanding will often come from description, from a synthesis which provides the links between sexual virility and the animal habitat and which may have only minor methodological significance, perhaps not even enough to pass university promotion committees.

Let me pursue this matter a bit further. In the eighteenth century, there was an intense interest in natural history (a side overshadowed by emphasis on philosophy, political, and social history); one need only mention the names of Pluche, Buffon, Pallas, Linnaeus, Tournefort, Bernardin de Saint-Pierre, and Banks. There were many reasons for this which we need not go into here, but one of them is pertinent to this discussion. Many men were dissatisfied with the knowledge of nature and natural laws which mathematics (and especially geometry) had yielded. The philosophy of nature of Descartes, for example, was too removed from reality, from the nature as observed by travelers in all parts of the world. Where in Descartes were the fragrances, stinks, blossoms, colors? Nature was too rich, too luxurious, too complex to be understood by mathematical deduction from first principles. Paul Hazard also has pointed to the contrast between the geometrizing of the seventeenth century and the interest in natural history in the eighteenth.[3] In studying natural history or in learning about it, men felt they were really learning something. The results of Cartesian deduction, once the premises were understood, had no surprises; they were like exercises. Although it would be incorrect to draw a parallel between this eighteenth-

[3] Hazard, 1954, p. 130.

century situation and that of the present, it nevertheless is a kind of problem that recurs in different forms and at different times. One discipline's meat is another's poison. High generalization and quantification in one subject may lead away from understanding to banality. At whatever period in which we look for interpretations of man-nature relationships we are confronted with mixtures which might include poetry, economics, and soil science. We readily enough admit myth, attitudes toward plants and animals, toward nature spirits in the study of nonliterate peoples. The nonquantitative aspects are equally important in complex societies.

In his analysis of existentialism, Wild, contrasting the classical ethics of Plato and Aristotle with the modern, says that "modern ethical theory is abstract and weak in phenomenological content. Little is said of moral habits as they are expressed in the concrete, and I know of no important modern treatise in which friendship is carefully discussed." Such shortcomings left opportunities for existentialist philosophers willing to grapple with the problems presented by behavior of human beings in the everyday world. Yet it is precisely this everyday kind of behavior that ethics should concern itself with in order to bridge the gap between the ethics of the philosophers and the everyday behavior of human beings. "Scientific theories of perception," he adds, "have popularized the notion that only the measurable, quantitative data of science have any objective status, and that all the secondary qualities, such as color and sound, must be disregarded as private phenomena. More and more realms of concrete data had thus been discredited and removed from the field of what is regarded as worthy of serious study." Or again, "The vastly rich and variegated fields of concrete experience are, as a friend once put it, *sloppy data,* too confused with one another and with biased interpretation to warrant careful investi-

gation. As a result of these tendencies, philosophers in the modern tradition gradually lost the habit of careful observation and description. This distrust of the concrete has penetrated very deeply into our scientific tradition, and has actually influenced our common sense, which is often willing, at least momentarily, to grant an epistemological priority to the elaborate inferences and constructions of some science when these conflict with immediate data."[4] It seems to me that the man-nature theme has certain affinities with these illustrations from ethics and the presuppositions of science; man-nature study has an enforced concrete and describable earthiness about it which resists a severe divorcement from detail and diversity. The continued development of quantification may well envelop vast fields of the social sciences, but the nonquantitative, normative, concrete, descriptive aspects will also increase in importance. The development of the resources of northwest China may employ a continually improving technology but it may also rest on survivals of traditional Chinese thought, and on Marxian teleology little changed from the nineteenth century. In this world, there are many aphrodisiacs which are associated with many rhinos. For centuries hence parts of California water law may still show the effects of the water law of Muslim Spain.

3

One of the knottiest problems in the literature on attitudes toward nature is that of representativeness. There are, for example, in this country strong literary traditions of urban castigation and of the value of communing with nature. The Whites have written about the history of American attitudes toward the city, but neither they nor their readers confuse the ideas of Thoreau, James, or Muir with

[4] Wild, 1959 (1955), pp. 23, 14.

those held by other thinkers or by the mass of the people. Several important writers of the nineteenth century glorified the rural, the frontier, and denigrated the American city or allowed it to suffer in comparison with the European city. But how representative were they?[5] There was much laughter in the Middle Ages, a fact not easily learned from the voluminous writings of the Church Fathers. When that resolute compiler of voyages, Samuel Purchas, wrote that the earth was decaying, losing the powers it had in its youth, we incredulously come to our senses and realize he was speaking of the Elizabethan Age.[6] I am groping toward a commonplace, that it is difficult in this field to isolate the ideas that have been enduring and influential. Excellence in articulation cannot be confused with unanimity of opinion.

In the beginning, much of American thought on the man-nature theme was derivative; this borrowing was to be expected whether the sources were in technical writings on agriculture, in poetry, or in landscape painting. An indigenous literature came into being when it became apparent that European knowledge, sentiment, and opinion were the products of an old civilization, of long settlement, of environments extensively modified by Europeans; the ideas required changing in an environment whose contrasts were much sharper. Circumstances in the history of the United States have been favorable to the rapid accumulation of a body of literature on attitudes toward nature; to document this would require a book,[7] but I might point out some major influences. First, there was the swiftness and massiveness of environmental change; slightly more than a century separates the observations of Chateaubriand that the forests through which he walked

and the clearings he saw had been untouched since the creation (*"aussi vieilles que le monde"*)[8] from the Governors' Conference on the conservation of natural resources called by President Roosevelt and held in the White House, May 13–15, 1908. Secondly, there was a strong association of scenery with wilderness, the forest, and other retreats to a nature untouched by man, compared with the European rural landscape, much changed by man and where natural scenery often had close associations with monuments, ruins, historical events. Indeed, one climbed the Alban Hills to see the natural beauty, but one could reflect there also on the tragic history of Rome. This kind of scenery of association was plentiful in Europe, almost entirely lacking in the United States.

In his "Essay on American Scenery" (1836), Thomas Cole said the most impressive thing about it is its wildness; an untouched nature affects the mind of man more than anything man has made, and the contrast with Europe here is striking. He defended American scenery for its "want of associations," meaning that European scenery often was suffused with human history. American scenery lacked this characteristic but to Cole the lack was also a strength.[9] Thirdly, it was seen very early that the outdoors was a laboratory of nature, unlike anything in changed Europe, for men of science who could study land unchanged (so they thought, aside from the activities of the Indians) since the creation.

The experience of the United States, however, is unique only in the sense that all such histories are unique; they differ from country to country and from period to period. They are unique because literatures on the man-nature theme accumulate around immensely divergent and contrasting situations, alike because they

---

[5] White, 1962; see also White, 1961.
[6] Purchas, 1614, p. 43.
[7] See Huth, 1957; Ekirch, 1963; Krutch, 1950, especially the prologue.

[8] Chateaubriand, 1828, p. 148.
[9] Cole, 1836, especially pp. 11–12.

often partake of traditions broader than the national ones. Today we are seeing before our eyes extremely important developments in the newly emerging countries of Africa where the man-nature theme emerges from tribal law, age-old practices such as burning and swidden, attitudes toward colonialism and colonial powers and their relation to international interest in preserving the rich African fauna and flora. This unfolding is different from the telescoping in time of American experience; the emergence of the African nations (whose culture is of primordial age) is occurring during an era of growing world population, unprecedented strains on natural resources, racial conflict, and of widespread alarm over the threatened destruction of some of the world's finest nature reserves. It is the contemporary example *par excellence* of the need for nonquantitative analysis: new assemblages of knowledge are needed; the world's physical and cultural patterns have always been incredibly complex; the accelerating interdigitations and blendings have added to the complexity and blurred it, and we are forced to paint what we see with broad and often faltering strokes. Elton has wisely remarked that in rich countries the attitude that the diversity of life on earth should be preserved for posterity is not uncommon, "but finds much less favour in those where making a living at all comes first."[10] One might add that it is easier in countries where such aspirations originated in their own independent past than in those countries where certain aspects of conservation and nature protection might be seen, however mistakenly, as lingering illustrations of colonial self-serving.

Attitudes toward nature throughout the world tend to be concrete; often they are composed of readily recognizable elements. I have already compared them with disease and ecosystems, and there can be no harm in saying that they resemble land-tenure systems in their variety and in their dependence on historical and political precedents, whether of law or custom, on ideas of the religious and the supernatural, on philosophical and esthetic conceptions. It is often difficult to detach the two; they seem to be part of the same cloth. A plentiful harvest could come from such a study (the economic and political aspects and consequences of land-tenure systems have been most studied and remarked upon for obvious reasons) whether it be the *ayllu* of the pre-Incas, the *mashà'a* of the Middle East, or American attitudes toward private property in land.[11] Since this Conference is concerned with North American habitats, I would like to discuss the problem of attitudes toward the land in complex modern societies. The concept of culture, as developed by the anthropologists over the last eighty-odd years, as I understand it at least, seems to assume a certain homogeneity in attitudes held by a given people, even with wide individual divergences and even though the existence of subcultures is recognized. This is implied in terms like "American," "German," or "Japanese" culture. Admittedly the concept of modal personality in culture is intractable. Are we justified in assuming any homogeneity at all? The man born in a slum who now has the wherewithal to live in a suburban development far more comfortable than the home of his immigrant parents may be quite different from the critic who sees in this development a dreary creation devoid of imagination or beauty. Cosmic values of nature are not involved; individual attitudes toward economic well-being are. It is easy to study attitudes toward nature and the land among writers, artists, college professors, and other

10 Elton, 1958, pp. 144–45.

11 See the many examples discussed in Parsons, 1956.

articulate groups, but are we justified in thinking of a generally held philosophy in complex cultures? Or is there merely a group of loosely held and perhaps contradictory notions (with unexamined presuppositions) resembling the platform of a major American political party? Does not a lot of planning occur which is innocent of any grounding in philosophy, esthetics, or the history of ideas? There are nonbooks; maybe there are nonphilosophies. It would be easy to write a history of American attitudes toward nature as seen through the eyes of Bryant, Thoreau, Marsh, Muir, Leopold, Bennett, and others, but what a one-sided history it would be!

In this country the history of legislation might be a sensitive indicator, but the problem is complicated by the constitutional provisions concerning federal and state power and as further defined by the Tenth Amendment. From this point of view the legislative history of an act of Congress may be even more important than the legislation itself. A study of the history and background of the Wilderness Act might be most rewarding.[12] In studying such legislation, one need not be concerned with its subsequent enforcement; the hearings, the legislative history, the law which follows, are the embodiment of existing attitudes whether or not compliance with them is secured. I first became aware of this indicator many years ago when I read the famous French Forest Ordinance of 1669,[13] prepared at the instigation of Colbert and approved by Louis XIV. Many lessons can be learned from it: the force of custom, attitudes toward trees, economic and social conflicts in a society, perhaps not

complex economically by modern standards but whose social fabric certainly was enormously complex. Whether the ordinance was enforced well or not is unimportant (it enjoyed an indifferent success), but one can clearly see the life of the forest, the valuable trees, the problems caused by careless shepherds, by poaching, by the brutality of prescribed punishment, the role of hammer marks on the trees to establish ownership and the consequent close guardianship of the hammers, the duties of the warden, the regulation of habitation within certain distances of the royal forest, and many other characteristics which show historically how complex the subject of man's attitude toward the land has been. The complexity is not a modern phenomenon; possibly in the past when land use and ownership were much more affected by custom and the sacred, relationships were even more complex, as indeed they still are in many peasant cultures today.

4

Since the war several developments have intensified interest in environmental questions; this interest is only natural in view of the widespread study of soil erosion, air and water pollution, effects of insecticides, the growth of city and regional planning, tourism, road building, and many other indications either of continuations or accelerations in environmental changes. An accompanying leitmotif (reminiscent of Élisée Reclus[14] and other critics of nineteenth-century industrial landscapes) has been that the combination of population growth and technological advance leads to environmental deterioration. Partly as a consequence of this realization, the period has also been marked by more subtle probings into the nature of the environment. There have been rumblings in landscape

[12] See, for example, Outdoor Recreation Resources Review Commission Report 3, 1962, Wilderness and Recreation–A Report on Resources, Values, and Problems, especially Chap. 1, "Wilderness Concepts."
[13] *French Forest Ordinance of 1669* (1883).

[14] Reclus, 1873, p. 523.

architecture, tourism has posed questions, there has been a greatly increased interest in plant and animal extinction. More recondite but symptomatic of closer attention to the nature of the physical environment have been renewed interest in the symbolism of environment by men as divergent in background as Scully, Shepard, and Eliade, and in environmental perception, in the role of scenery and landscape in evoking feeling and imagery, subjects which have interested men since the times of Rousseau, Chateaubriand, Georg Forster, Alexander von Humboldt, Henry Buckle, and William Wordsworth.[15]

The most striking development of the postwar period in generating revised attitudes toward the environment, however, has been the questions raised by the city, by urbanism as an idea, because the large city, the urban agglomeration, megalopolis, whatever we choose to call them, have become vast physical and social environments in their own right, dominant habitats for extremely large numbers of people. A new phase in the settlement history of the human race is occurring; the urban life of today, at least in this country, is quite distinct even from that of the very recent past. Cannot those who in their youth drove a Model T remember that a city of thirty or forty thousand may have had only a dozen

[15] In my opinion, the outstanding source in the United States of contemporary ideas concerned with environment, men's reactions to it, and the way in which it is perceived (with examples from many different fields) is *Landscape*, a magazine edited by J. B. Jackson in Santa Fe, New Mexico. Neither the articles nor the often arresting quotations are intended to be exhaustive, but over the years the riches have accumulated astonishingly.

Among the many articles and some books concerned with these questions the following may be mentioned; all of them will generate new leads into different fields; Eliade, 1961 (1959), especially Chaps. 1, 3; Heyman, 1964; Lowenthal, 1961; Lynch, 1960; Schafer, 1962; Scully, 1962; Shepard, 1961; Sopher, 1964.

traffic signals? The fact that a book on American landscapes including cities can be called *God's Own Junkyard*, the existence of freeways and air pollution, intensified study of neighborhoods, slums, and subcultures within the city raise the question (despite the existence of large cities in the past) whether such unique and massive milieus can in fact be understood. Contemporary interpretation, however, is only a small part of this preoccupation with the city. There is also world-wide interest in its functions, its role as a creative force in human history. The city's relation to the countryside optimistically interpreted by Gottman, critically by Lewis Mumford, is part of this inconclusive quest. The postwar period has been noteworthy as well for the persistence shown in the search for urban origins[16] and for comparative studies of urbanism, the origins question especially being bound up with concepts of continuity and the processes of civilization. Mumford, for example, has insisted that the modern city cannot be understood without understanding its origins.[17] Researches on urban origins, the literature on cities of orthogenetic and heterogenetic change, the study of the distinctive characteristics of cities produced by different world cultures, are further indications of the search for understanding the nature of urban environments, partly to see if they exhibit any discernible order. For if large numbers of men live in cities throughout the world, what are we confronted with in the habitats they create: order of a high degree, some order, minimum order, or none at all? They represent some order; otherwise they would not be habitable. Such searching seems to me indistinguishable from the quest for understanding the nature of modern life and the conditions under which it is lived. Attitudes toward the city and attitudes

[16] For example, see Kraeling, 1960.
[17] *The City in History*, 1961, especially Chaps. 1, 18.

generated within it are intimately bound up with attitudes toward the village, the countryside, the wilderness. Much of the literature on attitudes toward nature and to rural life has been written by men of the city, even if they were unsympathetic to it. The literature on urbanism thus cannot be divorced from that on the wilderness and nature protection; they have been closely associated in the past, perhaps negatively, because civilization has often been regarded as a control, conquering and obliterating nature. Now they must be associated in a more positive way because ideas and attitudes will largely be engendered out of conditions imposed by urban life. In much of the nature literature of the past, the city has been identified with the artificial, the opposite of a communion with nature; it has symbolized wickedness, clamor, sweat, gregariousness, or combinations of these. But such simple dichotomies will no longer do. Without advocating any determinism, it may be said that interpretations of the nature of the city are one key to understanding what is involved in our time in the study and rational use of all environments. It will continue to play an important role in the future because the main outlines of the world's population distribution probably will remain fairly stable. The great cores of population density which have developed in the recent centuries (very little is known of the early history of population distribution) will maintain themselves and new densities may appear. All over the world, to a greater or lesser degree, urbanism will have a great deal to do with attitudes toward nature, for in the cities are the offices of the automobile associations, the camera shops, and the window displays of the Audubon Society. It is for such reasons, too, if I may labor the point, that I would emphasize the nonquantitative aspects of these problems.

5

If one grants that the city and the attitudes it engenders will increasingly, and in a less negative way than in the past, influence attitudes toward nature, are there nevertheless certain enduring ideas which will exert their force in any new blend? I think there are, and I would like to comment on a few of them.

First, there is the question of anthropocentrism. On the basis of everyday observation, there is justification in the history of thought for man regarding himself as being at the apex of the creation, for the belief that he is God's vicar on earth. Such attitudes have not been confined to the religions like Christianity which make a clear distinction between human and other forms of life; even those religions like the Indian, which have not made such strong contrasts have recognized the superior endowments of man. And have not vast amounts of the time of each generation been spent on studying the behavior of man? What are history, the social sciences, philosophy, religion, and theoretical physics in the service of competing nationalisms but anthropocentric preoccupations? Such preoccupations, however, need not produce unimaginative and excessively utilitarian anthropocentrism. It was seen long ago that even if man to all appearances is at the apex of creation, it does not follow that all things were created in order to satisfy his wants; the earth with its plant and animal life might well have its own rationale, transcending its highest living form. In early Christian thought it was constantly pointed out that men must not be misled by their ignorance of the phenomena of nature into believing that because of their seeming irrelevance to human needs they have no purpose, or that because other life forms are lower in the hierarchy than is man that they have no purpose other than to serve the next higher forms. And even such a devoted adherent of teleological explanation as Aristotle rejected the idea that the end purpose of one form was to serve another. The deer has its own τέλος; it was not made for the lion. Cosmic humility was taught long before the Copernican revolution is alleged to have made man conscious of his insignificance: It is one of the teachings of Boethius' *The Consolation of Philosophy*.[18] Christian thinkers have been indefatigable in urging humility upon the human race not only as a matter of personal conduct but because man's place in the hierarchy of nature carries obligations among which is an awareness that this place is not of his making, that no credit accrues to him because of it, that it is an expression of the creative act of God. So we need not be worried that anthropocentrism, either now or historically, will necessarily be identified with smug utilitarianism. It is also hospitable to broader ideas.

The values which we find in nature and our attitude to it are human values which emerge from the immense variety of human situations. Ruskin was overly harsh on the pathetic fallacy while recognizing its historical importance; it may have been a crutch for melodramatic and less creative minds: But in exaggerated and distorted form it pointed to an area of thought of importance. Men bestow their feelings and their sentiments on nature; they give it human value when the cosmic value is unknown. In his criticism of the pathetic fallacy's shortcomings as creative and imaginative art, Ruskin was correct; it surely is easier to talk about angry winds, or surly dark overhanging clouds, than it is to find strong, fresh verbs to describe air movement and cloud formation. Even Milton saw nature grieving at the fall of man: "Skie lowr'd and muttering Thunder,

som sad drops/ Wept at compleating of the mortal sin." (*Paradise Lost*, IX 1002–3) And yet with its melodrama flamboyance, false imaginativeness, does not the pathetic fallacy send out signals worth looking into? Meaning is read into nature and its forces, even if we know that nature does not take sides, that it is neutral. Quoting the lines "They rowed her in across the rolling foam—/ The cruel, crawling foam," from Alton Locke, Ruskin said that the foam "is no cruel, neither does it crawl. The state of mind which attributes to these characters of a living creature is one in which the reason is unhinged by grief. All violent feelings have the same effect." The falseness which they produce in all our impressions of external things Ruskin characterized as the pathetic fallacy.[19] One can agree with Ruskin, but is this not a way of saying that human beings have normative attitudes toward life, the environment which supports it, is supported by it, and interacts with it? Today I think, one can see these truths with greater clarity than in the past when the idea of design in nature was dominant and it was much easier to find man's place in it, or when there was greater faith in secular teleologies, such as the idea of progress, or belief that evolution in the long-term view inevitably led to higher and higher forms. Human inventiveness has called a halt to such comforts. The mere fact that human power has reached such heights inevitably places more emphasis on human values and the weight of human decisions; easy correlations between the progress of civilization and the progress of knowledge are hard to come by. If men now have it in their power to destroy life and inanimate nature, then there are possibilities of an earth existing without man, or existing with a much reduced potential for modification of man. In the postobliterative pe-

18 *The Consolation of Philosophy*, 1962, Book 2, Prose 7.

19 Ruskin, p. 160.

riod who then would give significance to nature, ecosystems, life cycles, trophic chains?

The second enduring—perhaps ecumenical—idea is a body of thought which has clustered around the phrase "communion with nature." Often it is related to anthropocentrism and the pathetic fallacy. Serious men still speak of a sphinxlike nature who will only yield her secrets to the beguiling inquirer who will seek her out; the personifications of nature, often made for literary effect, reveal the force of such metaphors. The idea is expressed in the great religions. We know this to be a highly subjective experience; yet we know such exaltation is common. The views, prospects, scenes described in the prose and poetry of many peoples bear witness to its universality. I believe it to be religious in origin, to be related to the idea that we find in the creation itself evidences of the creator, but its modern forms are also secular. A typical expression is that communion with nature incites our minds to reflection and discovery. It has been said of Wordsworth, for example, that most often "his perceptions of spiritual realities are reached strictly through excited response to natural scenery." It was not that Wordsworth thought of himself as a poet of nature, "but that his coming to what he believed to be truth about human life was a process which cannot be separated out from his perception of natural scenery; so that the scene beheld becomes an image of spiritual reality hitherto unknown to him."[20] Similar sentiments were frequently expressed in the eighteenth century by Rousseau, Goethe, Georg Forster, coming to their finest fruition in the writings of Alexander von Humboldt. Both the religious and secular expressions are associated with the belief that in the solitudes of nature are to be found authentic manifestations of the life-giving

forces, that knowledge, emotional reinforcement, and inspiration (whether it be exaltation or incentive toward creative activity) come from that special kind of solitude found in the presence of nature. There are hundreds of examples of this in the literature of the eighteenth and nineteenth centuries; today it is frequently expressed in written commentaries accompanying collections of photographs of natural scenery. This idea has been important in the history of American attitudes toward nature. One of the most charming and authentic examples known to me is Asher Durand's painting "Kindred Spirits."[21] William Cullen Bryant and the painter Thomas Cole are shown gazing at the Catskill Gorges in the forest along the Hudson. As they stand on the ledge looking at the beautiful panorama, it is obvious what lesson is being taught: not only are the two men kindred spirits, but they are also one with the beauty, harmony, order, and life force surrounding them. Discovery of the beauties of landscape, understanding the elements of which it was composed, could not be attained until one felt deeply and strongly at one with the whole. Often certain corollaries were added to this: first, that the city, an artifact, could offer no such opportunities; even many rural areas had been too well raked. No, the essential environment was that which was farthest removed from man and his influence. Many American nature writings echo Cole's advice: Why go abroad when the virgin charms of our native land with its "want of association" have claims on our deepest affections? The concept of nature as wilderness has been an enduring influence on American attitudes toward the land—largely because it is a well-remembered relict environment. The wilderness was not pushed back to Merovingian or Carolingian times; it was described in Cooper's

[20] James, 1948, p. 75.

[21] A color photograph is beautifully reproduced in Eliot (1957), p. 213.

The Prairie. Another characteristic of the concept of nature as wilderness is that the nature untouched by man and through which one wanders softly without so much as breaking a twig, this kind of nature has sometimes figuratively, sometimes literally, been regarded as a simulacrum of nature at the creation. There is the assumption of order and harmony in a God-created nature, which are lost in part with the interferences of human beings. Considering the long history of this idea in Western civilization it is no surprise that one recent German work on nature reserves throughout the world was entitled *So wie am ersten Schöpfungstag,* another on the same subject, *Der Letzte Garten Eden.*[22] Clearly these authors did not wish to be taken literally, but the dramatic allusion would be lost on few. Many of our art books and collections of photographs of places famous for their natural beauty suggest the same thought, and advocates of wilderness protection often speak of a primordial order and beauty which must be preserved. To me, the nature-protection movement (far more so than the broader areas of conservation, resource economics, and population study) is a sensitive indicator of enduring attitudes. There is a great attraction to what appears to be fresh, untouched, pristine. How widespread such attitudes are today it is very difficult to say because there is so much blurring. How much is merely lip service paid to them? Often they are stimulated and conditioned by tourism, by desire to retreat from city life, by photography, camping, amateur nature study, sports.

The third enduring attitude is one which emphasizes the beauty, variety, and complexity of nature. The role of complexity in maintaining the stability of the ecosystem has been increasingly discussed from a scientific point of view by such students as Elton, Bates, and Fosberg.[23] Here a modern scientific concept has met an older religious, philosophic, and esthetic one. Ever since I read Lovejoy's discussion of the "principle of plenitude," I have been impressed with its importance in the history of natural history. Lovejoy, it will be remembered, says that there is either expressed or implied in Plato's *Timaeus* the idea that a beneficent deity, creating without meanness or stinginess, made all possible things; neither was he niggardly in creating variety, acting in Lovejoy's words according to the old saying that it takes all kinds to make a world.[24] Without going further into its history, it may be argued that complexity and variety of nature, especially in areas remote from human interferences, could evoke ideas of biotic assemblages, interrelationships, and harmonies, which are anticipations of the idea of a stable ecosystem, even though the scientific reasons now given for this stability naturally are not those of the older conceptions. Modern ecological ideas thus meet older ideas of the beauty of luxuriance, that there is full representation in nature of all possible phenomena, that variety of life form is an indispensable characteristic of the creation. Such ideas fortify, in both scientific and esthetic dress, beliefs (which are widespread in the world today) that it is unworthy of humanity to allow plant and animal extinctions, even though large-scale extinctions of plants and animals happened repeatedly in the geological history of the earth and before the coming of man. But within the span of human history the idea has wide appeal because it is closely linked with a similar desire to preserve historical monuments, primitive peoples, and environments of

[22] Born, 1961; Strohmeyer, 1958.

[23] Bates, 1961, p. 201; Elton, pp. 143–53, 155; Fosberg, 1963, pp. 1–6.
[24] *The Great Chain of Being: A Study of the History of an Idea,* 1948. (The William James Lectures delivered in 1933.) See index under "plenitude."

the past from extinction. The Italians set aside a typical *maquis* landscape in Tuscany, the French the famous ornithological reserve of the Camargue, the USSR landscapes typical of the Caucasus, and the magnificent sand dunes of Kara Kum. The nature-protection movement derives great strength from such ideas: it is not only the beauty that is to be preserved (by common standards an environment being protected may not be beautiful) but the variety also and the continuities with the past. Judging by the contemporary interest of many nations in nature protection and in the preservation of their historical monuments, it is fair to say that these attitudes may even transcend national pride, though today this is a powerful force.

I now wish to turn to the posterity argument. It too is closely related to anthropocentrism, communion with nature, and the idea of plenitude in nature. The posterity argument is so self-evident that I hesitate even to bring it up. When applied to the natural environment, the argument means that the living should regard their rights to renewable resources as usufructuary ones, and should hold themselves responsible for the preservation of natural beauty. In a broader sense it becomes a plea against setting irreversible trends in motion, against obliterating areas of beauty, or plants and animals which either are rare or are threatened with extinction. It is one of the most common and pervasive arguments in the literature of conservation. Examples of it are published every day.

"Every inch of unspoiled shoreline, every acre of open space will vanish; California will become a besmogged asphalt nightmare; and our descendants will look back with horror and rage at our ignorance and rapacity, our destruction of a heritage that should have been theirs."[25]

Although I am sympathetic with every

[25] Gilliam, 1964, p. 29.

one of these words, I wonder if such eventualities will occur. The argument assumes that our descendants will be as conscious, or more so, of beauty as are we. Perhaps, however, the vast majority will neither know nor care, and this "looking back with horror and rage" will be in the writings of historians with a limited audience. The posterity argument often assumes a self-consciousness pervading the whole society which one may very seriously doubt is in fact there. Of all the attitudes toward the natural environment, it has, however, I believe the most powerful appeal, if only for the reason that it is easily understood. It may be compared with the family system of traditional China which is like a chain linking the past, the present, and the future. The contemporary generation venerates the past but it is not all backward looking; it uses what it can and what it is entitled to during its temporary possession of material and nonmaterial treasures, and then passes on the inheritance, whether it be household furnishings, rice fields, or the good family name. The posterity argument is a way of forcing the past and the future to participate in the present, whether the case is being made for historical monuments, primitive peoples, or nature-protected areas. Civilization becomes a palimpsest; it cannot exist without mosaiclike qualities and historical depth. The posterity argument is thus meant for and most applicable to the generation which advances it; there is no assurance posterity will have the same values.

6

No one who has traveled in recent years or who has read and observed travel literature can have failed to observe the close connection between ideas of preservation (whether the old quarter of a city or natural scenery) and tourism. Tourism is old; tours were enjoyed by the

Greeks and Romans, but the tourism which has grown up since the end of World War II is a phenomenon of a different order. Many think it vulgar, thin, and unappetizing. Anyone who has seen fifty tourists crowding out of a chartered bus to take pictures of the same village dance or the same stained-glass window and then clambering back in the bus to the next church, crèche, or castle has a feeling for the disembodied nature of much of tourism. It seems to be the world of the museum, the travel office, the church, and the ruin. Nevertheless, it is a powerful force; perhaps it can also be a constructive one, even contributing to a minimum world agreement on the protection of nature which will be much more effective than exhortation and castigation. It is true that much of it is like stamp collecting; minarets, village brides, gates, changings of the guard are important only to the degree that they become subjects for slides. However, one cannot ignore wealth, mobility, and color photography in measuring attitudes toward land in the world today and especially in the United States. This triad produces more than color slides of French church windows, German castles, and Venetian street scenes; it produces slides by the million of fjords, geysers, canyons, and wildflowers. Although this is not the place to embark on such a venture, it is a simple fact that in modern Western culture there has been a close relationship between tourism and the history of attitudes toward nature. The English noblemen who traveled to Italy on the Grand Tour came back with the ideas of Salvatore Rosa and Claude Lorrain with striking effects on the English garden—and the English landscape. The sentiment for nature in the late seventeenth and eighteenth centuries is inseparable from the widening knowledge of scenery that came from travel. But it was not always one way. How many of the trips to Switzerland were made as pilgrimages to the scenes of *La Nouvelle*

Héloïse, to Vevey, Clarens, to relive the life of Julie and Saint Preux? Tourism needs study in relation to nature protection and preservation of the past. It will have to include the range from ideas and attitudes to studies of trampling effects. The influence of tourism might be conservative enough to challenge economic and practical interests, those who prefer a dam to the canyon, filled land for apartments to present bay shores.

Although the size and continuing growth of the world's population is the greatest single stimulus to environmental change, even with stable populations the desires and yearnings for a better life will continue because of the world's crushing poverty. Under these circumstances, the present world landscapes will change vastly; such changes are continuations, for the landscapes of China and the Mediterranean shore have experienced them for millennia; and people of small densely inhabited countries like Denmark realize that there are literally few spots left that have not been transformed. These historic processes of landscape change will no doubt continue and probably at an accelerating rate. Cosmopolitan tourism and nature-protection movements under these conditions might well be a brake on remorseless destruction of beauty.

A few words should be said about attitudes toward nature involved in the belief that certain environments should be protected in order to preserve them for scientific study and research. This belief is one of the cornerstones of national and international nature-protection movements. It is a relatively modern movement which has been helped and justified by modern ecology. The more that ecosystems are understood, the greater becomes the interest in such environments; even though it is apparent that because they are open systems they are inevitably affected by what happens outside them. It has been helped also by the sharp rise in awareness of the nature and extent of human modifications of the land. The assumption underlying this kind of nature protection (the scientific enclave) is similar to that of an enlightened tourism: the creative value of preserving the past. It has a wide appeal because the method of science is probably the closest approach we have in the world to ecumenical thinking; where the principles of ecology are understood, the need or justification of the enclaves is self-evident. In addition to the powerful scientific support, the scientific enclave also obviously benefits greatly from the posterity argument.

7

I hope I have not shamelessly neglected my responsibility to write on man's attitudes toward the land by talking, not so much about them, but about the problem of studying their nature. One of the great dangers in studying the literatures (with many Circes for each Odysseus) is the temptation toward monolithic summation. Let me give three examples. One often reads that Christianity has been contemptuous of life and nature on earth because it is concerned with eschatology and the City of God, that in consequence there is little love or affection, only tolerance, for earthly life and its environments. Or, conversely, one is instructed that the religion has encouraged the love of nature because its central theme is that the creation is the work of a beneficent God and what we see about us is evidence of it. Both points of view, for which ample evidence can be marshaled, ignore the fact that the question is of enormous complexity, both as to time and subject matter. The first interpretation, for example, would have to go very lightly over many of St. Augustine's writings, over St. Francis of Assisi's, or St. Thomas's thought. The second would also have to include St. Augustine. Equally oversimplified is the notion that Western thought has been characterized by a dichotomy of man and nature. Much

convincing evidence is at hand if properly selected to demonstrate this, but it would have to ignore large bodies of thought which have emphasized the unity of nature with man as a part of it, whether he is in the divine hierarchy, the great chain of being, the web of life, or the ecosystem. The history of American opinions toward nature is another enticing quicksand. The subject is too broad, too involved with science, philosophy and theology, governmental policy, to be tied to any specific body of thought such as, for example, the conservation movement.

The greatest opportunities might well lie with the posterity argument because implicit in it is a respect for the continuity and preservation of life and environment, an attitude essential to any nature conservancy. Schweitzer, who was much concerned with respect for life (*Ehrfurcht vor dem Leben*), said that the problem of ethics has been narrowly construed, the great fault of all systems of ethics being that they deal only with the relation of man to man. In his work on ethics, he wrote that beyond the need for food, ethical men should refrain from picking twigs and leaves, killing insects, and the like,[26] certainly an extreme view in Western thought. He would deny to humans what is done by wind, lightning, or by a dog bouncing through a weed patch, apparently not because life is saved, but because of the great human need to respect life for the sake of man's own well-being. One merit of Schweitzer's statement is that it calls attention to the inconclusiveness and uncertainties in attitudes toward nonhuman life, even granting the existence throughout the world of a large body of religious belief, custom, and law relating to the hunt, pet keeping, the abattoir, and vivisection. Attitudes toward plants have been much vaguer. It is hard tó imagine a harvest as a slaughter, but some writers have writ-

[26] *Kultur und Ethik,* 1948 (1923), Chap. 21, especially p. 240.

ten passionately not only of the destruction of human life in wars, but of the merciless slaughter of animals and the obliteration of planted fields. The redwoods, the rare flowers, and the flora threatened with extinction, however, call attention to this problem. There is also the ethical problem, as Darling points out,[27] of controlling population in wildlife sanctuaries.

Concepts of the food chain, population dynamics, range, and carrying capacity are generalizations which summarize the natural processes by which life comes into being and is taken away. Viewed as part of the cosmic order, we do not know why these processes and not others should exist; if we wish, we can accept the explanation that they are the results of evolution in which nature has been neutral, life and death being indispensable to its functioning. In this light, human attitudes are

[27] See Darling, 1964, pp. 6–7, for a sensitive appreciation of this ethical area. "We are faced with an ethical problem as well as the scientific and technical one, and it would be cowardly to ignore it and deceive ourselves by holding inflexibly to the idea of sanctuary. We cannot be Jains stooping and peering before each step lest we crush worm or beetle, because we know our feet must crush smaller life than our eyes can see, yet we should be ready to admit that animals exist in their own right and not by our permission."

aberrant and selective; they show a respect for life which apparently is irrelevant in nature as a whole. Respect for all life is subsumed in the dignity of human life. Since we lack both knowledge and agreement about the purpose of the creation, attitudes are attempts to give meaning to the world of nature in which men find themselves, paralleling similar attempts to find meaning in the social world.

Man has grown more aware of these questions since 1945. The general quality of the literature (despite some mawkishness, self-centeredness, and misanthropy) relating to nature protection that has appeared since the war has been high, whether it has concerned African flora or fauna or American canyons. Attitudes toward the land must ultimately be based on attitudes toward life; there are no bare and inanimate hills, seashores, or deserts. If human power has now made possible the destruction of much of life, it has also created a situation in which new perspectives toward the earth and its inhabitants are forced upon us. One of my lasting memories of *The Gallic Wars,* read when I was in high school, is that Caesar was always *in medias res.* I have never reread him to discover whether in fact this was the case, but like him we are moving into the heart of the matter.

BIBLIOGRAPHY

Bates, Marston. 1961. The Forest and the Sea. New York.

Boethius. 1962. The Consolation of Philosophy. Indianapolis and New York.

Born, Franz. 1961. So wie am ersten Schöpfungstag; die letzten Naturparadiese der Erde. Nürnberg.

Chateaubriand, Le vicomte de. 1828. Travels in America and Italy, vol 1. London.

Cole, Thomas. 1836. Essay on American Scenery, Amer. Monthly Mag. 7:1–12.

Darling, F. Fraser. 1964. Wild-life Conservation. The Ethical and Technical Problems. New York.

Ekirch, Arthur, Jr. 1963. Man and Nature in America. New York and London.

Eliade, Mircea. 1961. The Sacred and the Profane. The Nature of Religion. New York and Evanston, Ill.

Eliot, Alexander. 1957. Three Hundred Years of American Painting. New York.

Elton, Charles S. 1958. The Ecology of Invasions by Animals and Plants. London and New York.

Fosberg, F. R. 1963. The Island Ecosystem. In: Man's Place in the Island Ecosystem: 1–6. Honolulu.

French Forest Ordinance of 1669. 1883. Edinburgh and London.

Gilliam, Harold. 1964. The Lesson of Bodega. This World, San Francisco Chronicle (Nov. 22).

Hazard, Paul. 1954. European Thought in the Eighteenth Century from Montesquieu to Lessing. London.

Heyman, Mark. 1964. Space and Behavior. A Selected Bibliography. Landscape (Spring): 4–10. Santa Fe, N.M.

Huth, Hans. 1957. Nature and the American. Berkeley.

James, D. G. 1948. The Romantic Comedy. Oxford.

Keble, John. 1912. Lectures on Poetry, 1832–1841, vol. 2, Lectures 30–33. Oxford.

Kraeling, Carl H. and Adams, Robert M., eds. 1960. City Invincible. Chicago.

Krutch, Joseph Wood, ed. 1950. Great American Nature Writing. Sloane, New York.

Lovejoy, A. O. The Great Chain of Being: A Study of the History of an Idea. 1948. Cambridge, Mass.

Lowenthal, David. 1961. Geography, Experience, and Imagination: Towards a Geographical Epistemology. Annals of the Association of American Geographers, vol. 51:241–60.

Lynch, Kevin. 1960. The Image of the City. Cambridge, Mass.

Mumford, Lewis. 1961. The City in History. Harcourt, Brace, New York.

Outdoor Recreation Res. Rev. Com. Rep. 3. 1962. Wilderness and Recreation—A Report on Resources, Values and Problems. Wash., D.C.

Parsons, Kenneth, et al. eds. 1956. Land Tenure (Proceedings of the International Conference on Land Tenure and Related Problems in World Agriculture, Madison 1951). Madison, Wisc.

Purchas, Samuel. 1614. Pvrchas his Pilgrimage. London.

Reclus, Élisée. 1873. The Ocean, Atmosphere and Life. New York.

Rousseau, Jean-Jacques. 1761. La Nouvelle Héloïse, Paris (1925, ed. by Daniel Mornet).

Ruskin, John. 1873. Modern Painters, vol. 3.

Schafer, Edward H. 1962. The Conservation of Nature Under the T'ang Dynasty. J. Econ. and Soc. Hist. of the Orient, vol. 5, pt. 3:279–308.

Schweitzer, Albert. 1923. Kultur und Ethik (7th ed., München, 1948), chap. 21.

Scully, Vincent. 1962. The Earth, the Temple, and the Gods. Greek Sacred Architecture. New Haven and London.

Shepard, Paul, Jr. 1961. The Cross Valley Syndrome. Landscape (Spring): 4–8.

Sopher, David. 1964. Landscapes and Seasons. Landscape (Spring): 14–19.

Strohmeyer, Curt. 1958. Der letzte Garten Eden; durch die Naturreservate der Welt. Berlin.

White, Morton and Lucia. 1961. The American Intellectual Versus the American City. Daedalus, (Winter): 166–79.

—————— 1962. The Intellectual versus the City, from Thomas Jefferson to Frank Lloyd Wright. Cambridge, Mass.

Wild, John. 1959 (1955). The Challenge of Existentialism. Bloomington, Ind.

Wordsworth, William. 1944. The Poetical Works, ed. by E. de Selincourt, vol. 2. Oxford.

POPULATION PATTERNS AND MOVEMENTS†

William Vogt*

What a piece of work is man! how noble in reason! how infinite in faculty! . . . In action how like an angel! in apprehension how like a god!

William Shakespeare

Man is Nature's sole mistake.

W. S. Gilbert

Twenty-five years ago demographers (who were often economists) were nearly unanimous in their concern about the falling birth rate of the industrialized countries. Thus Gunnar Myrdal, in 1938, wrote: "Today the problem is how to get a people to abstain from not reproducing itself." In 1944 an elite group of American demographers projected "reasonably expected" populations for the United

† Material for a few of the following paragraphs on conservation and population has been drawn from the author's chapter in Robert Theobald's The Guaranteed Income, 1965, Doubleday & Co., Garden City, N.Y., with permission of the publishers.

* Dr. Vogt, Secretary of the Conservation Foundation, has had an unusually varied career since his graduation from St. Stephens (now Bard) College in 1925. He has been Curator of the Jones Beach State Bird Sanctuary, an ecologist with the Peruvian Guano Administration, Chief of the Conservation Section of the Pan-American Union, and National Director (throughout the 1950s) of the Planned Parenthood Federation. In his Road to Survival, 1948 and People, 1960 he projected his concern over the consequences of an increasing world population. He received an honorary doctorate in science from Bard College in 1953.

Kingdom and Ireland that a mere sixteen years later were exceeded by 12 per cent; Belgium, 12 per cent; Holland, 15 per cent; France, 17 per cent; and Myrdal's Sweden, 22 per cent (League of Nations, 1944). Parson Malthus was dead, and if he wasn't quite buried, it was because his corpse offered a convenient peg on which to hang current demographic mythology. The industrialized and urbanizing countries, according to beliefs then widely current, would continue to reduce their birth rates until they were below replacement rates.

There is generally, today, much greater caution in making population projections and even the U.S. Bureau of the Census, which has fairly consistently erred on the low side, in its projection to only 1985 allows for a variation of over 11 per cent between its high and low figures.

Certainly a nondemographer should be even more reluctant to risk projections. Since, however, no factor, including a thermonuclear war, is as likely to influence the face of North America over the next few decades as much as changes in size and distribution of human populations, it is unavoidable, in speculating about the future of North American environments, to give consideration to numbers and distribution of the human animal. It is obvious, of course, that the longer the projection the more suspect it must be.

We have some rather startling examples of swift population agglutinations.

The "standard metropolitan area" of water-short Phoenix, Arizona, for example, grew by 100 per cent in the 1950–60 decade; San Jose, California, increased 121 per cent during the same period; Anaheim-Santa Ana-Garden Grove, California, by 226 per cent; and Fort Lauderdale-Hollywood, Florida, by a whopping 298 per cent. The spread of these "wens," as Cobbett so aptly named early nineteenth-century London, already threatens Grand Canyon and Everglades National Parks because of growing water demands.

There are few of us who have not had experience with comparable changes. Kennedy Airport destroyed one of the finest salt-marsh habitats in the Northeast. The seaside sparrow, known to few Americans but certainly biologically as interesting as the condor, about which conservation organizations have expressed much concern, has already lost a substantial proportion of its range to the spread of Megalopolis; thirty years ago its habitat had been scarcely touched. This is probably true of far more species than is generally recognized, especially if changes in the winter habitats of migrating birds are considered. Reservoirs, thought to be necessary to growing population agglomerations, have drowned valleys, invaded some national parks, and threatened others. Commercial developments, almost as inviolate as holy sanctuaries under the doctrine of economic progress, have spread thousands of miles of slums along both our Atlantic and Pacific coasts. Parking fields, highways, shopping centers, and other urban and suburban developments have been flowing over areas that have been estimated (in a Senate hearing) at a loss of 3 million acres per year. Much of this has been prime land and our population has not—as of this writing—reached 195 million.

During the 1964 election campaign President Johnson confidently used the figure of over 300 million by the year 2000, an increase of 300 to 350 per cent in a century. Donald Bogue (in Hauser, 1963, p. 76), using U. S. Bureau of Census projections, cites and projects populations of American women in the childbearing age, chiefly estimated from those already born.

Year	Number of Women 15–44 (*millions*)	Number of Women 20–29 (*millions*)
1930	29	11
1940	32	12
1950	34	12
1960	36	11
1970	43	15
1980	54	20
1990	70	22

"No matter what the birth rates are during the next two decades," he points out, "they will apply to a population of childbearers that will double between 1960 and 1990." The "high" Bureau of Census projection for the year 2000 is 362 million; in 2010, a mere forty-five years away, 487 million (Population Bulletin, 1964, p. 116).

Philip Hauser, of the University of Chicago, one of our most astute students of population, in 1960 stated: "The continuation of our present birth rate could, by 2050, produce a population of over 1 billion!" Elsewhere, in the same book, he points out that "The United States, with approximately the same population density as that of the world (56 persons per square mile as compared with 52 for the world) and with about the same rate of increase (1.7 to 1.8 per cent per year), is faced with the same outlook of a density of one person per square foot of land surface in less than 200 years." (Hauser, 1960, pp. 89, 87) This *reductio ad absurdum* does not, unhappily, relieve us of certain absurdities that characterize factors influencing human populations in the United States at the present time, and which will be commented on in due course. With the boys and girls of the postwar baby boom coming into the breeding ages at the rate of nearly four million a year there would seem to be little justification to expect the birth rate to continue its brief descent (since 1958) except on the basis of assumptions that so widely misled demographers of twenty years ago.

In the first five decades of our national history, even though we more than doubled our territory, population density increased at the rate of 5.3 persons per square mile; in the next five, by 17.7; and between 1910 and 1960, by 29.1. ("People per square mile" is an unfortunate and widely used statistical fiction that is rarely, if ever, significantly applicable to large areas.)

As striking as the rate of growth of our population is its marked and rapid redistribution (U. S. House of Representatives, Committee on the Judiciary . . . 1964, p. 4). Richard M. Scammon, in 1962 Director, Bureau of the Census, pointed out that "a tremendous predominance" of counties within "a line from the junction of the boundary of Canada, Montana, and North Dakota, due south to the neighborhood of Laredo, Texas; then across just perhaps eighty miles back from the Gulf across to the Atlantic, around Savannah, Georgia, and then back northwesterly to the beginning point," lost population. Despite the rapid national growth, half the counties of the United States lost population between 1950 and 1960.

This resulted in part from increasing mechanization of farms with fewer men required for a given unit of output, and —somewhat ironically—from the consolidation of small farms and a trend toward the *latifundismo,* or large land holdings, against which we are campaigning in Latin America. Mechanization has probably exaggerated the tendency toward clean farming and over increasing millions of acres reduced the amount of habitat suitable for wildlife. On the other hand, small farms that were not incorporated into the large units but which were, nevertheless, abandoned for economic reasons, have been going back to brush and at least temporary wildlife production.

Net county population increases for the decade ran as high as 226 per cent for Orange County, Florida, 199 per cent for Adams County, Colorado, and 371 per cent for Brevard County, Florida. A list of changes in the fifty states, during the 1950s, follows:

State	Rate
Alabama	+ 6.7
Alaska	+75.8
Arizona	+73.7
Arkansas	+ 6.5
California	+48.5
Colorado	+32.4
Connecticut	+26.3
Delaware	+40.3
District of Columbia	− 4.8
Florida	+78.7

Georgia	+14.5
Hawaii	+26.6
Idaho	+13.3
Illinois	+15.7
Indiana	+18.5
Iowa	+ 5.2
Kansas	+14.3
Kentucky	+ 3.2
Louisiana	+21.4
Maine	+ 6.1
Maryland	+32.3
Massachusetts	+ 9.8
Michigan	+22.8
Minnesota	+14.5
Mississippi	0
Missouri	+ 9.2
Montana	+14.2
Nebraska	+ 6.5
Nevada	+78.2
New Hampshire	+13.8
New Jersey	+25.5
New Mexico	+39.6
New York	+13.2
North Carolina	+12.2
North Dakota	+ 2.1
Ohio	+22.1
Oklahoma	+ 4.3
Oregon	+16.3
Pennsylvania	+ 7.8
Rhode Island	+ 8.5
South Carolina	+12.5
South Dakota	+ 4.3
Tennessee	+ 8.4
Texas	+24.2
Utah	+29.3
Vermont	+ 3.2
Virginia	+19.5
Washington	+19.9
West Virginia	− 7.2
Wisconsin	+15.1
Wyoming	+13.6

Needless to say, with these shifts in human populations went the trappings of American civilization, motorcars, houses, schools, streets and highways, sewerage systems, water supplies, etc. The last two items were often inadequately provided and are, in some areas, threatening to impose a check on population growth or even a redistribution. As an example, ground water and sewage have been getting thoroughly mixed in some rapidly growing parts of Suffolk County, New York, and some Hudson River towns have had to place at least a temporary limit on building, for sheer lack of water. (The Hudson itself, of course, is thoroughly polluted by towns and industries over most of its length as are, perhaps, the majority of American rivers.)

In the great expanse north of our border it is widely held that Canada is "underpopulated," with only five people per square mile, doubling in twenty-seven years. Most of these square miles, because of short frost-free periods and limited insolation, are of little use in capturing solar energy for direct use by man. "It has come as a shock to Canadians to learn that one year's drought in the Prairies (1961) coupled with above-average exports of wheat as a result of a famine in China, could almost deplete the nation's stockpiles of wheat. . . . Most of Canada's good soils are now under cultivation" (Krueger, 1963, p. 97).

Canadians have begun to recognize that with their own population increase and that of other parts of the world, there will be a need for heavy dependence on technological progress—which is, of course, a gamble—in the next three or four decades. Canada is already losing not a little of its most productive land to urban sprawl.

A rapid examination of reports on Canadian forest management leaves me with the impression that here, as in so much of the world, a substitution of symbols for reality is obscuring the processes that are actually taking place on millions of acres of land. Economists, administrators, industries, and even landowners act as though the availability and exchange of little pieces of paper somehow represented the extremely complex and dynamic processes that are taking place from the water table and A-horizons to the microclimate at the forest crown and the air above it, which is the habitat at once of predators and the spores of diseases that are distributed throughout the ecosystem. Because more pieces of paper can be accumulated faster if one ignores the bio-physico-chemical processes that are taking place within the four-dimensional structure of the great coniferous forests, watersheds are being denuded, wildlife habitat destroyed, fishing ruined, catastrophic ecological changes

accelerated, and production of the biomass—especially the biomass useful to man—is being reduced. By and large, techniques for measuring the amount and trends of biomass have been neglected. Why bother, when instead one can ignore the existence of biomass and substitute the somewhat shaky symbols that are so appropriately denominated "currency"? The symbol is not the thing—or the process—but national and even international policies are formulated as though they were identical.

Across the border, in the prematurely born State of Alaska, politicians and chambers of commerce are attempting massive reorganization of the landscape that will involve drowning thousands of square miles of productive land—productive, that is, of carbohydrates, proteins, and other sources of energy—in order that more pieces of green and white paper can be brought to Alaska in exchange for minerals (of uncertain availability) and trees that have been a century and a half in growing. Along with the minerals and trees go, of course, a highly complex and vital society of plants and animals without which the trees could never have achieved the development that makes them dominant in the landscape. Canada, with its get-rich-quick aspirations, cannot afford to find out what it is doing—to make sure it perpetuates whatever kind of biota it has not taken the trouble to find out if it wants. The United States, which has belatedly recognized its destruction of the productive capacity of Appalachia, is still apparently only beginning to learn from past experience; land-use and resource-management practices such as could have perpetuated the productivity of the eastern area are not being utilized in Alaska. The Americans seem no more willing than their Canadian neighbors to find out what they are really doing before making radical changes in a harsh environment that by its very existence is testimony to its fitness for the edaphic-climatic-biotic complex in which it has evolved.

Unless Canada and Alaska plot their future courses by scientific rather than commercial criteria, they seem likely to compound the mistakes of their forebears.

South of the United States, between the Rio Grande and the border of Colombia, a region often included as part of North America (see, for example, various publications of the United Nations), there are great diversities in population numbers, changes, and distribution. El Salvador with more than 300 people to the square mile, has the second highest density of the Hemisphere; Nicaragua, with twenty-five, the lowest for Central America. Taken as a whole, Central America has probably the highest increase rate of any part of the world, as is indicated by the appended projections based on recent growth rates. Because of the age distribution of the people of Mexico and Central America, with some 40 per cent under fifteen years of age, and their retarded socioeconomic development, it seems unlikely that anything short of revolution, malnutrition, and starvation (all of which are not improbable) or epidemics can much slow their rate of growth. (Mexico's population actually decreased by more than 5 per cent during her revolutionary decade.) If death rates continue to fall, it is not impossible that Mexico should have 100 million people by the end of the century.

One of the primary impacts of popula-

	1963	Per cent increase p.a. since 1958	Estimated Population 1970	1980	1990
Mexico	38,416,000	3.1	47,570,000	64,500,000	87,590,000
Guatemala	4,100,000	3.1	5,077,000	6,982,000	9,349,000
Honduras	2,100,000	3.0	2,587,000	3,479,000	4,675,000
El Salvador	2,700,000	3.6	3,458,000	4,953,000	7,016,000
Nicaragua	1,600,000	3.5	2,036,000	2,872,000	4,051,000
Costa Rica	1,300,000	4.4	1,702,000	2,142,000	4,158,000
Panama	1,177,000	3.3	1,444,000	2,054,000	2,684,000
TOTAL	51,393,000	3.4	63,874,000	86,982,000	119,523,000

tion growth on the Middle American environment has been a shortening of the period of fallow in the shifting agricultural system, with a consequent increasing rate of reduction of residual fertility in soils, increased erosion and laterization, spread of cultivation to ever steeper and more remote areas, disturbance—to an increasing degree, at a growing rate—of hydrologic cycles, faster runoff, disappearance of springs, siltation, etc. What the Mexicans call *desertificación*, which has turned well over 50,000 square miles (Salgado Perez, 1950, p. 17) of once productive land to sterile flood headwaters, by washing soil down to bricklike *tepetate* or hardpan, continues to accelerate.

Areas formerly protected by remote-ness or topography have, in large part through foreign-aid funds, been brought within the impact of the increasing numbers throughout many parts of Middle America.

Increases in gross national product have benefited only minorities—in Mexico, which has had perhaps the most equable distribution, estimated at about 35 per cent (Navarrete, 1960, p. 90)—but even small changes have affected population niches. A .22-caliber rifle and shells cost relatively little, and in lands where protein is short and the common view is that wildlife has no value except in the market, the pot, or the cage, opportunities to see such magnificent species as the quetzal have shrunk rapidly. Perhaps the ersatz economist, who is sure there is a substitute for everything, has a solution for this scarcity, but I have not yet encountered it.

It is not only possible but probable that species of economic value will be exterminated before the end of the century and virtually certain that not only species but entire communities of tremendous interest to science will also disappear since nothing effective is being done to preserve them. Between Colombia and the Rio Grande there are a number of so-called national parks, but most of them are neither maintained nor protected. They are invaded not only by hunters but by lumbermen and small farmers. "Wilderness areas," preserved as scientific resources or for esthetic reasons, are nonexistent with the sole exception of Barro Colorado Island in the Canal Zone. And at this writing the very future of the Canal Zone is in doubt politically, and therefore physically.

In part because even the modest prosperity resulting from economic development is of small benefit in rural areas, and because of population pressures that even slight reductions in the death rate bring about, the trend toward urbanization is nearly as rapid in Latin America as in the United States. Mexico City, which in 1940 had a population of one and a half million, now has over three million, with five million in the Mexico City metropolitan area. In the 1950s, Guadalajara grew 95 per cent; Ciudad Juarez, 111 per cent; Mexicali, 126 per cent; and Tijuana, 153 per cent (Population Bulletin, 1964, p. 187; *Compendio Estadístico*, México, 1960; James, 1942; *UN Demographic Yearbook*, 1963).

The environmental impact of urban growth is, of course, much smaller in the less developed country, because the human niche is so very different from that of the motorized society. The bed of Lake Texcoco, around Mexico City, is covered with tens of thousands of insanitary shacks, but the suburbs and exurbs are not overrun with motorcars. Forests have long since been cut for fuel but the earth —what is left of it—is not yet covered with concrete.

At this point, it is perhaps desirable to consider our semantics. "Man" or "people," as a taxon, gives little clue to what human populations can be expected to do to their environments, or what they have already done. The Baffin Island Eskimo has contributed nothing to nuclear poisoning of his habitat; this has been left to his "advanced" neighbors to the south.

Since we are concerned with ecological impacts of human populations, we need to think of man in relation to his niche, in relation to what he *does* rather than to what he "is."

For nonecologists in this meeting it should perhaps be pointed out that "niche" does not refer to a recess in which an organism can be isolated like a statue. The term, chosen by Charles Elton (1927, p. 64)—rather unfortunately from a semantic point of view—is defined by him as an animal's "place in the biotic environment, *its relations to food and enemies.*" Eugene Odum clarifies its meaning by saying that "habitat" is where an organism lives, its "address," and that its "niche" is what it does, its "profession" (Odum, 1963, p. 27). This is of primary importance in considering human populations. It leads us to an "operational" description of human populations, in Bridgman's sense (Bridgman, 1949, p. 5).

Economic man has been a misleading concept during many decades; for example, we have been solemnly assured, over and over again, that as his income rose his birth rate would fall, and that all we needed to do to stabilize populations was to increase the gross national product.

"Economic development eventually also slows down population growth, without consciously induced efforts in that direction" is a conventional statement of this view by a recent Roman Catholic writer (Zimmerman, 1961, p. 180). This, in terms of the human animal and its habitat, is essentially meaningless since "eventually" is given no time dimension and the birth rate is not related to the death rate, which, thus far, has been demonstrated to be much more amenable to change. Central American death rates have plunged 36 per cent in twenty years while birth rates have actually risen 2.5 per cent according to UN estimates. (That these estimates are approximations is generally conceded, but the degree of error is inconsequential in comparison with the birth rate-death rate disparity.)

It should be noted that population increases during the past twenty-five years have, in most backward countries, accompanied considerable increases in national income (*UN Statistical Yearbook,* 1961, p. 486). Canada and the United States have also substantially increased national incomes while in the latter country the birth rate, in 1957, stood 51 per cent over its Depression low (Bureau of the Census, Historical Statistics of the United States, 1789–1945. Washington, D.C. 1949, p. 46). Because of the paramount relationship of population change to environmental change it is important to recognize that there is not self-limiting control in economic growth. Indeed, unless our North American descendants of two or three generations hence are to be condemned to live in what most of us would consider a dreary wasteland, current population practices of the U.S. government, a combination of *laissez-faire* and pro-natalism, some of which are related to economic growth, should be critically scrutinized.

The niche of man, partly as a result of economic motivations and activities, has changed at an exponential rate that in many of his environments exceeds population growth rate.

When we know that of California's seventeen million population some nine million hold licenses to operate more than eight million automobiles whereas, in 1960, thirty-five million Mexicans had 808 thousand motor vehicles, we know more about the niche of the respective peoples than population or GNP figures alone could tell us. Mexico extends over 758,000 square miles. Los Angeles County, according to reports of the Surgeon General (cited in Herber, 1965, pp. 52–53) and the Los Angeles *Times,* had more than 2.1 cars per acre and its inhabitants "are walking about in nearly 9000 tons of carbon monoxide a day, 1180 tons of hydrocarbons, 330 tons of oxides of nitrogen, and a sizable tonnage of aldehydes, sulphur compounds, acids, ammonia, lead, and other poisonous substances." "[A]s much as 80 per cent of the pollutants in Los Angeles smog is produced by the city's three million privately owned motor vehicles." (Herber, 1965, p. 15) Few statistics convey the horror of our second largest city as does this one.

The automobile, as an extension of the human organism, is especially significant in the U.S. environment. It has become such an integral part of the human ecosystem that communities are developed on the assumption of its availability and it is, therefore, indispensable for food-gathering and distribution, for the movement of raw and processed materials, as an adjuvant of school systems, as a means of distribution of health services, and maintenance of such essential utilities as heat and water supplies, not to mention recreation. It has become an adjunct of reproduction and probably has had a significant effect on vital statistics since many of the 20 per cent of American women who are pregnant before marriage, and mothers of the approximately quarter million illegitimate children born annually, have undoubtedly been inseminated in automobiles, which play a major part in weakening social controls on sexual behavior. As well as being a tool, the automobile's manufacture is one of the most important single channels (or industries) through which, by labor, energy resources of wage earners move from the primary producer and primary consumer, to the consuming American. The motorcar is our status symbol *par excellence* and the maturing adolescent feels unsexed without one. When Dr. R. C. Peale expressed the opinion, as a physician, that "The best thing that could happen to the American people would be a chronic shortage of gasoline," he probably did not consider what a revolutionary statement he was making. The automobile has become such a part of man, in the United States, that it is difficult to be certain, at times, that man has not become part of the automobile. Indubitably, in the foreseeable future, the two must be regarded as inseparable, and this is certain to influence North American environments even more profoundly than it has yet done.

The automobile, a *sine qua non* of the suburbia and exurbia that are taking over so much land, is also a prime mover in the expansion of roads with their immediate modifications of land, and cover, not to mention their increases of accessibility by human masses. Many problems of national parks arise from the Park Service's policy of expanding hospitality for automobiles, much as city governments continue to make the lives of metropolitan dwellers more difficult by improving, in the central city, the habitat for the motorcar.

On the other hand, the automobile and tractor have virtually banished the horse and mule from the farm and thus released millions of acres of land once required for pasture and fodder. What will be the result of alternative uses of the land, especially under heavy machinery, may be as unpredictable as were, thirty-five years ago, the physiological effects of cigarette smoking.

The bulldozer, which can be regarded as a monstrous offspring of the motorcar, is more or less limited to an elite that cannot, perhaps, be fully comprehended in the absence of extensive psychoanalysis. Their obvious enjoyment in wrecking a landscape in advance of a real estate development, or devastating hillsides to make way for concrete ribbons, has accompanied the destruction of millions of acres of forest, understory, topsoil, swamps, and stream bottoms. It has not been characteristic of the human race to restrict power to those who would use it wisely, and the bulldozer has been no exception. The Washington rumor that Job Corps trainees are to be turned into bulldozer operators by the hundred thousands injects a new variable into the man-machine ecosystem that expands the problem potential.

The suggestion, by a colonial administrator, at UNESCO's 1949 Conference on the Conservation and Utilization of Resources, that no bulldozer should be permitted in Africa without a special license showed an awareness of the vulnerability of that continent that has scarcely begun to dawn on the minds of Americans in relation to their habitats; we have not looked often enough at our muddy streams.

The population of the flying man does not yet have an impact on the environment comparable to that of the rolling man. There are no available government statistics on the number of individuals using the airlines. Private surveys are reported to have shown, however, that the median income of passengers frequently using airlines is $17,500, which (if even approximately true) would indicate that air travel is used by well under 5 per cent of our population. Sylvia Porter, the syndicated columnist, asserts that 70 to 80 per cent of Americans have never traveled by plane. Nevertheless, the air-pollution and the ear-pollution characteristic of environments surrounding major jet ports, maintained for the convenience of the small, privileged minority, have turned thousands of square miles of erstwhile pleasant human habitats into regions to be shunned. The supersonic boom, formerly a prerogative of the military, may—if airlines have their way—also be put at the service of the underwear salesman hastening from here to there. Costs may block the development of the commercial supersonic plane, but since costs often lose their identity in subsidies from the taxpayer, as in agriculture and the American merchant marine, too much reliance should not be placed on the cost factor. What the effect of multiple supersonic booms may be on the human nervous system apparently remains unknown. But since wildlife such as waterfowl, which has given little if any indication of reaction to the noise of subsonic planes, seems never to adjust itself to explosions, the new supersonic salesman could have considerable impact on wildlife in refuges and other habitats, not only within cities and all about Megalopolis, but across the nation.

Over vast empty expanses such as Canada's Pre-Cambrian shield there may soon be few places left where fish and other wildlife may hide. The helicopter has recently put the polar bear on the list of threatened species. A man may sleep in Minneapolis, but operationally extend his range well into the arctic. Policing such an area, on the other hand, would be prohibitively expensive for a government with as small a tax base as Canada's.

Man's niches are, obviously, functions of many factors of which the motorcar is merely one of the most powerful. But the influence of these niches, especially as North American populations move toward the half billion—or even billion—mark are certain to be profound. To the extent that Americans operate as "economic man," the future—for redwoods and those who cherish them, for river valleys such as that of the Hudson, for space and solitude for those who have the gumption to get to them on foot, for

the delight of spring water as it comes from its source, for the abundance or even existence of many species of plants and animals—looks grim indeed. Fortunately, however, as well as economic man there is esthetic man, intellectual man, and ethical man. Thoreau is far more widely read than John Stuart Mill, or even John Maynard Keynes.

Many of the processes that determine the value or impact of population variables are themselves variables—and most of them are dependent. Some are predictable; many are fortuitous. Perhaps not even that modern soothsayer the computer could cope with such dynamic variety and certainly—thus far—we do not have the information about many niches in adequate form to feed into computers.

A recent decision handed down by the U.S. Supreme Court, because it will result in a sweeping change in niches, may turn out to have a major impact upon our landscape. Its requirement of political redistricting on the basis of "one man, one vote" may, because of shifts in the historical distribution of our population alter the basic policies that have governed land use in the United States. In 1910, 46 per cent of our population was classified as rural, 54 per cent urban; in 1960, date of the last Census, 30 per cent were rural, 70 per cent urban. (These comparisons should not be taken too literally, because of changes in Census Bureau definitions.) Historical and traditional districting has long given both the Congress and most state legislatures a balance of power in favor of rural areas. Under the "one man, one vote" rule, legislative powers will shift to urban areas, where voters—to the extent that they consider such things at all—can be expected to have different values and points of view on many governmental policies and actions that influence the land. A very large proportion of them, unless there should be educational changes that now seem improbable, will have little if any understanding of how land *lives.* An increase in the range of the motorcar and perhaps motorboats, tote-goats, and private airplanes would seem likely. Beer cans, pop bottles, and Kleenex may well accompany them.

In the 1956 election only 60 per cent of the population over twenty-one voted; in 1960, 64 per cent; and in 1964, 61 per cent (*World Almanac,* 1963, p. 258; 1964, p. 44). Where there are well-organized political machines this voter apathy, if it continues, will leave a considerable proportion of the decision making in the power of big-city "machines," small groups of men who have never been noted for integrity, education, or taste—and certainly not for esthetic or ecological understanding. The need to develop countervailing forces, and to do it fast, is obvious. Remote though the Supreme Court decision may seem, it could prove to be the most serious, though inadvertent, setback conservation has ever had in the United States.

Some economists project a possible rise in gross national product to $2000 billion, or even $3000 billion, by 2000, and forecast disposable consumer income of $1500 billion. Since, under the definition of GNP, they do not include provision for quiet nights under the stars, the flight song of the upland plover, sweet corn ten minutes from the field, Northern Spy apples which were never bred to be shuttled from one side of the continent to the other, or really fine claret, which exists in limited quantities and for which no substitute has ever been found, I submit we should bite hard on the coin of the economists' values. Gross national product makes no provision for spacious silence, nor even for water that has not passed through someone's bladder within the past few months or days. A growing GNP signifies, in many ways, a falling living standard.

But one way or another, we shall likely witness a proliferation of artifacts of one kind or another, that will be exchanged for what passes for money, and Americans will have much more leisure time than any mass of people—except the peasantry of underdeveloped countries—has ever had before. Many of them may be more or less rich, and will differentially occupy niches such as the human race has never known.

Another group of economists, with much evidence on their side, sees cybernation and automation making man largely unnecessary except as a consumer of the products of his machines. Since many millions may be unemployed over a long period, and since our way of life depends on consumption of the things our machines make, it is proposed that these unemployed be given a guaranteed annual income that will, presumably, be squeezed out of the tumescent gross national product (by robbing Peter to pay Paul) or via the printing press.

The niches through which American populations function are, as has been said, dependent variables, and environments may be affected in a wide variety of ways by the size of the guaranteed annual income or whatever substitutes for it. Because it may support ten or twenty or even more million adults who will, presumably, not adopt celibacy as a condition of the GAI, these otherwise unoccupied people might give a thrust to the population bulge, especially if each infant automatically becomes eligible for the GAI. The last hired will likely be the first fired, and these are often not only the least educated but the most uneducable. The somewhat Utopian advocates of the GAI have not actually advocated that each unemployed be provided with an automobile, though it would not be surprising if this were attempted, if only in the interest of the GNP; the psychological need for a car is so strong among Americans, as is obvious from a walk through almost any slum, that it is probable some GAI money will hold jalopies off used car dumps for a time. On the other hand, the expansion of Megalopolis might also be somewhat retarded if GAIs are kept small, since small-town living is much less expensive than comparable living in large cities.

And to the GAI *panem* will almost certainly be added *circenses*. Cities, such as New York, that are neglecting essential services except on an emergency basis are already spending money on free theaters, band concerts, playgrounds, and other diversions as part of their defense against such social pathology as juvenile delinquency. It is quite possible that this type of expenditure will spill over onto lands that are now wild.

Americans have a foundation for nearly everything, including golf. The Golf Foundation recently calculated that in line with current population and economic growth, by the year 2000 we shall need ten times the number of golf courses we now have, or about 54,000 new ones. At an average of 125 acres per eighteen holes, this will mean some 6,850,000 or approximately the area of New Hampshire plus Rhode Island. The costs, presumably not adjusted for inflation, of land, construction, equipment, clubhouses, swimming pools, etc., are calculated at little short of twenty billion dollars. In a country where cities and towns are building basketball courts for their children "because there is not room for baseball," the Golf Foundation could possibly be overoptimistic.

Even with the total dreams of the Golf Foundation unrealized, golf courses will come to have increasing importance as open space, and it might be well for conservation-action organizations to revive the old project started by Arthur A. Allen to make golf courses bird sanctuaries. Water hazards and roughs may have conservation significance in the urban and exurban deserts as they spread through the next few decades, and in the landscape about cities.

De Grazia (1962, p. 503) criticized the projections of the Outdoor Recreation Resources Review Commission as biased because the samples were drawn from people actually engaged in outdoor recreation rather than from probability samples of our total population. (This survey incredibly does not list "gardening" as an outdoor recreation. My once-a-week cleaning woman who lives in New York City's Borough of Queens, keeps me supplied with flowers from June to October. Are her hours of recreation, or her pleasure, fewer than those of someone who drives in a line down Yosemite's four-lane highway during a two-week vacation? How many million additional gardeners have been ignored in the survey? I have not been able to get an estimate from the garden clubs, nor does the government seem to possess reliable figures. However, Lloyd E. Partain, Assistant to the Administrator on Recreation, Soil Conservation Service, summarizes [*in litt.*] some findings in a survey made by Dr. Arnon L. Mehring, for the National Plant Food Institute, of U.S. nonfarm homes using fertilizer. In 1959–61 these amounted to 50.9 per cent. Some fertilizer was undoubtedly used entirely for lawns, but if we include the grass-growers as gardeners, perhaps compensated for by gardeners who do not use fertilizers, gardening—conservatively—must involve over twenty million people, a number approaching the numbers of hunters and fishermen combined, exceeding those in attendance at major-league baseball games, and vastly exceeding the numbers of those who own motors and boats and who are such a pampered fraction of outdoor recreationists. In view of the day-to-day relationship of gardening to the way people live and would like to live, and therefore the impact it could—and should—have on the future development of our society, it is to be regretted that gardeners have not been given the consideration they merit in thinking about the future of the American environment.) With these reservations we can use ORRRC's findings as a basis of further consideration of the American environment. They project merely 73 per cent of 350 million (255 million) as living in metropolitan areas in the year 2000, with 60 per cent of the "consumer units" having an income of $10,000 of 1959 value. The number of passenger cars is projected at 100 million by 1976 and 180 million by the year 2000. (If they are the size of a current Ford or Chevrolet, bumper to bumper they will occupy about 600,000 linear miles of road or an area of over 2200 square miles, slightly greater than the State of Delaware. If they drive at an average speed of forty miles per hour and maintain the recommended one car length for each ten miles per hour between them, they will spread over three million miles. At the end of 1960 the United States had 3,546,000 miles of road. (Bureau of the Census, Statistical Abstract of the United States, 1962, p. 551.) If 73 per cent of these 180 million cars are distributed among the 255 million people projected as dwellers in metropolitan areas it is difficult to see how they can escape literal autointoxication. Something will have to give, and it will not be space; an acre is still seventy yards on a side. The high concentration of cars might well put the country back on its feet.

What technology may have in store for us is impossible to know. One might imagine that as life in conurbations becomes more intolerable the TV-equipped telephone could come into such common use at the executive level that such managerial power centers as Wall Street and New York's Park Avenue might easily become unacceptable. Should this develop a trend, to serve automated assembly lines, a real move toward decentralization could occur.

The University of Miami now houses under one roof a series of lecture halls where only one sixth of the students actually occupy the same room as the instructor, who teaches via TV. There would seem to be no reason why they should occupy the same city. The possibility of technological dispersal must not be overlooked. However, should this intensify the house-and-lot-*cum*-garden trend the environmental impact might be even more destructive of habitats as we now know them.

The income of the otiose will have considerable influence, over and above settlement patterns, upon what they do to environments. If 60 per cent of the "consumer units" have 10,000 1959 dollars in the year 2000, there will probably be few places in the country where one can escape ear pollution. Yellowstone Lake probably shows the shape of things to come. Motorboats will be fouling most reasonably still waters and with a population of 350 million to be served, the Corps of Engineers will probably have dammed most white waters. Except for a few preserves of exceedingly rich men, trout streams will be largely something grandpa talks about in his reminiscent moods. Trout streams may be replaced by trout pools into which hatchery-raised fish will be tossed; admission may be upon deposit of a coin which efficiency will reduce in cost year by year. It will certainly not be economically justifiable to produce trout by the old-fashioned ecosystem leading the food chain from watershed through mayflies to fish. It seems scarcely probable that under such conditions trout will retain either their flavor or their fighting quality; they will probably take on some of the more inert characteristics of human urbanites or tapeworms.

The rolling man has already made himself so obnoxious to landowners that considerable proportions of private land within reach of large cities are posted against hunters. Although both in terms of man hours per acre, and protein-per-acre harvested, private lands still contribute more to the hunter than do public hunting grounds, posting may well continue at an augmented rate.

Since many landowners do not themselves crop wildlife, this quasi-protection is an important factor in building excessive deer populations within 100 or 150 miles of conurbations. Unless there should be an improbable increase of predator populations this may be expected to have considerable impact on ecosystems over wide areas. Overbrowsing, for example, is notable in much of the Catskill region.

A recent reviewer in the London *Economist* (*The Economist*, December 12, 1964, p. 1257) averred that "there are probably no statistics on how many Indians shit in the street," nor have I been able to get any quantitative information on the activities of the Great American Slob. The Indian, as the writer pointed out, has the excuse of no alternative facilities. The American simply behaves that way. It has been reported that one way to spot productive fishing areas is by the beer can spoor left behind by fishermen. However this may be, the range of the rolling American is marked by heaps of offal, much of which is not "biodegradable," to use current cant from the detergent industry.

Ear pollution has been mentioned in relation to planes. It should also be recognized as one of the characteristics of outdoor campsites. When one walks from one tent or trailer to another, at North Lake inside the Catskill "forever wild" boundaries, it is frequently impossible to disentangle one radio station or one transistor receiver from another. Aurally, one might better be in a housing development in New York; there the walls would give at least a modicum of protection against the racket. The Sierra Club, commenting on the Humboldt Redwood State Park in California (Outdoor News Letter, November 6, 1964), reports that "Not a single grove in the park is beyond the sound of passing traffic." The sound of passing traffic presumably includes radios.

If our great museums and art galleries were used as recklessly and harmfully as are our wild lands, there would be a national scandal and a national sense of shame. Yet the environment of wild geese or the pasque flower, whose sighting Aldo Leopold recognized as a necessity for many of us (certainly as much of a necessity as a view of Picasso!), is as vulnerable as a Gobelin or the walls of the Sistine Chapel. So little respect for these environments have those in charge that they constantly advocate "accessibility" without provision for adequate protection. According to the Natural Resources Council (Executive News Service, 7, 20, p. 144), Senator Gruening is recommending that the central core strip of the Kenai National Moose Range in Alaska "be opened for disposal if it cannot be developed for public recreation." Is it too much to expect Alaskans to appreciate the value of some land that is not "developed" by man?

Obviously, with the third of a billion people which we may have by the end of the century, and a half billion which we might have a generation later, the pasque flower, the goose refuge, and the spread of moccasin flower can survive only through limited use of the outdoors. If our propensity for dumping large segments of our population into wild sectors of our landscape continues or is intensified, wonders far older than La Gioconda are going to be extirpated. At some point it is going to be necessary to say "Stop!" Upon whether or not we have the sense and ability to do this will depend the future quality of much of our land.

Little has been said thus far in this paper about our use of commercial natural resources and what this may do to the land. Appalachia is an object lesson that so far goes largely unheeded. Palliatives of great price are proposed but little attention is given to effective control of strip mining. Strip miners are generally penalized at such low levels that it is cheaper for them to pay penalties than to tidy up the landscape. And, obviously, any attempt at restoration cannot show much effect for a decade or more, in the production of small game, and four or five decades if anything like natural and esthetic values are to be re-established. There is little public recognition of the length of time required to restore a mature and complex forest. Acidity of mine-polluted waters appears to remain a largely unsolved problem.

One of the ugliest threats to our environment is the growing probability of exploitation of oil shales in western states. There can, I think, be no argument over the contention that many uses to which petroleum is put in the United States are not necessary. One thinks of a large proportion of motoring and flying, and the heating of nonessential buildings. Yet it appears that oil-shale exploitation is to be developed even though it turns thousands of square miles into dumps more gargantuan than those left behind by strip miners. If we may judge by past experience, industry will do whatever is feasible to promote use of petroleum—especially the nonessential because it is marginal—so the extraction process may become more economic, i.e. more profitable. Despite the verbal obeisances to esthetics in the Great Society, the landscape overlaying the shales appears headed for the same sort of spoliation as the forests that once cloaked northern Michigan, under climatic conditions that will make recovery much more difficult.

Nor, indeed, does appreciation of the forest itself yet outweigh the influence of the quick buck. It is usually discussed in terms of pulpwood or board feet. Many of our woodlands are apparently headed toward the monotony of the pulp planta-tion of Scandinavia, some of the world's dullest landscape. The Scandinavians, a decade ago, admitted they did not know what monoculture is doing to their lands and we may not find out until there is a Dendroctonus outbreak (such as the one now taking place in Honduras) too violent to be controlled even by our poisons. The elms are following the chestnuts, ashes, maples; and oaks are sick across a great deal of the country, and there is no reason to think our environment, as now managed, is going to cure itself. The biomass, from the B-horizon to tree crowns, is much smaller than it was before civilization took over the forests and variety is lost as fauna and flora are impoverished.

Americans are smug about their present food situation, as they may well be if we ignore the approximately thirty-five million of us who live in poverty and who certainly do not get their share of the reported 212 pounds of meat, per capita, a year. The 1963 *Statistical Abstract of the United States* lists only eight countries whose calorie intake is greater than ours, and two whose per capita meat consumption is larger. We are plagued by surpluses (which might well disappear if our entire population had adequate protein) despite having placed millions of acres in "soil banks." Yet the wheat and corn exported under the so-called Food for Peace program consists of production from only 19 per cent of our cropland. What is going to happen to our land as we increase production to take care of 100 to (conceivably) 150 million more people within thirty-five years?

The fact of the matter is, we do not know. The chemistry of our soils has been studied while the biotic processes that to a great degree govern nutrient exchanges remain (if the pun may be forgiven) *terra incognita*. There is, almost world-wide, a vast ignorance of even the taxonomy of soil animals, plants, and microorganisms. When we have not yet even identified the bacteria, mites, springtails, worms, millipedes, etc., that convert litter into organic and inorganic residues, we are scarcely in a position to evaluate the part these organisms may play in soil metabolism. Agricultural societies with long histories of sustained production, such as Scandinavia and the paddy lands of Southeast Asia, have been based on organic agriculture with a continuing addition of animal manures. One need not be a devotee of organic farming to recognize that chemical fertilization is a recent practice and that, because of absence of basic information, we have no facts that justify trust in substitution of chemical applications for the biotic exchanges that have been the basis of soil fertility since long before the dawn of human land management. Furthermore, soil structure was sustained under the use of animal manures as it may not be under modern practices.

By the end of the century we shall be competing, for food and fiber crops, on a world scale, with six to six and a half billion other human beings if UN projections, which are the best we have, can be relied on.

At the present time we import more than $2.25 billion of agricultural commodities (not including tropical products such as tea, coffee, spices and rubber) as well as $400 million in fisheries products. Imported forest products cost over $1.3 billion, and will be sought increasingly by the rest of the world as population pressures rise. Food production, per capita, has already failed to keep pace with population growth in Asia, Latin America, and much of Africa.

Can we double protein production without injury to the soil? Will there be land left over for game for the 83 per cent more hunting projected by ORRRC? Again, skepticism is not out of order.

Disposal of various kinds of wastes is a problem of which we are only beginning to be aware. President Johnson has spoken out against the used-car dump that has been "uglifying" America, but screening the graveyards is simply postponing the day of reckoning. As a nation we live by waste and the Public Health Service estimates that the cost to local governments of disposing of trash rose, between 1940 and 1961, from $300 million to "well over $1 billion." *The Wall Street Journal* (October 18, 1961) reports that New York City expects to run out of landfill sites for rubbish disposal "within the next twenty-five years." The city accumulates enough refuse each day to fill a freight train seven miles long.

There are varying estimates as to the cost of more-or-less cleaning up our rivers with the most popular figure about $700 million a year for ten years, an estimate that may well be too low in view of population growth. These funds must be sought in competition for billions needed for schools and colleges, hospitals, and care of increasing numbers of aged and infirm living more years, etc. Our practice of discharging wastes into rivers, following our European tradition, has destroyed fisheries and shell fisheries of enormous value. The take of oysters in Chesapeake Bay states, for example, is down from 117 million pounds in 1880 to twenty million in 1962, despite vertiginous price rises. The Delaware River produced over a million pounds of shad a year from 1880 through 1901, with a peak of 1,800,000 in 1890; in 1960 it produced 38,000 pounds. The impact of increasing tonnages of fertilizers and biocides washed into our streams and rivers is so far incalculable, though recent heavy mortalities of fishes along the Mississippi have given us an inkling of what to expect. Such chemicals will, presumably, be used in greater quantities as our population increases; we may not be able to support our population without them. A sharp drop in numbers of predators and other birds, such as grebes, that are at the end of the food chain seems to have no other explanation than poisoning. Circumstantial evidence is supported by high rates of DDT and related compounds found in the eggs of such birds as bald and golden eagles and ospreys —up to 48 p.p.m. (Conservation News Bulletin, Vol. 29, No. 22, November 15, 1964). Hydroelectric dams are, of course, compounding the habitat destruction caused by pollution.

A current dispute is raging over the construction of a hydroelectric plant on the Hudson River; its opponents claim, with considerable supporting evidence, that it will almost certainly terminate the run of both shad and sea bass. Pollution has already cut the numbers of these fishes and the flesh of at least the former has been made unpalatable by pollutants in the water.

River and estuarine environments have probably lost a higher percentage of productive capacity than most other American environments and the addition of 200 to 300 million more people within the next fifty years can scarcely fail to exacerbate the destruction. Sport fishing goes, of course, with commercial fishing.

The problem of water supplies for 400 or more millions is already foreshadowed by shortages in the Southwest, Texas, and the Great Plains, as well as in rising degrees of pollution. We now use about 350 × 10⁹ gallons of water per day (Abelson, 1965, p. 113) and with the desalting problem still far from solved, Bunyanesque projects—such as Americans might just be capable of executing—would divert rivers such as the Peace and Yukon across half a continent. Vast areas would be flooded and, in all probability, climatic changes engendered that might result in widespread vegetation changes. But what alternatives shall we have? In 1963, Bull Run, on the headwaters of the Potomac, was completely dry in its upper reaches except for effluent from

sewage disposal plants (Davies, 1964, p. 218). Prince William County, Virginia, grew 122 per cent in the 1950s and Fairfax County, 190 per cent. Both include the Bull Run watershed. At least four or five large sewage-disposal plants, to discharge into Bull Run, are now definitely planned.

Speculations of this sort could be extended almost indefinitely. We live in a complex ecosystem comprising interrelated dynamic processes most of which, except time, are dependent variables.

Of these variables the one that exercises the most powerful influence is human populations functioning through increasingly effective niches.

The growth of this human population could probably be considerably reduced by direct government action (Vogt, 1961, pp. 4–18). There is certainly increasing awareness in our national government that population growth can no longer be ignored; aid in birth control that has been more or less surreptitiously available through public health programs for two decades or more, is being offered somewhat more freely under the so-called Anti-Poverty plan. We are still, however, without a national population policy though many practices such as subsidized housing and tax relief for large families, draft exemption for fathers, etc., are pronatalist in effect. The Conservation Foundation is currently working with universities on projects that may break new ground in a path toward rational population policies.

No one who has traveled far and wide in today's United States is likely to agree with Shakespeare's apostrophe at the head of this paper.

Whether W. S. Gilbert is finally proven correct will probably be determined more by what man does with his population than by any other factor.

BIBLIOGRAPHY

Abelson, P. H. 1965. Sci. 147 (Jan. 8):3654.
Bridgman, P. W. 1949. The Logic of Modern Physics. New York.
Bureau of the Census. Statistical Abstracts of the United States for 1949, 1962, 1963, 1964.
―――― 1949. Historical Statistics of the United States, 1789–1945. Wash., D.C.
Compendio Estadistico. 1960. Mexico City.
Conservation News Bulletin. 1964. Vol. 29, no. 22 (Nov. 15).
Davies, William E. 1964. The Future of the Potomac: A Conflict in Values. Atlantic Naturalist, 19 (Oct.–Dec.):209–20.
Economist, The. 1964 (Dec. 12).
Elton, Charles. 1927. Animal Ecology. New York.
Executive News Service. 7:144.
Grazia, Sebastian de. 1962. Of Time, Work and Leisure. New York.
Hauser, Philip M. 1960. Population Perspectives. New Brunswick, N.J.
――――, ed. 1963. The Population Dilemma. Englewood Cliffs, N.J.
Herber, Louis. 1965. Crisis in Our Cities. Englewood Cliffs, N.J.
James, Preston E. 1942. Latin America.
Krueger, Ralph R., et al., ed. 1963. Regional and Resource Planning in Canada. Toronto.
League of Nations. 1944. The Future Population of Europe and the Soviet Union.
Myrdal, Gunnar. 1940. Population: A Problem for Democracy. Cambridge, Mass.
Navarrete, Ifigenia M. de. 1960. La distribución del ingreso y el desarollo económico de México. Mexico City.
Odum, Eugene P. 1963. Ecology. New York.
Outdoor News Letter. 1964. (Nov. 6).
Population Bulletin. 1964 (Sept.). Wash., D.C.
Salgado Perez, Felipe. 1950. Dinámica de la Conservación del Suelo y del Agua en México. Mexico City.
United Nations. 1963. Demographic Yearbook of the U.N.
―――― 1961. Statistical Yearbook.
U.S. House of Representatives. 1962. Committee on the Judiciary, Subcommittee No. 1. Study of Population and Immigration Problems. Wash., D.C.
Vogt, William. 1961. The Management of Human Population. Transactions of the 26th N. Amer. Wildl. and Nat. Res. Conf.
World Almanac. 1963, 1964. N.Y.
Zimmerman, Anthony, S. V. D. 1961. Catholic Viewpoint on Overpopulation. Garden City, N.Y.

General Discussion

GLACKEN: Thank you very much. Before opening this meeting to general discussion I would like to call attention to two ideas which appear in Bill Vogt's paper and also Ray Dasmann's.

First is the U.S. Supreme Court decision—the one-man, one-vote decision—and its possible bearing on conservation questions. It has interesting implications in many states, including California.

Second is the theme of urban mentality and its relationship to the preservation of nature. Many—I think sometimes without justification—have felt that people living in cities had no concern with these matters, that there was a divorcement from nature inherent in city life. I have never seen this field really analyzed, yet it is a worthwhile subject to explore. That is why I am making this suggestion.

VOGT: The question of decision making has come up several times here. We have to know what we want. We obviously have values. Don't those of us who want to protect nature and who like to study nature represent a minority group generally in a somewhat higher economic bracket—with somewhat better education—than the mass of the people in the country? I don't say there are no poor people who like nature or enjoy it. But in taking particularly the mass of urban people, I don't think you would find very many people who live in densities of 80,000 per square mile in Harlem who would be much concerned with nature protection.

Can we educate them fast enough? Can we by-pass them? Who is going to make decisions, how are they to be made, and then how are those decisions to be effectuated in a democratic society?

DURDEN: In their marketplace behavior, we do seem to observe differences between socioeconomic groups in their response to natural landscapes at resort colonies. The mass-market socioeconomic groups tend to think primarily of natural areas as providing a setting for active recreation.

It is not until we ascend into more limited socioeconomic groups that we find such developments as, say, Little Cumberland Island, where a deliberate attempt is being made for man to find his place as a part of nature.

For those of us who are interested in the general field of planning, one of our criteria is choice—to allow a choice of experience to the urban resident. So far we have had little success in giving the average urban resident the opportunity to experience a meaningful contact with nature. In the marketplace the choices that most can make are very limited.

DANSEREAU: Is this the fault of the planners? Could they do something toward educating people to free themselves from their class and esthetic prejudices and find something that is more truly congenial? Is anything at all being done? This is a job for the social psychologists, obviously. Have they stepped into the picture really?

STRONG: I would like to have Dr. Farber answer this. How much relief from stress is there in nature, and does it depend on the type of background to which we are accustomed? If you have been brought up in a very dense city neighborhood, do you find the same type of relaxation from a change to solitude that someone brought up in a different atmosphere would? Does variety again prevail here, and should the country dweller go into the city for his relief?

FARBER: There is first of all a habit pattern in the notion of beauty in certain groups. I don't think you can take people from the city streets or children or anyone who may not have ever seen a cow, and suddenly put them in a forest away from the blare of the truck horns, the noises of factory whistles, and all the other city things that we consider. They feel insecure—they feel lost. That is why you see millions of people on the floor of the Yosemite Valley. And if you just walk a mile or two miles up above there to May Lake or anywhere else, there are very few people. Most will stick right at the floor of the Valley.

This education and this effort at education must begin in grammar school. The hope that it will come from the parents is a fleeting hope, in my estimation. It must start very early, and it can be done. And the children can be made to feel a part of the great outdoors. It doesn't have to be the beautiful waterfalls, although they, too, should be admired. Some of the things debated here about ecology can be understood at a very early age by these children.

I do feel that there is a challenge to all planners, no matter what group they belong in, to consider bringing into our education a tremendous force from ecology.

SEARS: I would like to re-echo that, from the aged down to children learning their mother tongue. There are encouraging signs of progress, and I think it would be a mistake to link attitudes too rigidly with economic position. I don't know where you would assign the labor unions in the economic scale, but it is encouraging to see the attitude of some of their leaders in this matter.

WHITE: Much of what we have been saying this morning and yesterday has been in the nature of a statement of judgments about what would be right in the future for the environments of North America: horseback opinions about people's preferences, value systems, and modes of action.

What I have found lacking is on the one hand a sense of urgency of the kind which Vogt voiced this morning, but also a kind of urgency which it seems to me Boulding was presenting yesterday afternoon and to which no one really responded. Let me see if I can illustrate this by noting several other points in our conversation.

I would submit that no one today knows whether there is any significant relationship between wilderness, open space, and mental health. This is purely speculative at the present time. I suggest further no one today has any adequate understanding of conditions in which people make choices in most resource management situations. Although many of us tend to have opinions about this, they are largely unsupported.

Dasmann referred in his paper to the apparent irrational and silly action of people in moving into floodplains. Here is a place where we do know something about why people occupy floodplains, and we are beginning to find that it is not always simple. Some of the decisions are very rational. Some of them result from lack of information. Some result from imperfect perception of situations. Some of them result from very severe social constraints which permit no other choice.

The exchange between Tunnard and Meier the other day led to some assertions about what made people happy, what we knew about people being happy. Here we know very little. We know very little about the nature of the attitudes of people toward the physical environment. We know very little about how it is related to authoritarian views, to concepts of security in the universe around them, and to response to social-status situations. Most of this is just speculative on our part.

I come around also to Sears's comment yesterday about what is happening to our arid environments. A judgment was given in which a number of us joined. But in fact we know hardly anything about the nature of the systems which are being affected, and our basis for prediction about just what will happen and what the carrying capacity will be under given situations is extremely limited. Yet many of us, including myself, are making quite sweeping judgments about what should guide public policy.

Vogt was pleading for a sense of urgency here, but Boulding, as I suggested, was pleading for urgency with respect to our own investigations and knowledge. He was saying to the ecologist, why on earth are you all sitting back here making observations about what is right and wrong in the scene without seriously considering mounting what ought to be a massive and energetic research program to get answers to these questions?

When Clawson and Fisher asked what we should do to find out, say, what kind of land classification we ought to have, I am afraid we didn't respond very constructively.

My suggestions about our conversation are that perhaps it would be enhanced and made more fruitful if we stopped talking about being ecologists, economists, or geographers or planners, and we just stopped trying to designate disciplinary affiliation in defense of it, or attack on it, but instead we talked as men asking what are the significant problems that ought to be investigated.

Secondly, if we must ask ourselves, wherever we can, what it is we need to know as a basis for arriving at a more firm prediction of the nature of this North American habitat. Where are we now basing our judgments on horseback opinion? Where do we feel we have some sound ground of information? If we lack this, why aren't we moving ahead much more vigorously toward getting that information?

FOSBERG: I think every one of us will agree with what Dr. White has just recommended. This is clear, but it did come out yesterday that even though we don't know the answers, the details, the complete, the adequate answers to many of these questions, we still have to make these judgments. We make them from the best position that we have.

If we don't, the thing goes by default. There are plenty of people who will make judgments from far less adequate data or from a far more self-centered point of view.

As far as the massive attack on these problems, I don't know how many people here are aware of the fact that in the Department of the Interior there are serious considerations at the present time of the creation of what I conceive to be a mechanism for this massive attack.

It has been suggested that an Office of Ecological Research and Surveys be set up in the Department. The concept is still a little nebulous and there is no assurance whatever that the Secretary of the Interior will buy it, and much less assurance that Congress will support it. But such things are being talked about.

We must have free and independent inquiry, not mission-oriented, not tied to a single practical problem, but an inquiry that gets at the range of fields that we as ecologists think we are dealing with.

I think that this group could do much worse than to support such a suggestion, and lend its prestige for what it is worth to do this, to encourage the Secretary of the Interior and Congress to proceed with a thing of this nature.

DANSEREAU: I can see an ultimate response, if not an answer, to Dr. White's question.

There are essentially two areas that have to be developed. The first is obviously ecology. The ecologists have a great deal more to discover, and there is not much evidence that their message has been perceived.

At the next stage, for instance, in the esthetic and literary world, among those who create works in which people are able to recognize themselves— where recognition and therefore conscious expression become available to the ordinary person—ecology has contributed to literature only on the descriptive and not on the functional level. The functional message of ecology has not been conveyed in literature and in the arts.

Therefore the people remain bewildered, have no explanation for the contradictions of the frightening impact of nature and the soothing impact of nature. This contradiction is one of the many we face in the psychology of man and nature, the whole psychology of recreation, with its alternative needs of gregariousness and solitude. The motivational psychologists are probably working on this, but not relating it below to the ecological plane, and usually are not remotely interested in reaching out to philosophy for a further fertilization of their thought and a feedback all the way to ecology from philosophy. This is the kind of current that is very much lacking at the present time.

NICHOLSON: I would like to come back to the point raised by Gilbert White, which seems to me to go very much to the heart of the matter if this is not to be simply an academic discussion. I am not in any way criticizing the attempt to get a meeting of minds on this scale. I think it is most important. But it does strike me that altogether too much of the effort in this field, in this country, takes the form of a philosophic, a missionary approach.

May I give one or two illustrations of the active approach? In Britain, we have a comprehensive ecological program of the type which was mentioned by Fosberg just now. We have approximately 180 scientists working full time, and another seventy on contracts—say 250 scientists in all. I know from experience over ten years that we have a deficit of the order of 250 ecologists in order to do the minimum scientific program to validate the type of effort that we are talking about—the type of advice, the type of support and exchange of data, and so on. If we had about 500 people at this time, we would be able to attain the informational level we need to act.

But to apply these figures in the United States, if you look at the number of habitats here—perhaps 160 or so according to Küchler—it is difficult to believe that you have a deficit of less than 2000 full-time ecologists at this moment. I think that is probably a conservative statement.

I would mention one other line of approach. I have been concerned with the British conference on the countryside in 1970. At the moment we have twelve study groups working, not on the philosophy of it, but on what different groups can do. For instance, we have one group run by the National Coal Board on reclamation; we have another group run by the National Parks Commission on planning practice; we have another on forests and on the use of technology for conservation, both for the mitigation of technology and the positive use of technology; finally, we have a group being run by the Institute of Surveyors on the remaking of the curriculum. All of these people have to come up with not just positive plans but with things that they have actually done between these big organized groups, which include 175 of the main interests of the country. And they have to report to us what they have done, what they are doing, in order to implement their plans.

What worries me about this discussion is that I see so little emphasis on the channels of action in order to validate, to implement, or even to test the propositions that are being put up.

I would very much like to support what Gilbert White was saying. I think that unless you also are able to get some attention, national response, to this problem of validation—of execution, implementation, whatever you like—a great deal of admirable effort will be wasted. I never come over to this country without getting a lot of very viable ideas which I then go and apply over there. I have a very guilty conscience sometimes when I get an idea which I know came from here, and the only place I see it in action is across the ocean.

(*Laughter*)

GREGG: We have been talking about time scales here, and the ecologists are critical of the economists for having too short a horizon.

As a person who has spent some time wrestling with even more immediate problems, I will panic the ecologists further. I would like to suggest that what Mr. Nicholson has been implying has some immediate relevance to a lot of things that are going on right now.

To illustrate: We have fifty states and a couple of dependencies which are now preparing plans for spending 200 million dollars a year on outdoor recreation open space. Congress just passed, three or four days ago, the Water Resources Planning Act, which will provide a framework for making all kinds of decisions and establishing patterns within the next four or five years on land-water use.

While, of course, Dr. White's concern for a massive research program to get the kinds of answers that will provide sound, long-term guidance is important, it seems to me that there is just as high a priority, and perhaps a higher priority, in getting whatever it is that we know now applied now in the decision-making process.

LEOPOLD: Gilbert White and others have in the last two days pointed out how little we really know, how much more we have to know. As Mr. Gregg said, the immediate need is for application of what we do know—and the possibilities for applying what we do know are always, it seems to me, greatest in the vicinity of urban centers of high population density where need itself, created by density, lays the foundation and the groundwork for the application of ecologic principles.

I don't find it surprising that Max Nicholson can come over here and pick up concepts and ideas from American ecologists and get them applied in Great Britain because Britain, by its very maturity and the density of its population, is receptive to the application of these ideas. The further you go from a mature society back toward the frontier, the less acceptable is the ecologic viewpoint of how to plan resource use.

A classic example on the other end of the scale is Alaska, where we should be able, as trained ecologists, to plan an ideal program of land use, development of resources, and so on. Alaska is the least receptive of all the United States to good planning.

California, for example, an area of high density—of quite recent origin, admittedly—is making progress in ecologic planning that is still impossible in Nevada, right over the mountains from us. This is the result of low pressure in Nevada and high pressure in California.

Hence the place, perhaps, for us to start and apply what we know is in urban centers—and the slowest actual acceptance of ecologic planning is going to be in lightly populated areas, where, however, the problems are often extremely severe.

SEARS: How about the controls? A place like New York has many interests, each with its eye on the other fellow. A new state is likely to be under the control of two or three big economic groups. Is that a factor?

LEOPOLD: No, I don't think it is that simple. In Alaska there are many little groups. They all feel the same way—they want to develop and exploit. Any conservatism in this program of development and exploitation they look upon as fuddy-duddy thinking from California, particularly.

(*Laughter*)

MC HARG: I have found that a discussion of values is of the greatest interest to students of architecture, landscape architecture, and city planning. I have also found that the ethical implications of ecology, as reflected in the views of Aldo Leopold, are of consuming interest to these students.

I would like then to address this to Dr. Dansereau, who asked what a discussion of values and ecology provides for planners.

For five years I have given a course called "Man and Environment." This consists of four groups of lectures. The first, presented by natural scientists, develops the scientific view of cosmic evolution, the solar system, earth, geological history, the characteristics of life, the evolution of plants, animals, and man, and concludes with the ecological view of an interacting biosphere. The second group of lectures are presentations by theologians of the attitudes of the major religions on God-Man-Nature. The third group—given by natural scientists, social scientists, physiologists, and psychiatrists—is concerned with the perception of environment, human needs and responses, while the final lectures are synoptic personal statements by great and wise men.

The effect upon the students is quite marked. Their initial anthropocentrism and anthropomorphism are diminished. They are thoroughly dissatisfied with the concepts of God-Man-Nature represented by the major Western religions. They are almost all intrigued and often persuaded by the holistic aspects of ecology which does contain an intrinsic value system of Man-Nature. I would reaffirm Boulding's position to the effect that economics would be a much better value system if subsumed under ecology.

WAGGONER: My question arises because Mr. Vogt said that Latin Americans are hungry because they fail to employ ecological principles. Given the actual population and its actual growth during the next fifteen years—not the population that Mr. Vogt would like to see there, but the one that is really there—what kind of ecological principle, or, more important, what kind of ecological research would he begin that will feed them better? And feed them better so that they can afford the luxury of preserving the wildlife that they surely all would like to preserve there? I submit that a clear answer to this will win Mr. Vogt the complete respect and support of the economists.

VOGT: May I have the afternoon to answer that?

STRONG: I think it is time to propose some specifics for the Conference to report on. It seems to me that they could divide into two categories. The first would be those matters that we could agree that we know enough about now, in each of the fields we have been exploring, matters on which we could recommend implementation and action. Secondly, could we agree upon highest-priority questions for research, with some judgment as to what will be required in terms of time, money, or people to try to reach an answer. The questions could concern what man needs for his environment, how to sustain ecosystems, the field of law—any of these.

I would like us to offer two sets of recommendations: one, for action where we judge this timely, and, two, for specific, further research.

MILTON: I would like to support Mrs. Strong. We already have set a precedent at this Conference by producing discussion summaries for each session. I would like to suggest that the members of each session group, as they get together after the discussion period, try to produce such guidelines as Mrs. Strong has indicated. The recommended split into two different types of guidelines might be appropriate.

On another point I was stimulated by Max Nicholson's remarks on the need for a comprehensive ecological program here in the United States, and his estimated deficit of 2000 ecologists to carry out such a program. He is a supreme pragmatist, and anyone of this sort can be of tremendous benefit to such a highly diverse gathering as ours. Not very long ago I talked to Paul Pearson, who prepared the recent Ecological Society of America's membership list. He estimated that there were about 2800 ecologists who are members of the Ecological Society, with perhaps 2200 working in the United States. Of these, he estimated about 400 were full-time ecologists, with this as their primary function and interest. And of these 400 I would estimate very few would be available for the kind of program that we envision in just one area—the ecological survey brought up by Ray Fosberg. To be sure, the Society does not include all the ecologists in the country, but it does provide, perhaps, one of our few measures of ecological manpower.

It has been suggested that this apparent deficiency is a reason for pessimism; that it is a reason for saying we really can't do anything because we don't have the manpower to supply the programs we envision coming up in the future. I think we should look at it just the reverse. We should look at this shortage as a challenge, and I think the universities themselves will probably respond with an increase in training programs in ecology as they see the job openings developing for expanded employment. To be sure, there may be a two-, three-, or four-year lag. And for the top-level ecologists even a longer one. But no better argument could be made for the need to get such training underway promptly.

STEERS: Throughout the whole of this Conference so far one thing seems to me to come out as more important than anything else: the importance of educating the young in the love of the countryside. I am thinking really of what is done in Britain. The more people get to know and like the country as country, the easier it will be for ecological principles to be realized and for people like ourselves to make known our interests and expand them. But I am sure we have to build on the young.

Now may I comment regarding America? I have been to this country several times. I have been treated with enormous kindness. But I am never allowed to walk. I can't see the country—I can't walk it and appreciate it. It is the same at home. You find hundreds of people in Britain who drive on Sundays and go to the beach, sit in their cars with the windows closed, and watch the sea, and smoke or read the paper. They have "been in the country"—but really they haven't.

The only way to know the land is to go and put our feet on it and walk about it. The sooner we do that, the easier our problems will be, and this must start with the young, as part of education in the school and elsewhere.

LOWENTHAL:[1] Mr. Nicholson must be tired of getting answers to his questions, but I will give him a few more.

It seems to me a great deal of what is happening in this Conference is an indication of how Americans behave when they are trying to solve problems, problems like this one. Mr. Leopold has already suggested some of the conditions in Britain which make it possible to apply ideals perhaps more easily than they can be applied in many other countries. There is a general consensus of feeling, of willingness to accept leadership in ideas and in attitudes, a sense of pragmatism. I would add to that an ability to compromise; I like the story of the question about dandelions, the gardener who asks how do you get rid of them and is told you don't get rid of them, you learn to love them.

(*Laughter*)

There is in England an ability to use land in a great many ways at once, or a willingness to see it used in a great many ways at once, rather than to require specialized perfection. This leads, of course, to the observation that in this country we are rather different, we take an opposite line. May I suggest certain characteristics here which make it difficult for us to solve problems? These are based on historical analyses principally.

One is our tendency to consider that changes get made by missionary activity and not by institutional pressure. This has always been true in America. It probably has come about because we have been able to make some changes very easily. You can trace it in the antislavery movement, you

[1] Mr. Lowenthal attended the Conference as an observer from the American Geographical Society, in New York City.

can trace it among conservationists, you can trace it everywhere. There is always a feeling that if we talk loud enough about things, if we make recriminations, and if we beat our breasts, somehow these feelings are going to change institutions and the nature of society.

A second characteristic concerns our tendency to make dichotomies everywhere. We talk about man or nature. We talk about city or country. We tend to say 90 per cent of us are going to live in the city but 90 per cent of us would rather live in the country. We are very reluctant to try to make a combination of landscape or site or environment. Our zoning has tended always to break things apart. We have a kind of landscape to work in, another to live in, another kind to go and play in. If things get bad in the cities, we tell people to go out to the national parks. But they are supposed to turn on their vision only when they are out in the country, and to be blind in the city.

It is very difficult to educate children to an appreciation of landscape values when the environments they live in almost all the time do not demonstrate any such virtues. And here I think our planners, our engineers, our builders are not any more to blame than any of the rest of us.

But when Mr. Steers finds that he can't walk in America, we have to tell him that he is going to be able to walk even less because we are now building roads and bridges on which one is not permitted to walk. The Verrazano Bridge is an excellent example of this.

It is a very rare person—Edgar Anderson is one—who is able to take the point of view that environment is a whole and that landscapes exist in cities as well as in the country. I think Mr. Brinser made this point yesterday. But in general we tend to dichotomize everything.

Lastly, I think Americans tend more than other people to make a commitment to the future. We talked a great deal yesterday about the fact that no one would deny that what we want for our children is good. Not every nation would share these values to the extent that we do.

Foreign observers have always pointed out that Americans don't love their country as it is, but as it will be and as they are going to make it for future generations.

This is not admirable or otherwise, it is just a fact. But it makes it difficult for people to see the present landscape as anything of great importance. They like to think of the present as an abstraction from which to jump into the future.

I will conclude with the observation that I hope that when we make a set of study guides, we try to include some understanding of what the historical processes of decision making in this country are, and a comparative analysis also of how people live in landscapes. It seems to me that in these respects perhaps we know a little more than what Gilbert White has suggested we know in terms of motivational psychology.

COWAN: As another one of the foreigners here with Mr. Nicholson, I can take a slightly different view of landscape and people. We have lower densities in Canada. Our high densities are restricted to about one fifth of our nation and probably always will be.

What I want to say, though, is on a slightly different theme. One of the strengths of this Conference—one of its deficiencies at the same time—is the broad horizon through which we are approaching this common problem of interest. At one moment somebody is talking about landscaping for human survival, another is talking about landscape in the immediate living area and the pleasure of living in it, and another is talking about landscape for outdoor recreation.

Throughout I detect a feeling that we know so little about ecology that we can't get anywhere. But we are doing a great deal in applying ecological information from one side of this continent to the other. There are many extremely practical questions that many of us are asked daily, upon which we can give extremely practical answers. We can tell you the exact consequences of whether you burn this area or whether you don't burn this area, or whether you cut the trees in this way or in that way. We can tell you what this is going to mean in the number of species that are there, the rate of plant regeneration, what it will return to and the pattern in which it will return.

The largest single administrative unit in Canada—probably the largest single such unit in North America—is the Northwest Territory. This is managed by a small group of people; the carrying capacity is very low. We have partially known ecological bases on which to plan this management, and some of us have had to design firm management programs for areas bigger than many of the states in the United States for people who are living at the primary, extractive hunter level. These programs have worked. They are applied ecology.

Every conference I have ever been at comes out with the answer that we need more research. Nobody is going to deny this. Increasing pressures demand ever more finely honed instruments.

At the moment we are well beyond the ax stage in many parts of North America, and we need to hone our research instruments finer for the greater pressures that are to come.

GLACKEN: Before calling on the other members of the Conference who expressed a desire to speak, I will ask Mr. Nicholson if he cares to comment on these remarks.

NICHOLSON: I have two comments. First of all, I am concerned not to give the impression that it is anything but highly desirable to have the sort of discussion which we are supposed to be having this morning on the wider aspects of environmental problems, on esthetics, and so on. I think this is something which it would be hard to match in Britain, for example, and I think you are developing a valuable perspective for anyone who has any responsibility for action; I am not at all a supporter of taking action without an adequate appreciation of the background such as this meeting is giving.

Secondly, I agree that there is a great deal of research going on and there are a great many ecologists in wildlife management and so on in North America outside the ecological sphere. But however you look at it, there is a big deficit of ecologists who are organized in a team which can argue and reason with their opposite numbers in economics, in civil engineering, and so on.

I would put the stress not so much on the need for research as on the need for a body of researchers and staff scientists, not necessarily engaged in research—sometimes in advisory work, in management—who can get to grips with their opposite numbers, whether in forestry, engineering, or economics. This is what I think you most seriously lack.

GREGG: There is an organization in the country called the Interprofessional Commission on Environmental Design; ecologists are not a part of it, and perhaps they ought to be. This is a body established by the American Institute of Architects, the American Institute of Planners, the American Society of Landscape Architects, and the American Society of Civil Engineers. It has recently been expanded to include the National Society of Professional Engineers, the Consulting Engineers Council and the American Institute of Civil Engineers.

I have talked to these people but I have never heard them mention ecology as a design discipline. Yet I am sure that many of the planners—I think McHarg has been in on this—are trying to call attention to ecological principles within this commission.

This is something, an institutional arrangement, that might offer some promise for spreading an ecological point of view among related disciplines.

DANSEREAU: That there should be so many members of the ecological society is one thing, but the kind of ecologists who are able to contribute to the work mentioned by Mrs. Strong is another.

I feel extremely pessimistic about this. The ecologists are just not doing their own work. This map that we have on the wall has been done by a geographer. The best maps of vegetation that we have in North America are done by foresters, by land-use planners, by the wildlife people. Plant ecologists are not interested in vegetation and know a good deal less about vegetation than animal ecologists, who have on the whole a better understanding of it.

At this time the status of ecologists who are interested in vegetation is a wavering one. They are on the periphery of biology departments, however defined, somewhat welcome in geography departments, openly embraced by anthropologists.

So there is a state of flux among those who could contribute to such things as helping to describe the landscape, which is what we are interested in in this Conference.

What is the landscape like? We want it described. It has to be described and mapped in its own terms. Vegetation must be studied, not for what it does but for what it is. This is the first step. Then, of course, functional analysis should by all means be brought in. This can be done, presumably, much better by an ecologist than by anyone else.

But, where are the ecologists to do the job? I suggest that our supply is not adequate, that our graduate schools at this time are not turning out the people who can do the job.

DARLING: I want to mention something I felt yesterday, and feel even more today: Can we stop at the end of this Conference? There must be some kind of follow-up of our exchange of views. The aim of these four days is not to produce a blueprint of what the world is going to do, but to talk it over, to be conscious of the difficulties we have ahead of us.

If it is the wish of the Conference that there should be a follow-up I would be very glad indeed. That doesn't mean to say we can do anything about it at the moment.

CALDWELL: I would like to comment a little further with respect to John Milton's observation on the need for more ecologists and in so doing add also a word of support for what Frank Darling has just suggested by way of the importance of follow-up.

I think the number of available ecologists has a great relevance to the other questions that we have been considering this morning—namely, the relative priorities of research and action.

In higher education we usually find ways to pay for education and training where an employment market is evident. I am not sure that if we had several hundred additional ecologists produced the day after tomorrow we would be able to find appointments for these ecologists, that we would find places for them in the budgets of government agencies or research institutions.

Also, if we had such jobs for ecologists, we might initially find it difficult to recruit candidates into the universities. It is a common observation these days that the graduate student, at least in the university—and I would suppose most professional ecologists would be the product of graduate education—will have to be subsidized in some manner. There needs to be some kind of financial support, not only in fellowships, but in facilities for their studies. And these would not be forthcoming immediately.

We have here a kind of ecology of higher education that may throw some light on how one gets more of any kind of professional person. This is a simultaneous development of opportunity for employment and a corresponding enlargement of support to meet this need in the university. The two developments should be reciprocal.

This would suggest that the question of priority between the further development of knowledge, of more research and of action, is possibly best answered in this way: that we need both, and that both must go ahead simultaneously; that we will not get more ecologists simply because in theory we need them. We won't get them unless there is a demand for them someplace. Somebody has to provide the institutional and financial means for their preparation. They have to have an opportunity to go to work.

On the other hand, we won't have them even when we need them if we don't provide the training. It is a cyclical process. One has to break in probably at more than one point. I would like to conclude by suggesting that the professional ecologist also has a role in this development but it has not been adequately performed, partly because the ecologists are few in numbers. But it has been very adequately performed by some individuals.

For thirty-five years, for instance, Paul Sears has been speaking and writing on the need for and conditions of effective applied ecology. This has been a leadership function and we need more of it in applied ecology. We do not, for the most part, in education, engineering, or public health, attempt to take a feeling of the popular pulse before we decide what we ought to do. We do not really go to the mass of the people and ask them do they want more of this or more of that in most of these areas of public service.

We attempt certainly to find out what may be good for people. We may also discover, through various political processes, what people want. But we also have a history of leadership which can be demonstrated in the public health movement, in the movement for public education, civil rights, and many other areas.

We need to increase the leadership role on the part of the ecologists. It must be their task to interpret the meaning of ecological principles for public policies, to help the public official weigh alternative lines of action in environmental issues, and to persuade the public to consider ecological facts in the formulation of public program.

The more of these people that we can get through the universities, and the more that we can meaningfully employ in projects that can be interpreted to the public, I think the closer we will come to closing this environmental gap—of sufficient ecologists, adequate research, and meaningful interpretation of results to the public.

BOULDING: I would like to plead with the ecologists to realize what a treasure they have—one they don't seem to be aware of. The ecological point of view is an integrating point of view for all science, social and physical. You don't realize this.

You think of ecology as something that is a study of nature in the absence of man, and this is nonsense. The ecology of the aspidistra is just as interesting as the ecology of the whooping crane. The ecology of Harlem is just as interesting as the ecology of Yellowstone Park. In fact, much more interesting, more complex. The ecology of the suburb is much more interesting than the ecology of the wilderness. Who studies the ecology of the suburb? It is absolutely fascinating.

Yet ecologists have this absurd point of view that all they are interested in is the countryside. I have nothing against the countryside. In fact, I am in favor of people loving it. That is fine. But you ought to love the city, too, and especially the suburb, because this is where people are going to live. This is just as interesting.

You are missing an enormous opportunity in the schools. Ecology ought to be the guiding principle of elementary and secondary education. The physicists and mathematicians have caught on to this and have gone to the schools and absolutely reformed them, reorganized the teaching of mathematics and physical sciences in the schools. How many ecologists are really interested in the reform of the educational system of the level of the high schools and the elementary schools? Practically none. Yet here you have a key, it seems to me, to the whole reorganization of the education system of the whole world through the use of the ecological framework. You don't do this because of your hatred of man, because you think ecology is the study of nature in the absence of man, and there isn't any nature except in the absence of man. This is an absolute absurdity.

Man is an integral part of nature, even in the wilderness, even if he goes into it with a helicopter.

It seems to me the ideal of ecologists is a world of ghosts who just won't leave any trace, who won't make any paths, won't even disturb the air. This is so idiotic.

(*Laughter*)

Here we have man, by far the most interesting species on this planet. If you develop the ecological idea, as I suggested, and start studying social species, criminals, the role structure, the degradation of urban environments as well as natural environments, you have a key to enormous numbers of these problems; and you are just not using it.

I am mad at you. I am really mad at you!

(*Laughter and applause*)

NICHOLSON: I think this is so unfair that I must make a statement. The Biological Sciences Curriculum Study centered in Boulder at the University of Colorado is doing what Boulding suggested. It is brilliantly done and it is being applied in the American schools.

MC HARG: There is ecology, which has been described by Dr. Boulding; but there is also the ecological point of view. These are different things. The people who read Aldo Leopold, Huxley, Bates, and so on may or may not be ecologists, and it doesn't matter. They get a view of the physical and biological world which is more comprehensible, as a result of these insights.

I went to hire ecologists and built a program based on ecology, and I think this narrow view of ecology is much too small. One wants to see medical ecology reconstituted. Dubos says medical science is in a narrow compartment unconcerned with the physical world, unconcerned with the effect of environment upon great populations and distribution of disease.

Clearly the medical sciences have to be permeated with this ecological view. And I think this is absolutely true of planning. It is also true of engineering. The engineer is a man with the biggest blinkers on. Glaucoma is his by choice, a way of isolating most of the physical and biological world and seeing only big dam foolishness or a world of pipes. And finally this is true of the law, which still views nature as chattels.

I am much more concerned with seeing the ecological point of view permeating society and education than with seeing the sole preparation of ecologists in the narrower sense, although these are terribly important people, too.

If you look at the traditional Japanese agriculture, language, poetry, painting, architecture, village building, and their gardens, you see we don't need twentieth-century technology. They are very simple people with a tradition which can produce more art than we can dream about. It is good ecology and it is great art.

The things we do in comparison are brutish. Clearly, good ecology, art, can come from societies that don't have twentieth-century culture. On the other hand, in the Midtown Manhattan Study a lot of coldblooded people from Cornell Medical School sifted through the sample material and sampled 10,000 people and said 20 per cent of them should be in institutions, 60 per cent of them have demonstrable mental—whatever they are —aberrations, and only 20 per cent are clearly free of mental illnesses. From Park Avenue to the East River, including presidents of corporations, the leadership of America—and 20 per cent of them should be in institutions.

One really wants to know what effects the physical and biological environments we are making are having upon physical and mental health. This we absolutely have to know.

I have been given the job of doing a study of lower Manhattan and from Canal Street to the Battery, from the East River to the Hudson. What should I do? I have read the Midtown Manhattan Study. I have no good information. I have two choices. One, you can say people should live there; and the other reasonable thing to do is say clear-cut this son-of-a-gun and plant it to grass. These two extremes are equally reasonable and there is no evidence to support either of them, and this is outrageous.

(*Laughter*)

OVINGTON: At the beginning I put forward a plea for more ecological research. In a sense this has boomeranged a little. I was a bit shocked to hear this morning that we had such a knowledge of the effects of fire that we really didn't need to do any more research—that we had this knowledge of the multiple effects of fire.

I think this is complete nonsense. I don't think ecologists have got anywhere near enough information. This is not to say that they can't give an answer based on an appraisal of their own. I think many are very farsighted in doing this, and can make a good guess at what is the situation, and what is the answer to it, on rather limited knowledge.

There are some fine ecologists with this insight. But I think it must be recognized that the whole nature of ecology is changing. A few years ago "ecology" was a dirty word. I think ecology is growing up now and is being recognized. I think it important, therefore, that it be put on a much firmer foundation.

This isn't going to come quickly; it won't come quickly enough. But there has to be a starting point, and we do need to encourage the right kind of research. I think ecologists have to get themselves reoriented to try to answer the kind of questions which are now being asked them. This is our challenge. I think some of the knowledge we have isn't quite the information that is needed to answer the role which ecologists are having to play in this modern world.

GLACKEN: I certainly agree with a good deal of what Dr. Boulding has just said. There are, however, one or two matters that I think shouldn't remain unchallenged. One of these is that he is recommending, I gather if you take him literally, that we discard all of this nonsense about going out and studying anything but man, because man is the most important and most interesting organism we have to deal with.

We have had a whole horde of ecologists, if you like to call them that, who have done just this. They call themselves sociologists.

DICKINSON: And geographers.

FOSBERG: Some of those go out and look at the earth, which "geo" would imply. Most of them don't, I must say. I don't think that these people have necessarily revolutionized the civilization we live in, either.

People who have studied principally the natural ecosystems have found even there a complex they haven't figured out how to deal with, especially when they tackle the natural ecosystems that are closest at hand.

I have found that I have developed more understanding by looking at some of the apparently simpler ecosystems in the world. I have looked at a good bit of the coral-atoll ecosystem. This is a pretty simple one compared with the deciduous forest or even the prairie.

I rather think that maybe we aren't wasting our time in looking at situations that may be simple enough for us to gain some insight, before we tackle the highly complex interreactions between human beings and the environment that they are influencing.

I have found in comparing natural ecological patterns, such of them as are left in the world, that where similar patterns have been influenced by human beings, the picture becomes more and more blurred and confused with man's impact.

That doesn't mean to me that I shouldn't study it. In fact, I have devoted a great deal of my attention to studying these man-influenced patterns. But I also think I would be wandering around without any direction at all if I hadn't spent a good bit of my time looking at as nearly undisturbed patterns as I could and at some of the simplest natural ecosystems.

It is a good thing in my opinion that some of us are willing to go out and climb around the mountains or go up to the arctic or out to the desert or to the tropics and look at relatively undisturbed situations in order to have some basis for the rest of us to compare our observations of the man-influenced ecosystems which are all that most of us ever can work on. I think that there is room for the whole range of activity from the social anthropologist and sociologist on the one hand, clear down to the person who studies the culture of protozoa on the other extreme—or even the bacteriologist, who is still a kind of ecologist. I wouldn't exclude any of these things. I wouldn't criticize anyone for following his inclinations because that is what he will do best if he has the opportunity.

WHITE: McHarg seemed to me to make a cogent reminder to us that there is a major distinction between ecology and the ecological view. I take it most of us here share something we would loosely define as the ecological view.

Ecology, on the other hand, as I think most of us know, is a discipline which has made relatively modest contributions to scientific knowledge, to the problem with which we are dealing, and which seems unlikely in the near future to make radically larger contributions by virtue of the number of its practitioners and the character of the skills which they command.

We recognize that almost all the problems we have been discussing are ones that call on scientific insights and methods and artistic insights that go far beyond what the average ecologist gets. And indeed the ecologists around the table here are exercising a judgment, experience, and insight which is not being systematically cultivated in most of the schools which pretend to be teaching ecology today.

BRINSER: I think the frustrations that I feel as a consequence of sitting here arise from the fact that most of us seem to be approaching problems from this point of view: that we think of ecology *against* economics.

The problem is, I think, resolved somewhat in the position that Mr. Nicholson took: it is to find the places at which economics, ecology, or whatever sciences you want to bring together can produce supporting answers; and the issues really are to identify those areas in which their supporting answers will be relevant.

This involves, among other things, the very useful distinction between the ecological point of view and the economic. I think one of the most difficult problems for me is understanding what the ecological point of view is, and how useful this is in dealing with economic analysis, in problems involving economic phenomena. I would like to suggest that a fruitful line of approach to the activities of a conference like this is to identify the points of contact that are possible and the opportunities available to explore the ways in which these relevant contacts can be made.

OVINGTON: The point I am trying to make is that I feel an ecologist goes along, whether with an engineer or an economist, very badly equipped because these other people have certain facts at their fingertips. The ecologist often hasn't got the right kind of information to justify his arguments.

For example, the question might arise, should an area have a cover of trees or not? The question can be framed in terms of water supply. We are not in the position of knowing, really, to what extent various tree covers would affect water yield. I think we must first get to grips with this kind of problem, so that we can come in with basic facts.

We talk about human population explosions, and having to fit this in some way with the resources of the world. Yet we haven't any idea of what the over-all prime production of the world is. We don't know what are the major limiting factors. We talk generally without knowing what the gross primary production of the world is and what it might be if we did certain things. This is where I think the ecologist is still in difficulty.

We may have good ideas about this, and I believe some of the intuition is right. But I also think ecology has to grow; it has to come to grips quantitatively and qualitatively with this sort of question. I don't see at present that ecology is getting to this kind of basic question quickly enough.

BRINSER: I understand your position. I agree with it. I think there is this difficulty, however, that the ecologists, from the economists' point of view (if one, as an economist, is permitted to have a point of view about ecologists), have a tendency to collect their information in terms of an assumption about the nature of relevance and truth which overrides the frame of reference within which they operate. This does not happen to be relevant to other sets of decision making that are in the economic area.

What we need is availability of information that is transferable and is neutral with regard to the frame of reference within which it is collected and organized. This does not flow, it seems to me, from a great deal of what is called the ecological point of view. I don't know where it comes from. I think this is where some of our difficulties arise.

DICKINSON: I don't quite know how much longer as a geographer I am supposed to hold in. We are going to hear a good deal this afternoon about human ecology, whether we like it or not. I think much of the problem here, which has arisen, is that we don't seem to decide precisely what place is man's in this whole field we are discussing. This is why at the outset I am completely in agreement with Kenneth Boulding in his attitude.

Last week I was at a conference in Germany of twenty geographers from all over Europe. They were seeking guidelines. We decided that the one central core which gave us a clear objective and field of work was the study of human ecosystems and their special relationships. As Kenneth Boulding said, it is impossible, and absurd, to think of different areas of the earth only in relation to plants, animals, and birds. They are all intertwined, connected in various ways.

I will not forestall what I will say this afternoon. I think we ought to think of trying to get man placed here in his proper place with respect to the future of the environments of North America.

DARLING: I think Kenneth Boulding is flogging a dead horse.

The ecologists I know are distinctly interested in man-invaded habitats, and what man is going to do in the future in these habitats. That is just what we are doing. That is why we are here.

V REGIONAL PLANNING AND DEVELOPMENT

---

* Professor Tunnard has, since 1957, headed Yale's graduate program in city planning. His concern with the relations between the city and its landscape matrix has most recently found expression in *Man-made America—Chaos or Control*, 1963.

Introductory Statement and Summary Remarks

TUNNARD: Our title is "Regional Planning and Development." We hope, if possible, to stick to the subject.

I think this is probably as good a place as any to acknowledge all our debts to Lewis Mumford in the matter of regional planning. Since 1922 he has been writing and educating us all on this subject.

Perhaps it can be said of planners that they follow the advice of Alexander Pope, "Be not the first by whom the new is tried,/Nor yet the last to lay the old aside."

To put the subject in perspective, very briefly, I have two quotations. The first:

"The American city should be a collection of communities where every member has a right to belong. It should be a place where every man feels safe on his streets and in the house of his friends. It should be a place where each individual's dignity and self-respect is strengthened by the respect and affection of his neighbors. It should be a place where each of us can find the satisfaction and warmth which comes only from being a member of the community of man. This is what man sought at the dawn of civilization. It is what we seek today."

This is the President's message on cities of March 2 last.

Second, let me quote some figures:

At a time when the 1960 population doubles, around the year 2010, perhaps it will need seventy-five million additional acres of urban land. This is only 3.9 per cent of the land area of the continental United States, or 18 per cent of the area currently in use as cropland. In fact, some SMSAs have gained rather than lost cropland recently. In addition to these U.S. figures we have God's country to the north, where I was born and have emigrated from. So we are going to be faced with the extraordinary phenomenon of decaying centers, and the leapfrogging that is taking place in the usual urban-fringe phenomenon, as well as having plenty of other land to ruin as we choose.

One other point here. The economists yesterday were trying to find a relationship with the ecologists, but I think they may have already done so. The new discipline of regional science, which I suppose could be called a branch of economic geography, is in a way an attempt at the ecology of man. At least on the macroscale, because it shows (although in rather general terms so far) how man thrusts together in cities, what the rules are about this, what he seems to want to be doing through his use of the economic process. There appears to be an order to this process, and Professor Dickinson will probably have something to say about that.

Also yesterday the question of beauty was raised. For a scientist this can perhaps be a rather indefinite term. However, I think we can say that we know that beauty exists because man has always admired beautiful things, just as we can say that we know people *can* be happy because we know—through the work and writings of poets and the work of artists— that people *have* been happy. Presumably there may be even some people who are happy now whom we can examine and find out what this phenomenon really is.

And finally, I don't like to think of planners as just problem solvers. I like to think of them as people who are concerned with the quality of life, both in the city and in the country. If we think of all our work in terms of problem solving, we are not going to inspire anybody very strongly, or urge many people to action, even though we know there are frightful problems connected with urban life. If we could think about raising its quality, this would be a better approach.

I am going to call on our speakers. I will ask Dr. Dansereau to give us now a word on the ecology of man.

DANSEREAU: Mr. Chairman, if I might somewhat disrespectfully knock together the heads of Kenneth Boulding and Ray Fosberg, that might ignite the spark which I need to light the lantern of Diogenes which I seem to need now.

I find that I can agree with them on both sides of the statements that they made this morning. They are not contradictory statements. Whereas the ecological point of view, as Dr. White has pointed out, is an old philosophic concept which ecology has adopted as its center. The science of ecology has largely developed without man, and there is a good reason for that. The same reason, I suggest, that the science of psychology, which first developed by addressing itself to man as an object, had to backtrack in order to establish objective scientific principles to simpler and more controllable organisms. I think that we find in the same way that we have been obliged and still must refer to situations in nature, to the play of heredity and environment in nature without interference of man as a background for the establishment of a human ecology. We do not have at this stage, I suggest, a science of human ecology. Much of what passes for human ecology is sociology, just plain sociology. The rest is ecological research in which man's role in changing the face of the earth has been considered. This does not add up to an ecology of man.

We have reached the point where an ecology of man should be emerging, derived from the same methodology which has served us in good stead so far, and which will allow us to proceed by analogy, and maybe by something more than analogy, to describe habitat, to evaluate and measure the flow of resources, including money, which is not unlike the storage of starch and other forms of energy that are not immediately used but eventually usable in a system. I fully agree with Boulding that the suburbs and the cities should be studied as the habitat of man. In a very similar sense to what we have been doing about plants and animals.

Whereas we have convinced ourselves that the ecosystem is a whole and must be studied as a whole, yet it has to be taken apart, and a proper ecological study is not one which is based primarily on one organism but on all of the organisms that take part in the utilization of resources at a certain place during a certain period of time. In that sense, a man who lives in Westchester County and commutes to New York and works in a skyscraper participates in several ecosystems.

I think we have many leads, none of which has been very well followed so far. Regional planning offers us some hope of a framework within which we can work. However, human ecology and regional planning or city planning are not to be equated any more. I would suggest that city planning is to the ecology of man what hygiene or public health is to the science of medicine. The ecology of man is a very broad subject, one in which we are only beginning to find our way. The kind of training that should be available in our universities and in our schools in order to prepare people for this task is only emerging in the proportion that we become conscious of what the necessities—methodological and other—are.

By focusing our discussion this afternoon on the requirements of regional planning, and the more limited requirements of city planning, we come close to defining the variety of smaller units which are habitat units, ecosystem units, within which the ecology of man develops.

TUNNARD: Thank you. Professor Dickinson, of the University of Leeds, is another pioneer in his book *City, Regions and Regionalism*—and on another level in his *West European City*. However, I have asked him to talk not about Europe but about this country, if he will.

DICKINSON: My paper on the process of urbanization was a difficult assignment. I propose to concentrate now simply on one or two main points. In approaching this problem I have tried to keep in view the object of our Conference—namely, to consider the future of the North American habitat. Quite clearly, we are here concerned with the urbanized habitat.

It seems to me that the two key points in the spread of urbanism in this country are first mobility, and secondly the extremely high and constantly increasing level of living, which means that there are now more people engaged in providing services than there are actually manufacturing goods. My next point—my first main point—is a development from Lewis Mumford's concept, in that a city, or any urban center in a fixed place on the earth's surface, is a point of attraction and a point of repulsion.

In consequence it is essentially a center of reactions or of phenomena that are evident not only in the use of the land but in the attitudes, movements, and ways of life of people. In general, theoretically, we can assume that the number and complexity of these relationships diminish with increasing distance from the center.

The city will have what I call a city settlement area. This is the area within daily reach of the economic center.

My third point is that these areas, the cities—particularly the big cities—are often so close together that they interlock and overlap. We get these clusters of standard metropolitan areas, or even urbanized areas, which form what are often popularly referred to in this country as urban regions.

The fourth point emphasizes that we should have a framework of reference as to how far urbanization extends. There is no such thing as a clear-cut division between rural and urban. There is something that we will have to call a continuum. At any rate, urbanization extends further than urban land uses and the contiguous and continuous urban land uses.

With all due respect to Jean Gottmann, he didn't face this problem. He took a contiguous cluster of standard metropolitan areas. He didn't attempt to define the areas in which various degrees of urbanization prevail in terms of particular criteria.

I have attempted this. I have attempted to define the urbanized areas of North America in terms of three criteria. Using these criteria you get different areas. When I am told that one and a half per cent of the United States is urbanized, obviously it doesn't mean very much because that covers not much more than national parks.

So that I have taken three criteria and produced maps. It took about two years to do this. The first map is one based upon density of population, taking a density of 500 persons per square mile.

The second map, which was much easier to produce, was simply to map on an adequate scale the boundaries of the standard metropolitan statistical areas, which mainly are county areas, and which supposedly include the counties in which the people are predominantly oriented toward the centers of cities.

A third was much more difficult because neither of the former maps, it seems to me, ranges far enough to embrace those areas which are within reach of urbanization—in terms of commuting, in terms of entertainment, organization, and so on. One needs some sort of wider limit to use as a consistent basis for defining wider urbanized areas. I took—you can agree or disagree—a twenty-mile radius from the center of every standard metropolitan area with over 100,000 people.

The latter map reveals that the Atlantic seaboard area extends throughout upstate New York, central Pennsylvania, to the middle-western states as far as the Mississippi. It includes the whole of southern Michigan. In this vast area there are three inner layers which are more than twenty miles from a city. One of these is in the Catskills, a second is in the North Appalachian Plateau, and a third is curiously enough in the Middle West —right in the south between St. Louis and Chicago.

In other words, in nearly the whole of the northeastern states to well south of the Ohio, all places lie within twenty miles of one or more metropolitan cities. It seems to me safe to say that this area indicates the outer framework within which the urban growth of the next few decades will take place.

The final question is what kind of processes are going on within this area which are determining urban growth and urban expansion. There are two major processes to which a good deal of attention has been given and that we still don't know enough about. The first is the process of centralization, the second is the process of dispersion.

I am intrigued by the concept which I got from Mr. Tunnard on interurbia. Interurbia is embraced, you see, within this area of dispersion and centralization.

TUNNARD: Coleman Woodbury teaches regional planning. I would call your attention to the passage in his essay in which he defines the amorphous term "region." You see that there are many types of regions, and we will return to this afterward, I hope, in our discussion.

WOODBURY: My paper is essentially an essay in definition. I have four excerpts from it that seem to me worth calling to your attention in a summary.

First I defined a region. As the term is used in regional planning, a region is an area whose inhabitants are tied together in economic and social, and sometimes governmental relationships, many of which are determined or strongly influenced by history, tradition, and by natural features of the areas—for example, climate, physiography, and soil types. I am perfectly aware that there are other forms of definition, but this seems to me the one in fact that is being used in our attempt to do regional planning in this country.

As to what planning essentially is, I was foolhardy enough to try a definition of that. I am talking about one kind of planning. Someone said this morning there is a difference between ecology and the ecological point of view. I think it was Mr. White. This certainly is true of planning, too. One of the greatest difficulties for those of us who are interested in planning and are trying to discuss it, both among ourselves and with others, is the very loose and inclusive definitions and connotations of the word.

I am talking about governmental planning, central planning as distinguished from departmental or functional planning—central in the sense that it is done by an agency concerned with a region, and with a wide range of the activities called for in the development of that region. And I distinguish rather than separate it from planning for highways or open space or water supply or waste disposal or any other of these departmental or functional types of planning.

So I say that regional planning is the process of preparing in advance and in a reasonably systematic fashion recommendations for policies and courses of action, with careful attention to their probable by-products or side effects, to achieve accepted objectives in the common life of urban regional localities or communities. Most of my paper is simply a gloss on that definition.

I also tried to point out there are three conditions of effective regional planning—at least three. First, that the planning shall be done for a governmental unit that is coterminous in area with the area planned for, and that has powers that are roughly correlative with the range of the recommendations that come from the planners. Second, that the locality or area in which the regional planning is done must have a reasonably developed sense of community. Third, the regional planning process and the regional planning agency must have what some people call a constituency—that is, a group of people, supporters and in part critics, whose range of interest is roughly the same as that of the planning agency.

Very clearly, if you take these as conditions of effective regional planning in the United States, or anywhere else, there is no effective regional planning being done at the present time. There isn't a single regional area that I know of that can meet those requirements. We have made considerable headway in the last ten years, and at a slower rate previously, perhaps, but I don't think regional planning is what I would call effective yet.

Finally, implied in my definition, I look upon planning as simply one element in the policy-formulating or, as some people prefer to say, decision-making process. I think it is an important and even unique part of that process. The final steps in that process are taken not by the planners but in the political forum and by politically responsible people. I admit that sometimes the outcome of this political process is disappointing to many people; historically you can criticize it in pretty drastic ways. However, if anyone has found a more effective and more defensible way of arriving at those decisions, I don't know it.

TUNNARD: I think it is appropriate at this time to call on Dr. Farness.

FARNESS: Very briefly, I have identified five functional types of regional planning—that are actually occurring in society today—by their major purpose and objective, which shapes their perception and their images. I call them resource planning, aimed at economic development; urban planning, at the metropolitan scale, which is aimed at developing an urban habitat; regional facility planning, emphasizing technoeconomic efficiency; ecological planning for biological fitness and health; and social institution planning to effect progressive design and elaboration of our social institutions.

These forms of planning occur pretty much in isolation from each other. They are guided by different value orientations, and they result in different expressions or forms in the environment.

I then move on to a brief description of what I call economic dominance in our cultural value system. Our settlements in cities are obvious expressions of this kind of dominance of economic interest. The planning that is going on today is subsumed under merely mechanical growth projections, reductive explanations of city form, and so forth. There is no cultural understanding at the popular planning level today of the dynamics of social change. And from this perspective of economic dominance in the working of society the ecological, the esthetic, ethical, and other kinds of value orientations are simply by-passed.

If we presume some different organization of human settlement, this will require a modification of our cultural purposes, because the two are interrelated. The outer is an image of the inner.

I have a brief discussion of system size under the technological stimulus, discussing the problem of how we are to understand our systems, to comprehend them, where the span of human attention is limited.

We need to bring together these five types of planning and their value orientations in some kind of a new social institution organized around concrete geographic areas of the United States, where we can bring together this confusing array of federal, state, and private planning programs of all kinds with all value systems so that they can be interrelated in a concrete environment. And such institutions would take many different forms in many parts of the country. They could provide multiple-purpose functions, for field administration of federal and state programs, for regional research, policy making, planning center, academic research, and so forth.

I feel if this kind of institution is not invented and actualized that our political process will simply break down, that we will end up with some kind of decision-making system wholly run by the experts.

TUNNARD: Dr. Fosberg?

FOSBERG: I am not quite sure that I fit into this panel—that is, my paper on restoration of lost and degraded habitats has no very direct logical relation to planning. We were agreed last night that we would confine our remarks to three sentences, of which one had to do with regional planning. I don't normally, I hope, construct such sentences as I am going to read you. But in order to get it into three, I have to be a little bit Germanic.

(*Laughter*)

First, habitats and the kinds and degrees of destruction or degradation of them are so diverse that many techniques of restoration are necessary and available. Perhaps a truism.

Second, natural and seminatural habitats are rapidly becoming scarce commodities, and the time is approaching when the values placed on them will justify and indeed make mandatory the rehabilitation or restoration of any artificially degraded land available.

Third, the restoration of degraded habitats to natural or seminatural conditions will become an essential tool of the regional planner or, more exactly, of the agencies that execute the recommendations of the planners, since so much of the area of North America has felt or will suffer under the heavy hand of man.

TUNNARD: Mr. McHarg, please.

MC HARG: My paper on ecological determinism has an independent existence only if you assume that Dansereau said what he said before I am allowed to speak, and that I am qualified by the gentle historical sense of Christopher Tunnard. I exist because other people have said there are other things which allow me to exist.

However, this being so—this is entirely true. My statement is a brash statement unless taken in context, and can exist only within this context.

It starts from the presumption that a sort of primitive ecology accomplished a great amount in the eighteenth century. Clearly, this experiment was appropriate only for a pastoral environment in England. It never confronted the problem of the city. I know a little of Scotland, less of England, and not much of the United States, where I work in a variety of environments. I need ecological information before I can even begin to equal that which was accomplished by eighteenth-century landscape architects. This requires simply that ecologists subvert themselves to my purpose, or at least some ecologists subvert themselves to my purpose.

I want, first of all, an ecosystem inventory, which starts with Küchler. Küchler said the whole Allegheny Plateau is a forest, and it is not. Brown spent a lifetime showing that it wasn't. But Brown really isn't very exact when you get to the Philadelphia region. So while we accept Küchler and Brown as approximations we must proceed through the work of Drs. Wherry and Fogg to the flora of Pennsylvania and progress to the specificities of Dr. McCormick on the Pine Barrens, Dr. Ruth Patrick on limnology, and so on. But the available information varies in quality, extent, and mapping. The necessary information is simply not available in useful forms.

This is only the beginning because we need a description of natural processes. We want to know about underlying geology and surface soils and the water regimen and the degree to which marshes perform a role in the water cycle, diminishing flood, drouth, water storage, and so on.

We need identification of these natural processes in their larger context. One must be able to see Philadelphia with the coastal plain, the Piedmont and the uplands, but these in turn related to the Appalachian Plateau, the Ridge and Valley Province, the Great Valley. We want certainly to know something about the limiting factors.

I don't think I need to develop this. These are well understood in the regeneration of old fields. But many of these are enormously important as indicators of succession, stability, and retrogression.

We need desperately, I think, the attribution of value, even if these values are tentative. The ecologist should be able to tell us which of all the ecosystems does he believe constitute the greatest variety, for whatever purpose he believes justifies this value.

I made a tentative proposal of four types of value. First intrinsic, the land itself, without any intervention as a value, beautiful scenery, recreational use, beauty, scientific value. Second, productivity, in terms of its capacity to produce, value added by man's actions on a piece of land.

Third, the conception of work performed, which may be the role of water regimen, flood control, water storage, erosion control, air shed, and so on. And then the concept of negative value, those places where catastrophe or calamity can occur, where the land might subside, volcanoes, earthquakes, hurricane paths, avalanches, mud slides, forest fires, and so on.

Finally, the conception of the replacement value. The land, in fact, not only has a value corresponding to sale price or assessed valuation, but has a value in terms of natural processes at larger scales.

I would like to know, then, given this sort of information, the degree to which these environments are prohibitive to intervention, or permissive.

Starker Leopold called this friability and durability. One would like to know, of all lands, which lands can best support man or his interventions of one sort or another. And which cannot. For any region, where can man intervene in a massive way? Where can he not intervene at all?

Ross Mackay told us the tundras are enormously susceptible. Can we get some hierarchy of susceptibility? Can we get some hierarchy from which man can select to find areas which are tolerant to man—environments where man might well live?

Finally, we want indicators of stability and instability, and the most important of these, I think, are indicators within the city.

I want to know when the major inhabitants with man in a city are rats, starlings, lice, cockroaches, fleas, and bedbugs, and the only trees are ailanthus, whether or not a threshold has been crossed and evacuation or redevelopment is necessary. At what point does the canary expire, and the litmus change color? I want the morphology which the ecologist can give as the basis for the creative act of the landscape architect.

TUNNARD: Thank you. Dennis Durden works in the middle of downtown Cincinnati, but characteristically he has written about empty areas.

DURDEN: First, throughout interurbia there are numerous habitats where the landscape has heretofore shown no imprint of man's current activities—places where man is not dominant. These habitats, these "empty areas," are now being assaulted with recreation-oriented seasonal resorts on a large scale.

Second, this growing trend is fueled by our affluence and leisure but it is motivated in part by the desire of large numbers of people to experience nature in some fashion—often vaguely defined. However, as it evolves, this new type settlement is actually adding to the homogenization of our regional landscapes. The forms and the landscape expressions of these new colonies resemble suburban developments in and nearer the heart of the urban region.

Third, with only a very few exceptions, these new colonies make no pretense at recognizing ecological principles. Generally man in these new colonies appears bent on subjugating rather than harmonizing with the prevailing environment.

Fourth, the pattern of settlement by these colonies contrasts with our traditional notions of how empty areas are settled.

Fifth, because these new colonies are promoted by entrepreneurs in generally rural areas where governmental power is not well established or well staffed, this new type of settlement does not yet lend itself well to regulation by typical tools of planning.

TUNNARD: Mr. Nicholson this morning was telling us that we contributed to his knowledge, and that he had been able to apply the knowledge practically in the British countryside. We can also say the same thing in reverse —that the British have come over here and given us a great deal of expertise which we have been able to use practically. I especially mention the early housing movement in this country which the late Dr. Winslow, the public health expert, said had been greatly encouraged by visits by Raymond Unwin and Barry Parker. This process is still going on. We are profiting from the British experience exceedingly.

It is nice that we have in this particular field two British representatives. Of the two, I will first call on Dr. Steers.

STEERS: My topic is unlike that of other members of the panel. I am concerned with the coast. Although my direct interest is that of a physical geographer, I have also had a good deal to do with what might be called the use of the coast. It is from that point of view that I speak this afternoon.

It is essential to realize that the coast is a narrow belt. There is only one of it in any country, and it is all too easily spoiled, and once spoiled—that is usually the end!

Nevertheless it is difficult from this point of view to define the coast. The coastal area may reach back to a mountain range; in other types of country it is very narrow. Each separate locality presents its own problems.

In the United States the coast from, roughly, south of New York all the way to the Mexican frontier is very flat. There are numerous barrier islands and extensive marshlands. Human use of the sandy beaches is great and increasing. It is a coast which can suffer great damage in storms and hurricanes, and wave and wind action is all important. Dunes are extensive. Dunes, however, are very easily altered. Man, by making paths through them and by destroying the vegetation, may lead to the wind regaining mastery and the consequent blowing away of the sand.

Moreover, the buildings of whatever kind put up on these open sandy coasts often completely alter the natural landscape. It cannot be emphasized too much that man has already altered—many people would say ruined—many of the natural features of this long stretch of coast, and that relatively few parts remain in a natural condition.

North of, approximately, New York the coast is picturesque, and with its rocky promontories and numerous coves and harbors retains much of its beauty. Moreover, many of the small towns "fit" into this coastal landscape.

The Pacific coast is entirely different. There are many fine lines of cliff and a number of sandy beaches as well as spectacular features like the Golden Gate. It is nevertheless surprising how much of it is partly or wholly used by man, in one way or another. It is also subject to earthquakes, and profiles may alter considerably as a result of them. As along the Gulf and Atlantic coasts, there are several state parks, beautiful in themselves, but sometimes a little artificial in appearance.

It is most essential to emphasize the vulnerability of the coast and the ever-increasing pressure on it. In the last two decades the influence of the automobile has been profound. There is no doubt that the car is the greatest enemy of the coast, not only in the United States but also in much of northwestern Europe.

TUNNARD: Dr. Hall?

HALL: The research project I outline here is conceived within a specific British context. But I hope that it does relate to the central theme of this Conference, for it is easily applicable to a North American context, and indeed I hope that it may prove possible to set up a joint Anglo-United States project on this theme.

The problem is that of the impact of the city on its surrounding countryside and the changes in that impact over recent time. Of course there are many such impacts—residential, industrial, commercial, educational, recreational, and so on—and they will extend over different areas of rural land. One major aspect of the study will be to distinguish the impacts as carefully as possible.

I hope that this will provide useful generalizations for planners in telling them about the possible future impact of cities on their surrounding rural areas. To try to do this the central method will be to look at what people actually get: what they actually take in terms of categories of land. In other words, to look at their observed behavior—an essential method of the social sciences. But we shall have to ask, too, whether these choices expressed in events are in any way distorted. The economists may be able to tell us a great deal about this, about the ways in which land may go to the wrong purposes because the price system is distorted in favor of certain purposes rather than other purposes.

The essential method, though, will be to start with observed changes in land use, including those changes brought about by the use of the countryside by urban dwellers for recreation purposes—changes which are perhaps not strictly measurable in terms of formal categories of land use. Clearly, difficult problems of measurement are involved here. Then it would try to relate these observed changes to social and economic factors, so as to try to develop certain relationships, which might be used to project forward the likely future impacts, both in terms of measured land use and of educational impact. Finally, the study might lead to a last stage—

a stage coming well after the others—which would be an attempt to provide better criteria, especially economic criteria, for the decisions which have to be made by planners about the future use of land.

TUNNARD: My own paper deals mostly with scenic values and recommendations. We need a larger unit for scenic preservation than can be obtained by, say, the scenic highway or the easement of the scenic highway. This recommendation is made in the 1962 UNESCO report on the preservation and safeguarding of the beauty and character of landscapes and sites.

This does bring up a picture which I think was reinforced by Mr. Lowenthal this morning when he talked about multipurpose use in Britain. We do practice it in this country but perhaps not so consistently as he suggested it is done in Britain.

ECOLOGICAL IMPACT AND HUMAN ECOLOGY

Pierre Dansereau*

* Dr. Dansereau is head of the Department of Ecology at the New York Botanical Garden and Adjunct Professor of Botany at Columbia University. For a number of years he taught at Montreal, where he was Dean of the Faculty. An inveterate field man, he has accumulated an unparalleled firsthand understanding of the structure of vegetation from the tropics to the arctic.

INTRODUCTION

Ecologist, habitat, value. With what charge should we load these terms before we embark upon a consideration of their relevance to each other? Who are the ecologists? What is a habitat, how many kinds are there, and where are they? As for values, they are only dimly perceived by the scientist. Or should I say the scientist *as such?*

I will nevertheless argue that the ecologist is the only one who really knows about habitats and who can properly advise concerning their management if given reference to his society's values, with which, of course, he may or may not be in agreement! It is he who can assess renewability in space and time. In this he offers an *informed* opinion that should have more weight than the man-in-the-street's. But it is hardly he who can decide, as an ecologist, what is worth renewing, conserving, or sacrificing. As a citizen, he is of course no less competent and no less involved than others.

If my task consists in trying to outline his rôle by what he brings to it that cannot be expected of others, then some examination of the origins of ecology, of its field of operation, and of the variety of ecologists is in order. And then, a separate view of the requirements and values of the society in which we all live is needed in order to define the function and fitness of those who call themselves or are called ecologists. Finally, through the maze of work on man's impact on the landscape, can we perceive the lineaments of an ecology of man?

ECOLOGY AND ECOLOGISTS

There is no outstanding "history of ecology," in the form of a scholarly, encyclopedic text. Nor do we have the comprehensive "ecology of ecologists" that Paul Sears gave us a blueprint for in 1956. Such a work would fully document the relative determinism of developments in ecological science as strongly tainted by cultural allegiance and regional experience. Thus we might pay attention to the facts that Frederic Clements belongs to the same culture as Mark Twain and John Dewey; that Arthur Tansley is as English as Dickens; that Emilio Huguet del Villar is a compatriot of Salvador de Madariaga, and Josias Braun-Blanquet of Jean-Jacques Rousseau; that Einar du Rietz comes from the land of Strindberg, etc. This amounts to saying that a new science emerges within the matrix of one or more cultures and that long after it has attained its necessary measure of autonomy and has posed, if not answered, the questions that are hopefully encompassed by its competence, it retains something of the coloration and motivation of its intellectual origins, emotional stresses, and cultural formulation. Since it is our purpose to couple the power of the ecologist to the service of social values, this point of departure is germane to our topic.

Let us therefore consider the emergence of ecology as a great intellectual adventure, to be compared with the development of organic evolution and of nuclear physics. This of course has taken place within the walls of institutions and has been variously carried by their structures and curriculum, which in turn has served as a training ground for the release of a newfound science to society as a whole. These three aspects will be considered in sequence.

Emergence of a discipline

Without attempting a condensed history of ecology and even less looking for the more remote mutterings of the principles that guide us today, I think it may be useful to scan the surface of our contemporary science and to reach toward its roots.

I can hardly do this without adhering to a definition. Many years ago, about 1943, Frans Verdoorn had asked me for a contribution to *Chronica Botanica* and I wrote a paper entitled "The Scope of Biogeography and Its Integrative Levels." For many and various reasons this essay, terminated in 1946, was not published in *Chronica Botanica*. It appeared only in 1951, although an abridged version was published in Brazil in 1946. I had then taken my cue from Emmanuel de Martonne whose three-volume *Géographie Physique* (1925–27) devoted one third (by Auguste Chevalier and Lucien Cuénot) to biogeography. It is worth noting that, in the twenties and early thirties, in France, sociology was largely in the hands of the human-geographers and that both ecology and evolution were virtually excluded from the academies. In spite of many shortcomings in its details, infor-

mation, and coverage, it seemed to me that De Martonne, Chevalier, and Cuénot's compass was satisfactory. At least I found it very congenial for the kind of teaching that I wished to initiate in 1942 and 1943. It seemed to me then, as it has later when I published my *Introdução à biogeografia* (1949) and finally my *Biogeography: An Ecological Perspective* (1957a), that there was a need to cover at one sweep "the study of the origin, distribution, adaptation, and association of plants and animals."

In other words, environmental relationships in time and space need to be considered as an integrated subject. The manner of presentation (whether scholarly or didactic) can follow a time-space sequence which begins with geological history and paleobiology, with its movements and distributions of great amplitude (and small scale) and its relatively large gaps in the record ("history of biota"), and move on to the larger-scale and more immediately observable regional phenomena dominated by climate ("bioclimatology"). The next step, where the scale is considerably enlarged, brings the community into focus ("synecology"). Finally, none of this can be made understandable unless the individual organism is detected at the level where exchanges actually occur ("autecology"). Such a successive narrowing down of our visual angle inside the biosphere permits a virtually complete exploration of patterns and processes, of forms and functions in which the interplay of flowing heredity and changing environment operates.

Teilhard de Chardin's (1955) bold reconciliation of spirit and matter and of spirit-in-matter is a challenge to look more widely and more deeply. If man's impact is judged to be of a magnitude without precedent, then it rates a dimension of its own, and as the biosphere variously permeates the lithosphere and the atmosphere, so does the noösphere

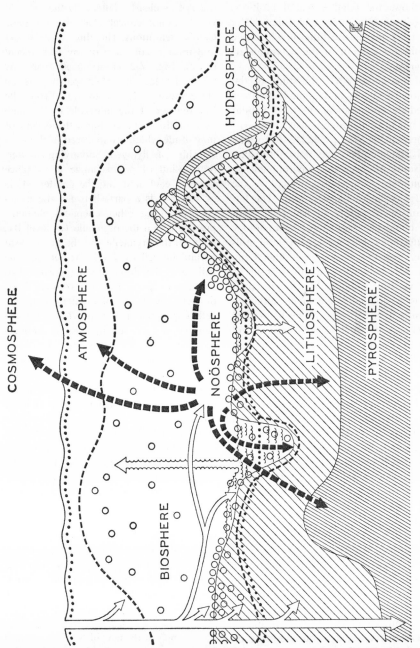

Fig. V-1. Man's environment: the noösphere has gradually penetrated far beyond the confines of the biosphere.

sink into the biosphere and beyond. Fig. V-1 shows the relative spatial positions of environmental units and forces. The year 1957 marks the time at which the noösphere burst out of the confining atmosphere.

I define ecology as "the study of the reaction of plants and animals to their immediate environment, to their habitat (and not to their geographical location)" (Dansereau 1957a, p. 323). According to this statement, ecology does not extend to a study of the whole environment, in its ultimate dimensions, which is the broader realm of biogeography. The latter consists therefore of historical plant and animal geography + bioclimatology + autecology + synecology + land utilization. For this reason and others, my Table I is somewhat modified from its 1957 version. I should like to present it not as a dogmatic statement, although evidently as a personal one. Whatever its merits and its tentative coherence, it will serve to give me my bearings in what is to follow, since it lists the disciplines which I believe to be related to ecology (whether they feed into or out of it).

I shall not press for acceptance of the above definition and of those definitions implied in Table I, as I am aware that they are not in general use. I value the distinction between ecology and biogeography and I maintain at least that we need such a solid framework for environmental science. But I am bound to emphasize also that ecology forms its pivot, and I will not take strong exception to the extension of its meaning which is so often implied or stated. For my present purpose, certainly the full swing of environmental responses is involved, and ecology, however defined, is at its center.

In a much condensed essay (1964a), I had been requested to outline some of the unfinished business of ecology, and I had pointed to the ecosystem and its study ("ecosystemology," says my friend Frank Egler) as the *hard core* of our

science. The term and the object itself are not as clearly defined as they should be. I cannot entirely base myself upon Cain's definitions (in this symposium) and must recall some of my own recent essays. Fig. V-2 (reproduced from my 1963, 1964a, and 1965 papers) is an eleven-note scale (A to K). From the low register of the molecule to the high note of the biota, it shows the orders of magnitude which are involved in the relationship of living to nonliving matter. Some kind of an exchange takes place between each unit and the greater whole of which it is a part: between the molecule (A) and other chemical elements present within the organelle (at level B); between the organelle and the protoplasm within the cell (at level C); between the cells and the differentiating tissue (D); etc. Thus organelle is "environment" for molecule; cell for organelle; tissue for cell; organ for tissue; individual for organ; population for individual; community for population; ecosystem for community; bioclimate for ecosystem; biota for bioclimate. At each level, that which is exterior to the object of study (cell, organ, ecosystem) strikes it in a peculiar manner, by means usually not possible at either a lower or a higher level. This interaction of forces induces a *process* (or series of related processes) that elicits *responses* in plants and animals which give form to a number of *patterns* separately definable at each level. Thus the combined forces inherent in the multispecific population of a community may induce the process of succession which will modify the pattern of the biomass from a predominantly graminoid structure to a scrub.[1]

[1] It is worth noting that whereas the principles that apply at one level (C) do not necessarily apply at the next higher (D) or lower (B) level, they cannot be properly proven unless they are tried at a different level. Thus an explanation of the overlapping ecological valences of the species observed in a stand and which properly determine the *community*

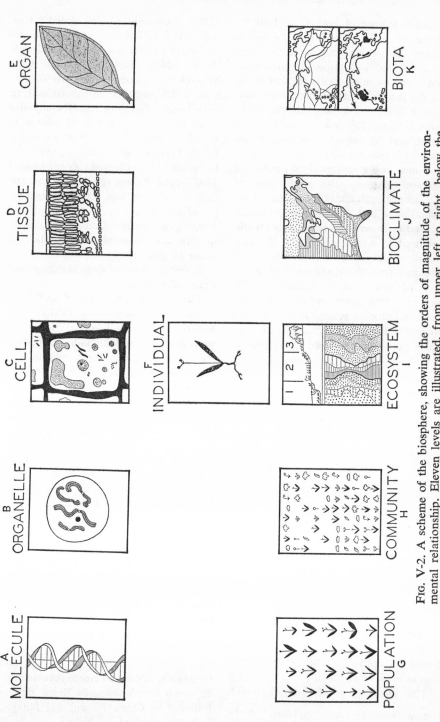

Fig. V-2. A scheme of the biosphere, showing the orders of magnitude of the environmental relationship. Eleven levels are illustrated, from upper left to right, below the level of the individual; from lower left to right, above the level of the individual.

A MOLECULE

B ORGANELLE

C CELL

D TISSUE

E ORGAN

F INDIVIDUAL

G POPULATION

H COMMUNITY

I ECOSYSTEM

J BIOCLIMATE

K BIOTA

Can a science of ecology usefully be drawn on so large a canvas? I would suggest that the levels shown on the lower panel in Fig. V-2 (from population to biota) and more especially the first three, are the proper object of study for ecologists. It is by establishing how the population is affected by soil, air, water, other plants, and by animals, and how it has fitted itself into one or more communities that some of the ecological dimensions of life are measured (this is the core of *autecology*). Similarly, the structure, composition, and dynamics of communities and their dependence upon site qualities need to be integrated into the ecosystem, which in turn is supplied with resources from the landscape (this is the core of *synecology*). Admittedly, the forces at work above and below do very much to influence ecological patterns and processes. But the truly ecological principles have been deduced from the recorded interplay of heredity and environment at levels G, H, and I below. In the Appendix I have drafted these laws as they appear to me. I had formulated them in 1956a and 1957a and restated them in 1962, and have slightly modified them herewith. The formulation is tentative but I believe it is unexceptionably ecological.

I hope to demonstrate the range of applicability of some of these "laws" presently. But I think it useful to consider first the historical origin of the growing autonomy of ecology which led to the insights of which the laws are a summary.

To be sure, ecology has many sources and it keeps going back to them, and receiving from them the steady flow of information upon which it must feed and grow. Turning to my Table I, herewith, I shall attempt to draw the principal filiation at each level.

The *plant geography* of Humboldt

pattern (level H) can be explained only by investigating the *populations* (level G).

(1807), Asa Gray (1846), and De Candolle (1855), followed and summarized by Engler (1899) has led, in our day, to Wulff (1943), Good (1947), and Croizat's (1952) recognition of world areas and, within them, to provincial and regional units. The most recent summation is to be found in the third edition of Good's *Geography of the Flowering Plants* (1964), and a close equivalent is to be read in Darlington's *Zoogeography* (1957). All of these rely heavily on geology, in fact they seek their principal explanations in geological events of the Tertiary and earlier. Cain (1944) made the first world-wide attempt to relate genetics to geography.

In *bioclimatology*, three different lines were followed.

The first can be traced back to Schouw (1823) and to De Candolle (1874) (who greatly influenced Köppen) and who were preoccupied with indicator species and, hopefully, indicator genera that would fit present or past climatic lines. Merriam's life-zone concept (1898) was developed out of this, and Meusel (1943) incorporated it into an historical scheme. Hultén is responsible for a new departure, in his several works that are based on much more detailed chorographical data, starting with his *Outline of the History of Arctic and Boreal Biota During the Quaternary Period* (1937), and his subsequent *Atlas of the Scandinavian Flora* (1950) which has led to even more detailed studies by Perring and Walters (1962) in Britain and by Kujala (1964) in Finland. The latter have employed computing devices.

In fact, Perring and Walters' work is directly derived from the second line of investigation, based on pollen analysis, which had originated under Lagerheim, Von Post, and Erdtman in Sweden, and Godwin in Britain. In North America this approach was initiated by Sears, closely followed by Cain, Hansen, and Potzger. Cain summarized its history and techniques in his *Foundations of Plant Geography* (1944). A probing of Pleistocene and postglacial deposits permits an accurate correlation of geological change and plant migration. It is here that the individual species cease to provide a satisfactory index, and that whole units of vegetation must be considered.

The third line springs from Humboldt again, who is truly the "father of biogeography"! It provides an escape from taxonomic categories and it requires an analysis of vegetation where no *a priori* emphasis is given to any systematic group. Various other properties of the plants are directly measured, and finally the entire plant mass is defined in its structure and behavior. Kerner's monumental *Natural History of Plants* (1896) remains to this day a model for the ecological approach to plant taxonomy, anatomy, and physiology, as his *Pflanzenleben der Donauländer* (1863) is a model for a regional vegetation monograph. Schimper (1903) and Warming (1909), following earlier leads, furthered the life-form concept, which was given a nearly definitive frame by Raunkiær (1905). Del Villar (1929), Rübel (1930), Du Rietz (1931), Allan (1937), and many others have continued in this vein, and more recently Meusel (1951), Schmid (1956), Lems (1960), and myself (1945, 1951b, 1958) have given it a new turn.

Synecology, the study of communities, in spite of Kerner's earlier efforts (1863), really came into its own with Warming (1909), and it was only after 1920 that quantitative methods were commonly used. Overwhelming importance has continued to be given to lists of species present in measured areas, whether the counts were based on estimates (as has been the usage of the Zürich-Montpellier school and of the early British ecologists) or on individual-plant counts (as in the Scandinavian school and in the practice of more recent British, American, and French workers: (Greig-Smith, 1964; Curtis,

1959; Gounot, 1959). The dynamics of vegetation in the landscape, prefigured by Kerner, caught the attention of Cowles (1901), Clements (1936), and Lucy Braun (1950), who had been much influenced by developments in the science of geomorphology.[2] It is at this level that the concept of ecosystem has originated and developed, from Tansley (1935) through Lindeman (1942) to E. P. Odum (1959), and Paul Duvigneaud (1964), very much in the same way as the concept of organic evolution, by successive aggregations and borrowings. We have been slow to realize that ecology is not a purely biological science since it must account for the whole environment and trace the origin and the effect of the resources which the plant and animal bodies are instrumental in cycling.[3]

It is only at the *autecological* level that the many responses of plants to environment are sensible. Schimper's (1903) "physiological basis" referred to the variety of tapping mechanisms that put plants (and animals) in possession of their livelihood and assign them a certain ecological role. Thus in each community, species can be grouped into *coenotypes* on the basis of their phenology and spatial development. But this phase could develop no more rapidly than physiology itself, behind which it has always lagged and still does, since physiology and genetics are both experimental and most workers in these disciplines do not care to relate their findings to field conditions, even less to repeat many of their experiments on "wild" species. In spite of the lead given

[2] Maybe it should be noted that these two trends are rather dangerously diverging at present: whereas some of the students of communities are so engrossed in mathematical formulations or in energy measurements that they have lost sight of the organismal nature of the community, the geographically minded accept too readily a descriptive approach.
[3] I have attempted a rather extensive development of this point of view in a recent essay (1965).

by Lundegårdh (1931) in Europe and McDougall (1931, 1949) in America, progress along these lines has been slow. The rather recent interest in productivity, at long last defined outside of its utilitarian value, and the brave attempt in Germany, Britain, and the United States to devise measurements of energy flow (Ovington, 1961; H. T. Odum, 1962; Lieth, 1962) are roping in the acquisitions of biophysics. Gates's recent book (1962) is a notable contribution wherein this is made apparent. Convergence from biosystematics or genecology is not very much in evidence: most of the best population studies are poorly focused as far as the definition of their ecological niche is concerned. Dobzhansky and his school, however, have opened up new perspectives[4] and some geneticists are now more conscious of the need for a new look at the (ecological) mechanics of natural selection!

Man's impact (at the *industrial* level) is so far-reaching as to be of geological magnitude, whence Vernadsky's (1945) and Teilhard de Chardin's (1955, 1956) noösphere (see Fig. V-2). If the emergence of ecology at all the preceding levels was conditioned by borrowings from other fields of knowledge and variously inhibited by lags in borrowing or indeed by a lack of progress in the adjacent field itself, human ecology is certainly the latest to emerge. A great survey (not really a synthesis) was made at the time of the Wenner-Gren symposium which was published under the title *Man's Role in Changing the Face of the Earth* (Thomas, 1956). That monumental work has given a whole generation its bearings on the complex problems which its title covers. But an ecology of man is something else again. The great French geographers of the twenties (Vidal de la Blache, Jean

[4] See, for instance, Dobzhansky, 1947, 1948, 1950; Brito da Cunha, 1960; Brito da Cunha and Dobzhansky, 1954; Brito da Cunha et al., 1959; Levins, 1963.

Brunhes, Emmanuel de Martonne, Maximilien Sorre) and their American colleagues in botany, zoology, geography, and anthropology (Sears, Adams, Leopold, Kroeber, Huntington, Sauer, Boas, Steward, and others) have blazed a trail and led us to a clearing where we now stand. A contribution such as *Man's Place in the Island Ecosystem* (Fosberg, 1963) consolidates that position, but we are still lacking a sharp definition of human ecology as a field. I shall try, in the latter part of this essay, to put up a few beacons.

It would be out of proportion to my topic, at this time, to make further comments on the emergence of ecology as a scientific discipline. I hope that my Fig. V-2 and Table I and the tentative compendium of "laws" in the Appendix sufficiently focus attention on what is to be worked upon and how various are the appeals to neighboring disciplines. They can at least orient us in what is to follow.

The training ground

How did those who now call themselves ecologists acquire their competence? What part is allotted to ecology in the curriculum at the various levels in the educational system?

If the holocenotic view which is at the focal point of the ecological perspective makes of ecology a synthetic field, calling for generalists and not specialists, does this not make education, not to mention training, very difficult? A "point of view" cannot very well be taught. If a synthesis is to be drawn, there has to be something to synthesize. And the time at which students can be supposed to have enough pertinent knowledge in many fields is late —too late to redress all their previous knowledge and harness it to a new point of view?

Or else, there is no such requirement, and indeed no such thing as a generalist's approach? All knowledge worthy of itself is specialized. No one can reflect on anything unless he has somewhere a store of personally earned information in a limited field of endeavor. No other knowledge, even less acquisitions from many unrelated sources, will have any consistency at all unless it can aggregate to a solid core.

Such is the paradox: in the study of the community and the ecosystem, ecology does have an object of study which it does not hold in common with other disciplines. No matter how many debts it contracts, its methodology is a specialized one, that cannot be substituted. On the other hand, it can less than genetics, pedology, sociology, live upon its own substance and is obliged to draw abundantly from other fields.

Pedagogically, it has developed as a sort of terminal chapter in general biology or as a lateral commentary in geography or sociology. In America, before the thirties, textbooks of botany, zoology, or biology did not, as a rule, have separate chapters on communities, although they had inherited a few notions on geographical distribution from the late nineteenth century. And thus, an afterthought on environmental relationship was *superimposed* on the implicitly more significant exposition of anatomy, morphology, physiology, genetics, and taxonomy. This distribution of materials makes it very improbable that any but a very few instructors in American colleges and universities gave their teaching an ecological slant. Unfortunately, it is fairly safe to estimate the contents and prevalent orientation by referring to the textbooks.

Separate courses in ecology, boldly recognized as such, are not offered in all American universities even now in 1965. In stating this I am not necessarily referring to the most backward, but having to include great centers like Princeton, Johns Hopkins, and until most recently, Columbia. It is in the Middle West, especially Chicago, Nebraska, Michigan, Illinois, Wisconsin, Minnesota, Ohio, Cincinnati, Iowa, Indiana, Kansas, Okla-

homa, that ecology has flourished. In the East, Yale and Rutgers are the major strongholds, and in the South, Florida, Tennessee, Georgia, and North Carolina. Actually, in the East and in the South, such strength has often rested on one or two men, as it did in other isolated universities (Washington, Arizona, British Columbia, Alberta, Saskatchewan, Montreal, Nova Scotia). It is only on some of the Middle-Western campuses that a student—in the forties and fifties—could take many courses in ecology from several instructors, who would submit him to a variety of tests.[5]

How, then, and why did ecology enter the curriculum? It is rather tempting to think that agriculture, forestry, fisheries, and wildlife management exerted considerable pressure in the Middle West; that in these fields the ecological aspects of the problem were so inescapable that they had to be incorporated into the teaching. Weaver and Clements' (1938) and Shelford's (1930) books are strongly marked with the stamp of the farm-and-wildlife economy: grazing, fire, erosion, pest control all figure prominently in these early textbooks. It must be noted, however, that the earliest of all, McDougall's (1931), is more nearly geared to a general-biology perspective. Of course, Conard and Fuller's translation of Braun-Blanquet appeared in 1932, but I doubt that it was very much used as anything but a reference book in most U.S. universities and colleges, although it stimulated a certain amount of research.

The late forties and the early fifties saw the emergence of quite a few textbooks: Daubenmire (1947), Oosting (1948), Odum (1953), Clarke (1954), Woodbury (1954). These manuals met the de-

---

[5] When I had the good fortune to teach at the University of Michigan (1950–55) some fifteen courses on ecology were offered. The instructors had extremely different backgrounds: European and American, foreign and U.S.A., experimental and field-based.

mands and responded to the spirit in which ecology was actually being taught.[6]

Accompanying this main inroad of ecological teaching on the campus were two kinds of support: development of genecology or biosystematics (Clausen, Keck, and Hiesey, 1940, 1945, 1948; Edgar Anderson, 1949; Stebbins, 1950), and a new perspective in plant geography (Cain, 1944) on the one hand, and a great collection of data, research, publication, and popularization in all of the applied fields: forestry, fisheries, wildlife management, agriculture, engineering.

It is precisely this support (often labeled "conservation") which provided ecology and ecologists with an overture that put them in touch with their society. Pressure from technology may have shamed the ecologists, who had advocated recourse to the principles they held dear, to deepen their knowledge of these same principles by doing more fundamental research. But it also increased their awareness of the inefficiency of their pleas for the preservation of nature, since their audience could not follow them. And it turned out that they (the ecologists) could also have been mistaken in their evaluation of the needs of society (Darling, 1964).

In two previous essays (1957b and 1959) I have tried to account for the relation of the academic ecologist to his world. What has come to pass since then rather confirms my views and prolongs my perspective, and yet I am bound to add some qualifications.

I believe that 1950 marks the turning point. It was then that Paul B. Sears initiated the Yale Conservation Project and that Stanley A. Cain inaugurated a new teaching program in the Department of Conservation of the School of Natural Resources at the University of Michigan.

[6] Criticism of contents and spirit will be found in Egler, 1951, and in Dansereau, 1958b.

The revolutionary aspect of the new curriculum consisted in providing an equally free access to conservation (better relabeled "resource administration") from the social, economic, and political sciences on the one side, and from the natural sciences on the other. For instance, students having majored in economics were required to take some courses in forestry, wildlife, fisheries, or even botany, zoology, or geology. Conversely, those who had come up through botany or forestry were obliged to study sociology, economics, regional geography, political science. Fifteen years later, we have the proof that this was a constructive design, since many of the graduates of this program of studies now fulfill an indispensable role in public administration and in private practice.

The attitude of the academic communities themselves has also been strongly influenced as the proving ground upon which this experiment is based was extended. There developed at the same time a number of similar ventures in American universities, as efforts were made to free the curriculum from the despotism of Departments and to break the iron circle of Faculties. For instance, at Ann Arbor, Kenneth Boulding's annual seminars on subjects requiring campus-wide faculty participation[7] brought much water to the mill, as did other interdepartmental and interfaculty seminars and study committees.

Pressures to develop and maintain such a program came from two directions and they still do. Our North American society as a whole (and possibly the public agen-

[7] As an example one of these was on "growth" and the contributions came from mineralogy, bacteriology, botany, zoology, psychology, pedagogy, philosophy, urbanism! Boulding has published a summary and discussion of this particular effort in 1953. Columbia University has developed similar faculty seminars in recent years (see Tannenbaum, 1964), one of which is entitled "Ecological Systems and Cultural Evolution."

cies above all) required experts with sophisticated technical training but also with
awareness of social structures.[8] These
men were needed for planning and for
implementation of public (and private)
policy on resource administration. On
these grounds alone, and in the good old
pragmatic tradition, the shift in curriculum was fully justified.

It is doubtful, however, that really efficient integration could have been devised and implemented on the campus if
intellectual pressure had not backed the
social urgency. Keeping the training of
young people for resource administration
on an ecological focus, and allowing them
at the same time to develop major
strength in some specialized areas, presented one of the great challenges our universities have faced in this generation. All
intellectual adventures are poised on contradictory premises such as these. We
must add to this the great anguish of drifting on a mounting stream of information
flowing in from many directions in unmanageable quantities.

ECOLOGIST AND SOCIETY

The ecologist (*sensu stricto*) stands at the
confluence of academic and social forces
and is called upon to play many roles.
Above all, he is required to convey an
understandable picture of the interplay of
environmental factors, in a particular region. Those who seek his counsel or his
collaboration are sometimes able to make
plain the values upon which they draw,
but not always the relation which exists

8 This, I suggest, is something utterly different from social consciousness, social awareness, and from dedication, none of which
per se has any scientific dimension! In other
words, a scientist's endorsement of a "cause"
(liberal or otherwise) offers no guarantee that
he can relate his skill or knowledge to it:
there are innumerable examples of the worst
kind of sociological illiteracy and/or naïveté
in scientists who comment on human problems.

between these values and the actual situation. Can the ecologist himself do it?

Technical investigation requirements

It is sometimes possible for an ecologist, if he is given separate reports on the
flora, the soil, the hydrography, and the
land use of an area, to put this information together in a meaningful way. But
this is seldom achieved. As a rule, the
data collecting itself must be geared to
an environmental, not a taxonomic or
economic or other, point of view.

Nowadays this requirement is reasonably often recognized, and ecologists are
frequently given freedom to direct their
study as they see fit and to gather the
relevant information. Thus, projects for
the preservation of public and private
tracts of land and water are frequently
based upon competent investigations that
fairly predict the consequences to the
landscape of various kinds of interference and of no interference at all.

A shift has occurred in recent years
with respect to protection vs. management. In an earlier essay (1957b), I had
suggested that conservation (as a social
practice rather than as a discipline) had
gone through four phases which I called
the *legislative,* the *biological,* the *ecological,* and the *sociological.* The last is the
one described in the previous section of
this essay. I now feel inclined to add a
fifth phase in my interpretation of conservation as it has grown in our society:
it may well be called the *engineering*
phase. With the increasingly obvious need
for multiple use of land, management has
taken precedence over preservation and
possibly over conservation itself.

If I may recapitulate: the "legislative"
attitude consisted in proclaiming a guarantee of protection usually directed to a
particular organism; the "biological" demand was for cessation of interference at
least during a period of study; the
"ecological" resolution was that no plant
or animal was safe unless a sizable por-

tion of its habitat was free from interference; and the "sociological" awakening brought home the fact that none of this was possible without constant consultation with society. The more recent "engineering" point of view takes stock of the fact that virtually all landscapes in the whole world are now under management of some kind and that this must be done rationally and not left utterly to local and/or unenlightened decisions.

Supposing that the science of ecology—however defined—is at the base of resource administration, conservation, landscape management, etc., how do we, ecologists, answer the following question: "Is ecology sufficiently advanced, firmly enough in possession of laws and principles, to guide landscape management securely?" Should we answer this question in the affirmative, no one will conclude that ecology (again, however defined) has solved all of its problems, for it has not even posed them and as a science it is engaged, inevitably, in an endless process of discovery and a perpetual recommencement. Nor is it very helpful to say that landscape management is merely applied ecology, any more than medicine can be reduced to applied biology. The fact is, however, that only part of our ecological knowledge is actually being applied and that we are not implementing now many things that science strongly and securely recommends. The excuse that we do not know enough and that much more research is needed, amounts to a withdrawal from responsibility.

This is no place to draw a comprehensive list of the unfinished tasks of ecology and ecologists. I have briefly hinted at this elsewhere (1964a) in an issue of *BioScience* in which other workers from the many provinces of ecology also took stock of the accomplishments in their field. It is no doubt inevitable that science should progress very unevenly and that many tasks well begun should remain unfinished—in fact, seemingly interrupted in full swing. Signal advances have always induced an abnormally high number of new vocations in the field of science where they were made. Whether the turnover revolves upon subject matter or technique, it necessarily deprives some of the neighboring areas of workers who would have been well qualified for them.

I hasten to add that I hold no belief in a specifically ecological vocation. This would be even more absurd than it is in some other disciplines, since a number of niches need to be filled and by men of extremely different talents: some with exceptional mathematical ability and some without it; some with great manual dexterity and some without it; some with verbal virtuosity and some without it; etc. This being the case, we can ask ourselves which ones of ecology's developments, at this time (in 1965), are being favored and which ones neglected and whether there is any real correspondence between current progress in ecological science and: (a) the needs of science as a whole; (b) the needs of society.

At a time when nuclear physics and molecular biology ostensibly proffer the greatest challenge to uncommitted young and future scientists, those who dominate these fields do not show much evidence of pursuing the consequences of their "breakthroughs" to environmental integrations. Looking back to my Fig. V-2, I see no great sweep from the molecule to the population (least of all to the community) in the thinking, speaking, and writing of the molecular biologists. In fact, some have given us to understand that efforts spent on species and associations can only be repetitive, and that taxonomy and ecology are closed chapters (Bonner, 1963). It is true, of course, that the bulk of scientific "production" is repetitive, confirmative, extensive rather than inventive or creative. The flood of literature that emanates from the newer disciplines does not avoid this law. It is true that the older (classic?) disciplines are also set in their ways; and if a renewal has not come about, the ecological "establishment" (if it exists) may be as much to blame for its immobility as the "new wave" for its absorption of all the current energy.

It remains that, at mid-point in the sixties, there is a shortage of certain skills that have traditionally given strength to ecology and a slowing of renewal in other fields where it has often been involved, and finally a failure to provide leadership in new directions. It is worth scanning these three areas.

Loss of skill

At a recent UNESCO conference on airphoto interpretation (Toulouse, September, 1964), Paul Rey spoke at some length of "vertical" and "horizontal" integration. The former is the work of the specialist and the latter of the generalist. In France, Rey contended, there are quite a few students of vegetation who also know *as much as is necessary* concerning geology, climatology, and agriculture to integrate and interpret raw data from all of these fields and to correlate them meaningfully. In America we also have had and still have a number of plant ecologists and animal ecologists whose understanding of climate, soil, geology, and human history is more than adequate to the task. Excellent memoirs and books published between 1930 and 1965 bear witness to this. The men who wrote them (and I have actually been out-of-doors with several of them) were thoroughly at home in the field. An easy familiarity with rocks, plants, and animals, a feeling for air, water, soil, and the textures of living things gave them the *direct line* that is so essential to the true naturalist. I do not say (although I probably belong to this family)[9] that this

[9] As witness, my 1963 essay entitled "The Barefoot Scientist."

is the best kind of ecologist, least of all the only true breed. I do say this is one of the several indispensable approaches to ecological problems. And I do fear that such people, trained in all of the natural sciences and responsive to the varieties of form and function as they occur spontaneously, are not emerging now in large enough numbers.

In fact, it is more difficult than it once was for ecologists to obtain the necessary support from taxonomists, who are barely maintaining their quota. Identification of rocks, plants, and animals, together with the implications (phylogenetic to physiological) that the specific appurtenance implies, is no less essential than it ever was to the mathematically minded contemporary phytosociologist who must gather more data than his predecessors in order to satisfy the hunger of the computer, and to the biophysically minded measurer who must know what he is working with. In fact, beyond and before the experiment, lies the very choice of materials for study; and what is the basis for selection where taxonomic myopia has set in?

Good descriptions of whole landscapes are in very short supply in North America. Frank Egler (1959, 1961) has given us bibliographies of vegetation studies, state by state, for the northeastern and southeastern United States, and has projected his inventory on maps. The end result is a very loose network, with many holes indeed. This does not stand comparison with Europe. The truth is, there have never been enough students of vegetation in North America and there are now fewer than there were. Moreover, many of them are not concerned with regional studies at all.

Mapping is where this crisis shows up most dramatically. Küchler's (1964) new "map of the vegetation of the conterminous United States" (1:3,168,000) is the first effort at over-all representation since Shantz and Zon (1923). Rowe's

(1959) "Forest Regions of Canada" (1:6,336,000) (a slightly modified version of Halliday's [1937] map); Porsild's (1959) map of the vegetation (1:20,-000,000) in the new *Atlas of Canada;* and A. S. Leopold's (1950) "Vegetation Zones of Mexico" (approximately 1:20,-000,000) complete the picture for North America. Other maps, on an even smaller scale, of Mexico, the United States, and Canada can hardly be considered serious contributions: there is one in every textbook of ecology and of physical geography and they run from one level of simplification to another. Some of the great international atlases (Brockmann-Jerosch, 1951; *Soviet Atlas of the World,* 1956; etc.) are altogether as useful, inasmuch as they carry alternative interpretations. As for mapping on a larger scale (regional, state, or provincial, county or township), very little has been done. Foresters in the United States and Canada have made the largest contribution. In conclusion, it must be admitted that we have almost no vegetation maps to work with and that very few workers are now engaged in this field, and almost no recruits are being made among graduate students on the campuses.

Slow renewal

Some of the central and some of the peripheral areas of ecology are now virtually dormant for lack of assimilating the discoveries made available by adjacent disciplines. The contact between evolutionary studies and synecology is very casual indeed. Most students of adaptive radiation and population dynamics make up their own ecology as they go along. Neither through their efforts nor through those of the synecologists themselves have the acquisitions of genetics been well integrated into the known facts and current interpretations concerning the environment. Conversely, it is apparent that the interpretations and formulations of ecology have not imposed themselves

to geneticists, physiologists, taxonomists, and others! A potentially crucial contribution to the heredity-environment conflict is therefore not being made on this front.

This lack is especially apparent in the virtual dropout of epharmonic studies. The large vein opened up by Raunkiær at the beginning of this century (1905) was once exploited all over the world. But, at this time, the question of life forms is sorely neglected, and the problem of relation (and lack of relation!) of form to function is not being tackled with these, our tools. (Lems, 1960, 1962, and Cooper, 1961, are exceptions.)

I will cite only one other area of diminished tension: physiological research. Light and water relationships, for instance, are now known to us in a very different way from that which inspired a good many textbook interpretations of their force in the landscape. The effects of light period on vegetative as well as sexual activity and the intricate interaction, in many communities, of inherited patterns of periodicity vs. light and/or rainfall rhythms are not the object of much study at this time. Nitsch (1957) and Bourdeau (1959) have, however, opened new vistas, and Brown (1961) has begun to explore antibiotic strategy in natural communities.

Failure to lead

If ecology, as a science, or rather: if ecologists as a group have either abandoned their traditional pursuits, given up their tried techniques, or surrendered to other developments in science, is there not, nevertheless, a group of pioneers who are leading us forward? E. P. Odum (1964) does speak of a "new ecology," and not without reason. It is true that the use of radioisotopes has provided us with the means of actually following the pathways of resources not only within the plant and animal, but in the environment itself and at various distances from their biological utilizers and transformers

(Carson, 1962). Also, the various developments that have followed Lindeman's (1942) early application of the "trophic-dynamic" concept of the ecosystem have sent us looking for a totalizing expression of environmental forces in terms of energy. Gates (1962) has recently given us a comprehensive review of this orientation. And now the International Biological Program has set its sights principally on the productivity of living matter. Darling (1964) says: "Knowledge of energy flow in conversion cycles is the stuff of ecology."

The arsenal which is needed to tackle the various aspects of this very central problem is impressive. Outstanding contributions have been made and highly sophisticated instrumentation has been devised by physicists, chemists, geologists, meteorologists, physiologists, and others; but it is no more hopeful to add all these up in order to obtain an ecological conclusion than it ever was. The productivity of an ecosystem can only be measured if we know what to measure, and also when to measure it. A knowledge of its behavior *as a whole* can come only from experience in the field with many ecosystems of greatly different composition, structure, and dynamics.

This, strangely enough, has come to be better understood by engineers (including the military variety), anthropologists, geographers, sociologists, and such than it has by many workers in the mathematical, physical, and biological sciences (what has traditionally been called "the" sciences). In physics, chemistry, and biology there has developed a great disaffection for "description" and a strong concentration on "function." This may be neither the time nor the place to explore the rather tenuous philosophical premises that underlie this dichotomy and that also plague the conscience of those who would be "objective." A reading of Agnes Arber's *The Mind and the Eye* (1954) and of Kenneth Boulding's *The Image* (1956) might induce many a sobering thought! Certainly if we are to interpret and to detect behavior and function, we cannot do so in the absence of thorough inventories and adequate descriptions. Pattern is the result of process (Watt, 1947), to be sure, but process operates within pattern. No study of function makes very much sense without recognition of form! These are ultimately the great issues, of course, to those who preoccupy themselves not merely with the unity of science but with the unity of knowledge, and beyond this with the intricacies of the learning process.

Down from this higher plane on which research may or may not be motivated, and on which a career may or may not be oriented, what demands is our society making of ecologists? The question is not: who needs ecology? but who thinks they need ecology and who is asking for help from ecologists?

Certainly, foresters, agriculturists, pedologists, and aquiculturists are obliged by their very operations to employ or to consult, or to be ecologists, and they may well be dismayed by the "loss of skill" mentioned above. It is not clear, however, that these groups, in practice, are led by ecologists or even by sound ecological principles.

Another cohort consists of meteorologists, geographers, geologists, prospectors, surveyors, town planners, public health officers, and the military. Most of them have no formal training in ecology, sometimes not even a grounding in the biological sciences. However, they have come increasingly, through necessity, to realize the interrelatedness of the living among themselves and of the living with the nonliving. In other words, the idea of ecosystems has imposed itself to them, and induced caution because they realize that the wholeness of the environment escapes them. And so they turn to ecologists for advice, collaboration, or participation in their undertakings—but not often for actual leadership. In fact, institutions are developing, public and private, in which ecologists are reduced to an ancillary role whereas sometimes poorly qualified "administrators" design the investigation as a whole. This has occasionally resulted in impossible assignments and purely promotional planning. The deep-lying popular mistrust of governmental interference, the abiding faith in the built-in virtue of private enterprise, and the methods of Madison Avenue all strongly support this development in which academic ecologists do not fit very well.

Understanding of values

The ecologists may or may not be consulted when they should be, but when they are, what is primarily required of them is a "scientific" answer. Surely they can provide a technical analysis of a particular (or more or less generalized) situation, and they are doing this (within the limits and limitations outlined in the previous section). But it is society as a whole that determines the goals, that makes the choices, and its leaders who give expression to these choices. If ecologists as such are hardly allowed a preponderant voice, this need not mean that they cannot guide the decisions to be made and not merely predict consequences and implement orders.

Scientific values

Maybe enough has been said above concerning the rise and fall of favor for one or another of the disciplines involved in the sciences of environment to convey the idea that the world of scientists operates according to a fluctuating priority of ratings as far as its internal developments are concerned. This is not uninfluenced by pressures from other quarters (as has also been illustrated above), but it does enjoy a relative autonomy.

The values accepted in scientific circles, which determine relative freedom of operation and efficiency of production, eventually control the means: space, money, and time, as well as prestige, are allotted to tasks deemed intellectually worthwhile and/or economically or socially urgent. In a utilitarian society the latter are dominant indeed. A beautiful exposition of one such situation was made by W. P. Thompson (1960) in his presidential address at the Ninth International Botanical Congress, when he retraced the history of botany in Canada and showed how closely botanical research (and most of its outstanding achievements) had been geared to the economic progress of the country.

In a society that trusts its own imagination, it is realized that "applied" science cannot progress more rapidly than the "pure" science upon which it feeds and depends. At the level of involvement in the research operation itself, the choice of subject matter and method is hardly conditioned by economic and social values. The atmosphere within the scientific segment of the society where he operates more immediately conditions the individual investigator's reflexes. I will not allow myself a discourse, at this point, on the wish, the hope, of the scientist to serve humanity (directly if possible, indirectly if he must) vs. the devouring egotistical curiosity which leads him to his object irrespective of any benefit to himself or to others. Actually, the exercise of the investigating function is seriously hampered if it is not permanently or periodically an end in itself, and objects can often be substituted without harm. I well recall advising some student in search of a Ph.D. subject to work on a cultivated plant, since the interest was not necessarily lesser than that of a wild species. A marriage with a rich girl may be no less successful than with a poor one.

Thus, the greatest of scientific values is study itself. In many instances scientists (ecologists, conservationists, and others) will fly to the defense of their research material and try to halt utilization that will disturb a landscape very much in need of technical survey. That such a movement is more nearly inspired by the desire to learn than by the desire to be useful to the proprietor society should not shock anyone. In order to be fully motivated, a scientist must have a strong feeling of identification. Who would condemn the egotism of the actor who rehearses before a mirror in order to give polish to his performance? The idiosyncratic requirements of every profession are difficult for outsiders to evaluate.

Economic values

There may or may not be much antagonism (at least in the consciousness of the individual) between the scientific values and the economic ones. The latter are determined by the potential productivity of the land on the one hand and the exploiting capacity of the humans who administer it.

Certainly the problem of the human population—whether it is the Mayan people in Yucatan, the Maoris in New Zealand, or the American farmers in Iowa—is to fit itself into an ecosystem which can support it in a sustained way. Exhaustion of the land—the declines and emigrations that history has many times witnessed—may be due to an absolutely excessive exploitation and consequently irreparable depletion, or it may be a lack of accord with the normal cycle of replenishment. Economic wisdom is shown by certain populations who practice shifting agriculture and who have discovered the efficiency of short instead of long rotations, of noncontiguous instead of contiguous exploitation, etc. In other words, a capacity to measure or to perceive in a global manner the natural rhythm of the environment has led them to harness the forces of their ecosystem(s) in a nonabusive way. And of course this depends in great part upon

the relative foreignness of the introduced exploiting agent: maize or wheat on a site normally supporting a forest ecosystem, for instance, or periodic flooding of rice paddies on a soil with an upland profile.

The ecologist who is consulted by his society on exploitation practices must ask: "What benefits do you seek?" For instance, many modern cities are built on highly fertile ground: Detroit and its industrial suburbs occupy rich alluvial soils, whereas the glacial deposits that cover the neighboring hills are being farmed. On the island of Terceira a large military airport now occupies the richest wheatfields that ever were in the Azores. This latter sacrifice seems to have been made knowingly, at a time when it was felt that more revenue would accrue to the population through this form of industrialization than by maintaining cereal crops. As for large cities, founded centuries ago and having grown without benefit of much planning, no clear choice was ever made, although some rather interesting reversals of age-old decisions are now being carried out. Gottmann's (1961) image of *Megalopolis. The Urbanized Northeastern Seaboard of the United States* shows us quite a few of these, including the recent increase of green spaces!

There are many other instances where the economic odds—above all, on the long run—are not neatly stacked in favor of one kind of exploitation. The forest and fishery industries, especially where they intersect, pose many ecological problems that hardly lend themselves to a sound solution for all time. Lumbering, as it has been practiced in the St. Lawrence Valley, has resulted in the regression of salmon all the way from Lake Ontario to below Quebec City. Deforestation has had all kinds of consequences: the regression of salmon, due to the lowering of summer level in the tributaries and streams, is one of many.

There is also silting, erosion, flooding, warming of the soil, etc. No one would contest that deforestation was needed for agriculture in the middle St. Lawrence and that lumbering was to be a permanent source of revenue on the Canadian shield and in the lower St. Lawrence. But a Swiss instead of a Canadian pattern of exploitation would have maintained seepage in the streams all summer long by conserving riparian forest belts.

The tired, yet orderly, European landscape sets the exploitation of wood in a much sharper focus. Where less waste is allowed, in other words more diversified and thorough use of wood, its cultivation (and the breeding of tree species) is worthwhile, whereas it is not in most parts of North America.

The inroads of the lumber industry have been variously appreciated and fought in many parts of the world, both by conservationists and by members of rival industries, and sometimes by large segments of society when it was realized that a regional catastrophe was at hand, such as a devastating flood.

In relatively unproductive areas, such as parts of northern Michigan and north of the Lake St. John region of Quebec, where poor parent materials conduce to poor soils and slow growth of economically inferior species (such as jack pine), almost any alternative is welcome. Thus, in the Lake St. John sand plains and granitic outcrops overlain with shallow soil, controlled periodic burning keeps the forest out and maintains the landscape at the blueberry stage of succession (Lavoie and Guillemette, 1962). This crop is a most successful one, at this time, its outlets on the Montreal and New York markets firmly assured. The ecological management of the landscape is by now fairly well understood. Where it has been judiciously applied, a change in regional economy will still allow a change in vegetation management: the site as a whole (especially the soil) will not have

been irreversibly altered and can be allowed again to bear forest. On sites that will grow aspen instead of jack pine or birch, such a course may be desirable now that the plastics industry has a need for this wood which had been, until recently, almost unusable. Such an *"économie de rechange"* is possibly the most important consideration in an ecological planning of land use.

Cultural values

If scientific requirements lend themselves to a strict demonstration, in spite of the emotional charges that motivate the engagement of scientists in a particular kind of work, and if economic advantages can be objectively plotted, in spite of the political necessities that dictate them, cultural values which are related to the areas of motivation in the other two are somewhat less tangible.

The religious customs of the people in the Ruanda who pasture large herds of cattle that cause erosion of the hills and then do not use them as food even in times of famine have been respected by the Belgian administrators who combated famine by introducing cassava and erosion by planting eucalyptus. The persistence of such potentially profitable commensalism to this day in the face of dire necessity (India) only illustrates the strength of its impact. Isaac (1963) makes a strong case for the religious (not strictly agricultural) origin of the domestication of cattle.

The sacred groves of the Druids in Brittany and elsewhere, of the Gas and other tribes in West Africa, and the mythical or ritual privileges awarded to many plants and animals have been instrumental in assuring their survival, witness the now universally planted *Gingko*, saved from extinction by Chinese monks. Conversely, the identification with evil and the imaginary as well as the real damage caused by some plants and animals has made for their suppression. This has sometimes had adverse effects, such as the destruction of wolf packs in deer-infested areas where the survival of the unfit became a burden (Olson, 1938).

In the same vein, the gratuitous use of plants for ceremonial practices can have various ecological consequences. The custom incorporated in the Christian church from Celtic populations of hanging the parasitic mistletoe and the live branches of evergreen holly and of cutting down spruce, fir, or pine for display at Christ-mastime undergoes many variations in Christian and post-Christian societies. Thus *Lycopodium* (eastern North America), *Laurus* (Madeira, Azores, Canaries), *Olea, Myrtus* (France, Spain), *Podocarpus* (New Zealand), *Chamaerops* (Spain), *Serenoa* (United States), *Thuja* (Quebec), *Pinus* (Philippines), and many other plants are introduced into the church and the home. Except for the Christmas tree in North America, which is the object of a veritable industry, and possibly the laurels in Macaronesia, these customs do not create a sensible ecological disturbance.

When it comes, however, to the areas of esthetics and recreation, we are dealing with even more varied requirements than those which are set down by the ritual and observances of religion. Wagar (1964) has attempted to break down "recreation" into its components which he lists: "exercise, healthful environment, esteem and prestige, esthetic enjoyment, understanding, freedom of choice and early traditions, self-reliance, change, solitude, companionship, new companionship, cooperative endeavor." He presents a series of diagrams where the quality of these attributes is made a function of the numbers of participants at one time and place. The graphs presented by this writer are reasonably convincing (and fairly predictable), but what is needed here is a more thorough attack on this problem by social psychologists. Maybe

Mr. Vance Packard will give us a book entitled *The Gregarious Hermits?*

What kind of landscape do the several cultures favor? In order to answer this question, and bearing in mind that we are ecologists, we must keep referring to the potential landscape, we must make at least some distant reference to its primeval balance. It is from there that we can move to the regional economy and recognize as a fact (not always a necessity) the kind of change which has come about as a result of disturbance. This, then, is the image that will have struck the eye and etched itself into the conscience of the residents as they grew up; this is the background against which their emotional, intellectual, social, and professional experiences will have developed. This is a sentimental esthetic, occasionally a bad one, that feeds on calendar art. But, good or bad, it is authentic and strong, and it backs the motivations that inspire landscape management and policy.

For instance, in the boreal forest region, the dark, needle-leaved, moss-carpeted, primeval forest, once felled, is replaced by shimmering birch or aspen that stand bare in winter; the wet places are choked with resilient mossy bog, the swift streams are bordered with twisted alders and willows and a thin screen of cottonwoods. On the contrary, in the heart of the hardwoods country, the forest ablaze with flowers in the spring becomes tenebrous in the summer and mellow with gold and scarlet leafage in the autumn. Where it has been destroyed, rigid pines with clattering needles that turn rusty on the forest floor will take over. Extensive swamps and marshes, lush but forbidding, clutter up the depressions and line the streams. And in the grassland country . . . But why continue? What I should need here to pursue my present purpose are quotations from Robert Frost, Ernest Hemingway, and William Faulkner, and the paintings of Winslow Homer, Homer Dodge Martin,

Clarence Gagnon, Tom Thomson, Kornelius Krieghoff. . . . And for mirrors of other regions: W. H. Hudson, and Chateaubriand, Thomas Hardy, the Prince of Lampedusa, Anton Chekhov, C. F. Ramuz, and many others.

It would take, in fact, a whole anthology to document the "sentiment of nature." Several humanists have written very learned books and essays on this subject, from Mornet's (1907) study on the late eighteenth century to more recent approaches. But it would well repay an ecologist to seek such documentation the better to define the values we are concerned with here. Lowenthal (1964), Lowenthal and Prince (1964), and Glacken (1965) have offered some valuable thoughts on the psychology of landscape, as had Huth (1957) in his *Nature and the American*. What, in fact, these studies make us see is the enormous amount of projection which is involved. It comes to matter very little what the landscape contains if it is envisioned through the glasses of a certain culture. For instance, in northwestern Europe, parts of the deciduous-forest country are shared by Spain, France, Belgium, the Netherlands, Britain, Germany, and Denmark. The treatment of landscape is utterly different and cannot be explained, in our present perspective, by economic factors. Rather, it matters a great deal that the French do not, like the English, have a reverence for the natural forms, shapes, and textures of living things; do not seem to prize plants and animals for themselves but almost always as a décor. If the landscape, in a French novel, is in harmony with a mood, it more likely reflects than triggers it. François Mauriac's guilty heroine, Thérèse Desqueyroux, is obsessed by the whispering pines outside her window, but D. H. Lawrence and Katherine Mansfield's characters are enraptured with the textures of leaves. French landscape painting, from Poussin through Watteau to Corot and Cézanne,

is so orderly if compared to Gainsborough or Constable! As for the Spaniards, is it not the very crust of the earth and the sound of the sky that loom largest in the landscapes of Cervantes and Pio Baroja? Of El Greco and Goya?

At a deeper level, Bachelard (1948) has explored the philosophical reveries that involve and tie up the consciousness and conscience of man-in-the-landscape.

In reaching out for such high examples, I am trying to show where the esthetic nerve of a culture can be prodded, in the work of art where widely shared perceptions are transposed. What is mere sentiment (and yet how deeply rooted!) in the people becomes esthetic in its formulation by a writer, painter, musician. And it remains recognizable. (I think of Sibelius' "Finlandia," which has spoken so well to the French Canadians, on their cold Laurentian shield, among their white birches and black spruces!) It must be added that the more successful of these formulations, as they are added to the "heritage," tend to confirm reflexes and to condition perceptions along the same lines: thus, the grooves are hardened and the cultural channels deepened.

It has long been established that this diversity of cultures finds expression in those specialized landscapes that we call gardens. Although some of the finest English gardens are in France and some of the best Italian gardens in Germany, etc., the styles developed by the French, German, British, Dutch, Italian, Arabs, and Japanese, among others, are indeed related to other areas in their respective cultures, to other forms, rituals, and customs. The ratio of utilitarian to ritual function in the distribution and spectacle of water in Arab, Italian, French, Spanish, Polynesian, and Chinese cultures is very revealing.

When we consider the esthetic requirements of conservation, we are therefore bound to recognize that "scenic beauty" means many things to many men, that mass, outline, texture, size, and color can only be assembled in a satisfying manner if they ultimately find resonance in other areas of experience. It is therefore not enough to refer to "scenic beauty" as an esthetic value. The sentimental is bound to intrude.[10] And so is the social, since "natural beauty" of landscape is generally intended to be shared. Certainly in North America, with its increasing leisure time, recreation has long since ceased to be a luxury or even a pastime, when it is not frankly therapeutic. But again, recreation takes on the local color of culture. Americans would never dream of undertaking the strenuous hikes that involve the whole family in New Zealand. The French have long been horrified by *"le camping,"* which is much below Spanish dignity as well. As for cricket, bullfighting, and jai alai, they are fairly endemic, whereas skiing is no longer Norwegian, judo no longer Japanese, and surf riding no longer Polynesian. Active or passive, recreation has cast its stamp on the landscape and its requirements compete with those of other social functions. Ski tows in Wyoming, New England, and Quebec, bathing beaches on the oceans and the Great Lakes are equally menacing the preservation of some nearly extinct plant communities.

As for hunting and fishing . . .

Relaying the message to society

Who will gather all these threads and weave them together? And who will display the tapestry? And who will make its design understood to society as a whole? The ecologist? Some ecologists, maybe; very few, I should think. But certainly those who call themselves conservationists.

Several generations now have been do-

ing it. Some of the essential messages have been received. For instance, the fact that whole tracts of land covering more than minimal *Lebensraum* must be left intact if certain valuable plants and animals are to be saved from extinction (see Heim, 1956). This principle seems so obvious to all of us who are concerned that we look with dismay at the maps of some "advanced" countries like France[11] that, until very recently, had no "national parks" at all! Maybe a second look will reveal that conservation was nevertheless well served by the admittedly more efficient means of education.[12]

Maybe this is the place and time to sound the conscience as well as the scientific awareness of conservationists, ecologists, and indeed of the scientific community as a whole. No one has done this better and more bravely than Frank Egler in a rather scathing paper (1962) that apparently could not be published in the United States, although a substantial formulation of the same ideas found their way under his signature into the *American Scientist* (1964).

In this latter contribution, Egler presented a diagram which accounts for the social structure within which information and opinion on pesticides and weed control flow. Many of the observers of Rachel Carson's *Silent Spring* (1962) are "silent scientists," who know and who say nothing either because they dare not oppose the economically strong and the socially prominent or because they would be ashamed to support them publicly. At the New York Botanical Garden we have made an attempt to open the lines of communication by publishing in our

[10] In spite of many years of scientific study of forests in various parts of the world, I suppose a "beautiful" forest to me will always be the one that comes closest to Gustave Doré's engravings.

[11] Conservation and restoration (overrestoration?) of historical monuments may have received more attention than "nature" in France.

[12] The Bulletin of the International Union for the Conservation of Nature (1952 to date) has been recording in every issue the facts of protection and lack of protection.

Garden Journal a series of letters entitled "Conversations on Ecology" (1963–64). It is hoped that no issue will be deemed too sensitive to be the object of these exchanges.[13]

Protection of human life and of property against pollution, pesticides, and radiation opens up a triptych that is inevitably painted in bold political colors. In our society where the controversies over blood transfusion and vaccination are not completely appeased and where fluoridation of water is contested, these more crucial issues are not even squarely faced! Our choices concern the very survival of the human species itself. The emotional impact is quite different from that of the extinction of the dodo, the great auk, the passenger pigeon; from the dwindling of caribou, elk, or bison; from the regression of salmon and trout; from the blight on chestnut and elm!

And what stands have conservationists, ecologists, and other scientists taken? It is not without interest to note that the politically conservative have been liberal to the point of favoring *laissez-faire* in matters of pollution and radiation. They have frequently argued, with a great display of technological data, that we could repair all of our damages, if not mend all of our fences. But almost in the same breath they would inform us that it was not sufficiently known how much damage had been done. And they would conclude: Let us do nothing, least of all legislate, until more research has been done. In contrast, the politically liberal have been conservative in advocating a stop to experiment where the consequences were not well known, and an immediate implementation of the knowledge which we do have.

[13] These letters by Frank Egler, Robert R. Humphrey, F. Raymond Fosberg, Luna B. Leopold, Peter Wardle, Virginia Weadock, Richard Goodwin, John Milton, Thomas H. Jukes, and Pierre Dansereau have been reprinted recently (see Dansereau, et al., 1965).

It is not necessary to summarize the considerable controversy that followed Carson's (1962) readable and provocative book in order to detect the many ways in which her message was received. Both positive and negative responses were motivated by an adhesion to values that are not basically scientific, although valid scientific arguments are quoted by both sides. A thorough study of this controversy by competent group psychologists might go a long way to inform us on the forces that are at work in man's conception of himself as a social animal.

What emerges vividly from the *Silent Spring* debate as well as from parallel controversies of recent years is the fact that modern man, at long last, has come to see himself *in* nature. Marston Bates, in his excellent book *Man in Nature* (1964), one hundred years after T. H. Huxley's *Evidence as to Man's Place in Nature*, has expressed this in accessible language, as indeed he already had in his book on the tropics (1952). Cumberland's (1962) description of the New Zealand situation is also a truly ecological approach. Sears's Condon lectures (1957), entitled "The Ecology of Man," show him condensing his earlier thoughts (especially 1937, 1947, 1954, 1955, and the several editions of his classic *Deserts on the March*, 1959). He contrasts "man the newcomer" with "man the dominant." Any further development of this theme will owe a great deal to Paul Sears.

It would therefore seem that the essential message now to be urgently conveyed to contemporary society concerns the need for a new human ecology. Or maybe I should say: at last, an ecology of man!

ECOLOGY OF MAN

Geographers have reviewed the history of man and his management of resources in ecological or near-ecological terms.

Maximilien Sorre (1947, 1948) had gone at least one step beyond his predecessors in his outline of the "biological foundations of human geography." Carl Sauer's (1952) search for "agricultural origins" is based upon the recognized solidarity of plants, animals, and man. In this and in other texts (for instance, 1950) he has often condemned the absurdity of a study of vegetation-without-man!

Sociologists, likewise, have made these attempts, but on the whole without very much success. Amos Hawley, for instance, in his *Human Ecology* (1950) did not really transgress the boundaries of sociology *sensu stricto*.

The anthropologists have been very preoccupied for two generations now with their debate concerning the precedence of environmental over cultural influences or vice versa. The determinism of a Huntington (1940, 1945) is anathema to a number of cultural anthropologists, and a good deal of cultural anthropology is just barely acceptable as "science" to many physical anthropologists, not to mention the reaction of natural scientists. I do not have enough erudition or knowledge to inquire into this debate. I must deplore this since I am under the impression that some of the problems may be scholastic or semantic (not unlike some phases of the "acquired characters" controversy among geneticists), and that very few either-or choices are allowable in this context. In concerning themselves so much with nonindustrialized societies, the anthropologists have helped liberate us not only from taboos but from implications concerning biological behavior itself which had been accepted all the way up and down the line. Thus, Benedict (1934), Mead (1928), and Lévi-Strauss (1955) were able to strip certain patterns of human conduct down to their fundamental triggering by a combination of historical and ecological forces. In our present view of the ecosystem, much that the anthropologist recognizes as "cultural" has to be defined as serving also an "environmental" function.

The ecologist now tries to extend his thinking to the categories of habitat and behavior in man which are at least analogous to those of plants and animals. There remains rather a gap between these anthropological studies and a more universal application of ecological concepts to human ecosystems as they have developed in the urbanized ambience.

A review of applicable principles

It seems to me that the intellectual compulsion to study man-in-nature or man-as-part-of-nature has not yet been strong enough to precipitate the development of an authentic science of human ecology. Rather, it is the realization of the harm that man has done and is about to do to himself which has made such a need felt. The incredibly powerful harnessing of the hidden forces of nature and the unwillingness to limit his own growth and discipline his own economy have opened a new chapter in the Apocalypse. Malthus' cry of alarm (1798) either was not heeded or else commented not so much on its central propositions as on its moral or theological implications. The latter loomed very large during the great surge of the Industrial Revolution when the triumphs of technology seemed likely to go on forever and to solve, as they arose, all of man's resource problems. This suicidal optimism is still alive in the 1960s.

It may well be naturalists like William Vogt and Fairfield Osborn, whose *Road to Survival* and *Our Plundered Planet,* respectively, were both published in 1948, who precipitated a crisis in the study of man's ecology. They made it mandatory for anthropologists to dig *all the way* into biology and forced biologists to look up to anthropology. Carleton Coon's *The Origin of Races* (1962) and Theodosius Dobzhansky's *Mankind Evolving* (1962) offer us examples of such striving toward an ecology of man. Although a similar design is involved in the present essay, no such searching investigation will be attempted, but maybe a few beacons can be erected.

Much as Coon and Dobzhansky have applied the full weight of paleontological and genetic knowledge to the study of man, may we not glance through the acquisitions of ecology and tentatively apply the principles derived from the study of environment to the human species?

Turning to the twenty-seven "laws" which are formulated in the Appendix, it is not difficult to cite examples applying to populations of plants, animals, and men. Thus law No. 1, the *law of the inoptimum,* reads as follows: "No species encounters in any given habitat the optimum conditions for all of its functions." In earlier formulations of this (1956a, 1964b), I had mentioned as an example the early-spring flowering plants of the Northeast American hardwood forest, many of which will either leaf, flower, fruit, or store more abundantly elsewhere. Other plants will not flower unless the water recedes to a very low level. The performance of reproductive functions in amphibians often involves short-distance habitat migration; in many birds, long-distance climatic migration. Human tribes show very similar patterns: seasonal montane transhumancy and other occupational migrations of one or both sexes. "Civilized" man has standardized the microclimate of kitchen, dining room, sitting room, bedroom.

The difference that we should consistently encounter in applying, one after the other, these ecological laws (physiological, strategic, climatic, or geographical) lies in the greater weight of *learned behavior* and even cultural conditioning.

Outline of human ecological processes

The conjunction of environmental forces results in the development of

regimes of various kinds (Dansereau, 1956b, 1965). Thus, the displacement of airmasses controls temperatures and precipitations in such a way as to offer plants, animals, and man a rhythmical array of resources. In a given place, energy, heat, light, water, nutrients, support, and other necessities are available in certain assemblages, quality, and quantity, and times, to which living beings respond in a more or less characterized fashion. Thus, the polar, the high-latitude continental, and the equatorial climatic regimes elicit a corresponding regime in the soil: gleization, podzolization, and laterization. The climatic and pedogenic regimes in turn determine a *vegetation* regime which is expressed by the prevalence of tundra, needle-leaved evergreen forest, and broad-leaved evergreen forest. The opportunities offered (and refused) to animal life are equally definable by "way of life" or response: storage, dormancy, molt, migration, etc. As for man: storage and clothing are in evidence, and also construction of shelter and insulation, and also migration.[14]

An ecology of man, properly conceived, would therefore concern itself with the variety of environments, in which it is well proven that resources are unevenly distributed, unevenly available, unevenly known, unevenly exploited. These last two are probably the most limiting. The evolutionary processes which have permitted phreatophytes like the mesquite to develop a root system that taps the underground water are not really analogous to the discovery by man that he can obtain fuel that lies buried below his sight.

What then are the processes exercised

[14] I should like to follow Boulding's lead in pursuing the many parallels between economics and ecology. For instance, the storage by a plant of a resource to be reused at a time when it cannot be synthesized anew (such as starch) seems to me functionally equivalent to money in the human economy.

by man in tapping the resources of his environment and what patterns has he created in the environment itself?

The broader stage was set by Vernadsky (1945) and by Teilhard de Chardin (1955, 1956) when they proposed the notion of noösphere to characterize the realm of man's deployment of energy. Fig. V-1 projects an image of the intersecting spheres of this greatest order of magnitude of the environment—where it is apparent, among other things, that man, at first confined to parts of the litho-, hydro-, pyro-, atmo-, and biospheres, has now virtually sounded the heights and depths of all of them and recently (in 1957) emerged into the cosmosphere. The new science of exobiology has been born.

The great compendium entitled *Man's Role in Changing the Face of the Earth* (Thomas, 1956) reviews virtually all the ways in which man has utilized and modified the mineral, vegetal, and animal elements. It certainly provides a rich offering of materials for a treatise on human ecology. But the task remains to *consider all the processes involved in the laws of ecology and to classify the emerging variety of patterns that specifically result from man's presence and action in this universe.* This very much exceeds both my present duty and my competence and capacity. I must be content with a rough sampling of processes and patterns in order to demonstrate how they relate to those already known to us from observation and experimentation with plants and animals; how they are in some ways unique; and how the preservation of habitats and scenic values is implemented.

In the introductory statement of Part 5 of my *Biogeography* (1957a), I had selected two aspects of man's ecological integration: "the upsetting of natural balances by the elaboration of completely *new ecosystems* on the one hand, and the deliberate molding of evolutionary forces in living organisms (including himself)

with the elaboration of *new genotypes,* on the other."

I then adopted a "scale of human interference," to which I have added two rungs in Fig. V-3. Some of the human *processes* can be followed all the way up this scale and will be seen to draw increasingly complex support from the environment. For instance, *construction of shelter* and *food gathering.*

Shelter

In B and C, shelter may be a natural, unmodified feature of the landscape, such as a cave or a dense grove; although some populations will resort to actual construction with snow and ice, with stones and mud, or with branches, sticks, leaves, grasses, and mammal pelts. The latter will be the rule at the pastoral stage (D). At the next level, further transformation of building materials is involved: reduction and shaping of timber, stonecutting, eventual use of metal and glass, conduction of water, artificial light, and indoor fires. At the industrial and urban levels (F, G), there usually remains very little of the natural shape and structure (sometimes even of the texture) of basic materials: brick, metal, glass, concrete have not been derived from local (or even regional) rocks, soils, or forests. They present a much more diversified microclimate than the simple conservation of heat in an igloo or of relative coolness in a straw hut. Air-conditioning, however, does not usually involve a control of atmospheric pressure, which is the case at level H, where the "flying fortress" has a climate of its own.

Parallel to this increasingly planned shelter-building is an increasingly complex system of clothing (where obviously cultural and physically nonfunctional patterns may prevail to an absurd degree). At the extreme extra-orbital level (I), protection from unfavorable pressure is obtained primarily from sealed clothing whereas insulation from other ambient

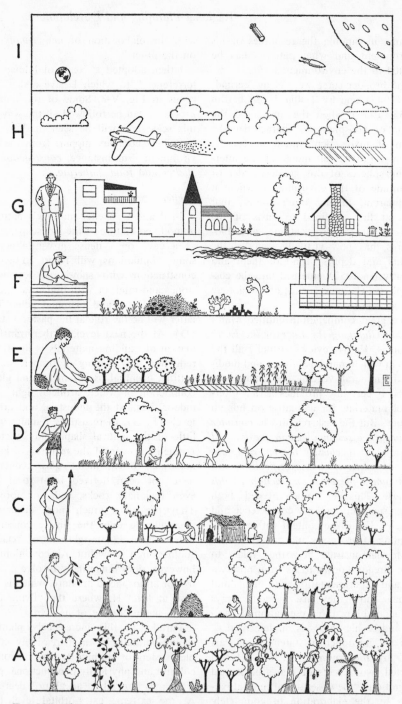

FIG. V-3. The scale of human interference in the landscape (modified from Dansereau, 1957, Fig. V-1): A. Virgin forest. B. Gathering. C. Hunting. D. Herding. E. Agriculture. F. Industry. G. Urbanization. H. Atmospheric control. I. Extra-orbital travel.

(now extra-atmospheric) effects is assured by shelter in a space capsule, where the pull of gravity itself has been cancelled.

Food

Human metabolism, at the B and C levels, is satisfied much in the same way as that of other higher animals that stand at the end of food chains or near the top of productivity pyramids, as consumers. A somewhat sparse population such as the Jivaris in the Amazon (Cruls, 1945) or the Pygmies in Central Africa (Turnbull, 1962) very nearly subsist by gathering, hunting, and fishing in a way that affects the plant and animal populations very little. At the pastoral stage (D) man begins to tamper with the genetic make-up of animals through selection, and he deliberately restricts the area of some plants (e.g. forest trees) and increases that of others (e.g. grasses). It is at the agricultural level (E), however, that truly drastic changes occur. I will cite only two. Exotic plants that could not possibly survive without constant care are sown or planted and variously nurtured and sheltered: maize has to be stored as seed and sown; apple trees must be planted and generally grafted. Animals are bred for a particular product (milk, eggs, meat) to the frequent detriment of some other normally vital functions. Thus, human management compensates the inability of maize to seed itself, the inability of Leghorn fowl to brood. In both of these cases, the natural life cycle is broken! Surely this is an important threshold.

It has been a long time since the farmers of otherwise industrialized countries have fed entirely upon what they produced. But in reality the distribution, in temperate areas for instance, of tea, coffee, bananas, spices, etc., has been industry's contribution to the agricultural communities and therefore an ecological phenomenon of the F level. In a city,

even a small city (level G), any food market offers ample evidence of the complex lines of supply that convey foodstuffs into the local economy. The urban population's very water supply may originate a hundred miles away; its bread and pastry are usually processed locally from ingredients produced under totally different climatic conditions. As for an airliner (level H) traveling between New York and New Delhi, it may offer bread from Dakota flour, wine from Chile, oranges from India, beef from Argentina, butter from New Zealand, tomatoes from Italy.[15] As for the food consumed by astronauts (level I), some of it is very similar to common occidental fare, and some of it quintessentially synthetic and owes its composition and nutritive value to the most advanced chemical technology of urbanized society.

The brief examination of shelter, of the privileged spaces which man builds for himself, and of food as it relates to an ever-increasing area away from this abode, gives us two keys to human ecology. One of the most remarkable features is the *growing distance in space* between the place and agents of production and man-the-consumer. This points to two relationships: the increased number of energy relays from harvest through storage, packaging, expedition, processing, presentation, and ritual of actual consumption (food) or utilization (shelter). Related to this is the *dependence-independence* ratio: at the higher levels the ultimate consumer is not physically present at the place of production-and-harvest and can only indirectly affect the ecosystem involved. Another important relationship is

[15] Such a menu makes fascinating reading if we further note that the Dakota flour is from a Middle Eastern grass; that Chilean wine is from a European vine; that Indian oranges come from a Chinese tree; that Argentine beef is from a Central European mammal, which also produces butter in New Zealand; that Italian tomatoes originated in South America.

the increasingly complex food chains (*sensu* Elton, 1927) that develop at the higher echelons, especially if one takes stock of the previously expended energy invested in domestication and migration, extraction of chemicals for fertilizers, etc.

It remains to fill in many additional dimensions if we are to cast the variety of human populations in a corresponding array of habitats. The processes of shelter building and food gathering involve a gradual loss of individual initiative and a greater dependence upon the community. They also make clear the increasing radius of resource tapping and the increasing need of technical imaginativeness in the community as a whole. *This particular ecological shift is a central feature of human ecology.* In search of a comparison, we may ask ourselves if any species of termites or ants, of cuckoos, muskrats, and beavers, since they first crossed their present specific threshold, have developed new techniques that have changed their exploiting capacity. Whereas such a progressive change is very much in evidence in both the plant and animal kingdoms in the long run of phyla involving the algae—ferns—flowering plants, or the amphibians—reptiles—mammals—and is still accelerating within the mammals, it not only reaches its highest pitch but its greatest rate of increase in man. What Teilhard de Chardin (1955) has called the "step of reflexion" is without precedent in the potential strength of its impact on environment. Thus the emergence of an hereditary innovation initiates a disproportionate rise to a higher energy level.

Psychological play of images on landscape

It would require a veritable treatise of human ecology (as defined above) to examine one by one the processes whereby man *exploits* his environment and to fix the patterns of this exploitation and their spatiotemporal integration in the plane-

tary economy. All the way up the line of living things, from microbes to apes, we shall have witnessed a number of different solutions to the individual-population (and to the individual-population-species) conflicts. Thus a goat-grass-soil chain may be broken through the excesses or deficiencies of one of its links. How different a chain of which the links are intraspecific (human) populations competing for control of a given agricultural-industrial region. In the crossings of the Rubicon, the Bidassoa, the Delaware, and the Moskova a relay of political-military-economic and cultural forces (more or less in that order) induced new commands in the turnover of regional resources. As much as anything else, the self-image of the populations involved changed their relationship to the landscape they inhabited.

The "post-civilized" world concerning which Boulding (1962) asks such searching questions and which Nicholson (1964) hopefully calls the "next Renaissance" is looking not only for new goals and new pathways to old ideals, but above all for new motivations. A more visceral philosophy is needed to replace the scholastic or idealist formulations that so tenaciously clung to the industrializing world of the nineteenth century. The first half of this century may appear to have been too wrapped up in Science (capital S) to have made the right efforts on time, or to have heeded the voices of Kierkegaard and Gabriel Marcel. A more existential grasp of flowing reality and an anguished sense of fluctuating identity need not lead to an acceptance of the absurd. But they have certainly shattered a number of images that the flimsy constructs of Madison Avenue cannot replace. A Parkinsonian anatomy does not answer any real questions. The nostalgic *Weltanschauung* of Boris Pasternak, a witness to a revolution in which he could not fully participate, will not do. Nor will the beatniks (bless their hearts) help us, since they have nothing positive to say after their thirtieth birthday. Possibly Camus (1958) speaks in a more virile voice to a more mature audience and projects a clearer image of ourselves.

But we must draw from various sources. The rehabilitation of the poetic approach, for one thing, seems to me a very important condition. It is rather revealing of the times that it had been largely eliminated from literature itself. In reading such a book as John Updike's *The Centaur* (1963), one measures a reversal of sensibility from that of Dreiser, Lewis, Dos Passos, Farrell! The value of poetic insight in science itself (with its attendant pitfalls, of course!) must be recognized. Maybe it will remain a privilege of the exceptionally endowed, like Teilhard de Chardin, on whose perspective Theodosius Dobzhansky (1962) concludes his *Mankind Evolving.*

It would not appear seemly for an ecologist to offer a blueprint for freeing modern man from his famous (and perhaps cherished) alienation, and I know I cannot rise to such heights. But I do feel that true statements of man's position in na-

ture cannot be made without prolonging our scientific perspective well into other realms. Thus, André Malraux's (1947, 1948) highly perceptive analysis of the "imaginary museum" is fully geared to the contemporary propension to abstract, to separate, to analyze, and above all to shift perspective by modifying scale. He demonstrates so well the emergence of pure pattern in many works of art which are, as wholes, realistic but laden, in their parts, with symbols and abstractions. The delight which we take in mathematical models and in the duplication and reproducibility of symbols extends all the way from the rigorously scientific to the esthetic and involves the same reflexes.

Our consciousness of environment, and of ourselves in it, is complex but not unfathomable. Our instruments of research and our means of expression are extremely powerful. We are more limited (as indeed man has always been?) by the failure of our imagination than by any obstacle outside ourselves. A valid imaginary reconstruction of our world is now our greatest task. It may even be the condition of our survival.

BIBLIOGRAPHY

Allan, H. H. 1937. A Consideration of the "Biological Spectra" of New Zealand. J. Ecol. 25:116–52.

Anderson, Edgar, 1949. Introgressive Hybridization. Wiley, New York.

Arber, Agnes. 1954. The Mind and the Eye. Cambridge Univ. Press, Cambridge, Mass.

Bachelard, Gaston. 1948. La terre et les rêveries de la volonté. Corti, Paris.

Bates, Marston. 1952. Where Winter Never Comes. Scribner's, New York.

—— 1964. Man in Nature (2nd ed.). Prentice-Hall, Englewood Cliffs, N.J.

Benedict, Ruth. 1934 (1948). Patterns of Culture. Mentor, New York.

Bonner, James, 1963. The Future Welfare of Botany. AIBS Bul. 13(1):20–21.

Boulding, Kenneth E. 1953. Toward a General Theory of Growth. Can. J. Econ. and Pol. Sci., 19(3):326–40.

—— 1956. The Image. Univ. Mich. Press, Ann Arbor.

—— 1962. After Civilization, What? Bul. Atomic Scientists 18(8):2–6.

Bourdeau, Philippe F. 1959. Seasonal Variations of the Photosynthetic Efficiency of Evergreen Conifers. Ecol. 40(1):63–67.

Boyko, Hugo. 1947. On the Role of Plants as Quantitative Climate Indicators and the Geoecological Law of Distribution. J. Ecol. 35(1–2):138–57.

Braun, E. Lucy. 1935. The Undifferentiated Deciduous Forest Climax and the Association-segregate. Ecol. 16:514–19.

Braun, E. Lucy. 1950. Deciduous Forests of Eastern North America. Blakiston, Philadelphia.

Braun-Blanquet, Josias. 1932. Plant Sociology, trans. by H. S. Conard and G. D. Fuller. McGraw-Hill, New York.

Brito da Cunha, A. 1960. Chromosomal Variation and Adaptation in Insects. Ann. Rev. Entom. 5:85–110.

——— and Dobzhansky, Theodosius. 1954. A Further Study of Chromosomal Polymorphism in Drosophila willistoni in Its Relation to the Environment. Evolution 8(2):119–34.

———, Dobzhansky, Theodosius, Pavlovsky, O., and Spassky, B. 1959. Genetics of Natural Populations. XXVIII. Supplementary Data on the Chromosomal Polymorphism in Drosophila willistoni in Its Relation to the Environment. Evolution 13(3):389–404.

Brockmann-Jerosch, H. 1951. Plant Communities of the World. Map 1:20,000,000. VEB Geographisch-Kartographische Anstalt Gotha.

Brown, Robert T. 1961. The Influence of Leaf Extracts on Pinus banksiana Seed Germination. Bul. Ecol. Soc. Amer. 42(4):156.

Cain, Stanley A. 1944. Foundations of Plant Geography. Harper, New York.

Camp, W. H. 1947. Distribution Patterns in Modern Plants and the Problems of Ancient Dispersals. Ecol. Monogs. 17:123–26, 159–83.

Camus, Albert. 1958. Le mythe de Sisyphe. Essai sur l'absurde. Nouvelle édition. Gallimard, Paris.

Candolle, Alphonse de. 1855. Géographie botanique raisonnée. Masson, Paris.

——— 1874. Constitution dans le règne végétal de groupes physiologiques applicables à la géographie botanique ancienne et moderne. Arch. Sci. Phys. Nat. 50(5):1–38.

Carson, Rachel. 1962. Silent Spring. Houghton Mifflin, Boston.

Clarke, George L. 1954. Elements of Ecology. Wiley, New York.

Clausen, Jens, Keck, David D., and Hiesey, William M. 1940. Experimental Studies on the Nature of Species. I. Effect of Varied Environments on Western North American Plants. Carnegie Inst. Wash. Pub. 520.

——— 1945. Experimental Studies on the Nature of Species. II. Plant Evolution Through Amphiploidy and Autoploidy, with Examples from the Madiinae. Carnegie Inst. Wash. Pub. 564.

——— 1948. Experimental Studies on the Nature of Species. III. Climatic Races of Achillea. Carnegie Inst. Wash. Pub. 581.

Clements, F. E. 1916. Plant Succession. An Analysis of the Development of Vegetation. Carnegie Inst. Pub. 242.

——— 1936. Nature and Structure of the Climax. J. Ecol. 24(1):253–84.

Coon, Carleton S. 1962. The Origin of Races. Knopf, New York.

Cooper, Arthur W. 1961. Relationships Between Plant Life-forms and Microclimate in Southeastern Michigan. Ecol. Monogs. 31(1):31–59.

Cowles, H. C. 1901. The Physiographic Ecology of Chicago and Vicinity; a Study of the Origin, Development, and Classification of Plant Societies. Bot. Gaz. 31:73–108, 145–82.

Crocker, R. L., and Wood, J. G. 1947. Some Historical Influences on the Development of South Australian Vegetation Communities and Their Bearing on Concepts and Classification in Ecology. Trans. Roy. Soc. S. Aust. 71(1):91–136.

Croizat, Léon. 1952. Manual of Phytogeography. W. Junk, The Hague.

Cruls, Gastão. 1945. A Amazônia que eu vi. Brasiliana, Biblioteca Pedagógica Brasileira, Série 5, 113.

Cumberland, Kenneth B. 1962. 'Climatic Change' or Cultural Interference? New Zealand in Moahunter Times. In: Land and Livelihood. Geographical Essays in Honour of George Jobberns: 88–142. N. Z. Geog. Soc., Christchurch, N.Z.

Curtis, John T. 1959. The Vegetation of Wisconsin: An Ordination of Plant Communities. Univ. Wisc. Press, Madison

Dansereau, Pierre. 1945. Essai de corrélation sociologique entre les plantes supérieures et les poissons de la beine du Lac St-Louis. Rev. Can. Biol. 4(3):369–417; also Contrib. Inst. Biol. Univ. Montréal, 16:369–417.

Dansereau, Pierre. 1946. Os Planos da Biogeografia. Rev. Brasil. Geog. 8(2):189–211.

────── 1949. Introdução à Biogeografia. Rev. Brasil. Geog. 11(1):3–92.

────── 1951a. The Scope of Biogeography and Its Integrative Levels. Rev. Can. Biol. 10(1):8–32; also Bul. Serv. Biogéogr. 7:1–27.

────── 1951b. Description and Recording of Vegetation upon a Structural Basis. Ecol. 32(2):172–229; also Bul. Serv. Biogéogr. 8:172–229 (1953).

────── 1952. The Varieties of Evolutionary Opportunity. Rev. Can. Biol. 11(4):305–88.

────── 1956a. Le coincement, un processus écologique. Acta Biotheoretica 11(3–4):157–78.

────── 1956b. Le régime climatique régional de la végétation et les contrôles édaphiques. Rev. Can. Biol. 15(1):1–71.

────── 1957a. Biogeography: An Ecological Perspective. Ronald, New York.

────── 1957b. Resource Planning: A Problem in Communication. Yale Conserv. Studies, 6:3–6. Also in: Science and the Future of Mankind: 131–40. W. Junk, The Hague. 1961.

────── 1958a. A Universal System for Recording Vegetation. Contrib. Inst. Bot. Univ. Montréal, 72:1–58.

────── 1958b. Trois manuels d'écologie américains. Rev. Gén. des Sciences 65(1–2):1–6.

────── 1959. The Meaning of Conservation. Trans. Northeast Wildl. Conf., 10th Ann. Meeting, Montreal, 1958, 1:7–13.

────── 1962. An Application of Ecological Laws to Woodlots. Proc. Lockwood Conf. on Suburban Forest and Ecol., March, 1962, New Haven; Conn. Agric. Exp. Sta. Bul. 642, 45–56; also Sarracenia 7:1–14.

────── 1963. The Barefoot Scientist. Colo. Q. 12(2):101–15; also Inst. Arctic and Alpine Res., Contrib. 10:101–15.

────── 1964a. The Future of Ecology. BioScience 14(7):20–23.

────── 1964b. Contradictions & biculture. Editions du Jour, Montréal.

────── 1965. Ecosystems of the World and the Play of Natural Selection (unpub.).

────── et al., 1965. Conversations on Ecology I–XIII. 1963–1964. Sarracenia 9:1–64.

Darling, F. Fraser. 1964. Conservation and Ecological Theory. J. Ecol. 52 (suppl.): 39–45.

Darlington, Philip J., Jr. 1957. Zoogeography: the Geographical Distribution of Animals. Wiley, New York.

Daubenmire, Rexford F. 1947. Plants and Environment. A Textbook of Plant Autecology. Wiley, New York.

Dobzhansky, Theodosius. 1947. Adaptive Changes Induced by Natural Selection in Wild Populations of Drosophila. Evolution 1(1–2):1–16.

────── 1948. Genetics of Natural Populations. XVI. Altitudinal and Seasonal Changes Produced by Natural Selection in Certain Populations of Drosophila pseudoobscura and Drosophila persimilis. Genetics 33:158–76.

────── 1950. Evolution in the Tropics. Amer. Sci. 38(2):209–21.

────── 1962. Mankind Evolving. Yale Univ. Press, New Haven.

Du Rietz, G. E. 1931. Life-forms of Terrestrial Flowering Plants. I. Acta Phytogeogr. Suecica 3:1–95.

Duvigneaud, Paul. 1964. L'écosystème forêt. Lejeunea, n.s., 20:1–36.

Egler, Frank E. 1951. A Commentary on American Plant Ecology, Based on the Textbooks of 1947–49. Ecol. 32(4):673–94.

────── 1959. A Cartographic Guide to Selected Regional Vegetation Literature. Where Plant Communities Have Been Described. Part I. Northeastern United States. Sarracenia 1:1–50.

────── 1961. A Cartographic Guide to Selected Regional Vegetation Literature. Where Plant Communities Have Been Described. Part II. Southeastern United States. Sarracenia 6:1–87.

────── 1962. On American Problems in the Communication of Biologic Knowledge to Society. Dodonaea 30:263–304.

────── 1964. Pesticides–in Our Ecosystem. Amer. Sci. 52(1):110–36.

Elton, C. S. 1927. Animal Ecology. Sidgwick & Jackson, London.

Engler, A. 1899. Die Entwicklung der Pflanzengeographie in den letzten hundert Jahren. In: Ges. Erdk. Berlin Humboldtcentenar Schrift 1899, Berlin.

Fosberg, F. R., ed. 1963. Man's Place in the Island Ecosystem. Symposium at Xth Pacific Science Congress, Bishop Museum Press, Honolulu.

Gates, David M. 1962. Energy Exchange in the Biosphere. Harper & Row, New York.

Glacken, Clarence. 1965. Man's Attitude Toward Land: Reflections on the Man-Nature Theme as a Subject for Study (in this symposium).

Good, Ronald. 1931. A Theory of Plant Geography. New Phytologist 31:149–71.

——— 1947. The Geography of the Flowering Plants. Longmans, Green, London.

——— 1964. The Geography of the Flowering Plants (3rd ed.). Longmans, Green, London; Wiley, New York.

Gottmann, Jean. 1961. Megalopolis. The Urbanized Northeastern Seaboard of the United States. Twentieth Century Fund, New York.

Gounot, M. 1959. L'exploitation mécanographique des relevés pour la recherche des groupes écologiques. Bul. Serv. de la Carte Phytogéogr. Sér. B, 4(2):147–77.

Gray, Asa. 1846. Analogy Between the Flora of Japan and That of the United States, Amer. J. Sci. and Arts, 52:135–36.

Greig-Smith, P. 1964. Quantitative Plant Ecology (2nd ed.). Butterworth, London and Wash., D.C.

Halliday, W. E. D. 1937. A Forest Classification for Canada. Can. Dept. Res. and Develop, Forest Res. Div., Bul. 89.

Hawley, Amos H. 1950. Human Ecology. Ronald, New York.

Heim, Roger, ed. 1956. Derniers refuges. Atlas commenté des Réserves Naturelles dans le monde. Elsevier, Bruxelles.

Hultén, Eric. 1937. Outline of the History of Arctic and Boreal Biota During the Quaternary Period. Bokförlags Aktiebolaget Thule, Stockholm.

——— 1950. Atlas of the Distribution of Vascular Plants in NW. Europe (English summary). Generalstabens Litografiska Anstalts Förlag, Stockholm.

Humboldt, Alexander von. 1807. Essai sur la géographie des plantes. Levrault, Schoell, Paris; Sherborn Fund Facsimile 1 (c/o Brit. Mus., London): i–35, 153–55 (1959).

Huntington, Ellsworth. 1940. Principles of Economic Geography. Wiley, New York.

——— 1945. Mainsprings of Civilization. Wiley, New York.

Huth, Hans. 1957. Nature and the American. Three Centuries of Changing Attitudes. Univ. Calif. Press, Berkeley.

Huxley, T. H. 1963. Evidence as to Man's Place in Nature. Reprinted, with an introduction by Ashley Montagu, in Ann Arbor Paperbacks, Univ. Michigan Press, Ann Arbor.

Isaac, Erich. 1963. Mythes, cultes et élevage. Diogène 41:72–95.

Kerner von Marilaun, Anton. 1863. Das Pflanzenleben der Donauländer, trans. by Henry S. Conard, 1951, as The Background of Plant Ecology. Iowa State Col. Press, Ames.

——— 1896. The Natural History of Plants, trans. by F. W. Oliver. Blackie & Son, London.

Küchler, A. W. 1947. A Geographic System of Vegetation. Geog. Rev. 37:233–40.

——— 1964. Potential Natural Vegetation of the Conterminous United States. Map and manual. Amer. Geog. Soc. Spec. Pub. 36.

Kujala, Viljo. 1964. Metsä-ja suokasvilajien levinneisyys-ja yleisyyssuhteista suomessa. Vuosina 1951–1953 suoritetun valtakunnan metsien III linja-arvioinnin tuloksia. (Über die Frequenzverhältnisse der Wald- und Moor-Pflanzen in Finnland–Ergebenisse der III. Reichswaldabschätzung 1951–53.) Comm. Inst. Forestalis Fenniae 59(1).

Lavoie, Victorin, et Guillemette, André. 1962. La production du bleuet dans la Province de Québec et les problèmes qui s'y rattachent. Serv. Info. et Recherches, Ministère de l'Agric., Québec.

Lems, Kornelius. 1960. Botanical Notes on the Canary Islands. II. The Evolution of Plant Forms in the Islands: Aeonium. Ecol. 41(1):1–17.

——— 1962. Adaptive Radiation in the Ericaceae. I. Shoot Development in the Andromedeae. Ecol. 43(3):524–28.

Leopold, A. Starker. 1950. Vegetation Zones of Mexico. Ecol. 31(4):507–18.

Levins, Richard. 1963. Theory of Fitness in a Heterogeneous Environment. II. Developmental Flexibility and Niche Selection. Amer. Naturalist 97(893):75–90.

Lévi-Strauss, Claude. 1955. Tristes tropiques. Plon, Paris.

Lieth, Helmut. 1962. Stoffproduktion der Pflanzendecke. Fischer Verlag.

Lindeman, Raymond L. 1942. The Trophic-dynamic Aspect of Ecology. Ecol. 23(4):399–418.

Lowenthal, David. 1964. Is Wilderness 'Paradise Enow'? Image of Nature in America. Columbia Univ. Forum 7(2):34–40.

——— and Prince, Hugh C. 1964. The English Landscape. Geog. Rev. 54(3):309–46.

Lundegårdh, Henrik. 1931. Environment and Plant Development, trans. by Eric Ashby from Klima und Boden in ihrer Wirkung auf das Pflanzenleben. Arnold, London.

Malraux, André. 1947. Psychologie de l'art. I. Le musée imaginaire. Skira, Genève.

——— 1948. Psychologie de l'art. II. La création artistique. Skira, Genève.

Malthus, T. R. 1798. Essay on the Principle of Population as It Affects the Future of Society. Reprinted as: Population: the first essay (with foreword by Kenneth E. Boulding). Ann Arbor Paperbacks, Univ. Mich. Press, Ann Arbor.

Martonne, E. de. 1925–27. Traité de géographie physique. 3 vols. Colin, Paris.

McDougall, W. B. 1931. Plant Ecology. Lea & Febiger, Philadelphia.

——— 1949. Plant Ecology (3rd ed.). Lea & Febiger, Philadelphia.

Mead, Margaret. 1928. Coming of Age in Samoa. Morrow, New York.

Merriam, C. Hart. 1898. Life Zones and Crop Zones of the United States. U.S. Dept. Agric., Biol. Surv. Bul. 10.

Meusel, H. 1943. Vergleichende arealkunde. Gebr. Borntraeger Verl., Berlin-Zehlendorf.

——— 1951. Die Bedeutung der Wuchsform für die Entwicklung des natürlichen Systems der Pflanzen. Feddes Repertorium, 54(2–3):137–72.

Mornet, Daniel. 1907. Le sentiment de la nature en France de J.-J. Rousseau à Bernardin de Saint-Pierre. Burt Franklin Res. & Source Works Ser. 59, New York.

Nicholson, E. Max. 1964. Conservation and the Next Renaissance. Univ. Calif. Sch. Forestry, Horace M. Albright Conservation Lectureship IV: 1–15.

Nitsch, Jean-Paul. 1957. Photoperiodism in Woody Plants. Proc. Amer. Hort. Soc. 70:526–44.

Odum, Eugene P. 1953. Fundamentals of Ecology. Saunders, Philadelphia.

——— 1959. Fundamentals of Ecology (2nd ed.). Saunders, Philadelphia.

——— 1964. The New Ecology. BioScience 14(7):14–16.

Odum, Howard T. 1962. Man and the Ecosystem. Proc. Lockwood Conf. on Suburban Forest and Ecol., March, 1962, New Haven; Conn. Agric. Exp. Sta., Bul. 642:57–75.

Olson, S. 1938. A Study of the Predatory Relation with Particular Reference to the Wolf. Sci. Monthly 46:323–36.

Oosting, Henry J. 1948. The Study of Plant Communities: An Introduction to Plant Ecology. Freeman, San Francisco.

Osborn, Fairfield. 1948. Our Plundered Planet. Little, Brown, Boston.

Ovington, J. D. 1961. Some Aspects of Energy Flow in Plantations of Pinus sylvestris L. Ann. Bot., n. s., 25(97):12–20.

Perring, F. H., and Walters, S. M., eds. 1962. Atlas of the British Flora. Bot. Soc. Brit. Isles, London.

Porsild, Erling. 1959. Natural Vegetation and Flora (map). Atlas of Canada. Can. Dept. Mines & Tech. Surv., Ottawa.

Raunkiær, C. 1905. Types biologiques pour la géographie botanique. Bul. Acad. Roy. Soc. Sci. Denmark, 5.

——— 1934. The Life Forms of Plants and Statistical Plant Geography. Clarendon, Oxford.

Rowe, J. S. 1959. Forest Regions of Canada. Can. Dept. North. Aff. & Nat. Res., Forestry Br. Bul. 123.

Rübel, Eduard. 1930. Pflanzengesellschaften der Erde. Verlag Hans Huber, Bern-Berlin.

Sauer, Carl O. 1950. Grassland Climax, Fire and Man. J. Range Mgt. 3:16–21.

———— 1952. Agricultural Origins and Dispersals. Bowman Mem. Lectures, Amer. Geog. Soc., New York.

Schimper, A. F. W. 1903. Plant Geography upon a Physiological Basis, trans. by William R. Fisher. Clarendon, Oxford.

Schmid, Emil. 1956. Die Wuchsformen der Dikotyledonen. Ber. ü. d. Geobot. Inst. Rübel, f.d.j. 1955:38–50.

Schouw, J. F. 1823. Grundzüge einer allgemeinen Pflanzengeographie. Reimer, Berlin.

Sears, Paul B. 1937. This Is Our World. Univ. Okla. Press, Norman.

———— 1947. Importance of Ecology in the Training of Engineers. Sci. 106(2740):1–3.

———— 1954. Human Ecology: A Problem in Synthesis. Sci. 120(3128):959–63.

———— 1955. Changing Man's Habitat: Physical and Biological Phenomena. In: Thomas, William L., Jr., ed., Yearbook of Anthropology. Wenner-Gren Fdn. for Anthropol. Res., New York.

———— 1956. Some Notes on the Ecology of Ecologists. Sci. Monthly 83(1):22–27.

———— 1957. The Ecology of Man. Condon Lectures, Oreg. State Sys. of Higher Educ., Eugene.

———— 1959. Deserts on the March (3rd ed.). Univ. Okla. Press, Norman.

Shantz, H. L., and Zon, R. 1923. Vegetation. In: Atlas of American Agriculture, U.S. Dept. Agric.

Shelford, V. E. 1930. Laboratory and Field Ecology. Williams & Wilkins, Baltimore.

Simonet, M., et Guinochet, M. 1938. Observations sur quelques espèces et hybrides d'Agropyrum. II. Sur la répartition géographique des races caryologiques de l'Agropyrum junceum (L.) P. B. Bul. Soc. Bot. France 85:175–89.

Sorre, Max. 1947. Les fondements de la géographie humaine. Tome I. Les fondements biologiques. Colin, Paris.

———— 1948. Les fondements de la géographie humaine. Tome II. Les fondements techniques. Colin, Paris.

Soviet Atlas. 1956. Vegetation of the World. 1:20,000,000. Moscow.

Stebbins, G. Ledyard, Jr. 1950. Variation and Evolution in Plants. Columbia Univ. Press, New York.

Tannenbaum, Frank. 1964. The University Seminars. A Riddle, a Complex, a Policy. Columbia Univ. Forum 7(4):33–34.

Tansley, A. G. 1935. The Use and Abuse of Vegetational Concepts and Terms. Ecol. 16(3):287–307.

Teilhard de Chardin, Pierre. 1955. Oeuvres. I. Le phénomène humain. Editions du Seuil, Paris.

———— 1956. The Antiquity and World Expansion of Human Culture. In: Thomas, William L., Jr., ed., Man's Role in Changing the Face of the Earth. Univ. Chicago Press: 103–12.

Thomas, William L., Jr., ed. 1956. Man's Role in Changing the Face of the Earth. Univ. Chicago Press.

Thompson, W. P. 1960. Canadian Botany: An Appraisal. Pres. Address, Proc. IX Internat. Bot. Congr. 1959. (Montreal), Vol. III:8–12.

Turnbull, Colin M. 1962. The Forest People. Anchor Books, Doubleday, New York.

Updike, John. 1963. The Centaur. Knopf, New York.

Vernadsky, W. I. 1945. The Biosphere and the Noösphere. Amer. Sci. 33(1):1–12.

Villar, E. Huguet del. 1929. Geobotánica. Editorial Labor, Barcelona-Buenos Aires.

Vogt, William. 1948. Road to Survival. Sloane, New York.

Wagar, J. Alan. 1964. The Carrying Capacity of Wild Lands for Recreation. Forest Sci. Monog. 7.

Warming, E. 1909. Oecology of Plants. An Introduction to the Study of Plant Communities. Oxford Univ. Press, London.

Watt, A. S. 1947. Pattern and Process in the Plant Community. J. Ecol. 35:1–22.

Weaver, John E., and Clements, Frederic E. 1938. Plant Ecology. McGraw-Hill, New York.

Woodbury, Angus M. 1954. Principles of General Ecology. Blakiston, New York.
Wulff, E. V. 1943. An Introduction to Historical Plant Geography. Chronica Botanica, Waltham, Mass.

APPENDIX: THE LAWS OF ECOLOGY

The following twenty-seven propositions are transcribed from previous publications (1952, 1956a, 1956b, 1957a, 1962), although some alterations and additions are made herein. I have credited some authors in parentheses, although I do not claim to have indicated strict priority. Where there are no actual quotes, I have reformulated the proposition myself.

A. PHYSIOLOGY OF ECOTOPIC FITNESS (1–9)

1. *Law of the inoptimum.* No species encounters in any given habitat the optimum conditions for all of its functions. (Dansereau, 1956a)

2. *Law of aphasy.* "Organic evolution is slower than environmental change on the average, and hence migration occurs." (Cain, 1944)

3. *Law of tolerance.* A species is confined, ecologically and geographically, by the extremes of environmental adversities that it can withstand. (Good, 1931)

4. *Law of valence.* In each part of its area, a given species shows a greater or lesser amplitude in ranging through various habitats (or communities); this is conditioned by its requirements and tolerances being satisfied or nearly overcome. (Dansereau, 1956a, 1957a)

5. *Law of competition-cooperation.* Organisms of one or more species occupying the same site over a given period of time, use (and frequently reuse) the same resources through various sharing processes which allow a greater portion to the most efficient. (Dansereau, 1956b)

6. *Law of the continuum.* The gamut of ecological niches, in a regional unit, permits a gradual shift in the qualitative and quantitative composition and structure of communities. (Curtis, 1959)

7. *Law of cornering.* The environmental gradients upon which species and communities are ordained either steepen or smoothen at various times and places, thereby reducing utterly or broadening greatly that part of the ecological spectrum which offers the best opportunity to organisms of adequate valence. (Dansereau, 1956a)

8. *Law of persistence.* Many species, especially dominants of a community, are capable of surviving and maintaining their spatial position after their habitat and even the climate itself have ceased to favor full vitality. (Dansereau, 1956a, b)

9. *Law of evolutionary opportunity.* The present ecological success of a species is compounded of its geographical and ecological breadth, its population structure, and the nature of its harboring communities. (Dansereau, 1952)

B. STRATEGY OF COMMUNITY ADJUSTMENT (10–14)

10. *Law of ecesis.* The resources of an unoccupied environment will first be exploited by organisms with high tolerance and generally with low requirements. (Cowles, 1901)

11. *Law of succession.* The same site will not be indefinitely held by the same plant community, because the physiographic agents and the plants themselves induce changes in the whole environment, and these allow other plants heretofore unable to invade, but now more efficient, to displace the present occupants. (Cowles, 1901)

12. *Law of regional climax.* The processes of succession go through a shift of controls but are not indefinite, for they tend to an equilibrium that allows no further relay; the climatic-topographic-edaphic-biological balance of forces results in an ultimate pattern which shifts from region to region. (Clements, 1916, 1936)

13. *Law of factorial control.* Although living beings react holocenotically (to all factors of the environment in their peculiar conjunction), there frequently occurs a discrepant factor which has controlling power through its excess or deficiency. (Del Villar, 1929)

14. *Law of association segregation.* Associations of reduced composition and simplified structure have arisen during physiographic or climatic change and migration through the elimination of some species and the loss of ecological status of others. (Braun, 1935)

C. REGIONAL CLIMATIC RESPONSE (15–20)

15. *Law of geoecological distribution.* "The specific topographical distribution (micro-distribution) of an ecotypic plant species or of a plant community is a parallel function of its general geographical distribution (macrodistribution), since both are determined by the same ecological amplitudes and ultimately by uniform physiological requirements." (Boyko, 1947)

16. *Law of climatic stress.* It is at the level of exchange between the organism and the environment (microbiosphere) that the stress is felt which eventually cannot be overcome and which will establish a geographic boundary. (Dansereau, 1962, 1965)

17. *Law of biological spectra.* Life-form distribution is a characteristic of regional floras which can be correlated to climatic conditions of the present as well as of the past. (Raunkiær, 1905, 1934)

18. *Law of vegetation regime.* Under a similar climate, in different parts of the world, a similar structural-physiognomic-functional response can be induced in the vegetation, irrespective of floristic affinities and/or historical connections. (Schimper, 1903; Rübel, 1930)

19. *Law of zonal equivalence.* Where climatic gradients are essentially similar, the latitudinal and altitudinal zonation and cliseral shifts of plant formations also tend to be; where floristic history is essentially identical, plant communities will also be similar. (Humboldt, 1817; Warming, 1909)

20. *Law of irreversibility.* Some resources (mineral, plant, or animal) do not renew themselves, because they are the result of a process (physical or biological) which has ceased to function in a particular habitat or landscape at the present time. (Crocker and Wood, 1947)

D. GEOGRAPHIC DISTRIBUTION (21–27)

21. *Law of specific integrity.* Since the lower taxa (species and subordinate units) cannot be polyphyletic, their presence in widely separated areas can be explained only by former continuity or by migration. (Gray, 1846; Wulff, 1943)

22. *Law of phylogenetic trends.* The relative geographical positions, within species (but more often genera and families), of primitive and advanced phylogenetic features are good indicators of the trends of migration (Simonet and Guinochet, 1938; Cain, 1944; Camp, 1947)

23. *Law of migration.* Geographical migration is determined by population pressure and/or environmental change. (Good, 1931)

24. *Law of differential evolution.* Geographic and ecological barriers favor independent evolution, but the divergence of vicariant pairs is not necessarily proportionate to the gravity of the barrier or the duration of isolation. (Gray, 1846)

25. *Law of availability.* The geographic distribution of plants and animals is limited in the first instance by their place and time of origin. (Good, 1931)

26. *Law of geological alternation.* Since the short revolutionary periods have a strong selective force upon the biota, highly differentiated life forms are more likely to develop during those times than during equable normal periods.

27. *Law of domestication.* Plants and animals whose selection has been more or less dominated by man are rarely able to survive without his continued protection.

TABLE I. A methodological comparison of the criteria and units involved at each integrative level in the study of environmental processes and relationships (modified from Dansereau, 1957).

Level	Sciences directly involved	Affinities with other sciences	Material studied	Object of research	Nature of the limitations	Methods of study	Conclusions	Units
I. Historical	Historical plant and animal geography Areography	Geology Evolution Phylogeny Paleoclimatology Taxonomy Geography Paleontology	Phyla to species	Origin, expansion, and decadence Migration Movement in relation to climatic change Distribution Areal affinities	Geological events Paleoclimatological fluctuations	Excavation of fossils Analysis of strata Location of relic areas Comparison of areas Plotting of areas	Evolutionary trends and sequences Occupancy of areas over periods of time Extension Disjunction and former continuity	Fossil floras Fossil faunas Isoflors Floras Faunas Areal patterns
II. Bioclimatological	Bioclimatology	Climatology Meteorology Phenology Vegetation science	Species to races Plant formations	Behavior in relation to climatic area	Climate or climatic factors	Mapping of coincidences of area Study of varvs, pollen profiles, tree rings	Responsibility of individual meteorological factors; cycles	Vegetation zones and formation classes Life zones Bioclimatic types Isophenes
III. Synecological	Synecology Vegetation science	Autecology Physical geography Pedology Geomorphology	Vegetation Animal populations Communities Ecosystem Landscape	Composition, structure and dynamics of communities	Cycling forces of ecosystem, from habitat to biotope	Physiognomic observations Quadratting Measurement Computing	Type of association Nature and orientation Static, dynamic and areal ordination of units	Ecosystems Communities Synusiae Biotopes

TABLE I. (cont'd)

Level	Sciences directly involved	Affinities with other sciences	Material studied	Object of research	Nature of the limitations	Methods of study	Conclusions	Units
IV. Autecological	Autecology	Physiology Genetics Anatomy Genecology	Populations, races, species	Reaction to habitat factors considered singly or holocenotically	Chemical, physical, and biological factors	Direct measurement of responses Experiment	Nature and gravity of immediate limitations Extensions and depth of possible reaction to individual factors	Ecotypes Coenotypes
V. Industrial	Human ecology	Anthropology Agriculture Forestry Human geography Sociology History Exobiology	Landscape Ecosystem Space	Influence of man Effects on man	Human intervention and ingenuity Human resistance	Historical recording Experiment	Nature, gravity, and duration of interaction	Land use and resource utilization types Human habitat

THE PROCESS OF URBANIZATION

Robert E. Dickinson*

This session is to be concerned with "Regional Planning and Development" insofar as these are relevant to what has been described by Dr. Darling as "the disturbance of the ecological repose of the planet" by urban growth. The leading question presumably is: What are the relationships between population growth and urbanization, with particular reference to the development of resources and amenities within some kind of undefined regional framework? I shall then address myself to three general matters. What are the trends of urban growth in the postwar years? What is the spatial impact of urbanization and how can it be measured and localized? What is meant by and how are we to define a regional framework as a basis for investigation and legal operation?

THE DYNAMICS OF URBAN GROWTH

The face of the land and the way of life of the people in North America and Western Europe are being radically transformed by the growth and expansion of urban areas. In the latter half of the nineteenth century the railroad facilitated the clustering of urban population in nar-

* Dr. Dickinson, of the Department of Geography and Planning at the University of Nebraska, was formerly Professor of Geography at the University of Leeds. A thoroughgoing revision of his classic *City, Region and Regionalism* of 1945 has recently been reissued under the title *City and Region: a Geographical Interpretation.*

rowly confined areas. During the past fifty years, and especially since the end of World War II, electric power and the internal-combustion engine have made it possible for urban land uses and urban ways of life to expand widely into the countryside. New industries have contributed substantially to this expansion. Moreover, the rapid tempo of economic growth, coupled with the increasing level of living, has prompted the increasing competition for building space in the heart of the cities, from which their tributary areas can be most effectively served. Urban sprawl and the skyscraper are the two major antitheses of this growth and they have made a varying impact in intensity and range both in different countries and different sections of the same country.

Economic development is clearly reflected in shifts in occupational structure. It is customary to recognize three rather ill-defined groups of occupations—the primary activities, concerned with the production of earthbound materials, mainly agriculture and mining; the secondary activities, concerned with the production of manufactured goods; and the tertiary activities, that are concerned with the provision of services of all kinds. A main feature of the twentieth century is the decreasing proportion of the working population dependent on agriculture. It has fallen in the United States from about 30 per cent in 1900, to 12.5 per cent in 1950 and 8.6 per cent in 1960. In Britain the figure has remained at about 5 per cent, but during the fifties the numbers of agricultural workers have been decreasing. The percentage of agricultural workers has fallen in Belgium and the Netherlands from about 30 per cent in 1900 to 7 and 10 per cent by 1975. In the Germany of 1939 there were 18 per cent in agriculture as compared with 27 per cent in 1907 and 40 per cent in 1880. West Germany had only 14 per cent so employed in 1960. In Italy the percentage fell from 59 in 1900 to 29 in 1961.

The rural exodus continued rapidly in the fifties. From 1950 to 1960 Italy lost 29 per cent of its agricultural workers, West Germany 30 per cent, Belgium and the Netherlands one third, and Great Britain one quarter. The United States lost a quarter and Canada one third of their farmworkers over the same period.

There has long been a surplus of agricultural workers in both the United States and Western Europe, and substantial and increasing numbers of the cultivators are moving from the land or are engaging in part-time work off their holdings. The steady transfer of workers from village to town during the fifties will continue in the coming decades. The continuing tempo of economic growth will mean the transfer of more people from agriculture to industry and service and thus the continued growth of the urban population.

The nonagricultural activities fall into the two major divisions of manufacturing industries and services. The proportion in manufacturing industries (secondary occupations), as classed in the national censuses, seldom passes above 45 per cent, not only in countries as a whole, but also in their constituent administrative divisions. The tertiary occupations embrace "trades and services." These generally include in the national censuses transport, commerce, finance, utilities, professional and domestic services. In the United States in 1950 they comprised about one half of the total employment. In Canada,

the Netherlands, and the United Kingdom the proportion is slightly lower; it ranges from 30 to 40 per cent in other areas of Western Europe. In all these countries, there is every indication that the tertiary services have constituted the most rapidly increasing section of the employment structure during this century. Moreover, today in the United States the gross personal income of tertiary workers far exceeds that of industrial workers. It is of interest to note by way of comparison that predominantly agricultural countries have only 10 to 20 per cent of their workers in the tertiary occupations (e.g. Yugoslavia 10.8, Turkey 6.9, India 16.2). Other agricultural countries with a substantial industrial component have 20 to 30 per cent in tertiary occupations (e.g. Japan 32.5, Italy 27.4).

These changes are rooted in technological developments. Geddes, fifty years ago, and Lewis Mumford, in our time, speak of the paleotechnic and the neotechnic eras. The paleotechnic era was based on the use of coal and iron, the railroad, and the steamship. This epoch was considered by Geddes to be nearing its end at the turn of the century.

New techniques became available to man with a chain of inventions between 1870 and 1930. They have resulted in an increasing change of tempo in the structure of human societies. Electrification, based on the use of the turbine, has facilitated the widespread distribution of power from both thermal and hydraulic sources. The advent of the internal-combustion engine has meant a revolution in means of transport, and the construction of a universal net of first-class hard-surfaced highways throughout these lands. New sources of power have come into use, brown coal (especially in Germany), hydroelectricity, and oil. New kinds of industry have also developed—automobiles, aircraft, artificial fibers, plastics, the distillation of coal, and (notably since the war) the petrochemical industries. Communications have been revolutionized by the automobile, telephone, radio, and television. Together with these changes has come about a raising of the standard of living and a growing social conscience which has been responsible for the steady increase of social welfare facilities undertaken by the state. If the Industrial (or Paleotechnic) Revolution is justified as a descriptive term, we surely have here another revolution covering a similar period of time about one hundred years later. This may be called the Neotechnic Revolution. It forms the basis of the urban dynamics of the twentieth century.

All these changes have come about at different tempos in different states and in different sections of the same state. The changes we have given above in the first half of this century reflect, in fact, growth under the impact of the techniques of paleotechnic society. The years of prosperity in the twenties were still based on late nineteenth-century foundations while the thirties were marked by stagnation. But in the interwar years there were many indications of changes to come. In Britain there occurred a great growth of new industries in northwest London and the Midlands at a time when the provincial industrial areas were hit by appalling unemployment. There was also the great growth of new thermal electric and chemical plants on a bigger scale in the United States. But the great impetus has come during and since the last war—within the last twenty years. The contributions of the new techniques, born in the preceding generation, have now gained full momentum. America experienced unprecedented growth as the Allied "arsenal" during the war years.

Rates of economic growth have been high on the Continent in the fifties. The "miracle" of American wartime production was followed in the fifties by a slowing down in the tempo of growth but a tremendous upsurge of consumer buying.

Germany has had its "miracle" and it would now seem to be Italy's turn, since the latter's rate of industrial growth is currently the highest in Europe. France has achieved wonders of reconstruction despite its crippling overseas commitments in money and men. Britain remains sluggish, if not stagnant, overburdened by the weight of its overseas economic and military commitments.

New highways and the prodigious increase in the number of trucks and cars are putting the railroads out of business. The consumption of oil and electricity has rocketed since the war. Western Europe must import most of its oil from abroad, and mammoth tankers are feeding refineries built since the war at the great port entrances for distribution by truck and pipeline to the interior. Coal, instead of being a basic British export, is now reduced in production and the export surplus has virtually disappeared. Big advances have been made in the production of electricity, and transmission lines carry power to most parts of every land, and, other things being equal, industry can be widely dispersed. Full employment means an ever-rising standard of living. This means an increasing demand for consumer goods, homes, and automobiles. Every country is trying to cope with these demands. The United States with the aid of thousands of miles of superhighways hopes to keep its vehicles on the move. The European countries—especially Britain—are being choked by the increase of vehicular traffic on medieval highways.

The increasing amount of business of all kinds results in the ever-growing number of persons engaged in the tertiary occupations. With this higher standard of living and the expansion of education and research, there is an ever larger number of young people in what Jean Gottmann calls the quaternary occupations. America aims at 50 per cent of its youth at universities, and this means the growth of many large new communities catering for the student populations. Great Britain is aiming at 10 per cent, and its program of university expansion is modest and exclusive. The continental universities are opening wide their doors, irrespective of the lack of accommodation. These vie in size with the American universities. The growth of all kinds of services is a white-collar revolution, an expression of the neotechnic era now in full flood. It is as fanciful to talk today about the "biotechnic era" as it was of the neotechnic era fifty years ago. We may be on the threshold of such a new era, but atomic power and space travel are harbingers of the future and as yet have made a negligible impact on society.

A higher standard of living means such things as the eight-hour day, five-day week, holidays with pay, substantial retirement pensions, and more education. People wish to live in new homes out of the cities in clean air with plenty of space around them. They like to spend their vacations in the country. Recreation and tourism are manifestations of the affluent society and are producing widespread effects in man's relation to the land. The senior citizens of America seek to retire and enjoy life in congenial physical and social surroundings. At present the heart of the desert is the vogue. The urbanization of the desert in the southwestern states is one of the most phenomenal new features of the American scene.

What effects are these changes having on the process and character of urban growth?

First, the highway. The advent of a universal system of motor roads over the last fifty years has greatly reduced the friction of distance. The great bulk of freight and passengers in most countries is today carried by road. The fact that the motor vehicle is a free agent and an economical short-distance and small-load carrier has greatly increased, and made virtually ubiquitous, the intimate contact between the city and its hinterland. "Rural and urban have truly met and . . . field and center are almost fusing."[1] The spatial expression of this centrifugal trend is fourfold. First, there is a development, or string-along-the-road settlement, along the highways radiating from the cities. Then there is the formation of satellite subcenters beyond the city, each with its own fringe, ribbons, and service areas. Thus "villages serve as centers for little fields; towns are centers for large fields; and cities function as centers for the largest fields. Each field, with its center is successively subsumed into the next larger one, in hierarchical fashion."

This urban expansion has hitherto been mainly in the form of compact private or municipal real estate developments. But individuals are now living in houses scattered far and wide. We have a new kind of area in which residences are scattered in the midst of farmland or woodland, a kind of semiurban landscape that in America Gottmann has described as having a "nebulous or quasi-colloidal structure." This is closely akin to what Tunnard has called "interurbia," in which houses and urban amenities are widely dispersed but easily reached by car. Furthermore, such houses frequently extend far beyond the limits of water or sewage facilities.

Second, while much of this dispersion is indeed caused by those who work in the city, it is also due to the establishment of factories out in the country to which residential areas have access by automobile or bus. The "suburbanization of industry"—establishment of plants on the urban periphery—began effectively in the interwar period and has continued to increase since 1945. Such plants are associated with the road rather than with the railway. The day of the exclusive pull of the railroad has gone. Highway and truck

[1] Firey, Loomis, and Beegle, "The Fusion of Urban and Rural," in Labatut, 1950.

are the principal determinants except for the heavy industries, such as oil refineries, chemical plants, thermal electric plants, etc., that of necessity must be accessible to the raw materials that they use.

Third, the growth of services, on the other hand, is having various repercussions. The chief of these is the increasing growth of the central business district and, in recent years in the United States, the loss of some of its activities to suburban shopping centers. Many communication-oriented pursuits need proximity to a host of other occupations and services. They seek such sites for convenience or prestige. Many can move out from the cities. This is eminently true of the retail services that naturally tend to follow the population. The change goes on freely in the States; in Britain it has been retarded by various factors, one of which is sheer inertia. The central business district is a vast and expanding nest of skyscrapers or "high-rise buildings." It is on the increase in postwar Europe and is marked since 1950 by the advent of the skyscraper—even in Britain. But the rate of metabolism is conditioned by the varying dynamics of economic growth between different areas and countries.

Fourth, in the central cities there is need for the replacement of obsolescent buildings, which date mainly from the period of 1850 to 1914 and lie around the central commercial district. Slum clearance has been prompted in the industrial towns of Britain by the unsuitability of houses for human occupation. But in these same British cities, the cleared or derelict areas lie in waste; and, ironically, the demand for land is far behind the rate at which the buildings can be demolished. Moreover, the process of demolition is held up by the relatively slow tempo with which new homes are built. On the other hand, in the United States private housebuilding is booming and city centers expanding, but the blighted residential areas are being removed at a very

slow rate. On the Continent, of course, and especially in Germany, the wartime destruction of cities necessitated speedy reconstruction, and indeed, through the fifties, Germany, with the same population as Britain, was building twice as many houses year by year.

Fifth, there is the rapid increase of housing and the spread outward of the urban area along the main lines of communication. Residential buildings and open spaces (including streets) make up about three quarters of all urban land uses. They are obviously the main contributors to the urban explosion; where they go, eventually services and industries will go. Stores will go to service the housewife, plants to tap the local labor supply, both male and female.

Sixth, there is the fantastic increase in tourism of all kinds. In the later nineteenth century this was limited to the spas for the wealthy. The seaside resort grew in the last decades of the nineteenth century and became popular over short distances, mainly in Britain. These new ways of living have given rise to a new kind of industry—tourism. Far and wide are to be found places in which the source of income is derived from the feeding and entertaining of urbanites, not only the wealthy or the professional middle class, as was the case fifty years ago, but also the so-called "working class" or the "blue collar" workers (as they are called in the United States) as well as the "white collar" workers. The highway is frequented by pulsating streams of automobiles. The motel is one of the remarkable additions to the American landscape and often forms continuous ribbons, miles in length, along main transcontinental highways on the outskirts of towns. This kind of development has been restricted in Europe owing to shorter distance between towns; but the holiday camp is one of its manifestations.

Finally, all these developments are reflected in the increasing daily movements of urban populations. These are the daily waves of movement to and from work, to and from the central or other business districts, and the factory. There are also the daily movements to school, to entertainment, and to shopping. These are not all focused on the center; they intercross in bewilderingly complex patterns. There are also the seasonal movements to and from places of recreation and along frequented "scenic" routes. A state such as California is having to give serious attention to the prospects of increased tourism with a rapidly growing population, which, more than any other in the world, is dedicated to the outdoor life. Around every city there is developing a circle of temporary summer homes, numerous retreats, and frequented beauty spots. The national-park movement is an attempt to provide such facilities and at the same time to preserve natural amenities from vandalism.

It has become almost customary to regard these changes in society, together with the increased rapidity and range of communications, as conducive to uniformity. In fact, standards of living, cultures, and aspirations vary immensely not only from one country to another, but also from one locality to another within the same country, whether in Western Europe or the United States, or in Africa or India. The spectrum of "economic health," as it has recently been called, varies enormously with local natural resources, the number and condition of the people, and the degree of their access to the poles of economic impetus in the great urban areas. The degrees of urbanization and the economic status associated with them vary from place to place. We need measures to locate them with precision before we can start to explain or remedy them.

These are the features of the urban explosion. It brings new trends in the location of urban land uses and in the spatial impact of urban ways. It brings new features and forces in the patterns of spatial relations, new problems in the organization of space.

URBAN REGIONS IN THE UNITED STATES

The phenomenal expansion of urban land uses around and between the central cities has resulted not merely in the growth of conurbations, but also in the coalescence of such areas to form predominantly urban regions in which cities compete with each other in the extension of their functional orbits.

The great cities of America are expanding on their peripheries at a phenomenally rapid rate. The urbanized areas are spreading to the boundaries of the SMAs and even beyond them. Not only are many SMAs contiguous, but their urbanized areas are now expanding and merging into one another. This process of "regional urbanization" is producing continuous clusters of large cities interconnected by sprawling and heterogeneous urban land uses. How are we to determine the extent of these areas? There are obviously degrees of urbanization, that depend not only on the extent of the urbanized areas and their immediate peripheries, but also on the facility with which homes in the country are accessible to work and service in city centers.

There were according to the 1960 census 208 such areas, but 107 of these can be grouped in about twenty-five contiguous clusters of two or more SMAs. These may be described as urban regions. There are also thirty-eight single SMAs, each with over 250,000, four of them with over one million inhabitants—St. Louis, Buffalo, Kansas City, and Atlanta.

The most obvious feature of the distribution of these metropolitan areas is the great stretch of almost continuously urbanized land which extends a distance of over 600 miles from Portland in Maine to Norfolk-Newport News in Virginia It contains thirty-three SMAs, including

Boston, New York-New Jersey, Philadelphia, Baltimore, and Washington. Here in 1950 there was a population of 27.3 millions and in 1960 31.6 millions. This is an increase of about 18.1 per cent in the decade, comparable to the national increase of 18.4 per cent. If you travel from Boston to Washington by air on a clear night, the lights clearly indicate the continuity of urban occupancy. There are open spaces, of course, but they are rapidly being filled up, and all parts are drawn closely into the functional orbits of the major places of work. The farmsteads in the rural islands are lived in today by professional people, factory workers, and others who travel daily to their plants and offices. For here and elsewhere growth takes place most rapidly along the highways. Miles of ribbon development—billboards, cafés, hot-dog stands, drive-in movies, amusement parks, gas stations, and even specialized stores —herald the approaches to every city. Bulldozers clear the way for housing developments that are completed within a few months, swallowing up farms and wood lots. Regional shopping centers emerge between outlying suburban subdivisions and are often physically removed from the actual residential areas. Industrial plants, covering hundreds of acres each, are located in the open countryside and workers' cars are accommodated in parking lots that far exceed the ground area of the plants themselves. Big-city department stores open up large branches in the suburban outskirts. The Atlantic seaboard has become the continuous urbanized area that Geddes and Wells envisaged fifty years ago and has recently been named Megalopolis by Jean Gottmann.

Outside the Atlantic seaboard, there are five other such clusters that dwarf the rest. Chicago-Milwaukee had 8.2 million, but on the basis of access this area reaches farther afield, extending through Michigan City to link up through the cities of southern Michigan with the Detroit region. The latter has some five million and is closely linked with its neighbors. Cleveland and Pittsburgh with their intermediate cities form a vast urban agglomeration with 6.3 million people. Together with Cincinnati (2.1 million) this whole cluster in Ohio-Pennsylvania has an aggregate population of about 14 million. Two giants are located in California, the most rapidly growing state in the Union. San Francisco and the Bay Area have over four million people. Los Angeles, with nine million in 1960, is the second largest aggregate in the nation and the fastest in growth. Eight other such city clusters have around one to two million inhabitants each, quite a drop in size from the major clusters. We should include with these, five "single" metropolitan areas of about one million inhabitants each—Kansas City, St. Louis, Buffalo, Atlanta, and Denver. Below the figure of about one million down to 250,000 there are forty-seven agglomerations. Especially noticeable are the two northeast-southwest series in the southeastern states, one from Birmingham through Chattanooga to Knoxville, and the other from Montgomery to Atlanta and thence through the cotton manufacturing towns of the Carolinas to Greensboro and Winston-Salem. The eastern coast of Florida is rapidly becoming a narrow urbanized coastal strip. The Puget Sound cities of Seattle, Tacoma, and Portland are closely interrelated but they are still physically separate. Of particular interest is the east-west series of cities in the Middle West that is bounded by Chicago and St. Louis. This series runs through central Illinois and Indiana from Indianapolis through Peoria to the Mississippi Valley and thence into central Iowa.

Let us note the rates of increase of these metropolitan areas for 1940–50 and 1950–60. The eastern seaboard belt increased by 18.1 per cent in the last decade, and its number of SMAs increased from twenty-four to thirty-three. This increase compares with 18.4 per cent for the nation as a whole. While some SMAs within the belt continued to grow rapidly (that is, above the national average), others had subnormal increases. The areas of most rapid growth in the nation were Los Angeles and San Francisco (1940–50, roughly 60 per cent, and the same in 1950–60 decade—fantastic rates for metropolitan areas of such a vast size). At the end of 1962 the seventeen million Californians surpassed the population of New York State, thus reflecting one of the most phenomenal migrations in history. Remarkable among the larger cities with over one million inhabitants are Dallas-Fort Worth and Houston-Galveston in Texas. Also highly significant are the tourist and retirement agglomerations of the Southwest. Phoenix-Tucson almost doubled in both decades. Florida also had great increases. Miami and West Palm Beach (1950–60, 161 per cent, 1940–50, 80 per cent) are seventy miles apart but are rapidly expanding toward each other. Tampa nearly doubled, and Jacksonville increased by one half. Lesser areas also recorded large percentage increases, such as Albuquerque.

The flood of urban expansion is in full spate and there is no apparent limit to it. It is likely that, if present trends remain unchecked, by the year 2000 the Atlantic seaboard belt will spread westward through central New York State and Pennsylvania, through the Middle West past Chicago, and possibly to Kansas City. It will expand southward beyond the southern fringe of the so-called manufacturing belt into Kentucky and Tennessee. New manufacturing centers are already growing in these latter states. The president of one of the greatest trucking companies in the country said in 1958 that in ten years one may have to travel 150 miles to get really clear of the big city of Chicago and he envisaged a "super-metropolis" in the Middle West running from Milwaukee through Chicago to Michigan City. He states that "the new interstate highways, the vast urban airports, and the huge industrial and residential growth along the expressways will run the big urban areas together into a blending of population and commercial enterprise." "Blending" is hardly the correct word for such a scrambling of uses, but it gives a general picture of what is taking place.

This expansion of urban uses is dependent on rapid transport mainly on highways between cities. Accessibility is a primary determinant of the range of urban expansion. The U.S. Census has not yet undertaken a thorough census of workplaces and consequently there is no basis for nation-wide assessment. We have adopted a simple but effective device to show the areas that are closely associated with central cities. We have mapped the areas in which all places are within easy reach of service and work in a large and well-equipped city. The standard metropolitan areas were given a radius of twenty miles, measured from the outer limits of their urbanized areas. All other towns outside these radii, with over 25,000 and, in effect, less than about 100,000 inhabitants, were given a radius of ten miles. All places within these circles are definitely within the reach of work and services of a well-equipped city center. These urban fields were linked together when the circumferences of two major cities lay within twenty miles, or of two minor cities within ten miles, and of a major and minor city within fifteen miles. The resultant areas were marked out in black. This is a conservative estimate of the extent of the urban and inter-urban areas.

This map reveals that the Atlantic seaboard area extends through upstate New York and central Pennsylvania to the Middle Western states as far as the Mississippi, including the whole of southern Michigan. In this vast area there are three inliers, one in the Catskills, a second in the northern Appalachian plateau, and the third in the Middle West, south of the Chicago belt. The groups of cities in the southeastern states do not quite qualify, on this basis, to be called a continuous belt, but the closeness of these lesser clusters indicates that here is one of the major urban regions of the nation. The Los Angeles and San Francisco regions are rapidly spreading into central California at an alarming rate. Houston-Galveston (plus Beaumont and Lake Charles) and New Orleans are extending tentacles toward each other and will soon merge. Seattle-Tacoma and Portland are substantial in size, and though functionally interrelated, they are still widely separated. It seems safe to say that these areas indicate the outer framework within which the urban growth of the new few decades will take place.

THE URBAN EXPLOSION,
SOME CONSEQUENCES

The phenomenal impact of the metropolitan city on the countryside has been a dominant feature of the internal scene in the United States and in Western Europe since the war. In order to emphasize the gravity and urgency of the "urban explosion" in its varied aspects, let us briefly enumerate some of its consequences.

First, there is the impact of urban land uses—"scatteration," as some Americans like to call it—on agricultural land uses. Over one million acres of farmland have been eaten up yearly by urban land uses for several decades. There is also a loss to agriculture of nearly another million acres a year through soil erosion, afforestation, waterlogging, and the like. Of 465 million acres of cropland only seventy-two million are in what is described as Class I land and over one half of this land is within reach of the urban areas. It was argued in the late fifties that if the

present levels of agricultural production and consumption continue, the nation, at this rate of loss, will produce by the mid-sixties no more food than will be required by the demands of its increased population. Some readjustment is obviously going to be essential. Will it be a decrease in production (and the disappearance of export surpluses) or increased production from a decreased area of cropland? There are those who are perturbed; there are others who are prepared to let economic trends take their natural course, through which the remaining agricultural land will be cultivated to bring higher yields—a general trend during recent decades.

Second, there is the question of water consumption that in some cities seems to be outrunning the existing supply. New Jersey, the most highly urbanized state in the Union, draws most of its water from wells. In the mid-fifties the state was using some 10 per cent more than its long-term average yield, and a subnormal year could bring disaster. The kitchen taps of Atlantic City sometimes yield saline water, yet the people voted against taxation for a new storage reservoir. Cities must seek increasing supplies from new sources over greatly increased distances, and often involving bitter conflicts between cities and states.

Third, there are sanitary problems, that arise especially where housing takes place without adequate cognizance of the physical conditions of the site, and especially when the pipe and disposal systems are in the hands of separate municipalities in one urban area. Septic tanks can absorb the sewage of plots of over one acre, but when houses are built on average suburban plots to, say 60 by 135 feet, the garden may become quickly waterlogged when the occupants first flush their toilets. Above all, there is the problem of widespread water pollution by the use of rivers as open sewers.

A fourth consequence of urban expansion is the steady decrease of the availability and accessibility of open space in and around the urban areas. Open space is needed to conserve water, to maintain special types of agriculture, to avoid flood hazards and land slips, to afford playing space, to form buffers against noise and nuisance, and above all for recreation. "The demand for outdoor recreation is likely to increase tenfold in fifty years, simply in terms of the expected growth in population, income, leisure, and mobility." (Wurster, 1960.) Much of this demand will be located in scenery and places far removed from the metropolitan cities. This is already evident over wide areas up to fifty and seventy-five miles from the cities, where there are cabins, and transformed farmhouses, on the shores of lakes and in the hills, motels along the highways, and extensive state and national parks. "If our present preserves are not rapidly expanded, overuse will create many wilderness slums by 1970." In New York a plan has been formed to increase the permanent open space by 60,000 acres but right now this would involve a cost of two billion dollars. A remarkable report has recently been published on public outdoor recreation in California. It points out that the present recreation facilities are "overused" by more than 30 per cent, with 60 per cent of the recreation being "water centered." Thus, greater access is sorely needed. By 1980 the population of the state will have doubled and the people will have more leisure and more rapid transport. By 1980 it is calculated that 30 per cent of the outdoor recreation will be spent within two miles of one's dwelling (day use), 25 per cent within 250 miles (overnight use), and 10 per cent beyond 250 miles (overnight use). In terms of "activity days," the demand will be four times greater than today. The state is thus threatened with an "overwhelming deficiency" and overcrowding of recreational facilities. Therefore, "the

state should lead a bold program to develop a comprehensive state-wide land-use plan in which recreational needs are adequately recognized."[2]

A fifth consequence of urban expansion is the need for drastic revision of the boundaries of municipalities. A large number of independent municipalities lie around each large central city, and owing to expansion beyond the boundaries of the central city to marginal municipalities and small incorporated or even unincorporated areas, that do not have municipal equipment of their own, boundary revisions and the cooperation of municipalities are needed in the interests of economy and viable system of taxation, and for the financial maintenance of mass transit by train and bus.

Transport presents a sixth problem. Mass transit (rail and bus) carries large numbers of outside commuters who are not required by taxation to support the system. It is suffering from the quite cataclysmic competition of the automobile that normally brings people to their work in the cities more quickly, more cheaply, and with greater comfort than the train or bus. Most companies have suffered a tremendous loss of passenger traffic (to automobiles) in the fifties, and most of them are in the red. The provision of new services will involve tremendous financial outlay (and tax increases) for the regional groups of municipalities, that would be concerned, as in the proposed system for the Bay Area of San Francisco.[3]

A seventh consequence of urban expansion is the need for a new geographic base for taxation. Municipal taxation depends almost entirely on land and buildings. Indirect taxation is small and irksome (e.g. retail sales tax). Industrial and

[2] *California Public Outdoor Recreation Plan,* 1960.

[3] There is vast literature on this topic. See Labatut, 1950; Owen, 1956; and Mitchell, 1954.

commercial properties have much higher assessments than residential property. Expenditures, on the other hand, for maintenance, protection, and public services are greatest in the residential areas, notoriously so in the suburban areas. The latter have inadequate revenue from their residential properties to meet the costs of providing sewage, water, police and fire protection, and especially schools, that are needed much faster than they can be built. Hence the suburban municipalities must seek outside aid, either by bringing in industrial plants or by receiving financial help from outside, for they jealously resist absorption with a larger neighboring city. There are municipalities in the metropolitan districts in which virtually the whole of the area is in industrial uses and the resident population numbers a mere few hundred. There is an urgent need for larger areas of taxation and government, more realistically related to the areas of the distribution of population and places of work.

Lastly, the central cities, confronted with the flight of people and their money to the suburbs, have suffered for several decades from the depreciation of land and property value and thus of tax revenue; from the steady deterioration of buildings; and from the virtual stoppage of building in the Depression years and then during the war. Meanwhile, many northern cities, if present trends continue, will soon have large Negro majorities, as southerner Negroes move in and the whites move out to the suburban peripheries.

The last ten years, however, have witnessed a new attack on these problems, and a large share of the financial burden is being carried by the federal government. Slums are being cleared, though so far the rate of demolition and replacement for the lower-income brackets is distressingly slow. Blighted areas are being "refurbished" and "conserved." Express highways are being built around, under, through, and over the central cities, often at three or four levels. Skyscraper apartments and office buildings are being built with exteriors of aluminum, stainless steel, bronze, and gold leaf. The building of colossal civic centers is in progress. Parking areas are appearing both above and below ground. But close to one third of the homes are still considered to be inadequate on current standards and the problem of rehousing their occupants, through federal aid (and this is the only solution), has scarcely been touched as yet.

Here are enormous tasks of planning and government that are becoming daily more complex since the process of growth is so alarmingly rapid. The essential problem for the immediate future, particularly in view of the great expansion of new highways (or "freeways") is to find effective ways and means of preventing urban sprawl. The states have constitutional powers for the acquisition of land for highway construction and for the purchase of development rights and rights of zoning in urban and rural areas that would permit immediate withdrawal of land from uncontrolled development. There is also need, however, for a new rationale of land-use planning on a nation-wide scale. This should reach beyond the usual practice of city and regional planning, and probably operate within the framework of a few major planning regions, and defined with due regard to the distribution of population. This will be a longer process and would call for greater federal powers and the education of public opinion on the issues at stake. Urban expansion is proceeding with such rapidity that immediate action on such lines is essential.

In conclusion, the problems of metropolitan government require further comment. They arise from the fragmentation and multiplicity of local municipalities and special districts of local government in the metropolitan urban areas. It is necessary to coordinate these districts and combine the municipalities so as to cope more effectively with the common problems of life and organization of the metropolitan community. Progress is slow, but there is a possibility, writes Perloff, that "within the next generation a new structure of urban government and metropolitan planning will have evolved in the United States."

PLANNING THE CITY REGION

The city has emerged more and more in the last hundred years as the focus of the activities of the towns, villages, and countryside around it. Indeed, the growth of cities has proceeded so far that the really great city is too large to offer the best conditions for human living. Disintegration has already started through the operation of centrifugal forces, the shift of factories, institutions, houses, and people out from the center—although hitherto in a haphazard fashion without any attempt at a "design for living." It is to be hoped that the future will see the continuation of this redistribution of urban functions and buildings from the congested centers, so that the city settlement area, and, beyond it, the city trade area, will emerge more and more as the effective grouping of real social and economic life, ready to be adopted in principle as the unit of democratic activity and land planning and regional development.

There is, however, every indication in the postwar years that economic growth has taken place so rapidly that the play of economic forces has resulted in the accelerated concentration of industrial sites in existing large urban areas—London, Paris, Ruhr, Stuttgart, and the great cities of America. There has been some dispersion but far less than the continued concentration. As Gravier has pointed out, in France dwellings and public services for industrial workers cost three to five times as much as the work-

place itself. Every time the problem of site arises, the entrepreneur is swayed by the mobility of industry rather than by the mobility of labor. Factories can be erected and come into operation long before the dwellings of the workers can be erected. Decentralization is one of the primary objectives of all planning authorities. The small industrial town is a feature of large areas of Germany, France, and the Low Countries. But decentralization can go much further in the shape of new towns and extensions of existing towns. Even the New Towns in Britain represent a small fraction of the four and a half million houses built and industries established in the last twenty years.

THE CITY AND ITS REGION

Many large urban agglomerations continue to increase in size at a faster rate than the countries in which they are situated. During the next decades even more people will be withdrawn from agriculture and transferred to centralized occupations. While planners aim at decentralization and its variants, these objectives have been of no avail in checking the more rapid growth of the big cities. Efforts by their governments to check growth of the regions of London and Paris have failed and hold out little prospect of being able to do so. Southeastern England is the fastest growing section of Britain. The population of the London region was ten million in 1938, 12.3 million today, and could reach 14.3 million in twenty years. The same is true of Paris and a new twenty-year plan anticipates that the present population of the Paris region (three Departments) will reach eleven million by 1975 and possibly sixteen million by 2000. Evidently not much is expected of the governments' plans for decentralization.

The city, in the fullest sense—and there are few cities that fill this ideal—will continue as the head of our civilization. It is argued that planning for the future should aim at reducing the size of the great urban agglomeration, while improving and making more widely accessible the amenities of city civilization in town and country alike. Decentralization of industry and population, in the sense of a widespread redistribution, far from the direct influence of the great city, was only an incipient development in the interwar years. It should more accurately be described as deconcentration, since the shifts took place merely to the margins of the built-up areas and tended to expand the area of the urban tract. Wartime evacuation of factories and commercial and administrative concerns was, on the other hand, real decentralization, real dispersal. The planned balance of activities in new and expanding towns is best called "recentralization." However far decentralization may go in the future and the urban agglomeration be reduced in size, the city as the fount of civilization provides the best it has to offer. And such a trend will inevitably tend to increase the reality of the extensive city region through the interdependence of its parts and their relations with the chief cities.

This means that a new kind of symbiosis of country and town must be strived for and especially in those areas in which the urban way of life is making increasing impact on the activities and way of life of the countryside. The diminishing number of farmers must be effectively integrated with the city, land must be open to urban dwellers for recreation and retirement and yet preserved as to its amenities. Residential evasion must be directed, water supplies must be assured, travel facilities must be adequate, etc.

Some writers, like Mumford, seem to be particularly pessimistic about the future of our urbanized society. Others, like Gottmann, the student of Megalopolis

on the Atlantic seaboard of the United States, and the Lloyd Rodwin and Kevin Lynch group are more optimistic. In any case, the explosion of the city is rapidly taking place in America. Efforts are being made to stop it in Britain by Green Belts, but while there is doubt about the efficacy of this concept, there seems to be no clear idea as to how the urban expansion of the future should be shaped. Central cities are being transformed, since they are obsolescent, damaged, derelict, often overcrowded, and unhealthy. This situation is probably worst in the "insensate industrial towns" in Britain, and any inhabitants of these areas must of necessity be pessimistic, so vast is the problem, so drab the environments. Large areas are derelict with tens of thousands of blighted dwellings in every nineteenth-century city, but progress is slow. In Britain in particular promises are still being made (as thirty years ago) for an acceleration of the slum-clearing and housing program, that is, in fact, far behind the tempo of development in Germany, where in the next ten years the housing problem will be solved.

The central business district is changing rapidly on the Continent and especially in the United States. Frank Lloyd Wright used to envisage the city center as a place for banking and prostitution, whereas the planners, such as Robert Moses in New York, are seeking to establish it as a seat of commerce and culture as the worthy focus of the vast population it serves. Such cities exist on the Continent, but at the present rate of progress, it will be many decades before such goals can be reached in the industrial metropolises of Britain. In any case, we have the curious paradox that this most highly urbanized people in the world is highly averse to the amenities and habits of living in cities.

Among the greatest problems of urban life are the betterment of the environment and indeed the provision and maintenance of services and amenities. This is a matter mainly of land ownership and costs. The costs of the provision of services—schools, libraries, utilities, police, fire protection, etc.—have to be set against the income derived by the municipal authority from its taxes (rates). The clearance of obsolescent properties and urban-renewal costs make demands far beyond the capacity of single municipal authorities. Expenditures are continually increasing as urban areas extend and as the social facilities increase. Water shortage, stream pollution, overcrowded schools, inadequate roads, urban renewal, etc., confront all cities with problems that are insoluble under the existing organization of municipal government, without financial aid from outside—the national government or a "regional government" of some kind or by the creation of large new units of government—the last still being matters of inquiry and dispute. Hundreds of municipalities and *ad hoc* areas make the need of coordination of these lines especially urgent. The problem is acute in the United States, for example, where the municipalities are still largely dependent on their own resources for the provision of services. Regional governments as well as state assistance are urgently needed in all the great urbanized regions of the Western world.

The central cities are full up and large areas are obsolescent. Land values are so high in the free market that purchase by the city for redevelopment is prohibitive from its own resources. The rehousing of people who cannot be accommodated also requires proper legal and financial facilities for joint planning by municipal authorities on a wide regional basis. In British cities, calculations are made of how many of the inadequately housed population in a city can be accommodated and how many must go elsewhere. The "overspill" must be arranged for by the provision of housing elsewhere by arrangement with another independent municipality. This leads to interminable wrangles with neighboring local government authorities. Deliberate decentralization obviously lies beyond the powers of town and advisory regional-town planning authorities, and can be effected only through the guidance and authority of a body with nation-wide or regional powers.

Attention on both sides of the Atlantic has long been drawn to the breakdown of the traditional corporate life of the historic city—both as a whole and in its component parts—through the great growth of numbers, the separation of home from workplace, and the increasingly complex scale of economic organization and social service. Metropolitan life must find new local associations, which the individual and the family need as an inherent part of human make-up. Traditional ties of local interest and locality have been usurped by nationwide associations. It is important that while diffuse associations of all kinds reduce personal dependence on local associations—be it churchgoing or shopping or club membership—the essential ties that remain are based especially on the children of the family, and it is understandable that the school and the school district remain as the keynotes of local community relations. And Europeans need to realize that the United States, with its very high postwar birth rate, finds its urban life strongly oriented to the life and needs of the family as the basis of new neighborhood relations. The primary geographical group is weakened since face-to-face relationships are diminished. But, as was said by John Dewey, "Unless local community life can be restored, the public cannot adequately resolve its most urgent problem: to find and identify itself." "Democracy," he said, "must begin at home and its home is the neighborly community." These are the new values that must be sought for. In concrete terms, they seem to lie in the provision of schools for the children, and in the physical separation of school districts by traffic arteries. Traffic islands, as they have been called, are currently favored as the framework for such community groups.

The problem is, says Mumford, "to overcome the barbarism of the submerged areas of the metropolis" through the medium of "an appropriate social nucleus" to serve as a meeting point in its suburban areas as well as in its higher focal points. The vast megalopolitan mass should be replaced by urban communities, with a balanced occupational structure, adequate in size to support a healthy social life, with an agreed arrangement of land uses, and surrounded by a guaranteed belt of green, sterilized from urban encroachment so as to prevent coalescence with other towns. The ideal size of such a town would be 30,-000 to 50,000 people. This idea was first put forward by Ebenezer Howard and put into practice in England at Letchworth and Welwyn and in the United States at Radburn and the Green Belt towns (a term that Mumford prefers to "garden city"). It is now embodied in the New Towns in Britain, and other new centers are being built elsewhere on the Continent both as town and suburb. Mumford goes further, as did Howard, in envisaging a cluster of such towns that would form a "regional city," focused upon a central "mother city," providing the facilities of economy, culture, and leisure, which such towns are too small to support. As Mumford never ceases to remind us, art and culture—religious, social, organizational, and recreational activities—are the most ancient and essential hallmarks of a real city. The central city would not have more than a million inhabitants and attention would be paid not only to the provision of economic functions, but also to museums, galleries, hospitals, concert halls, etc.

The ideas of the neighborhood and the Green Belt are today basic to the practices of town planning in various countries, most of all in Great Britain. Since both ideas come in for a good deal of criticism, especially in the United States, it should be made clear that they are an attempt to break away from the bigness and anonymity of modern urbanism. If there are errors, they lie in the planning practices and new ways must be tried. The far-flung English towns, with low-density houses, gardens, narrow roads, wide verges, and sidewalks, give an empty and monotonous sprawl that does not favor social cohesion or personal convenience. The argument of land is a myth. These notions and practices need to be superseded by others, aiming at a more compact unit, with a variety of dwelling types, and a more effective and accessible social nucleus. All these are variants working against the megalopolitan trend and in that sense are steps in the right direction.

It will be evident that many of these ideas reflect the actual spatial pattern of society that is inherent in the natural mode of growth before the advent of modern urbanism. They are not in any way novel. Mumford has emphasized in his works how the neighborhood group through history has given to the town in the past a sense of human scale. This is one of the main themes we have emphasized in our study of the historical town in Western Europe (Dickinson, 1953). Further, the arrangement of a family of towns and villages around a capital emerged in Europe during the Middle Ages and is still to be found in large areas where excessive urban growth has not taken place. Small cities such as Dijon and others in France—with about 100,000 inhabitants—or Würzburg or Bamberg in south Germany are regional capitals in this sense, and enjoy cultural attributes, embodied in centuries of regional associations, that are every bit as important as their economic functions, though they are difficult to measure.

We need to know, then, more of the size and spatial structure of urban communities; of the nature, location, and size of the nuclei of neighborhood groups; of the functions and trends and needs in central business districts; of the spatial distribution of towns and their relationships with one another; and the way in which they do, in fact, form groups of towns focused upon outstanding regional or mother cities. We have not been greatly concerned in this article with the philosophical aspects of the problem. We seek to promote study of the actual character and determinants of the spatial structure of urban societies. Out of the actual conditions we can obtain better understanding of the current needs of urban society. But this cannot be done without sound social values, and elasticity and experiment in planning practices.

BIBLIOGRAPHY

California Public Outdoor Recreation Plan. 1960. 2 vols. Sacramento, Calif.

Dickinson, R. E. 1953. The West European: A Geographical Interpretation. London.

Labatut, Jean, and Lane, Wheaton J. 1950. Highways in Our National Life. Princeton, N.J.

Mitchell, R. B., and Rapkin, C. 1954. Urban Traffic a Function of Land Use. New York.

Owen, W. 1956. The Metropolitan Transportation Problem. Wash., D.C.

Wurster, Catherine Bauer. 1960. Goal for Americans. Report of the President's Commission on National Goals.

USE OF EMPTY AREAS

Dennis Durden*

Urban centers in the North American environment continue their degrading use of adjacent habitats. Relentlessly, landscapes surrounding urban centers are overlain with anonymous residential suburbs, entwined with glaring ribbons of commercial development and veined with discarded urban wastes of all types.

This urban condition has been widely documented and lamented. In fact, the almost myopic attention given to metropolitan areas occludes some wider views. The landscape impacts of an urban society are far-reaching.

A persistent feature of American land-use patterns has been the presence of many areas whose landscapes display no significant imprint of man's current activities. These are habitats in which man, at any given time, is not visibly dominant. In this paper they are called "empty areas."

The name is anthropocentric. While man may be currently absent from these areas, other life abounds there and they are prime habitats for other species. Though empty of man, they are not empty of value for him.

In our nation's earlier history empty areas were generally associated with tracts

* Dr. Durden is Executive Secretary of Cincinnati's Downtown Development Committee and an Associate Professor in Yale's Department of City Planning. With a background in geography (from the University of Washington), his approach to planning has been marked by an attention to feasibility and the spreading impacts of urbanism.

beyond the frontier. Currently, in the midst of our heavily urbanized society, there are empty areas set aside by public policy such as forests, parks, wilderness and wildlife areas. Similarly, extensive private commercial areas have been deliberately kept "empty" by natural resource-based industries.

For these empty areas of today that have not been reserved by public or private commercial policy, new pressures are being generated by residential colonies in the form of resort and retirement developments. This growing use of empty areas by new part-time or specialized residential settlements, called here "new colonialism," is the major focus of this paper.

Before turning to an examination of the new colonialism, it is first useful to review an earlier definitive study of empty areas.

Klimm's study

A landmark study of empty areas was carried out in the early 1950s by the late Lester Klimm. The results of his inquiry were published as "The Empty Areas of the Northeastern United States" in the July, 1954 issue of the *Geographical Review*. Here, only a general outline of the findings are pertinent as a discussion framework.

In the northeastern United States from Delaware and Maryland north through Maine, Klimm found five basic types of empty-area regions. He classified the entire northeastern United States into one of the five. They are:

(1) Regions in which empty areas are large and continuous. These centered primarily on mountains such as the White Mountains, the Adirondacks, etc., but also included the New Jersey Pine Barrens.

(2) Regions of long, narrow, and parallel empty areas. These again were associated with mountainous areas, particularly the ridge and valley topography in central Pennsylvania.

(3) Regions in which empty areas appeared as small, scattered, and numerous parcels. These occurred chiefly in western Connecticut, southern Maine, Vermont, and western New York State—places where there is a significant but not particularly dense pattern of urban settlement.

(4) Regions in which the empty areas occurred primarily along the shores of bays, limited to Chesapeake and Delaware bays.

(5) Regions in which empty areas existed in the form of small, isolated parcels. As would be expected, this type of empty area region occurred nearest urban settlements.

Klimm's findings

In seeking causality for the pattern of empty-area distribution in the northeastern United States, Klimm was rather hard pressed to go beyond factors of geomorphology and climate. He estimated that perhaps 85 per cent of the empty areas were characterized by steep slopes or poor drainage or poor soil and that perhaps 60 per cent of the empty areas had some "climate" handicaps. However, he emphasized that these deterministic relationships between geomorphology, climate, and the pattern of empty areas were not as simple as they may seem.

Exploring an additional avenue of causality, Klimm noted isolation as a factor accounting for the pattern of empty areas.

To him, isolation had three connotations:

(1) Isolation in terms of distance from centers of economic activity—that is, remote from population concentrations.

(2) Isolation in terms of remoteness not from centers of activity but rather from corridors of intensive circulation. He felt that this type of isolation was especially important in the extremities of the region, particularly those peninsulas which, in effect, constitute "dead ends," rather than pathways for intensive circulation between urban centers.

(3) The third type of isolation which Klimm recognized as affecting empty areas was isolation related to the absence of local access routes. He noted that "In particular, many empty areas are the leftover country between the roads." Yet he qualified this by an assertion that a lack of local access roads is probably a result of an area being empty rather than a principal cause.

Klimm's prognosis for empty areas

For later students of empty areas Klimm felt that primary attention should be given to future potential uses rather than to attempting to explain the causes behind present emptiness. He remarked that "extensive field experience has led this observer to the conclusion that many details of the present landscape represent the 'frozen history' of decisions—once made with some rational explanation but now uncomprehensible—by people long since dead."

Klimm noted that man's assessment of empty-area potential for use is constantly changing. He cited those portions of New England which were tried for various types of agriculture but which have now been abandoned. He further noted that many of the topographic features which make land unprofitable for agriculture or other commercial use make it particularly well suited for recreation or to be set aside as a preserved forest or wildlife area.

From this position Klimm ventured briefly into predicting the future of empty areas. He felt that more favorable alternatives for industry, commerce, and agriculture would prevent most of the areas in the northeastern United States from ever being used extensively by such activities. However, he believed that in terms of forest, wildlife, watershed protection, and recreational use, empty areas would be set aside, permanently preserved, and perhaps enlarged.

From today's vantage point Klimm's cogent remarks about the recreational potential of these empty areas seem remarkably acute. Although he viewed his study results modestly and cited limitations of his study procedures, his work is of particular value today. It furnishes a carefully researched bench-mark analysis of empty areas at a given point in time. From this bench mark, contemporary studies can be carried out to measure the extent of change in empty areas.

Equally as important, Klimm's study did bring forcefully to light the fact that in the most highly urbanized portions of the United States a surprising quantity and variety of empty areas exist.

Classic notions of empty-area use

The patterns observed by Klimm reflect classic notions of empty-area use as modified by shifting public and private commercial policies. When he wrote, Klimm also observed the beginnings of new accelerated patterns of private residential empty-area use—a use pattern largely independent of classic considerations of the empty area's economic productivity for agriculture and other extractive industries.

Under classic notions of empty-area use, some essentials of man's recasting the habitat into one dominated by him include:

(1) An initial movement of users to those portions of the empty areas where the land resources appear to offer the greatest economic productivity. An area remains empty as defined here until, at some point, man makes an appraisal of the area's potential and decides that he will benefit more by directing his efforts to the use of the area in question rather than to some available alternate site.

Many of these use appraisals, often made with minimal information, are far from being rational. Moreover, the factors considered in the appraisal vary from man to man, and for any given appraiser the factors are constantly shifting in value over time. Behind these shifts are changes in his capability, public policy, his needs, and his available alternatives. Thus, the "emptiness" of any area has definite temporal limitations. As some formerly empty areas are being used, there is a reverse process at work. Areas formerly in use are reverting to emptiness as man's appraisal changes.

(2) The initial use of an empty area classically involves dispersed settlement. Within the settlement pattern small modes, or colonies, develop. These colonies are not fully balanced communities but are instead highly dependent on some established, often distant center for a wide range of goods and services.

(3) However, the classic pattern of empty area use generally assumes that the early colonies will eventually develop into full-time permanent settlements offering a balance of services and amenities. As an example here, it is useful to recall such anomalies as the grandiose opera houses developed in western mining colonies in anticipation of a settlement permanence and size which was not achieved. Along with this assumed community balance is a further assumption that eventually the formerly empty area will support a full range of governmental services and other local institutions.

(4) In his classic use of an empty area, man is little concerned with natural-habitat preservation, resource conservation, landscape amenities, or recreational opportunities.

Shifting public policies toward empty-area use

Underlying classic notions of empty-area use were public policies basically directed toward getting the areas settled, placing them into productive use, and achieving economic returns from natural resources there as rapidly as possible. Such public restrictions as were imposed directed themselves mainly toward standards for tenure and ownership.

Today, of course, public policy has been modified from its original thrust. The emphasis is toward rational use and better appraisals of empty-area potential in terms other than the extractive industries. In short, there are today public standards for the use of public empty areas.

Some of these standards seek preservation of empty areas near urban centers in the form of Green Belts, parks, and preserved open spaces. Even so, these formerly empty areas do undergo considerable landscape modification and the impact of man can become quite pronounced in preserved empty areas near urban centers. Farther from urban population centers, there are some public wilderness, forest, and wildlife areas which do remain "empty" as defined here, where the current activities of man have little landscape effect.

Emerging private commercial policy toward empty areas

Stimulated by changed public policy and by an awareness of resource-base limitations, private commercial activities are today much more concerned than formerly with conservation practices in their use of empty areas. Even though there are still flagrant examples of dev-astation by private commercial activities, better standards of empty-area use do exist and there is a growing acceptance of them, albeit a sometimes reluctant one.

Contributing to a more enlightened commercial use of empty areas is the increasing size of private commercial activities based on natural resource exploitation. This is especially true of forest-products industries. Many private commercial activities today carry out programs of empty-area preservation to assure themselves of a continuing resource base for production.

Moreover, areas which have been commercially devastated and are now lying empty are subject to increasing restoration and conservation practices. In short, there has been some progress in private commercial practices for the use of empty areas.

Characteristics of new empty area residential use

During our country's earlier history, empty-area residential use in connection with farming settlement was of great interest. Now there is a need to refocus concern about the residential use of empty areas. Although overshadowed by housing growth and problems within metropolitan regions, there is once again sizable residential land-use pressure on empty areas.

The new settlement arises from a complex of factors principally reflecting general affluence, mobility, and increased leisure time. As would be expected, there are sharp contrasts between the classic pattern earlier assumed for empty-area residential settlement and the newer pattern which can be observed today. Some of the more noteworthy of these contrasts are:

(1) *New settlement motivations and values.* In contrast to the classic settlement of empty areas motivated by desire to generate productivity from land resources, today's private residential settle-

ment in empty areas is based principally on consuming rather than generating economic gains. Today the asserted frontier settlement values of frugality, productivity, and enterprise seem almost irrelevant as empty areas undergo residential development.

(2) *New criteria for site selection in empty areas.* Today the empty areas chosen for residential settlement are not those where the potential for agriculture or other production from the land is necessarily greatest. Perhaps the most dramatic examples of these new site criteria are displayed in desert resort settlements of the Southwest or skiing and summer recreation colonies in mountainous portions of various regions.

(3) *New patterns of seasonal occupance.* Instead of being designed for full-time, year-round occupancy as in the classic pattern, the new residential settlements in empty areas are largely oriented toward seasonal occupancy with residences remaining vacant for large portions of each year. This occupancy pattern carries with it definite implications concerning the ability of the seasonal residents to support a full range of local institutions and participate in local government.

(4) *Changes in basic settlement pattern.* Instead of a dispersed pattern of individual dwellings on relatively large land holdings as in earlier empty-area homesteading, the bulk of today's new settlements in empty areas is clustered. Rather than individual holdings of several acres, the new pattern typically involves much smaller house sites approaching the size of the suburban single-family lot.

(5) *Limited horizons of community growth.* Instead of seeking to locate at sites which could ultimately be developed into large-scale centers, new residential communities in empty areas generally look to a low horizon of ultimate community growth. They do not assume

that their new settlements will ultimately evolve into balanced communities. Today's residential settlement in empty areas is predicated almost exclusively on residential and recreational development with only a limited layer of commercial activities. In effect, residents of the new communities plan to remain highly dependent on established areas for a wide variety of goods and services. They could be colonists indefinitely.

(6) *Extreme separation of job and home sites.* With this acceptance of more or less permanent colonial status, there is usually a considerable distance separating the residence in the empty area from the major place of work of the colonist. In the classic settlement of empty areas, home site and job site were the same.

(7) *A new outlook on colonial living levels.* Instead of moving into empty areas with the prospect of starting at a relatively low level of living and gradually developing it upward as in the classic mold, colonists today bring with them high levels of living and urban standards of consumption. Now empty-area settlement is clearly a mass-market phenomenon in which no discomforting sacrifices of urban living levels are anticipated.

The size, the development standards, and the conservation implications of this new colonialism warrant careful examination. Unlike public and private commercial use of empty areas, this private residential use is not yet covered by generally accepted standards.

Scale of the new colonialism

Estimates vary, but there is general agreement that the scale of second-home development currently is large and growing rapidly. This is partially reflected by the interest which the home-building industry and some of its major material suppliers display in the second-home market. These trade sources place the current pace of construction at approximately 75,000 units per year. Industry spokesmen estimate that the present pace is expected to double by the end of the 1960s. Eventually a level of 200,000 units annually is foreseen.

Basically, the construction of second homes takes two landscape forms: (1) buildings on individual scattered sites and in small tracts and (2) new recreational community development. Until recently almost all such construction took place according to the former pattern in and around established resort areas. Here small-scale developers construct a few homes each year on a more or less custom basis. The recreational facilities and the amenities for these scattered home developments are those of the general area and are not an integral part of the tract being developed. In this type of second-home building, raw-land prices are relatively high and the availability of sites is limited. Site competition is quite intense. Assembly of a large parcel is difficult, placing rigorous barriers in the path of achieving large-scale housing production.

Now the focus has shifted away from the limited sites and small tracts near established resort areas. Today the largest and fastest-growing segment of the second-home market takes the form of new communities in heretofore empty areas. For second-home builders, communities have been proclaimed by trade sources as "the surest way to success."

In these new recreation colonies the leisure-time facilities are an integral part of the community development. Freed from a dependence on the facilities of established resorts, colonies are relatively "footloose" in terms of location. The four prime locational requirements of a contemporary large-scale recreational colony are:

(1) Land prices that are relatively inexpensive.

(2) Sites within 100 miles of and certainly not over 200 miles distant from at least one major urban center.

(3) Topography that lends itself to golf-course and/or ski-slope development.

(4) Sizable lake frontage or a site that lends itself to the development of a man-made lake. This ability to offer access to a lake seems to be the *sine qua non* of marketing a successful second-home colony.

The acreage used for each second-home colony has varied widely to date. However, there seems to be a trend toward larger developments and currently 1000 acres seems to be the desirable minimum. There is at least one successful development of 8000 acres, but probably a size range of 1000 to 3000 acres includes the bulk of today's most imitated developments. Below 1000 acres it becomes difficult for a developer to house enough colonists to support some of the recreational facilities essential for successful marketing. For example, a consultant in second-home colony development estimates that a minimum of 400 families is needed to operate a full-scale community clubhouse at a financial break-even point.

Even though the colonies themselves encompass large acreages, lot sizes for the individual homes resemble large single-family suburban plots.

Moreover, there seems to be a gradual trend toward smaller lot sizes with the average near the one-acre mark and trending downward. Even after allowances are made for golf courses, lakes, roads, and other community facilities, it is easy to see that large family populations can be accommodated on a development of 1000 acres or larger.

Despite their sizable acreages and populations, these new communities are clearly colonies. Their seasonal occupancy patterns, separation from urban areas, heavy dependence on established centers, and the almost complete absence of any commercial or institutional facilities combine to cast these empty-area residential uses into a colonial mold.

Development economics of the new colonies

Out of our current economic prosperity have come the leisure time, the discretionary spending power, and the automobile-based mobility which have created the second-home market on a mass scale. A recent home-building trade advertisement featured the lead "Every family needs two homes!" This is clearly a different economic era from those earlier eras giving birth to such slogans as "A chicken in every pot" or even "Two cars in every garage." Within this present climate of general affluence it is important also to note those more specific economic factors that induce second-home developers to center their activities on empty areas.

First, quite simply, the empty areas are there. As extensive land-using sectors of our economy, particularly agriculture, have become more efficient, there has been a well-chronicled retreat from marginal areas. Today, in many regions, recreation represents a most aggressive land-use competitor. Thus, there has been a coincidence between a lessening general demand for empty areas and a heightened specific demand by recreational uses.

Second, this shift in land-demand patterns has been accompanied by tremendous public investment in highways and resulting economies in highway travel time during the past decade. Consumer ability to use private autos to reach empty areas has been immeasurably facilitated by the growth of arterials. Access improvement is continuing unabated. It seems likely that subsequent highway investments will bring even more empty areas within convenient driving range of the automobile-owning residents of metropolitan centers.

Third, new economies in earth-moving technology now have made it financially feasible to transform natural landscapes in a dramatic fashion. Dams, ski slopes, golf courses, and all of the man-made earth forms essential to outdoor recreation can now be imposed economically over a wide variety of terrain.

Fourth, and certainly the most important economic factor which concentrates second-home colony development on empty areas, is the profit potential which a developer can realize there through enhancement of land values. Because the new colonies must provide a wide range of recreational facilities to compete successfully, it is not uncommon for a developer to invest heavily in site improvements before land sales commence. In addition to site improvements, there are also marketing and promotional costs as well as property taxes to the developer over the period during which he will hold sites pending their sale.

Yet to reach the mass market which the developer caters to, he must keep his land-sale prices to the colonists as low as possible. A low initial land price permits this even in the face of the high development costs. Trade sources estimate that $50 to $100 per acre is the desirable *maximum* price which a developer can pay for raw land to be transformed into a large-scale recreational colony.

In special situations, this maximum can sometimes be exceeded, but there is every reason to believe that (at the time it was bought by developers) the land for most of the large-scale colonies now being built cost well below $100 per acre. This figure, of course, is very much below the typical suburban land values in and around urban centers and also below the price of better agricultural land. Within any feasible distance from an urban center the only land that can meet this price maximum of $50 to $100 per acre is to be found in empty areas.

After taking care of site improvements,

management overhead, and other expenses prior to sale, the entrepreneur in the recreational colony can market his land in quarter-acre so-called "offshore" lots for, say, $1500 each. Of course, the land in public facilities cannot be marketed but, nevertheless, there is a profound difference between the developer's $50 to $100 per-acre purchase cost and the lot sales price.

Moreover, the $1500 per-quarter-acre-lot figure is indicative of the sale price away from the waterfront at the beginning of development. Initially, waterfront sites sell for some two to three times this amount. Moreover, as the development progresses, initial land sale prices throughout the colony usually are increased from 25 per cent to as much as 200 per cent in the more successful large-scale developments.

Moreover, even after the developer sets aside a fund to take care of later maintenance and operation of public facilities when the colony is fully developed, the land profit potential inherent in recreation-colony development in empty areas is obvious.

Currently, new methods are being found to obtain longer term financing for the colonists' purchases of the site and the homes which are built on them. This will tend to broaden the market. At the same time, it can increase the profit potential for the developer if he participates in the financing profits as well as the development income from the project.

Doubtless, the future will see some increases in the developer's empty-area land costs. There probably also will be offsetting increases in his sales prices to the new colonists—thereby preserving the very favorable profit relationships between empty-area land costs and second-home lot sales.

Suburban genesis of the new colonialism

The resort colony is not a new feature on the North American landscape. There

have long been groupings of second homes intended primarily for recreation. Until quite recently, these colonies were almost the exclusive province of the economically—if not the socially—elite. The number of colonists and colonies was small, and, in terms of scale alone, today's new mass-market colonialism dwarfs its antecedents.

Apart altogether from differences in scale, there are significant landscape differences between earlier recreation colonies and those of today. The earlier colonies were generally developed as a group of estates, sometimes centered on a clubhouse. Usually their owners placed a high premium on the natural landscape. Some of these earlier colonies are responsible for pioneering efforts in conservation.

Today's new colonialism does not look to these earlier second-home communities except perhaps where street and project names are borrowed in an attempt to connote status. Rather than resembling the earlier colonies, today's new developments take as their model the suburbs.

Although many of today's new colonies advertise "a new way of life" and "a new concept in living," they seem actually to be a suburban landscape form and suburban living pattern transported outside the suburbs to empty areas. To the extent that there is "a new way of life," that way is suburbia at play.

Among the strongest ties between suburbia and the new colonies are those supplied by the home-building industry itself. The industry catering to the housing needs of the new colonies closely parallels and, in many areas, is an extension of the suburban home-building industry. Many merchandising techniques and some financing tools developed in the suburban home-building industry have been applied to new colony development.

The housing products being created in the new colonies very strongly resemble those in suburbia. Developments generally consist of variations on a few model homes. Only rarely is there a custom-built product. The feeling of spaciousness that characterized earlier resort land-scapes has been replaced by the closer feeling of suburban living. Some devel-opers assert that housewives in the new colonies are repelled by the notion of isolation and prefer the smaller plot sizes which they have been conditioned to in the suburbs. While there is some sensitiv-ity in the siting of individual homes, the new colonies demonstrate much of the monotony of the suburban street-scape.

Today's buyer of a second home looks for the same household conveniences in the second-home housing product that the suburban house buyer seeks. Most rustic ideals of "roughing it" are completely absent. The experience of most recrea-tion colonies indicates that few colonists are interested in the minimum suitable shelter. Rather developers speak of many colonists buying status symbols, not hous-ing alone.

The pattern of home tenure within the new colonies resembles that of suburbia. In the promotion of second-home colo-nies, the concept of a lifetime investment is highly touted. In reality, it is estimated that the average second home is sold once in ten years. Thus, the "lifetime" nature of the investment has not proven to be a reality. Instead, the turnover and mobility of the suburbs prevail. Further, as second homes in the colonies are sold, expe-rience to date indicates that the suburban policy of "trading up" to a more costly dwelling is prevalent.

In all, it is difficult to envision the new colonialism taking place without its first having been preceded by suburbia. Resi-dents of the new colonies are clearly seeking a familiar home environment combined with a wide array of mass-market recreation facilities.

Public programs in the new colonialism

Indirectly a number of public pro-grams, notably those covering highways, have set the stage for the rapid and sus-tained growth of new residential colonies in empty areas. Beyond this stage-setting, public policy largely has remained mute.

At present, the federal program most directly influencing new colony develop-ment is a small and comparatively ob-scure one carried out by the Department of Agriculture's Farmers Home Adminis-tration. Through it, a limited number of farmers to date have received assistance in converting marginal agricultural acre-age and empty areas into recreation de-velopments.

Of much greater future significance at the national level is the probable entry of the FHA into the second-home financing market. Legislation has been proposed but not yet passed that would allow FHA participation in the financing of second homes. It seems likely that future legisla-tive proposals for FHA participation will be forthcoming and soon approved.

A recent home-building trade maga-zine quoted the former chairman of the House housing subcommittee as saying, "I am for second homes which could be insured under FHA, but I was against their inclusion (as part of the Sec. 2031 program for low-cost homes) in the 1964 Housing Act because of the label. We would never have heard the last of the 'government building vacation homes and beach homes.' So if you get another name for second homes, we might be able to get it written into a new housing bill."

Surely from among all those interested in passage of such legislation some in-genuous new terminology will be found.

The entry of FHA could definitely broaden the mass-market appeal of the new colonies. Members of the home-building industry look upon financing as being the major present obstacle to fur-ther expansion. With removal of this ob-stacle by FHA's participation, the indus-try's optimistic growth projections seem likely to be met.

To many, FHA's involvement in the

new colonialism might seem a mixed blessing in terms of its landscape impact. As the godfather of suburbia, FHA will doubtless bring many of its suburban policies and practices to bear on any new colonial developments where it is involved. However, the suburban cast of the new colonialism is now so well established it is difficult to see how FHA's present policies could markedly affect landscapes in the new colonies.

Yet FHA's participation would provide the first national policy guidelines for the development of new recreational colonies. In view of this, the most fruitful course of action appears to be to try and influence FHA's programs toward the creation of better environments in the new colonies rather than continue to lament FHA's alleged failings in the shaping of suburban landscapes.

As with most facets of residential development, there are no noteworthy public programs relating to the new colonialism at the state level. With the interest that most state governments have in economic development, state policy makers presumably "favor" new colonies. One could predict quite confidently that if a study were carried out by any state it would be possible for it to show that new colonies do attract tourist dollars from out of state or at least prevent in-state tourist dollars from being exported.

It is at the local level that public programs currently exert the most influence over the development of new colonies. Local zoning and building codes as well as local taxing systems are applied directly to the new colonies. Unfortunately, from a public standpoint, the empty areas in which the new colonies are located are frequently those areas where codes are weakest and where local jurisdictions have the least professional help in guiding development. Moreover, there are few outside sources to which a local government can turn for advice and counsel. The problem is further complicated by

the fact that during the lifetime of any public body at the local level there will probably be only one or, at best, a few colonies within the local jurisdiction. Thus, it will be virtually impossible for a local public body to acquire and then later apply local experience meaningfully. Immediately the advisability of having some state- or region-wide professional resources for local agencies suggests itself. Through such broadly based resources, it would be possible to accumulate and later apply the experience of scattered local jurisdictions.

Despite strains imposed on local public authorities by a new colonial development, generally it is viewed as an economic asset to its local jurisdiction. Land which was formerly empty is brought onto the tax rolls at substantially higher rates. New buying power is concentrated for local businesses, and the area captures valuable outside tourist dollars. Moreover, as a seasonal community based on recreation, a new colony does not typically impose additional burdens on local schools or road systems. In fact, one of the local selling points used by developers is that most new colonies will provide their own community services.

The lack of coherent public programs for residential settlement in empty areas should not be particularly surprising. The entire range of settlement problems, from those of slum housing in the heart of the city to the mass-market suburbs to the specialized new colonies, lacks any coherent approach. As usual, a series of seemingly unrelated public programs have set into play a parallel series of unforeseen, indirect developments of which the new colonialism is a major one.

Conservation challenges of the new colonialism

The increased use of empty areas for seasonal recreation colonies holds significant conservation challenges. New colonialism typically does not place a high premium on the natural landscape itself but rather on the opportunity for mass-market recreation which an altered landscape affords. Any conservation qualities which the new colonies display stem from the efforts of enlightened entrepreneurs rather than from well-formulated public policies or demands of the new colonists themselves. Typically, within the new colonies conservation applies only to those landscape features and natural resources endowments that add to the salability of the second-home product which is being merchandised.

Because new colonialism is the transplanting of suburban development to heretofore empty areas, it further blurs the fading line between urban and rural landscapes. Structurally, it is a "leapfrog" development which bypasses transitional zones and radically transforms moribund habitats into those where man's dominance is very pronounced. As the new colonialism moves into empty areas, including many which conservationists would like to see preserved, there is a drastic habitat rearrangement. Not only drastic but sudden. There is little subtlety in the processes of new colonialism. Typically, large quantities of earth are moved. Vegetation clearance is extensive, as is dislocation of animal wildlife.

Although they do not particularly respect the natural landscape, entrepreneurs for the new colonies can afford to seek out choice empty-area sites. Promotional brochures for some new colonies depict suburban-style homes sited gracelessly in locations of outstanding scenic beauty. Landscape silhouettes of empty areas are punctuated with roof lines. Throughout the transformed habitat there are the new sound patterns of recreational use with the automobile and the motorboat supplying the underlying rhythms. The impact of this new settlement is not limited to the colony site itself or even to immediately surrounding habitats. Af-

ter they have once transplanted themselves for a few seasons of recreation, it seems likely that the new colonists will venture out into parks, forests, and other conservation areas in the vicinity. There is little reason to believe that purchase of a residence in a new colony will tranquilize the restless suburbanite and his auto. Further, it is doubtful that even the wide range of mass-market recreational facilities available in the colonies will provide sufficient outlets for the energies of the colonists over a sustained period. The greater likelihood is that the colonies will serve as "jumping-off places" or "launching pads" for assaults on conservation areas—especially those that, up to the present, have been relatively remote.

The question arises as to whether or not public conservation areas can adequately accommodate any new pressures to be generated by the colonies. Developers of the new colonies advertise that the recreation needs generated there are satisfied internally. This notion seems questionable and worthy of further study.

Still another conservation challenge arises if, as expected, FHA begins to participate in the financing of second homes. Because FHA's role seems likely to be so important, any conservation standards written into FHA's requirements would have widespread application. Moreover, because FHA would offer such financial advantages to developers, they would probably be willing to go to considerable lengths if FHA second-home requirements included conservation standards. The key question is whether or not any meaningful conservation standards could be devised on a nation-wide level to fit the wide variety of empty-area habitats into which the new colonies will be placed.

With or without FHA standards, however, a separate challenge of conservation education for new colony developers exists. These developers are highly organized, with strong, well-established trade publications. An education program could reach a wide audience of developers if properly channeled. Here the operative question is whether or not conservationists can be skillful enough to arouse the interest and, even more importantly, the active participation of the developers.

At least in a few instances, developers have seen such values. Some new colonies are being developed around a primary theme of conservation. In these select but possibly trend-setting developments, conservation has been made an integral part of the way of life which the colony offers to its residents. The Audubon Colony in North Carolina is one example. Another is the development of Little Cumberland Island, where a small group of conservationists are treating the natural landscape with great sensitivity. In both these colonies a major development objective is the least possible disruption and maximum conservation of the natural habitat. Not seeking an indiscriminate habitat dominance, these colonists are hoping to play a balanced role with other life there.

The predominance given to conservation in these developments indicates that the emphasis in new colony development need not be restricted to simply transplanting suburban landscapes and suburban values into an empty-area setting.

Directions for future studies of new colonialism

At present it appears that:

(1) The transforming of empty area habitats into new colonies cannot be stopped. Yet the nature of the transformation perhaps can be modified.

(2) The suburban landscape structure of the new colonies is rooted in strong financial and market considerations. Nevertheless, elements of conservation can perhaps be injected into this structure.

(3) Mass-market recreation will prob-

ably always be a major appeal of the new colonies, but current popular notions of recreation possibly can be enriched to include conservation values.

(4) The new colonies created by developers reflect the values and aspirations of an affluent mass market with growing leisure time and high mobility. However, in catering to his market, each developer has some latitude in the type of landscape and housing products which he offers to his potential customers. The developer is not a complete captive of market forces, but, if motivated, perhaps can shape and direct them.

(5) As with most aspects of housing and human settlements in our society, public programs and policies related to new colony development will always contain contradictions or at least lack coherence. Yet, over time, a more rational public-policy view of the new colonialism probably can be achieved.

Specific field studies

To date the bulk of our knowledge concerning new colony developments comes from their developers and from trade sources of the home-building industry. It is imperative that this information and the trade practices of the industry be appraised from the conservationists' viewpoint. Featured in the specific field studies would be such considerations as:

(1) Are there particular natural habitats within empty areas that seem especially attractive to new colony development?

(2) Are there development "constants" that recur from one new colony to the other?

(3) How do the business success and landscape impact of the typical new colony compare with the business success and landscape impact of the select few colonies that have been developed around conservation themes?

Impact of new colonies on established conservation areas

Separately, or in conjunction with the specific field studies above, there should also be studies of the impact which the new colonies have on conservation areas elsewhere in the region. Among the major questions here would be these:

(1) Is it true—as developers assert—that the new colonies are self-contained in their recreation needs, or do the colonies generate new pressures on existing public conservation areas elsewhere in their regions?

(2) Because the new colonialism provides for so many outdoor recreation needs, should there be a shift in the type of facilities provided by nearby preserved empty areas such as parks, forests, and wilderness areas?

(3) Specifically, what are the nature and types of uses which residents of the new colonies make of nearby conservation areas?

(4) Does residence in the new colony change the attitude of colonists toward conservation and toward publicly preserved empty areas?

State planning assistance to local jurisdictions

The local jurisdictions where new colonial development takes place typically are faced with unusual public planning choices and only meager local resources to help them choose. Studies should be undertaken to obtain and evaluate the experience of local governments which have faced problems of new colonial developments. Among the major issues in these studies would be:

(1) What are the common problems which various local jurisdictions face in dealing with new colonial development?

(2) What professional planning resources did they have access to either through the developer or through channels of their own?

(3) In retrospect, what changes in development policies or procedures would the local jurisdictions have made, given the experience gained in the completed developments?

(4) Corollary to this, what types of professional assistance, if any, would these local jurisdictions like to have had to aid them in their dealings with the developer of the new colony?

(5) Were there state or regional plans or programs available to guide them? If so, how helpful were they?

Studies of special FHA standards for new colony development

On the assumption that the FHA will someday participate in the financing of homes in the new colonies, studies should be undertaken to determine if viable conservation standards could be included as the prerequisite for FHA's participating in new colony development.

In these studies the basic questions considered should include:

(1) Could any FHA interest in conservation be tied to the interests of other federal agencies now active in conservation?

(2) Specifically, could the standards of use and development on land leased from federal agencies, such as the Corps of Engineers, be usefully applied to new colony development?

(3) Are there standards now being used in the small Farmers Home Administration program of assistance that could be adopted for FHA participation in new colony developments?

(4) Most critically, what types of conservation standards, if any, would have the widest possible application in an FHA second-home program that would reach into a wide variety of habitats in numerous regions throughout the country?

APPENDIX

1964 Field Survey of Some Empty Areas in Southern Connecticut

To directly observe landscape changes that had taken place in the last decade, a limited field survey was undertaken in August, 1964, in some of the empty areas designated in Klimm's 1954 study.

Klimm had recognized some ninety-four empty areas that lie partially or totally within the State of Connecticut. In his five regional classifications the entire State of Connecticut fell into two types of empty-area regions, namely regions where the empty areas were small, scattered, and numerous and regions where empty areas were few, small, and isolated. These reflect the relatively dense settlement pattern and high degree of urbanization within Connecticut.

The short field survey in August, 1964, examined twenty of the ninety-four areas identified by Klimm. These twenty areas are in south-central and southeastern Connecticut. As defined by Klimm's study, an empty area is one:

a. "containing no used structures (dwellings, factories, mine buildings, oil wells, hunting lodges, recreational buildings, and so on),

b. "containing no land used for agriculture (including even the roughest pasture) or for industry, and

c. "having a minimum dimension of at least one mile but not approaching a used structure nearer than a quarter of a mile."

The re-examination consisted of a field observation of the designated area from adjacent perimeter roads. Wherever road conditions permitted, the empty areas were traversed or penetrated.

The twenty empty areas observed were generally higher in elevation than their surroundings. Rock outcroppings were much more pronounced and appeared to contain many more bogs and other surface features associated with an irregular and interrupted drainage pattern.

At several of the sites, traces of past agricultural uses could be seen in the crumbling remnants of stone fences. In the past these had bounded fields and pasture areas. Today they meander through dense woodlands. Thus, in topography and appearance the twenty sites surveyed displayed the empty-area landscape features described by Klimm.

Out of the twenty areas examined in 1964, ten were found to be preserved public open spaces, consisting of portions of state forests with one reservoir watershed. Thus, half of the twenty empty areas which Klimm identified understandably remained as empty areas a decade later.

Of the remaining ten sites surveyed in 1964, only one still seemed to qualify as an empty area. The remaining nine showed varying degrees of development. On five of these the development has been of fringe suburban type. That is to say, along roads adjoining the empty areas, single-family, year-round homes have been developed. In view of the relatively isolated location of many of these areas, it was surprising to find such suburban developments. Although these small developments did not deeply penetrate the empty areas, they did clearly remove them from Klimm's definition.

Perhaps this type of suburban development in empty areas will be found only in a densely settled region such as southern Connecticut. Nevertheless, it was interesting to find that such a high proportion of the areas which Klimm designated as empty in 1954 had, a decade later, been used for year-round suburban residences.

In three of the remaining four empty areas surveyed, there were combinations of small, year-round suburban development and seasonal recreational colonies. Although quite small by contemporary standards, the colonies in these areas were pronounced landscape features.

Finally, in one of the small areas surveyed, the area which was empty in 1954 now contains a new colonial development of resort homes. Unlike developments containing year-round suburban homes which tended to cluster on the fringe of the formerly empty area, this resort colony penetrated deeply and was associated with a lake.

The limited field survey confirms that within the span of a decade substantial changes in empty-area use have taken place.

BIBLIOGRAPHY

Klimm, Lester. 1954. The Empty Areas of the Northeastern United States. Geog. Rev. (July).

RESOURCES PLANNING VERSUS REGIONAL PLANNING

Sanford S. Farness*

The term "regional planning" is loosely applied in the United States to a broad range of environmental research and action programs covering many different kinds of human purposes and geographic areas. The following are the major types classified according to primary objectives:

(1) *Resource Planning—"Economic Development"*

Programs for the development and conversion of water, land, forests, minerals, science, and historic artifacts into marketable goods and services. A vast range of public and private ventures is included in this category.

(2) *Urban Regional Planning—"Urban Habitat"*

Programs for urban living space for metropolitan areas, urbanized counties, and urban regions.

(3) *Regional Facility Planning—"Technoeconomic Efficiency"*

Specialized programs for large systems of facilities such as highways, airports, water supply, and utilities.

(4) *Ecological Planning—"Biological Fitness and Health"*

Programs for public health, air-

* Professor Farness is at the School of Urban Planning and Landscape Architecture, Michigan State University. He has been responsible for planning programs at the county and regional level in Michigan and has been particularly concerned with the impact of urban settlements on patterns of natural resource use.

and water-pollution control, soil conservation, wildlife propagation, and reforestation.

(5) *Social Institution Planning—"Implementation"*

Programs, usually as an adjunct to other types of planning, for new legal and institutional forms required to carry out plans. At regional levels such planning is seldom explicitly conceived as "institution building."

Rising population and the growth and diffusion of urbanization are imposing new and heavier demands on the natural environment. The human, social, and biological consequences of old unsolved problems such as urban deterioration, pollution, and crime have become intensified while new problems are arising. These factors are compelling the search for better ways of designing the environment as a setting for human life. In this search the above types of planning need to be seen as five aspects of the socioenvironmental system which, because they are both complementary and conflicting, require deliberate coordination in some degree as the system progressively differentiates and evolves.

Any improvement of present socioenvironmental conditions is now heavily dependent upon the degree of coordination that can be achieved between the numerous local, state, and federal agencies, the varied practice professions involved in the five modes of planning, and the "public"

—the collective client for all of these services in any particular region.

Unfortunately, on-going environmental problems and new needs are still being met through the creation of new single-purpose agencies and programs in closely related environmental matters. A continuing *ad hoc* proliferation of local, state, and federal agencies and programs as environmental problems increase will eventually so complicate and obstruct individual and group comprehension and participation that environmental defects will be extremely difficult to remedy—except by centralized decree.

In the remainder of this paper I shall only have space to note some of the main negative effects of present resource planning and urban regional planning together with suggestions for improved "harmonization."

Negative aspects of resource planning

We identify sociocultural facts by their component of meaning and purpose. Without meanings in human action there are only biological facts. Resource planning, in line with our historic economic interests, is proceeding largely under technoeconomic categories. The theory and practice of regional planning and facility planning are also heavily distorted by the same one-sided orientation. In the sphere of social theory we have even seen the birth of a discipline dubbed "regional science" based upon a single subsystem—the economic—of a manifold, complex cultural system. Regional planning agencies also tend to use largely economic spectacles in perceiving, researching, and reporting their environments. And in the last decade or two we have frequently witnessed university Schools of Conservation transform themselves into Schools of Natural Resources. The change in meaning is significant. The phenomena in the environment are thereafter perceived differently, more in line with the cultural drift.

In our one-sided emphasis upon producing and consuming in our technical-economic era we have acceded to viewing nature, ourselves, and our environments almost entirely in terms of exchange value—as natural resources or economic commodities. So we commonly speak in our planning studies and reports today of "natural resources" and "human resources." Now when we apply the concept "resource" to something we have already classified it as a "means"—an instrumental value toward our ends. This is the meaning of "resource." At this point we have already assumed the economic attitude and are geared primarily for economic decision making.

Over the centuries some fairly universal modes of thinking and intending preceded the economic manner which has become our favorite and almost compulsive approach within the last 200 years. The main fields of knowledge, the academic and practice professions, and our social institutions and roles correspond to our intentional modes of acting and have in fact been erected upon them as reflective, theoretical sciences and technical, creative arts. Each action mode has a distinctive meaning and logic that shapes decision making in that field and constitutes its rationality. We will briefly consider some of the differences between these and their relation to our environment and its design. Review of the following partial list of cognitive and decision modes indicates the compression of vision and myopia that may result from single-valued orientations and actions.

Some of the main categories of thinking, goal forming, and decision making, in addition to the economic, are those of interpersonal (human) relations, technics, health, art, government, and science. As these modes have evolved in Western culture, they have become distinctive with differentiated reasoning, goals, and action. Interpersonal action which we all undertake at times, aims at humanistic goals

Institution Social Role or Cultural Subsystem	Decision Method	Meaning–Goal
Economics	Calculation of costs-benefits	Maximize benefits
Religion	Contemplation	Spiritual truth
Philosophy	Logic, reason	Rational truth
Science	Experiment	Empirical truth
Ecology	Field research	Fitness, adaptation
Arts	Design	Expressive form, beauty
Technology	Invention, test	Efficiency
Jurisprudence	Hear evidence	Justice
Politics	Bargain, compromise	Equity
Law	Social need	Rights, duties, order
Personal	Integrative, sacrifice	Solidarity, love
Medicine	Diagnosis	Health

of mutual love, respect, sharing, understanding, and solidarity. It also extends the same personal and social relations to the world of nature—to animals, trees, water, land, and birds. Technical reason, the role of increasingly numerous technicians, is constituted through our valuation of impersonal, functional efficiency. The rationality of health as physicians and biologists enact it is distinctively based upon the given requirements of organic and ecological fitness. In the human dimension health also involves the need for emotional and mental wholeness and balance—the ability to participate in the varied types of knowledge and action we are now considering. Artistic reason aims at achieving symbolic meaning, beauty, expressive form, and knowledge beyond the range of merely rational thought. In our society governmental rationality is defined by legislators, judges, and administrators through the ends of justice, social control, freedom, protection, and an office for public decision making. Lastly, scientific action is directed by the goal of verifiable knowledge of nature and man—all scientists ideally act in these terms, even economists.

The specific economic sphere is originally constituted when we individually transform persons, cultural objects, things of nature, and even ourselves into commodities or "resources" and, through economic calculation, apportion these resources as means among multiple "wants" that we hold. Laws are then enacted to define the things which may become commodities. Prior to this conversion, objects such as persons, houses, land, trees, animals, and cities have unique, intrinsic meanings and qualities. They are invested with interpersonal, esthetic, moral, technical, scientific, and other meanings that we have previously reviewed. Within the sphere of economic reasoning these meanings must be repressed.

What has all this to do with the future environments of North America? The major modes of reasoning and planning that we have discussed are interdependent forms of knowledge making up our cultural system. They exhibit in many ways the creative conflict of opposites—the dialectical tension of complimentaries. The science and art of planning, as well as the science and art of life, is to combine them in a balanced program. When any particular mode of action is pushed to extremes it excludes the others. Planning is everywhere being reduced to technoeconomic-oriented resource planning. It neutralizes unique persons, places, and things into "natural resources" and "human resources" as we now universally name them—raw material for the input-output machine.

Economic-technical human action, because of its one-sided dominance, is and has been gradually destroying our natural environments and our cities as viable centers for positive, healthy human living. Isolated economic logic is also destroying its own ground, for the economic sphere is dependent upon a fit "biological" environment, a workable society of mutual personal relations, a body of balanced practical knowledge, and a government system defining available economic resources and structuring the economic system. These prior systems are slowly deteriorating, particularly in our large metropolitan economic machines whose urban overconcentrations are a prime economic phenomenon. Their biological and physical environments are heavily deteriorated and becoming progressively toxic. Yet we mechanically continue to predict their growth. There is hardly anything to be said regarding their esthetic environments. The paradox and irrationality of a rising economic standard of living, measured in dollar income, and a declining environmental standard of living, measured in ecological, esthetic, and social terms, is now manifesting itself. Social solidarity and interpersonal respect are declining under economic alienation into conflict and crime, while mental-health problems are increasing.

We must develop capacities to plan and decide in noneconomic and nontechnical terms as well.

The existential ends of human solidarity and love for man and nature, legal ends of justice, freedom, and control, economic ends of maximizing, health ends of organic, emotional, and ecological fitness, artistic ends of symbolic meaning and beauty, and scientific ends of verifiable knowledge must all play a proportionate role in the resource planning process. There is no other way to create humane cities and environments in North America. Resource planning will then be transformed into pluralistic, many-valued regional planning for a rational habitat for man in the constantly self-transforming evolutionary process.

Problems of regional planning

A primary difficulty affecting regional planning is that our society has no workable consensus regarding urban form or values for management of the environment. The entire history of American government policy, federal, state, and local, has been based upon the notion of growth indefinitely extended. Possible states of social or environmental stability are therefore automatically viewed as something abnormal and threatening. This cultural background provides a deep fund of social, economic, ecological, and esthetic irrationality full of conflicting movements with which the regional planning function attempts to operate.

Another important limitation involves the inadequate theory provided by the social sciences. This situation leads to crude logical errors and omissions in formulating planning analysis frameworks along with exquisitely refined computor and data-processing techniques. The resulting reports and representations of the planning unit often misrepresent and misinform the recipient public about the nature and dynamics of regional systems.

Many social scientists are well aware of the psychic and cultural components of social structures but they have remained abstract and have not often involved themselves in the concrete forms of social systems on the ground. We know almost nothing in a systematic way about the various forms of social space—existential space, esthetic space, sacred space—and other qualitative aspects of the living environment: such spatial relations all quite different from the abstract space of physical science. Political space is generally evident to us. Economic space, with our propensity for economic cognition, has also been analyzed in market and economic system studies in recent years. However, biological space at the ecological level has not yet been conceptualized in regional planning.

We have previously noted the specialized and very limited cognitive, decision-making, and value perspectives utilized in technoeconomic resource planning. Regional planning in its present stage also distorts and misrepresents sociocultural systems through a differently grounded omission. This practice can be indicated by reference to the following notation of empirical system levels:

System Levels
Personal
Cultural
Institutional
Biological
Machine (artifact)
Physicochemical

The above categories are organized according to my interpretation of their relative degrees of autonomy. Investigations in the philosophy of science, modern ontology, and general systems theory are building again upon the older "systems" knowledge couched in terms of the mineral, plant, animal, and human kingdoms. Logically and empirically it is beginning to appear necessary to identify distinctive entities, dynamic principles, and space-time relationships among the various strata.

Regional planning, focused primarily upon sociocultural systems, is currently hampered in theoretical clarity through absorbing the backwash of about two centuries of "reductive explanations." After the emergence of physics in the seventeenth century there followed a full century and more of intensive work formulating systems of "social physics." Again after Darwin, in the nineteenth century, great enthusiasm developed for formulations of social organics. Much of this material penetrated into the collective representations of our popular cul-

ture, and many segments of our general academic culture are committed by conviction or habit to reductive theory.

In regional planning operations this state of affairs blossoms in logical "confusion of the categories," awkward analogies, and muddled metaphors. Theoretical clarity and comprehension are weakened. One finds sociocultural dynamics explained in mechanical terms—pressures, forces, and even gravity. A popular conceptualization at present is to analytically define the "city" in terms of four components—the political, the social, the economic, and the physical city. The terms imply that economic and political relations are not "social," which hardly makes sense. The notion of a "physical" city is an additional logical barrier because if we are speaking with some degree of scientific precision, then by definition the category "physical" is noncultural and nonsocial.

Reductive theory and failure to comprehend the specific nature of sociocultural systems results in treating their dynamics mechanically. The policy decisions required for urban growth are then repressed out of awareness.

Consider the case of an urban or metropolitan planning unit. It can be flatly stated that unless additional urban facilities and services are provided in the future, little absolute population or economic growth can take place in the locality. We must assume in any absolute growth forecast, therefore, that a decision has been made to provide the public capital and urban facilities necessary to service the forecasted growth, otherwise the growth could not occur. But this is precisely the critical policy action that is ignored or glossed over in current projection methodology, nor is it implicitly or explicitly discussed in population and economic studies. Instead, trends are derived through a variety of mathematical population and employment projection methods producing a future growth estimate, which then becomes a bench mark for scaling plans and defining "future needs." Instead of treating these "needs" as results of self-generated policy, present methodology implies that they are the result of automatic, impersonal, socioeconomic technological "forces" playing over the region with relentless effects. The hidden policy decision is never brought to awareness and made explicit.

Such "planning" procedures are standard methodology for most resource, regional, and urban planning agencies. They are a major factor in generating our excessive and irrational metropolitan centralization. This occurs because important segments of the private economic sector benefit under present relationships from increasing agglomeration, spiraling land values, and growing regional mass markets and labor pools. However, the increasing social costs and diseconomies so engendered do not inhibit continuing centralization because they are, under present federal programs, largely absorbed by the public sector at the national level.

Federal responses to fiscal and environmental defects growing out of the original metropolitan agglomeration tend therefore to reinforce and ultimately increase centralization and the resultant problems. These effects are inherent in recent federal grant-in-aid policies. The programs absorb the increasing costs of scale, thus encouraging further metropolitan centralization. New and enlarged programs for mass transit, open-space acquisition, renewal, pollution control, water-resources development, highways, planning, and other urban services are thus continually evolving. Interlocked with the foregoing relationships are a series of private institutional structures affecting interest rates, capital supply and investment, transportation pricing, and similar factors which bring to bear powerful formative influences shaping metropolitan growth.

All of these relationships are obvious and well known but they serve to point out that federal metropolitan programs are more than political palliatives. In their directional effects they are unecological and uneconomic and we may conclude that they are poor examples of institutional design. On the one hand, federal agencies support regional planning, and on the other, they increase its problems by encouraging overdevelopment. We need to insert ecological criteria into eligibility for grant programs.

The "hard" impersonal, mechanistic treatment given to sociocultural dynamics in emerging regional planning practice and the continual elaboration of technology in urban environments raises the question of the future quality of the social environment—the qualitative distribution of the polarities of control and freedom in social space relative to personal, spontaneous human action. This question has a time dimension that requires a brief review.

History is created by human action. Anthropology and recent archeology have amplified our understanding of the record of human experience and the transformations of man's psyche. History can be read from this viewpoint as the gradual but uneven emergence and freeing of the individual from earlier collective social environments and modes of human action. Western culture, for the time being, is the dynamic center of this historical process. One can begin with the archaic, centralized theocracies of history and trace the gradual diffusion of decision-making powers toward individuals and subgroups in successive historical systems through the differentiation of culture and social institutions.

It is apparent that this long historical movement toward increasingly free individual decision making and action represents a key direction of human evolution. Much of the drama and conflict of recent Western life has centered about this issue. Powerful psychic forces and human needs are evidently centered here. Any substantial reversal of this direction of social change toward collective, centralized decision making would represent regression to earlier authoritarian forms of human relations.

A sudden breakthrough toward autonomous individual planning occurred during the Renaissance and subsequent centuries. The new capacity and achieved power for individual human action flowered into the age of individualism. Parallel with these events, persons involved in the new physical science and its applications helped bring into being our complex, technological environment. The social and environmental problems resulting from this phase have generated a strong countertrend toward restricting the scope of individual planning and enlarging the area of collective planning.

The various forms of planning that we have been considering are manifestations of this countertrend. Planning theory has evolved during our most recent phase of technological achievement. It has naturally absorbed the new scientific, technical, and functional rationalism into its theory and outlook. This is an outlook that is well informed about the technical order and it transfers the meaning and value of efficient organization to the world of human relations.

One of the primary characteristics of late technology, however, is its requirement for mechanical ordering—for the mechanical coordination of social functions and human relations in space-time relationships designed from a controlling, coordinating center. The evidence from environmental applications of technology to date indicates that the broader the scope of mechanized applications and the greater the efficiency the more collectivized and coordinated the mode of planning must be. Presumably, an efficient, high-output, and broadly automated environment would require completely centralized planning. This would represent a reborn, technically created, collectivized, and centralized social system. It indicates that at some critical point our kind of technology and emergent human needs come into fundamental conflict.

Regional planning is deeply involved in technical applications and coordination of social relations and its personnel have not faced this problem. Our dominant institutions, business, government, military, and research and development, and the ideals of planning practitioners stress the comprehensive coordination of human activity, with a view toward maximizing functional efficiency through collective action and technological innovation. The effect is to reinforce the inherent, centralizing effects of the technology created to date. We are faced with the need for regional planning operations to deliberately address and find ways to resolve this conflict in the ordering of our future environments.

Toward future environments

Two basic factors in modern life are now generating the need for regional planning to focus upon larger frameworks. First there is the well-known fact of the urbanization of society. The bulk of present urban populations, however, is now living in obsolete urban environments inherited from previous cultural periods. These environments are grossly inadequate in the light of emerging values and standards of living. They are particularly lacking in respect to ecological fitness, esthetic qualities, recreation facilities, and easy access to open space and nature.

There is manifest a growing repugnance for many of the urban and rural environments created in the last century and in which we are now living. Urban and rural settlements are the external expression of man's cultural systems, and as these values change over time the established forms and symbolic expressions of value become progressively obsolete and unsatisfying. We are now entering a period when there is a fresh awareness and demand for reshaping the landscape in symbolic-space forms that express richer human values and meanings.

Man, from this perspective, is seen as one unit in a total ecosystem of awesome complexity and order. Man's designs and activities, therefore, inevitably have far-reaching ecological effects throughout the systems. The task emerging for unified environmental planning is the collaborative work of providing theoretical and design bases for creating new cultural landscapes and reconstructing the disfigurements of the past. The science of ecology, yet to be fully elaborated, will provide a rational, practical foundation for this effort from one direction, while esthetic and symbolic principles of design developed to higher levels of meaning will provide the other source of knowledge for the coming synthesis.

From a psychological viewpoint, the regional planning movement represents new, evolving attitudes and capacities of man growing out of changing relationships with the environment. New forms of transportation and changing time-distance relationships are also modifying man's space perception. In vehicular movement landscapes are perceived first as general regional landscape and later at closer range as particular structures and small-scale landscape compositions. The feeling for urban landscape—the cityscape—is also growing. Architectural modes, street and highway patterns, the proportion of open and built-up areas, and other physical elements are blending together as components of a larger, qualitative urban whole, yielding the impression that each urban landscape has its own character.

Similarly, ecology is supporting the notion of designed and consciously managed evolving landscapes and life forms. Among the biotic factors that influence the quality of the landscape and human

cultural adaptation, vegetation is one of the most important. However, the kinds and density of plants that can exist in any region are determined to a considerable degree by climate and soil resources. The plants in their turn influence the distribution of fish and wildlife. These relationships produce a close correlation between the biotic and physical features of the environment.

Insights of this kind have led many biologists to maintain that regional environments are healthiest and least difficult to maintain when an approximate state of dynamic balance is sought—as between vegetation types, human and wildlife populations, the scale of resource conversion activities, and habitat conditions. A logical extension of such ideas is that of broad landscape design with species adapted to the most favorable land use, soil conditions, water management, view horizon, disease, biotic association, and other factors. Planting and forestation plans of various kinds—stream valley, headwater area, hedgerow, small woodland, wildlife area, park, farm, urban residence, and highway right-of-way will gain new esthetic and functional dimensions when considered as parts of an interrelated, composed regional landscape rather than as isolated plans and designs. The General Landscape Plan will then evolve as a new, needed component of community and regional advisory plans. This type of environmental planning will be functional in a scientific, instrumental sense as well as functional in an esthetic-symbolic sense. It will be related to erosion, pollution, drainage, disease, and microclimate control as well as expressing larger human meanings and purposes. It will join man and nature in a perceptible community of means and ends with mutual sharing of instrumental and final values.

We have recognized five basic types of planning which result in spatially organized environmental systems. Because they are simultaneously conflicting and complementary, they require continuous coordination. In review, they are resource planning for economic output, regional planning for urban habitat, facility planning for technical efficiency, ecological planning for biotic fitness, and social institution planning for implementation.

The future condition of our environments will be heavily dependent upon comprehension of these factors by the public and the degree of coordination that obtains between the increasingly numerous federal, state, and local programs. We are already reaching the point in organized complexity where coordination of planning agencies alone is a problem and even the professionals have difficulty grasping the systems they are working with. Inherent in this situation is a growing need to simplify and make more understandable institutional patterns and planning operations so that more persons can comprehend and participate in the decision making affecting their environments.

There is a clear need for a new type of multipurpose institution at regional levels in scale with the human span of attention, that can simplify environmental planning through grouping presently specialized institutions and programs. The new regional institutions should be joint creations of federal, state, and local governments, focused upon concrete geographic subregions large enough to permit comprehension and integration of the five basic types of planning. They should combine the functions of regional planning, academic research, technical services, extension, adult education, information center, data center, and field administration of federal-state programs. Only through this type of social invention, which would require many different forms in various parts of the country, will we get beyond the worst problems of today in building our environment, managing nature, and allocating resources into our economic subsystem. And let us keep as a watchword for our day—"the technoeconomic system is only a subsystem, one part of a many-faceted cultural system of values containing great noneconomic riches for future decision making."

RESTORATION OF LOST AND DEGRADED HABITATS

F. Raymond Fosberg*

INTRODUCTION

The Conference, so far, has dealt with the pattern of habitats existing in North America, with their uses, exploitation, and modification, with the human motivations and behavior responsible for changes, and with the possibility of planning such human activity so as to preserve as much as possible of the natural values inherent in what man found when he came on the scene.

Many mistakes have been made in the course of man's occupation and exploitation of the continent. Also, many exploitation processes and other uses result in unavoidable degradation or destruction of natural habitats. This has been so in the past—as much, or more, through ignorance of less wasteful and destructive methods as from the pre-eminent need to use resources. It will probably continue to be so as a result of heedless disregard of what we have learned, and because the sheer pressure of increasing human population will require utilization of more and more marginal situations. The prospect for the future is for increased restriction of anything like natural habitat and landscape, inevitably resulting in a premium on even seminatural

* Dr. Fosberg, recently appointed plant ecologist and taxonomist at the Smithsonian Institution, was for many years a botanist with the U.S. Geological Survey. He has participated in several expeditions to Micronesia, and in 1964 edited *Man's Place in the Island Ecosystem.*

conditions. This will force us to look for all possible means of restoring destroyed and degraded areas to something approaching natural conditions. The purpose of this paper is to examine some of these means. It must be emphasized that the author is not directly engaged in any such activity, does not consider himself an expert in the field, but is merely an observer of ecological processes, some of which may be involved in restoration of habitats.

At the risk of repetition, it seems necessary to examine some of the destructive processes in operation and their results. The resulting degraded habitats are in no way uniform, nor would the means of restoring them be uniform.

It is obvious that the end products of some of man's exploitation of his habitat are not subject to restoration. Areas that are devoted to intensive agriculture, such as the fertile plains of Illinois, to heavy industry, such as the Buffalo, New York, region, or to high-density human occupation, such as downtown New York, or any city and even most suburbs, are, so long as our present culture continues, likely to remain in a completely altered and unnatural state. This even applies to most parks and mass-recreation areas. It is only when such an area, because of pollution or other cause, becomes completely unfit for continued intensive use that it will be a candidate for any sort of restoration.

Biological consequences

We will consider first the general biological consequences of habitat degradation. These can be listed, at least in part, as follows:

(1) Changes in the composition and structure of vegetation and biotic communities.

(2) Creation of more nearly pioneer conditions, shifting successional status toward early stages, even in the most extreme cases creating the equivalents of new ground and primary successions.

(3) Changes that make a habitat less fit for one organism but that may provide an opportunity for another.

(4) Creation of biological vacua.

(5) Biological impoverishment.

(6) Creation of very adverse conditions for living organisms, even to the point of creating biological deserts.

Causes and kinds of habitat degradation

Then, in more detail, we should examine the degrees and kinds of degradation and destruction of natural habitats and their results. These can be grouped into a number of major categories.

I. Logging and other harvesting or exploiting of natural products.

    a. Hunting and gathering by primitive man resulted in degradation of habitats only when fire was used as a tool. Then it may have resulted in formation of savanna, brush, or grassland in areas that originally were forested.

    b. Tapping of trees for turpentine, gums, and latex altered the habitat only when carried to excess. Then it may have changed the composition of forests to some extent.

    c. "High grading" and selective cutting of timber result in an altered forest composition and some opening up of canopy and unevenness of spacing.

    d. Clear-cutting of timber without other treatment initiates relatively rapid forest successions which may lead back to forest similar to what was cut. If the trees are of sprouting species, a coppice forest may result with the readily sprouting species dominant.

    e. Clean-cutting of timber with subsequent burning of slash may result in significant impoverishment of composition both in plants and animals, and will certainly change the composition drastically. Frequently the resulting forests are dominantly of one species and are even-aged.

None of these processes leads to even extreme degradation, let alone destruction unless it is followed by conversion to agriculture. The return to a forest condition is likely to be rapid, unless the original forest was in a postclimax condition, when it is unlikely to recover. The practice of silviculture is aimed at restoring logged forestland and altering the resulting forest composition toward greater predominance of desirable tree species.

II. Agriculture and related phenomena.

    a. Shifting cultivation with bush fallow depends on natural recovery of soil fertility. Since it is usually accompanied by fire, it is a fairly destructive practice. Forest composition is normally completely altered, though this can be mitigated by leaving patches of uncut forest to serve as seed sources. Considerable loss of soil ordinarily results from this system, as well as very widespread destruction of primary forest for the support of a small human population.

b. Clearing for grazing or cultivation followed by grazing results in more complete destruction of the forest and its conversion to grassland or bush. Erosion often follows, especially if frequent burning is resorted to for pasture improvement.

c. Continuous cultivation for any length of time results in more or less complete elimination of the original flora and fauna, unless hedges or patches of wood are left. It may also result in marked changes in soils —either for better, or more likely, worse. Sheet erosion or even gully erosion may follow unless the cultivation is planned with the prevention of erosion in mind. Soil exhaustion is usually the reason for abandonment of cultivated lands. On abandoned land a secondary succession takes place, the course of which depends on the species available and the degree to which the soils were depleted.

d. Drainage: For hundreds of years swamps, fens, marshes, and bogs have been regarded by almost everyone as wastelands and it has been accepted as a matter of course that they should be drained. I saw a recent figure of something like 148 million acres of wetlands that have been drained in the United States. As a result, some of the most interesting and biologically rich habitats have become scarce, or have practically disappeared. Even lowering the water table enough to change the forest

from a swamp forest to pine forest means that the swamp has been destroyed, regardless of what has replaced it. Drainage normally results in replacement of a hydrophytic community by a mesophytic one, if natural vegetation is allowed to persist. Ordinarily, however, agriculture follows drainage. This alters the ecosystem completely. Burning of peat, leveling of land, diking, fertilization, all produce changes. Recently I had a discussion with a well-known plant geographer who maintained that the original vegetation of the part of the San Joaquin Valley, in California, where I grew up, now an area of fertile irrigated farmland, was tule marsh. I was so taken aback that the next time I visited my childhood home I studied the landscape with this discussion in mind. Several traverses across the valley revealed that a part of it had indeed been marsh—not the precise area I grew up in, but an adjacent section nearer the river, that now, except for the character of the soil, resembles the rest of it very much. The processes of drainage and agriculture have so altered *two* original ecosystems—sandy grassland and tule marsh—that they have become superficially identical to the point where they deceived my plant-geographer friend. What had been a very diverse landscape had been reduced to a monotonous, intensively cultivated plain. Usually it is only when such drained agricultural land is completely worn out that any restoration to natural conditions is permitted.

e. Overgrazing: Certain natural grassland habitats are normally subject to grazing, even rather heavy grazing, by wild ruminants. Substitution of domestic animals in reasonable numbers does not materially alter the system. Removing all grazing animals may change it profoundly. However, the line between reasonable and excessive stocking is not always very obvious. Ranchers, except the most careful ones, tend to overstock their ranges and their artificial pastures, through either greed or ignorance. And certainly it takes careful observation and either a good memory or good records to detect the increase in unpalatable herbs—*Ranunculus* and *Andropogon virginicus* here in Virginia, *Juncus* in New Zealand, woolly *Malvaceae* in other areas—that indicate the start of overgrazing. When these plants have increased to the point where the cattle or sheep cannot find enough to eat, or overgrazing has persisted to the point where gullies begin to be seen on the slopes, the rancher may wake up. By that time it may be hard to stop the process except by removing stock altogether. This the stockman cannot afford to do, or thinks he cannot. So the process goes on until the range or pasture is so cut up that it is unusable. At any time during this period the range is a candidate for restoration and rehabilitation.

f. Accelerated erosion: Erosion is a normal geomorphic process that has been going on since the first land appeared above the sea. It is directly responsible for the existence of a great many habitats, as well as for such scenic spectacles as the Grand Canyon, Zion and Bryce canyons, and Yosemite. It is also responsible for the deposition of almost all sedimentary rocks.

Ordinarily erosion proceeds at a very slow or moderate rate, and soil formation and the growth of vegetation keep pace with it and are in equilibrium with it. Occasionally under natural conditions, erosion can be so rapid as to remove soil and vegetation and to destroy habitats and expose raw subsoil or rock. This is a natural process, part of the natural scene, and actually creates habitats for certain pioneer organisms.

Man has caused accelerated erosion to occur much more frequently and in many cases more intensively than it would under natural conditions. He has also caused it to take place in areas where it would not have otherwise, and to destroy habitats that would not have been affected by serious erosion under any natural circumstances. Large areas suffer from loss of the surface layers of the soil, or even of the entire soil mantle. Vast areas are set back, successively speaking, to an absolute pioneer situation. Badlands topography, scab-rock exposures, gravel deposits, all result in an extreme impoverishment of the habitat and the biota. Streams and lakes are silted up and made unsuitable for the organisms previously inhabiting them. This, on such a scale as is now taking place, assumes the proportions of a biological disaster. Opportunities are provided for a few pioneer organisms to increase to great numbers, but the creatures that were there under climax or subclimax conditions are unable to exist.

g. Lateritic crust formation: This is an irreversible change that affects certain tropical soils when the land is cleared and exposed to sun and desiccation. Soils of low silica content to begin with, which have been leached until little or no silica remains and aluminum and iron sesquioxides are the predominant material, can, under the sort of exposure mentioned above, set like concrete to form an ironstone that is the despair of the cultivator. Vast areas in the tropics, not so much in North America as in Africa, are covered by a thick hard black "cuirass" that rings when struck by a hammer. Its vegetation is a poor savanna.

h. Salinization and alkalization by irrigation: In many irrigated areas where the water supply is not too abundant, and water is applied at no greater rate than is used by the plants and lost by evaporation, there is gradually built up in the soil a concentration of the soluble salts that were present in minute amounts in the water. Depending on the salts present, this is called salt or alkali. Above a certain concentration of these salts

most plants will not grow. Salt flats and alkali flats are the result. These have a very poor biota. Vast areas have been so altered, especially in Southwest Asia, but also in our own Southwest.

III. Urbanization, industrialization, and related phenomena.

a. City areas: In most cities all, or almost all, of anything like natural habitat has long since been destroyed. A few cities retain natural or seminatural parks, such as Rock Creek Park in Washington, Central Park in New York, and Fairmont Park in Philadelphia. However, most of the original habitats are completely gone. Where redevelopment, or slum clearance, is taking place, there is an opportunity for local re-establishment of something resembling natural conditions, but it will mean really starting from scratch. In such areas this rebuilding would be well worth the effort and would definitely be in harmony with the aims of the redevelopment schemes. I have not heard of anything of this sort in any redevelopment plan so far, but one can be optimistic, since the landscape and city planning professions are becoming aware of open spaces and ecology.

b. Industrial development: The blighting effect of intensive industrial development is well known. Little attention has commonly been given to preserving amenities in any heavily industrialized area. Traditional engineering and industrial planning have been geared to profits only, not to the living conditions of employees. (Of course, if more attention had been given to living conditions in the past, perhaps there would be less bitterness in labor's attitude toward management now.) One need only look around in the Niagara-Buffalo area (New York) or the Chester-Marcus Hook area (Pennsylvania) to see how thoroughly all natural habitat has been destroyed in a heavily industrialized area. One naturally asks what possible occasion there would ever be for the restoration of these habitats. Of course, New England could testify that industry sometimes moves, leaving a destroyed area behind. It is conceivable, also, that someday there may be some "slum clearance" or "redevelopment" in our industrially blighted areas. The tendency nowadays is for labor to insist on a share in the good things in life. Who knows how soon labor will even be asking for decent ecological and esthetic conditions in which to live? This would quite logically be one of the next "fringe benefits" to be scheduled by organized labor. Then there would be a sudden and great demand for restoration of pleasing and at least seminatural habitats in some of our industrial deserts.

c. Development of suburban subdivisions, parks, playgrounds, mass-recreation areas: Despite the aura of virtue associated with suburban development, the way it is commonly carried out destroys almost as effectively as does industriali-

zation all natural habitats originally in the area. A city or suburban park is better habitat for humans than a slum, but it has definitely nothing to do with the forest or prairie that was there before it was "developed." These areas must be regarded as destroyed habitats and may under some circumstances be candidates for restoration. They will not be as difficult to restore as city or intensive industrial areas, since the destruction has not been nearly as thorough.

d. Highway and airport construction: Ordinary highway or airport engineering is strictly utilitarian, with nothing in mind but providing the straightest, smoothest, fastest, and, sometimes, most durable highway or the safest, best-arranged airstrips and most economical surrounding areas. Robert Moses, in his New York Parkway System, established the idea of at least naturalistically landscaped highways for esthetically agreeable driving. Most highways, however, and their cloverleaves have deserts along their rights of way, to begin with, when construction is completed, and lawns at best, brownouts at worst, later. These, when the millennium comes, will be among the first destroyed habitats to be restored. The ground around airports may well be next. In both cases the start will be from almost raw subsoil.

IV. Flooding by impoundment of water.

Submerging a habitat or complex of habitats under water backed up to form a reservoir is a completely effective way of destroying it. The only opportunity for restoration is when the reservoir is silted up, or when it is permanently drained. This leaves a fertile soil but little or no biota. It is a situation in which natural restoration by invasion and succession takes place fairly rapidly.

V. Dredging and filling in shallow water.

The results of this common engineering process are complete destruction of the shallow-water habitat, both where the dredging is done, making the water deeper, and where the fill is deposited, creating dry land. Usually there is no practical way to restore the deep water to a shallow condition, although nature sometimes may do it. The land is at first barren sand, silt, or gravel fill, and natural development of a biotic community is comparable to primary succession. Usually, however, filled areas are utilized for building lots or industrial sites, so no restoration or creation of natural habitats is possible. Under some circumstances the land may be used as park, but it is commonly far too expensive for anything like a natural type of park, which presupposes a low intensity of use.

VI. Exploitation of the material of the substratum.

a. Open-cut, strip, or open-pit mining for coal, copper, clay, sand, gravel, or other mineral resources that lie close to the surface of the earth produces some pretty dreary landscapes. The surface soil is generally removed or mixed with deeper materials in such proportions that it loses its identity and the result is a sterile surface that takes a good while to develop a vegetative cover of any consequence. Very often ponds left in irregularities in this surface have high concentrations of dissolved substances, mostly inimical to plant growth. In some parts of the world, such as Germany, restoration of such land to a state of usefulness is compulsory, and highly developed methods are in use to accomplish this. The land is, however, normally restored to agricultural usefulness, rather than to any sort of natural or seminatural habitat. A few attempts have been made in the United States to utilize strip-mined lands for wildlife habitat and for parks.

b. Hydraulic mining and gold dredging cause even more thorough destruction of the habitat than strip mining. Both are done in areas of alluvium, usually mixtures of gravel and fine material, or of gravel overlain by finer material and soils. The washing removes the fine components of the mixture and leaves great expanses of gravel and boulders, with almost no plant nutrients and on which soil formation takes place extremely slowly. Without some sort of restoration, land that has been subject to these types of mining can only be used this once, at least in any reasonable time. In a society geared to "free enterprise" there is no easy way to control this sort of destruction, but we can scarcely afford an increasing acreage of unproductive and not even esthetically pleasing gravel wastes. It seems clear that restoration will be an eventual requirement wherever such mining is permitted.

VII. Habitat degradation by pollution. Pollution, or the introduction into a habitat of substances inimical to life, is perhaps not to be thought of as usually destructive to habitats, but, though it may not cause the kind of visible change seen in strip mining, the habitats are nevertheless rendered unfit for wildlife and human life. Pollution can take many forms. Perhaps the most thorough, outside of the local effects of nuclear explosions, is that from smelter smoke or other acrid industrial fumes. Classic cases of smelter-smoke damage result in deserts with little or no life for miles downwind from the source. Pollution of streams by salt water from oil wells or industries using brine can eliminate most aquatic organisms. The wastes from paper mills and chemical plants, or sometimes accidental escape of products, can likewise eliminate or seriously reduce aquatic life in streams. Sewage pollution, formerly merely esthetically bad and a menace to health, has, with increased use of detergents, become also very destructive to aquatic life. Petroleum, either on land or water, and on the beaches, also renders habitats unfit for most forms of life, as well as very unpleasant. Pollution of streams by mud from accelerated erosion eliminates those forms of aquatic life that require clear water. Finally, less conspicuous but probably far more effective in the long run in rendering habitats unsuitable to

support life are the slow but cumulative forms of pollution, especially by pesticides and radioactive contaminants. The very subtlety of these makes them far more destructive than such striking pollutants as smelter smoke. At low concentrations these are very differential in their effects. Certain animals, at the culmination of short food chains, may be eliminated first, even when general concentrations are very low. Eventually, the habitats will be sterilized. If the pollutants are especially long-lived, any restoration may be very difficult if not impossible.

NEED FOR HABITAT RESTORATION

The foregoing summary shows that the problem of habitat restoration is not a simple one, as the kinds and degrees of destruction and the resulting ecological conditions vary enormously. In most cases where habitats are destroyed there is no question of restoring them. With the human population situation what it is, most of the resulting space is required for dwellings, agriculture, roads, cloverleaves, and other works of man. Much of this space is already overcrowded with humans, and can no longer be kept in any sort of natural state. However, this very crowding, it is clear, will eventually be the thing to make restoration of all available degraded habitats a necessity. The ninety-five million people that visited the U.S. national parks last year and the 125 million that visited the national forests demonstrate that even now, when crowding is only very local, there is a great urge to get into the outdoors, away from the cities, and it is to the most natural places that are still available and accessible that people go. The visible deterioration from overuse shown by many of the British natural areas is another indication of the demand for natural landscape that is increasing as the available natural landscape becomes scarcer. As the pressure on land increases, areas that are totally degraded and not being actively used are likely to be in demand for recreational uses of various sorts. Many of these uses require natural or seminatural conditions which will have to be restored.

CURRENT ATTEMPTS AT RESTORATION

If we look for examples of habitats that have been degraded and are presently being restored deliberately, not just by letting nature take its course by default, the most obvious ones are clear-cut and burned forest areas where forests are being regenerated by silvicultural methods.

In some areas efforts are being made to rehabilitate overgrazed rangelands, though it must be discouraging to attempt this and at the same time continue to overgraze the same land. In some of the midwestern experiment stations it has been found that the climax prairie produced a better sustained yield of forage than planted pastures of introduced pioneer-type grasses. Hence attempts to re-establish a grass community similar to the prairie are being made.

In Texas there has at least been talk of retiring from cultivation large acreages of marginal agricultural land to establish big private hunting preserves which will be exploited commercially to provide hunting for paying guests.

Establishment of habitat suitable for game birds has been a very important preoccupation of state game management or "conservation" agencies for some time. *Rosa multiflora* hedges and other plantings that provide fruits and seeds for game birds are abundant in many areas as a result. These, however, can scarcely be regarded as restored natural habitats. Nor can artificially flooded waterfowl areas, nor the artificial fishponds of which there are hundreds of thousands in the United States.

There have been some attempts to re-habilitate strip-mining areas, some as public parks, some as hunting areas. In Europe, strip-mining areas are required to be restored to agricultural productivity and elaborate methods have been evolved to accomplish this.

In none of the above examples has there been much concern as to whether or not any natural habitat was being restored—merely that conditions suitable for a particular type of economic activity be achieved.

In the National Park System there have been attempts to re-establish natural conditions where these have been impaired or destroyed. A study of the results of these attempts would be of great interest, but to the best of my knowledge has not been made. In one or two cases that have come to my attention, there has been so little understanding of what constitute natural conditions that the methods adopted seemed ill advised. However, the new chief scientist of the National Park Service, George Sprugel, and his co-authors, Howard Stagner and Robert M. Linn, publicly quote from the Leopold Committee Report what would seem to be a policy statement that is encouraging: "The goal of managing the national parks and monuments should be to preserve, or where necessary to recreate, the ecological scene as viewed by the first European visitors. . . . Restoring the primitive scene is not done easily nor can it be done completely. . . . Yet, if the goal cannot be fully achieved it can be approached. A reasonable illusion of primitive America could be recreated, using the utmost in skill, judgment, and ecological sensitivity. . . ." (*Trends in Parks & Recreation,* July, 1964, p. 13.) If the last half of the last sentence were taken completely seriously, we would undoubtedly have, in the national parks, some excellent examples of restoration of natural habitats.

PRINCIPLES AND APPROACHES
TO RESTORATION

There seems no doubt that there will be increasing scope and demand for careful restoration of natural habitat. Now we must look at means by which this can be accomplished. That there is no single formula is obvious because of the variety of kinds of degraded areas and the multiplicity of sorts of habitat that might require restoration. This very diversity, also, makes it hard to arrive at any suggestions of a sufficiently general nature to be meaningful in the context of this Conference. A mere enumeration of suggested procedures for one habitat after another would be out of place and boring, even supposing that the present author were competent to write such an exposition. The same objection applies to an attempt to locate in the ecological literature all the available examples of attempted or completed restoration and to describe them.

It may be more useful, and certainly less dull, to try to state and perhaps justify certain proposed principles that might guide practical ecologists in approaching such restoration problems. Certain things are ecologically obvious enough to be safely suggested. Others may be debatable, or even unsound. It is hoped that any unsound ones that slip into the list will be vigorously attacked and debated by those assembled at the Conference.

(1) The present ecological nature of the degraded habitat should be defined as adequately and carefully as possible. This is no small task, but may be the means of avoiding great waste of effort and expense when restoration is attempted, and may also help avoid failure. It would seem rather axiomatic that to effect a guided change in a certain direction would require a pretty thorough knowledge of the starting point.

(2) It seems also clear that the nature of the habitat it is proposed to restore be equally well defined and understood. This may prove to be more difficult if the region is one that has been greatly affected by man. However, if this is not required, neither a direction in which to work nor any way of knowing when success has been attained will exist.

These first two requirements are sufficiently arduous that if they are adopted only serious projects are likely to be undertaken.

(3) If there is no time pressure to get the restoration finished promptly, and no exact specification of the habitat desired, by far the most economical and satisfactory approach is simply to permit natural succession to take its course. It is likely to be very slow, except where the habitat desired is an early pioneer situation. For example, disturbance of beach vegetation, or of creosote-bush desert, will be relatively rapidly healed by natural re-establishment of the native biota and their spontaneous grouping into natural biotic communities. On the other hand, to completely restore by natural succession a thoroughly destroyed tropical rain forest or southern Appalachian climax mixed-hardwood forest, with its subordinate plants and animals, may take centuries, especially if the area is large and remote from good areas of similar forests to provide the propagules or colonists required. Where conditions have been seriously altered over a large area there is perhaps legitimate doubt that an ecosystem essentially identical with the one that existed before will ever be restored. Nevertheless, this is the method that will bring about the most indisputably "natural" restoration, since man has no hand in it.

(4) Next to a completely natural restoration, perhaps the most economical and satisfactory, though still ex-

tremely slow method is to allow succession to do the restoration but to guide it by judicious management. Certain stages may be shortened, certain directions may be favored or discouraged by management practices—selective elimination of species, controlled grazing, controlled burning are examples.

(5) On raw subsoil, in order to achieve almost any desired vegetation in a reasonable time it is necessary to build up a significant organic matter content in the soil. The ways to do this are either by planting pioneer species, such as rye, lespedeza, and kudzu, or by adding quantities of organic fertilizers. The first of these methods is usually the only practical one for large-scale habitat restoration. The choice of plants is governed by the climate, the time available for restoring, the necessity for adding fixed nitrogen at the same time, and esthetic considerations. The possibility of the plants chosen becoming noxious weeds in neighboring cultivated land should also be considered.

(6) To check advanced erosion, certain pioneer plants may likewise be planted. Most of them need some encouragement to assure a good start. A layer of straw on the bare ground after seeding is an example. A fast-growing but deeply and extensively rooted species is essential, especially where the eroding material is soft and the process is rapid. Sod-forming and mat-forming species are also commonly used. Under some circumstances—of rapid erosion, or hurry for results—certain engineering work may be necessary, such as contour furrowing, terracing, and the erection of brush, log, or even concrete barriers to erosion. These measures are expensive and only used in cases of urgency (or abundant tax money).

(7) Short-cutting of succession is frequently tried—avoiding herb and shrub stages by planting trees. This may be difficult in extreme environments. Often the establishment of "nurse" plantings of trees of a species that is able to thrive in spite of extreme conditions, to provide protection for seedlings of ultimately desired species, is essential. Such species must, of course, be chosen with much care, to avoid antagonistic or antibiotic effects and to avoid species that persist and are difficult to eliminate when no longer needed. The common guava is an example of such a species, very hard to get rid of because of its root-sprouting tendency.

(8) Under conditions of frequent or constant strong winds or salt spray it may be necessary to protect young plants from undue desiccation. Windbreaks range from simple temporary cloths stretched between stakes to protect seedlings being established, to rows of trees or hedges, and to the elaborate plantings designed many years ago by George C. Munro in his attempts to rehabilitate the wind-eroded plateau of the island of Lanai, in the Hawaiian Islands. To withstand the wind and gravel abrasion he planted a belt of a large tough *Agave*. In the shelter of this a row of dense bushes, in the shelter of them small trees, and behind them several rows of tall *Eucalyptus*. This experiment started out with promise of success, but was abandoned and cattle turned in as soon as any grass appeared on the denuded ground.

Because the requirements of their component species are more nearly those usually found in degraded habitats, pioneer and successional communities may be the easiest to re-establish. If such are the objectives, the problem may be to keep them that way, rather than to establish them in the first place. The more mature subclimax and climax communities are more difficult to simulate but may show more stability when established. If they are unstable, it probably means that the simulation of climax conditions is only apparent.

One of the problems in true restoration is to know when a complete, functional community has been established. At times an inconspicuous species may be essential to the continued survival or reproduction of even a dominant member of the community—for example, a mycorrhizal fungus, a pollinating insect, or a nitrogen-fixing bacterium. We really know very little about these relationships as yet. Furthermore, the place in succession occupied by most species is not known, or is only vaguely known, and it may not even be the same for a given species under all circumstances. Failure to bring about regeneration of certain forest types in the tropics has been traced to the fact that the types under consideration were early seral communities but were being treated as a climax. The desired seedlings simply did not appear, or if they did, they did not persist. Among the hundreds of thousands of species of plants and perhaps millions of species of animals, the autecology of only an infinitesimal fraction is well known.

Under the term "lost habitats" not only those destroyed by direct action of man should be considered. Habitats can also be lost by vegetational succession or by natural catastrophe. Probably a much greater proportion than is commonly suspected of the existing apparently stable plant communities are really arrested successional stages, held at a particular level by some relatively minor factor or complex of factors. If these are changed, further succession may take place. Or many of them are disclimaxes, degraded to a certain level by natural populations of grazing or other animals. Or they may be the result of balanced competition, situations in which any one or more of the species present would reach a much greater development but for the presence of other species competing for the same environmental resources. Interference in

any one of these types of situations by man, or by natural factors, may cause profound changes. The introduction of a competitor, such as *Bromus tectorum,* the cheat grass, or a pathogen such as *Endothia parasitica,* the chestnut-blight organism, or a noxious animal, such as the goat, can destroy some habitats as effectively as would a bulldozer.

The restoration of some of these habitats lost, destroyed, or degraded by succession or biotic processes may be fully as difficult as that of those destroyed by more obvious and direct means. In fact, such a one as the oak-chestnut forest, in eastern North America, cannot be restored, as the chestnut cannot recover as long as the *Endothia* fungus is in the region. And since it has other hosts, it is likely to remain. In the kind of cases just discussed, even where no absolute factor is involved, restoration must be by manipulation of biotic components and processes. The knowledge essential for doing this does not, in most cases, exist.

So far most of our consideration has been given to restoration of single biotic communities. It is true that these form habitats for many organisms, and complexes of habitats for many more. However, the main subject of concern to this Conference is an adequate habitat for man. Man in certain parts of the world does inhabit a single biotic community, such as the prairie, steppe, wheatfield, cornfield, rain forest (Pygmies), or savanna, but this is not usual, and it is dreadfully monotonous.

It may be that our descendants will, of necessity, be conditioned to monotony, as there may be little natural diversity left and all human cultures may by that time have been reduced, by mass communication and the tendency to imitate, to one vast monoculture characterized by "togetherness." However, in the meantime, monotony seems to be what we would give anything to escape. Solitary confinement, characterized by complete monotony, is the most dreaded of punishments. Man, in his present state, is incapable of being a fully developed personality in monotonous surroundings. Yet crowding and social pressure are pushing him toward a life of monotony. This is relieved only by his occasional forays into the outdoors. And the outdoors available to man may be, in the not at all distant future, mostly the reconstructed habitats here under discussion. It is certainly not enough to think merely in terms of restoring a particular type of community. The demand will be for complexes of communities, varied landscapes that will in some measure satisfy the deep craving for variety that characterizes present-day man.

If there is a single pre-eminent guiding principle in the field of restoration of lost habitats, it is to work toward re-creating the full diversity, both of single communities and of landscapes. We must think in terms of mosaics of fully developed communities, of the normal complex of habitats that make up a satisfactory habitat for man, rather than being satisfied with simplified artificial assemblages. Again, before we can consider such natural complexity in any adequate way, enough biohistorical research must be done to know the nature of the original mosaic that occupied the region.

Such a program of restoration of lost habitats has, of course, practical values in providing more usable space in a shrinking world, and in creating a more satisfactory place to live in some areas than would otherwise be available. What is probably more important is the opportunity it offers for ecological research. The chance to see what various species of plants and animals do under varying and often extreme conditions, to watch different combinations of organisms adjust and form equilibria, to be able to manipulate populations and communities under varying and often controllable conditions, and to make many other types of observations under disturbed or controlled circumstances is complementary to observing under natural conditions on the one hand, and to experimental ecology on the other. The opportunities for getting at basic ecological information on tolerance, behavior of species, dynamics of invasion, colonization, population phenomena, and many other aspects will be a priceless asset to ecology. It is only hoped that we will provide ourselves with a more effective mechanism for taking advantage of these opportunities than now exists. Valuable chances to observe infrequent but highly significant ecological events are commonly lost because no one is in a position to drop what he is doing and go to the place where something is happening. Possibly this could turn out, eventually, to be the most important function of the proposed Office of Ecological Research and Surveys now under study in the Department of the Interior.

URBANIZATION AND THE BRITISH COUNTRYSIDE

Notes Toward a Research Project

Peter Hall*

1. THE BACKGROUND

In North America the impact of urbanization on the countryside is relatively well documented. In Britain it is not. Yet in a sense the problem is more urgent in Britain. In England and Wales, at the 1961 Census, 46.1 million people lived on 37.3 million acres at an average density of 1.23 persons per acre. But this average conceals the real degree of concentration; for of these 36.1 million people, 78.3 per cent of the total lived within twenty-six counties forming only 43 per cent of the total area. These counties, lying within an irregular figure bounded by Lancaster, Swansea, Southampton, Southend, and York, had an average density of 2.24 persons to each acre. It is a salutary reflection that at the current North American standards of new residential zoning, such a population could hardly be accommodated within this zone.

This concentration is perhaps the outstanding feature of the economic and social geography of contemporary Britain. It is a phenomenon as remarkable as that of Megalopolis on the eastern seaboard of North America, though, apart from some exercises in the 1930s (Fawcett, 1932;

Taylor, 1938), it has not been accurately delimited or analyzed. Its dominance is slowly but surely increasing, for between 1951 and 1961 its share of the population of England and Wales rose from 78.0 to 78.3 per cent. It has profound implications for the future of the British countryside. For the degree of concentration is uneven. There are very dense agglomerations of people in and around the major conurbations, of which five[1] occur in this zone; and it is at the edges of these conurbations that the most significant changes in British land use are taking place at the present time. Suburbanization on a large scale is occurring in Britain, as in North America. Between the Censuses of 1951 and 1961, there was a pronounced tendency for the large urban areas to grow less fast than the areas of their fringes. The smaller county boroughs and municipal boroughs were growing faster than the large cities and even faster than the great conurbations of which the cities form the centers. Rapid increases were observable in rural districts despite stagnation or continued decline in the farm population (Table 1). These trends are observable even from aggregate national figures, but they are even more pronounced in those counties most subject to the outward push of populations from the major urban agglom-

* Dr. Hall is Reader in Geography with reference to regional planning at the London School of Economics. He is the author of *London 2000*, 1963 and *The World Cities*, 1966 and the editor of *Land Values*, 1965.

[1] Greater London, West Midlands, Merseyside, South East Lancashire, West Yorkshire.

TABLE 1. England and Wales: Population changes, 1951–61

	Increase or decrease, per cent per year, 1951–61	Percentage of total population 1951	1961
Conurbations	0.01	38.7	36.6
Large urban areas elsewhere, 100,000 plus	0.27	13.9	13.6
Smaller urban areas elsewhere	1.11	28.3	29.9
Rural areas	0.99	19.1	19.9

Source: Census 1961, General Tables

erations. Between the 1951 and 1961 Censuses the population of the Greater London conurbation (roughly within a circle of radius fifteen miles from the center) fell by 165,000 but the population in the ring fifteen to forty miles from the center, including the Green Belt and the belt of the new towns beyond, rose by no less than 966,000—roughly two fifths of the net growth of the entire British population. Similarly the population of the West Midlands conurbation rose by only 110,000 or 4.8 per cent, while the population in the ring roughly twenty miles wide outside it (but excluding the city of Coventry) rose by some 150,000 or 15 per cent.

Although suburbanization is as important for Britain as for North America, its precise form may be very different; for this there are many reasons. British incomes are still on average lower, housing standards more modest, car ownership much less widespread, public transportation better developed. As important as these social differences are differences in public policy. The British have embraced since the Second World War a philosophy that land use should be publicly controlled in the interests of the community. Since 1947, development rights have been in effect vested in the state, and all significant development may take place without the permission of local planning authorities,

who must work within the framework of development plans, regularly reviewed and approved by the central government in London. These powers have enabled British planners to limit the physical spread of the conurbations and of individual towns by placing Green Belts around them; the growth of population has been diverted into communities outside the Green Belts. In detail, the areas for new residential development have been set out in the plans, while other areas have been held for rural uses. In practice many of the achievements of postwar British planning have been less impressive than the elaborate machinery might suggest. But there can be no doubt that over all, planning has produced profound changes in the physical form of suburbanization, and that the differences are likely to become more profound in the next twenty years as the pace of suburbanization increases.

We can have no doubt however that suburbanization will take place, on a more rapid scale than ever before. The population is now rising at an accelerating pace, due to a birth rate which has increased in every successive year since 1955. The Registrar General's 1964 projection was that the population of England and Wales would rise by 7.4 million to 1983 and in all by 17.7 million (or by over one third) by 2003. The program of slum clearance in the major cities is similarly accelerating and is leading to over-spill programs on a large scale, since British standards of urban density commonly allow only half the former inhabitants to be rehoused in clearance areas. Changes in the age structure of the population are leading to a rapid fall in the average size of household and consequently to a rapid increase in the numbers of households requiring separate dwelling units. Standards of space required, especially in the private sector, are likely to rise. Car ownership is officially expected to increase, on the basis of trends and of international comparisons of income and ownership, from roughly 0.16 cars per head (one car to every two households) in 1965 to approximately 0.36 cars per head (one car per household) by 1985.[2] All these trends are likely to lead to increased movement outward from the congested inner cities in search of space.

The precise implications of these changes for particular regions of the country are by no means clear, and detailed research is urgently necessary. A preliminary estimate of expected land-use changes for the country and for individual regions has been made by Robin H. Best of Wye College in the University of London. He calculates that between 1960–1 and 2000–1 the urbanized area of Britain may increase from four million acres to six million acres, or by 50 per cent. The impact will be much larger in regions which already have large urban elements and where rapid population increase is taking place, as in the southeastern part of the country. Here, Best estimates that in the twenty years 1961–81 there will be an increase in urbanized land of 300,000–350,000 acres, or 3.1–3.6 per cent of the present area (Best, 1964). This may seem a relatively small increase; it compares with a probable increase of over one million acres per an-

num in North America in recent years but it merely illustrates the difficulty of working in terms of large aggregate regions. The southeast embraces all that land southeast of a line running from Lyme Regis in Dorset to the Wash in East Anglia, and it includes very large areas which will remain almost completely unaffected by urbanization, now or in the conceivable future. Yet an estimate made for the ring roughly between fifteen and forty miles from the center of London, on the basis of expected population trends, is that while in 1961 there was one acre of developed land per eight acres of undeveloped land, by the end of the century there would be a ratio of less than four undeveloped acres to every developed acre.[3] This clearly indicates that the major impact of suburbanization will be felt within fifty miles of the centers of the major urban areas, where it may well raise acute problems of competition for land use.

Some of these competing uses are traditional ones. Within fifty miles of the major conurbations some of the most intensive agriculture of Britain can be found, exploiting the relatively rare areas of first-class land. Examples are the market gardening of the Sussex plain behind Worthing, the intensive horticulture of the mid-Bedfordshire gravels, and the vegetable cultivation of the silt lands of south Lancashire around Ormskirk. These occupy relatively small areas and might be regarded as inviolate, though at least one New Town, Skelmersdale in Lancashire, is invading such land. More problematic are the large areas of prosperous mixed farming, with an emphasis on fresh-milk production for the major sites, found on the better-class soils just short of the high-

[2] Road Research Laboratory, 1963, Table 6, p. 13.

[3] Standing conference on London Regional Planning, 1963, p. 15. This was on the basis of a growth of one and a quarter millions per decade. The official *South East Study* of March, 1964 assumed a slightly lower rate of increase for the area.

est grade. Much of the land within fifty miles north of London, in the sector from Berkshire through to Essex, for instance, falls in this category; so does much of the Cheshire plain within the forty-mile radius south and west of Manchester. Both these areas have provided objects of controversy over the location of new towns since the Second World War, and in the Cheshire case indeed the attempt to build on farmland was repelled. In these conflicts there has been a limited amount of research to try and establish economic criteria as a basis for decision. Outstanding here is the work of Professor G. P. Wibberley of Wye College. In a detailed analysis of the costs and benefits of a construction of a New Town in Cheshire, Wibberley concluded for instance that it would have been worth the community's while to spend an extra £750,000–840,000 in extra investment in higher densities of development in Manchester to avoid development on the good-quality land on the New Town site (Wibberley, 1959, p. 212).

This type of analysis urgently needs extension to a variety of different circumstances. There is considerable scope, for instance, for examination of the costs and benefits of the redevelopment of existing areas of cities (the slum and the surrounding twilight areas) at varying densities, with different repercussions for overspill housing outside the cities. Such an analysis, which has been developed by Dr. P. A. Stone, takes into account factors like the cost of building high versus low structures, the costs of movement and disturbance, and servicing costs (Stone, 1961, Chap. 9). Again, Stone's work has produced important conclusions but it has been carried through for only a limited number of circumstances, and it urgently requires extension. It goes without saying that this type of analysis depends to a great degree on the accuracy of the data about farm yields on different types of land; and that if the results of the research

are to be applied widely, it is essential to have an accurate understanding of the comparative capacity of land on a nationwide basis. It is already evident to workers in this field that the existing national maps of the value of agricultural land, which were compiled on the basis of limited data by the Land Utilization Survey of Britain in 1944,[4] no longer meet the need; and work is proceeding to try to establish a new basis of land evaluation as a basis for mapping.

The other major competing use for rural land, recreation, should itself form a major subject for research inquiry. Yet until the present time the work done in this field in Britain has been very small. A basic limitation is that information is very scarce. The British Hotels and Travel Association make estimates from limited data from which it emerges that leisure demands on land are rising at an unprecedented pace.[5] With higher average income and increasing mobility, the British people are taking more and more holidays: in 1937 fifteen million people (or one third of the population) are estimated to have done so, in 1954 about twenty-three million or half, in 1963 over thirty million or over three fifths, and by 1970 about forty million or nearly three quarters. In addition there are currently some four and a half million short extra holidays and about seven and a half million day trips. At Whitsun 1963, a sample survey showed that five million people (10 per cent of the population) stayed overnight away from home; ten million (20 per cent) made fourteen million day trips; and fourteen million made shorter trips. In all, 56 per cent of the population engaged in pleasure travel during the holiday (BTHA Survey).

[4] Cf. the account in Stamp, 1962, Chap. 17.
[5] See the BTHA data quoted in Cullingworth, 1964, pp. 196–97, and the evidence in *Staggered Holidays*, 1963, pp. 1–2.

From the much closer analysis made of recreational demands in the United States, we would expect to find a close correlation between this growth and factors like the general growth of population, its age structure of the population and its distribution, incomes, education, occupation, available leisure time, and car ownership. The U.S. study concluded that "By 2000 the population should double; the demand for recreation should triple."[6] In Britain the population explosion is unlikely to be as dramatic as this; but an expected one-third increase in population is likely, in Britain also, to produce a much more than proportional increase in recreational demand. For, in the words of the U.S. report:

"A dynamic is at work. The children of today do more kinds of things outdoors and acquire experiences and skills in things like swimming and camping that their parents never had. The new generation, as it grows up, will spend a great deal more leisure time outdoors than the parents of today and so will their children and their children after them."[7]

There is another basic similarity between the British and the North American situations. The U.S. report stresses the paradox that recreational areas make up one eighth of the entire area of the nation but that recreational areas tend to be where the people are not, especially in the West and in Alaska.[8] Precisely the same situation obtains in Britain, as recent research by Mr. Burton and Professor Wibberley of Wye College shows. The best possible estimate is that in England and Wales about three million acres, or about one ninth of the entire area, can be counted as rural recreational land available for public use. But this land is heavily concentrated in the uplands of the country, in the north and

west: nearly half the available acreage is here. There is a profound inbalance in relation to the distribution of population, so that Wales and the West Midlands have together 150 acres per thousand persons while the East Midlands have only twenty acres per thousand (Burton and Wibberley, 1965, Chap. 2).

Any inquiry into changes in the countryside is perhaps bound to be focused primarily on changes in land use. And for a study of recreation, as for a study of residential growth, this approach will bring useful results. But the limitations are evident. In the first place, there is the difficulty of classification: much recreational land is in fact in multipurpose use, and its intensity of use for recreation, in comparison with other uses, is difficult to establish. The more basic difficulty is that the impact of recreation on the countryside does not express itself primarily in terms of land use. A caravan site here, a petrol station or snack bar or parking space there are perhaps not significant features of the landscape, and may pass unnoticed on a weekday winter afternoon. But the same scene on a summer Sunday may be transformed. The impact of people, and above all their cars, on the countryside is a very elusive thing to measure, because it is so transitory. Yet because of the rapidly increasing impact, and because of the geographical spread of that impact into regions previously little touched, it is exceptionally important to incorporate this element in any research program.

Urbanization and suburbanization do affect the countryside in many other more or less indirect ways, which are readily observed. A new motorway across Charnwood Forest or perhaps across the Berkshire Downs; an extension of the electric supergrid across the Sussex Chalklands; a Post Office telephone tower on the crest line of the Chilterns; a nuclear power station in North Wales; a plan to withdraw water from Ullswater

[6] Outdoor Recreation Resources Review Commission, 1962, p. 25.

[7] Ibid., p. 29.

[8] Ibid., p. 49.

n the English Lakes—all these individually may have a profound local effect on the countryside. Yet just because the effect is localized, it is difficult to give precise expression to. The most fruitful line of inquiry would seem to be an analysis of the real costs to the community of alternative decisions: for instance, a decision to reroute a motorway via a less direct route, or a decision to put power lines underground, or to relocate a nuclear power station where land may be more expensive.

This necessarily discursive account has tried to analyze some of the problems which arise from new and increasing impacts on the countryside, to dissect the resulting choices which face the community, and to suggest some ways in which research can aid the resolution of those choices. This second section of this paper turns to outline a program which would apply these research methods in a comprehensive analysis of current and projected changes in the countryside and of the alternative possibilities which offer themselves for public decision.

2. A PROJECTED STUDY

Any research program on the impact of urbanization on the British countryside will contain two main elements. First, there is the analysis of data which is already available, or which will become available in the current period, 1965–6. Outstanding here are the full results of the 1961 Census. Secondly, there is the need for new primary data which must be collected as part of the research program.

These two types of information would be used in the following types of study.

(1) *A study of land-use changes*

Clearly this is the most important phenomenon with which the study must deal. Those facets of change which can be expressed in terms of land-use changes should be so expressed.

A basic source for this study is the land-use maps compiled by all planning authorities as part of their original surveys for development plans in the years immediately after the Town and Country Planning Act 1947. Most of these surveys date from 1948–51 and so are reasonably contemporaneous with social and economic data in the 1951 Census. If necessary they may be supplemented from the extensive air-photo cover on the six-inch and twenty-five-inch scales flown between 1947 and 1949, and publicly available through the Ordnance Survey. The picture which thus emerged would be compared with air-photo data from a recent date. It is believed that Air Ministry cover exists for the period ca. 1960, though it has not so far been made generally available.

It is not proposed that the whole countryside be analyzed in this way, because the aim would be an inquiry in depth. Instead, sample areas would be chosen. One method would be to consider a belt of uniform width, or alternatively a widening sector, stretching for some considerable distance (say, sixty to seventy miles) outward from two or three major conurbations with different socioeconomic characteristics (say, London, the West Midlands, and South East Lancashire; Central Clydeside would be another possibility, though there are difficulties of noncomparability of Scottish Census data). It might be possible to analyze all land in this belt or sector; alternatively, sample squares or sample local-authority areas might be considered.

The biggest problem in this study would be to develop a methodology for analysis. It would be necessary to devise some convenient measure (or measures) of the impact of development on the countryside. This would incorporate not merely the amount of development that had taken place (in terms of percentage cover of the ground) but its visual impact in terms of concentration. For instance, a relatively self-contained suburban extension may have much less impact than a low-density scatter of buildings, though both might represent the same percentage degree of cover of an area. Some measure of local concentration must therefore be devised. It may also be desirable in practice to distinguish particular types of development on the grounds that some are more intrusive than others. This would have to depend to some extent on value judgment.

(2) *Relation of land-use changes to socioeconomic data*

A basic assumption would be made that the observed changes can be meaningfully related to statistical data relating to administrative or census units. In published form a great amount of Census data is available for local authority units; a basic difficulty is that in the countryside much of the data relates to large and often heterogeneous rural districts. Much of the 1961 Census data can be obtained for relatively small Census tracts, but this information cannot be compared with data from previous Censuses.

Census data in the 1961 Census relate to migration, socioeconomic status, occupational structure (including retired), place of work, size of dwelling, and improvement of dwelling. Information not available from Census data includes: household income, car ownership, data of construction of house, lot size of house, and whether part-time (second-home) owner. Therefore it may be necessary to conduct detailed surveys in certain local authority areas in order to supplement Census information in depth. It is thought that certain correlations might thus be developed (for instance, between occupational structure and car ownership) which would hold good elsewhere.

From this, the next stage of analysis would be to try to develop mathematical relationships which would "explain" the amount and type of development in terms of selected socioeconomic characteristics. The experience of transportation surveys in the United States (and latterly in Britain also) offers the hope that such analysis could then be used in a third stage: to develop models of future land-use development on the basis of certain assumptions about the economic growth of the conurbations, income changes, social shifts, future car ownership, and planning policies. These models would offer a picture, on a regional scale, of the expected changes in land use around the major conurbations for two or three decades ahead. They would offer a more detailed picture of future development than the broad regional estimates so far developed in Britain. They would not, however, attempt a detailed allocation of land to particular uses, at least at this stage. The aim would rather be to obtain a clearer picture of the impact of the conurbations in broad concentric rings at increasing distances from the conurbation centers, and perhaps in sectors within these rings.

(3) *A study of temporary outside impacts on the countryside, with special reference to recreation.*

But the urban impact on the countryside by no means ends with changes in land use. The transitory impact of thousands of conurbation dwellers, seeking holiday or weekend recreation, is no less important. Yet as already indicated, it poses acute problems of measurement. It is suggested that an answer must be sought in terms of *an index of intensity of recreational use.* This will be expressed in terms of numbers of people (and numbers of cars) per square mile per day. Since cars have a bigger impact on the countryside than people without cars, it will be necessary to make a quantitative allowance for this. The impact of the car is big because the car is much bigger than the total volume of the people in it, and because the car is much more limited than people in the spaces it can occupy. Probably, therefore, two indices of impact must be developed: people per square mile of public recreational area (per unit of time); and cars per square yard of public road (per unit of time). Both these indices will need further definition. The experience of urban transportation surveys, with their emphasis on the distinction between person trips and vehicle trips, and their techniques of analysis of trip ends in relation to area, should be useful here.

Even when these definitional questions are resolved, this part of the study will pose acute technical problems of measurement. What is needed, in fact, is a limited type of exurban transportation study, similar in methodology to the urban transportation study. The urban study has traditionally depended in large measure on the home interview, supplemented to a limited degree by roadside inquiry. Such a method is more feasible in the case of a discrete urban area, where the great majority of trips begin and end within the area, than in the case of the exurban fringe. Insofar as the impact on the countryside derives from the conurbations, it might be possible to derive information as a by-product of the urban transportation studies now being set up in areas like the West Midlands and Merseyside. But it is notable that in the London Traffic Survey and in other conurbation studies so far set up, the boundaries of the transportation study areas have been much more narrowly drawn than in the case of most similar American studies. Consequently, the impact on the countryside of the rapidly growing outer suburban fringes—the fringes outside the conurbations themselves—may be neglected. To overcome this, two solutions would be possible. One, the simpler, would involve sample roadside checks in the countryside areas themselves. The

other and more reliable means would be to try to extend the method of the urban transportation studies into the exurban fringe, as part of the total social study, referred to earlier, which may well be necessary to supplement Census data. If funds could be made available, there is little doubt that this latter solution would be preferable.

(4) *Development of criteria for planned choices in urban land use.*

This last stage would be conceptually by far the most difficult part of the study. It would start with projections of land-use patterns and of recreational travel patterns. On this basis it would seek to devise criteria for making choices about future land use according to certain planning criteria. It would seek to resolve questions like the following. Given that some agricultural land will be lost, which land should we seek to preserve? What types of land should be preserved in their natural state, and what implications has this for the provision to be made for access by car? What will be the demand for high-intensity recreation areas, and what types of land will be best suited for this purpose? How can we group development so as to leave as large a part of the countryside as possible relatively untouched? What will be the impact of projected highway developments on the pattern of provision of recreational facilities? And many other questions.

The criteria which might be developed for these purposes remain obscure. At present *ad hoc* choices are made as the result of an amalgam of contradictory pressures from private individuals and groups, local authorities, and the central government. There is no indication at all that the community interests are best served by the decisions that emerge. What must be found is some common measure of community advantage. One solution, which has been employed in many questions of public decision making, is the economist's solution. This stresses the advantages of free choice expressed through a pricing system. But such a system is seldom completely possible, and failing its complete application the economist stresses the achievement of a rational, comparable set of investment criteria for different public projects.

A pricing solution poses exceptional difficulties in choices of rural land use. An investment solution has however been applied in certain case studies, most notably those of Professor Wibberley and Dr. Stone. In such studies of the real community costs of different methods of urban development, involving computation of the value of agricultural land, there seems little doubt that the economist can provide criteria for decision, and that through further work these criteria can be progressively refined. But in the sphere of recreation even an investment solution poses very large theoretical problems, involving the valuation of leisure time. Economists in the transport field are trying to overcome these problems and it seems possible that ways may be found of computing (for instance) the value of providing recreational areas near cities rather than farther away, which would have to be reckoned against the benefits from putting such land into agricultural use or developing it. Mr. Burton and Professor Wibberley have made a first attempt to estimate the relative value of land in Britain for recreation and for agriculture on the basis of a calculation of the amount people are prepared to pay to visit an area.[9] They recognize that this is a very partial and inadequate measure of the total gross benefit derived from recreation; but they point out that it is the only satisfactory measure and must suffice. Their calculation depends on national data about the percentage of the population which is prepared

[9] Burton, Chap. 7. The method is a modification of that devised by Trice, 1958.

to travel more than a certain distance for recreation. It is clear that this proportion could later vary significantly with increases in mobility due to rising car ownership and better roads. The conclusion was that in 1963 for two low-quality agricultural areas (Ashdown Forest and the Black Mountains of Breconshire) agriculture yielded a marginally higher return than recreation but that in a high-quality farming area (The Fenlands), the advantage of agriculture was very marked.

These conclusions are based on very broad regions of the country, and the application of the techniques to small areas clearly presents difficulties. Given a general valuation of leisure time, it may be very difficult to resolve which of two neighboring areas should be used for recreation, which for housing. Here indeed it may be necessary to enlist the help of other skilled professions. The landscape architect in particular should be able to develop techniques of evaluation of landscape, which could be used in conjunction with estimates of the value of leisure time to provide a framework for decision. In conjunction with the traffic engineer, too, he should be able to devise a methodology for determining whether an area should be developed for higher-intensity use or not. It cannot be pretended that such work will be easy, or that it will not be subject to wide margins of error and differences of personal judgment. But it seems important, in view of the scale of the problem, that efforts be made.

CONCLUSION

The four stages of the project outlined here follow one from another. It would indeed be possible to carry any number of stages out without proceeding to the next. It is suggested though that stages one and two make a coherent study in themselves and that stage three could be developed separately, though there are clear economies of organization in combining the socioeconomic survey of stage two with the traffic study in stage three. Stage four is extremely speculative and experimental, and could well be developed after the results from the first three stages began to emerge.

BIBLIOGRAPHY

Best, Robin H. 1964. The Future Urban Acreage. In: Town and Country Planning: 350–55.

Burton, T. L., and Wibberley, G. P. 1965. Outdoor Recreation in the British Countryside. Wye, England.

Cullingworth, J. B. 1964. Town and Country Planning in England and Wales. London.

Fawcett, C. B. 1932. Distribution of the Urban Population of Great Britain. Geog. J. 79: 100–16.

London Regional Planning. 1963. Population, Employment and Transport in the London Region: Meeting the Situation. LRP 180: (Dec. 4).

Outdoor Recreation Resources Review Commission. 1962. Outdoor Recreation for America: A Report to the President and to the Congress. Wash., D.C.

Road Research Laboratory. 1963. Road Research, 1962. H.M.S.O.

Staggered Holidays. 1963. Comnd. 2105, H.M.S.O.

Stamp, L. Dudley. 1962. The Land of Britain. London.

Stone, P. A. 1961. Housing, Town Development, Land and Costs. London.

Taylor, E. G. R. 1938. Discussion of the Geographical Distribution of Industry. Geog. J. 92:22–27.

Trice, A. H., and Wood, S. E. 1958. Measurement of Recreation Benefits. Land Econ. 34: 195–207.

Wibberley, G. P. 1959. Agriculture and Urban Growth. London.

ECOLOGICAL DETERMINISM

Ian L. McHarg*

* Professor McHarg is Chairman of the Department of Landscape Architecture at the University of Pennsylvania. He has been directing his own efforts (and those of his graduate students) toward exploring the ways ecological principles can be applied to landscape architecture and regional planning.

INTRODUCTION

In the Western world during the past century transformation of natural environments into human habitats has commonly caused a deterioration of the physical environment. However, much improvement to the social environment has been accomplished in these transformations; city slurb and slum are less attractive physical environments than forest, field, and farm that preceded them. In earlier times, because of the slow rate of change, unity of materials, structural method and expression, this was not so. Few among us regret the loss of ancient marshes on which Venice and Amsterdam sit, the loss of even more ancient hills which now seat Athens and Rome. History testifies to human adaptations, accomplished with wisdom and art, which were and are felicitous. Yet the principles which ensured these successes are inadequate for the speed, scale, and nature of change today. In the seventeenth century it required a third of the treasury of France, the mature life of Louis XIV, and the major effort of André Le Nôtre to realize Versailles. Three centuries later Greater New York will urbanize at the rate of 50,000 acres and absorb 600,000 people into its perimeter each year without any plan. In the interim the classical city has been superseded by the industrial city, by metropolis, megalopolis, and now, in the opinion of Lewis Mumford, is en route to Necropolis. Paradoxically in this period of change the city plan has remained the Renaissance archetype which motivated Versailles, a poor symbol of man-nature in the seventeenth century, an inexcusable prototype for the twentieth century.

It is clear that the principles which contributed to historic successes in urban form have failed dismally since the Industrial Revolution. The success of the subsequent city as provider of employment and social services is its best testimony, but as a physical environment it has continually retrogressed. New principles must be developed for human adaptations, for city, metropolis, and megalopolis.

The problem is an enormous one both in extent and speed of change. Three hundred million Americans are expected to populate the United States in the year 2000. If indeed 80 per cent of these will live in urban places, then this involves the urbanization of fifty-five million acres of nonurbanized land. If one extrapolates from the present megalopolis to this future population, then 10 per cent of the land area of the United States, 200 million acres, will fall within urban influence, comparable to megalopolis, in a mere thirty-five years.

Today, the prescriptions for urban location, form, and growth derive almost exclusively from the social sciences. Both analytic and predictive models are based upon economics. The natural sciences have remained aloof from the problem, yet the understanding of physical and biological processes, which reposes in these sciences, is indispensable for good judgment on the problems of human adaptations of environment.

Many central questions can best be answered by natural scientists but at the onset one alone can suffice. What are the implications of natural process upon the location and form of development? The answer to this is vital to administrators, regional and city planners, architects and landscape architects. For the last it is the indispensable basis for their professional role. As the representative of a profession with a historic concern for the relation of man to nature and the single bridge between the natural sciences and the artificers of the urban environment, it is not inappropriate that the spokesman for this group ask for the formulation of an ecological determinism.

LANDSCAPE ARCHITECTURE

In the Western tradition, with the single exception of the English eighteenth century and its extension, landscape architecture has been identified with garden making, be it Alhambra, San Gall, the Villa d'Este, or Versailles. In this tradition decorative and tractable plants are arranged in a simple geometry as a comprehensible metaphysical symbol of a benign and orderly world.

Here the ornamental qualities of plants are paramount; no concepts of community or association becloud the objective. Plants are analogous to domestic pets, dogs, cats, ponies, canaries, and goldfish, tolerant to man and dependent upon him; lawn grasses, hedges, flowering shrubs and trees, tractable and benign, man's cohorts, sharing his domestication.

This is the walled garden, separated from nature, a symbol of beneficence, island of delight, tranquillity, introspection. It is quite consistent that the final symbol of this garden is the flower.

Not only is this a selected nature, decorative and benign, but the order of its array is, unlike the complexity of nature, reduced to a simple and comprehensible geometry. This is then a selected nature, simply ordered to create a symbolic reassurance of a benign and orderly world, an island within the world and separate from it. Yet the knowledge prevails that nature reveals a different form and aspect beyond the wall. Loren Eiseley has said that "the unknown within the self is linked to the wild." The garden symbolizes domesticated nature, the wild is beyond.

The role of garden making remains important. Man seeks a personal paradise on earth, a unity of man and nature. The garden is such a quest for a personal oasis, a paradise garden. In these, man can find peace and in tranquillity discover, in Kenneth Rexroth's words, "the place of value in a world of facts." He can respond to natural materials, water, stone, herbs, trees, sunlight and shadow, rain, ice and snow, the changing seasons, birth, life and death. This is a special microhabitat, a healthy cell in the organism of the city, a most humane expression, yet clearly its relevance, depending upon ornamental horticulture and simple geometry, is inadequate for the leap over the garden wall.

In the eighteenth century in England landscape architects "leap't the wall and discovered all nature to be a garden." The leap did not occur until a new view of nature dispelled the old and a new esthetic was developed consonant with the enlarged arena.

Starting with a denuded landscape, a backward agriculture, and a medieval pattern of attenuated land holdings, this landscape tradition rehabilitated an entire countryside, making that fair image persisting today. It is a testimony to the prescience of Kent, Brown, Repton, and their followers that, lacking a science of ecology, they used native plant materials to create communities which so well reflected natural processes that their creations endured and are self-perpetuating.

The functional objective was a productive, working landscape. Hilltops and hillsides were planted to forest, great meadows occupied the valley bottoms in which lakes were constructed and streams meandered. The product of this new landscape was the extensive meadow supporting cattle, horses, and sheep. The forests provided valuable timber, the lack of which Evelyn had earlier deplored, and supported game, while free-standing copses in the meadows provided shade and shelter for animals.

The planting reflected the necessities of shipbuilding but the preferred trees, oak and beech, were climax species and they were planted *de novo*. On sites where these were inappropriate, northern slopes, thin soils, elevations, pine and birch were planted. Watercourses were graced with willows, alders, osiers, while the meadows supported grasses and meadow flowers. As long as the meadow was grazed, a productive sere was maintained and meanwhile the forests evolved.

The objective, however, was more complex than function alone. Paintings of the *campagna* by Poussin and Salvator Rosa, a eulogy of nature which obsessed poets and writers, had developed the concept of an ideal nature. Yet it clearly did not exist in the raddled landscape of eighteenth-century England. It had to be created. The ruling principle was that "nature is the gardener's best designer," applied ecology of yesteryear. Ornamental horticulture, which had obtained within garden walls, was disdained and a precursory ecology replaced it. The meadow was the single artifice, the re-

maining components were natural expressions, their dramatic and experiential qualities exploited, it is true, but deriving in the first place from that observed in nature.

Nature itself produced the esthetic; the simple geometry, not simplicity but simple-mindedness, of the Renaissance was banished. "Nature abhors a straight line" was declaimed. The discovery of an established esthetic in the orient based upon occult balance, asymmetry, confirmed this view. In the eighteenth century, landscape began the revolution which banished the giant classicism and the imposition of its geometry as a symbol of man-nature.

This tradition is important in many respects. It founded applied ecology as the basis for function and esthetics in the landscape. Indeed before the manifesto of modern architecture had been propounded, "Form follows function," it had been superseded by the eighteenth-century concept wherein form and process were seen to be indivisible facets of a single phenomenon. It is important because of the scale of operation. One recalls that Capability Brown, when asked to undertake a project in Ireland, retorted, "I have not finished England yet." Another reason for its importance lies in the fact that it was a creation. Here the landscape architect, like the empiricist doctor, found a land in ill-health and brought it into good heart and to beauty. Man the artist, understanding nature's laws and forms, accelerated the process of regeneration so well indeed that who today can discern the artifice from the untouched?

It is hard to find fault with this tradition but one must observe that while the principles of ecology and its esthetic are general the realization of this movement was particular. It reflects an agricultural economy, principally based upon cattle, horses, and sheep. It never confronted the city, which in the eighteenth century remained the Renaissance prototype. Only in the urban square, parks and circuses, in natural plantings, was the eighteenth-century city distinguishable from its antecedents. The successes of this tradition are manifest. No other movement has accomplished such a physical regeneration and amelioration. Its basis lies in applied ecology. It is necessary that modern ecology become the basis for modern interventions particularly at the scale of city, metropolis and megalopolis, if we are to avert Necropolis.

ECOLOGICAL DETERMINISM

Processes are expressive; morphology is a superficial expression of the process examined. The creation of a twentieth-century tradition requires an understanding of natural process and the morphology of the artifacts of man as process. Thus, natural processes are deterministic, they respond to laws; they then give form to human adaptations which themselves contain symbolic content.

Beehive huts, igloos, stilt homes on marshes are morphologically determined. We need today an understanding of natural process and its expression and, even more, an understanding of the morphology of man-nature, which, less deterministic, still has its own morphology, the expression of man-nature as process. The eighteenth century developed a morphology for a pastoral landscape in England. What are the prerequisites for discerning the appropriate morphologies for our time?

I believe that there are six elements which are required:

(1) Ecosystem Inventory
(2) Description of Natural Processes
(3) Identification of Limiting Factors
(4) Attribution of Value
(5) Determination of Prohibitions

and Permissiveness to Change
(6) Identification of Indicators of Stability or Instability.

The final step for the artificers is then the perception of the revealed morphology and its realization.

(1) *Ecosystem inventory*

The eighteenth-century landscape architects were only fair taxonomists, but, by using collected material, transferring from site to like site and planting in communities, they avoided the errors of caprice, ornamental horticulture, and much traditional forestry. In the intervening years descriptive ecology has developed the concept of community. In the Philadelphia region the identification of open water, reed swamp, sedge meadow, secondary succession, mixed mesophytic forest, and pine barrens has great utility. Recent work which refines these descriptions by identifying gradients adds value to this technique. The conception of range from hydrosere to zerosere is of great value but it is the conception of succession, sere, and climax which adds dynamics to the eighteenth-century view. The first prerequisite for the application of ecology to the planning process is the preparation of ecosystem inventories. This involves the creation of ecological maps at various scales in which communities are identified. The inventory should also include the city. The ailanthus-pigeon-starling "community" is quite as important as the oak-beech-hickory forest. The ecosystem inventory is the basis for planning related to natural processes.

(2) *Description of natural processes*

Inventories and ecological maps have to be supplemented by explanation of natural processes. In particular the stability or instability stage in succession of ecosystems must be described. While this is important for all communities it is particularly necessary for major physiographic regions—coastal plains, piedmont, uplands, etc., and for certain discrete environments—pine barrens, estuarine environment, mixed mesophytic forest, sand dunes, etc. In the city the relation of atmospheric pollution to insolation photosynthesis CO_2 consumption is typical of a human process which affects ecosystems. Transformation of farmland to subdivision and erosion-turbidity-reduced photosynthesis and natural water purification is another example. Descriptions of natural processes and the degree to which they are affected by man are a vital component of this body of information.

(3) Identification of limiting factors

It is important to establish what factors are necessary to ensure the perpetuation of any ecosystem; apart from factors in abundance, which elements are critical —water-plane-table elevation, alkalinity, acidity, fire, first and last frost, etc. This category must be extensive enough to include limiting factors external to the ecosystem under study as, for example, transformation of a fresh-water into a salt-water marsh through channel deepening and river widening.

(4) Attribution of value

In eighteenth-century England the land was thought to be the arena for the creation of a metaphysical symbol—all nature a garden. Nature was attributed a value which transcended any concept of productivity, the landscape was also productive. In the twentieth century, when nature desperately needs a defense in the face of disdain, disinterest and remorseless despoliation, the first defense is certainly noneconomic, the insistence that man is a co-tenant of the universe, sharing the phenomenal world of living and inert processes, an organism in an interacting biosphere. From this some men will conclude that nature is a manifestation of God, others that the cosmos is unitary, all processes subject to physical law yet having infinite potential, that man is an inhabitant free to develop his potential. Each of these views contains an inherent deference, a posture of serious inquiry, and the instinct to exercise care, intelligence, and art in accomplishing human interventions. Such a view characterized eighteenth-century landscape architects, nineteenth-century naturalists, and today is associated with conservationists.

The search for a theology of man-nature-God does not exclude exchanges which involve the coinage of the time and place. This requires that the proponents of nature also attribute values to natural processes so that these may be recognized as parameters in the planning process. Indeed, given ecological inventories, explanation of natural processes and identification of limiting factors, the next increment of knowledge essential for an applied ecology is precisely the attribution of value to these natural processes.

Four major divisions of value can be discerned: intrinsic value, value as productivity, value as work performed, and, finally, negative value as discouragement to use.

Intrinsic value is thought to exist wherein the landscape neither is "productive" nor "performs work" but simply is. Areas of wilderness, scenic beauty, scientific value, and educational value might fall into this category.

Productivity would include agriculture, forestry, fisheries, extractive minerals, recreation, gamelands, a concept in common usage.

The attribution of value based upon work performed might include water catchment, water purification and storage, flood, drouth and erosion control, hydroelectric power generation, "air shed," climate, and microclimate amelioration.

Negative value would include those areas wherein there is a hazard and whence occupancy should be discouraged. No occupancy would avert costs and damages. Thus areas subject to earthquakes, volcanism, hurricanes, avalanches, floods, drouth, subsidence, and forest fires should fall into this category.

All of these subdivisions can be subject to the concept of replacement value, a most useful concept which can apply at several scales. For example, in the case of a city park planned for an expressway intersection, the value is not "land value" alone but rather the entire cost of replicating the park including the cost of equally mature trees, shrubs, etc. Where it is intended to fill a marsh, the replacement value would include the cost of equal flood protection, water equalization, and wildlife habitats on another site. In the case of transforming prime agricultural land to housing, replacement value would include the cost of upgrading poorer soils to prime capability. Given attribution of value to natural processes, the concept of replacement value provides an important measuring device for alternative choices. No other device offers a comparable restraint to thoughtless despoliation.

Clearly the concept of value poses many difficulties, the change of value over time is one. Low-grade ores, presently marginal farmland, undistinguished rural areas can increase in value with increased demand and shrunken supply. In addition, value is relative. If, as in the Netherlands, survival is linked to the stability of the dunes, then marram and sedge are valuable. If no such role exists, then dune grasses are merely decorative. If diatoms are needed for water treatment, then they have value. If water is treated with coagulants, rapid sand filter, and chlorine, then diatoms have, in this local case, no value. Marshes can be seen either as costly obstructions to development or as invaluable defenses against flood; in one case they represent costs, in another they represent values. Another problem arises from the geographic scale

of natural process and interdependence. The Mississippi watershed unites suburban Chicago with New Orleans; effects upon water quality will affect values in the entire downstream area. The requirements of clean air unite western and eastern United States. There is no method of accounting which relates snowfall in the Rockies to the value of water in California, no accounting which attributes value to forests of upstream watersheds and flood control in the lower Mississippi. The final difficulty in attribution of value lies in unmeasurable qualities. Who will attribute value to whooping crane, grizzly bear, or pasque flower? Yet the inability to attribute value to serenity, happiness, and health has not deterred economic determinism. In spite of difficulties, the attribution of value to natural process is a necessary precondition for applied ecology as a basis for determining nonintervention, intervention, and the nature, scale, and location of such intervention.

(5) Determination of prohibitions and permissiveness to change

Given descriptive ecological inventories, supplemented by descriptions of natural process and limiting factors, with a scale of values, the necessary information is available to establish the constraints inherent in natural process which should affect the location and nature of development.

This finally produces the program. No longer is nature an undifferentiated scene, lacking values, defenseless against transformation; it is seen to be a complex interrelated system, in process, having discernible limiting factors, containing values, present or prospective, and, finally, containing both constraints and opportunities. For example, the arctic and antarctic, bare mountains, oceans, and perhaps beaches are highly tolerant to human use. Other systems are highly intolerant, wild animals retreat or succumb, natural plant communities are erased and superseded by man's cohorts in the processes of agriculture, industry, and urbanism. Can we select environments, more suitable than these extremely tolerant examples, which, satisfactory for man, are unusually tolerant to him? Can one set limits on transformation of natural habitats implicit in the processes themselves? Thus, how much housing can a forest absorb and perform an attributed role in the water regimen? How much development can occur on a marsh without destroying its role of water equalization, emergency flood storage, or wildlife habitat? What proportion of an aquifer can be waterproofed by urbanism before its percolation performance is diminished below a required level? The answer to such questions, and many others, is prerequisite to the application of ecology to the planning process.

For the regional planner, landscape architect, city planner, and architect, the development of concepts of prohibition and permissiveness inherent in natural process is the beginning of a modern applied ecology, the gift of natural form, the program for intervention which has relevance to the house and its site, the subdivision, hamlet, village, town, city, metropolis, megalopolis, and the nation.

(6) *Identification of indicators of stability or instability*

The concept of ecological determinism requires criteria of performance. For pond ecosystems it may be possible to determine stability or instability from the entropy in the system. It seems unlikely that this concept will be capable of dealing with extensive geographic areas or with the problem of the city. Clearly for the moment some simpler devices are necessary by which stability or instability, succession, sere or climax can be discerned; indeed, there is a desperate need for a concept of a "healthy" and "healthful" environments. We need analogies to

litmus paper, the canary in the cage, indicators of health and change. Dr. Ruth Patrick has developed histograms from which the "state of health" of Pennsylvania streams may be discerned. Dr. Luna Leopold has propounded the measure of a "duration curve" against which stability or instability of stream processes can be examined. This writer has advocated the use of the "coefficient of runoff" as a planning determinant for land use relative to the water regimen. "Sky blue" is a measure of the relative presence of atmospheric pollution. The presence of trace metals in the environment is being investigated as an indicator of health. The technique of indicators is established, but it must be extended, not only to "natural" environments, but also to include those dominated by man.

Can we proceed from broad presumptions which have utility while evidence is collected and analyzed? Can one say that where trees cannot live, then man should not try? Can one say that when the most abundant inhabitants, with man, are pigeons, starlings, and rats, a threshold has been crossed and either evacuation or redevelopment is necessary?

It is important that stable and healthy forests, marshes, deserts, rivers, and streams can be defined, that succession and retrogression can be identified, but it is even more necessary to find comparable definitions and indicators for the city. This moves the subject from the orthodoxy of ecology yet those concerned with the environment are the cohorts of medicine. Pathology is the concern of the medical sciences, the environment of health must be the concern of the artificers, but they require from ecologists an identification of healthy and healthful environments.

The role of the ecologists would include the identification of "healthy environments"—that is, for example, a forest wherein trees, shrubs, animals, and fish were conspicuously healthy and a determination of those factors which were contributory to this condition. Healthy natural environments could then be used as criteria against which adjacent urban environments could be compared.

In the city, examination of health or pathology devolves upon the social and medical sciences. It is necessary to determine stressors, the pathology of stress, and the environment of stress. Among stressors the poisons of food, atmosphere and water, density, noise, sensory overload, and sensory deprivation would be included. The pathology of stress—mortality, cancer, heart disease, suicide, alcoholism, crime, neuroses and psychoses —might be mapped as isobars, and from the incidence and distribution of both stressors and stress disease the environments of stress may be located.

Given identification of healthy "natural" environments and the urban environments of stress pathology, diagnosis of environments becomes possible and therapy can be prescribed. There are environmental variables linked to most urban stressors. In this search for health and pathology in environments, indicators could serve a valuable role in diagnosis. In Philadelphia does the presence of hemlock indicate a tolerable level of particulate matter in the atmosphere? What plant pathology indicates a dangerous level of lead? Are there indicators of sulphur dioxide or nitrogen dioxide at "safe" levels? What creatures can coexist with levels of noise preferred by man? What indicators can be found for the optimum distribution of trace metals? Which reveal optimal concentrations? What can be inferred of human environments when trees degenerate?

This line of inquiry might well be unproductive yet there are now no operative standards of environmental quality, no limits are placed upon density, poisons, noise, no criteria are available as measures of existing environments or as programs for new environments. It is clear that criteria are needed, and for the empiricist planner, indicators could be a vital tool. The conception of succession or retrogression, stability and instability must be utilized in the examination not only of wild environment, but of those environments dominated by man.

Where does the canary expire, the litmus change color? Where is the disgenic zone, the area of apathetic survival, the environment of full health—and what are the indicators?

THE MORPHOLOGY OF ECOLOGICAL DETERMINISM

Each year a million acres of rural land succumb to hot-dog stands, sagging wires, billboards, diners, gas stations, split-levels, ranches, asphalt and concrete. Most of this is accomplished without benefit of planning, landscape architecture, or architecture. Where these professionals intervene they utilize some part of available knowledge, the best of them are pressing for better information, yet action must occur even when information is inadequate.

This apologia precedes a description of three experiences in which the writer has been involved, each crude in terms of the available information and the interpretations made, yet, for all of their crudity, so effective in giving form as to justify description. These experiences permit extrapolation on the form of ecological determinism.

New Jersey shore

From the fifth to the eighth of March 1962 a violent storm lashed the northeast coast from Georgia to Long Island. For three days sixty-m.p.h. winds whipped high spring tides across 1000 miles of ocean. Forty-foot waves pounded the shore and vast stretches of barrier islands and bay shore were flooded. In New Jersey alone, 2400 houses were wrecked, 8300 partially damaged, and eighty million dollars' worth of direct damages incurred over a three-day period. Almost all of this damage was caused by ignorance of natural process and the resultant destruction of the natural defenses against flood. In this case an ecological inventory existed, natural processes in the beach-bay-shore communities had been described and limiting factors identified, the values involved could be inferred from damages and costs. The requirements requested by this paper for all ecosystems were satisfied in this one situation.

The theory of dune formation is well understood as is stabilization by vegetation. The ecological communities from beach dune to bay shore have been identified as have been their limiting factors. In the Netherlands the value of dunes and their stabilizing grasses, and the important role of ground water are known and attributed value, but not, however, in New Jersey. It is common knowledge that beaches are highly tolerant to human use but that dunes and their grasses are not. Development of the Jersey shore included breaching of dunes for many purposes—home building, beach access, etc. No constraints were placed upon use of dunes so that vegetation died and the dunes became unstable; no effective restraints were placed upon withdrawals of ground water which inhibited vegetation growth. Considerable areas were waterproofed by buildings, roads, parking areas, which diminished recharge of the aquifers. The consequences were inevitable: with its natural defenses destroyed, the shore was vulnerable and was extensively damaged.

Had development responded to an understanding of natural process, ecological determinism, much if not all of the damage could have been averted. The form of development, however, would have been quite different. The beach, highly tolerant, would have been intensively utilized; the dunes, generally two in number between sea and bay, would have been inviolate, protected, stabilized

by marram; access to the beach would have been made possible by bridges over the dunes; woody vegetation would have been protected in the trough; development would have been excluded from dunes and located only in wide areas of trough and on the bay side. Roads and parking would have been constructed of flexible, permeable materials; drainage would have been used for aquifer recharge; buildings would have been of columnar construction; withdrawals of ground water would have been regulated. The application of this determinism, responsive to natural process, would have located buildings, roads, and drainage systems and determined their form. It would have been the principal determinant of planning, landscape architecture, and architecture. It would indeed produce the morphology of man-dune-bay for the New Jersey shore.

The Green Springs and Worthington Valleys

Seventy square miles of beautiful farmland adjacent to Baltimore were made accessible by the construction of a new expressway. The present population of 17,000 was predicted to rise to 75,000 by 1980, to 110,000 by the year 2000. It became necessary to determine where best this development would be located to ensure the conjunction of optimum development and optimum preservation. The conception of ecological determinism was invoked.

The area is characterized by three major valleys contained by wooded slopes with a large intervening plateau. It transpired that the valley bottoms were coterminous with the major aquifers in the region, that in the valleys were the major surface water systems, flood plains, and extensive soils unsuitable for development using septic tanks. The major source of erosion lay in the slopes defining the valleys. The plateau in contrast contained no major aquifers or minor streams; floodplains were absent as were soils unsuitable for development using septic tanks.

Ecological determinism suggested prohibition of development in the valleys, prohibitions of development on bare slopes, development limited to one house per three acres on wooded slopes. In contrast, development was concentrated upon the plateau in a hierarchy of country town, villages, and hamlets, related in response to physiography. Development in wooded plateau sites was limited to one house per acre; this standard was waived on promontory sites, where high-rise apartments were recommended.

In this example, ecological analysis revealed the morphology of development; it selected the plateau as most tolerant, the valley bottoms and side slopes as least tolerant. It suggested densities of use appropriate to natural process. When this analysis was carried to a more detailed examination of the plateau, this, too, demonstrated variability in both opportunity and intolerance which suggested a hierarchy of communities, hamlets, villages, and a country town instead of pervasive suburbanization. Here the utilization of a very few determinants—surface water, ground water, floodplains, alluvial silts, steep slopes, forest cover, and an interpretation of their permissiveness and prohibitions, revealed the morphology of man and the Maryland piedmont.

METROPOLITAN OPEN SPACE FROM NATURAL PROCESSES

The Urban Renewal Agency and the states of Pennsylvania and New Jersey supported a research project to establish criteria for the selection of metropolitan open space. The hypothesis advanced was that such criteria can best be discerned by extending the inquiry to examine the operation of the major physical and biological processes in the region. It was suggested that when this is understood, and land-use policies reflect this understanding, not only will the values of natural process be ensured, the place for nature in the metropolis of man, but there will be discerned a structure of natural process in the metropolitan area, form-giving for metropolitan growth and the identification of areas for metropolitan open space, recreation, and amenity.

In the country at large and even in metropolitan areas, open space is seen to be absolutely abundant. In the Philadelphia SMSA only 19.1 per cent of the area is urbanized; twenty years hence this may reach 30 per cent, leaving 2300 square miles of open space.

The problem of metropolitan open space lies, then, not in absolute area, but in distribution. The commodity concept of open space for amenity or recreation would suggest an interfusion of open space and population. The low attributed value of open space ensures that it is transformed into urban use within the urban area and at the perimeter. Normal process excludes interfusion and consumes peripheral open space.

Yet as the area of a circle follows the square of the radius, large open-space increments can exist within the urban perimeter without major increase in the radius or in the time distance from city center to urban fringe.

The major recommendation of this study was that the aggregate value of land, water, and air resources do justify a land-use policy which reflects both the value and operation of natural processes. Further, that the identification of natural processes, the permissiveness and prohibitions which they exhibit, revealed a system of open space which directs metropolitan growth and offers sites for metropolitan open space.

The characteristics of natural processes were examined; an attempt was made to identify their values, intrinsic value, work performed, and protection afforded. Large-scale functions were identified with the major physiographic divisions of uplands, coastal plain, and piedmont, smaller-scale functions of air-water corridors were identified, and finally eight discrete parameters were selected for examination. These were: surface water, marshes, floodplains, aquifers, aquifer recharge areas, steep slopes, forests and woodlands, and prime agricultural lands.

For each of the discrete phenomena, and for each successive generalization, approximate permissiveness to other land uses and specific prohibitions were suggested. While all were permissive to greater or lesser degree, all performed their natural process best in an unspoiled condition. Clearly, if land is abundant and land-use planning can reflect natural process, a fabric of substantially natural land can remain either in low-intensity use or undeveloped, interfused throughout the metropolitan region. It is from this land that metropolitan open space can best be selected.

When this concept was applied to the Philadelphia SMSA, the uplands were discerned as performing an important role in natural process and offering a specific range of recreational opportunity. The coastal plain was observed to perform an equally important but very different role and offered another range of recreational potential. Uniting uplands and coastal plain to the central city are major air-water corridors while at the lowest level exist the distribution of the eight parameters selected.

In general, planning for natural process would select uplands, coastal plain, and air-water corridors to remain relatively undeveloped; it would confirm urbanization in the piedmont. It would protect surface water, and riparian lands, exempt floodplains from development by

	Recommended Land Uses
Surface Water and Riparian Lands	Ports, harbors, marinas, water-treatment plants, water-related industry, certain water-using industry, open space for institutions and housing, agriculture, forestry, recreation.
Marshes	Recreation
Fifty-year Floodplain	Ports, harbors, marinas, water-treatment plants, water-related and water-using industry, agriculture, forestry, recreation, institutional open space, open space of housing.
Aquifers	Agriculture, forestry, recreation, industries which do not produce toxic or offensive effluents. All land uses within limits set by percolation.
Aquifer Recharge Areas	As aquifers.
Prime Agricultural Lands	Agriculture, forestry, recreation, open space of institutions, housing at one house per twenty-five acres.
Steep Lands	Forestry, recreation, housing at maximum density of one house per three acres.
Forests and Woodlands	Forestry, recreation, housing at densities not higher than one house per acre, other factors permitting.

land uses other than those unimpaired by flooding or inseparable from waterfront locations, exclude development from marshlands and ensure their role as major water storage areas, limit development on aquifer resources and their recharge areas, protect prime farmland as present and prospective resources of agricultural productivity and scenic beauty, ensure the erosion-control function of forested steep slopes and ridges, and ensure their role, with forests and woodlands, in the water economy, and as a scenic-beauty and recreational potential.

This concept, if realized, would ensure a structured system of open space within the metropolitan area within which only limited development would occur. It would produce the "natural" morphology of the metropolis. Due to the small number of parameters examined, this is a course-grain study. By increasing the number of phenomena and replacing the descriptive account of natural process by accurate quantitative analysis, the value of this information could be compounded.

The importance of these three examples lies simply in the fact that the commonplaces of natural science, where applied to planning, can be intensely illuminating and provide form in a most dramatic way from the level of the house on the shore to the form of metropolis.

CONCLUSION

Today, in the face of momentous change in which urbanization is one of the most dramatic phenomena, nature is seen to be defenseless against the positive acts of transformation. The proponents of nature emphasize preservation, a negative position, one of defense, which excludes positive participation in the real and difficult tasks of creating noble and ennobling cities in fair landscapes. Meanwhile, the positive acts of urbanism proceed without perception of natural proc-

ess, blind to its operation, values, and form-giving rules, scarcely modified by appeals for preservation and protection, remorseless in destruction, and impotent in constructive creation.

The negative view of conservation and the disinterest of natural science in problems of planning and urbanism is a disservice to society. The redirection of concern to include, not only wild environments, but those dominated by man is a challenge which the natural sciences and their public arm—conservation—must confront and accept. Understanding of natural process is of central importance to all environmental problems and must be introduced into all considerations of land utilization.

The burden of this paper is a request to natural scientists, particularly ecologists, to provide the indispensable information which the artificers require—ecological inventories, explanation of natural processes and identification of their limiting factors, the attribution of value, the indicators of healthy and unhealthy environments, and, finally, the degree of permissiveness or prohibition to transformation, implicit in natural processes.

Given this information, those who bring good will to the problems of resource planning and urbanism may add knowledge. This information can provide the basis for persuasion in both private and public domains; it can indeed provide the basis for a federal land-use policy based upon natural processes.

Such information can identify roles with geographic locations and attribute values to them. Thus, catastrophe-prone and danger areas would be prohibited to development—earthquake, volcanic, hurricane, avalanche, flood, drouth, fire, and subsidence zones; areas having great intrinsic value—wilderness areas, wildlife habitats, areas of great scenic beauty, areas having important scientific and educational value, would be identified and exempted from development; the concept of "work performed" would permit identification of constituent roles—water-catchment areas, dunes, flood, drouth- and erosion-control areas, floodplains, air sheds, etc., etc., on which only limited development, responsive to natural process, could occur. Positively this information could select areas suitable for development, tolerant to man. The final component, the indicator, would permit diagnosis and prescription for existing environments.

This ecological information is thus deterministic and might well be called ecological determinism. It reveals the megaform of natural processes at the national level, the mezoform of the region, the microform of the city. From the city down to the level of its parts, ecological determinants become participant parameters in the planning process, but still influential as form-giving.

Precursory ecology made possible the leap over the garden wall in the eighteenth century, but the landscape created was a pastoral one. Modern ecology can enable us to leap more surely into many different environments, reserving some, intervening with deference in others, accomplishing great and wise transformations for human habitats in certain selected locations. When the program is developed and understood, when pervasive, then the artist will make it manifest. His interventions will become metaphysical symbols revealed in art.

The search is then for the place of nature in the city of man and, even more profoundly, for the place of man in nature.

BIBLIOGRAPHY

McHarg, Ian L., et al. 1963. Sea, Storm and Survival, A Study of the Jersey Shore (mim.).
———— 1965. Metropolitan Open Space from Natural Processes (mim.).
Wallace, David H., and McHarg, Ian L. 1964. Plan for the Valleys.

COASTAL CHANGES

J. A. Steers*

Coastal Changes

The title allotted to me is "Coastal Changes." It is a wide one, and by no means easy to assess, either briefly or at length! Perhaps I should begin by saying that I know the coast of Great Britain fairly well, and also that I have had opportunities to see either from the land or the air most of the coast between San Diego and the Oregon-Washington boundary, much of that between the eastern part of Padre Island and Apalachicola including the Mississippi delta; I have also seen a little of the west coast of Florida, most of its eastern shore, two of the sea islands of Georgia, and I have had brief glimpses from the air of the east coast as far as New York. I have also visited one or two parts of the coast of New England. This hardly seems to be sufficient for me to venture to write this paper which must refer largely to the United States. Fortunately, however, the nature of the causes which bring about change are much the same on all coasts, and so I shall make considerable use of my more detailed knowledge of Britain.

* Mr. Steers is (1966) Professor Emeritus of Geography in the University of Cambridge and the first Emeritus Fellow of St. Catharine's College. His lifelong observation of the coastal environment led to the publication of *The Coastline of England and Wales* (Cambridge University Press, Second edition, 1964). Except for a spell in the late fifties, he was a member of the Nature Conservancy until 1966, and remains a member of the England Committee.

I hope, too, that through my using to some extent a comparative method my contribution will have wider interest.

When I have lectured in America about the British coasts, two points in particular have appeared to impress Americans—the great variety of scenery, even in very short distances, along the coast of Great Britain, and the shingle which is found on nearly all our beaches, and some of them are almost entirely formed of it. That there are magnificent beaches of sand and shingle in the Pacific northwest, and also in New England, I am well aware, but shingle is less common in the United States than in England. On the other hand, I have been astonished at the enormous extent of white sand beaches between Florida and Mexico, where there is not a single pebble placed there by nature(!), and also by the extraordinary development of barrier beach, lagoon (or estuary), and salt marsh along many hundreds of miles of the Atlantic coast. By choosing these two points, I do not wish to imply that there are not many other features which have impressed me. The Pacific coast is very different; there are magnificent areas of dunes in Oregon, but a great deal of the coast consists of fine cliff scenery and, let us remember, nearly all of it is in a region of active seismicity.

It follows from even these very brief remarks that a great deal of the American coast is particularly vulnerable to what I will call human attack. In this context it would be valuable if someone familiar with the laws of both the United States and Great Britain were to write a summary account of how planning and other legislation affect the coasts of both countries. The subject is complex, but a proper understanding of many of the problems posed by this Conference would be helped by such a study.

Coastal changes in the ordinary sense usually imply those brought about by the sea, and therefore refer to but a very narrow band, roughly that between the extreme limits of high and low water. But we must take a wider view and extend the coastal zone a little inland. There is no precise way of doing this, but probably we shall all agree that if we could just wave a wand and obliterate all that spoils our coasts, we should like to see a belt of varying width kept clear, and that we should take particular care of skylines as seen from the beach or cliff top. But it is impossible to be consistent! Leaving aside ports and towns which, after all, must be on the coast, there are other man-made features which often beautify the scene. In Britain, castles like Bamburgh and Dunstanburgh in Northumberland or Criccieth and Harlech in West Wales add enormously to the landscape. A lighthouse is often an attractive element, and there is all the difference in the world between a pleasant layout like Carmel in California and the towering skyline of Miami. Moreover, at this present time Americans and Britons alike are, very rightly, extremely self-conscious about the blemishes of their coasts; and those of us who think in terms of natural beauty are extremely anxious that unsuitable buildings should not be erected on or close to the coast. But will our successors think the same? In Britain the sea fronts of, for example, Sidmouth and Southwold—two small places, one on the south and the other on the east coast—are regarded by all as not only good but as fitting the landscape.

I think the same view holds about some of the smaller fishing towns in New England. Will this always be so, or will the characteristic high boxes of the twentieth century be regarded by our grandchildren as of real beauty and appropriately placed?

It is, I maintain, worth mentioning this, because tastes change and since we must, willy-nilly, develop large parts of our coasts, it is by no means sensible to be too rigid in our ideas. Nevertheless, it is this direct attack by man on the coast which is far and away the most serious problem. The United States is particularly unfortunate in this respect. Just because so much of the Atlantic and Gulf coasts consist of long sandy beaches, whether they are attached to offshore islands or barriers or to the mainland, they are extremely vulnerable. Nearly all the beaches are easily reached by car and the others by boat; the numbers of people visiting them, already very large, are increasing yearly at an alarming rate. The demand for more and more accommodation on many of these beaches inevitably means that their natural beauty is threatened if not already ruined, because, unless cleverly placed and landscaped, even a small building is conspicuous on a more or less open beach. What is more, these beaches are often backed by dunes which, in the natural state, add greatly to their amenity value. But dunes are, by their very nature, perhaps the most unstable of land forms, and the more people that roam about them, the greater the danger.

In Britain the same trend is apparent. The population is, of course, less than that of the United States, and even if the length of the coastline is proportionately longer, the pressure on it, especially in England and Wales, is nevertheless great and continually increasing. As in America, most people want to go to good beaches, of which there are many, but they are much smaller than those in America, and a great many of them are enclosed by cliffed headlands. This in it-self locally makes the problem of trans-port unusually difficult. In 1963 I visited one of the most popular parts of the Cornish coast during the August Bank Holiday period in order to see the prob-lem in the field. Local rural coastal roads were in places jammed with cars, cars were often driven onto the beaches, and car parks had to be improvised. For per-haps nine months of the year, the roads and beaches are almost deserted; but in ten or twenty years' time the summer pressure will be far worse. Between the beaches the cliff scenery is magnificent. Yet how few people were on the cliffs, except in those parts near a town so that a car could be driven onto them!

The real enemy of the coast is un-doubtedly the car. Americans may have set the lead in this way, but other coun-tries have only too willingly followed! There is nothing wrong in this, but a car and a reasonable road system along the coast mean that all, or almost all, parts of an accessible coast are affected. When in Corpus Christi for a few days in 1964, I was taken a considerable distance along the main beach of Padre Island; nearly all of it is possible for the motor-ist. The flotsam and jetsam on the beach was not wholly derived from the sea! Taking a car along an open beach which may be covered at high water, or at par-ticular tides, is from the point of view of nature relatively harmless; and cer-tainly it is so on Padre Island, which is not situated in an area of dense popu-lation. On the other hand, similar access along an open beach in an area of high-density population means that the dunes behind the beach are invaded by thou-sands and therefore the plant cover is disturbed, probably destroyed, the sand begins to blow, and, unless care is taken, dunes may disappear. The making of paths through dunes is often most dam-aging, and once the dunes have deterio-rated they have a much smaller esthetic

appeal. In the many coastal parks in the United States some control can be ex-ercised in this respect, and in fact must be. If that in its turn means that the tourist must keep to particular paths, the pleasure of a visit may possibly be limited. This, however, is a matter that must be faced in any country because everywhere the pressure on the coast is increasing, and unless measures are taken in time, dune landscapes will be ruined by the very people who want to preserve them! At the mouth of the Wash there is a nature reserve known as Gibraltar Point. It is within a mile or two of Skegness, a popular resort. Visitors to the reserve are numerous, but trails, like those in American reserves, have been made and have been remarkably success-ful in letting large numbers see and ap-preciate the reserve without doing dam-age to it. In short, persuasion and a little "courteous ingenuity" can do a great deal! The double threat of buildings of all sorts encroaching on the coast and of tourists unintentionally aiding in the destruction of what they most want to preserve is indeed formidable. Planning legislation has undoubtedly helped the conservationist in Britain; can more be done in America? If a stranger may so comment, it seems that in America the problem is often intensified by the fact that so much of the coast is privately owned. At the beginning of the century, even twenty-five years ago, conditions were completely different, the motorcar was in its infancy, and the train took people to resorts. There was little pres-sure anywhere else. The same is even more true of Britain. With the change, more advanced in America than in Brit-ain, of the visit—long or short—to the seaside by car instead of by train, *all* the available coast is in demand and the problem of the privately owned beach is emphasized.

Coastal problems are quite different in Canada and in much of Scotland. In both the population density is far less than in that of their southern neighbors; in both the climate is generally less attractive for a seaside holiday. Apart from a limited development (in comparison with the total lengths of the coasts of Canada and Scotland) of built-up areas, there is an abundance of open coast. In Scotland some beaches in the east and southwest are popular, but not in the same way as those in southern England. But much of the coast of both Canada and Scotland is beautiful, but it must be seen in a different way. In Scotland roads give reasonable access to nearly all places; some of the most spectacular parts of Canada can be seen only from the sea or air. I may appear to be wandering far from my thesis in saying this, but this is not so. This Conference is concerned as much, even if not more, with the future as with the present. If we are to preserve what we have in the easily accessible areas, I suggest we must try to influence people so that they begin to take an interest in the coast from a different point of view. This may seem impracticable, but will it not be just as impracticable to double, in relatively few years, the use of popular beaches? However sociable people may be, there must come a limit to those who are willing to spend holidays on a beach that, throughout the season and not just on one or two days, is as crowded as the sidewalks of Broadway or Piccadilly!

This problem is one with that of increased affluence and more and more leisure. In Britain an ever-growing number of people take their holiday abroad; this is probably true in the United States, too, although political conditions in Europe may have an appreciable effect from time to time. But it is unlikely that this outlet will afford any real relief to the beaches, which, when all is said, remain the ideal holiday place for most families. Unfortunately there is only one coast for any country, and it is but a narrow strip. Once it is spoiled, there is no way of repairing it. The primary problem is education, and by education I mean not only at school level, but at all levels including especially big business. Unless it is generally appreciated that a fortune made by the "development" of an attractive beach, while it may please a few, may well be a calamity for the nation as a whole, little can be done. Free enterprise in the modern world may be a real danger. It is highly alarming to read the several recent surveys by the National Parks Association and other similar bodies in the United States, and to realize how little good unspoiled coast remains, and, as I have said above, so much of this is of the most vulnerable kind—open beaches and dunes. It is an unpopular thing to say, but the only way of saving some of it in both America and Britain is to make it accessible only to the walker!

One of the finest features on the Atlantic Coast is Cape Cod. That I have not exaggerated the points made above let me quote from Elmer C. Martinson (1959): "Today, so many visitors agree that it [Cape Cod] is in grave danger of obliteration by summer cottages, resorts and commercial enterprises of all kinds. If this happens—and it is already progressing with alarming rapidity—the very beauty which makes Cape Cod so greatly beloved will vanish under the surge of development." And, later on: "The expense of acquiring the land subject to life estates is considerable—estimated at $16,000,000. But with each passing year that cost will rise. At the same time the opportunity for preserving an adequate portion of the Cape will dwindle. If the opportunity passes, the American people will have lost more of inspirational value than dollar values can ever reflect." What is true of Cape Cod is equally true of other places.

I have dwelt on the broad effects of human impact on the coast at some length because it is the major factor with which we have to contend. It will now be proper to consider in more detail some of the ways in which the coast can be spoiled as a result of natural processes, and also by some processes instigated by man.

Since the coast is the borderline of land and sea, the major natural factor at work on it is wave action. It will be unnecessary here to consider past changes of level, and we may concentrate on the sea-land border as it is today, as long as we remember that in some places slight but measurable vertical movement of either land or sea, or both, is in actual progress. In southeastern England, for example, there is a slow and very slight downward movement of the land relative to sea level. It has been going on for a long time, and if it continues, precautions will sooner or later have to be taken about the level of dock sills and similar matters. On the open coast a sinking movement of this sort also implies the possibility, even the actuality, of increased wave attack. The reverse happens if a coast is slowly rising, as is part of eastern Scotland and also part of New England.

Wave action, however, is continuous; it is strongest during gales and at high water, especially during surges which not infrequently occur in, for example, the North Sea. Not all surges are dangerous, but in 1953, when one of some magnitude coincided with a violent storm, much damage ensued. The level of the North Sea was about six or seven feet above normal for the tide in question, and wave action was excessive. Hence, there was locally severe erosion of cliffs, and in Lincolnshire the effect was to remove the beach almost completely. A beach is not static; on an open coast it is always in transit, although the movement is not noticeable in ordinary weather. The 1953 storm washed a great deal of the Lincolnshire beach inland

over the sea walls, and presumably also scoured a great deal away seaward. The result was that great damage and loss of life took place, and the beach was replaced by the underlying boulder clay. Immediate repair work was begun; new walls were built, and new groynes were erected. Fortunately, Dr. King and Dr. Barnes of the Department of Geography of Nottingham carried out a long and most valuable series of profile measurements, which showed conclusively that it took approximately ten years for the beach to reach the state it was in just prior to the storm. This is not unique; similar and even more violent effects may take place in a hurricane on the Gulf and Atlantic coasts, but seldom if ever have such careful measurements been made. Much damage took place all along the east coast of England in the 1953 storm, but it is interesting to note that little if any change took place in salt-marsh areas; the sea flooded them to an unusual depth but, as far as could be estimated, little significant change occurred. The effects of storm and hurricanes are often somewhat unexpected. The damage to property, sea walls, and harbor installations is usually severe. Hurricane Audrey, 1957, was studied in detail by the Coastal Studies Institute at Baton Rouge. J. P. Morgan (1963) writes: "After formation of the normal beach cross section (near Cameron, La.) the entire coastal marsh was inundated . . . (up to a maximum of twelve feet). Storm wave action distributed the beach sediment both landward and seaward leaving the area out of equilibrium with normal wave action. For a period of eighteen months after the storm, wave activity caused abnormal shoreline retreats until the beach finally returned to an equilibrium condition. The significant fact was that coastal retreat did not occur during the height of the hurricane but rather during the months following the storm." The storm of 1953, referred to above, was most uneven in its effects on cliffs of soft sandstone and glacial beds on the coast of Suffolk. A few miles north of Southwold, cliffs about thirty feet high were locally cut back thirty to forty feet; just to the north, where their height drops to about ten feet and then to beach level, eighty to ninety feet disappeared. At a similar distance south of Southwold, where the cliffs are equally unresistant, no measurable change took place although throughout history this part of the coast (Dunwich) has suffered severely.

An interesting example[1] of the way in which man can influence the effects of natural processes on coasts is given by coral cays. These are either small sandy islands developed by wave refraction on reef flats or accumulations of reef debris built up where larger coral blocks are lodged on high-standing reef flats by storm waves. Vegetation plays a major part in stabilizing these somewhat ephemeral constructions: seeds brought by the sea or by birds establish themselves, forming a pioneer strand community which progresses through low scrub to a climax stage of broadleaf woodland. On most of the coral cays in the Caribbean this woodland has been largely or even entirely removed in post-Columbian times and replaced by coconut plantations. Traces of it remain only in a few patches of *Bursera, Neea,* and *Ficus,* and in more widespread littoral hedges of *Cordia* and *Tournefortia.* In 1961 an opportunity occurred to assess the physiographic significance of this change in the vegetation cover, when Hurricane Hattie crossed the reefs of the British Honduras coast shortly after a study of the reefs and cays had been

completed. Winds during the hurricane exceeded 200 m.p.h., and near the center of the storm sea level rose up to fifteen feet above normal. Since no cays are higher than ten feet above sea level, this meant that many of them were submerged during a period of exceptionally severe wave conditions. The broad pattern of damage to islands and reefs was roughly zoned north and south of the storm track; it was greater in the north, where winds were onshore, but within this general pattern major variations in damage could be correlated with vegetation cover. Where natural vegetation had been replaced by coconuts, and there was usually no undergrowth, storm waves were able to overtop islands and caused severe damage and sometimes complete destruction. Where the natural vegetation remained, however, it proved well adapted to storm conditions, maintaining its roothold and acting as a baffle to the storm waves and surge, with the result that erosion was much less and deposition occurred along the edges of the vegetation. In places this was sufficient to raise the surface of the cay as much as five to seven feet above pre-storm levels. On islands only partly used for coconuts, the cleared part was usually heavily eroded and damaged, whereas the vegetated part was built up during the storm. It is known that coconuts spread widely on these islands in the second half of the nineteenth and in the early twentieth centuries, because the nuts became an export crop, and it is also known that at least twenty islands have completely disappeared from these reefs since 1830.

There is a growing interest in the reefs as a tourist attraction, a new clearance of vegetation has begun by means of mechanized methods, and there is no doubt that, just as clearing for coconuts disturbed the equilibrium exisiting among sediment accumulation, vegetation, and storm conditions in the period since

[1] This paragraph has been contributed by my colleague David Stoddart, who was able to map the coral cays of British Honduras both before and after Hurricane Hattie. I am most grateful to him for an interesting and pertinent contribution.

1800, so this new and more intensive clearance will result in even more massive damage to cays during future hurricanes. It is hardly going too far to say that it is only in this interaction between sedimentation processes and vegetation growth that cays are able to build up to their present form, and once this system is disrupted, a rapid change takes place; sediments once held together largely by vegetation reach a new equilibrium and a very different topographic form. This trend may, of course, be halted if the natural vegetation is allowed to re-establish itself. After a succession of recent hurricanes and an increasing shortage of capital to finance coconut plantations, it may be that the vegetation will revert to littoral thicket, and that the old equilibrium will be re-established.

This kind of thing has happened time and again in the Caribbean and the Gulf of Mexico; nature destroys and, on the seacoast, often rebuilds in her own way. But this is not so on a cliffed coast; if the cliffs are easily eroded, that which is lost is not replaced but swept along the coast. The magnificent till cliffs facing Great beach on Cape Cod are always retreating; this is not an isolated example, and many others will doubtless occur to the reader. If such cliffs are at or near a town or settlement, they must be protected either by a sea wall or by groynes, or by both. The remedy may be successful locally; its main objects are to resist erosion and especially to attract a good beach on which the waves can expend their energy. But the beach can grow only as the result of the longshore travel of sand and stones; if these are held up by groynes, it clearly follows that the coast immediately down-drift is deprived of its normal supply and erosion, often serious, ensues. In Britain, the building of groynes or harbor piers at Great Yarmouth and Lowestoft on the east coast and at Shoreham, Newhaven, and other places on the Channel coast

illustrates this action. It is but natural that a seaside town should try to protect itself; it is more logical that the country or nation should take over-all action to protect its coast—but has any country except Holland ever done so?

Coastal erosion is often a serious problem. In parts of Britain it has gone on more or less continuously for centuries. It is most evident along cliffs of boulder clay and little-resistant sedimentary rocks. On the Holderness coast (southeast of Yorkshire) it is estimated that as much as eighty-three square miles has disappeared since Roman times along a cliff about thirty-four miles long. Along the cliffs of Norfolk and Suffolk, erosion is also serious, but erosion is by no means wholly the work of the sea. Land water draining through the cliffs is a potent cause, especially if there are impervious clay beds dipping toward the sea. In boulder clays there is often a mixture of sands, boulders, clays; sometimes they are contorted and if water drains from the cliff top, local movements and slides are easily set in motion. The scalloped top of boulder clay cliffs, originating in this way, is a characteristic feature. The step from simple erosion to landslips is not great. The extensive slips on the Dorset-Devon coast at Christmas 1839 were the result of movement along a clay stratum. There are many other examples that might be quoted from both the United States and Great Britain.

It is possible by means of expensive sea walls to restrain erosion and to stop it completely for a period. But since it is usually impracticable to build a wall of considerable length, it follows that erosion usually continues at its ends, and a time may come when the protected part stands salient. This has happened to a limited extent at Hornsea and Withersea, two small towns on the Holderness coast. Indeed, it is not unusual for short lengths of wall to be completely isolated by the sea, which has either undermined them or cut in behind them. Protection of a limited piece of cliff or, for that matter, of any type of coast sooner or later provokes serious reactions on the unprotected parts adjacent to it.

On a cliffed coast of resistant rocks little change is likely to take place under ordinary conditions. An earthquake may cause large falls or indeed considerable changes of level. Those that took place in the Yakutat Bay earthquake of 1899 were considerable. Changes of this type, however, are uncommon.

The lateral movement of beach material leads to the formation of spits across the mouths of rivers and re-entrants if local circumstances are favorable. The long barrier islands characteristic of the Atlantic and Gulf coasts of the United States and, on a very much smaller scale, those off the coast of northern Norfolk in England are built by direct wave action, although they may, and probably do, lengthen by beach drifting along them once some degree of stability is attained. All their features are vulnerable to natural as well as to man-induced change, of which we have already spoken. The dunes behind the beach are the direct result of the wind carrying the surface layer of sand with it, and depositing it, or some of it, on and around obstacles of one kind or another. In Britain the first obstacle is usually a shingle ridge, since nearly all our beaches are topped by shingle. If shingle is not present, the sand may drift landward and possibly lose itself in the lagoon behind. But once the waves have raised the beach above the level of ordinary tides, vegetation will come in. Seeds are washed in by the water, carried by birds, often carried by man himself, and many are blown to the place in question. If some come to rest at the top of the beach, a few may strike and begin to grow and send up shoots. The plants that can tolerate this exposed habitat are few, but in Britain certain grasses, especially of the genera *Agropyrum* and *Ammophila,* are usually successful. Once these plants have begun to grow, they become obstacles and help to collect sand. The process may start around a few scattered plants; sooner or later these grow upward and sideward; two or more clumps may coalesce, and eventually a longish dune ridge parallel to the sea may evolve. This now forms a rather different habitat; it is mainly outside normal wave action, although spray and storm will affect it. In course of time other changes take place; the dune area increases, there is more local shelter, more plants arrive, the surface cover is more continuous, the decay of the vegetation produces humus, and the original white or yellow dunes become more and more gray as a result of these changes. All this is very familiar to physiographers and ecologists, but the ordinary tourist seldom realizes how delicate is the balance. He, or at any rate his children, may dig in the dunes and pull up some of the plants. This seems quite harmless, but once it is done a new *bare* surface is exposed on which the wind can act, and large blowouts or complete furrows cutting through a dune can often be traced to such a small cause. Before the advent of myxomatosis in Britain, rabbits burrowing in coastal dunes often had a similar effect.

Dunes present special problems. The rate at which large areas can be changed may be illustrated by two examples, one from Scotland and the other from Oregon. On the northeast coast of Scotland, between the small towns of Nairn and Burghead, there is an extensive coastal flat, an integral part of the twenty-five-foot and fifteen-foot so-called raised beaches. On part of this flat, just west of Findhorn Bay, there existed up to 1694 a fertile estate of some size, the Culbin estate. Sand dunes existed to the west of it, but the estate produced good crops and was prosperous. Its history can be traced back to the thirteenth century. In medieval and later times the pulling of bent (*Ammophila arenaria*) had been unlawful, but the estate suffered no danger from blowing sand. But at the end of the seventeenth century sand had become to some extent a menace, and by 1694 the estate was so encumbered that cultivation ceased. The sand continued to accumulate, buried the house of Culbin, and in 1937 there were dunes which reached the 100-foot contour. Every now and again the moving sand exposed some of the old plowland. A few years earlier the Forestry Commission decided to plant the dunes; some had been planted by 1937. Others had been thatched—that is, branches and other material had been spread over the dune surface, pegged down, and stable sweepings scattered. Some planting of *Ammophila* was also done. Now, in 1964, nearly all the dunes are held, and the old farmlands of the seventeenth and earlier centuries are replaced largely by a forest growing perhaps eighty or more feet above them. It will, of course, be appreciated that the forest cover holds the sand, but when it is cut some precaution will have to be taken to prevent blowing.

An interesting experiment was carried out on Scolt Head Island, Norfolk, in 1963. On a few chosen places, high and low, the dunes were sprayed with an oil-extended synthetic rubber compound which allowed sufficient stabilization for the germination and growth of grasses and also for the continued deposition of sand. The film was effective for six months, and even resisted occasional coverings of sea water. Further experiments at Blakeney Point were also successful. The National Parks Service of America has shown interest in this experiment (Haas and Steers, 1964).

There are some magnificent dunes along the coast of Oregon. They, too, are liable to move and locally encroach on the land within. Man has altered them a good deal, both by introduction, usually casual but sometimes deliberate, of exotic plants and by cutting of forest, clearing, and grazing animals on the cleared areas. Burning has also taken place, and large areas have been rendered more mobile. The introduction of gorse, in 1873, from Ireland, when two twelve-foot hedgerows were planted near Bandon, has given rise to serious problems. In 1949 it was estimated that 25,000 acres were covered by this shrub, and it has become a pest both costly and difficult to eradicate. But man has intensified the problem by building townships, and also by the construction of jetties across river mouths. On the Clatsop Plains overgrazing and a jetty so upset the natural balance that there were about 3000 acres of bare sand in the 1930s. The building of jetties may produce exactly the opposite of the effect desired; nowadays an experiment can be made in a wave tank, and proper precautions taken. In the past this was not possible, and jetties in Oregon and elsewhere have caused erosion in some places and deposition in others. The jetty in Tillamook Bay led both to the undermining of forest and to the building of extensive new flats. On the east coast of Florida one or two outlet channels which obstruct the lateral movement of beach material are by-passed by a mechanism which sucks sand from the one side and carries it either over or under the transverse channel to the beach beyond. It cannot be insisted upon too strongly that in coastal problems generalizations only too often lead to serious difficulties, and that each and every locality demands individual study over a reasonable period of time. If model experiments can also be made, so much the better.

If any barrier island or spit at the mouth of a river is watched, still better mapped or photographed from the air, over a period of years it will be seen that it is in a constant state of change.

Sometimes the changes are slow and hardly measurable; at other times, they are violent. Further acquaintance will show that there is often a close interaction between vegetation and sand or shingle supply. If for some reason the supply of beach material is reduced, then the waves are likely to cut away a good deal of the depleted area. This may come about in many ways: a wreck may be washed up on to the beach and act as a groyne and so upset the lateral movement of material; a storm may break through a ridge and make a new in-and-out channel which may also act as a barrier to beach drifting; or perhaps a change in bottom conditions offshore will alter the incidence of waves or tidal currents on the beach. All these may seem trivial, but they are not, and in the long run may have profound effects. Unless the users of such a place understand and appreciate the very delicate balance that exists in nature, they may unwittingly cause serious damage. Since so much can happen as the result of often small natural causes, it is no wonder that devastating change can follow the arrival of a multitude!

The United States up to, and for some considerable time after, the arrival of Europeans was relatively little affected by man except as a result of fire. The Indians burnt large areas of forest, often near the sea, and this set in motion a series of changes. The white man soon began to clear forests, and in more recent years he has been ruthless in many places as a result of the use of modern machinery. The clearing of forest means that soil erosion is often begun or intensified, the load of the rivers is vastly increased, and the amount of sedimentation in estuaries and sheltered waters is greatly extended. There are many examples of this in the Northwest; maps of areas of salt marsh made at different times show how rapidly they have grown

if the amount of sediment has been increased as a result of forest clearance.

"The Final Report of Some Recent Physical Changes of the Oregon Coast" (Dicken et al., 1961) is a most interesting and revealing document. The basins of the Umpqua River and its tributary the Smith are heavily wooded, and lumbering is the main activity. Along the Smith River the forest is mainly new growth since devastation by fire about a century ago. There is no direct measurement of the rate of filling of the estuary as a result of this, but it is thought to have been considerable. The Kilchis River (Oregon) has changed its course several times in its delta on account of increased load, and therefore sedimentation, following the severe forest fires of 1939 and 1945. The tidal marshes in Kilchis Bay were mapped in 1867, 1939, and 1961, and the changes reflect the amount of load carried by the rivers. It should be emphasized that the delta region of these two rivers has filled considerably during the era of the Europeans. "From 1867 to 1939 the accretion . . . resulted in a shoreline advance of 500 to 1500 feet (about 14 feet per year on the average); in the last 22 years the margin has extended 200 feet on the average (about 9 feet per year) across formerly bare mud-flats. Therefore, the rates have been roughly the same and it may be assumed that the process will continue. As the marsh expands it may be assumed also that dikes will be built and extended, and that material dredged from the sloughs and stream channels . . . will be used to create dry land of high value."

This last point is significant. Flat reclaimed land is in demand for many purposes, including the building of airports; a local example is that in Coos Bay, Oregon, near the city of North Bend. On a much larger scale the continuing reclamation of parts of San Francisco Bay is noteworthy. This bay illustrates extremely well the effect of the incoming of the white man. The silting increased rapidly, partly through forest clearing, but especially because of the effects of early hydraulic mining, a subject brilliantly studied by G. K. Gilbert (1917). The threat to wetlands is serious, and has been emphasized by the recent IUCN publication "Liquid Assets." There is no need here to insist on their scientific and educational value, and on the devastating effects on the fauna and flora which results from their reclamation. Again it is the naturalist, *sensu lato*, versus big business; moreover, there is also an increasing desire for more land which is easily cultivable or of use in other ways. In Britain the discussions concerning the enclosure of Morecambe Bay and a part of the Solway Firth illustrate this. The Morecambe project arose through the threat of Manchester to use more water from the lakes of Cumberland and Westmoreland, and by so doing to spoil their natural beauty. An impounded freshwater lake in Morecambe Bay might be associated with a new highway along the barrage, and with two or three power stations on its margin.

It is difficult to preserve an open mind on many coastal problems of this sort. America has for long been used to pumps and other installations associated with oil; they are common off the Californian and Gulf coasts. The same problem may now face the countries around the North Sea. The island of Texel has already suffered. It is perhaps too early to comment on the possibilities, but one can only hope that the several important coastal nature reserves on the east coast of England, to say nothing of the intervening areas and seaside resorts, will not be adversely affected. Apart from disfigurement and the effects of oil on beaches and marshes, there is also the possibility of subsidence, only too evident at Long Beach, Los Angeles.

In Britain much of the country was formerly more forested. Occasionally, as for the navy in Nelson's time, more timber than usual was cut, but great areas were not cleared as they were in America. There is a local but interesting example of the probable effect of early forest clearing in the Weald—the southeastern corner of England. The small rivers which drain the Weald and flow in to the English Channel have been carefully analyzed, and a curious difference was found between the Arun and the Rother and neighboring streams. There was no apparent physiographical reason why the Arun and Rother should have cut somewhat deeper into the alluvium of their valley floors and thus leave a prominent terrace on either side of the streams, a few feet above water level. It has been suggested that this slightly deeper cutting was at any rate in part the result of the clearing of the ancient forest of Anderida.

In estuaries and behind barrier beaches, and often on beaches facing shallow water, salt marsh may grow. The marsh consists of particles of silt and clay brought in mainly by tidal action, which settle in favorable places. The surface on which the marsh grows is often a sand flat, or even rock. Sediment accumulates first in the most sheltered places, and perhaps also on the slightly higher parts of the surface. Often a bigger tide or a storm will wash it away, but in course of time some degree of stability will take place. When this occurs, possibly earlier, the seeds of halophytes carried by the water or other means fall on the mud or even on the bare sand flat. Some of these seeds will strike, and plants begin to grow. Just as on a dune, once the plants on a newly forming marsh begin to spread, they too become an important factor in the growth of the marsh. They have a filtering effect on the flowing and ebbing tides, and cause increased deposition of fine particles around them. In fact, once an area is covered with plants, its upward growth will usually increase until a time arrives when it has reached such a height that only a few of the bigger tides inundate it. There is no need to discuss the general ecology of salt marshes—the relation of plant species to both the substrate on which they grow and the number of times they are covered by the tide in the course of a lunar month, or in a year. We must, however, note that the gradual spread of marsh need not be regular or continuous. Channels of streams from the land may intersect it; creeks develop as it grows upward. Both streams and creeks meander, often considerably, and they undercut their banks and erode the marsh. The meander may pass downstream or swing away from the undercut bank, and then at the lower level, the level of the floor of the retreating stream, plants may begin to grow, and these will probably be distinct from those at the higher level or on the terrace left by the retreating meander. The reason for this is simply that more tides cover the lower than the higher level, and therefore the plants may differ. Waves set up by strong winds in an estuary or lagoon often cut into marshes and make low cliffs, and lumps of the eroded marsh often partially cover the flat which the waves are producing. These lumps are in effect small islands of higher marsh, and if conditions change so that erosion ceases, they will remain, and at the same time plants will grow on the slightly lower flat on which they stand so that two distinct levels, physical and ecological, are produced.

We have seen already that silted-up parts of estuaries are sooner or later reclaimed; the same is true of ordinary salt marshes. The scientific and educational value of marshes needs no notice in the context, but a word about what is happening on some English examples may be appropriate. In 1870 a hybrid grass, *Spartina townsendii*, appeared on the south coast; it spread rapidly and is very abundant in, for example, Poole Harbour and Southampton Water. In recent years it has suffered from dieback; the interior parts of large spreads and clumps begin to decay. The reason is uncertain, but one effect is to open up the sward to some extent. *Spartina* itself is an excellent accretor of mud and can be of much use in helping to reclaim low flats. Partly for this reason it was introduced into eastern England, and now it has spread by this means into Scolt Head Island and other nature reserves. At Scolt it is spreading rapidly and changing the character all too rapidly of certain parts of the island. Hence, various means to prevent this have been tried out, since its spread threatened communities which were valuable food resources for various grazing birds. The Nature Conservancy experimented both here and at Bridgwater Bay and found that certain herbicides such as Dalapon and substituted urea compounds killed *Spartina*. Experiments on trial plots at Scolt showed that Dalapon, at fifty to seventy pounds an acre, gave a high kill, and that Ureabur at 2000 pounds an acre, and Fenuron at fifty pounds an acre, gave a complete kill in trial plots.[2]

It would not be difficult to make this paper longer by giving other examples and by discussing particular localities and experiments. Enough has been said, however, to emphasize what seem to the writer to be the two fundamental factors: the very delicate balance that exists in all natural coastal formations, and the impact of man. Until it is more fully realized how easy it is to damage the coast irremediably, we cannot hope to do much. Education is far and away the most important criterion, and this

[2] It is worth emphasis that in a country like England, and probably also the United States, mountain and coastal vegetation (dune, shingle, marsh) is the only natural vegetation which most people see. So much elsewhere has been modified or eliminated.

means education of adults as well as of young people and children. There is no doubt that adults are the worst offenders, so often because the damage they do springs from a real desire to benefit their fellow men. It can also be noted that the educational value of coastal reserves— using "educational" in its ordinary academic sense—is particularly high. Not only is there a considerable range of natural and seminatural communities, but their changes and evolution are relatively rapid and so can be observed and appreciated by any intelligent observer.

In Britain, at this time, there is an appeal being made by the National Trust, an unofficial body, to collect two million pounds in order to buy up some of the best parts of the still unspoiled coast. The money will not go far, but the interest which the appeal may inspire should be of even greater value in bringing home to people what the coast should mean to the nation. It is difficult to convince inland dwellers who only go to the sea for a holiday that it is necessary to take steps to preserve the natural beauty of the coast. The same problem presum-

ably applies even more strongly in America, where so many millions of people live hundreds of miles from the sea. It can be argued that, since so many parts of the American coast are privately owned, there is no need to worry from the purely conservational point of view about them. Is this so? How many private, how many collective, owners are interested in the coast as a natural phenomenon? The coast must be accessible to people, and they will come in increasing numbers, but some parts must be kept as far as possible inviolate, and because there is but a limited amount of coast, exploitation by industry, urban development, private dwellings, or in other ways must be curbed otherwise little, if any, natural coast will remain. One last point—if this is done in countries like the United States and England, there is an increasing chance that newer and less developed countries may follow suit.

I am grateful to Dr. Max Walters and Mr. P. Haggett for their comments and criticism.

BIBLIOGRAPHY

Dicken, S. N., et al. 1961. Report on an Investigation Carried Out under Contract No. 2771 (04), Project NR 388-062, between the University of Oregon and the Office of Naval Research. U.S. Dept. of the Navy. Dept. of Geog., Univ. Oreg., Eugene, Oreg.
Gilbert, G. K. 1917. U.S. Geolog. Surv. Prof. pap. 105.
Haas, J. A., and Steers, J. A. 1964. Geog. J. 130:265.
Martinson, Elmer C. 1959. Nat. Parks Mag. (Oct.).
Morgan, F. P. 1963. Contribution 63–65, Coastal Studies Inst.

PRESERVING THE CULTURAL PATRIMONY

Christopher Tunnard*

1

The French call it *"biens culturels,"* a term which has overtones of being useful or valuable to the public. At the Rome Center the translation is "cultural property." I prefer the Middle English term "patrimony," meaning inheritance from one's father or ancestors. The implication here is that somebody else has worked for it, and that an element of trust may be involved.

What, then, is to be included in the cultural patrimony, especially as the term might apply to this continent?

The spectrum is broad and cannot be covered in all its aspects here. For instance, there is a temptation to include for discussion many of our unique or priceless natural resources—soils, mineral deposits—as part of the cultural heritage. Leaving these to better-qualified contributors, I shall confine my considerations to the landscape values which may be associated with them. It is the esthetic patrimony that I hope to stress. On the other hand, the man-made landscapes, buildings, and structures must be included, at least down to the scale of the individual house and garden. At the furthest end of the spectrum are the smaller, movable artifacts, not necessarily limited to those produced on native soil. The contents of museums, libraries, and public archives

* Professor Tunnard, who presided over the session on "Regional Planning and Development," is identified in a note on page 411.

should be included, regardless of their country of origin. This group, again, will not be discussed here.

Apart from the natural and scenic patrimony then, we should include historic monuments, such as those registered by the Historic American Buildings Survey. Since this list can never be complete, we must make local surveys based on the National Trust for Historic Preservation's method, broadening it to include historic town-planning and settlement patterns, of which more anon. Buildings of architectural value should be included, as well as those of historic value. Social and technological history must not be forgotten, as witness the recent interest in preserving monuments of the Industrial Revolution —early ironworks, bridges, mines, and mills. Parks and gardens may be considered historically important, too, always remembering that parkland should be inviolate, and that an open-space policy is actively pursued for reasons other than preservation.

Which brings us to social riches heretofore neglected or considered borderline. They have mostly to do with land and the activities centered thereon.

Woods and fields? Certainly one can insist that a legacy from nature is part of the cultural patrimony, especially in her grander forms, which are apt to be mountains, lakes, river valleys, and wild seashores. No one has seriously questioned this aspect of preservation for a hundred years. Spectacular scenery may have been slow to acquire, but except by a few vested interests the principle involved has not been attacked, and we have been praised abroad for initiating a national park and forest system. Less spectacular scenery with intimate views has also been established as a public trust, notably by the Trustees of Public Reservations, now approaching their seventy-fifth anniversary.[1] Few people would call Governor Hutchinson's Field in Milton, Massachusetts, spectacular, although it does afford a fine view of the Neponset marshes. It wasn't until four years after the Trustees began their work that Britain's National Trust was founded, its first acquisition, significantly enough, being four and a half acres of cliffland overlooking the Barmouth Estuary in North Wales.[2]

Woods and fields, then, have been included in the patrimonial scheme, especially when they are unique for one reason or another. Blood-soaked battlefields, like Gettysburg or the soon-to-be-opened Lexington-Concord Battle Road area, have always qualified, but of special interest are scattered examples of flora or habitat, like the Medfield rhododendrons or the Oregon myrtle groves. Surely this type of landscape will in future be considered an inalienable part of the cultural patrimony, too. The work of the National Audubon Society, the Wilderness Society, and the Nature Conservancy, to name only three private organizations devoted to preservation, ensures a bright future for thousands of acres which would otherwise have gone unprotected. Significantly, much of this acreage has been acquired

in quite small parcels, such as a duckpond at a crossroads or a key piece of woodland.

Close to these activities is a kind of preservation hitherto considered foreign to these shores. Admittedly the problem may be more acute in some countries of Europe, but what means are being used here to preserve our agricultural inheritance? There are countries which include farming as a visual amenity. The Swiss give the words *"la nature"* and *"le paysage"* equal weight in their conservation legislation. A Swiss farm usually *is* a visual amenity, but then so is an Iowa farm, or a Wisconsin farm, or a Connecticut farm, for that matter. The term "countryside," which is one equivalent of *"paysage,"*[3] remains little used by us. I daresay it was common in James Fenimore Cooper's time[4] but of recent years we have preferred "rural land" (denoting something apart from the *real* centers of civilization) or "back country" or "agricultural area," whereas "countryside" is a friendly designation, embracing both farming and wildlife but essentially suggesting the idea of a controlled environment. The result of the modern, less friendly attitude has been to throw all conservation measures back on hardpressed landowners; we do not think of a farm as worthy of preservation by society. When a big agricultural tract like

[1] As of 1963, the Trustees held for the public benefit thirty-nine reservations comprising some 5909 acres of land.
[2] This was immediately followed by another acquisition, representing a type of preservation for which the Trust is better known, and which had been anticipated by the earlier-established Society for the Protection of Ancient Buildings—a fourteenth-century timber-framed Clergy House at Alfriston in Sussex.

[3] "A stretch of country which affords a view of the whole." Larousse.
[4] Paul Shepard provides an anecdote of an American visitor to Britain in 1820 being shown the countryside near London from the top of a tower. "The fields, fenced by hedgerows, gave way in the distance to tree-tops, so that the highly cultivated land actually had the aspect of a broken forest becoming more and more compact toward the horizon. 'Do you call this beautiful?' the Yankee asked. 'In America we would consider it to be one of the most desolate scenes that the mind can conceive. It resembles a country that has never been cleared of wood.' " "They Painted What They Saw," in *Landscape*, Vol. 3, No. 1. p. 6.

the Killerton estate in Britain, or a whole village like the recently acquired Branscombe in Devonshire, is given to their National Trust, not only does the Trust gain much-needed revenue from the farms, but these come into the hands of a landlord who will give priority to seeing that they are run efficiently and thus contribute to the amenities of the landscape.[5] Although agricultural zoning, scenic easements, and other relatively new devices may save some of the North American "countryside," we are a long way from giving it equal status with "wild nature" as a scenic resource.

Similarly, we are quite iconoclastic as to scenic values when they are disassociated from nature. We complain about billboards in the country and tolerate them in the city. Our urban lake shores and river fronts are a national scandal. Skyline and silhouette are violated at will.[6] The battle to save landmarks and preserve historic districts is never-ending. It is one thing to promote the idea of historic house museums, and quite another to save the district in which they are to be found. The surroundings of the Old Merchant's House in New York or of the Shirley-Eustis House in Boston are testimony to this neglect on the part of urban authorities, in spite of the fact that the

5 J. F. W. Rathbone, "The National Trust: Its Growth and Problems," in *The Preservation and Development of Ancient Buildings and Historical or Artistic Sites*, p. 68. Council of Europe, 1963.

6 "The twentieth century equivalent in London of the spires and towers of medieval and 17th century London could have been, and indeed still could be, the slender towers of modern commerce and of London flats. The sinister compromise between the towers available to us through the development of modern building techniques and the low roofs of traditional building is the multi-storey slab; the building which turns streets into sunless canyons, makes the citizen crane his neck for a glimpse of the sky, and rubs out, with its india-rubber profile, the grace and romantic variety of London's skyline." *The Architects' Journal*, October 13, 1960. p. 522.

historic house museum is enjoying phenomenal popularity. In 1895 there were twenty of these in the whole country; today there are probably nearer a thousand. State activities in preserving historic houses and sites have mushroomed; since 1935 the National Park Service has developed and administered hundreds of historic "shrines," as the late Harold Ickes liked to call them; and we have had the National Trust for Historic Preservation in the United States, first incorporated in the District of Columbia in 1947 as the National Council for Historic Sites and Buildings. In 1949 it received its Congressional charter as a private nonprofit educational organization.

It was the National Trust of Washington which showed us that preserving a house here and a site there was not the answer to the problem. The comparatively recent concept of the historic district, pioneered first in New Orleans and Charleston, South Carolina, has been encouraged by the Trust, but remains essentially a local endeavor. There are now about seventy of these districts in about half of the states. Over fourteen states have enacted historic district enabling legislation, while many cities and towns have special ordinances established without state action. "Historic district architectectural controls," according to the Cambridge lawyer and preservationist Albert B. Wolfe, "aim at preserving appearance without change in ownership or use; where the setting is important as well as the buildings, or the relationship to each other of a sufficient number of historic buildings creates a whole that is greater than the sum of its parts." Few cities have established historic or architectural control on a city-wide basis, although recent activities in Quebec City suggest that a comprehensive effort is being made there. Mexico for many years has had its museum cities, and government sponsorship of the arts there has consciously developed archaeological sites as part of the "image" which that country presents to the world. In the United States, one large city, Philadelphia, has an official Municipal Historical Commission and can use means other than the historic district to halt demolition of structures.

Typical of the historic district are Beacon Hill in Boston; Nantucket, Massachusetts; Bethlehem, Pennsylvania; and Wethersfield, Connecticut. Wethersfield aims to preserve good examples of architecture within a relatively large district, stressing the fact that it is "an early Connecticut River community in continual growth from the year 1634." Bethlehem was a center of the Moravian religious sect, and Nantucket a home of the whaling industry of the eastern seaboard. I will have occasion to speak of an extension to the historic district idea in another context, but will mention here that the operation is similar from state to state: the District boundaries are drawn and described, a Historic District Commission is established, and the Commission issues a "Certificate of Appropriateness" upon submission of plans involving change in exterior architectural features. Sign control is also usually exercised by the Commission.

No billboards here, and it may very well be that Historic District controls will form the entering wedge for improved scenic appreciation in urban life.

2

Turning now to the realities of current spoliation, can we identify the changes that are taking place, with a view toward achieving better management of our scenic and cultural resources?

Ninety years ago William Cullen Bryant published his *Picturesque America, or The Land We Live In*. The selections, by different writers and illustrators, are interesting to us as descriptions of the then most admired scenic places in the country. Many, like Yosemite and the canyons of the Colorado, would still head our list; but others, then quite beautiful, we now scarcely consider important or else think them too far gone to save—for instance the Connecticut shore of the Sound, the valley of the Housatonic toward its mouth, or the southern shore of Lake Erie, now an industrial slum. The efforts being directed in these places toward renewal or conservation—and there are some, as exemplified by the new wildlife refuge near Sandusky, Ohio—are not likely to remake them into the beauty spots that once they were.

At the beginning of the second volume of *Picturesque America*, author and artist explore the Hudson Valley, "scenes of our most beautiful and perfect river." The only blot they can discover is "the smoke from the busy founderies [sic] at Poughkeepsie," but even these, the account goes on, are redeemed at night—"They light the river like weird beacons, and the sound of their great furnaces comes across the river in the stillness, as the panting of giants that toil when the weaker forces of the world are all asleep."

The furnaces with their strange peaked roofs and ramshackle chimneys are all gone. The blots which threaten today are larger, more permanent, more damaging. They are not likely to disappear. It is thus that the second half of the twentieth century will see bolder steps being taken to discourage the behemoths; even as this is being written a bill to block "destructive intrusions" along a forty-two-mile stretch of the Hudson River is being introduced in Congress to ensure the long-term preservation of the "historic, scenic, archaeological, recreational and wildlife character of the river."

Yet we know that we have to build and that we are faced with twentieth-century tasks.[7]

[7] "One of the broad points which seems to emerge from the chart is the very heterogeneous nature of the activities and operations responsible for impacts on the countryside,

Why do we think that there is anything new about our situation? Certainly there is no novelty in the sight of men trying to achieve a symbiotic relationship between themselves and their landscapes. We have only to learn of the Stone Age peoples of the North American continent and their notions of living with the land, or of eighteenth-century Englishmen who romanticized the orderly pastoral scene. If in North America it was not necessary to destroy much, and if in England it was the rich who benefited most (driving Goldsmith's peasants either to industrial slavery or to "the terrors of a horrid shore") surely these two tenancies left an incomparable wilderness and a gardened landscape which are both our envy, and, where we have managed to save them, our pride. Neither of these past imprints was, in fact, careless; whereas in our own time we have trodden without gratitude or love.

Not new attitudes, but new attempts, are necessary. Recovery of some old attitudes, yes. Understanding of new forces, essential.[8][9][10]

One of the new forces is thought to be sheer numbers. Consider the probability that in the next forty years there will be an increase of 150 million people in the United States, or a number almost equal to the total population in 1950. Is this increase supportable? By present production quotas, yes. By present con-

---

and the apparent lack of awareness among those concerned of their role in this respect. Those whom Dr. Bracey in "Industry and the Countryside" has named the Guardians of Amenity are themselves a miscellaneous band, but they are all aware of a common interest, whereas those whose activities alarm or antagonize them often have no links with one another, or even recognition of one another's existence. Admittedly they tend to have little in common, and their interests may often conflict, but if they could learn to look at themselves as jointly and generally having some responsibility for the rate, duration and character of changes in our countryside, they would not only help in conservation and preservation, but might find more effective and less often challenged means to fulfill their ends." From paper No. 2, "Chart of Human Impacts on the Countryside," E. M. Nicholson and A. W. Colling, London, 1963.

8 "We students in the field of design find ourselves standing on the unbearable gap between our traditional ways of the arts and crafts and the techniques from abroad which

adapt themselves to the practical life of today. We find these approaches merging and at the same time fighting each other. The designers who represent the two points of view have nothing in common because they have confined themselves to their own limited worlds, even when they are in the same school." Letter to C.T. from a student of landscape architecture at Chiba University, Japan.

9 "We note with pleasure that even those nations which have lately acquired their autonomy demonstrate by their presence at this meeting the same ideals as those nations of long experience, promoting the identification, conservation and supervision of the cultural patrimony; and thus, the transmission through the vestiges of the past of a vitality capable of reinforcing the present. From these roots spring the genuine values of national development." Speech of welcome by Pietro Gazzola, Second International Congress of the Architects and Technicians of Historic Monuments, Venice, 1964.

10 "The initiative and drive generally lie with the opponents, who invoke vital necessities—the need to innovate, social progress, public health, planning based on birth or traffic statistics—while the champions of the cause of culture are all too often living in the past. Contemplation of our cities clearly shows that, so long as the defenders of historical and artistic sites and monuments allow themselves to be drawn into battle on these terms, they will be doomed to defeat, and time will remain on the side of the 'jungle of concrete.'

"The real need is for the development and strengthening of active cooperation between those who devote all their efforts to keeping the past alive and those who are endeavoring to foresee how mankind will live in the years to come and to guide its development towards better living conditions.

"This cooperation, which is both desirable and necessary, is made easier by the fact that both parties are by definition opposed to destruction." From Document 1570, Council of Europe, submitted to the Consultative Assembly, May, 1963.

servation and preservation practices, scarcely. We have already seen enough landscape overcrowding to realize that the increase can be a blessing only if it is well accommodated. The question of appropriateness presses on us now much more urgently. The issue in the case of the threatened Hudson River highlands is not so much that a giant public utility wants to build a $162-million hydroelectric power plant in the wrong place (which is a fact) as the more ominous statistic that this corporation serves ten million people in the New York region and that the population of this region will probably increase by 80 per cent by the year 2000. We have only begun to see the penetrations of cherished scenery that will be made if such activity is neither controlled nor made visually acceptable.

It is not sheer numbers which are intrinsically bad, it is their location, mobility, and culture patterns which threaten. For example, those of us who are professionally concerned with the urban settlement pattern must necessarily ponder the question of its limits. But suppose that the future settlement pattern need have no limits, threading its way through the continents unchecked?[11] The thought frightens us, in spite of the fact that in everything but a physical sense, for a very long time the city *has* contained much of the world. Even the tiny circumscribed dot in the sea that is Mont Saint-Michel dominated the fat grazing lands that stretched out for miles behind it, powerful Norman dukes having established there the monks of Monte Cassino as "the highest influence of the time." It is a commonplace that ever since the city's Chaldean beginnings man's chief institutions have been centered there, and if, as in the fourth to the tenth centuries in Europe, there was a decline in urban dominance, it soon returned with the Commercial Revolution and the rise of new towns. The difference between our own time and any past period of urbanization is that there seems to be no boundary to the developed landscape, no obstacle to growth, no limit to travel by very large numbers of people, and no barrier to visual or oral communications issuing from the city's maw.

There are those who think that all this can be exciting and good, if it is subject to proper societal directives. But—and there's the rub—the new settlement pattern implies *more* of everything, and we must be much cleverer than we have been heretofore in how we share it out. More land? Yes, there is plenty more, but *where* it is allocated is a critical matter, since the new urban pattern tends to grow in belts and is not evenly distributed. More food? Yes, there can be more of that, too, with the revolution in agricultural technology. More jobs? This will require great political and economic ingenuity, but they *can* be secured. And we can be sure that along with them will go a great increase in leisure time, a condition fraught with the greatest implications on both the national and the international scene.[12]

11 "The old antithesis (between city and country) will, indeed, cease, the boundary lines will altogether disappear; it will become, indeed, merely a question of more or less populous. . . . Everywhere . . . over the land of the globe between the frozen circles, the railway and the new roads will spread, the network of communication wires and safe and convenient ways. To receive the daily paper a few hours late, to wait a day or two for goods one has ordered, will be the extreme measure of rusticity save in a few remote islands and inaccessible places." H. G. Wells, *Anticipations of the Reaction of Mechanical and Scientific Progress Upon Human Life and Thought,* New York and London, 1902. pp. 70–71.

12 Within the last ten years itinerant tourism has endangered some of the most beautiful scenes in Greece, which are becoming the victims of new financial interests. The capping of Mount Parnis with a gigantic boondoggle of a hotel is one such blot. The fact that the ensuing scandal nearly toppled the conservative Greek government is small consolation for its continued existence. More serious is the new hotel on the beach below Cape

The kinds of loss or damage vary, but not as much as one might suppose. For Great Britain, they are conveniently grouped under a few main headings in the "Chart of Human Impacts on the Countryside" already quoted. Most of the categories occur in North America. (For indiscrimate grazing of unfenced woodlands in Scotland read: extension of suitcase farming on prairie lands; and for violations of rural scenery by followers of the hunt substitute the new spectator sports like drag racing which have invaded rural quiet over here. It would not be difficult to enlarge the list for North America; we have always been able to think up quite fancy ways to despoil the environment, of which incendiarism is the most cataclysmic. It works more speedily than "calculated ruin," a device sometimes used by speculators in historic districts where demolition is forbidden). I will only mention a few of the most aggravating occurrences.

A great many of the immediate causes of ugliness come under the heading of nuisances. They are not necessarily permanent, and may, as J. B. Jackson has argued, be far less damaging to the landscape than changes in methods of cropping or afforestation.[13] In the case of billboards, most of the existing blight is there by "sufferance or inertia of public officials," as J. J. Dukeminier has put it,[14] since it is no longer doubted that billboards in a wide variety of situations can be controlled. That part of this change is due to the fact that other forms of advertising have become more efficient and that outdoor advertising is said to account for not more than 2 per cent of the national total spent should not necessarily make us complacent about the matter. Roadside controls have done much to eliminate the nearby commercial sign, but, and especially since some states have adopted a no-billboard policy on interstate highways, the entrepreneurs have scaled new heights beyond the prescribed limit and raised giant signs which can be seen for thousands of yards. Some of these, in river valleys and on private property in mountainous areas, have made visual intrusions on historic ground.

Nowhere in the world, I suppose, is the contrast greater than the view of Fujiyama from the train which runs between Tokyo and Kyoto, the foreground strung with advertising signs, and the sweep of the green hills around the latter city, which the mayor told me were protected from all such intrusions, even though much of the wooded slope is privately owned. If the lower Palisades had been totally instead of only partially protected from building and advertising, what a superb backdrop to the whole western view from Manhattan they would have remained.[15]

More permanent, but sometimes recoverable in a visual sense, are mineral excavations, of which gravel pits and the stripping of topsoil are the most ubiquitous. There are many examples of communities prohibiting such damage; on the

---

Soúnion and the Temple of Poseidon, which the combined protests of the Service for Historic Monuments and the Committee for the Preservation of Landscape were unsuccessful in preventing. Nearby, the new highway to the Cape cuts a cicatrice around the mountains as viewed from the sea.

[13] "Limited Access," in *Landscape*, Vol. 14, No. 1., pp. 18–23.

[14] "Zoning for Aesthetic Objectives," in *Law and Contemporary Problems*, Vol. 20, No. 2, pp. 218–37.

[15] "The view of the river was magnificent, quite the finest which the city had to offer; but it was ruined by a hideous gas-tank, placed squarely in the middle of it. There was nowhere in it a beautiful sight on which a man could rest his eyes, without having them tortured by something nearby. . . . Across the river the Palisades were being blown to pieces to make paving stone—and meantime were covered with advertisements of land companies. And if there was a beautiful building, there was sure to be a tobacco advertisement beside it. . . ." Upton Sinclair, *The Metropolis*, p. 180. New York, 1908.

other hand, the building industry needs gravel and the huge federal highway program crushed rock as well. Some of the restrictions on such excavations have been upheld on esthetic grounds; the Supreme Judicial Court of Massachusetts upheld a town ordinance prohibiting stripping of topsoil on the basis that unsightly land depressed the taxable value of the neighboring properties. But these activities will take place increasingly with the expansion of the housing and highway inventory; where they should occur and which hills and stream beds should be inviolate have not yet been considered a matter of prime concern on a regional scale. Rock cutting has recently destroyed whole chains of hills in the vicinity of several metropolitan areas. Here, where natural landmarks would seem to count for much in the way of psychological orientation to nature for millions of people, the loss may be considered calamitous.

As for the junkyards which Secretary Udall has been using as the ultimate symbol of an ugly America, the city I live in has for years required that they and auto-wrecking yards be attractively fenced in. This is only a partial solution to the visual eyesore of reusable waste—a "cosmetic" approach, the scornful would term it—yet it does help in protecting the vulnerable entrances to cities and towns, to which the most objectionable land uses are so often relegated.

The wires and stanchions of communication and power—ranging from television relay towers to oil derricks—stretch out beyond the ports and cities and in some cases form a grid over the entire country. I can remember the outcry raised against the central electricity grid taking its pylons over the South Downs in England between the wars. One must now travel southwest from London into Wiltshire to escape the plague, and a great many telecommunication items have been added, some of them provided by the BBC. A symposium by leaders of the

power industry and their technicians is not particularly reassuring on the methods which can be used to disguise or otherwise improve the siting of pylons and wires. Neither does it give any indication that government-owned facilities are more imaginatively placed than those of private companies on this side of the water. Placing the smaller cables underground in areas of rural charm seems to be the most daring solution proposed.[16]

In North America the grids are sometimes farther apart, but this isolation is more than made up for by the profusion of new installations which develop constantly as the space age progresses, and the careless placing of main lines. A small example may suffice: An eastern seaboard city recently showed civic enterprise in reclaiming land on its harbor front for a waterside park, where people could sit and enjoy a historic view, not very different from the prospect of colonial days. The local power company now wishes to run a new high-voltage cable across the harbor, stringing it from 230-foot high pylons standing in the water. At an aldermen's hearing on this matter, the company was surprised to hear testimony from a private preservation trust, given on esthetic grounds. It was quite obvious that no esthetic considerations had been taken into account in choosing the route. It was merely the cheapest. The issue is in doubt, but it seems likely that if the line is prohibited in that particular spot, it will largely be due to the protests of airport officials, who pointed out that one of the towers was on the line of flight to a nearby field, and not to the arguments of the preservationists. What to do? According to Peter Cooper, of the Yale Law School and the Master of Urban Studies Program, it would be healthy to see esthetic arguments being given con-

[16] "Power Production and Transmission in the Countryside: Preserving Amenities." Two papers by Sir Christopher Hinton and Sir William Holford. London, 1959.

sideration at a far earlier stage than in the courts. He thinks that a "single dimension" agency (such as the water company mentioned above), whose locational decisions have an impact on esthetics, should be required to submit to early review—either by the agency itself, by a referral agency, *or* by the courts on a preliminary basis—before the planning decisions have solidified. This is a better alternative than reliance on the courts to resolve "stretcher cases" (in which all the basic planning decisions have been made by unilaterally minded agencies long before). The courts, according to Cooper, and I think we could agree, should be used only as a last resort, only when all else has failed and litigation is essential to prevent esthetic destruction.

The intrusion of buildings of various types is the last category I shall mention here. We all know how three houses spaced along a country road with their garages and outbuildings can cut off thirty acres of view. But a single house on the edge of a marsh can do as much damage. Time is running out for communities which have not taken steps to protect their edges, let alone their centers. A picturesque town of 10,000 people recently turned down historic-district zoning around its green, in spite of the fact that it was rich in eighteenth-century timber-frame houses; this was the result of an organized campaign by the opposition, led by a department-store owner who thought it would prevent expansion of his business. The town then turned down an offer to sell it a meadow of about forty acres, near the center, by a farmer who was giving up his dairy business. The town also turned down a zoning appeal which would have allowed him to build garden apartments there. The result is that it will become a subdivision of single-family houses occupying the entire acreage. Finally, the town has done nothing to protect the marsh which borders it, not realizing that marshes can be filled, or

dredged to make marinas and black-top boat-launching parking lots. The meadow should have been purchased as a future investment in open land near the heart of town, or a scenic easement obtained. In the case of the marsh, which is a breeding ground for birds, fish, and shellfish, one can point to a new Massachusetts law which has just passed its first legal test; this forbids the removal, dredging, or filling of any bank, flat, meadow, marsh, or swamp bordering on coastal waters if such action would be detrimental to marine life. In fact, the National Audubon Society has pointed the way by recently acquiring 130 acres of tidal land above the town in question.[17]

With a hotel-amusement complex threatening Mount Greylock, motels encroaching on Gettysburg, and Hyde Hall falling down from neglect, we can see that the variety of preservation problems present us with a never-ending task, especially if we are to consider the cultural patrimony as embracing them all.

3

If current trends indicate an increasing interest in saving the past, partly because of the fact that it is disappearing before our eyes,[18] what can we say about the somewhat-further-away future?

There is not much question about a future audience for beautiful or historic artifacts and sites. In its economic review of

[17] Among other financial aids available to communities for acquisition of open space are the funds allocated by the Urban Renewal Administration and the Area Development Administration, Public Law 566, for multipurpose watershed development, including recreation.

[18] "The Historic American Buildings Survey, inaugurated in the 1930s, has recorded more than 10,000 buildings. It was estimated in 1963 that 30 per cent to 50 per cent of these buildings, significant in America's history and culture, had already been destroyed." R. L. Montague III and Tony P. Wrenn, *Planning for Preservation*, American Society of Planning Officials, p. 1. Chicago, 1964.

the year, *The New York Times* says that in 1964 "Americans spent nearly $400 million at theaters, concerts and opera halls. They bought a billion dollars' worth of books. They shelled out [sic] $200 million for paintings, prints, color reproductions and art materials [If some of this results in a revival of the art of landscape sketching, we can be hopeful. C. T.], $600 million for musical instruments, and $300 million to operate art museums." Superhighways and jet planes have brought localities out of their cultural isolation, says *The Times,* and there is greater mobility of more people at less cost than formerly. There is unfortunately no cost-benefit analysis yet made of parks and historic sites, but with the floors of many a historic house about to cave in from foot traffic, one can assume that the important sites and monuments are receiving their share of attention.[19]

Against this encouraging audience total, one can place figures and examples which are more disquieting. "In addition to the soaring gate receipts," one could read on a sports page recently, "the National Football League is able to fall back on a $28.2 million two-year contract with CBS, and the American Football League can draw on a $36-million five-year deal with NBC."[20] On the same page appeared an interview with a twenty-one-year-old player who confessed that "being with a winner is very important to me, almost as important as money," as if to give the spectacle its proper tone. How many people on how many Sunday afternoons and goodness knows how many reruns at other times are involved (using the verb in its passive form) here? And

we have Daniel Boorstin's account[21] of an image of a man (in a Chevrolet advertisement) looking at an image (a set of color slides in a General Electric viewer) and being photographed as he does it by his daughter with her Eastman Kodak, all this taking place on the edge of the Grand Canyon, at which nobody is looking.

As image piles on image, is reality being pushed out of sight? Does the advance of technology include the knack of so rearranging the world that we don't have to experience it, as Max Frisch has suggested?

My guess is here—it is not an answer—that by 1984 we shall have a much more sophisticated population than we have now and that its cultural demands based on an understanding of the past will be much greater.[22] Already we can forecast a much larger middle-income group in proportion to today's population composition, and this, together with the new movement for better visual training in schools, will make for a larger cadre of discerning folk. As a matter of course, the popular sports and nonintellectual pastimes will boom with population increase; but here we may take heart in the fact that bread and circuses did not notably diminish the artistic output of our cultural forbears. Even the presently underprivileged groups may find an enlargement of their perceived horizons if experiments now going on bear fruit—in preschool instruction of children and their parents, the enrichment of school life for teen-agers, and the special preparation of promising

---

[19] The first historic site to be preserved through the organized endeavor of a private group was Mount Vernon, Virginia, which, since 1950, has achieved the total of over a million visitors a year.

[20] "Giants First: Deny Sneak Picks." New Haven *Evening Register,* November 10, 1964.

[21] *The Image: A Guide to Pseudo-Events in America,* p. 250. New York, 1961.

[22] Projections of the Bureau of the Census suggest that by 1970 almost one third of U.S. households will have annual incomes of over $10,000, and that by 1980 the educational level of persons of twenty-five years or more will have risen to 38.1 per cent for those with four years of high school and 11 per cent for those with four or more years of college. U. S. Census, Series A.

youth for entry into leading colleges. Perhaps it will not be deemed invidious here to mention a trend at Yale, where prior to the last war about one tenth of the undergraduate body elected a course in the history of art, and where now over one third do so. While this rise may in part be due to a decline in fashion among other disciplines (we remember how the Rector of Justin was outraged when he heard that his school had substituted art appreciation for Greek) nevertheless it is an established trend which indicates some acquaintance with the cultural patrimony among a considerable group. One can also say with confidence that a healthy result of the cultural "ferment" is that the government will follow along with expanded art and conservation programs in response to private initiative and public needs.[23]

Another force beginning to affect the "cultural front" and which may be important in the future is the growing realization of our vulnerability as a potentially unstable society. The closed world of mass production, the increasingly artificial culture of the marketplace, the triumph of nonmanual skills, the simultaneous multiplicity of the mass media— none of these draws on the past or on nature for its existence. We face a giant, senseless attack on our cultural inheritance, all the more damaging because it is ignorant, springing from a basis in compulsion and routine.

Where are our strengths to come from, in such a crisis?

Like the ancient skill of the Greek wrestler, one art is resistance.[24] If, as

Josiah Royce implied, we Americans are all too prone to injure our surroundings, then surely one way to counter senseless new depredations is to stiffen the forces acting against destruction. To spend money for a land bank, for instance. To say no to urban growth beyond a certain distance from central places. To speak up against "progress" when it is too grossly material. To be against the bulldozer approach to urban renewal and *for* the kind which endeavors to merge the future with the past. To be for the classical ideal in architecture and design.

Another strength can come from the intelligent use of social controls. Beside the correctives already mentioned, there is a larger issue at stake—by what means can our ways of dealing with the environment be brought into focus for the community at large? The report of the Cultural and Scientific Committee of the Council of Europe (1963) suggests that the best way to reconcile the demands of economic progress with the preservation of esthetic surroundings is by town and country planning.[25] We hear, too, the recommendation of UNESCO that "the uncontrolled encroachment of suburban growth, the dispersal of houses, the unconsidered siting of factories or houses, and haphazard or crude engineering structures demand that *one general course of action be reflected in the town*

---

[23] A rough estimate discloses that 65 per cent of historic preservation in this country is done under private auspices, a figure which often surprises foreign visitors whose governments have taken over the whole operation.

[24] "Monuments, archives, libraries and objects in museums of art, history and science— all things that individually and collectively may be described as the cultural patrimony of nations—these have come to be recognized

in the present age as one great treasure common to humanity.

"The Rome Center has one simple object, to build up the strongest bastion possible against the forces of destruction." From the prospectus of the International Center for the study of the Preservation and Restoration of Cultural Property.

[25] "Care for historical groups of buildings should be apparent from the very beginning of regional and town planning. It is particularly important not to lose sight of these essential points in zoning and traffic planning and in steps to be taken for the protection of the landscape." Resolution adopted by International Federation of Housing and Planning at its conference at Santiago de Compostello, 1961.

and country planning of each individual state [my italics]." A significant document, the Message of the Federal Council to the Swiss Federal Assembly (May 19, 1961), stresses this point in speaking of conservation; it recommends federal action in the protection of nature and the countryside, singling out "interests of a public character—hydraulic systems, national roads and the decentralization of towns"—which require action to be taken not by the cantons alone but by the whole country.[26]

Similar thinking lies behind current recommendations here requiring that the Department of the Interior be consulted before the Federal Power Commission issues licenses for new installations, a suggested course of action brought to a head by the Storm King controversy.[27]

Administrative action may in the future be important in setting the pace for esthetic improvement, but I will briefly review here a few of the tools at our disposal now. Agricultural-zoning and tax-assessment laws can be helpful, according to William H. Whyte, but are essentially a holding action.[28] In practice, the par-

ties who benefit therefrom have often been too demanding and inconsiderate of the public interest involved. Rather than acting as a stringent exercise of the police power, agricultural zoning amounts to an agreement with the owners not to sell, but, when values rise, it is easy for them, say, to petition to be annexed to the nearby growing city and have the zoning set aside. Also, inclusion in an agricultural zone does not actually guarantee the owners a lower assessment on their land; here, much depends upon the individual policy of the assessor. Mr. Whyte thinks that a purchase and lease-back policy[29] might save money for municipalities and states, and help to accomplish the purpose which would be aimed at by landscaping grants along highways and watercourses. The purchase and lease-back policy would continue the land in farming, which, in the case of farms that have not become marginal, is the best scenic investment that can be made.

The use of the easement device works best when people understand its purpose. With this fact in mind, the State of Wisconsin first explained its easement program to lawyers and others at a large conference, and then was careful to designate the type of easement under different headings: conservation easements, scenic easements for roads, fishing easements, and so on. Since in the ordinary course of events the easement program is handled by several departments of govern-

---

[26] "The authorities, officers and institutes of the Confederation in the accomplishment of their tasks must take pains to develop the characteristic aspects of the countryside and its settlements, those sites which evoke the past, natural curiosities and monuments, and to preserve them intact where there is a preponderating general interest. They will do this by: Giving an appropriate form to the building and installations which they are constructing, or renouncing their construction; by withholding subventions for public works, agricultural buildings, changes in watercourses, purification plants and communications facilities, etc., etc. . . ." Roughly translated from "*Avant-project: Loi fédérale sur la protection de la nature et du paysage,*" Berne (mimeo., no date.) At the time of publication, a Swiss correspondent writes that this law is not yet fully applied.

[27] "Mr. Rockefeller's Wrong Move." Editorial in *The New York Times,* December 14, 1964.

[28] In a conversation with the writer at Yale University, January 12, 1965.

[29] Mr. Cooper writes: "In some circles this device might be criticized as a system which puts local government too much in the real estate business. Whether this is a valid criticism or not, the device does raise problems on maintenance and tort liability. A well-drafted agreement could mitigate such drawbacks, however, insofar as the purchasing agency is concerned. From a political standpoint, the device might have to be limited to cases in which the owner was voluntarily willing to sell; however, a compulsory purchase and lease-back arrangement could be available in selected cases so long as a legitimate public purpose could be shown."

ment, it has proved helpful to spell out what each is required to do, especially since in some states parks and forests may be more active than fish and game, or vice versa.

The scenic easement will be much in evidence as the national program for scenic roads and parkways gets underway.[30] Spurred by its Advisory Committee on Scenic Highways,[31] California already has laws on the books[32] creating a scenic highway system, in the development of which "the department shall give special attention both to the impact of the highway on the landscape and to the highway's visual appearance." California has offered us the term "scenic corridor," which is interpreted in the acts as "a band of land generally adjacent to the highway right-of-way" in which local governments will be required to regulate land use and intensity of development, control outdoor advertising, earth-moving, and landscaping, as well as the design and appearance of structures and equipment. "Within the scenic corridor," the Advisory Committee recommends, "the basic need is to preserve lateral sight distances along one or both sides of the highway." Well and good, and another report[33] contains detailed suggestions for landscaping, thinning of trees, and placing of structures, as well as establishing an "immediate zone," an "intermediate zone"—from three hundred feet back from the road to approximately half a mile—and a "distant zone." All these recommendations in-

volve the highway department *and* other authorities, many of them local. This could ameliorate the present situation; in one state, currently, the highway department, acting alone, is proposing to take land in twenty-two parks throughout the state. This may very well lead an aroused citizenry to demand legislation curtailing the department's power of eminent domain or instituting a process of referral to another authority.

What else will the growing cultural awareness of our "sophisticated" population demand?

There are two courses of action now in the experimental stage which may achieve status in the years ahead. I have mentioned the historic-district device already in use here, but not the fact that in practice it presents some questions of boundary delineation and does not always penetrate to the root of the problem. In France, the preservation-planning idea has been carried a step further, to protect whole towns and villages as well as their historic sections. Realizing that the existing laws only provided for the protection of individual buildings and the exteriors of urban districts (façades and roofing), the present Minister of Cultural Affairs sponsored the law of 1962, which changes the approach to preservation.[34]

Briefly, the new approach includes social measures to ensure sound utilization of old buildings. It is now considered insufficient to achieve an attractive exterior appearance if behind an improved façade there remains a dilapidated and substandard dwelling. In France many of the old parts of towns are occupied by people of small means who seldom own their own houses. Rent is usually insufficient to cover maintenance. Since the country al-

30 "A National Program for Scenic Roads and Parkways." Recreation Advisory Council, Circular No. 4, Washington, D.C., 1964.
31 "A Plan for Scenic Highways in California." Citizen's Advisory Committee on Public Highways, Sacramento, 1963.
32 Senate Bill No. 1467 and 1468, an act relating to the state scenic highway system, etc., etc. (both 1963).
33 "Recreation-Vacation-Tourism in Northern Berkshire, Massachusetts." Technical Planning Associates, New Haven, 1964 (prepared under the Technical Assistance Program of the Area Redevelopment Administration).

34 I am indebted to Professor F. Sorlin, Inspector General of Historic Monuments, Paris, for a copy of his paper "The System in France for the Safeguarding and Sound Utilization of Historic Urban Sites," delivered at the Venice Congress in May, 1964.

ready had an urban-renewal procedure in use by the Ministry of Construction, it was decided to tie in with this operation, but whereas before the passage of the 1962 law urban renewal tended to destroy rundown areas and build new living quarters, now, wherever the Ministry of Cultural Affairs considers the conservation of towns or villages necessary, the urban-renewal funds are applied to the restoration and interior modernization of existing buildings. ("Modernization" in this context would apply to rudimentary facilities such as running water and other plumbing, electricity and other fundamentals rather than to radical structural changes.) Not all buildings are restored, but an effort is made to preserve the atmosphere of the town by maintaining the old roadways and the general arrangement of volume and mass. The result is not a museum village but a revitalization of the old quarters by developing an activity for them appropriate to the economic framework of the community. Tied in with a plan for the entire town, they are thus protected from intrusions in the form of new highways or other public works.

The legal, technical, and financial measures for achieving all this in France are interesting, but would vary from country to country and will not be discussed here. The syndicates that are set up under the 1962 law would in this country involve the private sector of the economy much more than in most European countries. The principle, however, is valid and has been tested on a small scale on The Hill in Providence by private rehabilitation groups, without, however, the social controls operating in the Marais sector of Paris or the central sectors of Aix-en-Provence. I would like to see it extended to communities in rural areas which are threatened by sudden change or slow deterioration. Instead of Sarlat, Uzes, or Pezenas—towns which are receiving the treatment in France—

one might substitute a chain of white valley towns in Vermont—say, Chelsea, Tunbridge, and South Royalton—or a string of river towns in Missouri, or of mining towns in British Columbia. We tend to forget that the appeal of such picturesque spots is not that of great age but of their unique architectural character and plan, both due to be changed out of all recognition by the activities of nation-wide stores or state highway departments. The fact that in many cases the subjects for urban preservation are to be found in parts of the continent which are depressed economically gives an added reason for treating them as precious reminders of a past which is not entirely forgotten.

The second course of action, applicable to natural and man-made landscapes, is to be found in the UNESCO recommendation of 1962 on the preservation of the beauty and character of landscape sites.[35] This includes a recommendation that extensive landscapes—our old friend the *éntendue de pays qui présente une vue d'ensemble*—should be scheduled by zones. I find this more comprehensive and at the same time more realistic than the "highway belt" form of scenic preservation, which is entirely based on the automobile. After all, who is going to guarantee that the rush of new plans for scenic highways and parkways now being prepared in several states will not destroy certain landscape and wildlife values while presumably creating new ones? The UNESCO recommendation suggests that control should be exercised over a larger area—presumably a river valley or mountain region—setting up standards of an esthetic order which would cover the use of materials, their color, height stand-

[35] "Scheduling of Extensive Landscapes by Zones," Articles 16–19, Recommendation concerning the safeguarding of the beauty and character of landscapes and sites, adopted by the General Conference of UNESCO, Paris, December, 1962.

ards, precautions to conceal disturbances of the soil resulting from the construction of dams and the operation of quarries, regulations governing the cutting of trees, and other considerations. UNESCO suggests that this action should not involve large-scale compensation, although the organization does allow the possibility of compensation for individual sites in cases of direct and definite prejudice resulting from the scheduling process. In this country a stronger exercise of the police power would have to be considered and might present some problems. One can easily see how this device might be used in the surroundings of important villages and towns, lying on the one hand outside the scope of the roadside easement and on the other, too far away to be included in the great natural reservations. This is not a green-belt concept, but could resemble Ebenezer Howard's agricultural zone surrounding Garden City, in which everyday activities were not curtailed if they proved compatible with Garden City life. The chief difference would be in the multiple ownerships—in Garden City the land is owned by the corporation. I would add to the standards several of the recommendations of the Venice Charter[36] including the importance of *using* historic buildings in the zone, preserving them as they have come down through the years rather than restoring them to an arbitrary early period, and prohibiting the reconstruction of ruins, except for the reassembly of existing but dismembered parts

[36] Adopted at the same meeting as the foundation of ICOMOS (International Council for Monuments and Sites) held at the Isola di San Giorgio Maggiore, May, 1964.

(the last item would mark a small but significant step forward in the preservation movement). Away from the cities and towns, one can imagine the scenic zones in inhabited beauty spots like the banks of the lower James, in the hunting estates southwest of Washington, D.C., and in the bayou country of Louisiana, to name only obvious candidates.

A final word about the "climate" in which the continuing preservation movement can flourish. It has been stressed in the latter part of this paper that planning measures are essential to its ultimate success, and while land-use controls in this country are not as strong as in Europe, I have mentioned several that have been used with varying degrees of satisfaction to private individuals and the community at large. The future need for planning of all critical areas presupposes to me a changed approach on the part not only of architects and planners, but of highway engineers, municipal officials, renewal administrators—in fact, of all those who are shaping the future environment. Eagerness to develop and build must be paired with a better appraisal of the past, and a broader cultural approach must replace the attitude becoming common among our administrators, as well as the general public, that the new is more exciting than the old, a well-established myth originally spread by American "moderns." A changed attitude to old buildings and beautiful sites would mark the maturity of the environmental arts in North America. There is no room for slick opportunism if we are to treat the past with the honor which we all hope the future will hold.

BIBLIOGRAPHY

Anonymous. 1960. The Architects' Journal (Oct. 13).

Anonymous. 1964. Giants First: Deny Sneak Picks. New Haven Evening Register (Nov. 10).

Anonymous. 1964. Mr. Rockefeller's Wrong Move. New York Times (Dec. 14).

Boorstin, Daniel. 1961. The Image: A Guide to Pseudo-Events in America. New York.

Bracey, H. E. 1964. Industry and the Countryside. Baton Rouge, La.

Bryant, William Cullen. 1872. Picturesque America, or The Land We Live In. New York.

Citizen's Advisory Committee on Public Highways. 1963. A Plan for Scenic Highways in California. Sacramento, Calif.

Council of Europe. 1963 (May). Document 1570.

Dukeminier, J. J. 1955. Zoning for Aesthetic Objectives. Law and Contempory Problems, 20(2):218–37.

Gazzola, Piero, ed. 1964. Second International Congress of the Architects and Technicians of Historic Monuments. Venice.

Hinton, Sir Christopher, and Holford, Sir William. 1959. Power Production and Transmission in the Countryside: Preserving Amenities. London.

International Council for Monuments and Sites (ICOMOS). 1964 (May). Venice.

International Federation of Housing and Planning. 1961. Conference at Santiago de Compostella.

Jackson, J. B. 1964. Limited Access. Landscape, 14(1):18–23.

Montague, R. L., III., and Wrenn, Tony P. 1964. Planning for Preservation. Chicago.

Nicholson, E. M. 1963. Chart of Human Impacts on the Countryside, pap. 2. London.

Rathbone, J. F. W. 1963. The National Trust: Its Growth and Problems. The Preservation and Development of Ancient Buildings and Historical or Artistic Sites. Council of Europe.

Recreation Advisory Council. 1964. A National Program for Scenic Roads and Parkways, Cir. 4. Wash., D.C.

Shepard, Paul. 1953. They Painted What They Saw. Landscape 3(1):6.

Sinclair, Upton. 1908. The Metropolis. New York.

Sorlin, F. 1964. The System in France for the Safeguarding and Sound Utilization of Historic Urban Sites. Delivered at the Venice Congress (May).

Technical Planning Associates. 1964. Recreation–Vacation–Tourism in Northern Berkshire Massachusetts. New Haven, Conn.

UNESCO. 1962. Scheduling of Extensive Landscapes by Zones, arts. 16–19. Recommendation concerning the safeguarding of the beauty and character of landscapes and sites. Paris.

U.S. Bureau of the Census. 1960. U.S. Census, Series A. Wash., D.C.

U.S. Senate Bill No. 1467 and 1468. An act relating to the state scenic highway system. Wash., D.C.

Wells, H. G. 1902. Anticipation of the Reaction of Mechanical and Scientific Progress upon Human Life and Thought. New York and London.

THE ROLE OF THE REGIONAL PLANNER IN PRESERVING HABITATS AND SCENIC VALUES

Coleman Woodbury*

Papers of this genre (the role-of-the-planner-in-) seem usually to have suffered a common fate. With some exceptions they have turned out to be rather weak and unhappy mixtures—unconvincing discussions of either the planning process or the substantive areas in which planners are thought to be able to play a useful part. In trying to avoid this outcome I propose to focus this paper on planning as one part—albeit a significant and in some respects a unique part—in the policy-formulating processes of our society. From this central concern a few suggestions will follow on how regional planners, *with others,* may help to assure habitats that will be kindly in the lives of men and other species of life—both those now living and those to come after. The primary emphasis, however, will be on regional planning in the United States today—its nature, possibilities, limitations, and the relationships of its practitioners to other persons and groups, official, quasi-official, and private.

Of course, this approach to my subject is made at the risk that its product may be even less useful than those of earlier discussions of similar subjects. Also, it

entails some description and comment that may seem to some of you to be an elaboration of the obvious. Omitting all mention of all such topics, however, would result in a distorted and disjointed outline of this view of regional planning in our society. Several aspects of this symposium, on the other hand, as well as some parts of the current scene seem propitious for the attempt.

First, the conception of planning to be presented is based on an essentially ecological view—our Chairman's "wide web of causes and consequences"—of the natural and social environments within which and as a part of which planning is carried on. Further, as to the characteristics of those environments, the conditions of their healthful existence, and the dangers that threaten it, other members of this Conference can speak from more knowledge and understanding than I. If I can add anything, it may be on the planning process as a part of and as an influence within the ecologic web.

Also, it seems to some observers that planning struggles under a net of conflicting and ambiguous definitions and hopes. Just one example: Not many years ago several articulate and influential groups in this country were trying to equate planning with authoritarianism, regimentation, and other threats to a free society. Although this charge is heard less frequently these days, it by no means has

* Dr. Woodbury is Chairman of the Department of Urban and Regional Planning at the University of Wisconsin. His active involvement in urban and regional issues is reflected in his *The Future of Cities and Urban Redevelopment,* 1953 and *Model State and Regional Planning Law,* 1955.

died out. On the other hand, planning now suffers in some quarters from an uncritical popularity; too often it is being looked upon as a panacea—some kind of snake oil good for all the social ills of man and beast. Many officials and prominent citizens in cities, urban areas, and states caught in difficulties generated in part by unexpected population growth and shifts and creeping inflation seem to think that hiring a few planners is all or most of what needs to be done. It is, of course, only one of the indicated first steps in dealing with the difficulties and problems. Even a few planners seem to think that a reasonable mastery of the planning process in one area of human activity qualifies a man to plan in many if not all other areas—in other words, that the planning process per se holds some kind of magic that is quite independent of knowledge or understanding of the substantive areas in which it may be applied. Fortunately, relatively few planners espouse this view.

Even among less naïve planners and serious students of public affairs wide differences of opinion exist as to what planning is essentially and what it might become. At one extreme, it is argued that planning should be recognized as a fourth power of governments, more or less equal with the legislative, executive, and judicial, and with a veto power over a considerable range of legislative action—to be sure, a veto that could be overridden by the legislative body but nevertheless a veto. At the other, planning is simply "collaboration with the inevitable." It cannot really shape or control or guide the basic forces of urban or regional growth and change; it can only go along with them and try to make them a little more orderly and their results a little less painful than they otherwise might be. A variant of this latter view is that rational planning in most parts of a society as complex as ours is impossible. Planners, therefore, would be well ad-

vised to forget their pretensions and join from time to time one or more shifting coalitions of power groups temporarily united, for varying reasons, on short-term objectives. Thus the planners might achieve a few worthwhile results through clever participation in the devices of "disjointed incrementalism."

Without accusing any members of the Conference of holding the extremes of any of these views, it does seem proper to suggest that they, as thoughtful men concerned with one of the crucial issues of our day, might well take a careful look at this process and try to evaluate its potentialities and limitations in dealing with the great problem of this Conference. Hopefully this paper is one introduction to this task.

Among the ambiguities in the planners' vocabulary is the term "region." No finely spun definition seems necessary here; a region (as the term is used in regional planning) is an area the inhabitants of which are tied together in economic, social, and sometimes governmental relationships, many of which are determined or strongly influenced by history, tradition and by natural features of the area—e.g. climate, physiography, soil types, etc. Some river basins are the archetype. Of course, very few if any regions are self-contained or self-sufficient, and their boundaries often are not lines but bands of considerable width.

Some planners and others also speak of metropolitan or urban regions—central cities of considerable size plus suburban and rural-urban fringe areas that are closely tied to the central city or, sometimes, even more directly to major suburban localities. Because nearly all parts of these areas are essentially urban in character or undergoing urbanization or economically and socially dominated by the urban centers, ordinarily it seems preferable to label planning for them as urban planning. In this paper, however, planning for these areas is considered regional planning.

A principal reason for including them was succinctly put recently by Frank P. Zeidler, formerly Mayor of Milwaukee and later Director of the Department of Resource Development of the State of Wisconsin, before a class: "Why," he asked, "can we not plan and build urban centers so that the first impulse of nearly everyone who has some free time on a weekend would not be to hop into a car and try to get out of them?" Of course, Mr. Zeidler is not arguing for imprisoning city dwellers in or near their places of residence. Neither is he denying that occasional or even frequent escape from even the most satisfactory urban environments helps to meet certain deep-seated human needs. His question simply points to the well-known but often neglected fact that the network of interactions that competent planners must be concerned with cannot, for many sectors of their work, be arbitrarily chopped up into neat pieces labeled urban, metropolitan, regional, state, or national.

Another rapidly developing phenomenon of our times should also be noted at the outset of this discussion. It is the growing together of metropolitan and urban areas into great bands or strips of urban development, which are variously called regional cities, megalopolises, or strip cities. That of the northern Atlantic seaboard is only the best-known and furthest-advanced example; several others on both coasts and in the Middle West can now be identified and are developing rapidly. They, too, are regions for the purposes of this paper.

Finally, although few states are regions in any close sense of the term, they are governmental entities of considerable power and many of them are now showing a new or revived interest in at least some kinds of planning. State planning, then, is taken here to be one variety of regional planning.

Just one more preliminary comment: The planning discussed here is primarily governmental planning, although some regional planning agencies are hybrids, in personnel and financing, of public and private efforts. It is central planning as distinguished from but, of course, closely related to functional or departmental planning—e.g. planning by highway, welfare, or conservation agencies of local and state governments. Finally, it is done largely by professional planners, both full-time officials of public agencies and consultant offices. As will be pointed out, however, this does not imply the exclusion of laymen from a significant part in the process.

Planning—a definition

Quite probably the best way of delineating regional planning thought and practice in this country would be to trace their history or evolution in the context of the nation's social, economic, and political development and with frequent side glances at concurrent changes in nongovernmental central planning—e.g. in large-scale corporations, the military services, or in quasi-public welfare agencies. This, however, would be a formidable task, partly because competent and thorough research has not yet been done in many parts of this history. Besides, a summary that would be at all enlightening or persuasive on what is now known about it would run well beyond the space limitations of this essay.

Instead of this historical or evolutionary approach, then, let me try the "ideal type" form of description and analysis used so effectively by the well-known German scholar Max Weber and others. In essence, an ideal type is a construct that has no exact counterpart in empirical reality but that does usefully represent and emphasize essential elements and relationships, actual and potential, in some part of society. Some ideal types—e.g. the well-known "economic man"—are highly abstract in the sense that what has been abstracted or pulled out for analysis is a relatively small part of the whole. Other ideal types, like the rather cumbersome one I am going to try to present for consideration, are much closer to what one may find in the actual world. It should be clear, however, that it is not a description of the work of any one planning agency and that the word "ideal" in this usage does not connote perfection or a standard of excellence.

In other words, I will inflict on you a rather formal definition of regional planning as it is being developed in this country and then try, quickly and maybe inadequately, to dissect it and to suggest some of its implications as well as some of the adverse criticisms that have been leveled against it.

Reduced to its essentials, *regional planning is the process of preparing, in advance of action and in a reasonably systematic fashion, recommendations for policies and courses of action (with careful attention to their probable by-products, side effects, or spill-over effects) to achieve accepted objectives in the common life of regional localities or communities.* A few comments on key words and phrases in this definition may give it more substance and meaning.

"Process" certainly implies a continuing, on-going activity, not the *ad hoc* drawing of a master blueprint or other document, which then only needs to be followed out or "implemented." The best-laid plans of mice and men do indeed "gang aft a-gley"—too often in a complex, ever-shifting, poorly understood world. The only practical response is continuous study of the regional scene as it is affected by population growth and migrations, scientific and technical developments, by changes in national income and in its distribution, by shifts in the preferences and value systems of various classes and groups of people both within and outside of the region. Making the necessary adjustments and revisions, however, requires rather more than further study, essential as that is. It calls for rare qualities of judgment. In respect to them as in the preparation of the initial plans, every effort must be made to look ahead, to try to foresee how the area will develop under existing trends, and then what influences can be brought to bear that seem likely to guide that development closer to the desired objectives. But a plan that changes too often and too much loses much of its usefulness. Here is one of the persistent problems in regional and many other kinds of planning: Where, in specific situations, lies the balance between sensitive appreciation of changing conditions and emerging needs, on the one hand, and reasonable stability, on the other?

May I emphasize as crucial in the planning process two steps that often have been slighted both in practice and in discussions of planning: (1) A competent planner must make the best estimates he can of what seems most likely to happen in those aspects of his region with which he is concerned if no further plans were to be made or no additional public action were to be undertaken in accordance with such plans. Would the residential blight simply deepen at about its present rate; the air or water pollution simply get worse; the congestion of automobile traffic or mass transit simply increase? Or are there possible changes in the offing either as to the character or spread of these ills—changes that may or may not be effective correctives by themselves, but that might well supplement or defeat certain possible changes in public programs now being considered? (2) The planner also must look carefully for the most effective "points of leverage" that could be used by public agencies in trying to guide future development "closer to desired objectives." Should he propose new police-power measures, public acquisition of easements or development rights, some form of public enterprise, intensive education of mortgage lenders, conditional financial aids, or . . . ? Quite possibly, no one device will do the job; if so, what combinations would seem most promising? Obviously, if the planner is to give expert advice on such matters, he must know more than a little about his region and about past and current experience with these tools.

Anyone who thinks even a little about the responsibility of regional planners on these fronts will have to reject the notion of all-purpose planners as put forward by the snake oil or planning-as-panacea school.

Much has been said, possibly too much and too glibly, about the ability of planners to look ahead, to plan *in advance* of coming events. Without belittling this part of the planner's responsibility, two observations seem in order.

(1) In very few regions can planning start with a fairly clean slate. Nearly always planners are, in fact, pushed into devising corrective measures to deal with the mistakes of the past—e.g. to clean up areas of residential blight and slums, to relieve traffic congestion, to correct serious shortages of public recreational and open space, to reduce air and stream pollution. Often, even in localities with long-established planning agencies, a large proportion of staff time and energy goes into such essentially remedial measures. It is difficult to do the basic analysis of conditions and trends soon enough and thoroughly enough that the remedies for specific ills stand some chance not only of correcting obviously unsatisfactory conditions, of not creating other serious difficulties, but also of fitting into the longer-range development of the area as a whole.

(2) Foresight in respect to trends and needs of an entity or system or subsystem as complex as a sizable re-

gion is not only dependent on hard work, judgment, and what might be called education intuition, it also is a function of the depth and breadth of one's knowledge and understanding of that system. Here is the Achilles' heel of most, if not all, urban and regional planning. Not long ago one of the most perceptive critics of urban planning in the United States said, in effect, that earlier in this century various individuals and agencies were operating on the urban body social and politic in light of a knowledge about its anatomy and physiology roughly comparable to the notions about the human body held by an old-time medicine man at a country fair.[1] This may be an exaggeration, but certainly not a gross one. Altogether too much of what passes for knowledge of urban and regional localities even today is superficial, spotty, and unreliable. This seems to me especially true of the human-social dimensions of urban and regional life and their relations to the natural environment; it may be less true of the nonhuman components of ecosystems.

Here the responsibility lies not so much with the practicing planners as with universities and other agencies of inquiry and research. They simply have not and are not now providing knowledge, explanations, and theory about localities and their functioning that would undergird the planning profession as, in fact, other professions—e.g. medicine—are now supported by steadily increasing and deepening knowledge of their subject matter.

A planner, however, is more than a part-time student of regional life and affairs. Our definition indicates that he makes *recommendations* as to policies and courses of action and, further, that

[1] Lewis Mumford in *The New Yorker*, May 15, 1951, p. 80.

he prepares these recommendations *in a reasonably systematic fashion*. It is a mistake, of course, to assume that the form or medium in which a planning proposal is presented is any evidence of its validity. Maps, drawings, perspectives of areas for development and redevelopment are often required. So, too, are written reports, drafts of possible legislative bills or administrative regulations, charts showing the desirable time sequence of parts of a program of public works or capital investment. Within very broad limits, the forms of communication have little or nothing to do with the nature of planning, let alone with the merits of specific proposals.

"Recommendations," however, raises another and much more substantial question that has been debated for years in planning circles—and the end is not yet. The word clearly implies that planning is advisory, that the final determination of policies and courses of action lies with others. The others, the nonplanners who make the final decisions in all major planning matters, are those legislative and administrative officials directly responsible to the citizens of the locality or community. On some points, to be sure, they may share some of this responsibility with representatives or elected officials of a larger political unit and, in some respects, with high appellate courts. The principle, however, is clear. Planners as an identifiable professional group are advisors, and by no means the only advisors, of politically responsible officials.

Sometimes, however, the debate referred to above does not turn directly on this point. Rather it is on the question of whether at least some of the recommendations of planners should have a preferred position, so to speak, as against the proposals of others. For example, should the legislative body of a local government be able to go against the planning agency's recommendations on zoning or the location of major public works

only by an extraordinary majority—say two thirds or three fourths—of its members? Other devices to the same end have been put forward and sometimes tried out. No extended discussion of them can be undertaken here, but they deserve one comment.

In respect to most of them, no hard and fast, yes-or-no answer seems defensible. In my opinion, in specific situations the doubts should usually be resolved against the proposals for preferred position. To be sure, the recommendations of planning bodies should be entitled to respect and to fair and full consideration. Trying to achieve this end by these formal means, however, often runs the danger of taking more and more of the substance of planning out of the area of public concern and discussion and of putting it in the category of technical specialization—by definition less amenable to lay criticism and discussion. Admittedly some parts of regional planning, particularly the standards on which regulatory measures of land use are based, largely fall in the latter category. Clearly, however, many professional groups show a tendency to enlarge this area of their operations at the expense of the former. Professional planners, as a group, are no exception. And quite as clearly, the more the technical area grows and the area of public concern and discussion contracts, the more difficult will it become for planning to command strong and widespread public support without which its greater ends will not be realized. And at present that difficulty is certainly one of the greatest weaknesses of regional planning.

In this context, therefore, planning is one component or factor in the complex and fascinating process of policy formulation. Other influences can readily be identified. They include the opinions, preferences, and ideas of the elected officials themselves, the positions taken on major issues by political parties, the less clearly articulated notions of political leaders, the recommendations of administrative heads of operating agencies of local and state governments, the proposals of budget and finance officers, the pressures of organizations of business, labor, and professional groups as well as those of civic, neighborhood, and district associations. In most general terms, this is the political or social environment in which regional planning takes place.

The phrase in our definition, "in a reasonably systematic fashion," suggests (possibly rather indirectly and clumsily) that the role of planning agencies differs, in some respects, from those of most other groups in this process. In my opinion, there is a difference, but the line cannot be drawn too sharply and the contrast is not that of black with white.

In general, however, the proposals put forward by most of the other groups and organizations tend, naturally, to be colored by a strong concern for their own interests and often for their advantage *vis-à-vis* other elements in the locality. Also, they usually are argued for in short-run terms. Finally, they seldom reflect much care in identifying the ends sought —these are more or less taken for granted —let alone much consideration of other possible ways of reaching them.

Planning, on the other hand, is rational or, at least, quasi-rational in the sense that the planners try to identify clearly certain objectives or ends to be sought, recognize and try to accommodate conflicts and inconsistencies among them, consider various possible ways and means of reaching them as well as the approximate costs and benefits of each, and recommend the one that, on balance, seems best. Furthermore, a planner pays careful attention not only to the measures and courses of action at hand but also to the interrelations of any one proposal with others. In other words, he looks for and into "by-products" or "side effects." For example, what will a major public investment in additional traffic and transport facilities do besides facilitate the movement of more goods and people into, out of, and within the regional area? Will it lead to traffic congestion in some districts not now so afflicted? Will it eliminate some slums and, possibly, accelerate the blighting of other property adjacent to rights-of-way? Will it strengthen the tax base in the central city? Will it encourage further urban decentralization or deconcentration? These questions indicate only some of the complexities that have to be considered—not in general terms but specifically. A deep-seated and unremitting concern with interrelationships among programs and projects and with the by-products or side effects of courses of action are among the hallmarks of good regional planning.

"Policies" and "courses of action" may seem redundant. The distinction between them in this context is simply as to the degree of generality. A course of action normally should be rather more detailed and specific. It should include carefully thought-through subprograms for its major sectors, including their timing, financing, appropriate means of regulating or inducing private action, public and quasi-public development and use of land and facilities, etc.

Although many practicing planners and students of planning accept without much objection a definition quite similar to the one under consideration, some of them, particularly those concerned with urban as distinguished from regional planning, often use another phrase that indicates a serious misunderstanding of this conception of planning. That phrase is "implementing the plan." Assuming that "the plan" is the end product of the planning process, "implementation" is something added to or undertaken subsequent to the planning. Too often in this usage it is quite clear that the plan is not a course of action but a picture, in words, maps, drawings, or whatever, of some desired end result. Implementation or "effectuation" refers to measures and devices appended to it that may make it a reality.

This, it seems to me, is more than a question of semantics. In my definition the courses of action recommended are not appendages but vital parts, in fact, often the heart and core of the plan itself. They require, therefore, just as careful and imaginative shaping as any other part, and should be examined just as thoroughly as to their appropriateness to the immediate objectives and as to their probable repercussions throughout the social and ecosystems in which they are to take place.

"Objectives" in the planning process have been mentioned several times above. It seems to some students of urban and regional planning that one of the more notable advances in thought and practice during recent years has been in more explicit and sophisticated recognition of the central place of goals or objectives in the whole process. After all, when an individual or group or public agency or government plans, it plans *for* something. Certainly the range of objectives of public planning is wide. What are the more common *kinds or classes of objectives* for regional planning today? What is the proper part played by planning agencies in the setting of goals or objectives?

One classification of regional planning objectives, with some illustrative but by no means complete detail, follows:

(1) *Livability*—reasonable convenience for all persons in their normal activities, including recreation and the journeys to work of those gainfully employed; sufficient open space, particularly but not only in and around dwellings, to give some sense of relaxation from the routine of work and from the constant stimulation of interpersonal contacts; the separation of incompatible land uses; safety and pleasant facilities for all children's activities—at home, in the neighborhood, at school, and going to and from it; opportunities for but no compulsion to neighborliness; the removal and prevention of slums and blight—urban and rural.

(2) *Efficiency*—physical development in such patterns and of such densities of population and of land uses in its component districts that it makes for reasonable efficiency in the provision of public services and in the activities of business and industry.

(3) *Amenity*—a setting for all land-use districts that encourages development marked by a degree of both variety and unity as well as by "character," beauty, and a sensitive and imaginative treatment of the natural site.

(4) *Flexibility and Choice*—again, an urban structure and density pattern that allows many use districts to grow or change at least moderately without drastic disruption of adjacent areas; measures to ensure the healthful and otherwise desirable qualities of residential and other areas during their youth and old age as well as during their early maturity; a considerable range of choice open to families and unattached individuals in all income groups as to where, in what kind of housing, and under what kind of tenure they wish to live.

(5) *Minimum Harm to Natural Communities of Plants and Animals*—assuming changes in these communities near areas of enlarging human settlement, these changes should be no more disruptive than is unavoidable and should be estimated in advance to determine what offsetting steps could be taken in behalf of desirable new equilibria in the near future; this consideration should extend not only to massive invasions by residential or industrial development but also to highways, areas for active recreation, dams or

other interruptions of streams, disposal of human and industrial wastes, etc.; early identification and means of protecting natural areas of museum quality, both wilderness areas and other.

(6) *Optimum Use of Resources*—an allocation of human and capital resources among the various types of public investment and between new development and redevelopment that *represents some approximation* (no one should claim more than this) to their optimum use; priorities[2] among the needs for urban investment at any one time that will both meet the most urgent needs first and minimize future shortages of facilities and services; a system of local public revenues (including grants-in-aid and shared taxes) that will both distribute the costs of local and state capital outlay in some fair relation to ability to pay and encourage private development to accord with other planning objectives.

(7) *Public Participation*—"public" here refers to nonofficials, nonprofessionals in planning; "participation" to some meaningful part in the planning process itself through regular rather than chance opportunities for criticism and voicing of preferences, either directly (whenever possible) or through acceptable representatives; implies nearly everywhere the need for inventiveness and experimentation with political devices—new or revised—for this purpose; both an objective of urban planning and a means of setting and achieving its other goals.

This or almost any other classification of regional planning objectives touches upon many sectors of life in which at present we have no satisfactory units of

2 "Priorities" in the sense of a scheduling of outlays in light of the relative urgency of the needs each might help to satisfy. Of course this does not imply that the outlays would be made *seriatim;* several or many of them usually would be going ahead at any one time.

measurement or comparison. It is apparent, however, that pressing too hard for any one group of goals often would endanger some or all of the others. For example, the highest degree of efficiency in an urban or regional structure quite surely would not be compatible with a corresponding degree of livability or amenity. On these as on other parts of the planning process, our reliance must be on the planning officials' judgment and devotion to the general welfare, plus, of course, on the controlling institutions of public discussion, debate, and decision.

Those persons who find this view somewhat vague or otherwise unsatisfactory might well reflect on two further opinions that have intellectually respectable advocates. The art of planning is still in a relatively early stage of development; it may soon reduce somewhat, although it never can eliminate, the area of personal judgment and controversy in such matters. Again, there is no compelling reason to believe that any *one* combination or set of priorities among objectives of this order will necessarily further the general welfare of a locality better than all others. Quite possibly, two or more sets would be substantially equal.

If this listing or something like it indicates roughly the range and character of objectives for urban and regional planning, what is the responsibility of planning officials in determining specific goals for any area? The whole thrust of the argument here rules out the planner as the determiner and imposer of major objectives. But what should he do on this vital front? Should he make up his own mind as to objectives and then try his best to persuade others, including legislators and community leaders, to his opinion? Should he stand aside from the whole matter, saying in effect: "When you responsible officials decide what should be the objectives of development in this locality, I will be at your service to advise you how you may attain them most

rapidly and effectively"? Should he prepare several sets of possible objectives,
with the priorities within each set clearly
indicated and with a judicious analysis of
the pros and cons for each set, and then
present this statement to the decision-
making officials and possibly to others
as well? Should he prepare such a document and then add to it his judgment as
to which set seems to him, on balance,
the most appropriate for that locality at
that time?

With due recognition again of the substantial differences among regional localities (and the status of planning agencies
in them) and for any one from time to
time, the last possibility named seems
usually preferable to any of the others.
But it does not exhaust the potential usefulness of planners in goal determination.

The objectives set forth by legislative
bodies usually are broad and general. So
are those assumed to exist in some general community consensus. It is a proper
and necessary function of planning to
make them more precise and almost always, in doing so, to set intermediate,
middle-range goals consonant with the
more general objectives and, in time and
inclusiveness, on the way, so to speak, toward them. For example, in a comprehensive housing law passed in 1949, the
Congress of the United States declared
the broad objective of "a decent home
and a suitable living environment for every American family." Similar language
can be found in many supplementary
state laws and in resolutions adopted by
local governing bodies requesting financial aid under the federal statute. Well
and good, but what is a decent home or
a suitable living environment? What are
reasonable standards for judging housing
and neighborhood quality? Further, once
the areas of substandard housing are
clearly marked out in a locality, what
should be the strategy of attack on them?
Should the worst slum areas be cleared
first and rebuilt? If so, should they be

rebuilt with housing or for other purposes? Should the occupancy in these
areas be reduced, by building elsewhere,
before acquisition for clearance starts, in
order to ease the problems of relocation
and, possibly, to soften the asking prices
for blighted properties? At any one time,
how much public outlay is justified for
clearance and rebuilding operations in
proportion to that used for opening up
areas for new development? Should the
initial program—say, for the first three
years or so—emphasize rehabilitation of
badly but not hopelessly blighted areas?
What should be the quantitative objectives of the first five, seven, or ten years?
In other words, how fast should the program go?

It would be easy to list literally pages
of questions of this order. In the context
of this paper, they clearly are planning
questions. Many of them imply the need
for intermediate, middle-range objectives.
Unless they are asked and intelligently
answered, any program started to realize
the fine-sounding general goal easily
could fail or even make matters worse.

Over a period of years, planning can
and should influence goal setting in still
other ways. Planners should propose
working programs that keep the activities
in behalf of all the objectives in some
kind of balance. They can warn against
the easy optimism that occasionally seizes
well-intentioned officials and citizens
when a long-debated program finally is
approved and started. From time to time
they can suggest new objectives or modifications of those already established. By
no means least important, they can educate other officials, leaders, and groups
in the possibilities of regional development. Many persons, even intelligent and
sensitive persons, find it difficult to appreciate the range of regional goals, both
in physical and institutional development,
that are now quite attainable. Since they
are not very knowledgeable in such matters, their imaginations are often limited

by the conventional, by what they have known and seen around them. They readily see only the possibilities of relatively minor or more or less traditional improvements. In addition to his primary responsibility for program and policy recommendations, the professional planner ought to take seriously his opportunities to be an educator, to help shake off these blinders, to make real and vivid the possibilities of urban forms, including some of those now in the stage of experimentation, invention, or intellectual exploration, to enlarge some officials' and lay leaders' conception of the "realm of the possible"—as someone has put it. Questions of methods and tactics on this front are clearly beyond the scope of this essay.

Clearly, central planning has a major role to play in this vital matter of community goals. Certainly no planner should feel belittled because he and his associates do not have the final word in setting the goals. If he lives up to his responsibilities and opportunities in this process, he will have more than enough to do—however fine his intelligence or great his talents.

"In the common life of urban and regional localities or communities" raises the question:[3] What things on the urban and regional scene should be planned by local public agencies? Questions of process and objective aside for the moment, in what substantive areas of regional life should central planning by local governments be recognized as necessary or desirable?

The conception of planning put forward in this paper recognizes at least seven areas in which central planning agencies of regions have definite responsibilities. They are parts of the *common life* because whatever is done within or

[3] Here "common" is used not in the senses of ordinary or usual or mediocre but in the sense of shared or in common.

to them affects, quite directly, the welfare and ways of life of many people and groups in the area. They are:

(1) *Land Use*—the allocation of land[4] to fairly broad categories of uses—e.g. residential, industrial, commercial—within which the real estate market may continue the allocation process; the sizes of such use districts and the linkages among them; selection of sites for public uses and facilities—e.g. schools, hospitals, public parks and open areas of various kinds, parkways, playgrounds, water supply and sewage disposal facilities, etc.; less well developed but receiving increasing attention is what Professor J. H. Beuscher, my colleague at the University of Wisconsin, calls "the pacing of urban development"—i.e. regulation and guidance of the rate of urban expansion or development (changes in land use) in and around urban centers.

(2) *Standards for Development and Maintenance.* Closely related to (1); minimum and desirable standards as to density of development, setbacks, floor-area ratios, minimum lot sizes, off-street parking of motor vehicles, etc.; made effective by means of such police power measures as zoning and housing ordinances and subdivision regulations as well as by inducements such as the acquisition of sites and "write-down" of land prices (as in urban redevelopment or renewal programs) and the preparation of sites for new towns; in many parts of this work, notably in the provisions of police-power ordinances, planning officials must collaborate closely with others who have more expertise in such fields as public health, public recreation, and schools; poses questions of how best to protect the public health and welfare without unduly limiting imagi-

[4] "Land" in the broad sense, not merely the solid surface of the earth.

native design and innovation in building and site layout; the protection of sites and buildings of special historical or architectural interest or value.

(3) *Circulation*—i.e. space and facilities for traffic, transit, and transport—the moving of people and goods into, out of, and within regional areas; might be considered a subtopic of (1) *Land Use* but seems to deserve separate listing; closely related, nevertheless, to both (1) and (2).

(4) *The Economic Base of Localities or Regions*—useful and often essential to population forecasts, both of numbers and of probable family and income status; means of strengthening and diversifying major sources of employment; has obvious implications for over-all tax-paying ability of the area, which, in turn, conditions many other possible policies and programs.

(5) *Capital Programing*—and its variant, capital budgeting; establishing time priorities for major public investments or capital outlays; recommending ways and means of financing, including utilizing grants-in-aid from federal or state governments; one experienced planner in this country remarked that any urban planning that neglects or omits capital programing is simply the adult equivalent of writing letters to Santa Claus; in rather more dignified terms but to the same effect the Schuster report (British) said: ". . . when cost is ignored—as indeed appears to have been the case in some of the contemporary planning proposals—then planning is just so much waste paper."[5]

(6) *Special Problems of Urban and Rural Redevelopment*—determining in some detail the extent and character of blight as a step in deciding on the appropriate method of treatment in

specific areas—e.g. clearance and rebuilding, clearance alone, rehabilitation, conservation, combinations of clearance and rehabilitation; the terms and conditions, including land prices of sites, for rebuilding; relocation policies and practices; measures for prevention of deterioration in rebuilt districts.

(7) *Site Planning*—in many respects on the borderline between planning and the functions of architects, landscape architects, and engineers in designing large-scale projects for residential and other purposes; important, however, in assuring economy, variety, and amenity in residential neighborhoods and elsewhere; planning agencies, however, are more often the reviewers than the creators of site plans; might be listed as a subsection of (1) *Land Use*.

Some students of planning and of state and local government have suggested that other substantive areas would also be proper concerns of over-all or central planning agencies. They point out that the seven areas just mentioned all have to do more or less directly with capital investment, both in money and human resources, for physical equipment or facilities, public and private.[6] (To be sure,

[6] Very often—in fact, usually—this kind of planning is called "physical planning." This seems to me a most unfortunate and misleading term. It implies that not only is the end product physical, but also that the process of planning for it is concerned entirely or primarily with physical things—i.e. roads, houses, industrial plants, land, etc. "Capital facilities planning" would seem a much preferable term because it clearly implies that the physical entities, whether privately or publicly owned, are constructed to provide certain goods and services for which there are human demand and needs, primarily but not exclusively from the residents of the region. Thus the emphasis is placed where it must be if regional planning is to be useful and effective—on the kind, amount, spatial distribution, and relative urgency of the demand and needs for shelter, privacy, recreation, community life, aesthetic enjoyment, potable water, consumer goods, physical mobility, etc.

[5] "Report of the Committee on Qualifications of Planners." London: His Majesty's Stationery Office, Cmd. 8059, 1950, p. 19.

these areas are not, by any means, exclusively of this character, but they nevertheless do share this component or characteristic.) This seems to these students, in respect to public facilities at least, an unnecessary limitation. They point out that the wisdom of adding to the public capital equipment of a community—say, a park or a public building or a highway—cannot be competently judged without considering (a) the alternative of using existing facilities more intensively or efficiently and (b) what the new investment, if made, would require for maintenance, repair, and operation. Both (a) and (b) clearly have to do with the operating budget of the local or state government. Therefore, they argue, the central planning operation should include responsibility for preparing the operating budget.

As a practical political and administrative proposal this suggestion certainly is weak. Very few if any planning agencies now have sufficient reputation and prestige to make this organizational shift feasible. Also, the wisdom of the proposal can be questioned. Central planning has to stop somewhere; it would go into many detailed matters only at the cost of unnecessarily weakening the responsibilities and morale of other vital parts of local government and at the serious risk of poor performance in the wide and complex areas for which it now has responsibility.[7] To be sure, in respect

7 These are two of the principal considerations for an answer to the persistent question: What should be the scope of central or over-all planning for any region? The other two are: (1) Central planning should be concerned with elements or components of regional development that are long-lived and, therefore, cannot be readily or frequently changed—e.g. with a major water supply system, but not with the number or salaries of persons who check on the purity of the water. Both are "important," but the latter can be changed on relatively short notice in the light of experience. (2) It also should be concerned with those elements of regional development

to the relations between capital outlays and operating expenses, the planning agency and the budget office should work together. Although this has proven rather difficult in some local governments, experience in others indicates that it is by no means impossible.

Recently this proposal has taken a new twist, particularly in some of the discussion that has come with the revival of central planning in state government. The argument is that the only thing approaching an effective plan for state government is the budget. If one stresses the coordinating or integrating function of central planning—i.e. the adjusting, fitting together, and minor filling out of plans, proposals, and programs from operating departments such as those for highways, industrial development, conservation, institutional care, etc., into some reasonably coherent whole—there is some truth in the contention. And some recent developments toward program and performance budgeting promise to strengthen this function in these agencies. If, however, one maintains that innovation or creativeness is an equally significant part of a central planning agency's job, he may fairly ask what innovations in substantive governmental programs have come out of budget offices.

So far the only answer has been an admission that, with all due respect to the many able and devoted financial officers in state and local governments, they have not contributed on this front, *but* this could be changed for the future by adding to their staffs persons trained and experienced in planning. This, of course, sounds quite a bit like solving a chess problem by moving both the black and white pieces. To most people with

that have the most and most far-reaching side effects or consequences in the ecosystem—e.g. with the location of all kinds of major recreational or shopping areas, but not with the regulation of camping or the pavement in the parking lots.

experience in sizable governmental agencies it also sounds rather naïve to expect a minority of nonbudget personnel to make over long-established attitudes, practices, and traditions. The chances would seem long that the planners would find themselves outmanned and outargued, and either would go elsewhere or resign themselves to helping out in the important, but essentially different, task of coordination.

"Urban and regional localities or communities" indicates very roughly the area for which this kind of planning is done. "Localities" and "communities" are both listed to indicate a distinction between them.

"Locality," in the sense intended here, is a rather neutral word. It means a number of people and groups of people living within an area that can be marked out or bounded, at least approximately, in some way—e.g. by municipal or county lines, or by commuting radii, or by the drainage of a watershed.

Unfortunately the word "community" has more than one meaning in common and scientific usage. Here, of course, it means a *local* community—one that has a geographic or areal base rather than a professional or functional community—as one might speak of the scholarly community or the business community. Even when the word is limited to local community, however, it is not unambiguous. At least two broad, related, but distinguishable meanings are common.

One well-known scholar writes: "Koenig would accept the specification that community must be identified with place, a location in which the individual maintains certain fairly habitual relationships. To Parsons it is the base of operations for a group. In his words, 'A community is that collectivity the members of which share a common territorial area as their base of operations for daily activities.' Another observer might argue, however,

that it is important to think of a community as a place where a collectivity shares experience, where the interests of people are localized. . . .

"One very often quoted definition of community is that offered by MacIver: 'Any circle of people who live together, who belong together, so that they share not this or that particular interest, but a whole set of interests wide enough and complete enough to include their lives, is a community. Thus we may designate as a community a tribe, a village, a pioneer settlement, a city, or a nation. The mark of a community is that one's life *may* be lived wholly within it.' "[8]

"Community" is often used both in the sense of place—a locality—and also in the sense of MacIver's definition—with the emphasis on people and their shared interests, sense of identification, and recognized responsibilities. Here the second meaning is intended. It should be clear that planning of the kind outlined in this paper will reach its full flowering only in a local community like or approaching MacIver's conception. It can be practiced, and in fact often is, in localities that are not communities. Some planners and students of planning argue, sometimes rather wistfully, that planning for a locality over a period of years may help to develop within it a meaningful *sense of community.* Maybe so; some, but by no means conclusive, evidence can be adduced for this opinion.

Without exploring this subject further here, may I emphasize, as a partial sum-

[8] Nels Anderson, *The Urban Community: A World Perspective.* New York: Henry Holt & Co., 1959, pp. 26–27. The original materials referred to are: René Koenig, "Die Gemeinde in Blickfeld der Sociologie," in *Handbuch der kommunalen Wissenschaften und Praxis* (Berlin: Springer, 1956) p. 23; Talcott Parsons, *The Social System* (Glencoe, Illinois: The Free Press, 1951) p. 23; and Robert M. MacIver, *Society, Its Structure and Changes* (New York: Richard R. Smith, 1932) pp. 9–10.

mary, three suggestions that already may be evident to those who share or follow this general conception of the character and place of regional planning in our society?

(1) Although central planning has many potentialities for improving the environments of life, it is not an autonomous activity, but rather is embedded in and strongly influenced by much of the institutional and sociopsychological components of our culture.

(2) Although the relations between intelligent and vigorous planning and other parts of our culture are reciprocal, in and of itself central planning is not a major force in cultural change. If it is to become such a force, it must be joined, necessarily as a junior partner, with a continual, varied, and vigorous effort of agitation, public education, and political pressure in behalf of *not* this or that particularized program or immediate objective with which planners are concerned, but rather in behalf of the whole range of their activities and potentialities. To put the matter in other terms: it has often been noted that central planning lacks a constituency. When central planners are working on some specific issue or component of regional development (be it open space, transport, water use, or whatever), which usually means that they are collaborating with functional or departmental planners of one kind or another, they often have the support or friendly criticism of groups of citizens who seem to think that more open space or more concrete pavement is the *summum bonum* of civilized life. When, however, the current focus of the regional planner turns, for example, from highways to open space, most of the concrete lovers lie back in the traces. Their attitude is: "Let someone else worry about that, and if the planner gets his ears pinned

back on that one maybe in the future he will pay more attention to highways."

In short, if the regional planner is to be truly effective, his appreciation of the natural and human ecology of regions, imperfect as it may be, will have to be matched by that of at least many of the present battery of friends and supporters of programs for parts of those regions or for particular activities carried on within them.

Should regional planning become a major force in cultural change? Maybe not; certainly a case could be made for the view that planners should be content with a less ambitious and demanding role. As an admittedly prejudiced witness, however, I cannot see how our restless, changing, and increasingly complex society can help to create for itself the kinds of environments, natural and social, that most people would thrive in unless it has in some places of major influence people of trained intelligence and professional orientation who think in terms of "the wide web of causes and consequences" that does in fact characterize and condition all that is done or attempted to this end. This, in my opinion, is the core of the need for regional planning and the principal justification of it as well.

(3) One of the principal limitations of central planning stems from the fact that usually it is being practiced in and for localities that are not communities.

Some criticisms and objections

This conception of planning has many critics on many points—too many, in fact, for all of them to be considered or answered here. Four of the more common objections, however, should be briefly noted.

(1) Discussions similar to this one on central planning for regional locali-

ties or communities, carried on usually by units of general-purpose governments, have drawn the criticism of overcentralization. No one should infer, however, that this kind of planning is all the planning or all the significant planning for the development and improvement of regions that is being done or should be done. Functional or operating departments of local governments—e.g. departments of water supply and waste disposal or of streets and highways—plan for their objectives; so do semi-independent, *ad hoc* authorities; so do civic and semipublic organizations concerned with local affairs; so do many private enterprises having to do with regional growth and development. And it is important to note that these latter kinds of planning go on concurrently with the central planning.

Regional planning, as set forth here, can provide important aids to these other kinds of planning: reliable information and analyses of the natural and social make-up of a locality and of its economy as well as estimates of its future, coordination, professional collaboration and encouragement. Conversely, these other agencies can help the central planning office materially. As suggested above, many of them have valuable, specialized knowledge on which the general planning should draw. Continuing informal discussion and interchange of information, ideas, and proposals can strengthen the entire fabric of the planning process.

Of course, when one looks at the actual position of most regional planning agencies the charge of overcentralization becomes almost ludicrous. A large proportion of them, including nearly all in the more populous and rapidly changing areas, are attached to no general-purpose government with powers at all commensurate with the scope of the planning that is being

carried on. Rather, the planners prepare recommendations that depend for their execution on the action of many governments of all kinds—federal, state, county, municipal, and *ad hoc*—i.e. special authorities and districts. Furthermore, the regional planning recommendations often call for further and more detailed planning by agencies of these governmental entities, as the cliché has it, "within the framework of the regional plan." Usually, however, these other governments and their planning units are under no formal or legal obligation to respect or even to consider seriously the recommendations of the regional planning unit. It must rely almost entirely on persuasion and the substantive merits of its proposals.

For anyone concerned with results the danger is not overcentralization but lack of jurisdiction and responsibility.

(2) Sometimes it is objected that planning of the kind considered here, at least that in sizable and rapidly changing areas, is beyond the capabilities of men. The variables to be dealt with are too many and too varied; the systems of relationships are too complex; the questions of values are too puzzling for human judgment over all. According to this view, planning, in these localities at least, should only be expected to accompany, so to speak, the great, uncontrollable forces of environmental change and content itself with simply making them a little more orderly and correcting some of their most obvious crudities. As indicated above, someone has called this role "collaboration with the inevitable."

This question is often posed in terms of the qualifications and responsibilities of "the planner." Is there, can there be any such animal as "the planner" who can, in fact, make the conception of planning outlined above a reality—

not on paper but in the rush, bustle, contention, and change of our world? A large part of the answer is that planning is not a one-man job; it is a team task. Where the word "planner" appears above, it should be read as the planning team, the planning office, or the planning department.

To be sure, a team must be led; and the leader, although not a master of all the tasks and techniques, must know quite a bit about them, including how to combine their results into a balanced and consistent whole. This, admittedly, calls for men of extraordinary abilities, but the planning profession has some of them, and could use more. A corollary of this view is that not enough time, effort, money, and attention have been given so far to recruiting and educating men and women of the caliber needed.

(3) Another criticism is somewhat similar to but quite distinguishable from the one just noted. Often it is said that regional planning, particularly that for urban regions, really is "physical planning," and the urban planner is or should be a "physical planner." In other words, the end result of urban planning, the urban environment, is physical—houses, streets, schools, water mains, recreational areas, and other buildings and facilities as well as the spaces around and among them. The purpose of planning is to assure that they will be so designed, built, and arranged on the land that the final composite will be useful, convenient, and beautiful. Of course, in this view, urban planning has to pay some attention to such matters as population forecasting, the analysis of problems of slums and residential blight, legal controls of land use, public participation, and many related policies and programs, but only as they may aid or facilitate the physical result and only to the degree necessary to enable plan-

ners to achieve their conceptions (in arriving at which, they will take into account the views of others) of the good, the beautiful, the appropriate physical setting for human life. Thus urban planning is, at bottom, design, and the true planner is a designer in the grand manner.

My counterargument does not deny the importance of the well-designed physical city. Neither does it deny the physical designer a role as a member of the urban planning team. Quite the opposite. It does dispute, however, the assumption that the only dimension of environment is physical. Man does indeed live and work and play in houses, neighborhoods, shops, factories, parks, and playgrounds; it is highly desirable that they and the areas of which they are component parts be well and beautifully designed. But, quite as truly, urban man lives also in an economic environment, a social environment, and a political environment. To the quality of these, too, urban planning can make contributions. It cannot, of course, determine all of their nature and characteristics; neither can it determine all aspects of the physical environment. But to all these environments or, more accurately, to urban environment seen in these several dimensions, urban planning, as defined in this paper, can contribute much.

Although what can be properly and effectively planned by public agencies varies from one of these environments to another, it seems just as much a mistake for planning to concentrate on one and neglect the others as it would be, within the physical environment, to plan, for example, only for traffic and transport and to ignore housing development, recreational facilities, and open space. A capital program that schedules public works and facilities with sophisticated judgment of relative needs, of the most appropriate sources of funds, of ability to pay, and of the claims of well-organized and aggressive groups as against the needs of relatively inarticulate publics, may be making just as significant a contribution to the political and social environment of the citizens of an urban area as the buildings and other facilities may make to their physical environment.

Very clearly, too, this criticism of urban-regional planning overlooks or badly underestimates the significance, even in essentially urban and urbanizing areas, of the needs of other than human forms of life. It is faulty both in social and ecological perspectives.

(4) The last objection to be looked at is of a rather different order. Students of government, including notably those primarily interested in local government, are paying much attention these days to "the political process." Although scholarly definitions of this phenomenon vary somewhat, for our purposes it can be thought of as the ways and means by which various groups in a society contend for what they take to be their interests and for influence in public affairs, by which any group tries to counter the actions of others that it sees as threats to its own position, and how these diverse and conflicting interests, pressures, and maneuvers are resolved into policies and programs or, it should be added although it often is not, how they may result in stalemate, frustration, and alienation.

This has been and still is a fruitful idea or concept. It has been recognized not only by professional scholars, but also, often without the label and the special vocabulary that has grown up around it, by newspaper reporters, heads of government departments and agencies, officers of civic and neighborhood associations, public-relations specialists, and many others. Particu-

larly in scholarly circles, however, many of its more ardent and generally less experienced devotees tend to become a cult that is surrounding this basically straightforward idea with an unnecessary and rather confusing mystique. Many years ago it used to be said that if you could teach a parrot to say "supply and demand," you had an economist. In some circles today, if you could teach him to say "the political process," he would be a recognized political scientist. Of course, many professional scholars and others interested in this process are not cultists at all; they see this concept as one of several useful aids in observing, studying, and otherwise trying to understand the societies of our times.

To most of the cultists and even some of the noncultists, however, planning, and particularly the kind of planning I have been trying to examine, seems an alien, disturbing, or even faintly undemocratic idea. Some simply denounce it as unrealistic—a figment of naïve imaginations. Often without trying very hard, they see nothing in their world that resembles planning so outlined. Some try to fit it into their system of thought and analysis by declaring, with little or no empirical evidence, that urban and regional planners, however defined and whatever their scope, are simply one more claimant or contender in the political process. As a group they are not basically or significantly different from the chamber of commerce, the labor-union council, or the west-side property owners association. Each has its own value system, its own immediate objectives, its own wish to be influential in shaping policies and programs, and its own brand of tactics, stratagems, and maneuvers.

I have still to find anyone who makes this assertion who has also bothered to try to test it by a respectable comparative inquiry into how planning offices actually work. Only when this is done shall we have any solid basis for judging to what degree, if any, this opinion is justified. Until then, it certainly is the opinion of many persons who have been in and around planning offices for years that the statement is false in many important respects. To be sure, most planners would like to see their recommendations followed and, naturally and properly, employ various means of persuasion to this end. Equally clear, however, is the impression that most planners' attitudes, rationale, and methods are markedly different from those of most interest or pressure groups. If what has been said above about the planning process has any merit (and at least it is based on many years of observation and acquaintance with the practicing profession), this view of planners as just another pressure group is mistaken and misleading.

To make an extended defense of planning as defined here against the charge that it is alien to or opposed to democratic political processes seems hardly necessary. Of course it is not. On the contrary, it is essentially a means of bringing into those processes a longer and more inclusive look at a wide range of community considerations, a more explicit definition of objectives, and a more thorough exploration of the pros and cons of various possible ways and means to these ends. To repeat, its direct results are recommendations, not decisions. As Professor John Gaus once put it very succinctly: Planning is an attempt to improve the making of decisions. Without it, in many burgeoning regional areas in this country with governmental and quasi-public agencies under severe and mounting pressures from population growth and financial stringency, the policy-formulating process may well become what one of my friends calls an exercise in pure and applied chaos. If or to the degree that this happens, it seems quite clear that those who will suffer most will be the relatively weak and inarticulate groups in our society as well as those other forms of life that have no direct voice in our affairs.

In Conclusion

One of the difficulties of "ideal type" description and analysis, at least in inexpert hands, is that it tends to present a static picture rather than one of movement and change. If that is the impression this essay gives to readers, let me simply say that it is, of course, completely false. Change—rapid, often bewildering, sometimes almost frightening change—is probably the dominant characteristic of most regions in our society today. And although planning for their development and redevelopment is changing less dramatically and probably not rapidly enough, it certainly is not standing still.

In my opinion, the most significant and promising change in regional planning over the past several years has been the movement, often uneven and awkward, toward an essentially ecological view of the regions or other areas for which central or over-all planning is being done. Earlier there may have been a glimmer of this conception in the emphasis on the need for "comprehensive planning." Unfortunately, this term often was taken to mean that central planners thought that their hands should be in everything—or almost everything. Today, however, we see and hear much more about systems, subsystems, side effects, spill-over effects, by-products, networks of influence, etc.—all terms that connote a growing appreciation of both the complexity of regions and the interrelatedness of their parts. So far, to be sure, the plant and nonhuman animal ecosystems often have been ignored, but even here a change seems to be under way.

Finally, some thoughtful observers and students of our society think that it may now be on the edge of technical *cum* economic change that may well deserve the label of revolution: the widespread automation of much of that society's economic processes—in production and distribution, blue-collar and white-collar jobs—with the probable consequence that large numbers of people will have more leisure or, at least, nonwork time on their hands than most of them have ever dreamed of. When one considers what a much less drastic increase in the amount and distribution of leisure has helped to do to the development and patterns of regions over the past generation or so, he certainly should be puzzled or even exasperated that most planners seem so little moved by the current prospect. If, as some of us think is likely, urban and many other regions in this country during the latter years of this century may well be as unlike those at the end of the nineteenth as they, in turn, were unlike those at the end of the eighteenth, both our understanding of ecologic processes and the practice of regional planning soon may be facing their severest test.

General Discussion

TUNNARD: Let us now turn to the substantive issues. First is the limitation of suburban growth. My own feeling is that one doesn't look for limits. One looks, as Professor Dickinson has said, for a framework in which urban growth should take place—which naturally leads one toward the planning point of view.

I have been reading the proposed National Housing Bill recently, and in it are provisions to make it easier for private new-town builders on rural land; cheap loans for developers in areas outside the suburbs and acquisition of open space in the old center—an excellent idea.

It is in many ways a most statesmanlike proposal. However, if the provisions of this act were carried out without planning safeguards, what we see happening to the urbanized areas today would just be accelerated in the old form. Luckily the foresight of Congress suggests that there will be planning controls. I am not going to go into the type that presumably would be in operation here or how the administration, through the HHFA, would provide them. I bring it to your attention because one has to qualify any statement which is so bold as to say that urban growth may have no limit. One can qualify it by suggesting that growth can be controlled, even though its spread may be larger than our present urban areas.

Incidentally, we have some space to give away to the Organic Environment group who asked for ten million acres for experimental purposes. We can give them a great deal more if they would like it and still have lots of room for our projected population.

That is one point we might discuss. Then I suggest we might discuss regional planning. There is already a difference of opinion in the group here that I detected, between Dr. Woodbury and Dr. Farness. Dr. Farness asked for a new administrative organization. Dr. Woodbury said it should be done through the existing ones, if I understand him rightly.

And third, I hope we might make some rather practical and smaller suggestions, as Dr. Dansereau suggested; change the scale a little bit, and make some recommendations about the use of empty areas: such as whether government military installations should be sold off to developers when peace breaks out or whether they should go to public parks. Perhaps a previous inventory ought to be made of such areas so that a future use could be suggested.

I was interested this morning to hear Mr. Eichhorn say that the earliest study of the national parks in the twenties had focused on the green chain of mountains stretching from Canada down into Georgia. In the light of our growing urban regions, massive effort should be made to control and limit urban growth in such an area, which is presumably within a day's drive or less for many people on the eastern seaboard. This kind of thing I hope we might get into toward the end.

GRAHAM: I have never before been confronted with such a formidable array of planners. I must confess that I see a potential power that is almost terrifying. They are going to use some of us for certain planning purposes; they are going to use the economists; they are going to use the ecologists; and they are going to use every technician and discipline they can get hold of.

While I may have been amused or annoyed by some of the comments which were made earlier in this meeting, I am beginning to be frightened with some of the things that these fellows are talking about. They are very practical men, and I don't think we want to let them kid us into an evaluation of concepts and principles. None of us, I think, has wanted to feel that we had to live in a planned society. I know that after the First World War the word "planner" was a bad word and you couldn't use it. In the Soil Conservation Service we couldn't even talk about our technicians as farm planners because this implied that the technician was planning the area for farming.

The only hope I see in the discussion so far is that Mr. Woodbury said that the planners don't make the decisions, that the decisions are made in the political arena. But I am being led to disbelieve this. At least I think there is a question, and I think this is as pertinent to the objective of this Conference as any question that has been raised in my mind. These men are going to shape the environment. I don't think there is any question about this. But how are they going to shape it? I live in Fairfax County, Virginia, where there is now a 7500-acre development called Reston which is important largely because of private investment. It will supposedly house 75,000 people. A little farther north there is Columbia City, which will house 110,000 people on 15,000 acres.

My question to Mr. Woodbury is: What choice do we provide the people who are going to live in these developments, which are relatively signed, sealed, and delivered as planned units, changed environments, supposedly to provide all the needs and necessities of man?

I don't see the political forum or the place for individual or even community decision in the development of that environment. It seems to me that it is gone, it is lost, because the plan is made, it is imposed upon the area, and we have lost even then the power of choice and the right of decision.

I may be overemphasizing this, but I do believe that the power and influence of the urban regional planner in North America in the future will be a terrific thing. I would like to know how we avoid the trap of living in a completely planned environment where the only choice available is to either buy a town house or a suburban house.

WOODBURY: Mr. Durden on my left knows more about Reston and Columbia than I do. Let me offer two comments:

First, both of those are developments, private developments, and private speculations, if you wish. The limitation of choice, the type of residence and so forth that you suspect they may make, are, after all, only restricted to a relatively small part of the metropolitan area of the District of Columbia. If some people cannot find in Reston or the District the kind of housing they want and can afford, most of them can look elsewhere in the Washington area.

Certainly one of the tenets of my conception of planning is that the public planners of the area ought to give a wide range of choice to residents as to location and type of house. I happen to be one of those who is a dispersalist, if that is the word. I think that this is the trend of the future. I welcome it. But I admit in the very next breath that there are many people who do not wish that form of development.

I think they are in a minority. But certainly any regional planning for the metropolitan district of Washington ought to recognize the preferences of that minority, ought, as a matter of fact, to make some estimate as to how large the minority is, to provide locations and encouragement for the kinds of dwellings that members of this minority would prefer.

I don't think we want to get the idea that any type of regional planning, at least any kind that has been suggested this afternoon, is going to have the degree of detail and restriction that may be necessary in a private corporation development like Reston or Columbia.

TUNNARD: Whatever may be said about Reston—and there are a lot of things that are lacking there—there is an attempt to save space, which I think is commendable. It is clustered rather too tightly, I think, for some people. It is going to be a real "togetherness" community, because the first part of it at least is down around an artificial lake, and the distances are being minimized.

It is rather like some of the British densities that you see in the Roehampton development and other housing projects.

DANSEREAU: It is rather distressing to hear Dr. Woodbury say there is no effective regional planning being done in the United States right now, and then to say, in response to Dr. Graham's question, that the public planners are going to surrender their powers before they have ever used them.

I wonder if it is naïve to conclude that the majority of the American people have made such a religion of private enterprise that the public planning will never get off the ground.

Franklin Roosevelt failed to convert this nation to socialism, and I think "planning" is still—not was, but still is—a bad word. What planners are working against is a political block and nothing else; primarily a political block.

TUNNARD: Could I draw your attention, though, to the intervention of government in the banking business, farming, and in almost every aspect of our national life? We are quite used to the effect of government and private enterprise going hand in hand in this country since Roosevelt, wouldn't you say?

DURDEN: I think it is rather archaic to make too much of a difference between public planning and private planning. There is good planning and bad planning.

The first point I would make to Dr. Graham is that you had your chance in the public arena to speak up. There were public hearings, inadequate as the public-hearing mechanism is.

From my knowledge of it, the public hearings at Reston were for a number of reasons, much more sanguine than, say, the hearings on Columbia. In any event, the planner's role is very well circumscribed with all sorts of presumed safeguards.

The residents had a chance to speak. Whether they chose to speak or not, I don't know. Why they chose not to, I don't know. There have been people for years, urging more interest in the landscape, urging people to step forward. They don't always do it.

The second point that I think you spoke of concerned a lack of choice. This really speaks to the skill of the entrepreneur. I think the more skilled entrepreneurs operating in urban developments are the ones who are attempting to provide the most choice. They do this not because they like choice in some vague way. They offer choices because in developments of large size they are going to face a long period of development and they want to be able, when the market softens, say, for single-family-homes, to get into a rising market such as housing for the elderly. When that levels off, they would like to tap another market. As they encounter these cycles, they would like to be able to meet them with a variety of housing types.

Again, we need more skilled planners, more skilled public scrutiny. And this, in turn, I think will give us more skilled entrepreneurs.

I don't fear the entrepreneur. I fear public apathy more than anything else when I look at the regional landscapes of our country. It is public apathy which to me is the big question mark.

TUNNARD: I wonder if our lawyer member, Mrs. Strong, might have something to say on this matter of public and private interests.

STRONG: More from a planning than from a legal point of view, I would answer Mr. Graham by saying planners have not nearly enough power. I should state first that we have about 110 Restons now under way across the country, and there is every expectation that we shall have further large-scale development in the coming years because we will have larger and larger private investment.

I fear that the public planner, at the regional level, does not have the power to determine, with public governing bodies' support and endorsement, what type of development these new towns should be. I fear that there is too much power in the hands of the private entrepreneur.

I would like the proposed Housing Bill to be far more specific as to the type of plans that are to be submitted prior to the payment of public funds for land acquisition. For example, Charles Abrams has for a long time supported the requirement that plans should specify that housing would be provided for low-income groups. There is nothing of this sort in the bill.

CALDWELL: I would like to comment further on Dr. Graham's question. Mr. Woodbury suggested that planning was most effective where the planning agency or function was performed in a manner that was closely related to its clientele.

Very regrettably, in planning over any very large area for the kind of purpose that Dr. Graham is speaking of, there is a disjunctiveness between any kind of meaningful region and the political units. What we have seen again and again across the country is the failure of the political powers of government to be effectively used—a point that Mr. Farness referred to earlier.

The private entrepreneurial groups all too often have subverted—I think this is a correct word—the machinery of planning and the machinery of surveillance in local government. If you look at the composition of the members of the county planning commissions, you will see them often heavily weighted with representatives of the real estate interests. These people primarily have sought to protect, quite understandably, their own freedom of action. This is not an irrational sort of behavior. They are following a clear rationality.

I certainly share the fear of public apathy—the failure of people to use the powers available to them. To be sure, as Mrs. Strong has said, the planner does not always have as much power as he needs, and we haven't often anticipated these land-use developments so that we could have a fruitful relationship between the private entrepreneur and government, which certainly could be quite consistent with good planning.

Therefore, what has happened has been really a failure of public responsibility and hence of government. The private entrepreneur has moved ahead.

MUMFORD: The question, Dr. Graham, isn't whether we have planning or no planning. But whether we have responsible planning—planning that is adequately related to public need—or whether we have planning done by irresponsible authorities, by real estate operators, by individual agencies like highway commissions, like the Federal Housing Agency, and so forth. They are all doing planning, but not responsibly.

Why? Because we haven't got an adequate regional unit to handle planning. Here I think I would like to make a reconciliation of the two points of view that both Woodbury and Farness brought forward. It isn't a personal contribution of mine, but you will find it in a rather remarkable report that the State Office of Regional Development, New York State, brought out last summer or last fall. This report is one which I am not entirely enthusiastic about. I am highly critical of some of its assumptions. But in one respect it made a remarkable advance. It took the State of New York as it was, and analyzed the resources, analyzed the population distribution, the distribution of the cities—and then using the existing county units, combined them into ten regions, each of which had a real or a potential regional capability. It didn't go far enough, unfortunately, for it should have suggested that each of these regions had to have a political body capable of making decisions within that particular region.

Here is a reconciliation of Woodbury's proper demand that we use, if possible, the existing governmental units instead of inventing them all over again, and Farness' notion that we have to act boldly and create a new unit capable of handling the entire situation. The real trouble with all of our planning agencies is that they act as though they were alone in the world and that all of the other necessary contributions are just secondary to what they are going to do.

So the highway department has been ruining large parts of our scenery, not just by invading it with superhighways, but by making accessible very valuable parts of the landscape that should have remained accessible only to those who would work a little in order to get there.

A great deal of the country which could have been kept free—like the Lake Tahoe country—for hundreds of years for a very special kind of recreational purpose has been ruined. I think we ought to get into the question of what is an adequate unit for controlling all the forces and processes at work within a region. This must be a unit in which these processes are arranged concentrically, not in any rigid way, but with relation to the mass of the population and to the rough geographical boundaries. The boundaries will always be rough. But as long as there is sufficient centrifugal force, that won't be a real obstacle.

WOODBURY: May I make two comments, first on what I think is an essential understanding of planning? Mr. Mumford implied it very strongly in what he said. And this is in partial answer to Mr. Dansereau. My conception of planning is that it is not an activity that is concentrated in government: governments plan, corporations plan, individuals plan. I think in many respects the crucial question is who plans what, and in what detail?

I was trying to present a case in my paper of what I considered the proper scope and limits of governmental planning for regions. Certainly I think there is a part or a place for planning by private developers. I think there is a place for planning by private house owners and lot owners, and their architects and landscape architects.

I don't think we will get far by posing public against private planners with the assumption that the government is going down to the last detail and tell you where you are going to plant a tree in your back yard. Obviously not. But just where those boundaries are for proper government planning is a matter of strong difference of opinion. Yet I don't think that anyone should feel that the advocates of effective governmental planning wish the government to be planning everything.

My second point is simply a question of what I think is a misunderstanding of my position on governmental organization and regional planning. Both the Chairman and Mr. Mumford thought I felt it would not be necessary to reorganize governmental units in regions in order to do the kind of planning I had in mind. If two such distinguished listeners to my remarks drew the same conclusion, I am sure many others did too, and I was less than clear. But I thought I said that I considered one of the conditions of effective regional planning a governmental unit with region-wide jurisdiction and with powers roughly correlative with the things the regional planner was dealing with. And I thought I also said that we don't have that situation today. For some of the smaller urban regions the county government might meet the first requirement but not the second. I see no essential difference between us on that point.

If I may take the discussion just one step further, we were talking this morning about institutions, the institutional side of ecology. I think that if you want to promote effective regional planning in this country today, the first step ought to be to encourage all of the state governments to establish departments of urban affairs. Why? Because I think we do have to have some rationalization, some reorganization, of local government structure in the metropolitan regions of this country if we are going to get effective regional planning. We have tried to bring about such reorganization in many ways in the past. And the results have been almost total failure.

If you look at the methods that we have tried, while they have varied in certain details, they have all been *ad hoc* jobs. You appoint a commission or you set up a quasi-governmental body supported by local citizens. They make a study, they hire some publicity people, and eventually the reorganization proposal gets to a referendum and is voted down. This has become very tiresome. If there is anything clear it is that this is not the way you do it. And I suggest that it is worth trying to see if a continuing agency of state government (which, after all, is responsible for the local governmental structure in its area) can take on the responsibility for pressing this issue day by day, week by week, year by year; then I think you have some chance.

If we can get this started and moving in the direction I think it will take, we might take by an indirect route perhaps the greatest steps we can toward regional planning in this country.

ORDWAY: In your opening remarks you rather calmed the thoughts of those of us who were concerned with the needs stated in our first session, the need for preservation of open spaces and enough areas for a variety of wildlife, by stating that we need not worry because there will be ample lands left after the urban planners get through taking care of the great increase of urban population we see ahead of us.

I would like very much to see some discussion of whether there are, among the urban and regional planners, any planners who can lend direction and take into consideration in their planning the need to keep out private and local people from areas that ought to be preserved, and can give direction to the planning needs for preservation of the right areas in the right places in the future.

TUNNARD: This is an extremely good question that needs a rather detailed answer. I hope also that we will be able to ask our panelists and others in the room whether there is a consensus about regional planning and whether we think the United States and Canada are ready for this. Is this the moment when we should start to plan on these larger areas or not.

Mr. Ordway's question on the appropriate place for public and private developments, places where certain things should go and where certain things should not go, brings to mind in a somewhat closer fashion the form on the macroscale that development might take. I mentioned the mountains behind the Atlantic urban region which are already penetrated in certain places.

I don't think one need assume a total green band extending for many miles across the mountains but judicious penetrations of the area, very much as some of the earlier settlers thought of it in settling in the valleys and avoiding the higher ground.

This is of course the exact opposite of what Mr. McHarg suggested in his development.

A matrix of open space into which urban development fitted with its highways and all the other appurtenances of urban life would presumably provide room for all kinds of development, public and private, in places where they might be appropriate.

To do this—and I have used a very crude example—we would have to have a framework that Mr. Dickinson has suggested, and which I am sure Mr. Meier, too, will have ideas on: What should be in very rough outlines the extent of this particular kind of development? And should it fade off at the edges? Should it be intense in certain places—as in some of the colonies which Mr. Durden has suggested might be intense centers of activity?

LEOPOLD: I would like to come back to a question posed by Mrs. Strong as to whether the planning process really has enough teeth in it to be effective.

In the San Francisco area south of the Bay between Oakland and San Jose, roughly, was one of the richest pieces of productive agricultural land in California; it was used primarily for apricots, truck gardening, and cut flowers. This is deep soil, and there is nothing better in the whole state.

Despite the fact that San Francisco, the whole East Bay, has planning services associated with various cities, and we have a strong Department of Regional Planning in the University, still here is an area whose usefulness to the community, meaning the whole region, certainly should have been in agriculture; yet it is now essentially converted to housing communities.

This discourages me in terms of the planning process. We talk about planning, and yet here is a conversion that obviously is poor planning. I am wondering, as Mrs. Strong wondered, what is the mechanism? Can any of you suggest how this sort of ecologic mistake can be avoided by putting more teeth into the planning process?

STRONG: I think the failure there has been in the inability to convince the people in Santa Clara County—which is the governing unit that imposed the agricultural zoning requirements—that it was more important to keep the agriculture than to have the development. Any owner could be annexed to an existing municipality within the county upon his request. Specifically, a municipality can go out along a road and take a farm which the farmer wants to have annexed. The farmers did not want to be so restricted that they could be prevented from having development on their property when they wanted to.

If there had been sufficient conviction within the governing body and within the populace of the county that the farming was more important than leaving this choice of individual land use to the farmers, there is no reason whatsoever that the zoning couldn't have been worded differently from the way it was.

LEOPOLD: In that case, Mrs. Strong, no one is planning that. The individual landowner is obviously going to sell for the maximum income.

STRONG: The County Planning Commission said that they wanted to keep all the agricultural land, but they didn't get the backing politically to have the kind of ordinance that would enable them to do this.

The owners know how much that land would be worth as agricultural land. The owners also are perfectly well aware of how much it is worth for development. Since it would be worth considerably less for farming, if the county or the Bay Area wishes to keep it as farming land, I think they will have to face up to the question of compensating the owners for certain loss in its market value for development.

LEOPOLD: Whose responsibility is it to sell this idea, if not the planners'?

STRONG: I think it is the planners' in part, but I think they haven't had sufficient ammunition.

DURDEN: Here, I think there is a lack of meaningful concepts in regional planning. When faced with problems on a regional scale, the planner speaks of how mammoth they are and yet when it comes to conceptionalizing, he seems able only to deal effectively with sites.

In other words, we have no overriding vision, no wide view of human ecology to relate specific sites. I agree with Woodbury. We don't plan regions, we plan sites. We act like the way to attack urban environmental problems is to concentrate on sites.

TUNNARD: My feeling is that the lobby is one of the most effective means in our democratic situation. Unfortunately, in a democracy one can never get enough of it. Presumably public participation should be at a much more intense level than it is in many of these matters. It is not ignorance entirely, but it is partly that. And also strong interests are at work. This room, for instance, represents a lobby. It doesn't have to be a lobby in the sense that we think of some of the ones that operate in the halls in Washington. And I think it is more important than a public hearing, which comes often much too late. Certainly in the case of highway planning, public hearings often come very late in the proceedings.

To be active, to participate, to represent other people: this is a movement stirring all over the country now.

NICHOLSON: I feel doubly depressed about what we have heard about the absence of teeth in planning, about the great difficulty of getting enforcement of the ideas and concepts of the planners. I also feel depressed beyond that: this apparent defeatism about the future of the city and the way things are going. It looks as though people have already moved out of the city and to the suburbs, and are now moving from the suburbs, having ruined that. And when will this process end? Where will they go when they ruin the exurban areas?

Are we getting any information about the positive driving force to get some value which can't be found in the city, such as living on the coastline? In what way is it a refuge from some preventable evil which is offered to them?

I am sorry Dr. Farber isn't here. Perhaps 40 per cent instead of 20 per cent would have needed mental treatment if they had stayed, and I think I understand their wanting to get out.

Is it possible to construct an alternative type of city in which perhaps only 10 per cent of them would need treatment?

In Ottawa, a very concerted effort has been made to provide a Green Belt and internal parks and so on, to try to make the city more livable, to make it less necessary both to drive out of it, short term, into the country, and also less necessary to live out of it.

Is there any attempt to evaluate what this means in terms of city patterns? How far is this pressure ever outwards from the city inevitable? How far is it curable by different types of city design? It seems to me if it is not curable in the long run, the future for North America will be pretty poor.

TUNNARD: Are you suggesting that distances are getting so long that cities will not actually work physically?

NICHOLSON: In the case of Ottawa I understand the concept was that if you provided not only more park space but also a great variety of facilities in the parks, that not only could you enable people to spend more of their leisure time fruitfully in the city, but that you actually reduced the pressure to live in the suburbs because people could just walk into these parks and have a wide variety of facilities not normally provided in the park. That is what I understand.

TUNNARD: It does happen, I am sure. Toronto is an interesting case. With the immigration of lots of people from Eastern and Central Europe after the war, living in rather bad conditions, doubled up in the central-city tenements and in overcrowded frame houses, they used the parks—the central-city parks—for the first time properly. These people were used to city parks, and they enjoyed them in their new surroundings.

I would like to ask you, though, if you think that the British system in which there is a plan for every acre of land on the Island provides certain advantages over our many multitudes of plans that we have in this country, state and local.

NICHOLSON: I think we have multitudes of plans in Britain as well. They do collectively, as you say, cover the whole Island, but there is no integrated regional planning as yet. I do think that at least we have been able, with the Green Belt policy, and with the zoning, to prevent a number of cities from physically joining, and we have prevented a good deal of this urban sprawl.

I wouldn't regard our planning as at all a model. It seems to me that you have to create a type of city which people sufficiently want to live in to relieve a part of this pressure. If you have pressure, sooner or later the plan is going to be defeated and resisted.

TUNNARD: I think there are two points here. One is that we must have a vision of what the city ought to be, that enough people can agree on in different parts of the country, perhaps. We wouldn't want everything to be the same everywhere.

The second is, what kind of administrative framework can be devised to produce this city, or to regulate it when it is built?

FARNESS: I want to say that many discussions of planning tend to be somewhat superficial unless they really try to comprehend that social form, urban form, comes out of a deep cultural impulse. Unless you get back to thinking about the formalized institutions, where these ideas are that form the framework within which people move and live, you don't really connect with this.

The Santa Clara case goes back to many of our fundamental institutions. The plans have been laid down in these institutions years ago. Planners are in competition with other kinds of planning; very weak competitors they prove, too, because they are a minority group. But the point is, unless we can think about how we can redesign or reconstruct many of our formal institutions, we simply will not change the way things are happening.

TUNNARD: There are more ecologists than planners, judging from the figures Mr. Milton gave this morning.

FARNESS: On the one hand, we probably agree that one of the fundamental problems is the overconcentration or overdevelopment of our big urban systems. Problems arise and then the federal government begins to develop and evolve a series of programs which have had the effect of limiting or wiping out the cost of scale these overconcentrations generate. So the overconcentrations are then enabled to grow larger.

So you have, on the one hand, government making a superficial remedial action that fundamentally makes the problem more serious.

TUNNARD: There is a very good point here—that the lateral spread of cities has been from many points of view unnecessary, or rather a poor way of dealing with city growth, or not dealing with it, and that densities could be increased in our central cities, which would still be perfectly livable. Some of the densities of our urban areas in this country are perfectly laughable if you think of them as cities at all. A great many more people could be accommodated within existing city boundaries and still provide open space.

The scale question is an extremely difficult one and it is hard to deal with in conversation because we need graphic examples as illustrations.

MC HARG: I would like to answer Starker Leopold's question. If this situation had been posed on the one hand in Holland, Denmark, or England, the answer would be predictable—that is, by public decision it would be determined that prime agricultural land cannot be used for development.

In Britain every borough, every county, every city is required to produce a development plan, and it has to be reviewed every five years. This plan, when reviewed and approved by the Minister, has the force of law.

The Minister has said that he is unlikely to accept any applications to white areas, which are open agricultural land, not now developed. His presumption is that land not now developed will not be developed. And only inordinate pressure will cause this to change in the case of Denmark, Holland, or the United Kingdom. Here the planner is a public agent, responsive to public process, who produces a plan which is in fact realized. The plan may be good or bad. The process may be authoritarian or not, but the planner is an agent of a public process and the plan is realized.

In America the program is not so. The planner may be an agent of a public process but it is no guarantee the process will realize the plan. We have lots and lots of plans produced but there are no powers—either created by agencies for the purpose of realizing a plan, or federal or state powers—which are any guarantee to any planner producing the plan with the consent of the Planning Commission that he will have this realized.

You have to say that the planner is a man engaged in an enterprise which need not have any product at all. But the powers which he can invoke are only zoning powers—which are as good as politicians are honest, subdivision controls which produce the worst horrors of architecture and site planning. In England there is the Green Belt concept which Sir Patrick Abercrombie drew in pastel around London and which is effective. It is being protested but nonetheless it has the force of law. This is the Green Belt. I don't happen to think that is a good way to determine the nature and location of open space. But it is certainly one way of getting it by fiat.

ORDWAY: I think this raises again the question that I was asking. Why should there not be in this country—adopted by federal law if necessary—a flexible master plan, with the kind of white spaces that you referred to in England.

If this is impractical for reasons I don't understand, I should like to know them. If it is practical, then I should think we can put our minds to the forum of seeking that new form of institution which might do something to achieve this reservation of natural landscapes that we envision.

HALL: The great achievement of British planning has been a purely negative one. It has held land against development.

ORDWAY: May not the negative be good?

HALL: Negative may be good in itself. This negative achievement was made possible because of the legislative framework, and the legislative framework was the 1947 Planning Act, which in effect nationalized development rights. Without this you can't achieve it. You have to nationalize the rights so that in fact people lose the automatic rights to develop a plot of land. This demands that you pay compensation for the loss of rights.

The British government in 1947 had to establish a fund of 300 million pounds to pay for development rights that people expected to have at that time.

ORDWAY: This doesn't shock me.

HALL: They didn't say that they paid this as a right. They said they paid it to deal with cases of hardship.

As a matter of fact this fund was never paid out, and the law was changed so that the payments were made only when people made application to develop, but the basis is the same.

ORDWAY: Would you be opposed to an effort to attain similar programs in the United States?

HALL: Certainly not. This has been successful and certainly the great achievement of postwar planning has been to channel urban growth in a way that planners thought was right. You can quibble about the way they have done it, but the effect has been a powerful one. It has led to the end of surburban sprawl which was taking place in England between the wars and would have taken place at a greatly accelerated pace, and which is still taking place in the United States.

ORDWAY: The same thing is true in Denmark. They are developing a similar type of plan which sets aside certain conservation areas not to be invaded.

TUNNARD: They have a plan which is different from the Green Belt idea. There are green fingers going out from the center, which some planners think is a more effective method than the Green Belt, but which may increase distance rather severely.

STRONG: I second Mr. Ordway's suggestion. We do need a federal plan to be carried out in more detail, of course at state and regional levels.

I also feel as a country we have never faced up to the need for paying when we take away development value. This is the heart of the problem. Santa Clara County is a perfect example of this. We have wanted to achieve plans through zoning. Zoning fails because it doesn't provide for compensation for landowners. When the hardship becomes too great on the property owner, he manages to exert sufficient pressure so that the zoning will be revised and something more favorable to him will be initiated.

If we decide, as a people, that we wish to preserve certain areas and, as a result, cause people severe loss in value, we must be prepared to pay for it.

FISHER: On the matter of planning in metropolitan jurisdictions, there is not so much a failure of concept as a failure of political instrumentation. This has been mentioned already by Mumford and Woodbury and perhaps others.

I can give a couple of examples. For instance, in my county—Arlington —we have, I think, a pretty good master plan and a competent planning staff. Our difficulty comes in carrying the thing out and in making arrangements with our neighbors so that it can be carried out. One of our neighbors is the federal government.

To give you a couple of examples of how, if you find the right button to press, you can really go quite far, even against the political difficulties: one case would be the Federal Land and Water Conservation Act, passed in the last session, which puts up money to the states to acquire land and water resources for recreation. But the states have to have some kind of a state plan and planning process before they get a penny. And in response to this, my own state of Virginia, very quickly got up a Commission to go into this with plenty of money to do a decent job; and this isn't in a state that is very much given to planning experiments, at least, since the War between the States.

(*Laughter*)

In another case, the federal highway legislation required that the Washington metropolitan area, along with others over the country, have going by this June a metropolitan-wide planning process, otherwise they convince us we won't get any more money. This immediately moved the General Assembly of Virginia to pass a law enabling the northern Virginia region to set this going, and they were breathing down our necks to get moving.

I could give you another case under the Economic Opportunity Program; here we are in the realm of social planning, I suppose. The federal officials of this act are going to dish the money out through a united planning organization which operates for the whole metropolitan area, and they say they won't dish it out to anybody else.

These are examples of what I call political instrumentation which can make big improvements in the way land is developed and used in metropolitan areas.

I don't think it is so good to be looking around for some way of making a total comprehensive metropolitan plan come into being. Much more important, it seems to me, is to look for button after button to press which will make at least some facet or some sector of planning a good bit better than it was before, and then hope that as this goes along the different planners and military leaders in the metropolitan area will be reasonably clever and quick to find ways of coordinating these.

The great need, as I see it, projecting along this line a little further, is to get these massive federal programs hitched together a little better. I will give an example. There is a tremendous federal program moving in the interstate-highway field, by far the biggest internal improvement program under one concept we have ever had in history. It will spend about sixty billion dollars in fifteen years' time. Another big program that hasn't moved so far, but I think will in the future, is federal aid to acquisition of open space. A third one is the Renewal Program that now is under lots of fire.

What is happening in the metropolitan area that I know best seems to me something like this: The big highway program moves in with great force, and highways are put down the stream valleys and through the parks because land is cheaper and fewer people object, and so on. A little while later in the next cycle, five years later, I am sure there will be a massive program, much larger, to acquire open spaces—so we will have to go make open spaces someplace else. Meanwhile, urban renewal goes on, and nobody ever thought of perhaps moving some of these highways through areas that will have to be acquired under public authority anyway.

It seems to me that though we are pushing separate buttons in order to get highway planning and open-space planning and so on, we need now some kind of console or instrumentation so that these buttons can be pushed and some kind of harmonious music will come out.

WOODBURY: On Mr. Leopold's question, I think there are two other things that ought to be said. One is that we are in a curious position in this country in that the first attempts at public planning—area planning—are in the smallest areas, geographically: the cities and municipalities. It is they that were first given control powers in zoning and so on.

I would suspect, without knowing the situation that you referred to in any detail, that what happened there was that a relatively small unit of government focused on its own problems and, not looking at the regional development at all, decided on the change of zoning and let development take place along that line. Certainly one of the concomitants of the sort of proposal that we were working on before, a reorganization of local government on some sort of a regional basis, ought to include giving to the governments of those regions at least many of the control powers.

This would not necessarily avoid the sort of thing Mr. Leopold has cited, but it would certainly make it less likely.

The other point concerns what we have to do if we are going to get an ecological view of planning. One of the reasons probably that Mr. Leopold's unit of local government gave in so readily was that a fairly substantial portion of its revenue is from the property tax. Therefore, if you have more buildings on the land, you get a higher yield. That one thing has been distorting as many planning proposals in American cities of all sizes as any one other thing that you can name.

I think if you are going to get effective plans, you have to look not only at the legal position and the legal powers, but at who exercises them, and in what context on the financial side.

The fact is that a very substantial amount of local revenues these days is coming from State and Federal governments. Not many people realize that of the total revenues of American cities, the proportion must now be something like 30 per cent from state and federal government grants-in-aid of one sort or another. Again this is all being done on an *ad hoc* basis. And it is having another effect upon planning—that of distorting programs to take advantage of the juiciest grants-in-aid.

If we are going to take an ecological view of regional development, and if we are going to include man, we have to include his institutions. To get effective action in many of these areas we have to go into some of these institutions that at first do not seem immediately involved: the tax system, the local government setup, the grant-in-aid program, and so on.

This is a formidable job. Yet I think our experience indicates that it has to be done. And those of us who believe that this essentially ecological concept of regional development is the only one that makes much sense have to follow this to its conclusion in the types of action that we have to seek.

DARLING: I was pleased, a few moments ago, to hear such support for the idea of—if I may use the word here—nationalizing development values. Of course it was very hard for some of us to take in Britain in 1947. It was a magnificent idea. In general it has worked. Now I don't think very many of us would wish it to be otherwise. Unfortunately, the government of the past twelve years has whittled away the Town and Country Act very seriously, for which I am sorry.

When I came to work on the national-parks survey, which our Foundation is doing, I came bang up against this whole subject, the effect it has against the keeping of the edges of national parks in reasonable condition.

Whenever any ground is set aside as an open area or a national park, the values of the edges go up out of all reason and it is possible for a large area of countryside to be damaged which would not have been touched had not the open space of a national park been established.

That is one side. And then when it comes to inholdings in national parks, it operates heavily against the National Park Service to acquire them. It puts the value up out of all reason.

What has struck me particularly as an Englishman, the average Englishman has no notion of your land-taxing laws—what we call rates. You tax upon potential development, as far as I can see.

An American friend of mine has seventeen acres on the top of a hill, very poor ground. But he has his home and two or three other houses up there. He is being taxed almost out of existence because he will not allow subdivision on his seventeen acres on the top of the hill. Such a subdivision would deteriorate amenity over a much larger area.

The English system, of course, is to tax when development takes place, not before. I can imagine in Starker Leopold's case that the land holders in Alameda would be pushed into the housing development two ways: by the chance of getting the big money for the land and also because if they didn't sell, they would be taxed at a much higher rate than they would were it not taxed on potential.

TUNNARD: Dick, would you say something about regional planning from your point of view?

MEIER: It seems to me that when you look at the kinds of things that are coming up in the next ten or twenty years, the planners cannot look backward, and a good share of what we have been saying has been looking backward rather than forward.

We have to identify sufficient new stresses in this system that have only the very tiniest beginnings at the moment, but will become very sizable in the future.

I tried to identify in my paper one where there is an amphibian population in the United States. It is already bidding up the price of seashore plots in Florida as far as a hundred yards inland. Plots with mooring facilities are going to cost about $6000 more than identical plots without any kind of dock at the back door.

This move toward the marine frontier has to be taken into account. And it seems to be strongest within about 100 miles of the urban centers, and it will continue to become increasingly strong because the technology is getting cheaper. Not only is there increasing demand, but the cost is also declining.

There is another new stress developing, too, when one makes projections of air space, not water space; already the queue at O'Hare Airport is two hours long. It is often longer here in the megalopolis in the East, so that planes, before they leave the ground 500 miles away from Chicago, are already in the queue to get into O'Hare Airport. As we try to project into the future problem of providing air channels, we find congestion, particularly when you are bringing traffic over the poles or across the ocean and bringing it along the megalopolis line. Transport becomes intolerable. Educated people like ourselves will no longer be able to interact without running into the fact that one third may not arrive.

Something will be done about it. I suspect from the way the projections go, about five billion dollars' worth will be done about it, and that some of the major elements in the capital budget in the development of urbanism are going to enable us to get around.

I have had my students exploring what were the implications for the formation of a megalopolis on mid-continent over the next two decades, given what we know now about technology, about the growth rates and demand, and we begin to see a new kind of region evolving that stems in the long shot from Guttman. As Dickinson indicated, he stopped short from drawing all the inferences from the data which he had collected.

It appears that one will have to have an underground tube. The pictures are in the April, 1965 issue of *Fortune* of the studies from MIT.

These tubes will go up to 400 miles an hour. They will have stops fifty to 100 miles apart in general. These stops then begin to have the equivalents of an airport but they are likely to be very close to urban centers.

Therefore we begin to get rather high-density flows of educated mobile people showing up again, not only in the great metropolitan centers but also in the smaller metropolitan centers—but only those along the main line.

Our students were horrified to discover that Ann Arbor had virtually all of the pressures of a mid-continent megalopolis funneling into it, being at the center of it, and having most of the growth activities of the next two decades showing up in Ann Arbor, particularly within a half mile of their classroom.

But to go a little further. We also found that the demand for space was such that most people wanted to get away from the metropolitan area, and that therefore this dispersed urban kind of population is the kind that would account for a very large share of the new settlement; and therefore there seemed to be no demand for two thirds or three quarters of the land which was being cleared of slums for urban renewal.

We are going to have a desert around the CBD [Central Business District] in the major metropolitan areas, a desert in the sense that for a long time we will be in a quandary as to how to devalue that land to use it for some other purpose than had originally been intended. Instead, people will be out there, providing a kind of flesh around the spine of a 600-mile megalopolis which has grown along the line of Detroit, Chicago, and Toronto.

We can then see a kind of distribution of densities coming into these foci fifty to 100 miles apart, with a peak where the parking buildings and the apartment houses may get up to twenty stories high. This is the urban form that appears to come out of existing pressures. One cannot see too many things against it at first blush.

TUNNARD: May I ask what happens to this expensive network that has been projected and mentioned by Dr. Fisher?

MEIER: It is utilized to get the cars from the dispersed urban areas to these centers where a small proportion, 5 per cent or so, wants to get up and down the megalopolitan main line because it is more convenient than the airport system. The airport is still there.

TUNNARD: I think the picture is an interesting one. I would like Professor Dickinson, then Dr. Clawson, and then—hopefully—an ecologist to respond, by giving us a view of what he thinks the city of the future ought to be.

DICKINSON: I have tried to define this area of urbanized impact in the United States, to get some indication of what has happened. I said this covers seventy-five million acres. That brings it up to a total of 3.6 per cent of the United States.

If you take all these areas that lie within the orbits of the big cities, within a radius of fifteen or twenty miles, which I defined, it will bring you in the neighborhood of 20 per cent of the United States. I would like to know therefore what the conservationists propose to do. This is Mr. Ordway's question, what he is really getting at. What do the conservationists propose to do with this area? What guidelines would they suggest for controlling or checking or developing or improving this area?

ORDWAY: They want you to answer that.

DICKINSON: It is quite clear in the whole of this area there are great differences in terms of land use and in terms of human settlement. Parts are very highly urbanized. There will be separate communities. There are still going to be large areas, presumably, of open land, including a large section of the United States. From an ecological point of view, what is going to be done with it?

CLAWSON: It seems to me that the essence of planning is the assumption that we are not going to leave the decisions to an unregulated private market.

This I am quite willing to accept. But I do think that planners generally —and if I am being critical now of planners I am being even more critical of economists—have not carried the economic value, the dollar-value implications, into our plans.

If we talk now about a particular use of land in an area, who will benefit from this use of land and to what extent? And who will lose?

Believe me, in many instances people would lose. In Santa Clara County the farmers were the ones who were most opposed to keeping this land in agriculture because they wanted the opportunity to sell it at development prices.

I think it is fair to say that in almost no instance are the economic implications of regional plans or city plans so conducted as to say what is the total gain to the whole community, and particularly to which groups, and which ones are going to lose.

If you propose, by legal powers, to do something which is not the most profitable line to somebody, then you certainly have got to have the legal power competence to withstand the pressures. And this we generally do not have.

I think it would help a great deal if we had some concept of what kinds of economic pressures we are going to meet. In some cases they are slight, and therefore the zoning or other legal powers may be sufficient. In others they are great, and it would certainly take substantial legal powers to stand up under the pressure, purchase being oftentimes the only one.

TUNNARD: Since the subject this afternoon is so big, and we haven't heard from them, I think we should wind up with hearing from the ecologists. Particularly because this Conference so strongly emphasizes open-space and wildlife concepts, it would be good to hear from the ecologists now as to their vision of the future of the city.

ALLEN: I was wondering what kinds of technical principles are being developed in this art of planning, and I wonder particularly when I look around my own local community. I know that the point that Dr. Woodbury brought up is involved here, the matter of getting more land on the tax rolls at a higher rate. Sometimes I think it is the only thing that some of the planners know. It could be, and it is no reflection on the good planners.

We have a river bottom. It flooded once at a very high level, as I remember, and did a lot of damage, and it has flooded at lesser levels since then. Now we have a great hole dug in one side of the river bottom and a big shopping center built on top of the earth that was piled over a forty-acre plot. We also have apartment houses built down in the river bottom.

It seems pretty evident that if anyone understood the dynamics of the river and had any respect for the natural river-bottom scenery at all it would have been a simple thing to locate a park down there, which would give us a part of the open space that we need in an area that at least at one time was rather inexpensive land. Then when it floods you tie down the park benches.

What do you do now? After a flood comes we will appeal for a big dam up the river, and mud is going to fill any reservoir that is built. Then what happens when the reservoir is filled? This is an ecologist's nightmare I am building here, instead of an ecologist's dream. But I think it is realistic.

Some of the problems that we are creating now are going to be pretty difficult to solve fifty or more years from now. In the meantime, of course, we are collecting more taxes from the river bottom and we are trying to locate parks somewhere else.

What this boils down to in my terms is a plea for paying close attention to and developing some principles relative to integrating the natural scene with the man-developments.

I think all of us have seen what architectural triumphs are achieved sometimes when a dwelling house is fitted into the scenery. A few miles south of us in the Carolinas we have some little towns built in the middle of stands of old-growth pine, and the streets run around among the trees. They didn't cut the pines down to run the streets in straight lines. Why they didn't I don't know, but this was certainly an imaginative approach that can make a small town startlingly beautiful.

I think it shows what man can do if he fits himself into the scenery and does not approach his development problems with the ultimate degree of arrogance that always involves the use of a bulldozer and other similar techniques.

I remember such simple things as small marshes. Most marshes in little towns—and I know some very good examples—have become dumps, and of course they are unsightly. Sooner or later they are filled and someone uses them for building sites.

Around my home, where I grew up, there was a little marsh. Maybe it bred mosquitoes. It also had frogs in the spring and a lot of other things. It was a little open space and a touch of wild nature that with imagination could have been kept, even as a marsh.

Some people see no beauty in a marsh. Many people do. It is a natural habitat that, if used with imagination, could be incorporated into a plan for an environment that would make the most of inexpensive natural beauties.

I am sure the economists would say you are giving up something if you keep that. You are giving up a building site.

They are quite right. I suppose when I say inexpensive I am to some extent wrong. But at least it doesn't cost a lot to preserve some of these small, accessible natural areas. They only need to be kept the way they are.

TUNNARD: I am glad to have these smaller-scale examples because this really gets us down to the ground we live on. I suppose if we had time we could really come to some kind of consensus about stream valleys in relation to urban areas. We know certain things are being done with floodplains and catchment areas in relation to cities. I think we are also going to see more attention being given to keeping agricultural areas within metropolitan centers, as in a city like Hartford, for instance, where within the metropolitan area there are tobacco farms and cash crops and grazing lands, water meadows, and so on.

To add up the natural part of the picture of North America's future environment and to relate it to the city is not an easy task. It indicates an approach more than a blueprint, and we have to give the ecologist his say in the urban area. This has obviously been a great lack. We have heard for three days that the ecologist isn't having his say. He could prevent many bad developments from happening, and could also suggest many good and interesting new approaches to forming a better urban environment. How he gets this say, how he enters the picture, is, I suppose, up to the ecologists as a group to decide.

COWAN: This function of the ecologist-biologist in the planning process I think is well known to you from the excellent progress made in southern Ontario in some of the recent minor river-basin developments in the vicinity of Toronto.

A beautiful application of intelligent, unified planning of this sort was initiated in Ontario. I think the first steps were taken by a society of naturalists stimulated by J. R. Dymond of the University of Toronto. He was able to mobilize a group to excite the people of the communities to accept the work of the planners and to see it implemented.

We have all of us been exasperated—as I am sure the planners have—to see the piecemeal adoption of well-thought-out plans, and to see that with every change in civic governments a new set of planners is brought in to begin the process anew.

If the question is asked, what should we do with this land, the conservationist and ecologist has a standard answer: We will do what we have to do and as little as possible to achieve the desired effect. And this is the desirable approach to much wild land planning.

The ecologist, in planning, has been involved in the ecology of cropland. In this he teams up with the highly competent people in agronomy and the agricultural sciences. He is involved in the ecology of forestland, which will continue to be a very large part of the North American scene in perpetuity. After all, 75 per cent of Canada will probably always be wild land.

The ecologist is heavily involved in planning for use of wild recreation areas, but has not been involved in planning for intensively used recreational areas to the same extent.

There are large parts of the North American public interested in fishing and hunting, and at this level the ecologist is heavily involved with the agriculturalist, the forester, and with the other people who are interested in land use at this level. And an important part of our interests is the marine littoral and the immediate subtidal. Our immediate competence beneath the water is taking hundreds of thousands of Americans beneath the water every year and they are finding their recreation, finding their fascination in the subtidal down to 100 feet.

Our government discovered some years ago that there were almost no publicly owned lands around the coasts of southern British Columbia. They made an immediate enclosure, and now it is impossible to buy government land there. Our coastline is seven thousand miles long with some of the finest fjords in the world. It is now completely removed from alienation until the government has had a chance to prepare a comprehensive plan including the identification of areas that must be used for public recreational development later on.

There is an important part that the ecologist or economically oriented biologist can play as a member of the team that associates with the other people interested in the landscapes of North America.

TUNNARD: Very good. I assume, too, that if we could get that ecological survey that was mentioned this morning, and also get Mr. Dickinson's grid, and the kind of transportation system that Mr. Meier worked out, we would begin to have a useful research basis for what we want to put on the land.

I think if I may close the proceedings, unless somebody is simply burning to have a last word—

MC HARG: I am burning.

TUNNARD: All right.

MC HARG: I am looking at Clawson, if he will raise his head. There is one plan, at least, where some people really did try to put economic values on open space, and I would like to speak about that.

Once upon a time some four thousand families lived a bucolic life in Baltimore County, in the Green Spring and Worthington valleys. A new highway had been constructed opening their rural retreat. Existing zoning protected them not at all. They had the sense of an imminent Homestead Act whereby every developer was waiting to load gas stations and diners, hot-dog stands and billboards, ticktacky houses, and smear them over their beautiful landscape. They said this is no way for Americans to achieve their destiny or hand down their patrimony—what can we do about it?

They raised $100,000 in quick order, and they hired my colleague Wallace and myself, and we hired some other people, and we did two things. First, we did what was called an uncontrolled-growth plan in which we predicted how developers were likely to behave, the sites they were likely to select, where public investment in water, highways, and sewers was likely to go, and we assumed that the landscape architect would be called in to design all these subdivisions, and we saw what the product would be, and we called it a specter.

At the end of this a lot of money would have been made but nothing to justify the people living there.

We calculated how much money would have been produced by this to the landowners, to the entrepreneurs, subdividers, and how much money the community would get from taxes and used that as a base line. We turned around and said how can an understanding of natural processes determine where the development should best occur.

Fortuitously, the valley bottoms were coterminous with the best resources of ground water in the region. We said if you don't want hepatitis, don't build in the bottom of the valleys. We found, of course, that there were surface waters and flat plains in the valley bottoms.

The valleys are beautiful, they are the genius of a site, but they are vulnerable and not the wise place to develop. Then we looked at the plateaus.

Physiographic examination of them disclosed that instead of pervasive developments, there were locations where hamlets, villages and a country town could be built. From our physiographic analysis we concluded that the valley bottoms were vulnerable and should not be developed, that the wooded side slopes were also vulnerable and should support only limited development, and that the new development for some one hundred thousand people should be best located on the plateaus as a hierarchy of communities with normal low density housing limited to forest areas. We calculated what the income from this plan might be. We found what it was. We found it was somewhat in excess of what it was within controlled growth, which allowed us to say that the income to be derived from development as proposed could pay for 30 per cent of the land not to be developed at all, and to pay to the landowners, whose land should not be developed, that sum appropriated for the loss of value produced by the plan.

Mrs. Strong went through an enormous analysis of devices by which this might be utilized, including the public and private sector. Of all of the proposals perhaps the best was the real estate syndicate under which the landowners would conjoin as a real estate syndicate and give them development rights in exchange for cash or stock.

Up to this point this private plan has been accepted by the public. It is very crude ecology. This is high school natural science. But nonetheless this high school natural science still allows the people in this place to see that they can develop and absorb 180,000 people without despoliation and that this process is just as profitable and distinctly preferable to inchoate despoliation.

TUNNARD: A few words in summation.

We began this afternoon with the administrative and the scientific side rather than with a vision of what we thought the future city might be.

I think that approach was appropriate enough, in the light of the talent that we have and what it was able to contribute, which was considerable.

Although we don't have a vision of the regional city except in very general terms from this afternoon's discussion, I think we have begun to see where a lot of people might fit into the urbanization process, and the nature of the institutions and facilities that would either have to be devised or encouraged or suppressed in the achievement of a regional environment.

I think we got a little further into the future than we have at some of the sessions, although this may be because I have been shown things myself that have given me a better picture of the future, because of the excellent testimony that we have heard.

I hope you are not too depressed. We didn't bring up examples like Stockholm, which has no suburbs, practically, and is redeveloping the central city by the municipality without the need of much pump-priming. We have kept away from too many examples from Northwestern Europe, though we were very glad to have the British picture given to us.

We may not be clear about an ecological approach to planning, but I can see after these meetings that there could be an ecological approach. This is very encouraging to me. My fear is that this voice is not heard loudly enough: in conservation matters, yes, but as a creative field, I think a lot of education has to be done.

The economists have been very quiet this afternoon. I would like to mention that they also should have had their say. Ecological determinism may produce a beautiful living environment, but the economist would tell us that we can't abolish our great urban belts because of the means of mass production and distribution, the linkages between industries, the way automobiles are manufactured, specialization, and so on; that in our free market system we must continue to have these things occurring among rather large agglomerations of people. They were restrained and didn't paint that picture. But I think it is part of the vision of the future, too.

VI ORGANIZATION AND IMPLEMENTATION

* Mr. Ordway, a member of the New York Bar, was President of The Conservation Foundation from 1962 to 1965. He was formerly a member of the United States Civil Service Commission and, as Captain in the Naval Reserve, was in charge of the Navy's civilian manpower in World War II.

Introductory Statement and Summary Remarks

ORDWAY: Having listened to four days of our deliberations, I found myself yesterday thinking of Laski's "Ultimate Judgment"—that the ability to be optimistic in the face of disillusion is the only breath of hope.

This morning I feel that premature disillusion is only a beginning of the realization of the ecological dream.

This session deals with organization and implementation—that is, with institutional means, including education, for advancing our approach to our goal of long-range environmental health on our continent.

We shall discuss institutional forms, present and projected, innovations to cope in time with the most pressing ecological issues of today and tomorrow, institutions to foresee the consequences of choice, to guide and perhaps control the future of our landscape within constitutional bounds.

More specifically, we will explore institutional means for better systematizing the classification of land and land use, habitat types, and ecosystems, and to improve the variety, distribution, and use of our various resources, perhaps even the determination of policy and choice. We have suggested, in our inadequacies, that all these are the obligations of institutions. We know in our disciplines only what we know. What we do not know and now need to know we should be in haste to find out through ourselves, our disciplines, and with the help of our institutions. But we should be in haste also to apply what we do now know considerably faster and better than we have yet done. This asks much of our institutions, which are, admittedly, still inadequate and which, after all, are only means to our ends.

Institutions include law and education, economics and government, even politics, among the social sciences, and they embrace the physical and chemical and ecological sciences that Boulding also found inadequate. There were reasons for that dark hour before the dawn.

We have talked about the pressures on modern man, stresses of population growth, of urbanization and crowding, of the imposition of automobiles and TV and noise and pollution. We have talked also about the pressures of man and his technology as stressors on the land itself, on ecosystems, and on natural beauty. What institutional means are there that are most likely to alleviate both sorts of interrelated stress? I sometimes wonder whether the great variety in our institutions is healthful. They seem less productive at times than a tropical forest of equally diffuse and more healthy variety. Dr. Caldwell here is a political scientist. Ann Strong is a lawyer who speaks as much with the voice of the planner as the voice of Blackstone or Holmes. Paul Brandwein is, among many things, an educator and an innovator. I have suffered the pangs of institutional administration.

In our four papers, which I shall soon ask each author to relate briefly to all that has been said here in the last four days, I find a common element: the effectiveness of all institutions depends on societal understanding and, indeed, consensus. Ann Strong says this boldly about the law. I quote: "Law emerges from . . . the area of societal consensus." Caldwell says: "If ecological perceptions and values are underdeveloped in society, they are not likely to be influential in government." And Brandwein is concerned also with full conceptual understanding by future leaders. My own brief indicates a steadily broadening interpretation of the scope of the police power to regulate the uses of private property in the public interest.

Thus has societal consensus become ready for change. And yet I'm not sure that we are wholly right about this position. The idea that law emerges from consensus seems to me a degradation of a learned profession. I wonder whether, even in our present diverse human ecosystem, so full of variables and variety, there can be such a thing as a consensus. Institutional recommendations, pioneering in nature, however politically dangerous, have helped develop, not always followed, societal consensus. Caldwell's paper includes examples.

Indeed, if Ibsen was right, as I like to believe he was, when he said the majority is always wrong, there would be little progress if our institutions serve only a belated consensus of opinion. Moreover, I submit that sometimes a minority which is sharply critical, yet constructive and consequential in the sense that it foresees and points out impending consequences, often influences action before the minority becomes wrong by becoming a consensus. Having planned for institutions, having worked for institutions, having won and lost with institutions, fully knowing their weaknesses and their tribulations, I still have faith that they can accomplish what our disciplines, freely acknowledging inadequacy while willing to help with the knowledge they have, doubt that they can accomplish through wisdom alone.

I am now going to ask each of the authors on this panel—and there are only four of us—to take six minutes on their subjects to provide you with hope. We will then suffer the crossfire.

I think we should begin with Paul Brandwein, and I'd like to say that not only is he a sound critic of educational methods but he is also an innovator. He sees clearly the failures for the present world of past instructional processes to prepare our future leaders to be learners, to comprehend change and environmental interdependencies. He proposes ways to apply today the conceptual approach to that end to enable our future leaders to acquire knowledge, skills, and attitudes that are not yet known, and thus prepare them to lead in a world whose technology does not yet exist.

BRANDWEIN: I wish—for reasons that no longer exist—that this Conference had been held in a *favella* in Brazil or in a slum in Harlem, and we would have had different aspects of the future. Possibly we would not have been concerned as much with the condor but more with the Kabluna Eskimo and with poverty. But perhaps this is past, and we cannot see Airlie Houses dotting the landscape for all people. But we would wish the amenity of the Airlie House and all its landscape for people.

Let me attack the problem in the short time in another way. One million or two million years ago, depending on whose geologists you prefer, man came up from pithecanthropoid ancestry. Seven hundred to eight hundred years ago all of us, except those who chose our parents properly, would have been slaves, except we would have been called serfs. Only a short time ago, man began to educate others in time-binding institutions called schools. And I will return to the word "time-binding." In 1900 in this country the last state made compulsory education law. Thirty years ago we educated in our high schools only three out of ten. Now we get seven out of ten through high schools, however bad they are.

So I must take an evolutionist's point of view toward education. And evolution need not be optimistic. It just can indicate trends. And the word "optimism" has no value except to say that if you are human you tend to be humane, and the word itself implies optimism.

Let me project the school of fifty years from now. First, we will not assume that competence means learning. We will assume that the educated man is as compassionate as he is competent. Indeed, that's the fault of the American school, which eliminates the European notion of competence as the aim of education. We will consider that education is not only a profession but it is also a mercy, that we must take all who come to us —even those who didn't choose their parents properly—and, further, we will assume that, if education is a mercy, we cannot use children as implements of psychological warfare as we do now—that is, to serve our ends —but that each child will be of supreme moral worth, because even the dullest and most moronic is a work of art that has taken three billion years to develop.

We will further go ahead to assume that human variability is the guarantee of full freedom. And that to me is, of course, the conservation ethic: that if you permit variability, it is the guarantee of freedom. And freedom is the only thing I find essential in order to be human.

And we will not assume that equality of opportunity means identity of exposure—that is, with identical teachers and identical textbooks, identical time spans, because you know some children grow faster than others.

And we will take Einstein's definition of education as experience in search of meaning as exceedingly important.

I think Mr. Steers was saying yesterday in my absence that, above all, we should conserve environments of beauty so children would have experience with environments of beauty. Otherwise, how can they search for meaning?

And so we see a kind of education in which teachers are not defined as those who regurgitate what they know, that teaching will not be telling even on the college level, and that teachers will not rob children of the right to discovery. Indeed, teaching will be consequent with intelligent failure and the appropriation of the right to make errors, and we will give children the psychological safety and psychological freedom to develop at the fastest rate.

This is no figment right now in my own "experiments," if you will, "in education." It is different from experiments with learning. Such works as the process approach are experiments in learning. But with experiments in education you are concerned with conservation.

Education is, in the end, the fullest expression of conservation. It is the human use of human beings.

In the Western world, what we do for children up to the age of eight is a good operational definition of the kind of world we want. After the age of eight we tell them to go to the devil, and after twelve to sixteen they can join the Marines. But up to the age of eight it's the Western code to love little children, and we would make a world for them that's fit.

Now, I see a school then—I could name dozens of places—where children proceed at the rate of growth which is consequent on their development.

To be specific, children can do calculus in the ninth grade, eighth grade, without emotional consequence. Children can design landscapes, beautiful landscapes, at the age of twelve. Children can do original research work in science—and this is the area with which I have been particularly concerned—oh, before high school, and publish papers, and have scientists say, "These are indeed of value."

There are these kinds of children, called idiosyncratic children, and there are children who are not.

We see, then, a school system in which all these assumptions that I have laid down exist not as hot air but as practice. Children are now proceeding because teachers are not supposed to know everything but are supposed only to know something of the way children learn, proceeding at their own level, very rapidly.

This was not present except in very isolated cases thirty years ago.

So that at least in three great cities that I know, and at least forty others that have been reported on—and that's quite a rate of growth—children will be doing the equivalent of what we call, for want of a better word, college work, right through high school.

Furthermore, experiencing the things that we have been talking about, it is not impossible for children to take six months out of their environment any more—it is not impossible—and to visit other environments and to have the experiences in search of meaning, while others proceed at their own level.

The reason for this is that we now assume something we did not assume before, and it took twenty years of research to come upon this very stupid thing. I will say it this way: Mental activity is not directed by problems.

It is almost never directed by problems. It is directed by objects and events.

If the object and event are not recognized, the problem cannot be stated. And if the concept is not understood, the problem is not clarified. Otherwise, why couldn't Aristotle have stated everything we state today? All he had to do is face the problems.

In short, you do not proceed from unknowns to knowns but from knowns, however sad, to unknowns and to knowns.

And, therefore, we can now organize schools not on the basis of grades —that's Neanderthal—but on the basis of conceptual understandings, and concepts are structures. In Piaget's sense of the term, the teacher creates situations, experiences, Mr. Steers, by which children uncover the structure. And as soon as they uncover the structure or the concept, they proceed to the next conceptual level.

This is actually the case. Perhaps later we can talk about it.

And so our school is changing from one which is bound in time by teachers' experience in grades to that which is bound by scholarship in concepts and experience, so that children can move as fast as experiences can permit them.

ORDWAY: Thank you, Paul, very much.

I am delighted that we have Ann Strong with us and that not only is she a lawyer who will make some of our problems clear but that she also has had experience in planning which she has applied successfully.

STRONG: I was asked to talk about how to secure an adequate distribution of open space. And as I faced the problem I realized that no one had before defined for me what an adequate distribution was and that, therefore, I could hardly say how we were going to achieve it. So, instead of writing what I think you probably expected on the land-use-control aspects of achieving open space, it seemed to me essential to try to explore what an adequate distribution would be.

I started with the premise we have all accepted here that variety in the natural environment was a desirable thing and then asked myself whether this also meant that, since man lives in both the world of his own creation as well as the natural world, it might be possible to suggest that it was equally important for him to have variety in the man-made world. I have moved on from the premise that it is desirable, without any proof that this is so.

If one is to have variety in both the natural and the man-made world, one would wish to maximize opportunities in both. Since there is no evidence that one is more important to man than the other at this point, one would therefore assume that you should try to optimize opportunity for variety of both.

We have noticed, and it's been commented on here several times, that man has a tendency to separate and stratify and destroy variety, and this is certainly evident in his man-made world. In America the zoning trend of the last forty years, or since 1920, has been to have a separation of uses, separation of people by income, and, of course, racial stratification. Under my assumption none of this would be desirable, and we would seek instead to get a mix of activities and people and economic levels.

I then started to wonder on what scale we would do this. If we were to do it at the national level only, we could achieve variety by separation. We could have open space in one place, the cities in another place, the small towns somewhere else. But this would hardly give us variety for everybody. Therefore, I think you must have the variety penetrate down to the lowest level of urban development, down to the neighborhood. I also think that one must, in seeking this variety, try to preserve as much choice for man as to the type of environment that he might have as is possible.

However, as we have been talking here about the wishes of man to live out in the country and have this dispersed-urban type of settlement, we also know that man wants to live near the water and that he likes the temperate climate. It seems quite evident that not all people can have their choice in this way and that we are going to have, as a society, to place limitations on choice in order to maximize choice for all people. This would mean in terms of urban settlements that we would set both minimum and maximum size and density limits. I cannot say what these should be.

We should also assume that we are going to have to force people, by policies of redistribution, to settle where we want them to, that we will have to have our urban centers more distributed than they are at present, that we also must try to provide open space in relation to people's daily lives as part of these urban settlements, and that the open space should be keyed both to the size and the density of the urban community, also to its accessibility to the people there.

This might mean that, if you had a very large urban core, you would need more open space immediately adjoining it than you would near a smaller community where the accessibility would be easier and your time-distance costs would be lower. In going through this process of trying to develop the type of urban community that we would have and relate this to law, I conclude, if Mr. Ordway does not, that one must first know whether this is desirable and that we must persuade people. I believe with F. S. C. Northrop that positive law really is a reflection of the living

law. I wouldn't deny, Mr. Ordway, that we should be the leaders in trying to develop what the living law is. But, in order to do this, I think
that we must conclude among ourselves as to what is desirable, whether
the type of design of centers that I have proposed here is, in fact, one
that is most healthy for man.

ORDWAY: Dr. Caldwell's paper interested me particularly because of the historical development that he presents concerned with the evolution of our
political approaches to this problem of land use. He goes beyond this, of
course, and analyzes some of the institutional efforts that we have made
in the past and suggests some that we can look forward to in the future.

CALDWELL: My remarks this morning will be directed to the future and in the
spirit of that great Virginian who said, on the eve of the new experiment
of the American republic, "I hope this will be an age of experiments in
government." Well, it has not been the age of experiments in government
that Jefferson had hoped for. We have been a conservative people in the
United States in the shaping and reshaping of our institutions.

I shall not attempt in what I have to say this morning to deal with the
institutional and administrative situations of our Canadian neighbors or of
the area south of the Rio Grande. They present interesting problems and
could be instructive, I'm sure, to future developments in the United States.
But the situation that we confront in the shaping and reshaping of our
governmental institutions in the United States is so large and complex
that we can only deal with it in a very superficial way in a session
like this. I submit that ours must indeed become an age of experiments
in government for very obvious reasons growing out of the impact of science and technology and world political and economic pressures that have
been discussed in this room during the past several days. We must also
attain to an age of experiments in government if the objectives that have
been implicit in these meetings are going to be realized even in approximation.

Though we in the United States have lived under an eighteenth-century
Constitution that was designed primarily for political stability and in such
a manner as to be difficult to change, we have seen some remarkable innovations. We have, of course, a method of constitutional amendment
which has been used to reshape from time to time relations between
the national authority and the states and among the states. We have
seen the Constitution of the United States amended by the Supreme
Court. Within the Constitution there are devices for gaining flexibility
and gaining variety in public institutions, for example, the device of the
grant-in-aid, which has been referred to many times throughout these sessions, as one way of obtaining certain kinds of action throughout the nation for which we do not have explicit institutional arrangements.

We have, through the federal compact clause, an instrumentality for
intergovernmental cooperation at the state level, and we have seen this
used in the case of certain of the river-valley compacts and the interstate

sanitation compact in the New York area, used frequently for purposes of what we might call environmental administration.

Nevertheless, it is quite possible that this kind of *ad hoc* flexibility that we have enjoyed may not be adequate to meet the kinds of challenges that we are beginning to encounter and that the particular devices for flexibility in the Constitution themselves may not be adequate to obtain the kind of control over our own futures that we may now wish. I think, therefore, institutional innovation, even though it is something that most Americans do not like to contemplate, is in the long run inevitable. And perhaps the long run will be shorter and more immediate than we might think.

Let me suggest to you several reasons for this inevitability, as it seems to me.

First of all, we have heard in the sessions here and elsewhere that we are undergoing a very rapid and massive reconcentration of wealth and population in the United States. The megalopoli are already a fact. And this is creating an economic and a demographic imbalance on our eighteenth-century federal system.

Less and less does it make sense to consider Arkansas, New York, California, and Delaware as equal and sovereign states; even though this is in a sense a legal fiction, the fiction has also a kind of legal reality. This may seem a contradiction; there are many contradictory sorts of things in human arrangements. A convincing case can be made for regional and local government. But our present federal pattern seems to fall farther and farther behind the needs of the times. Increasingly initiative is passing to the federal government under the euphemistic name "creative federalism."

Secondly, we can see very clear evidence of the strain on this system in several constitutional developments for example, the reapportionment changes that the Supreme Court has mandated transfer power from the rural and small-town areas increasingly to the great cities, further emphasizing the power of the great and populous states in the American Union. The civil-rights decisions, regardless of ethical or juridical merit also undercut the assumptions on which the traditional federal system was established.

A third factor which I think is very significant from a political and legislative point of view is the rapid decline in the power of the rural South. We have seen in the events of the past few weeks further evidence of the rapid loss of political power by the South, by the Gulf states particularly. In the American federal system and in the structure of our Congress, it has been possible for any cohesive veto group to shape policy by inaction.

I think it is quite clear that this now rather rapid loss of political power will mean a corresponding increase in the power of the political groups in the northern cities and a change in the mobility, at least legislatively speaking, of the Democratic Party and the Congress, and that kinds of legislation that would have been difficult to achieve because of apathy or conservative misgivings might become more readily achieved in the future.

A fourth element that augurs for institutional change, I think, is the enormous significance of the American defense and space establishment and the precarious international situation with which we must live. This is an obvious influence for massive federal leadership. The enormous fiscal powers that the government of the United States must have to maintain our present position in a very dangerous world, the implications of space technology—and the economic planning implications of all this make it very improbable, I think, that the federal system as we see it in the future can really be thought of as a partnership between states and the nation, unless we are prepared to recognize that the partnership of the future will be much less equal than it has been in the past.

Now, this leads to the obvious conclusion that national policy and action affecting natural resources, transportation, urban affairs, already relate to a situation in which a federal responsibility and initiative have been greatly accelerated.

Moreover, we can see that in the areas of natural resources administration, in urban affairs, and in transportation, although in a rather inadequate way, we already have massive intervention by government throughout the United States and by the federal government in particular. We have referred to the urban-renewal program, the open-space program, land- and water-conservation legislation, housing legislation. We are engaged, in fact, in massive environmental administration in all of these areas, even though we do not have as yet a cohesive or consistent national policy with respect to them.

On the other hand, we see at the local level—and it's been documented again and again in these meetings—an apparent inability to innovate. Mr. Ordway referred to the frustration that is often experienced by great multitudes of units of government presumably at the local level, and he spoke of these as a kind of variety in our political, sociopolitical ecosystem.

There is a variety there, but we have also a great deal of monotonous uniformity in structures of government that have been replicated across the country, such as the American county, without any regard to the particular kinds of tasks that government now needs to perform.

Institutionally, we have a kind of disjunctive incrementalism, to use the word that came up in one of the papers, that makes it very difficult to mobilize action at the local level.

We are being forced, in the absence of effective devices at the local level, to seek some way through federal action to stimulate or, if need be, to coerce local action. Administrative possibilities for the more effective development of environmental policy imply a number of things at this federal level that we already see in the making.

In two areas we are in the midst of a slow and sometimes discouraging effort to restate the responsibility of government in this country in terms appropriate to new conditions. One of these has to do with natural resources, the other with urban affairs.

We have taken steps in the past through the Resources Planning Board and other devices to try to develop a concept of what the natural resources role of government ought to be, but now, under the pressure of events, we are coming closer to some realistic answers. We also see that natural resources have a common element among them through their relatedness to the environment. We also see that much of our social and welfare functions, particularly those dealing with urban affairs, likewise involve the human ecosystem—man in relation to his environment. And I therefore look for a coalescence of our urban policy and our natural resources policy through the common denominator of environmental policy. President Lyndon Johnson has already suggested this in his statements on the "new conservation."

To turn from the federal government to the state and local level, we have had some discussion about the problems of regionalism. It is difficult to see how we will be able either to reform or abolish fifty states. It is not at all certain that the cumbersome methods of interstate compacts and collaboration and cooperation will achieve the kinds of ends that we have been positing in this session.

I suspect that we will continue to find through combined federal, state, and local action ways of devising institutions, institutional arrangements that will be superimposed upon those that we already have.

This will be a rather expensive and apparently irrational way of going about the task, but we are a pragmatic people, we are a sentimental people, and we also love our politicians. Moreover it's inconceivable, to put it very bluntly, that fifty Senators times two are going to commit political suicide and enable us to combine states and recast the regional structure of government in this country in a more meaningful manner.

And so I think we will probably find other ways of doing this.

Now, these kinds of changes will probably not come about as a result of any new kind of national constitutional convention or any theoretical concern with the end and means of government. I suspect that they will come about in pursuance of the kind of problems that we have discussed here and that Mrs. Strong particularly focused on in the question of the reorganization and arrangement of community open space.

In other words, these changes will come about incidentally to policy and programatic changes, and the critical force for innovation will be the functions to be served, the functions needed, rather than any theoretical perception of what the ideal form should be.

In conclusion, I would like to suggest two or three kinds of things that we might see as coming out of this process of innovation.

Firstly, ecologists will be increasingly employed at all levels of government and that we will create new kinds of positions in the public service such as those that have been suggested in other places by Fraser Darling and F. R. Fosberg. I mean community ecologists or conservators, people who will be at levels in which there is direct comprehensive environmental administration. There will be more ecologists who serve the public interest in a direct way as well as through research and teaching.

Secondly, the management of waste for the first time in human history is going to become a major and increasingly technical public responsibility. I think it could be shown that in the greater part of the United States of America, geographically, the management or disposal of waste is not even a public function. But in an age of high technology, with increasing technological obsolescence, we are going to find that this is a problem that must be coped with. We shall have to devise ways of dealing with it institutionally in places where it is not now dealt with, and we shall have to find ways of relating the activities of the Atomic Energy Commission, of the federal defense establishment, of the municipalities, of industrial establishments to the general public health and environmental amenity aspects of our public life.

Thirdly, the boundaries of private and public action are going to interrelate increasingly, and frequently to merge. The more rapidly we can close the gap between environmental planning and the private entrepreneurial development use of land, instead of seeing these as antipathetic kinds of action, necessarily hostile, the better. The sooner we can make sense out of what the government does and what the private sector does and can bring these into some sort of constructive relationship in the public interest, the better.

But I would in passing observe there are, of course, problems of the clarity of public responsibility when you do get such a merging of functions.

I think in all of this we have an opportunity to plan for a greater degree of variety and to protect the personal freedoms that we now enjoy. In fact, one of the reasons for this kind of institutional innovation that I suggest is that our present institutions are not serving us very well in these respects and will serve us increasingly less well as times goes on.

I don't, then, share the fear of some who have felt that, with this growth of planning and enlarged responsibility and particularly increased federal involvement, we will necessarily jeopardize personal freedom or variety. We could, but it is not, it seems to me, inherent in the process.

Unless we can devise institutions that will help us cope with these problems, we are going to lose a great deal of personal freedom and a great deal of variety, not through planning but through what you might call sociopolitical entropy that will result from a complete lack of effective, responsible handling of these complex problems.

ORDWAY: Thank you.

My own paper is a brief review of the evolution of decisions in the state courts of the United States and in the Supreme Court of the United States to expand the concept of the police power particularly in relation to private property and its use.

We are presently seeking institutional ways to protect environments and habitats so that they will be available in the future to support a diversity of fauna and flora and a diversity of human uses for factories and homes and transport and recreation, for amenities of every kind.

Once the scientists have determined the nature and the scope, the sizes and the contents and the evolution of the many kinds of natural habitats we shall wish to preserve, and once the planners have devised a master plan for the continent, for each of the nations and for the states and regions, mapping the essential land uses for megalopoli and agriculture and recreation, for factories and homes and transport and wildlife, the institutional problem will become one of requiring and implementing, democratically and economically, the land usages essential to meet these needs in the long-range public interest.

Invocation of the police power to regulate the use of land, in cities and villages, through "comprehensive" zoning plans and ordinances began in the 1920s. The constitutionality of zoning, which deprives owners of free choice in the use of their property, was immediately challenged in many court cases and ultimately, of course, in the U.S. Supreme Court.

The paper then continues to list and quote from some of the pathfinding decisions which extended the scope of the police power.

"Regulations applicable to existing conditions which are now uniformly sustained would have been rejected half a century ago as arbitrary and oppressive."

It took a considerable length of time for the courts to extend approval of the use of the police power to advance esthetics. This problem of going beyond the health and safety as a basis for use of the police power occurred in 1954 in the well-known *Berman* case, where the Court said:

"The concept of the public welfare is broad and inclusive. . . . The values it represents are spiritual as well as physical, esthetic as well as monetary. It is within the power of the legislature to determine that the community should be beautiful as well as healthy, spacious as well as clean, well balanced as well as carefully patrolled."

These early cases centered around the problem of zoning in cities. Rural zoning developed much more slowly. Obviously there was less pressure and less need.

Gradually, zoning was extended to the rural districts. Today most states have authorized rural zoning. Among specialized and specified purposes of rural zoning ordinances, under the public welfare doctrine of the police power, are: prevention of wasteful scattering of the population, prevention of overcrowding of land, conserving scenery, conserving and developing natural resources, and promotion of desirable living conditions.

While most of the planning controversy over the last twenty-five years in the United States has related to urban and suburban planning and related zoning and building regulations, England as early as 1943 recognized the value of a national policy for all land use and development. Parliament declared:

"It shall be lawful for his Majesty to appoint a Minister of Town and Country Planning, to be charged with the duty of securing consistency and continuity in the framing and execution of a national policy with respect to the use and development of land throughout England."

We have heard some discussion of the Town and Country Planning, and creation of the Nature Conservancy.

This paper then cites the history of the Santa Clara agricultural zoning which we discussed yesterday.

It then reports on the recent state-wide planning legislation in Hawaii, and proposed National Planning in Denmark.

It next discusses the tax and revenue implications of zoning. You have this problem of fair and just compensation. Zoning under the police power does not compensate the owner. Eminent domain, of course, does. And we had some discussion yesterday of the very high cost of extending the proper controls over rural land.

ORIGINS OF PUBLIC POLICY AND PRACTICE IN CONSERVATION: EARLY EDUCATION AND THE CONSERVATION OF SANATIVE ENVIRONMENTS

Paul F. Brandwein*

Pectinatella magnifica is a microscopic bryozoan; its habitat is the clear, cool, not overly unruly stream; its diet, microscopic protozoans and algae and the detritus its cilia bring to it; it occupies the usual food niche of microscopic organisms in the presence of voracious young fish; somehow its reproductive bodies manage to be distributed (by the unknowing largesse of birds that dip their feet into the stream); thus far, in itself it has no market price—except perhaps to yield some patient student a doctorate and to furnish me with a study of the vagaries of a small country stream. One might say, with Wordsworth, "and oh, the world to me," but the harsher realities are that although *Pectinatella* is the result of some 3×10^9 years of evolution, it is succumbing—in the stream I am studying—to various new breeds of natural selection, one especially, known by the name of "pollution." The industrial product "causing" the pollution has its market price; it is valued; *Pectinatella* is not. That is to say, 3×10^9 years of

* Dr. Brandwein, whose teaching, editorial labors, and writing have brought millions of American students their first glimmer of relatedness to the biotic environment, is Director of Education for the Conservation Foundation and Director of Research with Harcourt, Brace & World. In 1963 he was appointed Co-Director of the Pinchot Institute for Conservation Studies.

evolution or not, for the present, *Pectinatella* has no value. In *Pectinatella* we recognize the archetype of the sequoia, elephant, panda, trumpeter swan, passenger pigeon, perhaps Pribiloff seals, or perhaps Galápagos tortoises; we recognize the archetype of events which stem from one form of exploitation pressure or another. I almost insist on calling these exploitation pressures modern forms of natural selection, although one could say justly that it is man who is the agent of the new forms of natural selection; it is he, not industrial products, that causes pollution; he uses pesticides; he exploits land; he has the socioeconomic choices to make. He determines—or should determine—the quality of life he wishes to lead.

Surely, my choice of *Pectinatella* is precious; who, after all, requires a bryozoan to make life complete? Or a panda? Or a trumpeter swan? Or an Ainu? Or a Pigmy? Or a Bushman? Or a Laplander? Or an Eskimo? Or—?

Now the point is that *Pectinatella* need not be destroyed, if reason and morality, or competence and compassion, prevailed. Or if a certain population of *Pectinatella* (using *Pectinatella* as *bête noire*) were to threaten an ecosystem, a selected number could be destroyed—again with competence and compassion. And the point is again that it is not reasonable, nor moral, to destroy *Pectina-*

tella or *Carex*—or *Procyon* or *Halcyon*—
or even *Homo* (or choose your own species)—without acknowledging that the destruction is being accomplished. The least
we owe to a species that has come up
through 3×10^9 years of evolution is the
acknowledgment by public statement that
it is giving up its life in our interest. This
acknowledgment is biological good manners, biological *noblesse oblige,* if not
reason and morality, and might as a matter of good taste be accompanied by a
sense of loss.

What kind of education is relevant in
this moment of history when comprehension of the fitness of the environment and
the interdependence of environments, or
organisms, and of men is essential to securing sanative environments and sane
men? All our future scientists, economists, historians, conservationists, politicians are presently in our schools. Public
policy and practice are affected by the education of those presently in our schools;
otherwise, why our concern for what
goes on in the schools? Indeed, why this
Conference which is, in a primary sense,
a venture into public education?

What kind of individuals will bring
competence and compassion to an examination of the environment which now is
affected by economic, social, political,
cultural as well as ecological components? Let me put it tentatively, against
further probing in this paper, that if we
wish to secure sanative environments in
the future through sanative public policy
and practice, then we must secure for
children an early sanative environment.
There is an overwhelming literature that
supports this view. That is to say, against
further analysis, that the early education
of children in both substance and style
is of prime relevance in a response to the
question: Who is it that conserves?

Clearly, there is no intention here to
set up the persistent and meretricious
dichotomies of economist and ecologist;
technologist and conservationist; spiritual
value and market value; these are not
dichotomies but antiphonies. Rather, they
should be antiphonies but are not because
education has not been harmonious; we
have educated for ages past, not for ages
present. Conservation is concerned, in
good part at least, with fitness *to* the
whole environment, socioeconomic and
bioeconomic, and fitness *of* the whole environment, socioeconomic and bioeconomic. Education, definable as the conservation of man, also has its prime
concern with the fitness of man to the
environment.

We find, for instance, that practically
every school system (elementary and secondary) has in its stated curriculum a
series of activities under the rubric "conservation." These are generally conglom-
erates of readings (e.g. nature of soil,
erosion, etc.), some experiences (e.g.
water-holding capacity of the soil), field
trips (e.g. to fields), films (e.g. life in a
forest). But if one examines what actually goes on, one finds in about 50 per
cent of the cases that the topic is not considered—and this mostly in city schools.
Reason: the teacher cannot "cover" the
course as it is; he or she tends to gloss
over, or neglect, an area which is not important or is thought to have little intellectual rigor. Particularly in city schools,
conservation is thought to have little importance and no intellectual rigor. Besides, in a city, what fields or ponds or
streams are available for that necessary
field trip? In country schools, experiences
in conservation are thought to be super-
erogatory. In any event, more than any
other curricular area, conservation is
honored in the breach. This would not
be possible if the ecological, economic,
and psychosocial concepts underlying
practices in conservation ramified, or pervaded, the curriculum.

At other times, conservation education
(truly a euphemism) is often a rubric for
the occasional walk in the woods, or what
is worse, a nature trail, for the trivial

naming of specimens (rarely their study); for the remnant rules of an ancient agronomy, for a set of "don'ts." Too often, these "field trips" are conducted by agencies outside the school: that bus trip to a concentration camp for organisms which cannot otherwise survive. Almost never is conservation a study which combines the biological and the physical sciences, the behavioral sciences and the social sciences, in a conceptual structure, an art-science, which is relevant to the kind of world now in the making.

Indeed, this Conference is called, in part, because, among other failures, educational practices have not prepared young people for life in a changing environment, an environment in which science and technology have increasing impact, a world in which above all, in Lewis Mumford's terms, "The moral sense needs mothering."

If education is experience in search of meaning, what kind of early experience is relevant to securing the sanative environments we seek? What kind of early experience secures for the world the kind of men who comprise what Mead (1964) calls "evolutionary clusters"; the men who, in any moment of history, create and give life its quality, the men who will create the philosophies, policies, and practices which may secure the future of the sanative environment? For the purposes of this paper, it is useful to define conservation as *the recognition by man of his interdependence with his environment and with life everywhere, and the development of a culture which maintains that relationship through policies and practices necessary to secure the future of a sanative environment.* This Conference is a long step toward the definition of conservation, of the sanative environment, and philosophies, policies, and practices which will conserve it.

To secure the future of a sanative environment—that is, to conserve—one must first understand what is to be conserved

and why, to state the proposition simply. Understanding requires that the concept of *environment,* as bioeconomic and socioeconomic (ecosystemic, if you will) shall have meaning to men and women if we require them to become a part of it. A fish is part of its environment, man is often alienated from it: this mainly through lack of understanding: this through lack of sanative experience with and in the environment.

What experiences can we give the child, who is father to the man, which will give meaning to the environment? Einstein has defined science as experience in search of meaning. For me, education has always had the same aim: experience in search of meaning.

Which experiences?

Which meanings?

To make more sense, I should like to deal with meanings first; these are our means to the end we seek: meanings are anvils on which philosophies, policies, and practices are molded. But meanings, understandings, *concepts,* must also be related in a structure because education is a kind of ecosystem in which the various parts are interrelated. That is, a school has structure, and it develops educational structure through curriculum. Our web of meanings, the structure of meanings we would propose is *an environment of mental constructs (concepts) in which the teacher finds direction and scope, and the child finds psychological safety and freedom to experience; but these experiences are in the search of meaning.* Here the teacher plays a significant role, he is a guide to full development of children, a guarantee to idiosyncratic development in a sanative environment; he is not a guardian of the archives, not a Cerberus, nor Procrustes. To "see" and understand structure is to see the interrelatedness of things —whether parts of an ecosystem or parts of a philosophy.

In light of this, we shall develop first

a structure in which the teacher finds scope as well as the genera of meanings which give the structure its function. We shall see that a structure, in which intellectual disciplines thrive, does not enslave; rather, it furnishes psychological safety and freedom for the widest experience in search of meaning.

SUBSTANCE: STRUCTURE AND MEANING

Evolution (I modify Julian Huxley's thoughts in this matter) implies transmission and transformation of DNA. Various baskets of adaptation to the environment—that is to say, various experiments in creative evolution—occurred before matter was able to contemplate itself; that matter so adapted turns out to be man. That basket of adaptation we call *Homo sapiens cum faber* is, however, not the result of biological evolution only; cultural evolution has, in part, made man what he is. Cultural evolution implies transmission and transformation of knowledge, attitudes, values. Physical adaptation is, for man per se, no longer of as great significance in terms of natural selection (survival value) as is his basket of cultural adaptation—the basket of knowledges, attitudes, and values. Each man carries the basket everywhere with him and before him; much of the basket is filled early—in the school years. There is a vast horde of evidence, which it would be presumptuous to cite, that supports the claim that what happens to men and women in their school years presages what they do—or, what is as important, do not do.[1]

We speak of the "problems" posed

by pollution, population, pesticides, pressures on resources. Why doesn't everyone recognize these as "problems"? Precisely because the clarification required in framing of a *problem*—in counterpoint to a *question*—is an art requiring great skill, based on searching knowledge. An ability to recognize and clarify problems is precisely an ability to frame and penetrate into strategies for solution: there is all the difference in the world between asking a question and framing a problem.

Mental activity, I would affirm, is purposed and directed—*but not by problems, rather by objects and events. If the object or event is not recognized, a problem is not clarified. Indeed, it seems clear that an object or event is recognized only when the concept to which it has relevance is understood. Otherwise the problem is not clarified.* To most of our population, problems in conservation of our resources—pollution, pesticides, population, pressure on resources—are not problems per se precisely because the objects and events which signify pollution and pressure on resources, among others, are not clearly perceived. And this because the basic concepts underlying conservation of environments are not understood.

If statements of questions were all that were involved in the processes alleged to take place in inquiry, one would be at a loss to explain why Leeuwenhoek did not ask, "What is the relation of ATP to the energy consumption of my animalcules?" or why Priestley did not ask, "What are the respiratory enzymes responsible for the O_2-CO_2 exchange in the microecology of mouse and green mint?"—or why Darwin didn't ask, "How does mutation of DNA act in the origin of the species?" or why Adam Smith didn't ask, "How is deficit spending related to the business cycle?" or Hammurabi, "What is the relation of the ego to the self-image?"

Clearly the scientist (whether natural, social, or behavioral) doesn't arise bright

---

[1] For an excellent summation, see Erikson, 1963 and Gerth and Mills, 1964. These are chosen as a kind of summary; the case for the general position we have stated ramifies, to one extent or another, much of the work in psychology, psychiatry, sociology, cultural anthropology, and general folklore. Clearly different environments in early youth breed antisocial behavior. (See also the work of Sheldon and Eleanor Glueck.)

and naïve in the morning exclaiming: "What great, new, astonishing discovery shall I make today?" His problems arise not *de novo* but *in vitro;* they arise out of his comprehension, his conceptualizations, not out of curiosity naked of prior experience. When he is confronted with an object or event which does not fit his conceptualization (however wrong the latter may be) he *may* recognize a problem. Understanding—that is, possession of a concept—is antecedent to recognition of a problem; this seems clear to us. The depth and subtlety of a scholar's comprehension then enable him to clarify the problem and develop it as a strategy for solution. Bear with me—for a clarification of what activity is antecedent to clarification and solution of problems is also antecedent to insight into the kind of education with which we are concerned, and the kind of "evolutionary clusters" or cadres we develop, and the kind of knowledges, values, skills, attitudes, we put into the baskets of cultural evolution.

There was a time when it seemed simple to base education on a recounting of facts. Facts seemed so relatively stable. Now A. N. Sullivan tells us that in all probability nothing that was "true" (i.e. a fact) in the last century is "true" today. Mere facts seem no longer to hold their authority. While there is nothing mere about facts, it is also true that facts per se are inundating us to an unconscionable degree. Thus it is calculated (there is someone always doing these calculations) that it would take an omnilingual scientist to the year 3363 to read all that was published in 1964—if he worked eight hours a day without lunch. The explosions of population and of knowledge are running neck and neck.

Clearly the point is that the school can no longer be a place where the "facts are covered." Clearly that part of the early sanative environment we call "school" must be a place where the student learns how to learn. In a word, he learns an art which prepares him for acquiring knowledges, skills, and even attitudes which are not yet known or desired: that art should prepare him for a world whose technology does not presently exist. Is this possible? Yes.

There are continuities within discontinuities, there is uniformity within diversity, there is a certain stability within continuous flux. There are, in short, *concepts* which remain fairly stable over several decades. Furthermore, these concepts become the *preconceptions* which are *prelude* to recognition of a "new" object or event, leading perhaps to newly developed concepts. Inquiry does not occur unrelieved by prior history. If Newton stood on the shoulders of others, it is to say that one concept stems from another. Concept replaces concept, but this rather slowly, for a concept is based on prior networks of inferences and on prior observation of objects and events.

To be specific. The term "mammal" is evocative: different *objects,* horses, dogs, cats, pandas, elephants, kangaroos come to "mind": also different *events,* suckling of young, a long epitomizing evolutionary history, and the like. A little individual experience is worth undertaking to press home the point. Suppose I were to ask you to think of a reptile; closing one's eyes helps. One might "see" in the "mind's eye" a crocodile, a garden snake, a boa constrictor, an iguana. One doesn't see a "reptile." Similarly, per se one doesn't "see" a mammal, or fish, or town meeting, or family, or tax structure, or planned community. These are constructs, or conceptual structures, or in a word, *concepts.*

A concept is a network of inferences stemming from critical observation of objects and events leading to class identities; in turn a comprehension of class identities enables us to identify as yet unobserved objects and events. A concept enables us to unite a seemingly chaotic array of objects or events within a relationship.

Thus pH, markets, energy, city, Ming dynasty, house, C major, deficit spending, ecosystem, young river, taiga, floodplain, surrealism, romantic poets, Elizabethan era, Neanderthal man are concepts. Taxonomically concepts can be brought under a larger head, "conceptual schemes," and ordered into subconcepts, etc. (see pages 634–35).

The possession of concepts helps us to associate or combine, as well. Thus the goose, frog, and rabbit are also vertebrates; the inclined plane, pulley, and lever are also simple machines. We expect a goose to have feathers and a warm body, and to lay eggs; these are associated in the concept "bird." Concepts, therefore, help us combine, or associate, or synthesize also. The area of conservation is a congeries of concepts.

Thus a concept is never a single thing; it helps us achieve *meaning* through discrimination or association. As we indicated earlier, it was Einstein who defined science as experience in search of meaning. May we not define science as activity in search of concepts? *Concept seeking, together with its end, concept formation, becomes a legitimate, indeed the central, objective of the teacher.*

Similarly, if we accept science as consisting of a series of conceptual schemes which help us understand the physical world, then conceptual schemes are made up of concepts; concepts, of a series of related elements or facts; and facts, of the data which result from observation.

A *conceptual scheme* (such as evolution) involves many concepts (for example, mutation, variation, sedimentation, geographical barriers).

A *concept* includes similar elements, related generalizations, and related facts (for example, the concept of mutation for any specific case includes the generalization of "gene," the generalization of mutation, stemming in turn from observa-

tion of a change of one gene into another; thus the gene for red eyes in *Drosophila* changed into the gene for white eyes).

A major objective of teaching, we have said, is to foster understanding of the major conceptual scheme which scholars have developed. Curriculum planning and lesson planning are simplified when teachers consciously undertake to develop a course of study around the major conceptual schemes of the area being considered, and to plan their daily work around the concepts underlying these conceptual schemes. The laboratory and the classroom then become places for discovery, for discriminating and associating data into facts, facts into concepts, and concepts into conceptual schemes.

It is almost obvious that individuals could not discover for themselves all the conceptual schemes already known, and probably not even all they need for daily living in our society. Hence, the need for teaching and teachers to recreate efficiently for the young the heritage of the past—both in attained conceptual schemes (the product) and in the means of attaining them (the process). We shall develop the thesis later that this is best done through experiences in which thought is related to action, i.e. through inquiry. In this way, children may have opportunity to acquire the apparatus of attaining the conceptual schemes of the future.

It is, in short, our proposition that the very nature of learning, as we understand it at present, consists of concept-seeking activities leading to concept formation. The concepts formed are to be so important, so functional, that their understanding and application leads young people to live more effectively.

Now the point is that a conceptual framework can be developed to give education intellectual discipline; that is, a network of inferences, of relationships can give structure to a curriculum. To learn structure is to understand the relation-

A Structure for the Elementary School Science Curriculum

CONCEPT LEVEL	CONCEPTUAL SCHEME A	CONCEPTUAL SCHEME B	CONCEPTUAL SCHEME C	CONCEPTUAL SCHEME D	CONCEPTUAL SCHEME E	CONCEPTUAL SCHEME F
	Energy may be transformed; it is neither created nor destroyed. (Total sum of matter and energy is conserved: see Conceptual Scheme B, Concept Level VI.)	Matter may be transformed; in chemical change matter is neither created nor destroyed.	Living things interchange matter and energy with the environment (and with other living things).	A living thing is the product of its heredity and environment.	Living things are in constant change.	The universe is in constant change.
CONCEPT LEVEL VI	Energy gotten out of a machine does not exceed the energy put into it.	In nuclear reactions, matter may be destroyed to release energy. (The total sum of matter and energy is conserved: see Conceptual Scheme A, Concept Level VI.)	Living things are adapted by structure and function to the environment.	The characteristics of a living thing are laid down in a genetic code.	Changes in the genetic code produce changes in living things.	Nuclear reactions produce the radiant energy of stars.
CONCEPT LEVEL V	Once an object is in motion, it tends to remain in motion, unless energy is applied to produce an unbalanced force.	In a reaction, the totality of matter remains constant.	The capture of radiant energy by living things is basic to the maintenance and growth of all living things.	The cell is the unit of structure and function; a living thing develops from a single cell.	Living things have changed over the ages.	Universal gravitation and inertial motion govern the relations of celestial bodies.
CONCEPT LEVEL IV	Molecular motion can be altered by the absorption or release of energy.	Matter consists of elements and compounds.	Living things capture matter from the environment and return it to the environment.	A living thing reproduces itself and develops in a given environment.	The earth's environment is in constant change.	The motion and path of celestial bodies is predictable.
CONCEPT LEVEL III	Energy can be changed from one form to another.	Matter exists in small particles.	There are characteristic environments each with their characteristic life.	Plants and animals reproduce their own kind.	Organisms are related through structure.	There are seasonal and annual changes within the solar system.

	CONCEPTUAL SCHEME A	CONCEPTUAL SCHEME B	CONCEPTUAL SCHEME C	CONCEPTUAL SCHEME D	CONCEPTUAL SCHEME E	CONCEPTUAL SCHEME F
CONCEPT LEVEL II (*Analogical*)	There are different forms of energy.	Matter can change its state.	All living things depend on the environment for the conditions of life.	Related living things reproduce in similar ways.	Forms of living things have become extinct.	There are regular movements of the earth and moon.
CONCEPT LEVEL I (*Analogical*)	Energy must be used to set an object in motion (i.e. when work is done).	Matter exists in various states.	All living things are affected by their environment.	Living things reproduce.	There are different forms of living things.	There are daily changes on earth.

ships of objects and events to each other. The interrelatedness of an area of knowledge (such as conservation) can be demonstrated—that is, the knowledge can be disciplined so that the way further knowledge is acquired has discipline. This is, of course, the meaning of "discipline" which unfortunately has been replaced by a "sequence of courses."

This does not mean, nor must it ever mean, that the teacher lays before the student the concept whole. Teaching, after all, is not telling; the teacher does not "cover" a text, he "uncovers" it. Only regurgitators (and these are not teachers) spill their collected knowledge over a year's time. The concept is uncovered or perhaps developed by the student, not discovered per se—for after all, scholars have spent their lives in the discovery that was prelude to it. Nevertheless, the student acquires knowledge and skills through inquiry; this simply means to me that the student expends the energy in learning and is not robbed of the right to bend his own efforts to uncover the concept, or if you wish to "discover" it, while the teacher's art is expended in preparing the learning situation. But we digress; we shall come later to the ways by which students have opportunity to develop membership in evolutionary clusters.

We mean to say that experiences in early education lose meaning if they are helter-skelter and subject to whim. We mean to say that early education in conservation can be based on a structure which is sound because it is built on concepts, hence the elements of the structure are related and relevant. And yet at no time can the structure be labeled "conservation" because it is in essence education in the knowledges, skills, and attitudes which are basic and are the warp and woof of the art-science we call conservation. Those who will conserve need grounding in the full scheme of man's past, not in the parochial specifics of con-

servation of land, or water as practiced in an outworn agricultural economy.

Furthermore, the structure of concepts gives meaning to experiences we call "experiences in conservation," since its constructs (concepts) pervade the school experience—that is, the curricular structure in which the experiences take place. It is otherwise when unrelated bits and pieces are stashed together in a period of time.

We have had occasion to investigate the feasibility of a conceptual structure in development of curriculums and have found such a structure desirable, practical, and serviceable in the best administrative, curricular, and pedagogical practice. One structure basic to an intellectual grasp of the modern natural environment (ecological and technological) follows.[2] The levels of conceptual understanding are given in order to emphasize sequence; as soon as a child has come (through experience) to grasp one concept, he proceeds to the next level; or if he is of high intellectual competence, he may encompass a group of these at one intellectual swallow.

As we shall see (Manner of Learning Through Inquiry and the Nurture of Evolutionary Cadres), possession of a class identity, or concept, enables a learner to relate knowledge, to be able to recognize objects and events (overpopulation, pressure on resources, effects of pesticides, pollution, etc.) and to clarify problems. Furthermore, these problems do not remain in the area of a question without vector: the problems become strategies for inquiry.

[2] Similar structures may be developed for the social sciences and the humanities. Mathematicians have begun to develop a structure for elementary mathematics (see the work of the School Mathematics Study Group).

This structure was first advanced in "Substance, Structure and Style in the Teaching of Science" by Paul F. Brandwein, given at the General Motors Conference for High School Science and Mathematics Teachers, August, 1964.

Permit me to be presumptuous, even temerarious. Note how this conceptual structure differs from an elementary school curriculum based on a series of rubrics, biology, chemistry, physics, geology, conservation, or ecology, etc., each in its own cubicle, each subject to the whim of an administrator and to the vagaries of fashions in education. Besides, conservation owes its knowledges, attitudes, and skills to all the major disciplines; a biological orientation is parochial. Note, too, how it varies from a curriculum based on a series of activities or so-called "problems"—e.g. "How to Make an Aquarium," "The Generation of Static Electricity," or even the so-called "processes of science"—hypothesis making, problem framing, and the like. A hypothesis, a stated problem, or the like is not a "process of science" but a product, much as a laser is.

A conceptual structure is a home for "original" activity of all sorts; indeed without some such structure, it is our thesis, "original" problem-solving activity is merely problem doing. That is, in what is normally called problem solving the teacher "knows" the answer and the children's activity in inquiry is merely error reduction to come up to the teacher's standard. This bears further examination, and we turn to this next. For it is of utmost importance to the future of society that we develop each child's intellectual tools to their fullest and that we give fulfillment to all children, those who will develop leadership in evolutionary cadres and those who did not choose their parents properly but will nevertheless furnish the charismatic social environment in which evolutionary cadres may flourish. A sanative environment is not sustained by the minority.

MANNER OF LEARNING THROUGH INQUIRY: THE NURTURE OF EVOLUTIONARY CADRES

The Kipsigis are a people of Nyanza, a province in the southwestern corner of Kenya. Long before they became colonials, their virtue, viewed ecologically, was that they lived within the environment and were, as much as pre-Western technology permits, part of it. In time as colonials, they began to plant maize as food, and then as a cash crop; to make a long story of acculturation short, today's Kipsigis venture into cultivation of tea, as well as maize, as well as cattle, as well as milk. With this perceptible change in using the land for cash rather than subsistence comes the inevitable growth of a middle class of artisans, service and professional personnel; we see the full flow of a change, if you will, of the human ecosystem. And one can predict that with the increase in the cash crop, more and more Kipsigis will depend on wage labor; further, with the expansion of cultivation of tea and coffee, and the increase in milk cows, the population will expand and growth of the economy will press for use of the remaining land. The Kipsigis ecosystem, a human ecosystem of a kind, is changing (Bohannan and Dalton, 1965).

Now why don't the Kipsigis maintain the values that come with living close to the land? Is the life of the centuries, and the values inherent in living in close harmony with the land, so easily set aside? Yes, so it seems. Most men seem almost always to take those new ways which enable them to control and modify the environment to the end of securing food, longer life, and the amenities which eliminate drudgery. Nevertheless, what kind of education should the Kipsigis have? Indeed, what kind of education is useful for any people who would conserve the sanative nature of the environment and yet secure adequate food, longer, healthier life, and the amenities which eliminate drudgery? The act of conserving, it seems, is its own cause and effect.

Indeed, Kipsigi and Londoner, Yakima Eskimo and New Yorker, Parisian and the *favellas* of Brazil have in the long evolutionary run similar fates. Kipsigi and *Pectinatella* seem oddly related; both are being subjected to what we have said, *ad nauseam,* is, for organisms, a modern form of natural selection—exploitation pressure.

Let us proceed. Kipsigi and Londoner, European and African, American or Russian are all born completely alien; this, too, is the fate of every child. This alien —this child—is early an intervention in the social order. Our thesis has been that the men and women who comprise our social order are first ordered by the early environment. Not only DNA but the *moment of history*—that is to say, the moment in which the experiences we call education are available to him—seem *generally* to determine whether a man shall remain an organism or become an individual, and whether once an individual he can become a person—compassionate and competent. The evidence seems to be that early education with that all important group of primary teachers (his parents and the community) and his second group of teachers (in his early school years) seems paramount in determining the bending of the intellectual twig and its subsequent growth.

All organisms vary. All children vary. Freedom to develop to one's fullest is the practical guarantee of biological and cultural variation. Which of these variations, which characteristics, shall we nurture— that is to say, conserve?

Every child is of supreme moral worth; teaching is a mercy as well as a profession, and teachers—as physicians— must take all children who come to them. Nevertheless, equal opportunity does not mean identical opportunity; indeed, it means opportunities tailored to the child's gifts and capacities; it means wise use of these gifts and capacities; conservation implies wise use and children are easily as important as resources as the land. Wise use means, then, wise education, which in turn should at least mean full opportunity for personal fulfillment in gifts and destiny.

The characteristics of children who have later become scientists and scholars in other areas have been studied; similarly, the past histories of scientists and scholars have been studied in order to yield clues as to the characteristics which have been central to their development. These are the individuals who are central to forming the evolutionary cadres we have been considering.

The spectrum of qualities which *may* lead to original contribution to knowledge and to the development of the individual as a member of an evolutionary cadre can be summed up in the word "giftedness." I prefer it to "creativeness." Everyone is creative to some degree. "Giftedness" is not necessarily a weasel word, if we use it to mean a high and remarkably consistent order of creativeness resulting in original contribution to the field. It can, of course, be limited to a specific field (music, art, engineering, athletics, nuclear physics) or it can be general. The central outcome of giftedness, to repeat, which I deem distinguishes it from "talent" or creativeness is the work of the individual, that is, his *original* contributions to the field.

"Gift," in its German usage, can mean poison or venom, but we may consider these individuals poisoned by their art or science and unable to rid themselves of the poison; the only antidote is original contribution. These are the children who, to my mind, will form evolutionary clusters, if they are nurtured. What does the ability to make original intellectual contributions imply?

It implies at least the ability to hold various salient alternatives in mind, to use relevant concepts and data in their analysis, to design critical investigations where those are needed, to synthesize fresh concepts where the analysis permits, to seek confirmation of these fresh concepts, and to collaborate with others in testing them. In short, it requires *intelligence and methods of using that intelligence.*

It implies at least a kind of attitude toward new knowledge, new attitudes, new skills, new phenomena which Jones, Freud's biographer, has called "gullibility." Perhaps this is only the open mind, thrilling to the fresh and new phenomenon. Nevertheless, there are too many who believe that nothing should be done for the first time; yet those who have the characteristic of gullibility appreciate innovation, succumb to its examination and delight in its presence—but nevertheless retain the critical faculty of enlightened skepticism.

It implies the ability to indulge in *fantasy*, yet with a hard focus on reality, so that the *free association* assigned to fantasy is at the same time eventually subject to sober analysis.

It implies the possession of what I have called "questing." Questing implies the inability to accept present explanations of reality, hence the need ever to seek fresh explanations. By questing, I do not mean curiosity, nor high motivation, I mean curiosity directed by intelligent analysis; questing means the linking of analysis with the seeking of explanations.

It implies *persistence*, which must be defined specially as the ability to work in the face of such obstacles as failure, disapproval, or illness. Persistence implies nonconformity with ordinary goals of comfort, and the psychological massage of modern comforts.

It implies a certain amount of *physiologic vigor*, the health necessary to persist in long drouths of work.

Perhaps I have not defined giftedness.

If I were to do so, I should be certain that the definition could not include that gifted individual who because of the nature of his equipment would leap out of the definition and confound it and make an original contribution to it. Giftedness is also its own cause and effect.

Nevertheless, given the qualities which I have briefly sketched, the *intelligence* which permits critical analysis of alternatives and the ability to test one's conceptualizations by means of critically designed investigations, the *gullibility* and *fantasy* with its highly creative untrammelled free association, yet with a high focus on reality, *questing, persistence*, and *physiologic vigor*, we may have an incipient member of evolutionary cadres, we may have a contributor of original works provided—

the individual is given the early sanative environment which permits fulfillment of these characteristics, the environment in which the child can become what at first he pretends to be.

What are the *essentials* of this early sanative environment in which those who could form evolutionary cadres in the conservation of present and future sanative environments can seek expression and build the strong tissue of background for a future in original contribution or in intelligent collaboration? Certainly these essentials must be furnished in the home, the community (which includes many educational experiences, church, the natural, social, political environment), and the school. The deliberations of this Conference—if appropriately implemented in policy and practice—would affect education in the home, community, and school. I should place these essentials (using Roger's terms but taking license to extend their meaning) under two heads: psychological safety and psychological freedom.

Psychological safety, in good measure, would imply that the child is developing in a sanative home environment. This would imply that the interpersonal relationships within the family are healing (sanative) and that gentleness and warmth, firmness and quiet surround the child: the child is of supreme moral worth and is loved for its own sake. In such an environment, the child develops respect and ego strength; its self-image, given other essentials, can develop into one of tough fiber. Although the Western code is to love little children, this is not as true as it might be. The origins of delinquency, vandalism, in a word, disrespect for the environment can have their root, and often do have their root, in a disruptive home environment. If the child does not have respect for itself and does not develop ego strength, how can we expect it to have respect for the environment? How can a child be expected to conserve the environment if it, itself, is not conserved?

Psychological safety would imply the permissive environment in which failure is expected, even desired, as a concomitant of growth. For the child, or adult, is not always successful in new enterprises. Ego strength—that is, confidence—is established in such an environment. Confidence precedes competence. Psychological safety cannot exist without psychological freedom.

In a sanative environment, *psychological freedom* secures that "precious lawlessness" which was once the birthright of every child. Once, so long, long ago, a child could truly be part of the environment. A step away from his doorstep wilderness began. The natural environment became progressively civilized, clearing overcame the insouciance of plants and animals. But still the natural environment could beckon the child. To run free, to be part of an ecosystem, gave precious lawlessness; even the tree house was given indulgence. Often only the child could find it. For the present, for too many children, the window box and the house pet are the weak guarantees of life with a broad margin. Can children deprived of a natural environment, sanative because of its beauty and peace and guarantee of the mild yoke of lawlessness imposed by children, guarantee the future of an environment? Can they conserve, having never been faced with the alternative, to conserve or not to conserve?

Psychological freedom, if not available to a child, must then become part of the corrective environment of the school. If the environment of the home and community be not sanative, then the school environment may well have to undertake to provide for the shortcoming. Furthermore, we cannot legislate the home environment, but we can, and do, legislate the environment of the community and school. This Conference is concerned with legislating the environment of the community—and through it that of the home. This Conference is also concerned with affecting the school environment.

To safeguard the psychological freedom which is the psychological environment antecedent to attitudes which would safeguard future environments, the school might well commit itself to furnishing at least three "models":

a. a "model" of the intellectual environment (conceptual in nature) in which the alternatives the modern world presents might be considered;

b. a "model" of the psychological framework in which evolutionary cadres could survive—and in securing this provision, ensuring the survival of all individuals, whatever their ancestry or destiny;

c. a "model" of the natural environment from which may come an element of understanding and appreciation of a kind of environment from whence man came.

We have tried to deal with the restrictions of this Conference with the *intellectual environment* antecedent to understanding of present and future environments: we have sketched, by way of example, a framework of concepts in one area which are basic to understanding *what is to be conserved*. We have begun to sketch the psychological environment antecedent to forming attitudes basic to an appreciation of the present and future environment: we have sketched the essentials of psychological safety and freedom which condition *those who are to conserve*.

We need also to emphasize the requirement that in the future, no school should be built without securing a good sample of natural environment, woods, field, and stream which would be available to children. In such a natural environment, children see auguries of future environments; films and pictures are fraudulent; they tell what has been, not what is, what has been missed, not what is being missed. If land cannot be acquired with every future school site, then there must be its moral equivalent—land (a modest wilderness) easily accessible to children in which sense and sensibility can be educated. There is no substitute for the woods—the ecosystem in the flesh, as it were. There is no education without it.

There is nevertheless precious equipment which the school in its function as corrective of the ills of society could give children. This equipment would fit the child to roll questions toward its universe, however small or large, would fit the child to explore its environment, would fit it for confrontation by new events and new objects—to the limit of its ability. Granted the early environment might be sanative or not, still the child could acquire the tools with which to ask *corrective questions* of society: the tool is *skill in inquiry,* obstinate in the face of custom and conformity.

The skill of inquiry is based on the understanding that personal desire or wish is not the key to understanding the universe. It is based on the understanding that explanations of the way the universe

works—to be accepted by scientists—must be testable.

The teacher's framework of concepts enables him to *plan inquiries*—that is, plot the child's experiences in search of meaning, but the library of conceptual schemes (the intellectual filing cases) thus obtained must be antecedent to *true-and-free inquiry,* in which the child plans his own experiences, in his own idiosyncratic manner, in search of meaning. Free inquiry is true inquiry; the teacher's use of the technique of teaching through planned inquiries is merely a tool to make the acquisition of known concepts more interesting, hence more palatable; hence more of the student's energy is expended. In true-and-free inquiry, the gullibility, fantasy, questing, persistence, intelligence—the total apparatus of the student—are energized and initiated by *his own processes;* in inquiry planned by the teacher, the initiating processes are those of the teacher.

We emphasize, then, that whatever the environment, sanative or not, an educational environment which fulfills the idiosyncratic nature of the student through permitting true-and-free inquiry may be furnishing the social corrective which will, in the end, invent the methods by which the sanative future environment is brought into existence. An educational environment, therefore, which permits true-and-free inquiry is perhaps one guarantee that we may secure sanative environments because it nurtures the evolutionary cadres which would invent it, and the educated individuals (the nonexpert citizen if you will) who would understand the purposes of the men and women who comprise the evolutionary cadre, and would thus sustain them. What is the nature of this true-and-free inquiry? Put another way, what is the scientist's "art of investigation" (Beveridge, 1950)? How does it bear on education in true-and-free inquiry?

We do a disservice to both scientist

and science teacher by oversimplification of the scientist's art of investigation by blessing the scientist with a "method" with its inevitable steps leading to success. Further, we crown this method by calling it the "scientific method." Bridgman tried to get out of this impropriety by calling it "a method of intelligence." Very few have adopted the term; nevertheless, to my mind, it is far more evocative than scientific method. Elsewhere,[3] I noted that if the scientist did indeed have a method it was more in the nature of a melee, rather than a procession of one stately step to another, all crowned with discovery. Process and product feed on each other; there is feedback; there is unity between process and product, not dichotomy.

Nevertheless, an analysis of essence in the scientist's art is useful *if* it reflects more truly the nobility of the task, and its complexity, rather than a recipe which can be applied equally to cooking a ragout, to repairing an automobile, and to investigating the nature of an ecosystem or an economic system. The procession of the rationalized "scientific method" runs somewhat as follows:

a. a problem is stated;

b. a hypothesis is developed;

c. observations are made (an experiment may be part of controlled observation);

d. the observations are checked;

e. a conclusion is reached.

This series of steps, appropriately followed, lead to inevitable success.

For one, a scientist doesn't "begin" his work with a "problem." A scientist is an informed individual; particularly in his field. The scientist reads avidly the work of his colleagues. He has a *comprehension* of his field; he has a general (but useful) *comprehension* of the con-

3 The Burton Lecture "Elements in a Strategy for Teaching Science in the Elementary School" from Schwab and Brandwein, 1962.

ceptual schemes and concepts, or relationships, which explain the way the world *works at this given historical moment.* Certainly he has a conception of the "schemes" delineated on pages 634–35 —and this to incredible sophistication. He brings this comprehension with him to his daily life and to his work.

Does a scientist, then, ever engage in "problem solving," to use the term? Surely, as part of an investigation, but the elaboration of the problem is part of a strategy of solving the problem; the statement of the problem is but one tactic. But there is a prelude to the statement of the problem. I wish we did not have to engage in the fraudulence of schematizing the stigmata which accompany true-and-free inquiry, but we owe it to the children not to make them subject to the busy work of problem doing (with solution foreordained) in the name of problem solving (with solution unknown). Problem solving may result in failure, intelligent failure if it leads to insight into cause; problem doing is crowned with success. True-and-free inquiry defies description; it is idiosyncratic; it is creative. Nevertheless, we can try to plot the general area of the scientist's art. These general areas may perhaps be subtended as follows:

The scientist has a present comprehension of the way the world works. The comprehension could be erroneous (as was the homonculus theory, or the notion of an actual philosophers' stone) —but since the scientist is a part of history, he is sometimes the victim of these comprehensions. Because of the personality which sent him first into the area of scholarship and then of science (that is, his complex of intelligence, gullibility, fantasy, questing, etc.), he is never satisfied with his comprehension. Experience as a scientist has led him to doubt that there is any certainty as such; he has learned to live with uncertainty and change. In any event, comprehension of the way the world works is combined with an awareness of the imperfection of any concept or theory, a sensitivity to discrepancy, to disconformities, to error.

The scientist, then, is ready for any confrontation which casts doubt on the validity of his comprehension. Thus Copernicus, and Galileo, and Darwin.

Once a confrontation occurs, it would seem it triggers, as it were, the *preconscious,* inchoate activity of the mind which, perhaps, led Bridgman to say that "science means doing one's damndest with one's mind no holds barred." From my own investigations into the way scientists work,[4] it seems that before the scientist enters his laboratory he has a decently clear idea of the *operations* which he will pursue to meet his confrontations. In some form or another, at the moment of true confrontation, the flashes of insight (*preconscious* in nature) point the way to a fruitful way to solution; a full-formed strategy and tactics (in broad outline) catch him, as it were, by surprise. In a word, his "problem" comes to him imbedded in a matrix of probable solutions to it. Why not? All his life has been a preparation for this moment. Who was it who, speaking of so-called accidental discoveries, said "accidents come to him who is prepared"? It wasn't an accident that Wallace and Darwin came to similar insights.

In these preconscious flashes of insight, the path is laid for more formal statement of the mentifacts which others have called "the scientific method." In other words, statement of a problem, or hypothesis, or a critical design of an investigation, or a conclusion is each a mentifact; that is to say, they are all *products* of *processes* as yet undefined; yet we may consider that product and process feed each other. The processes of science, to my observation, are pre-

[4] Brandwein, 1955. See also Roe, 1953.

conscious; we have yet to identify processes of the mind which can be called "scientific." Simpson's definition of science (Simpson, 1964) as an exploration of the material universe in order to seek orderly explanations of phenomena, which are testable, sheds light on a more productive approach. We can, nevertheless, give opportunity to youngsters

a. to explore the material universe (to inquire);

b. to explain their findings (to form concepts);

c. to test their explanations (to formulate empirical tests).

When, as teachers, we present a segment of the universe to explore with observations and explanations (a concept) in mind, we are plotting the inquiry. When we come upon a segment of the universe as yet explored, without the observations and explanation in mind, we invite true-and-free inquiry; we invite the student to expend his own energy and his own idiosyncratic talent.

It would be more suitable to consider the "scientific method" as normally framed in steps as an outline for the preparation of a research paper, or oral report, once a segment of the research is finished. Then a stately and logical procession of *problem, hypothesis, experimental design, conclusion* seems appropriate. The paper or report itself, however, is antecedent to one of the most important aspects of the scientist's way: scientists have invented a pure capsule of democracy in communication. It is one of their major accomplishments and assures the necessary critique through confirmation and collaboration. Anyone who abides by the rules of evidence of this highly refined method of intelligence may open his mind's work to others and receive the benefit of their advice. Scientists make wise use of each other and their work; they conserve.

This *brief*, oversimplified discussion of the essence of the scientist's way (call it inquiry if you must) emphasizes the bright luminosity of his creativeness as well as the sober processes in the library, laboratory, and conference room. Nevertheless, the seat of science is an individual's mind, not the laboratory.

THE CONSERVATION OF EVOLUTIONARY CADRES

We now must focus more closely on the early school environment and its conservation of those who *will* generate public policy and practice. I say *"will"* simply because *all* those who will make policy go through some form of school. To repeat, our strongly defensible thesis is that the early environment of children conditions whether future environments will be sanative. There is little, if any, evidence to the contrary. This is not to say that later environments—say of the university boy or girl—are not important; they are. But the majority of our children do not yet go to the university, and once in the university only a minority tend to put themselves in the hazardous position of leadership. There is a vast amount of evidence that early childhood is the time of life where the seeds of leadership are laid. What the school does to children is of considerable moment insofar as evolutionary cadres are concerned.

The teacher's way, like the scientist's way, is imaginative; it is idiosyncratic, but it deals not only with what is, was, or will be *learned*, but also with a *learner*. However this may be, the teacher's way and the scientist's way are congruent; they support each other. I have been engaging in a kind of "research" over these past years; I have been observing eighty-two teachers who are considered excellent by their colleagues, by their community, indeed by their works:

students who have gone on to contribute.[5] What is it these teachers do?

This way of a teacher who conserves children, who unites gifts with opportunity, what is its image? In it is an unquenchable desire: to construct and disseminate a meaningful world. In it is a faith: the universe has its uniformities; it can be explained if explanations are sought honorably. They would say, with Einstein, "The universe is not fickle."[6] In it is a creed: each child is of supreme moral worth; the fullest development and fulfillment of each child is goal and duty. In it is a morality: teaching is not only a profession but also a mercy; we must take all children who come to us; compassion is wedded to competence. In it is a mode: teaching is not telling: a child must not be robbed of the right to discovery.

In it is an attitude: children should be permitted their fullest expression and this idiosyncratic; differences are cherished. Equal opportunity does not mean identity of exposure to identical experiences, identical books, with identical methods in identical spans. To repeat, freedom to learn and grow is the practical recognition of biological and cultural variability. With these teachers the school environment is sanative, it is luminous and illuminating.

More precisely, the teachers I have briefly sketched teach by freeing the youngster's energies; it is the youngster who is the learner. To teach the learner the art of learning is to teach him to find "hidden likenesses" (Bronowski, 1958); in short, to find relationships.

Armed with a structure of relationships (such as the one we have delineated on pages 634–35), the teacher plots in-

[5] There are other criteria observable in the classroom: their presentations are captivating, their personalities luminous; they are scholars who bring two loves together: children and their field of learning.

[6] Actually *"Der Gott ist nicht boshaft."*

quiries to be undertaken; planned experiences in search of meaning. Since the relationships are related in a web of scholarship, proceeding from simple relationships to complex ones, the teacher can proceed with a flexible ordering of investigations, or *inquiries, planned, or originating with him.* Thus he may plan field trips in the spring to place young children face to face with the early life of the woods: the incredible development of a frog's egg, the collaboration of insect and flower. Older children may be faced with *Drosophila:* thus with the mystery of DNA, and the simpler explication of their chemistry in "laws" of heredity. These are inquiries planned by the teacher; the teacher would make relatively certain that children do not pass the world by without having the full advantage of the work of humanity antecedent to them; that is, the work of those who use the scientist's way.

Why should the teacher plan experiences in search of these meanings? Wouldn't it be simpler to "tell" the child, through lecture? Perhaps the lecture can be defended as an approach to teaching older students (college students, wise beyond their years—that is, disillusioned). But the child needs not to learn, but to learn how to learn. This is not to say that a child learns only by experience with hardware or nature. He studies nature and books (Agassiz studied books as well).

What does a scientist do once he observes a discontinuity—however you wish to state the moment of his confrontation, followed by a commitment to investigate? He may consult his colleagues, he certainly spends time in thinking, he certainly brings all his training, all his imagination, all his free association to bear on the nature of the critical investigation he is designing. Certainly he reviews the literature; he has always spent much time in *reading.* Now he reads even more to derive sustenance from his colleagues. The library is as important to him as his laboratory, but the primary tool remains his brain.

Finally, he goes to the laboratory—or to the field—or to the observatory—or to the blackboard—or to a notebook filled with his mathematics—or to the armchair. The scientist's activity is a "mix," not pure unadulterated laboratory work.

The emphasis is on the phrase *mix of activity* and the emphasis is on the individual exerting the energy: that individual is to be the student, not the teacher.

If inquiry is the focus of the teaching activity, then the textbook is to be *read and studied* by the student prior to work in the laboratory, not regurgitated, as it were, by the teacher. The text and talk, to repeat, are prelude to inquiry; the text is to be uncovered by the teacher, not covered. To repeat, the teacher uses the classroom to help the students explore the material universe, to seek satisfactory explanations of the objects and events explored—always putting these explanations to the test. If some bit of this universe presently under scrutiny is not clear, then appropriate questions may point a way to further clarification. But teaching is not the way to "right answers" but rather a way to assisting boys and girls to learn more than any one teacher could know.

Some concepts must be subjected to discussion, others to investigation at home, or in the class, or in the laboratory. Some time must be given to the calisthenics of discovery (the so-called laboratory exercise): a student should learn to use the lens, the ruler, the microscope, a variety of tools; he needs to dissect plants and animals; he needs to become expert in the "human use of human beings."

Significantly, these teachers also made opportunities for children to originate their own experiences in search of meaning; they gave the children opportunity *to science* (a new and useful verb).

Limited plans for experiences in search of meaning ("problems" planned by the teacher) or great ones (depending on the ability of the student) but in any event "problems" for which there are easy solutions, and those for which there are no easy solutions, or solutions which come only after considerable effort should be made available to the student. In other words, if the problem can be solved in a planned period of time (say a laboratory) it is within the domain of the calisthenics of discovery, or *problem doing*. In *problem solving* the solution must be deferred if only because inquiry and subsequent data gathering in line with the strategy of the critical investigation takes time. Problem solving involves the true-and-free inquiry we have been discussing.

Where does a teacher obtain such problems for investigation? Hordes of them have been developed by BSCS,[7] CHEMS, PSSC. Others can be garnered from the quantities of books now available. But then, teachers have always been ingenious.

Where the teacher does most of the work, through lecture, through directions by work sheet and assignments, through insistence on recall of lecture material and text, through laboratory work which is designed to illustrate (by deed) for the student what has already been illustrated in the text (by word and picture)—then inquiry and the independent learning associated with it are minimized. Teaching is then equated with telling; truly an impoverished road to the young mind.

Where the student has opportunity to do most of the work, then slowly but surely he assumes responsibility for learning, and the library becomes a tool as does the laboratory. The teacher becomes a guide and the classroom a place to clarify; the text and talk are a springboard for further work, not *the* end.

In sum, we have put forward the the-

sis that a sanative, a healing environment developed for the young is one guarantee that the young, now become men and women, will place value on a sanative environment for their young. But the Biblical injunction is that one doesn't get figs from thistles. One must plot and scheme —in a human way—to secure the early sanative environment. It has its intellectual and emotional parameters. Indeed, judgments affecting conservation must be based on a strong intellectual component; love of outdoors, if diffused and undirected by an intellectual vector, may even be antagonistic to appropriate conservation measures, e.g. balancing of population of organisms.

We secure the intellectual parameters by securing one critical aspect of early environment, corrective and full of hope, the school. In order that the environment make sense, we need to plot experiences in search of meaning; to do this, we must first persevere in making meaning of the world. A conceptual ordering permits us to see structure and through structure relatedness. A contemplation of intellectual structure is sanative, for a contemplation of order (synonym: intellectual beauty) is sanative. However, when *we* plot experiences for the young, even in the interests of the child's idiosyncratic development, we introduce *our own values* as ends.

We have need to stimulate independence in students, for it is the independent student who can see structure, who can plot independent searches for meaning, who becomes part of an evolutionary cadre seeking to ensure independence of search for others. Men and women in these evolutionary cadres, in turn, invent the means by which sanative environments are secured. That is to say, when children have freedom to invent their own investigations (in true-and-free inquiry) they have opportunity to develop their own values; in the end, values which come out of healing experiences

[7] For instance, see American Institute of Biological Sciences, 1962.

tend to be those that value healing. These values are powerful instruments in conserving the sanative environment.

We secure the emotional parameters by making possible the return by man, as species, to his womb—the natural environment. To conserve beauty, one must experience it: have perennial access to it: live in it.

When we secure a sanative environ-ment for the young, we are extending the bounds of human sympathy. Conversely, extending the bounds of human sympathy through the riches of experience in search of meaning means building and disseminating not only a world of meaning but a world of beauty: a world fit for all life and for all that will live.

BIBLIOGRAPHY

American Institute of Biological Sciences. 1962. Teaching High School Biology: A Guide to Working With Potential Biologists.

Beveridge, W. I. B. 1950. The Art of Scientific Investigation. New York.

Bohannan, Paul, and Dalton, George. 1965. Markets in Africa. Garden City, N.Y.

Brandwein, P. F. 1955. The Gifted Student as Future Scientist. New York.

Bronowski, Jacob. 1958. Science and Human Values.

Erikson, Erik H. 1963. Childhood and Society. New York.

Gerth, Hans, and Mills, C. Wright. 1964. Character and Social Structure. New York.

Mead, Margaret. 1964. Continuities in Cultural Evolution. New Haven.

Roe, Anne. 1953. The Making of a Scientist. New York.

Schwab, J. J., and Brandwein, P. F. 1962. The Teaching of Science. Cambridge, Mass.

Simpson, George Gaylord. 1964. This View of Life. New York.

ADMINISTRATIVE POSSIBILITIES FOR ENVIRONMENTAL CONTROL

Lynton K. Caldwell*

The purpose of this paper is to explore the utility of public administration for the control of man's biophysical environment. Attention will be directed primarily to the *natural* aspects of the environment rather than to those contrived by man, although man and his artifacts are also natural phenomena. The biophysical combinations and interactions on Manhattan Island are no less a part of nature than those at work in Muir Woods, even though the environmental contrast is extreme. There is, however, a valid logic in a focus on man's efforts to control the biophysical environment which he has not created but out of which he has evolved. It is one means to man's understanding of himself and of the world upon which his continuing survival depends.

The context of the discourse will be at the level of national policy and action in the United States. This choice is made for two reasons: first, in order to hold the length of the essay to appropriate proportions; and second, because given the distribution of constitutional, statutory, and fiscal powers in American government, and the incongruity of political and environmental boundaries, public policy

* Dr. Caldwell is Professor of Government at Indiana University. He has been a leading advocate of public responsibility for the quality of the human environment and for the use of ecological concepts in the coordination of natural resources and conservation policies.

at all levels of government is today heavily dependent upon national policy.

To treat fully the role of government in the control of North American environments, attention should also be directed to Canadian experience. However, to deal adequately with natural resources and environmental policies in Canadian government would extend this chapter beyond available limits of space. The argument developed in this chapter applies in principle to both American and Canadian government, although the illustrations and historical analyses are drawn from south of the international border. Until the recent past, the pressure of man on his environment has been much less in Canada than in the United States. This circumstance is now changing, and comparative study of Canadian and American experience in environmental control will increasingly gain pertinence in both countries.

The political context of environmental policy

In an analysis of environmental control through public administrative means, two sets of ecological relationships are involved. The more inclusive relationships are those between American society and its biophysical environment—the ultimate focus of our concern. But examination of the possibilities for control over these relationships involves consideration of the more specific political context, the psychosocial environment of the organizations through which public administration takes place. The availability of administrative means to govern relationships between men and their biophysical environments is largely conditioned by the contextual matrix of perceptions, values, ideas, institutions, and relationships within which public action occurs.

The public official responsible for some particular aspect of public action affecting the biophysical environment (pollution of air or water, for example) is therefore concerned not only with the internal operations of his agency, but equally he must be concerned with what the psychosocial environmental matrix within which his program must be administered will permit him to do. On occasion he may need to consider how these limiting factors (of public opinion, for example) may be changed to permit a more effective realization of the purpose that he believes it his responsibility to serve. Each public agency operates not only in the general environment of public life, but within its own unique contextual matrix. This contextual matrix imposes constraints on the agency as diverse as those that bear upon the National Park Service and the Corps of Engineers. Thus, factors that condition the ability of federal agencies to cooperate with one another are frequently external to their formal administrative structure. Common among these factors are clientele groups, citizen organizations, Congressional committees, and other governmental agencies (state and local as well as federal).

Where (as in American society) there is substantial popular control of government, it is essential that the larger purposes and goals of public action be defined and accepted with essentially the same meaning both inside and outside the formal structure of government. The availability of specific administrative means, and of organizational structures

suitable to their utilization, depends ultimately upon what goals and purposes have been accepted in society. The perceptions and values which predominate in public life thus ultimately influence the objectives that administrative action will pursue.

In the analysis of administrative possibilities for environmental control, the selection of specific means is therefore incidental to the definition of *purpose*. Determinations as to who defines public purposes, how they are defined, and to what ends are of course functions of politics. But politics in the broad sense operates through the administrative process as well as outside of it, and is one of the fibers that tie together the internal and external aspects of public administration, giving it functional coherence. The character of administrative action often reveals the extent to which this coherence has been achieved in politics, and can be expressed in public policy.

In an open democratic society, environmental policy can hardly be more coherent than popular consensus will permit. There may be so little social consensus on environmental goals that environmental policy based exclusively on currently prevailing attitudes would be little more than a patchwork of contradictions. For this reason the practical problem of environmental administration involves much more than the application of administrative means to actualize whatever environmental goals and purposes society appears to have adopted.

Environment-affecting goals in our pluralistic society *are* often incoherent and contradictory, and some of them are of doubtful consistency with what we know to be necessary to human well-being. Ours is a government intended not only to serve popular wishes, but more importantly to safeguard and advance human welfare. The task of environmental administration is thus not only to imple-

ment public decisions affecting the biophysical environment, but also to help
ensure that those decisons are the ones
that a society knowledgeable of its own
needs, interests and potentialities *ought* to
make. Basic to the task of environmental
administration are therefore the functions of research, education, training,
and public information which influence
the contextual matrix of public policy
making in ways that will make "better"
environmental decisions possible.

Meaning of the "possible"

Man's capacity to improve or to destroy his environment is large and is
growing. But it is not unlimited. The
"possible" affords a greater latitude for
choice than man is likely to utilize, but
it also has parameters set by the biophysical realities of the universe. Within
biophysical limitations, man's capacity to
effect environmental change is largely
culturally determined, with technology a
salient factor. Through his technology
man manipulates his biophysical environment and his present actions thus help
to determine future possibilities. But only
in the relatively recent past has man
been able to assess the consequences of
his technology on the biophysical environment against a yardstick provided
by his knowledge of the biophysical
world—including knowledge of his own
physiological and psychological needs.

This knowledge, derived through science, is of course merely the tested, systematized, and corrected accumulation
of perceptions and interpretations of
natural phenomena. The way in which
man organizes and interrelates this knowledge is determined by the culture through
which his goals and purposes are expressed. For example, *natural resources*
and their *conservation* are culture-derived
concepts. There are no natural resources
except as perceived and classified by man.
Resources conservation (including the

meaning attributed to *conservation*) is an
aspect of a culture that postulates certain cause-and-effect relationships and is
the product of its own interpretation of
its historical experience (such as the influence of the frontier on American ideas
and values). To take another example,
the concept of *use* has been so generally
understood in exclusively economic or
physical terms that the preservation of
undisturbed natural areas for scientific or
esthetic purposes is equated in the minds
of many Americans with *nonuse*. The
urge to extend the multiple-use concept
to all natural environments, regardless of
suitability, follows from concepts of economy, efficiency, and utilitarianism—concepts that are culturally and historically
derived, but which are also subject to
future modification and change.

Inherent in present attitudes and action
are possibilities for enlarging or foreclos-
ing future opportunities. To maximize the
range of choice tomorrow and in the
more distant future, the effect of decisions taken today must be understood. In
relation to the biophysical world, knowledge of what should or should not be
done now, as well as in the foreseeable
future, is derived from the sciences and
particularly from ecology. But ecology is
a young and not yet fully developed science, and what it has to offer by way of
guidance in environment-affecting decisions is often neglected. The development
of ecology would be a major contribution
toward enlargement of the possibilities for
effective environmental administration.
But policy and action can be informed
only by knowledge now at hand. If we
seek wise decisions with respect to future
possibilities we have no choice other than
to make the most of the potentialities of
the present. The extent of our ignorance
of environmental relationships is disheartening but, in the words of Dr. M. King
Hubbert, "Our ignorance is not half so
vast as our failure to use what we

know."[1] Present ecological and environmental knowledge could enable us to make more and better environmental decisions if we possessed the vision and the means to do so. How, then, do we obtain the vision and how do we acquire the means?

There are no obvious or easy answers to these questions. But there are clues that indicate where answers may be found. One of these clues has already been provided by our discussion of the ultimate dependence of public action upon public opinion. This indicates that vision—a conceptualization of the possible—must precede political or policy implementation. Means can be appropriate only in relation to specified ends. Thus, somehow, a concept of environmental ends must be developed throughout society to an extent, and with a degree of coherence, that will make possible the development of means to serve these ends. If, in addition, one is concerned that ends and means promote the public happiness and welfare, then there is need for public consensus with respect to the qualities of "good" environments. To enlarge the possibilities for human well-being through environmental administration there will also be needed a corresponding growth in both scientific and popular understanding concerning the ecological basis of human society.

Prerequisites for public action

It is evident that the American people, in effect, are already engaged in the comprehensive "management" of their biophysical environment. But it is also apparent that this "management" is largely the sum of the unplanned, uncoordinated, and often cross-purpose pursuits of individuals, corporations, and government agencies, all seeking their own objectives,

[1] Comment in National Academy of Sciences-National Resource Council, "Renewable Resources," by Paul Weiss, 1962, Publication 1000A, p. 106.

and seldom with regard for the cumulative consequences of their actions. In American society there is as yet no well-defined and generally accepted doctrine governing man's behavior toward his biophysical environment as an environment. Government in America has no charge to deal comprehensively with environmental questions; it approaches environmental issues only through some specific environment-affecting responsibility such as the protection of water supply (a public health measure), prevention of soil erosion (an aid to agriculture), or prohibition of overkilling wildlife (for economic, recreational, or scientific reasons).

Before government can become generally responsible for safeguarding the quality of the biophysical environment, at least three prerequisites must be met. These can be identified and described under the headings:

a. vision and leadership,
b. minimal consensus, and
c. instrumental means.

Vision and Leadership. The first of these prerequisites may be divided for discussion, but must be united for action. Someone must be able to visualize how society can deal comprehensively with its environment before the other prerequisites can acquire a practical relevance. This vision is less an act of individual inspiration than the slow and random accumulation of concepts and ideas from many sources that one day fall into place as a coherent and persuasive doctrine of social responsibility. To make this vision meaningful and to catalyze consensus is the function of leadership. This function is not only one of interpretation; it is also one of integration. The diversity of interests and values of people in relation to the biophysical environment are major factors in the fractionalizing of public responsibility. Comprehensive environmental policy becomes possible only when a sufficient number of these diversities and resulting conflicts are reconciled, adjusted, or transcended to permit the degree of consensus needed for public action.

Minimal Consensus. The level of consensus necessary for public action will of course vary with the character of society, with the political situation, and with the issue upon which consensus is sought. Under effective authoritarian rule, minimal consensus may be very minimal indeed. In open, democratic, politically active societies, a large percentage of the population—perhaps a strong majority—must be agreed on basic legislative concepts. However, on specific issues, such as those affecting environments, agreement among small but relatively influential minorities may be sufficient for public action. The history of rivers, harbors, and reclamation projects illustrates the way in which the machinery of government can be mobilized on behalf of relatively local, minor, and short-term interests. It is also true that public action on behalf of unique habitats or specific natural areas and wildlife has often been the work of dedicated minorities. But for comprehensive public policies some breadth of popular consensus must be won. The efforts to enact the federal Wilderness Bill illustrate the ways in which a necessary minimal consensus is developed.

Public action on behalf of these projects (good, bad, or indifferent) is possible because of a vague, inarticulate consensus that public "improvements" or conservation of resources are in the public interest. Lacking an adequate comprehension of ecological cause-and-effect relationships and of a strong or clearly defined concept of environmental values, Americans generally tend to be apathetic and uncritical in matters of environmental change. To arouse public interest, environmental issues have to be posed in most dramatic form, as in Rachel Carson's *Silent Spring*. Efforts to institute more comprehensive environmental policies and controls in government characteristically meet the concerted opposition of natural resource users whose economic interests are threatened, without gaining support from the public-at-large that is the intended beneficiary.

Absence of consensus for comprehensive environmental policy is no more inherent in our social or political system than formerly was absence of consensus for old-age insurance, employment security, or space exploration. Prior to the forming of a minimal public consensus on these matters, their realization through public action seemed quite as hopeless as comprehensive environmental administration seems today. Crisis is often a creator of consensus, and ideas widely viewed as utopian may, under compelling conditions, become public demands. The economic debacle of the early 1930s wrought changes in public opinion that made possible sweeping innovations in public law and policy for which only a few years earlier no popular consensus could be found.

The crises of environmental change, however, tend to be "quiet crises." The more violent environmental catastrophes (fires, floods, drouths, and earthquakes) tend to be viewed as discrete events or "acts of God," and the remedies sought are characteristically directed to the event itself with little regard to the combination of circumstances which made the event, in man's view, a catastrophe. Thus, millions are spent in an ultimately futile effort to contain floods rather than to follow the less costly and more dependable course of environmental planning. But the more widespread and ultimately more disastrous environmental changes are those occurring so slowly and steadily as to escape attention until possibly irremedial harm is done. Cumulative environmental poisoning by wastes, pesticides, or radioactive materials proceeds in this unobtrusive manner. Soil erosion and depletion, disappearance of wildlife habitat, breakup of open space, spreading deterioration of settled areas both urban and rural are other examples of progressive environmental decline with which government, as now constituted, is poorly equipped to cope.

Instrumental Means. The machinery of government may have been adequate to do what it was originally intended to do. But it falls short of adequacy in the performance of many of the tasks that confront it today. It has not, for example, been intended for the coordinated public management of the biophysical environment. Law and the weight of judicial precedent tend to favor particularist interests—ecological concepts and the public interest in its environment are as yet inadequately developed in American legal doctrine.

For the most part governmental agencies act upon the biophysical environment only in pursuit of the special purposes that they have been constituted to serve. These purposes have come into being at the behest of particular groups and interests, and not infrequently are in mutual conflict. The spectacle of interagency collision over environmental issues has been most prominently dramatized in the management of rivers.[2] Recommendations by the Hoover Commissions and other investigatory bodies for a greater coordination in natural resources administration have largely failed to win acceptance.[3] The reason is obvious and simple: the political forces representing particularized interests in environmental matters have been collectively stronger (although very possibly less numerous) than the forces favoring a more comprehensive and balanced approach to public action on environmental and natural resources issues.[4]

Limitations of administrative means

It would be erroneous to conclude that inadequate consensus and divided opinion are the only obstacles to effective coordination of environmental administration. Should these barriers be miraculously overcome tomorrow, there would remain some very obdurate limitations on what government could readily do. The more obvious limitations would be those of knowledge, personnel, and institutional arrangements.

Knowledge of man's environmental needs is far from adequate even though our society is also far from utilizing the knowledge that we do in fact possess. Our most reliable environmental knowledge relates to what is demonstrably harmful to man. But there are ranges of tolerance among individuals for specific environmental phenomena—noise, for example. Qualitative environmental standards tend to be subjective: purity of water, purity of air, freedom from noise, freedom from disorder are conditions that different persons will interpret and evaluate differently. Nevertheless the gross boundaries of environmental tolerances are definable and if we cannot at present be confident that we can describe an environment that everyone would find "good," we can at least identify environmental conditions that virtually everyone would agree were "bad."

A second limitation of administrative means is personnel—people able to assimilate the requisite knowledge and to apply it through analytic and operational skills. Such people are not numerous at the present time and their numbers could not

---

[2] Cf. Pealy, 1959; Hart, *The Dark Missouri*, 1957; Maass, 1951.

[3] Cf. Commission on Organization of the Executive Branch of the Government, *Concluding Report—A Report to the Congress* (May, 1949), pp. 27–30, 65–67; and *Organization and Policy in the Field of Natural Resources—A (Task Force) Report with Recommendations*, January, 1949. See also Barrow Lyons, *Tomorrow's Birthright—A Political and Economic Interpretation of Our Natural Resources*, 1955.

[4] Cf. Wengert, 1955.

be increased overnight. Environmental analysis and planning requires knowledge and skills obtainable only through multidisciplinary education. Skills of communication are especially necessary for cooperation with diverse specialists if their particular contributions are to be brought into a coordinated relationship. A comprehensive public environmental policy objective would imply greater emphasis on environmental considerations in those fields of education (agriculture, civil engineering, city and regional planning, and public health, for example) that inevitably would be involved in environmental administration.[5]

The present limited capacity of higher education to prepare individuals for environmental planning and administration ought to be recognized as an important sublimitation on the use of administrative means for environmental control. In the absence of significant demand for persons trained for the tasks of environmental administration, educational preparation for these tasks is not likely to be provided in the universities. There are, however, indications of growing concern for environmental relationships in such fields of professional education as civil engineering[6] and public health.[7] As the need and demand for persons of broader competence in environmental matters grows, higher education will find ways of providing the requisite training.

A third limitation on environmental administration today can be found in the institutional arrangements through which

environmental issues are administered. From both a jurisdictional and functional viewpoint the structure of American government tends to impede rather than to facilitate the solution of environmental problems. The federal structure of national government is poorly designed to deal with environmental issues (it was not intended for this purpose). Nevertheless, under strong national leadership, fiscal control, and certain legal and structural innovations, the federal system could be adapted to cope more effectively with environmental problems. Interstate cooperation can show some successes, but in the main the states cannot be counted upon for effective voluntary action on environmental issues. Their generally ineffectual performance in air- and water-pollution control illustrates the problem.

Finally, the functional divisions of public administration impose formidable barriers to effective environmental policy. At the federal level, coordination of natural resources policies and their administration has long been a matter for study and concern. The National Resources Planning Board represented the closest approach to comprehensive environmental planning attempted for the nation as a whole.[8] The Tennessee Valley Authority is, of course, an instructive example of comprehensive public environmental planning in action.[9] But federal organization generally reflects the interests or needs of special resource users—in forestry, grazing, mining, navigation, irrigation, and outdoor recreation, for example.

The principal but only partially effective coordinating agency in relation to

[5] The need for multidisciplinary education and training has been stressed in *National Academy of Sciences-National Research Council Report of the Committee on Natural Resources to the President of the United States*, 1962, Publication 1000, pp. 33–34; Publication 1000A, pp. 95–106; and 1000G, pp. 34–52.

[6] Cf. Grimm, 1961, pp. 17 ff., and American Society of Civil Engineers, 1964: "Urban Planning Definitions," pp. 15–19.

[7] Cf. Rosen, 1964, Part II, pp. 1–6.

[8] Cf. Charles E. Merriam, "The National Resources Planning Board," in Galloway and Associates, 1941, pp. 489–506, and Millett, 1947, pp. 137–52.

[9] Lilienthal, 1944; note Chap. 7, "A Seamless Web: The Unity of Land and Water and Men"; Durish and Macon, 1951; Wengert, 1951, pp. 369–92; and Martin, ed., 1956.

these user interests has been the Bureau of the Budget. Its concerns, however, are primarily fiscal and secondarily economic (cost-benefit justification, for example). The Bureau is assumed to apply the over-all policy guidelines laid down by the President. In actual fact, presidential policy must often be a product of bargaining, maneuvering, and compromise among the federal administrative agencies. The Bureau's functions are largely political and, in a narrow sense, technical. It is seldom in position to provide the analysis and integration of substantive policy that environmental issues require. At best it may require the administrative agencies to iron out their differences and coordinate their efforts. Meanwhile the basic environmental issues at stake may never be posed; the questions that matter most may never be asked.

The fact is that the federal government is not structured for the effective administration of complex environmental issues. Compensatory measures have been sought through legislation requiring joint consultation and planning in specified cases of natural resources administration. The effectiveness of these measures is difficult to assess. They represent an improvement in environmental policy making over the earlier exclusiveness and competitive behavior of the natural resource agencies. But they are palliatives rather than basic reforms, and their accomplishments are largely at the technical rather than policy level.[10] Nevertheless these legislative requirements for interagency consultation evidence recognition of the need for coordination in environmental policies. These measures may prove to be transitional stages toward future and more fundamental re-

forms, but they do not answer the need for high-level-policy leadership.

The emerging concept of environmental administration

In America, government (particularly at the federal level) has traditionally played a mediating role between the claims of differing interests in the development of the natural environment. Contrary to the recommendations of Washington, Hamilton, and Gallatin in the early years of the Republic, public opinion and political interest did not support a conservative national responsibility for guiding the physical development of the continent. Individual initiative was unfettered and the attitude of "Come and get it" was prevalent late into the nineteenth century. Not until the closing years of that century did historians and geographers, following the lead of earlier European scholars, begin to investigate the influence of environment upon the shaping of the American social character and institutions.[11] The influence of man on his environment received less attention, but the pioneering work of George P. Marsh (*Man and Nature: Physical Geography as Modified by Human Action*, 1964) marked the beginning of a slowly growing awareness that man himself was a major factor in environmental change. By 1908, when Theodore Roosevelt called the first conservation conference at the White House, the elements of a doctrine of public responsibility for the biophysical environment had begun to take shape through the conservation movement.

From its beginnings, the movement tended to divide into two courses of intellectual development: economic and ecological, which although related could also conflict.[12] Conservation as an economic concept was concerned primarily

---

[10] Cf. Pealy, op. cit., and comment "Interagency Relations," in Commission on Organization of the Executive Branch of the Government, 1949: *Task Force Report on Natural Resources* (Appendix L), pp. 25–26.

[11] E.g. Semple, 1903, and Turner, 1921.
[12] Cf. Elmo R. Richardson, 1962; Swain, 1963; Hays, 1959, especially pp. 189–98.

with the "wise use" of natural resources. Its focus was upon discrete resources of economic benefit to man: upon water power, timber, minerals, fisheries, and agricultural productivity of soils. Its regard for environmental factors tended to be secondary or coincidental. The ecological concept of conservation was concerned more with the quality of the biophysical environment than with economic resources. To sharpen the contrast between these viewpoints, it can be said that the economic concept was concerned with wealth, the ecological with health; the economic with quantities, the ecological with qualities; the economic with analysis, the ecological with synthesis.

In the early years of the conservation movement these dichotomies were not always apparent. Neither concept was well developed, and the divergencies resulting from specialized emphasis on one or the other of the two viewpoints only gradually emerged. During these years the term "conservation," however generalized, possessed sufficient coherence to permit the establishment of departments of conservation in many of the states and to be studied in the classroom as if it were a unified concept. But by mid-twentieth century "conservationists" not infrequently found themselves opposing "conservationists" in public debates and on legislative issues. In more than one state, administrators of conservation departments saw "nature-loving" conservationists as their number-one annoyance. And ecological-minded conservationists frequently saw in economic resources-minded conservation commissions and administrators the agents of anticonservation. The motto "Conservation Means Wise Use" poses the ambiguity of the conservation concept. What use is wise? Who is qualified to make the determination, and what should be the criteria for judgment?

By mid-twentieth century the inadequacy of the traditional conservation concepts for conciliating or adjudicating conflicting interests in environmental issues was becoming apparent. Public administration, in the main, tended to follow the economic resources view of conservation. But economic reasoning was unable to cope adequately with a growing number of environmental problems that involved the conservation of noneconomic values. There were, of course, major economic questions involved in problems of water pollution, air contamination, pesticides, wilderness areas, and the preservation of open space. But the basic factors in these problems were not altogether economic —there were also issues of physical and mental health, of the quality of life, or ethical, esthetic, scientific, and military values. The administrative machinery of public conservation, based on vaguely defined and economically oriented concepts, increasingly demonstrated its inadequacy to deal with a growing number of public controversies over the shaping of the biophysical environment.

The major problem of public environmental administration has thus been a matter not so much of appropriate tools and techniques as of guiding concepts. When the issues of conservation could be resolved on the technical level by regulating the cutting of timber, setting bag limits on wild game, and reducing soil erosion, the traditional conservation doctrines made sense and pointed the way to public action. Value differences in issues like these tended to diminish as the consequences of unlimited exploitation became clear. But in such issues as the proposals to construct a power-generating plant on the face of Storm King Mountain on the Hudson River; in the leveling of the Indiana Dunes for a great steel mill and industrial harbor; in the bisecting of the natural beauty of Woodside, California by a high-tension power line, neither the doctrines of traditional conservation nor the jurisdictional allocation of public responsibility afforded an adequate basis for public decision. The conservation concept could help guide the resolution of issues like these only if it were infused with a substantive content that afforded a basis for the setting of priorities—that gave objective content to the meaning of wisdom.

Out of the evolution of our society—demographic, technological, and cultural—has grown the need for a concept of public responsibility in relation to the biophysical environment and man's habitat that extends or transcends the historical conservation movement. To conserve, in the narrow sense, is not enough; if man is to shape his relationship to his environment with regard to his ultimate well-being and satisfaction, some goals and guidelines for his developmental urge are imperative. For better or worse, man will continue with increasing powers at his disposal to attempt the management of his environment. There is no point in debating over whether there will or will not be environmental administration. Its occurrence, however disorganized, segmented, or shortsighted, is a fact of public life. The question now is not "Shall we have environmental administration?" but rather "What kind of environmental administration, and to what purposes?"

Implications and Probabilities. If, as this essay contends, a comprehensive public responsibility for the character and quality of the biophysical environment is necessary to man's future welfare and happiness, it is desirable to ascertain the circumstances under which acceptance of this responsibility is likely to occur. For evidence does not support the conclusion that such a sense of public responsibility will *inevitably* emerge—however logical or advantageous its emergence may seem. In our prior discussion of the possibilities and prerequisites of public action we stressed the importance of public attitudes and understandings as basic to whatever administrative action government takes. Only in relation to these con-

ceptual factors does discussion of particular administrative tools and methods have meaning.

Interaction of Attitudes and Events. It does not necessarily follow, however, that the beginnings of comprehensive (or at least coordinated) environmental administration must await a fundamental change of popular attitudes. Events, perhaps more often than theories, initiate change in human affairs. Theories and concepts may be adopted as a means of coping with events, and of rationalizing unavoidable change. Expression of an idea may be an event and may figure both as a cause and an effect in a sequence of events. It thus seems probable that the slow leaven of ecological thought that has been at work in many aspects of modern society has been preparing the way for an enlarged concept of public responsibility which will be crystallized under the pressure of events. Unfortunately, the most instructive events are often painful.

Such events are recorded with increasing frequency in the public media—in the press, in politics, in scientific and cultural affairs. Familiar examples are the condemnation of cranberries and milk in Wisconsin because of harmful chemical residues; the smog in New York and Los Angeles; the imminent biological death of numerous lakes, streams, and coastal waters illustrated dramatically in the lower Mississippi Valley and in Lake Erie; the impending extinction of numbers of plants and animals owing to the disruption of their natural habitats. Hitherto, comparable events when deplored, have often been described as the "price of progress." But if the "price" increasingly exacts payment in the health and happiness of people, even those unversed in ecology may be moved to ask whether the price must necessarily be so high, and whether the alleged progress is in a desirable direction. Yet, thus far, the impact of these well-publicized disasters is limited to relatively few people. The cumulative effect of environmental deterioration is only beginning to be generally comprehended.

Americans for the first time in their national history are being compelled to reckon with the finite nature of man's environment, but there is still widespread failure to distinguish between the *material elements* of the environment (minerals, gases, organic compounds, for example) that man may fabricate or simulate, in some cases indefinitely, and the unique *environmental combinations* of living and inanimate things that, once destroyed, can be neither replaced nor simulated. The "conquest" of outer space affords temptation for irresponsible romanticizing concerning alternatives to the necessity for a self-renewing administration of man's earthly environment. Mining on the moon and migrations to Mars may be more than phantasy, but too often they are invoked in defense of an indulgent and exploitive attitude toward the earthly environment. Ironically, the true lessons of space exploration underline the enormous importance of the environmental factors in human welfare.[13]

Effect upon Political Values. Environmental administration based upon regard for the quality of man's total environment suggests important implications for American government and politics. The effect of changing environmental concepts upon political values can be illustrated by reference to questions of local and personal rights, or property ownership, and of the adaptability of our traditional structure of government to new public responsibilities.

The American belief in the constitutional right of people to govern themselves in their own communities has been

[13] A fact emphasized by Stephen H. Dale and Isaac Asimov in their popular version of a Rand Corporation Research Study, *Planets for Man,* 1964, Chap. 8, "An Appreciation of the Earth."

markedly modified by the constitutional and political trends of recent times. Mandatory and prohibitory action by federal and state governments has continually narrowed the latitude of independent action by local governments. The enlarged scope of permissive taxation and an increase in local governmental functions in some localities are only a partial exception to the trend. The foreshortening of time and space by jet-age technology is redefining concepts of environment, locality, and community in ways that contradict many of the traditional assumptions of American government.

To the resident of the Boston-New York-Baltimore megalopolis, Quetico-Superior, Jackson Hole, and the Florida Keys belong potentially to his recreational environment. The San Franciscan need not live in the Sierras to consider it his own "back yard." America's public lands and domain more than ever in the past have come to be viewed as belonging equally to all of the American people. This viewpoint has angered local users and prospective developers of resources. Grazing, lumbering, mining, real estate, and resort interests have loudly and frequently protested the abrogation of their "rights" on behalf of faraway city dwellers. Traditional boundaries between individual rights and public interests have been breaking down as popular demands upon the environment grow. As in race relations, foreign affairs, and public health, old moralities are under attack by new and antagonistic concepts. It is not to be wondered that the man who, when trying to wrest a living from nature after the fashion which three centuries of American history found good, may explode in frustrated, uncomprehending outrage at the suggestion that he is selfishly exploitive. The pioneer with ax and gun and plow is still revered in American folklore; it is difficult for those who would emulate his psychology today to see themselves, at best, as anachronistic and, at worst, as destroyers of the national heritage. Unhappily, this differential time lag in attitude among Americans gives rise to incomprehension and bitterness in political controversy over environmental policies. But ultimately the exigencies of a crowded and mobile world seem certain to override traditional values that are yet widely ascendent.

This redefinition of local and personal rights is closely related to the idea of property ownership, which is of course a legal concept. As with other legal concepts its meaning has changed over the years. Ownership of property in land or other natural resources has never been absolute, nor has it necessarily been consistent with the concept of personal freedom—even for the owner. Were environments, as distinguished from discrete resources (in land or water, for example), to become more clearly the objects of public responsibility and the subjects of legislative and administrative action, the rights of property in the biophysical environment might be further modified by overriding public interest. In fact, zoning and other forms of restriction upon the uses of property are widely accepted instruments of environmental administration. And the concept of public (or private) rights in environments-as-such is being further reinforced through the use of easements and building codes to protect scenic, natural history, cultural, or esthetic values in environments. Comprehensive environmental policy would not, of course, escape the old and continuing problem of determining who pays and who benefits when public action is taken. The broader ecological approach to natural resource and environmental problems does not in itself resolve questions of equity of treatment and of property rights. But it may provide an institutional setting in which laws and policies pertaining to the environment may receive more thoroughgoing scrutiny and may be more fully evaluated through broader based tests of public interest.[14]

Effective environmental control implies comprehensive control. The nature of the biophysical environment and the concentration and interrelatedness of the modern industrial economy necessitate this conclusion. The tools and techniques that technology and administration make available for environmental administration are most effective when used in combination. But their coordinated use has been largely prevented by definitions of public responsibility—in law and practice—that emphasize the separate and competing use of natural resources. The economic rather than the ecological concept of conservation has dominated our political and administrative doctrine. Emphasis on resources and not upon environments in the structuring of government has tended to reinforce the popular view that administration of the natural environment and its elements is primarily a matter of economics. Implicit in the concept of comprehensive environmental administration is not only an extension or, more accurately, a redefinition of public responsibility, but also a reorganization of the administrative structure of government for natural resources and environmental purposes.[15] The emergence of a popular ecological concept of the responsibility of government has been slow and painful. The following pages will recount briefly the struggle between the two approaches to conservation and the difficulty experienced by the comprehensive,

[14] As a case in point to demonstrate that environmental policy making in detail would be neither simple nor easy see Ostrom, 1963, pp. 98–111.

[15] Compare the observation by Ostrom, 1962, p. 72, that "Since patterns of organization have a fundamental influence on the development of perspectives, values and ideas regarding resource policies and patterns of resource development, any question of comprehensive planning must necessarily involve questions about the design of organizational arrangements."

integrative, ecological concept in making headway against prevailing natural resources concepts which have traditionally been atomistic, competitive, and economic. Focal point of this struggle has been the effort to achieve a coordination of natural resources policies.

Efforts toward coordinating administrative action

As previously noted, the machinery of American government has frustrated coordinated public action on environmental issues through the fractionalized allocation of responsibility for specific resource decisions. Agencies such as the Federal Power Commission, the Corps of Engineers, or the Bureau of Reclamation act on criteria and on behalf of objectives that are often narrowly specified by law or policy. Control over the several parts and segments of the biophysical environment has been divided among separate agencies each of which pursues its unilateral course independent of the others and seldom with sufficient regard to the larger environmental consequences of their actions. The environment as a whole is not a public responsibility. There is presently no administrative machinery through which comprehensive public environmental policy can be developed and applied.

The Conceptual Basis of Public Action. An understanding of why the American people have found such great difficulty in coordinating or integrating public policies pertaining to natural resources and the biophysical environment can be gained by comparing the possibilities and conditions of public administrative action detailed in the preceding pages with the cursory summation of historical events in the pages that follow. To facilitate this comparison it will be useful to focus attention on two basic considerations.

First, possibilities for administrative action in relation to the biophysical en-

vironment have been severely limited in the American historical context by deficiencies of concept, leadership, consensus, and instrumental means.[16] Efforts toward coordination of natural resources policy have failed, as we shall see, *not* primarily because of the complexity of the problems involved, but principally because there existed no generally accepted structuring of priorities to postulate the substantive ends or goals of coordination. The ecological concept of man in relation to his environment formulated for Americans by George Perkins Marsh made very slow headway in a society in which the dominant values were essentially economic and particularistic. The conservation motto of "wise use" was unable to provide an integrating concept, and it afforded a basis for coordination only at the technical level. Economy and efficiency are instrumental as technical concepts and offer no guidance toward substantive goals. The "wise use" motto even when related to the idea of the greatest good for the greatest number still lacks content. Democratic ideology has traditionally defined "good" through political bargaining. Democratic public administration, lacking any authoritative conceptualization of good environment, has dealt with the environment in its discrete parts as "natural resources." The unhappy environmental consequences of this approach have led to demands in and out of government for what, in fact, was coordinated *environmental* policy, but which has been customarily misconstrued as a need confined to coordinated *resources* administration. Only with repeated failure to achieve a unified approach to environmental policy through the coordination of natural resources administration has the fundamental contradiction in this approach begun to be evident.

Second, the possibilities for administrative action in the future depend in large

16 Cf. Ekirch, 1963.

measure upon the conceptualizing of environmental goals and of related public responsibilities at the highest and most influential levels of public life. The development of instrumental means and popular consensus for better environmental administration necessarily proceed simultaneously and in mutual interaction; new concepts of public responsibility call for new forms of public action. The adaptability of existing natural resources agencies to the tasks of environmental administration is limited by the internal and external factors described earlier in this essay. Continued operation of these agencies along traditional lines and on the basis of traditional assumptions is a major obstacle to the effective exercise of public responsibility for the biophysical environment.

Administrative Reorganization Efforts: 1907–57. Dissatisfaction with the organization of government for the coordination of policies pertaining to natural resources and the biophysical environment dates back at least to the beginning of the conservation movement. As early as 1907 Senator Francis G. Newlands of Nevada proposed legislation to establish a commission for comprehensive water-resource development. This measure remained before the Congress for some ten years until it finally succumbed to the united hostility of the federal water agencies and the special resource interests in the Congress.[17] Reorganization of the Department of the Interior and reallocation of natural resources and public works responsibilities were proposed by the Joint Congressional and Presidential Committee on Reorganization of 1924. No action was taken, but the issue remained.

In 1937 the President's Committee on Administrative Management recommended a reorganization of federal natural resources agencies under a Department of Conservation that would "advise the President with regard to the protection and use of the natural resources of the Nation and the public domain" and would "administer the public lands, parks, territories, and reservations, and enforce the conservation laws with regard to public lands and mineral and water resources."[18] This proposal also incurred the enmity of federal resources agencies and special purpose users and became, for the time being, a historical conversation piece. But the issue still remained.

An argument for the coordinative approach to natural resources administration, but one that inadvertently demonstrates its inadequacies, was published in 1946 by the resources economist S. V. Ciriacy-Wantrup. He declared that "improvements in the administrative coordination of conservation policies can best be brought about, first, by establishing or strengthening general planning agencies in the executive; second, by better integration and more effective functioning of the legislative; and third, by facilitating federal-state and interstate cooperation."[19] He opposed the idea of a federal department of conservation as an "administrative monstrosity." The comprehensiveness implied in a national conservation policy would, he believed, impinge upon nearly every other department of the federal executive. A federal department of conservation must either absorb important functions delegated by Congress to other agencies or subordinate them to its own administration. He also opposed the idea of a general federal conservation act as neither constitutionally feasible nor politically wise. "It appears probable and politically desirable," he concluded, "that conservation policies

[17] Hays, pp. 199–240.

[18] President's Committee on Administrative Management, 1937, *Report with Special Studies*, pp. 34–35.
[19] Ciriacy-Wantrup, 1946, pp. 48–58.

will continue to be formulated through numerous individual acts."[20]

Ciriacy-Wantrup's conclusion appears to have been influenced by his premise that "conservation is only one phase of the general problem of economic planning," and by his assumption that to attempt the coordination of the widely ramifying aspects of conservation in any single agency of government would be technically unmanageable—would impair constitutional checks and balances that he believed necessary for democratic government. Nevertheless, he was doubtful that coordinate agencies could coordinate themselves effectively without assistance. He therefore proposed a Federal Planning Division, with review and advisory powers only, within the Bureau of the Budget, and a number of Regional Coordinating Boards representing federal, state, and local agencies under the chairmanship of a regional representative of the Federal Planning Division.

The position taken by Ciriacy-Wantrup illustrates the conclusion that would tend to follow from an economics-oriented view of natural resources. The need for action to correct duplicate and cross-purpose effort was evident. But the problem was construed to be one of coordination of discrete elements—not of managing the interrelating parts of the seamless web of the environment. Public policy remained at the level of attempted coordination of the conflicting or inconsistent acts of separate resource agencies. It could not, in Ciriacy-Wantrup's view, wisely be extended to the level of integration, to bringing natural resources development under the unifying policy direction implicit in a national conservation statute and agency.

A closer approach to an integrative viewpoint was taken in the report of the Commission on Organization of the

Executive Branch of the government (Hoover Commission) in 1949 which provided the most detailed and explicit examination of the problem hitherto undertaken. The actual recommendations of the Commission corresponded generally to those of the President's Committee on Administrative Management a decade earlier. Although more conservative than the proposals of the Commission's Task Force on Natural Resources and the views of several of the commissioners, its recommendations went far beyond the point of Congressional acceptance. But of possibly greater future significance than the Commission's final recommendations was a minority report submitted by Vice Chairman Dean Acheson and Commissioners James K. Pollock and James H. Rowe, Jr.[21]

This minority view evidenced an ecological orientation implicit in the statement "that the conservation, development and use of our public resources is a single indivisible problem. It can be solved wisely," the minority declared, "only by the leadership of one governmental agency which would relate each part of that problem—forests, water, public lands, minerals, wildlife, fisheries, recreation, power—to the others and develop all of our natural resources together" (Hoover Commission Report, 1949, p. 54). The minority found that "This Nation has reached a stage in its growth that calls for a new concept in the relation of these resources to our economy" (Hoover Commission Report, 1949, p. 55).

This new concept was expressed in the proposed establishment of a Department of Natural Resources replacing the Department of the Interior and providing for a unified administration of public land and water resources functions. Unified management of natural resources on

20 Ibid., p. 51. For his economic interpretation of conservation see his *Resource Conservation*, 1952, pp. 51–52.

21 Commission on Organization of the Executive Branch of the Government, 1949. Reorganization of the Department of the Interior, pp. 53–80.

a regional basis was recommended, with the TVA as a model that might be extended to some river basins. At highest political levels a Board of Review in the Executive Office of the President "would coordinate the programs of the Department of Natural Resources and those of the new regional authorities—if any—with each other and with other interested Government agencies such as Agriculture and the National Military Establishment" (Hoover Commission Report, 1949, p. 57).

In 1953 a Mid-Century Conference on Resources for the Future gave considerable attention to the growth of cooperation in the administration of natural resources. The record of the discussions, although in themselves inconclusive, indicate that voluntary cooperative efforts thrive best against a background of clearly expressed public policy and among a citizenry informed regarding the issues before it.[22] As with "coordination" in the history of resources administration, so "cooperation" in the Mid-Century Conference appeared to be desirable as an end as well as a means. In the words of the Conference report, "the focus was on cooperation itself" (Mid-Century Conference, 1954, p. 333). The ultimate ends of cooperation were never made articulate; the substantive goals around which cooperative effort might be effected were not explored.

In 1955 the President's Advisory Committee on Water Resources Policy added its recommendations to the growing list of rejected proposals.[23] The high-level board of review that had characterized several earlier plans was again proposed. A permanent federal interagency committee under the chairmanship of a co-ordinator of water resources was rec-

ommended. But even this conservative proposal—confined essentially to water resource problems—found insufficient acceptance.

By 1957, after fifty years of relatively futile effort to coordinate natural resources administration, there was a growing belief among students of the problem that something was wrong with the approach. This belief was evidenced not so much in criticism of earlier reorganization efforts as in an ecological rather than functional approach to administrative organization. The basis for this viewpoint could be found in published writings on environmental and resources policy that were soon to be followed by proposals for a new approach to the coordination of natural resources policy through the integrative concept of environment.[24]

National Academy of Sciences Report: 1962. Of indirect but meaningful implication for federal administrative action were two reports on the state of research on natural resources prepared at the request of President John F. Kennedy. The first of these was prepared by a Committee on Natural Resources of the National Academy of Sciences-National Research Council; the second was prepared by the Federal Council for Science and Technology. These reports exemplify the two major contrasting viewpoints that characterized the conservation movement since its inception. The Academy report was ecological and integrative in its outlook; the Council report tended toward the technological and coordinative. Economic values were a major consideration in both reports, but were more heavily stressed in the report of the Council. Both reports recognized the need for

---

[22] Mid-Century Conference on Resources for the Future, 1954.

[23] Presidential Advisory Committee on Water Resources Policy, 1956.

[24] A notable contribution to the ecological viewpoint was the international symposium in June, 1955, at Princeton University, the proceedings of which were published in the volume edited by William L. Thomas, Jr., 1956. An ecological approach was also taken in the volume edited by Charles H. Callison, 1957.

more comprehensive and coherent national policy on natural resources.[25]

The Academy committee proposed a central natural resources group within the federal government as a means toward meeting this need. This group would stimulate, evaluate, and assist "an integrated program of resources research involving a great majority of the departments of the Federal Government."[26]

A more comprehensive and incisive statement of what this new agency should be appeared under Proposition VII of the report of the study committee on *Renewable Resources* prepared by Paul Weiss:

"Such a body would function in essence as an intelligence agency in matters of human ecology. It should keep itself constantly informed of all physical, biological, sociological, geographic, and economic events and developments of potential bearing on man's optimal adjustment to his environment, and attempt to evaluate in scientific terms the probable net effect of their mutual interactions of man's future—short-range and long-range—in national, regional, and global respects. In this pursuit, it should avail itself of the cooperation of the best talent of the country in the natural sciences and relevant branches of the social sciences. It should determine for any single alteration in the total scene—manmade or beyond man's control—the net balance between risk and benefit, not in absolute terms of the intrinsic properties of that particular change, but in relative terms of its putative consequences for the whole fabric of human affairs. In view of the ever-increasing rate of man-made alterations, with their ever-widening circle of sequelae,

such an intelligence agency of broad scope would have to cultivate the highest degrees of perceptiveness and sensitivity so as to be able to feel the pulse of the ecosystem, as it were, and to register and assess incipient developments before they have reached critical dimensions. These diagnoses would then serve as guides for action programs, precautionary measures and the exploration of alternative courses. By its cultivation of a total integrative overview, such an organization would be in the most favorable position to detect signal gaps and incongruities in the map of existing knowledge in need of filling or reconciling by further research. And by its anticipatory point of view, it would be singularly qualified to identify what kinds of research might be undertaken or intensified in order to forestall, counteract or rectify predictable *future* disruptions and imbalances of the human ecosystem. The contemplated agency should not, however, be given powers of decision or enforcement and it should steer clear of the political arena."[27]

In this statement a conceptual threshold was crossed; government transcended its traditional role of umpire among conflicting resource interests to become guardian of man's biophysical environment. To be sure, the study-committee proposal disclaimed any political or administrative role for the new agency. But the proposition would have no meaning unless public policy were somehow influenced by agency findings. In one very important respect the Weiss report appeared to misconstrue the circumstances under which such an ecological intelligence agency would necessarily function. Even though it did not possess powers of decision or enforcement, and steered clear of involvement in the grosser forms of partisanship, it could not

[25] For a detailed comparative analysis of these reports see Ordway, et al., 1964.

[26] National Academy of Sciences-National Research Council: Committee on Natural Resources, 1962, Publication 1000A, p. 33.

[27] Op. cit. supra note 1, p. 15.

avoid contact with politics. A government agency is in the broad sense of the term inherently *political*. The establishment of such an agency would be a political act, and its continued support by public moneys would also involve political action.

The findings of such an agency, directly or through sponsored research, could be presumed to have wide-ranging implications for American society. The urgency of the need for such an agency is an indicator of the magnitude and power of the environment-shaping forces with whose interactions the agency would be concerned. The environment-shaping forces in human society—ideological, technological, economic, and military—are neither impersonal nor nonpolitical. They are personified in individuals and organized groups with emotional and often economic commitments to environment-shaping activities. Some indication of the impossibility of isolating major ecological research findings from the political arena can be gained by recalling the reaction of the tobacco industry and the tobacco-state politicians to the report of the Surgeon General on cigarettes and public health; or the public furor created over Rachel Carson's polemical but nonpolitical *Silent Spring*.

Nevertheless, the Weiss report was surely right in its separation of the ecological-intelligence functions from direct administrative action. Less certain is the extent to which the proposed agency should have a review function with respect to natural resources and environmental decisions in government. Should this agency fulfill the function of the Board of Review proposed by the Acheson group in the first Hoover Commission? The power of recommendation in itself may be very great when vested in a body of high competence, prestige, and objectivity! To exercise strong influence, it would not be necessary for such a board or agency to have the power to approve or disapprove proposals. Its evaluation of proposals for approval by the President or the Director of the Budget could be a major factor in the process of policy making.

Matching administrative means to environmental ends

At the beginning of this paper we observed that possibilities for administrative action were dependent upon congruity between the internal and external forces influencing the behavior of organizations. We found that in American government this congruity existed between specific resource agencies and their particular publics but did not extend to a more generalized public responsibility for the protection and management of the biophysical environment. We also saw that, of the conditions upon which administrative action depends, elements of vision, leadership, and popular consensus favorable to public environmental administration on ecological principles appeared to be gaining strength, but that instrumental means for developing environmental policy were inadequate. American government has had no forum appropriate to the exercise of an ecologically oriented leadership in environmental policy. Means for exercising policy leadership and so broadening and deepening the basis of popular understanding and consensus are an urgent and unavoidable need.

Inducing a National Environmental Policy. The struggle to preserve, protect, or wisely manage America's natural environments has in the main been a losing battle, although not without significant victories. It has been a losing battle in part because the institutional arrangement in American society—economic, administrative, and juridical—is better adapted to the exploitation of the biophysical environment than to its protective custody and self-renewing development. Public action on behalf of natural environments has almost uniformly been defensive—until recently there has been no positive public policy to place any but the most spectacular of them under the protective custody of government, or to formulate guidelines and standards for their management. Government has indeed too often been an agent of those who were prepared to sacrifice environmental values to economic, military, or political advantage. In consequence, persons who would protect natural areas have often endeavored to wall off or immunize these areas from the blighting hand of public "improvement."

There are, of course, specific short-run legal devices and remedies by which particular natural habitats can be protected from direct invasion by either public or nongovernmental action. But the larger environmental settings and the larger distinctive habitats that by definition must be extensive—grasslands, deserts, mountains, and estuaries, for example—cannot be safeguarded in the absence of public action. Public ownership affords no guarantee of safety in the absence of public environmental policy that will lift the level of public decision above bargaining among the various resource users. Until the ecological concepts expressed in reports of the Committee on Natural Resources of the National Academy of Sciences-National Research Council, and in the writings of our policy-minded ecologists are somehow reflected in the public law of the United States, available administrative means for environmental control cannot be utilized with full effectiveness.

Nevertheless, there has been a very slow yet discernible growth of a larger concept of public and national responsibility. The evidence can be found in the arguments for such specific legislation as the Wilderness Bill (88th Congress, Public Law 577); the Land and Water Conservation Bill (88th Congress, Public Law 578); in inducements to the control of

advertising on interstate highways; and in presidential and Congressional inquiries into the effects of air and water pollution and of pesticides. Thus, the building blocks of a coherent national environmental policy are in the making.

It is, of course, sensible and realistic to cope as best one can with existing facilities. Attention should be given to enlarging and improving the specific devices of law and administration available for immediate use in relation to environmental issues. But it is equally important to develop the basis in law and policy upon which a more effective and ecologically informed environmental administration can be established at all levels of government. It is especially important that this be done at the federal level, where the financial and administrative power in our federal system is concentrated, where responsibility is located for the use, development, and protection of our national public lands and waters, and where ultimate responsibility for national action pertaining to the atmosphere, the oceans, and international environmental issues must be placed.

The development of institutional means for public environmental administration requires research and innovation. There have been suggestions and proposals but we have no procedural manuals to tell us exactly how it should be done. Some guiding considerations, however, can be deduced from the history of efforts toward coordinated national conservation policy and from the recommendations of scholars and study commissions.

The first and fundamental consideration is that efforts at major-policy coordination among coordinate resource agencies are foredoomed to failure and in any case cannot achieve comprehensive environmental policy. There are times and places where coordination of resource uses at the technical level is feasible. But the task of coordination has little significance beyond considerations of economy and efficiency, unless undertaken against a more explicit and authoritative standard for social goals. The quality of the biophysical environment might afford the substance of such goals; this possibility was implicit in President Lyndon B. Johnson's description of the tasks of the "Great Society" delivered at the University of Michigan on May 22, 1964.

"The challenge of the next half century," he declared, "is whether we have the wisdom . . . to enrich and elevate our national life and to advance the quality of our American civilization." And he added, "Your imagination, your initiative and your indignation will determine whether we build a society where progress is the servant of our needs, or a society where old values and new visions are buried under unbridled growth."[28] The heart of his address was concerned with the remaking and safeguarding of America's urban and rural environments and was expressed essentially in ecological terms. It is doubtful if the President would have expressed himself in this manner if he had not been confident that what he said would be understood by his audience and, being understood, would be approved. His intellectual commitment to the ideas expressed may be less significant than his political judgment that these were the "right" things to say to a youthful audience in an election year.

Qualitative environmental standards must necessarily be derived from the biological and behavioral sciences, but they must also necessarily take into account the whole man even as they take into consideration the comprehensive environment. Thus, some way must be found to reflect in public standards the psychological, ethical, and esthetic needs of men rather than to reject as idiosyncratic whatever cannot be reduced to rigorous

economic logic, or calculated on slide rules or on computers.

Administrative Institutions for Environmental Control. These considerations point toward the need for a high-level public agency that in addition to being a focal point for policy-oriented research, would also be evaluative and expressive —would define and clarify issues, consequences and alternatives, but would leave the decision on environmental issues to the politically responsible institutions of the federal government: the Congress and the President. The basis of this function and agency would necessarily be a statute which would state in general terms the responsibility of government for safeguarding the public welfare through surveillance over changes in the biophysical environment. This, in effect, corresponds to the recommendations of the National Academy of Sciences-National Research Council Study Committee on Renewable Resources and to earlier suggestions advanced by Gilbert White.[29]

The novel and unique functions of this agency would be to sharpen the process of political choice. After analyzing the failures of coordinative and cooperative efforts, Gilbert F. White concluded that the key deficiency in the administration of natural resources and environmental policy was absence of the kind of analysis that "would present estimates of the consequences of each of the politically practicable lines of public action. Thereby the political process of choice would be sharpened rather than curbed, and governmental intervention seen in perspective with the alternatives" (Jarrett, 1958, p. 223).

A major consequence of this focusing of issues on a large perspective should be the broadening of popular perceptions of the environment. The educational merit of this evaluative function could be very

---

[28] Office of the White House Press Secretary, 1964, pp. 1–4.

[29] In Henry Jarrett, ed., 1958, pp. 220 ff.

great and would hopefully lead toward much greater popular understanding of the stakes in resources and environmental decisions. This function thus answers the need for visualization of issues and for articulate leadership that comprehensive environmental policy requires. It would provide the instrumental means by which popular consensus could be induced. In these ways such an agency would greatly extend the real possibilities for legislative and administrative action on environmental issues.

Changes in the existing structure of government for natural resources administration are nevertheless needed, no less now than they were when recommended by past committees, commissions, Presidents, and scholars. The Acheson version of the first Hoover Commission report on natural resources affords the best basis yet proposed for an integrative approach to a resources administration that could be regardful of ecological and environmental considerations. The further problems of integration among levels of government and the need for special arrangements in particular regions and localities are complex matters requiring an experimental and innovating approach. Experience indicates, however, that initiative at lower levels of government depends upon a more adequate resolution of the problem of integration at the federal level.[30]

The role of the citizen in environmental policy is also in need of innovative thought. Environmental administration is neither inherently nor necessarily a technocratic nor bureaucratic process. It could become so if exigencies of health,

safety, or gross inconvenience resulting from environmental mismanagement should necessitate summary governmental action beyond the level of general public understanding. A widening gap between scientific (particularly ecological) knowledge and popular perception and comprehension could lead to an alienation of public opinion from environmental administration regardless of its ecological soundness or its promise for human welfare. It is possible, however, to develop institutions for environmental policy making and execution that are much more broadly representative of the diversity of citizen interests and values than is the present structure of resources administration, responsive (as it is) mainly to special client groups.[31]

The effectiveness of organizational change, however, depends (as has been noted) upon a reciprocal influence between structure and attitude. Administrative possibilities for environmental control will depend upon the attitudes and understandings of the public officials whose decisions shape public environmental policy. In this process of decision, relationships between the "natural" scientists and economic and political advisors to top policy officials become especially important. The need for improved communications between scientist and administrator has been widely recognized.[32] To the extent that mutual understanding and effective communication are lacking between "natural" scientists and "social" scientists and administrators, administrative possibilities are correspondingly limited. Specific, formalized measures to improve this understanding and commu-

---

[30] Cf. recommendations of the Commission on Intergovernmental Relations (Knestnbaum Commission), 1955, pp. 240–41; e.g. "a permanent Board of Coordination and Review to advise the President and the Congress on a coordinated natural resources policy within the National Government and between it and the States." Natural resources advisory councils were recommended for each state.

[31] Examples of innovative ideas that bridge the gap between professional ecological management and popular understanding are F. Fraser Darling's "conservator" (professional managing ecologist), in Macfadyen and Newbold, 1964, pp. 39–45; and Fosberg's "The Community Ecologist," in Fosberg, 1957, pp. 24–25.

[32] E.g. Murray, 1964, pp. 360–70.

nication are needed for the betterment of public policies generally.[33]

The Need for Action. Unless political and administrative innovation can move government significantly along the foregoing lines of development, it is doubtful if more than a marginal "conservation" of the remaining natural environment of North America can be expected. Private means cannot be mobilized to a degree sufficient to buy the lands and the easements and to fight the legal battles necessary to safeguard ecological values everywhere. The setting aside of specific natural areas and sanctuaries through private and public effort should be pushed with full vigor. But the prospects for their survival as ecological islands amid environments of biophysical ruin could hardly be optimistic.

Even though America's population growth were arrested today, the present industrial technology would continue its push to exploit every niche in the North American biosphere. The convergent effects of the triple explosions of technology, science, and population make comprehensive environmental administration inevitable in the long run. But the preservation, restoration, and wise management of the biophysical environment will become progressively more difficult the longer it awaits comprehensive treatment. Even to let the natural environment alone now requires positive protective action. Nothing will remain untouched that public administration does not protect. There is at present no end of talking and writing about the environmental crisis of our time, but action proportionate to the need has yet to appear.[34]

Our current knowledge of public atti-

tudes is inadequate for gauging the readiness of public opinion to support comprehensive governmental action on behalf of environmental well-being. For public opinion to be catalyzed it may be necessary for people everywhere to be hurt environmentally as acutely as many were hurt economically by the great Depression of the 1930s. The overdue legislative and administrative changes required for effective environmental administration may require this impetus.

An imperfect but suggestive analogy of the course that might be followed would be the history of the Employment Act of 1946 and the surveillance of the national economy by the Council of Economic Advisers.[35] And by analogy, one may ask whether the state of the biophysical environment is less important to the public health, safety, and welfare than is full employment, and whether the knowledge of man's environmental needs as understood through the biological and behavioral sciences is less "hard" and less reliable than knowledge of his economic welfare. A generation ago the idea of public responsibility for the state of the economy was utopian. Is it less conceivable that public responsibility for the quality of the biophysical environment may be generally accepted (if not sooner) within the generation ahead?

The White House Conference on Natural Beauty convened by President Johnson on May 24–25, 1965 may have marked the threshold of such an enlarged concept of public responsibility. Although the specific focus of the Conference was upon beauty, it nevertheless dealt broadly with questions affecting the quality of the total environment. The argument for a high-level citizen advisory body to help formulate the issues and alternatives in environmental policies, which in various forms has had advocacy for more than a decade, was again urged by the Confer-

[33] This argument is elaborated in my "Biopolitics: Science, Ethics and Public Policy," *The Yale Review*, 1964, pp. 1–16.

[34] As a random sample of the literature of protest see: Blake, 1964; Carson, 1962; Dasmann, 1963; Tunnard and Pushkarev, 1963; and Udall, 1963.

[35] Cf. Bailey, 1950.

ence. Implicit in the proceedings of the Conference, in President Johnson's Message on Natural Beauty to the Congress on February 8, 1965, and in his remarks at the conclusion of the White House Conference, was a new interpretation of public responsibility that moved far beyond the concept of conservation that pervaded President Theodore Roosevelt's White House Conference on Conservation in 1908. President Johnson expressed the essence of the change in his Message on Natural Beauty:

"To deal with these new problems will require a new conservation. We must not only protect the countryside and save it from destruction, we must restore what has been destroyed and salvage the beauty and charm of our cities. Our conservation must be not just the classic conservation of protection and development, but a creative conservation of restoration and innovation. Its concern is not with nature alone, but with the total relation between man and the world around him. Its object is not just man's welfare but the dignity of man's spirit."

BIBLIOGRAPHY

American Society of Civil Engineers. 1964. Urban Planning Definitions—A Report by the Committee on Terminology used in the Practice of City Planning. J. Urban Planning and Develop. Div., Proc. Amer. Soc. Civil Engineers, 90:15–19.

Bailey, Stephen Kemp. 1950. Congress Makes a Law: The Story Behind the Employment Act of 1946. Columbia Univ. Press, New York.

Blake, Peter. 1964. God's Own Junkyard: The Planned Deterioration of America's Landscape. Holt, Rinehart & Winston, New York.

Caldwell, Lynton K. 1964. Biopolitics: Science, Ethics and Public Policy. Yale Rev. 54. New Haven, Conn.

Callison, Charles H. 1957. America's Natural Resources. Ronald, New York.

Carson, Rachel. 1962. Silent Spring. Houghton Mifflin, Boston.

Ciriacy-Wantrup, S. V. 1946. "Administrative Coordination of Conservation Policy." J. Land and Pub. Util. Econ. 22.

———— 1952. Resource Conservation. Univ. Calif., Berkeley.

Commission on Intergovernmental Relations (Knestnbaum Commission) 1955. A Report to the President for Transmittal to the Congress. Govt. Print. Off., Wash., D.C.

Commission on Organization of the Executive Branch of the Government. 1949. Concluding Report—A Report to the Congress. Govt. Print. Off., Wash., D.C.

Commission on Organization of the Executive Branch of the Government. 1949. Reorganization of the Department of the Interior. Govt. Print. Off., Wash., D.C.

Commission on Organization of the Executive Branch of the Government. 1949. Task Force Report on Natural Resources (Appendix L). Govt. Print. Off., Wash., D.C.

Dale, Stephen H., and Asimov, Isaac. 1964. Planets for Man. Random House, New York.

Dasmann, Raymond F. 1963. Last Horizon. Macmillan, New York.

Durish, Lawrence L., and Macon, Hershal L. 1951. Upon Its Own Resources—Conservation and State Administration. Univ. Ala.

Ekirch, Arthur A., Jr. 1963. Man and Nature in America. Columbia Univ. Press, New York.

Fosberg, F. Raymond. 1957. The Community Ecologist. AIBS Bul. VII.

Galloway, George B., and Associates. 1941. Planning for America. Holt, New York.

Grimm, Sergei N. 1961. Physical Urban Planning—System of General Concepts and Principle Features. Syracuse Univ. Sch. Arch., Syracuse, New York.

Hart, Henry C. 1957. The Dark Missouri. Univ. Wisc., Madison.

Hays, Samuel P. 1959. Conservation and the Gospel of Efficiency—The Progressive Conservation Movement 1890–1920. Harvard Univ. Press, Cambridge, Mass.

Jarrett, Henry, ed. 1958. Perspectives on Conservation—Essays on America's Natural Resources. Johns Hopkins, Baltimore.

Lilienthal, David E. 1944. TVA—Democracy on the March. Harper, New York.

Lyons, Barrow. 1955. Tomorrow's Birthright—A Political and Economic Interpretation of Our Natural Resources. Funk & Wagnalls, New York.

Maass, Arthur A. 1951. Muddy Waters: The Army Engineers and the Nation's Rivers. Harvard Univ. Press, Cambridge, Mass.

Macfadyen, A., and Newbold, P. J., eds. 1964. British Ecological Jubilee Symposium. Blackwell, Oxford.

Martin, Roscoe C., ed. 1956. TVA, the First Twenty Years. Univ. Tenn., Knoxville.

Mid-Century Conference on Resources for the Future. 1954. The Nation Looks At Its Resources. Resources for the Future, Wash., D.C.

Millett, John D. 1947. The Process and Organization of Government Planning. Columbia Univ., New York.

Murray, Allan S. 1964. The Relationship Between the Administrator and the Scientist in the Renewable Resource Field. Can. Pub. Admin. VII.

National Academy of Sciences-National Research Council: Committee on Natural Resources. 1962. Reports Constituting Publications 1000, 1000A and 1000G. Nat. Acad. Sci., Wash., D.C.

Office of the White House Press Secretary. 1964. Remarks of the President . . . (As Actually Delivered).

Ordway, Samuel H., Jr., Bowman, Wallace D., and Milton, John. 1964. Research on Natural Resources: A Review and Commentary. Nat. Res. J. 4.

Organization and Policy in the Field of Natural Resources—A (Task Force) Report with Recommendations (January, 1949).

Ostrom, Vincent. 1962. The Water Economy and Its Organization. Nat. Res. J. 2.

——— 1963. Property, Proprietorship and Politics. Paps. of Reg. Sci. Assn., West. Sec., Univ. Oreg., June 14–15, 1963. Univ. Oreg., Bur. of Bus. and Econ. Res., Eugene.

Pealy, Robert H. 1959. Comprehensive River Basin Planning: The Arkansas, White, Red Basins Inter-Agency Committee Experience. U. Mich., Bur. of Govt., Ann Arbor.

Presidential Advisory Committee on Water Resources Policy. Rep., December 22, 1955. 1956. Water Resources Policy. Govt. Print. Off., Wash., D.C.

President's Committee on Administrative Management. 1937. Report with Special Studies. Govt. Print. Off., Wash., D.C.

Richardson, Elmo R. 1962. The Politics of Conservation—Crusades and Controversies 1897–1913. Univ. Calif., Berkeley.

Rosen, George. 1964. Human Health, Community Life and Rediscovery of the Environment. In: Man—His Environment and Health (suppl. to Amer. J. Publ. Health and Nation's Health 54).

Semple, Ellen Churchill. 1903. American History and Its Geographic Conditions. Houghton Mifflin, Boston.

Swain, Donald C. 1963. Federal Conservation Policy. 1921–1933. Univ. Calif., Berkeley.

Thomas, William L., Jr., ed. 1956. Man's Role in Changing the Face of the Earth. Univ. of Chicago.

Tunnard, Christopher, and Pushkarev, Boris. 1963. Man-made America: Chaos or Control? Yale Univ., New Haven, Conn.

Turner, Frederick Jackson. 1921. The Frontier in American History. Holt, New York.

Udall, Stewart L. 1963. The Quiet Crisis. Holt, Rinehart & Winston, New York.

Wengert, Norman. 1951. TVA—Symbol and Reality. J. Politics 13.

——— 1955. Natural Resources and the Political Struggle. Random House, New York.

TRENDS IN LAW AND OTHER INSTITUTIONS[1] FOR THE NURTURE OF DIVERSE HABITATS

Samuel H. Ordway, Jr.*

Flood-control effort, begun after a flood has damaged the land, reveals lack of human foresight. Flood-control planning, based on recognition of the consequences of causes, requires knowledge of the soils of valley and upland, the flora and fauna they have supported over the years, the changes wrought upon them by nature and by man, normal and abnormal rainfall, absorption and runoff—many land-use factors which interrelate in making the environment what it is. When relevant knowledge has been marshaled, studies follow to determine how human institutions—law, engineering, organization, land management—can be applied to prevent flood damage in the future with least cost and greatest advantage to the community.

So it should be with habitat protection: timely, knowledgeable, and institutionally feasible.

The well-being of a great variety of environments, which constitute the diverse North American habitats of the present,

is threatened by a flood of developments initiated by men, in our ever more affluent societies. It is timely that we are seeking ways to control this threatened flood before irreparable damage is done. We are exploring environmental knowledge to foresee causes and consequences of social change. We are reviewing institutional means to prevent abuses and destruction our descendants would otherwise suffer and find insufferable. We are presently seeking institutional ways to protect environments and habitats so that they will be available in the future to support a diversity of fauna and flora and a diversity of human uses—for factories and homes and transport, and recreation—amenities of every kind. Although our descendants may never agree on what is "the good life," we want them to inherit a sufficient variety of healthy habitats in which life can be enjoyed.

This search of ours is complicated by the cultural as well as the physical aspects of our North American inheritances. We, in the United States, are proud of constitutional safeguards of individual property and personal freedom. The control needed to preserve the diversity of our habitats must be accomplished through democratic institutions within the framework of constitutional evolution.

I would here trace some of the landmarks in our constitutional and institutional evolution to indicate ways we may foresee by which habitat diversity can

---

* Mr. Ordway, who presided over this session of the Conference, is identified in a note on page 613.

[1] This paper draws heavily on the assembly of relevant cases and legislation by Charles Haar in his casebook entitled Land Use Planning, Little, Brown & Company, Boston-Toronto, 1959; and on the admirable discussion of "Institutional Arrangements" found in Chapters 12 and 13, Land Problems and Policies, by V. Webster Johnson and Raleigh Barlowe, McGraw-Hill Book Company, Inc., New York, 1954.

be democratically though forcefully preserved.

Once the scientists have determined the nature and the scope, the sizes and the contents and the evolution of the many kinds of natural habitats we shall wish to preserve, and once the planners have devised a master plan for the continent, for each of the nations and for the states and regions, mapping out the essential land uses for megalopoli and agriculture, and recreation, for factories and homes and transport and wildlife, the institutional problem will become one of requiring and implementing, democratically and economically, the land usages essential to meet these needs in the long-range public interest.

In 1927 the U.S. Supreme Court dealt liberally with this problem of the conflict of personal freedom and the public interest. Neither land use nor zoning was before the Court, but the decision dealt forthrightly with the fact that public welfare must prevail over individual, most personal prerogative. Mr. Justice Holmes spoke for the Court:

"We have seen more than once that the public welfare may call upon the best citizens for their lives. It would be strange if we could not call upon those who already sap the strength of the state for these lesser sacrifices, often not felt to be such by those concerned, in order to prevent our being swamped with incompetence. It is better for all the world, if instead of waiting to execute degenerate offspring for crime, or to let them starve for their imbecility, society can prevent those who are manifestly unfit from continuing their kind. The principle that sustains compulsory vaccination is broad enough to cover cutting the Fallopian tubes. Three generations of imbeciles are enough." (Buck v. Bell, 274 U.S. 200, 1927)

This was not an easy decision to make. And it took the mind of a Holmes to express so simply the nonfascist, thoroughly democratic resolution within the Constitution of that ultimate issue: the right of the peoples' elected representatives to determine what is best for the greatest number.

In terms of the public interest in ultimate land-use planning and habitats protection on the North American continent, it should follow that the long-range public interest will prevail over the property rights of individuals, be they speculative developers or home-loving landowners. Mrs. Buck has become an unfortunate symbol of the right and interest of the many to prevail over personal tragedy.

The lands of this continent are in part owned by various levels of government, in part by quasi-public institutions, and in part as private property by corporations and individuals. Much government-owned land is dedicated to specific public purposes and uses which can be as difficult to alter as are uses of privately owned land. Vested interests exist in the public, through governments, quite as emphatically as in corporate and individual owners.

Property rights are among the oldest rights established in and protected by law. Ownership of both real and personal property has long been the subject of contest, first *vi et armis* and then, as the law sought to establish order, through litigation. Regulation of ownership and of the usage of property has been the concern of legislators from early times, and legislative enactments have in turn been subject to varied interpretation by the judiciary, as has, of course, the Constitution itself—the supreme law of the land.

Article XIV, Section 1, of the U.S. Constitution provides: "Nor shall any State deprive any person of life, liberty, or property, without due process of law."

Under the constitutions of each of the states, except North Carolina, today, no property may be taken by eminent domain without just compensation.

THE NATURE AND LIMITATIONS OF THE RIGHTS
OF OWNERSHIP OF PROPERTY

Ownership of land imports the privilege of exclusive use—the right to exclude others—and the privilege of determining to what use the land is put. But from early times the courts have recognized and enforced limitations on the owner's exercise of these privileges, where the exercise infringes upon the "equal" rights of neighboring owners. A long line of cases, leading to reasonably established doctrine, proscribes the commission of "public," "common" as well as "private" nuisances on an owner's land which injure the privacy or enjoyment of other owners. Creation of noise, flooding of water or sewage, noxious odors, pollution of a neighbor's air or water are examples. Charles Haar suggests that the courts by

evolving and enforcing this doctrine of nuisance establish in fact the power of the state to control land use for the protection of others (Haar, 1959, pp. 95, 96).

Another line of cases involves the resolution of conflicts between variant neighboring land uses: cattle grazing adjacent to a golf course and a bathing beach adjacent to a glue factory are examples. Conflict between group interests and individual interests extends the scope of interpretation of property rights. Once the public interest is introduced, the issue is not merely one of "nuisance" or "trespass in the case" but exercise of the "police power."

THE CONSTITUTIONALITY OF ZONING

It is through exercise of the public power, authorized by the Constitution, and interpreted and sustained within limits by the courts, that land-use planning and zoning are most frequently justified.

The U.S. Supreme Court has stated that the police power "is universally conceded to include everything essential to the public safety, health and morals . . . the State may interfere wherever the public interests demand it, and in this particular a large discretion is necessarily vested in the legislature to determine, not only what the interests of the public require, but what measures are necessary for the protection of such interests. . . . To justify the State in thus interposing its authority in behalf of the public, it must appear, first, that the interests of the public generally, as distinguished from those of a particular class, require such interference; and, second, that the means are reasonably necessary for accomplishment

of the purpose, and not unduly oppressive upon individuals." (Lawton v. Steele, 152 U.S. 133, 1894)

Invocation of the police power to regulate the use of land, in cities and villages, through "comprehensive" zoning plans and ordinances began in the 1920s. The constitutionality of zoning, which deprives owners of free choice in the use of their property, was immediately challenged in many court cases and ultimately, of course, in the U.S. Supreme Court. A leading decision on this subject was handed down by that Court in 1926 in the case of Village of Euclid, Ohio v. Ambler Realty Co. (272 U.S. 365). While the Court did not pass on "the wisdom or sound policy" of the restrictions enacted, it held that this zoning ordinance was not unconstitutional, on the ground claimed, as "having no substantial relation to the public health, safety, morals or general welfare." In the course of its opinion, three Justices dissenting, the Court said:

"Building zone laws are of modern origin. . . . Until recent years urban life was comparatively simple; but with the great increases and concentration of population, problems have developed, and constantly are developing, which require, and will continue to require, additional restrictions in respect of the use and occupation of private lands in urban communities. . . .

"Regulations applicable to existing conditions which are now uniformly sustained would have been rejected half a century ago as arbitrary and oppressive."

The Court cites traffic regulations sustained today that would have been rejected as arbitrary and unreasonable before the advent of automobiles, and concedes that the scope of the application of constitutional guarantees of property rights must expand or contract to meet new and different conditions.

"In a changing world it is impossible that it should be otherwise."

On safety and health, the Court states that experts are agreed that segregation of residential, business, and industrial buildings will increase "safety and security of home life; greatly tend to prevent street accidents . . . decrease noise and other conditions which produce or intensify nervous disorders; preserve a more favorable environment in which to rear children, etc."

Charles Haar has said that the history of the *Euclid* case is the story of the acceptance of zoning in this country. He writes:

"Two opposing lines of decision in the state courts were presented to the Supreme Court. . . . After the first argument, a majority of the Court apparently concluded that zoning was an unconstitutional interference with property. . . . However, a dramatic reversal of the vote followed an equally

dramatic rehearing. . . . If you like so to express things, 'Smug reaction gave way before the enlightened forces of social advancement' (Isaacs, 1930)." (Haar, 1951, p. 165)

It took the courts a comparatively long time to extend approval of the use of the police power to advance esthetics. In 1944 a Connecticut court, upholding legislation to restrict billboards on state highways, said that early cases and a number of fairly recent decisions condemned regulation of billboards because esthetic considerations were regarded as the predominating or sole motive of the restrictions. "However, there has been a growing tendency to regard the power more broadly. Restrictions on billboards have been upheld on the grounds that they may be a source of danger to travelers, that they increase fire hazards, and produce unsanitary and immoral conditions." (Haar, 1959, pp. 304, 305) The Connecticut court then cited a Massachusetts decision which, after reviewing recent cases, upheld a regulation forbidding billboards near highways "where, in the opinion of the authorities, having regard to the health and safety of the public, the danger of fire and the unusual scenic beauty of the territory, signs would be particularly harmful to the public welfare." (General Outdoor Advertising v. Department of Public Works, 289 Mass. 149)

Approving this language, the Connecticut court then said:

"These authoritative pronouncements justify, in our opinion, the extension of the police power to the prohibition of billboards and advertising devices in places where they deface natural scenery, and places of historic interest." (Murphy, Inc. v. Town of Westport, 131 Conn. 292, 1944)

Finally, in 1954, in Berman v. Parker, 348 U.S. 26, the Supreme Court said:

"The concept of the public welfare is broad and inclusive. . . . The values it represents are spiritual as well as physical, esthetic as well as monetary. It is within the power of the legislature to determine that the community should be beautiful as well as healthy, spacious as well as clean, well balanced as well as carefully patrolled."

Mr. Justice Douglas, writing the opinion of the Court in the *Berman* case, which involved condemnation of property for urban renewal, added:

"It is not for the courts to oversee the choice of boundary line nor to sit in review of the size of a particular project area. Once the question of the public purpose has been decided, the amount and character of land to be taken for the project and the need for a particular tract to complete the integrated plan rest in the discretion of the legislative branch."

RURAL EXPERIENCE

I turn now to the subjects of *rural* planning and zoning, subjects in which we have less experience and literature. Rural areas are far less crowded with people, and suffer less pressure of building, traffic, and conflicting use. Health, safety, and welfare have only recently been seen to be in jeopardy, and the police power has not often been invoked for public protection.

Nevertheless, in farm and ranching country and in private forests, conflicts of interest have arisen, and been solved in part by common action, institutional in nature. Water districts have been formed and regulations adopted which require the minority to conform to usage declared by the majority to be in the common interest. Soil conservation districts, with which state and federal agencies cooperate, also (not always) possess compulsory powers to prevent a recalcitrant owner from practice which may set to nought the expensive and often extensive conservation effort of cooperators. A recognized need to educate small woodlot owners to improve the management of woodlands has resulted in the passage of State Forest Practice Acts and the provision of technical assistance to voluntary cooperators.

Most of the efforts by governments at the federal and state levels to regulate rural land use have been tentative, sporadic, unintegrated, and often inconsist-

ent. Note the shifting and diverse methods of disposal by the United States of parts of the public domain. More recently complex agricultural legislation aimed at crop controls, invoking indirect taxation, tariff changes, subsidies, even bounties reflects shifting policies and uncertainty about ultimate goals. Johnson and Barlowe suggest "Congressional action in declaring policy goals might be very important today, particularly if Congress would then take the necessary steps to coordinate all the existing programs into one over-all place or system." (Johnson and Barlowe, 1954, p. 97) They suggest need for public leadership although they recognize that policy cannot be static and that the problem of policy direction and program integration is a continuing one.

Johnson and Barlowe in their chapters on "Institutional Arrangements" (Johnson and Barlowe, 1954, pp. 296–350) summarize the obstacles to national or even state-wide policy integration, direction, or control. Rural zoning and public land acquisition on a broad-policy level may fail to differentiate sufficiently between different types of land use areas and different local interests. "Such differentiation necessarily awaits a more adequate classification of land than is available in most states." (Johnson and Barlowe, 1954, p. 307)

Land classification is obviously a necessary step in planning broadly—statewide, nationally, or continentally—for habitat development and protection, which is the necessary ultimate aim of land-use policy planning and zoning. Such classification has local as well as continental social implications and difficulties. As a simple instance, there may be important pockets of excellent agricultural land in extended areas generally unsuitable to production. Patterns of settlement, affected by classification and zoning, can affect the cost of government and change the economics of regions. Land classification becomes in fact social planning.

Charles Haar says on this:

"If the law is to meet its claim as the science of social organization, it must concern itself with the creative handling of the principles of ordering and the formation of institutional means for the achievement of accepted goals." (Haar, 1959, p. 757)

Let us look at some of the experience of rural land-use planning and zoning. Johnson and Barlowe aver that rural zoning began in Wisconsin in 1929 when the legislature amended its enabling legislation related to urban zoning to allow county boards to "regulate, restrict and determine the areas within which agriculture, forestry and recreation may be conducted. . . . Regulations are applied by districts, and within each district they must be uniform; but in different districts, different regulations may be applied." (Johnson and Barlowe, 1954, p. 327)

Today most states have authorized rural zoning. Among specified purposes of rural zoning ordinances, under the public welfare *doctrine* of the police power, are: prevention of wasteful scattering of the population, prevention of overcrowding of land, conserving scenery, conserving and developing natural resources, and promotion of desirable living conditions (Johnson and Barlowe, 1954, p. 328).

If all of these purposes were declared everywhere on the continent, we should have an institutional base for implementation far better than we yet have. Today the scope and purposes of the various state enabling acts differ widely as does local use of the police power. This will doubtless remain the case until a broad Congressional statement of national policy, based on land classification and a comprehensive land-use plan, has been adopted. Then all states can review and more reasonably conform their enabling legislation to open the way for establishment of habitat protection of the many kinds that will be needed to accommodate economic and population growth, assure resources and space, and preserve the amenities of living for people and wildlife as well.

Once such a comprehensive system is established severally in the United States, Canada, and Mexico, international coordination on a continental basis will become far less difficult.

But enabling legislation with a comprehensive view is only the beginning. There remains local adoption and enforcement of the zoning provisions, and this is obviously a slow process beset by local pride, local special interests, and discordant ideas of what is best for a local community. There is certainly small local awareness of the complexities of the future national and continental need in the absence of declared national policies based on comprehensive national plans.

Comprehensive classification of land and the development of national land-use plans will not be easy, but the task can be accomplished with the skills that we now have and with the education of the people that will accompany evolution of the planning process.

ON PLANNING

At this point, a word of caution about the concept of planning may be useful. To some the idea of a comprehensive plan suggests a rigid blueprint that will dominate or control all future land uses. That would not and could not be desirable. David Lilienthal speaking of planning in relation to the TVA states that the life principle of democratic planning is an awakening in the whole people of a sense of a common moral purpose—not one goal, but a direction, not one plan once and for all, but the conscious selection by the people of successive plans (Johnson and Barlowe, 1954, p. 698).

There have been many definitions of planning. I like best the following derived from a New Jersey Court decision in 1948 (Grosso v. Board of Millburn Township, 137 N.J.L. 630):

"Planning is the accommodation of variant interests in land use to the interest of the community as a social unit. It is a science and an art concerned with land economies and land policies in terms of social and economic betterment."

While most of the planning controversy over the last twenty-five years in the United States has related to *urban and suburban* planning and related zoning and building regulations, England as early as 1943 recognized the value of a national policy for all land use and development (Johnson and Barlowe, 1954, p. 47). Parliament declared (6 & 7 Geo. VI, Chap. 5):

"It shall be lawful for his Majesty to appoint a Minister of Town and Country Planning, to be charged with the duty of securing consistency and continuity in the framing and execution of a national policy with respect to the use and development of land throughout England."

It is reasonable to conceive that the British, with limited open land areas and rapidly expanding cities, felt the need earlier than we to plan to preserve diverse natural habitats. But some of our own city planners sounded early warnings that the affluent society was forgetting its need for beauty and nature as survival values. Lewis Mumford said in 1943—the year the British act was adopted:

"Typical urban environments no longer offer the possibility of a significant or healthy life. Something more genial to the human soul is desired: contact with the soil . . . the esthetic joys of sunrise and sunset, of passing cloud and rising moon . . . the invasions and perversions of a dying civilization contaminate even the countryside. . . ." (*The Social Foundations of Post-War Building*)

And Stein in 1957 said eagerly and hopefully of the evolving form of cities:

"Nature will dominate, and all cities will be green cities, with parks in the heart of each block and encircling belts of agriculture, natural playgrounds and wilderness. Man's desire for a good life and his love of nature will determine the form of the town." (*Toward New Towns for America;* Johnson and Barlowe, 1954, p. 57)

The point I offer here is that urban planning, with its growing sense of the need of society for open space and natural amenities, is the forerunner of national planning such as that initiated in England. Frank Darling says that the act of 1943 came far too late. Our own trends today on this continent suggest that we cannot long delay national master planning for variant and diverse habitats.

The planning needed now for this continent is a vision of the many varied habitats that the people will need for their many purposes, a vision of where these habitats are or may evolve, and the desirable and undesirable approaches to their nurture. Goals may change, compromises will occur, but the direction of the aim must be clear and the ways made known.

The pioneering Wisconsin enabling act that authorized rural zoning was part of a plan to rehabilitate the economy of vast overcut abandoned forest areas of the state. Although the plan contemplated new land uses based on the environmental characteristics and possibilities of the areas concerned, it was hoped-for over-all economic improvement that won it support. Where that rural zoning was implemented in Wisconsin, it is now conceded that it improved economic and social conditions by "preventing such rural poverty as would logically result from bringing of unsuitable land into agricultural use, protecting and preserving the recreational resources of the area and encouraging the development of forestry, recreation and wildlife on lands best suited for these purposes." (Johnson and Barlowe, 1954, p. 330)

FURTHER EXAMPLE OF RURAL ZONING

Another significant experience in rural zoning occurred in Santa Clara County, California. This began in 1953 when the county enacted an "exclusive agricultural zone" ordinance. The Santa Clara Planning Department states that "the lush Santa Clara Valley" of which San Jose is the core city, within commuting distance of San Francisco, had "vast acreages of fine farms and productive orchards" with "deep alluvial soils built up over many thousands of years." In the last twenty years "urban development has progressively spread out over the prime soils of the valley floor, population doubled . . . we had traded much of this heritage of fertile areas for the asphalt covered acres of urban sprawl."[2]

Under Agricultural Zoning in Santa Clara, landowners could continue to engage in any kind of farming enterprise; but use for subdivisions, factories, or stores was prohibited. By 1958, 40,000 acres of land in Santa Clara County were included in the zone "exclusively for agriculture." It soon appeared, however, that county zoning was inadequate to prevent annexation by San Jose city of land so zoned. State laws authorized annexa-

tion of "uninhabited territory" with the consent of owners of 50 per cent of the assessed value of total land annexed.

The county sought and obtained a change in the state law to exclude annexation of any "A-zoned" land without each individual owner's consent. Even so, the acreage of A-zoned land began to decrease, as prices offered by developers continued to soar, and owners consented to annexation in order to accept the speculative offers. The county is now seeking federal or state action to provide "a democratic and equitable method of creating permanent reserves of agricultural open space." The county proposes "public acquisition of nonfarm development rights from owners of agricultural land, leaving title in the owner and compensating him for the development value acquired." Thus "the farmer retains incentive to manage his land and keep it in a high degree of productivity. The public at large gains the assurance of open space and a continuing food supply."

Need for federal or state action to protect rural areas is becoming ever more apparent today. The difficulty lies in providing a democratic and equitable process. Enforced zoning under the police

[2] Green Gold, 1959.

power, always without compensation, may deprive the owner of values. Acquisition of development rights with compensation is less costly than condemnation, or purchase of title, at full value; and it leaves the land in production. But it is still unpopular. Farmers on bare subsistence want to know they can sell their land when they have to, and get developer's prices.

STATE ACTION

The State of Hawaii has recently taken a major step toward centralization of zoning power in a state government. (Act 205 S.L.H., 1963). In 1957 the Territorial Legislature created a Territorial Planning Office and directed it to create a comprehensive state-wide land-use plan. In this act, the form of zoning and subdivision control was left to the four counties. With statehood this Territorial Office became the State Planning Office. In 1961, the Office completed "a state-wide general plan" in four sections, one for each county, knowing that the plan would not bind the counties. For each county the state plan included "an analysis of land use and industrial, agricultural and population development, and projections and objectives in basic economic areas of land use, agriculture, industry, tourism, military use, conservation and open space, public facilities, parks, water, and circulation and transportation."[3] (This section of this paper is derived, with quotations, from Hyman's report.) The Planning Office, pursuant to legislative direction in the act, had prepared the plan in cooperation with county officials. Each section of the plan would become effective only on adoption by the county.

In 1961 the Hawaiian state legislature further created a State Land Use Commission charged with classifying all the land in the state into one of three classifications: urban, agriculture, or conservation; and with drawing boundaries for "such districts" and imposing use regulations therefore, *which would be binding*

[3] Hyman, 1964, p. 248.

on the counties which thereafter would not be permitted to allow inconsistent development within the stated districts.

The act provided the following definitions:

" 'Agriculture' means the raising of livestock or the growing of crops, flowers, foliage, or other products.

" 'Conservation' means: protecting watersheds and water supplies; preserving scenic areas; providing parkland, wilderness and beach reserves; conserving endemic plants, fish and wildlife; preventing floods and soil erosion; forestry; and other related activities.

" 'Urban' means areas characterized by 'city-like' concentrations of people, structures, streets and other related land uses."

The act provided: "The Commission shall set standards for determining the boundaries of each class; provided, that in the establishment of boundaries of urban districts those lands that are now in urban use and a sufficient reserve area for foreseeable urban growth shall be included; in establishment of the boundaries for agricultural districts the greatest possible protection shall be given to those lands with a high capacity for intensive cultivation; and in the establishment of the boundaries of conservation districts the 'forest and water reserve zones' (provided in prior Act 234) are hereby renamed 'conservation districts' and . . . shall constitute the boundaries of the conservation districts, provided that thereafter the power to determine the boundaries of the conservation districts shall be in the Commission."

The Commission found difficulty in classifying either as urban or agricultural a considerable number of borderline areas where "isolated subdivided areas only partially filled with buildings" and "spots" of residential, commercial, and industrial uses were mostly surrounded by land of high agricultural capability. In 1963 the legislature amended the law to establish a fourth classification, rural districts, stating: "Rural districts shall include activities or uses as characterized by low density residential lots of not more than one dwelling per half-acre in areas where 'city-like' concentration of people, structures, streets and urban level of services are absent, and where small farms are intermixed with such low density residential lots. These districts may include contiguous areas which are not suited to low-density residential lots or small farms by reason of topography, soils, and other related characteristics."

Another Hawaiian statutory provision affords significant tax relief for owners of land in nonurban districts. Hyman states: "It provides that owners of parcels in such districts can dedicate their land for specific ranching or other agricultural uses and have the land 'assessed at its value in such use.' A petition for dedication is followed by an investigation by the appropriate governmental agency to determine whether the land is reasonably well suited for the intended use and is not in conflict with the general plan; if the findings are favorable to the owner the petition is approved and favorable tax treatment afforded. Approval disables the owner from changing uses for a ten-year period. Unauthorized change in use subjects the owner to retroactive tax liabilities plus penalties." (Hyman, 1964, p. 250)

Commenting on this pioneering extension of state authority over local land use, and its impact on individual property owners, Hyman says: "Local governments have been deprived of the power to permit uncontrolled urbanization or to select areas other than those designated by the state agency for such development. This is a substantial inroad on conventionally conceived powers of local government. But in an age of population increases and demonstrated interdependence of population centers it is difficult to say that the inroad is unjustified. In fact, it seems a rather nice compromise between state and local needs and desires. In many instances land within agricultural districts would have a higher market value if it could be used for urban purposes. Courts, by and large, have rejected constitutional attacks on zoning based simply on loss of value. . . . The older cases were concerned primarily with health, safety and morals. . . . Zoning enabling acts still echo these concerns. . . . Starting in the thirties, however, and of a great currency now, is legislative and court reliance on the public welfare as a [or "the"] legitimate aim of land-use regulation. . . . Acceptance of the 'public welfare' as a legitimate object of land use regulation has permitted controls which are more of a positive (benefit-inducing) than negative (harm-limiting) nature. . . . The judiciary is beginning to find in constitutional phrases no blanket prohibition on regulations which require people to limit their use of land to purposes which are beneficial (in a positive sense) to the community." (Hyman, 1964, p. 251)

There will always be some conflict between the exercise of the police power through zoning without compensation in the over-all public interest and the Constitutional guarantee against taking private property without just compensation. Some courts have struck down such zoning where (in Hyman's diagnosis) "the affected owner was deprived of all or nearly all economic use of his land, or . . . was alone or as part of a very small group of owners affected by the regulation. In typical legal language, the regulation was either confiscatory or discriminatory." (Hyman, 1964, p. 251)

This Hawaiian experiment seems to me to have extraordinary significance in exemplifying the institutional trend that as it spreads will ultimately make possible both national and continental allocation of diverse habitats to the varied uses required to sustain the future health and amenity of our civilization.

Hyman senses this significance when he suggests that "a court might be induced frankly to accept the idea, rarely if ever mentioned in land-use regulation cases, that land (in addition to minerals such as oil) can be regulated for conservation purposes because it is an asset in short supply and thus invested with unique public attributes. This last notion is basically at war with our alloidal theories of land ownership, but it would not be surprising to see legal developments along this line in the decades to come as population increases and room for expansion is at more of a premium."

NATIONAL PLANNING AND ZONING

Experience in national planning and zoning is comparatively limited to date. There are, however, two quite notable examples; first in the British Town and Country Planning Acts, along with the institution of the British Nature Conservancy, and the more recent National Zoning of Denmark, 1962 (*Zoneplan 1962 for Danmark, Landsplanudvalget,*[4] August, 1962).

In 1932, in England, a Town and Country Planning Act authorized "local authority" to prepare a scheme with respect to any land within its jurisdiction. But a resolution adopted under this authority shall not take effect unless and until it is approved by the Minister who may vary the extent of the land included in the area of the scheme (22 & 23 Geo. V., Chap. 48).

In 1943, the Minister of Town and Country Planning was "charged" with the duty of securing consistency and continuity in the framing and execution of a national policy with respect to the use and development of land throughout England. (6 & 7 Geo. VI, Chap. 5)

In 1947, a new act provided: "Every local planning authority shall carry out a survey of their area, and shall . . .

submit to the Minister a report of the survey together with a plan (hereinafter called a 'development plan') indicating the manner in which they propose that land in that area should be used. . . . Such plan may define the sites of proposed roads, public and other buildings and works, airfields, parks, pleasure grounds, nature reserves and other open spaces, or allocate areas of land for use for agricultural, residential, industrial or other purposes . . . and designate lands subject to compulsory acquisition by any Minister, local authority or statutory undertaking . . . for the purposes of any of their functions." The Minister may approve any development plan with or without modification (10 & 11 Geo. VI, Chap. 51).

When a development plan was so approved, a "local planning authority" was "authorized," by order to require that any use of land be discontinued, or to impose any condition on continuance thereof—"regard being had to the development plan and to any other material considerations." But no such order could take effect unless confirmed with or without modification by the Minister.

If any person suffered damage in consequence of any order by the deprecia-

[4] *Zoneplan 1962 for Danmark,* p. 22.

tion of any interest in his land, he shall be compensated by the authority in repect of that damage. (This differs from U.S. zoning without compensation.) Further, if, by reason of the order, land becomes "incapable of reasonably beneficial use,"[5] the owner may request and force public purchase of the land.

"Development" includes not only discontinuance of uses and removal of buildings, but also the preservation of trees and woodlands, the control of advertisements, and the proper maintenance of wasteland (Minister, Town and Country Planning, 1951, pp. 138–41).

"In a highly industrialized country, whose future depends on its ability to use its material resources to the full, there must often be a clash of interests over the use of land. . . . [It is] the Minister's *duty* to secure the right use of land in the national interest." (Minister, Town and Country Planning, 1951, pp. 138–41)

This 1947 act provided what has been referred to as "a nationalization of development values," and also made possible acquisition of reserve land for future needs.

In 1951 the Minister reported that "no serious criticism had been made of those Parts of the Act which relate to development plans and development control. There may be complaints of the way in which the powers in those Parts of the Act are administered, but responsible critics have not suggested that the powers themselves are unnecessary or too comprehensive." (Minister, Town and Country Planning, 1951, pp. 138–41)

A fund of 300 million pounds was provided for compensation, and the Minister stated "the power to plan without the continual fear of compensation, which crippled pre-war efforts, has made it possible for the first time to allocate land to the best advantage. . . . It is this

which has made practicable the preservation of open country round overgrown towns, the safeguarding of good farmland, the provision of open space in built-up areas—measures which in a remarkably short time have been the commonplaces of planning." (Minister, Town and Country Planning, 1951, pp. 138–41)

The Nature Conservancy in England is a different sort of instrument, but it is an important supplement and complement to Town and Country Planning. It is a body of scientists and laymen first chartered by the Crown in 1949 "to provide scientific advice on the conservation and control of the natural flora and fauna of Great Britain; to establish, maintain and manage Nature Reserves . . . and to organize and develop the research and scientific services related thereto."[6] This summary report states: "Our country, as we used to know it, is vanishing before our eyes. We see its coasts and fields chosen as sites for houses and power stations. Its green hills sprout steel masts and pylons. Its old oakwoods are clear felled. Its grasslands, once bright with flowers, are now ploughed up and are reseeded. Its water and its air are polluted. . . . During and after the Second World War, Parliament decided to try to safeguard the national heritage in the countryside. Instruments had to be created to fulfill the new public purpose." (Nature Conservancy, 1959, p. 1)

"Preventing destruction or injury to habitats and keeping them in the right state to enable the most varied plant and animal life to flourish in them is what we call *conservation*." (Nature Conservancy, 1959, p. 2)

This, of course, is the purpose of the explorations of this habitats Conference.

The Conservancy uses annual grants voted by Parliament to purchase or lease *National* Nature Reserves, and to man-

[5] Minister, Town and Country Planning, 1951, pp. 138–41.

[6] Nature Conservancy, 1959, p. 5.

age them, scientifically; to assist counties in acquiring *Local* Nature Reserves and managing them; to negotiate agreements with private societies and landowners to establish and maintain nonstatutory nature reserves; to select Scientific Sites that need present or future care and protection and "notify them to local planning authorities"; to carry on scientific research and dispense scientific information and advice to public and private bodies.

A Nature Reserve is a place, as large as 40,000 or as small as four acres, deliberately and permanently managed with the aim of conserving nature, but it may serve other purposes too, such as "recreation, sport or the grazing of livestock." Large Reserves are managed by full-time paid staffs. Small ones may only be watched by a part-time honorary warden.

More than a thousand scientific sites have been "notified to local planning authorities." The Conservancy states: "Local planning authorities have been most helpful in consulting the Conservancy before giving planning consent to any development affecting these sites. Prospective developers have also often recognized that it is in their own interest to avoid selecting sites likely to give rise to controversy."

The Nature Conservancy's long-term program in basic research, to which it devotes the largest proportion of its funds, aims to conserve nature in damaged areas—"to intervene, and where necessary to manage the evolution of the habitat. We cannot manage it without understanding how it works." Research carried out in the Conservancy's own reserves and field stations is complemented "by grant-aiding other researches in universities and elsewhere." It also provides postgraduate studentships "to train more

scientists for its staff, for teaching posts and for the Colonial Service."

Some features of the Conservancy's program could be of great use if adapted to North America's fading and essential habitats. It is one thing to set aside national forests, parks, and recreation areas for public use, and quite another for government to cultivate knowledge of ecological and environmental requirements and be able to apply that knowledge in places, large and small, where it is needed.

In North America the need for protection of the public interest in rural land use is increasing today faster than most of our citizens recognize. Speculation in farm and ranchlands hundreds of miles away from large cities is mounting with increase in leisure time, speed of transportation, and affluence. A measure of the monetary value of grazing lands has long been the carrying capacity (for cattle or sheep) of the acreage. Developers today are purchasing thousands of acres of such land all over the nation at prices largely above that measure. Assessed valuations increase accordingly and the farmers and ranchers are feeling the tax squeeze. Developers expect to subdivide this acreage and sell summer homes and recreation facilities, "far from the madding crowd," in years ahead. As publicly owned national and state parks and forests and recreational preserves increase in size and numbers, the value of adjacent private lands for private lodges and resorts will mount also. It is time now for the continent to take stock of its rural land needs for the future and plot out, while there is still space, a pattern of varied adequate habitats and desirable usages and a plan for orderly control of such resource use.

DENMARK

This is what Denmark has already begun to do for all its land and people. In 1961 the Danish government established a National Planning Committee "to integrate government policies for the allocation of public funds to influence the location of future urban and industrial expansion, and protect landscapes of recreational and cultural value and agricultural areas." The Committee reports to the Ministry of Housing.

By the end of 1962, the Committee presented its first report (*Zoneplan 1962 for Danmark*) with maps, dividing the entire nation into four recommended zones:

(1) Urban and industrial areas;

(2) Areas potentially suitable for future urban and industrial development;

(3) Landscapes of recreational and cultural values; and

(4) Agricultural areas.

The Committee report explains the reason for its creation and the aims of the program in relation to existing "inadequate" town and local planning efforts. It mentions improved technology, population growth, shifts from rural to urban residence, increase in motor transportation, and development of summer-cottage and recreational resorts, in addition to manufacturing and urban sprawl, as influences changing the socioeconomic structure of the community.

"Shifts in the employment structure have radically changed the settlement pattern. . . . Development is beginning to jump outside the present Town Development Areas [local planning units]. Depopulation of more remote rural areas has made it difficult to maintain or develop a reasonable level of service and employment. School costs, and public works, and welfare expenditure climb rapidly, although not sufficiently to keep up with all demands. . . . The increasing amount of scattered development is in many areas jeopardizing the essentially rural character of the country, destroying recreational values." (Zoneplan, p. 2 of English introduction)

The purposes of the National Planning Committee are:

(1) To provide data and methodology for policy and decision making with regard to location of public works and social facilities;

(2) To collate and evaluate information on natural resources, distribution of population, and other economic factors;

(3) To coordinate the activities of the various government departments and "ensure that they pursue physical planning policies in accordance with the general lines laid down from time to time."

There are provisions for consultations and, in the event of disagreement, discussion between the Permanent Undersecretaries of State "from all the Ministries" with the Chief of the Economic Secretariat of the government who is finally responsible "for the subject in question."

The English introduction states: "The Zoning Plan is not visualized as having itself the force of law, but is intended as a basis for coordination of the planning carried out under present legislation." It is "a first step towards a more detailed land use planning, and at the same time a plan for the expansion of local and regional planning controls. . . . All municipalities containing an urban area with more than 1000 inhabitants must produce a town plan and a building and zoning by-law to the satisfaction of the Ministry of Housing." (Zoneplan, p. 14 of English introduction)

There are some comments in the report which indicate problems of conflict of interest that arose in the fashioning of the four zones. Basic zoning criteria include in the urban zone both existing urban communities and a sufficient area around them for "double the estimated need for expansion" in the next fifteen years. Zone 2 comprises circular belts in the vicinity of Zone 1, for recreation, and other uses recommended by local planning bodies. Zone 3 comprises scenic and unique landscapes for summer-cottage location and recreational and cultural use, and farming; this includes woods, seaports and lakefronts, and prospective national park sites. (The report says Zone 3 covers 43 per cent of the country and is spacious enough to "accommodate the inherently conflicting interests between landscape preservation and summer-cottage development.") "Prevention of summer-cottage sprawl is the key issue in Zone 3." Included in Zone 4 are "agricultural areas in which no development should be encouraged for the time being."

The major conflict faced by the National Planning Committee was in reconciling boundaries between Zones 2 and 3 —that is, between potential urban, industrial, and cottage development on the one hand and the long-term recreational and amenity consideration on the other. Where these interests overlapped on the original charts, the conflict "was settled summarily for each conflict area."

In conclusion the Committee states: "If the plan gains political acceptance, it will be a tentative framework for further local, regional and national planning—a policy of preservation without undue restriction of development interests."

While this national land-plan program in Denmark has only begun and is not yet implemented, it is another national recognition of pressing need.

It states well a national aim, to assure the preservation of diverse forms of habitat, both economic and natural, which need nurture on the North American continent quite as much today, tomorrow, and for the future.

CONCLUSIONS

Trends in constitutional interpretation of the police power and eminent domain suggest that rural as well as urban planning laws, land-use zoning, and public acquisition of lands where needed are institutional methods which can be used to protect and nurture diverse habitats for the benefit of future plant and animal (including human) life and amenity.

Institutional trends from early enabling acts through compulsory land-use programs (local, state, and national) indicate that representatives of the people in legislatures and on commissions are capable of approaching these problems in a democratic fashion and are ever more able to solve them.

Methodology is available to implement legislative and administrations policies as may be needed.

Among important prerequisites to arriving at effective national and international policies and their implementation are these:

1. Determination of the nature and sizes of diverse habitats that do now and will hereafter require protection and nurture. International teams of geographers, biologists, ecologists, and economists can identify such areas and define their values and requirements;

2. Determination of need for limiting to a single, predominant use certain types of habitats, and providing for more than one use, or multiple uses, of some types of habitats;

3. There should then follow systematic classification of all the land on the continent for four primary uses:

(1) URBAN (residence, commerce, transportation, manufacture, and trade)
(2) SUBURBAN (homes, industrial parks, shopping centers, power, recreation, golf course, water sports, picnic areas, local recreation)
(3) AGRICULTURAL (crop production, marketing, service, grazing, range)
(4) CONSERVATION (forests, parks, watersheds, wildlife, wilderness, open-space recreation).

4. Flexible master planning by national planning commissions on a national and international basis, in full consultation with regional, state and local planning districts;

5. Determination of fairest and most economical means of compensation to private owners deprived of property values as a result of the zoning or condemnation;

Finally, national legislation and ultimately international treaties, and collaborative enforcement thereof, can and should derive from the proper completion of these prerequisites. To advance this end, I submit that a comprehensive national, and hopefully an international, land classification and master plan for zoning land use of diverse habitats on this continent should be initiated as soon as practicable and implemented locally as a proper exercise of reasonable police power to advance economic prosperity, provide recreation, and protect natural beauty and wildlife, all as part of the health, safety, and welfare of all our peoples and their children's children.

A healthy continental environment will be as vital in the future, as a healthy city is today.

CASES CITED

Buck v. Bell, 274 U.S. 200, 1927.
Lawton v. Steele, 152 U.S. 133, 1894.
Village of Euclid, Ohio v. Ambler Realty Co., 272 U.S. 365, 1926.
General Outdoor Advertising Co. v. Department of Public Works, 289 Mass. 149, 1935.
Murphy Inc. v. Town of Westport, 131 Conn. 292, 1944.
Berman v. Parker, 348 U.S. 26, 1954.
Grosso v. Board of Millburn Township, 137 N.J.L. 630, 1948.

BIBLIOGRAPHY

Green Gold—A Proposal for a Pilot Experiment, County of Santa Clara, Calif. 1959.
Haar, Charles. 1959. Land Use Planning. Little, Brown, Boston.
Hyman, Ira Michael. 1964. Planning Legislation: 1963. J. Amer. Inst. Planners (Aug.).
Johnson, V. Webster, and Barlowe, Raleigh. 1954. Land Problems and Policies. McGraw-Hill, New York.
Minister of Town and Country Planning. 1951. Cmd. 8204:138–41.
Nature Conservancy, The: The First Ten Years. 1959. Chiswick, London.
Zoneplan 1962 for Danmark. 1962. Landsplanudvalget.

AN HYPOTHESIS FOR AN ADEQUATE DISTRIBUTION OF OPEN SPACE

Ann Louise Strong*

PREFACE: THE ROLE OF LAW

At present, as well as at any other time, the center of gravity of legal development lies not in legislation, nor in juristic science, nor in judicial decision, but in society itself.

Eugen Ehrlich

Because law is the will of society, it can be a force to implement open-space goals only so far as these goals are commonly shared by most people. Laws emerge from the area of commonly shared goals —the area of societal consensus. Analogizing this area to a circle of given radius, society will accept laws representative of any viewpoint within the circumference of the circle but will reject laws incorporating attitudes beyond the circumference, because such laws are too divergent from the consensual center of gravity. Lawyers, legislators, and judges are the immediate authors and interpreters of the law, but their freedom to act always is circumscribed by the current mores of society. Techniques for implementing law can be freely innovative; law itself cannot pioneer beyond the periphery of the

* Mrs. Strong, a lawyer, is Research Associate Professor of Regional Planning, University of Pennsylvania Law School. In recent years she has participated in the formulation of a prototype system of open-space planning as applied to the metropolitan area of Philadelphia.

area of societal consensus. For example, were we to propose mandatory redistribution of people into cities of 30,000 evenly spaced across the continent of North America, to achieve goals of protecting natural resources and placing man in close proximity to nature, it is inconceivable that such a proposal could be enacted into law and enforced. The proposal would lie beyond the periphery of the area of societal consensus. In developing a design for an adequate distribution of open space, it would be most fruitful to form the design with awareness of the area of consensus. The area can be expected to shift over time; if the direction of the shift is predictable, the design can contemplate future action currently outside of society's goal structure.

ENVIRONMENTAL GOALS: AN HYPOTHESIS

Accepting this view of the role of law, one must define open-space goals and evaluate their acceptability to society— here the people of North America—before fashioning a legal structure for the implementation of the goals. It is postulated that a dominant goal for man is achievement of a healthy environment. We shall examine conceptually the open-space implications of this goal and their possible public acceptability.[1]

[1] See "Controls and Incentives for Open Space," Ann Louise Strong, Institute for Ur-

Variety of species—plant, animal, and human—is assumed to be the principal measure of a healthy natural environment. Can it be established that a healthy natural environment is synonymous with a healthy environment for man? Certainly man needs the abundant food supply, the pure water, and the clean air of a healthy natural environment. However, do factors detrimental to a healthy natural environment contribute to the health of man? Man, unlike other living species, has created an inorganic environment of elaborate structures, distant communication, and complex exchanges upon which he is now dependent. In seeking a healthy environment for man, to what extent can —or must—this inorganic environment be substituted for a varied natural environment? Further, if variety is the measure of a healthy natural environment, is it also the measure of the health, for man, of his inorganic environment? Variety, after all, is multifaceted. Variety of climate, soils, altitude, geological formation, and precipitation contributes to variety of biota. Variety also abounds within the man-made environment; there is variety of markets, production, and transportation; of density, housing, education, and leisure activities; of income and consumption patterns. However, although there is much variety within this inorganic environment, man has tended to separate and stratify the elements, thus stratifying his environment, in a manner disparate from that of the healthy plant and animal world. Does this stratification by function of land use and by age, income, and race augment or detract from the health of the man-made environment?

ban Studies, University of Pennsylvania, November, 1964, for a detailed discussion of a possible legal structure for protecting the natural environment; and see "Plan for the Valleys," Wallace-McHarg Associates; Ann Louise Strong, Consultant on Law and Organization, June, 1964, for recommendations of action steps for a specific area.

Taking as the goal the achievement of a healthy environment for man, it is the premise of this paper that man is dependent on both the natural environment and the inorganic environment of his creation. Further, if variety is necessary for a healthy natural environment, it is necessary for man as well as for other life in the natural environment. Therefore, it is posited that, for man, variety also is crucial in the inorganic environment. A healthy environment for man, then, is dependent on maximization of variety in both the natural and inorganic spheres. This necessarily means a decision not to maximize the health of the natural environment alone, since, in many instances, support of the inorganic environment will have as an unavoidable concomitant the diminution or destruction of some living species. This is a stated choice not to maximize variety of biota in disregard of the resulting impact on the structure of the inorganic environment.

MAXIMIZATION OF VARIETY

The next task will be to develop a system which maximizes variety in both the natural and inorganic portions of man's environment. Costs and benefits, calculated in terms of man's physical and mental health, must be determined for the system and its components, so that man will know not only for what he is paying but also the nature and amount of the costs and the benefits. Given a cost-benefit analysis of the proposed system, man may elect an alternate system; he may reject variety as a fundamental principle or he may stress either the natural or the inorganic portion of his environment at the expense of the other portion. However, a reasoned decision either to accept the form of system advanced here or an alternate one will rest upon knowledge of the costs and benefits of the proposed system.

The natural environment

Already much is known about the conditions, both natural and man-made, which contribute to or detract from variety among biota. However, it is doubtful whether it is possible to state with sufficient precision the costs of suppression or destruction of a species or a combination of species or the contribution to the natural environment of their preservation. We may know that too heavy a load of sewage will consume the oxygen supply in a stream, that lack of oxygen in the stream will kill mayfly larvae, and that lack of mayfly nymphs will eliminate game fish, but can we measure the value of the mayfly nymphs and the cost of their preservation? Since the system maximizing variety will be composed of weighted values for the elements of the system, it is necessary to approximate the value and cost not only of the total system, but also of the component parts.

How near to man need variety exist to provide him a healthy natural environment? Despite population trends, the North American continent has adequate space. If one were to maximize variety in the natural environment for three quarters of the continent and variety in the man-made environment for the remaining one quarter, how much conflict would arise between these goals? Man's use of the inorganic environment—his air and water pollution, for instance—would still affect those areas devoted to the natural environment. Also, it is presumed that many of the benefits of the natural environment accrue to man only when he is in continuing contact with that environment as part of his daily life. By far the greatest number of conflicts between the natural and the man-made environment will occur within and adjoining urban areas, and so it is within these areas that the most critical weighting of the system for maximization of variety must take place.

The man-made environment

For the man-made environment, there is imperfect knowledge of which actions of man will encourage variety. It can be observed that mass-production techniques, as well as rapid distribution of goods, transmission of ideas, and transportation of men, have reduced variety. There also are few guidelines for determining the relative value of different forms of variety. Existence of variety at different scales and existence of variety for all people are suggested as two measures of value.

One of the major decisions concerning variety is the scale at which it should be promoted. Probably all scales from the neighborhood to the continent should be stressed equally, for emphasis on variety at one scale is likely to be at the expense of variety at another. For instance, if only variety at the national scale is given weight, it may be achieved by a limited number of combinations of a few metropolitan and neighborhood components; conversely, if only variety at the neighborhood level is required, the national scene may consist of little more than multiple duplications of the same neighborhood pattern.

Availability of choice to all people is suggested as another major measure of the value of elements of the man-made environment. Choice for all, of jobs, housing, education, leisure activities, modes of transportation, goods, and location, is included here. How much choice? In the world of plants and animals, when a healthy variety exists the niches are full and the system tends to stabilize. Stability has not been a characteristic of the man-made structure; the structure has been in a constant flux as a result of man's continuing introduction of new elements which displace the old elements from their niches. Therefore, the range of choice can be expected to vary as new elements are introduced and as the existing elements of the man-made environment change character. Demand within the range also will alter with variation in the elements, and availability of choice will be determined in part by demand. Then, too, the range of choice for one element of the environment may well be interdependent with the range of choice for another element. Job choice, for instance, is necessarily affected by the range of educational choice. Restriction of choice should be imposed principally by the self-selection and the personal limitations of the individual rather than by limitation of the range of elements in the man-made environment. Given this aim, it is recognized that the costs of a varied environment also will impose some boundaries to the range of choice available to all.

Taking as a premise for future life in North America the maximization of variety in the natural and man-made environments, what are some of the alternative patterns of living which might emerge and what would be the role of open space? We in North America are fortunate that nature and past development combine to give us one vital range of choice for the future: we have enough habitable land for our present and anticipated population to be able to choose where and how to live. This, of course, would not be true if North America were subject to heavy immigration from more densely populated parts of the world.

Even given our increasing capacity to provide a climate-controlled urban habitat, it is assumed, on the basis of present behavior in such countries as Brazil, Finland, and Great Britain, that, where a choice exists, people will congregate in the more temperate areas. Therefore, continued sparse settlement in the vast and frigid north, a shift of people away from the most torrid areas of Central America, and increased population for the temperate areas are predicted. Despite the anticipated population increase for North America, total space in temperate areas should be adequate both to sustain us and to permit our accommodation in an urban structure of our choice.

Anticipating small populations for the arctic and tropic areas, the open-space question there is not one of adequate area or distribution but of resource management to maintain the health of the natural environment.

Within temperate areas, we can expect not only many more people but also an almost entirely urban people. However, regardless of the pattern in which the urban population is distributed, the bulk of the temperate land of the continent will remain unurbanized and thinly populated. This land will be open, either used for farms, grazing, forests, wildlife, and recreation or not used at all. Again, as with the arctic and tropic areas, the question is not one of an adequate supply of open land but rather one of resource management. For this unurbanized land, maximization of variety in the natural environment will require some restrictions on man's activities. However, the restrictions should have a very low cost in comparison to the benefits to man which can be expected to accrue from protection of the land.

The questions of adequacy of amount and proper distribution of open space arise almost exclusively in and near urban areas, where open-space uses conflict with development. Open space and development can be combined to yield myriad alternative patterns of urban living. Originally, natural resources and water were the principal determinants of urban location and urban form. The time and money costs of transportation and communication reinforced the locational choices and contributed to growth of these urban centers. Now, increasingly, improvements in the speed and quality of communication as well as of transportation of resources, goods, and people are facilitating freedom of location and structure for urban communities. Reliance on water for transportation is diminishing, although its availability for industrial and domestic use remains vital. Better water management through capture of precipitation, control of floods, sea-water conversion, and pollution abatement will augment the capacity of different areas to support urban development. Assuming that we now have and will have increasing freedom in the location, size, and composition of our urban settlements, what choices would be consistent with maximization of variety in both the natural and man-made environments?

Location and distribution of urban centers

Water and climate will impose the only environmental restrictions on location of urban centers throughout the temperate portion of the continent.

Assuming better water management, there still will be upper limits to the population which can be supported by a given water supply. Water-deficit areas can import from water-surplus areas, but the costs of transporting and storing water may exceed the benefits of continued development of the water-deficit areas. This question already has arisen in portions of the southwestern United States, where recent urban development and irrigation of crops has depended on ground-water supplies which are being depleted rapidly. There already is a history of years of litigation over allocation of the waters of such rivers as the Colorado and the Delaware. Increasing conflicts over water between different areas and different segments of the public can be expected as urban development spreads in location and volume. Legislation limiting urban development because of a shortage in the available water supply can be anticipated. Such legislation might be tied to

a legislatively adopted allocation formula for the available water supply and on legislatively established standards relating the water supply and population maxima.

Even within the temperate zone there are areas with extremes of climate which militate against growth of urban centers or which foster only limited types of development. The advent of air-conditioning has contributed greatly to the recent popularity of the Southwest and of Florida and the Caribbean, but much of this popularity is as a vacation land or for retirement. Elderly persons prefer warm climates, and air-conditioning protects them from extremes of heat. Climate, both natural and man-made, increased leisure time, and faster transportation all contribute to the burgeoning vacation industry in these areas. Existence of central heating has not sparked any similar boom in development of such areas as Montana and the Dakotas, which experience long and very cold winters. However, greater affluence and leisure have fostered a growing interest in winter sports, and now the economy of a number of new and growing urban centers is dependent on this recreation demand. Thus, climate will influence the composition and economy of urban development as well as its location.

An even spatial distribution of urban centers across the continental area possessing an adequate water supply and a temperate climate is unlikely because of people's preferences. People like to live near large bodies of water; the skyrocketing popularity of water for recreation has already been documented. People also prefer moderate year-round temperatures to a moderate mean annual temperature which encompasses summer and winter extremes. Therefore, if people are to be given their choice of urban location, it is predicted that the greatest concentration of urban centers will be in those areas enjoying a moderate year-round climate, which are located near large bodies of water. For the most part, this is where the present urban centers are located, although the principal reasons for their original settlement differed from those now advanced for their continuing popularity. Other urban centers will be scattered in relation to special-interest demand, particularly that of vacationers, the retired, and the extractive industries.

If there will be a sharp peak in the urban location demand curve, will the principle of maximizing variety in the natural as well as the man-made environment conflict with the distribution of urban centers by choice? It probably will, if the assumption proves correct that elements of the man-made environment destructive of variety in the natural environment become increasingly destructive with expansion in the size and density of urban development. On the basis of this assumption, there would be an upper limit for urban development within a given area, and a mandatory spacing of urban developments. Open space would, in part, be a by-product of these distribution requirements. In fixing distribution policy, maximization of individual choice of location would yield to maximization of variety. Actually, reduction in the opportunity for individual choice of location would probably result in a greater extent of realization of individual preferences. If everyone were allowed to choose to live in the San Francisco Bay Area, the resulting urban development very likely would be less satisfying to people than the urban development which would result from imposing size maxima on locational choice.

Adherence to the principle of variety would be expected to cause a broader distribution of urban centers within the temperate zone than would occur from the exercise of individual choice. Insofar as the policy causes divergence from locational preference, it is essential that there be public acceptance of the policy.

Referring again to an earlier illustration, if the principle of maximizing variety led to a policy of even distribution of urban centers from the Atlantic to the Pacific, it seems certain that the public would rebel and that the policy could not be implemented. Distribution could be shifted within the limits of public tolerance, and these limits will be influenced by an understanding of the rationale for the distribution policy.

Size and density of urban centers

Assuming that it is the open space of daily accessibility which has the greatest direct impact on man's health, size and density of urban development are major determinants of whether man has an adequate distribution of open space. Size and density affect both the accessibility and health of the natural environment. The more accessible the open space, the more subject it is to intrusions from the man-made environment. To achieve an adequate supply and distribution of urban open space and to maintain that open space in a sound natural condition, it will be necessary to place limitations on the size and density of urban centers. Assuredly, man's opportunities for contact with natural open space increase with faster transportation from his home or work to the open space, and so accessibility standards in part should be those of time-distance. Mileage-distance and location in relation to patterns of daily living also are important, so that it is not only possible but likely to achieve daily contact with open space.

Man's ability to alter the man-made environment so as to reduce damage to the natural environment will make it possible to resolve many conflicts as they develop. However, man's inventiveness must keep pace with population expansion, for controls which assure a tolerable natural environment at one population level will be wholly inadequate at higher population levels.

Because of improving technology, the controls on the man-made environment necessary to achieve an accessible and healthy natural environment in and about urban areas will change over time. Size and density will be among the elements of the man-made environment to be controlled, but it is probable that, as technology improves, the size and density limits can be raised. In considering permissible size and density limits, the dichotomy of man cannot be overlooked. He belongs to the natural environment and to the environment of his shaping as well. We must consider the impact of the man-made environment on man's health, yet so far we have concentrated on amassing evidence of its effects on plants and animals. We must know what maximum size and density of urban concentration are healthy for man and also what factors raise or lower these maxima. Substantiation is needed, as well, for the assumption that, for man, the man-made environment cannot be a total substitute for the natural environment. Lacking such proofs, we nonetheless assume that size and density limits will be necessary to maintain a healthy natural environment intermixed with urban development. We also assume that man's needs for links with the natural environment are such as to require that it be accessible to him on a daily basis. Since a given area of open space has a maximum use which it will support without deterioration of the plant and animal population, the higher the urban density the greater the amount of open space required.

The total size of an urban area also may be limited by a need of man for access to nonurban open space of low-intensity usage. Since choice is desirable for all, money cost as well as time cost will be relevant in fixing maximum distances from urban centers to this type of open space.

In contemplating the possible need to fix maximum size and density limits for urban areas, it is presumed that these limits will be sufficiently high to include the large, centralized concentrations of persons which seem most conducive to production of certain public and private services, ease of personal communication, and support of cultural activities. After all, these are elements of variety in the man-made environment and, as such, should be protected. However, the maximum limits might bring about a change in the pattern of land use moving away from the high-intensity center. A densely populated, high-intensity center might be adjoined by substantial areas of open space, in turn adjoined by some form of satellite communities. In hypothesizing shifts in the size, density, and structure of urban centers, it is important to recognize the relaxation of the economic pressures toward enormous metropolitan concentrations and to realize that size and density limitations could be imposed at little cost to the economy.

Public policy should be used, also, to achieve a minimum size and density for urban settlements. Variety in the man-made environment is dependent on minimum size. Even without public action, people's desire for a wide choice of goods and services, of educational and leisure opportunities, and of jobs and homes can be expected to cause the continued wasting away of small settlements which are not satellite to large urban centers. Some current programs of the United States government are questionable from this viewpoint, since they seek to keep alive communities too small to offer adequate variety without providing enough strong external support for the communities to become self-sufficient and attractive to people. Acceptance of a minimum-size concept would lead to a re-evaluation of these programs.

Following the principle of maximizing variety in man's environments, with reference to size and density, urban man would live either in medium-sized communites offering a range of densities and a modest but well-distributed internal system of open space or in large communities with densely populated cores separated from outlying settlements of varying density by large areas of open space. Density and size would be determinants of the total amount of urban open space. Time-distance and cost-distance, related to the topography, would govern the distribution. At one extreme, the undifferentiated continuum of megalopolis would be restricted because of its total impact on the natural environment and because of the limitations of cost and time which it places on man's ability to reach open space of low-intensity use. At the other extreme, small urban settlements would be discouraged because of the varietal limitations inherent in their size. Special-purpose urban communities —resorts, retirement towns, centers serving rural areas, and cities existing because of a single natural resource—can be expected to be smaller than other suburban areas because the range of human needs they serve is more limited.

Range and distribution of activities

Achievement of variety in the natural environment and the man-made environment of urban areas will require changes in the present distribution of open space and in the current patterns of land use.

When we look first at the natural environment, we find that at present the amount of open space in urban areas declines as the density rises. The larger the urban area, the farther this places people from open space. In addition to the time-distance and cost-distance minima already proposed, qualitative standards for urban open space also are necessary. A need for amenity is not likely to be satisfied by a series of macadam-covered vacant lots equipped with basketball hoops. If daily exposure to the natural environment is of importance for man's health, open space must be incorporated into the urban design to increase the incidence and quality of exposure. The principal routes of man to work, school, stores, or play should be located in open space of high amenity value. For greatest benefit from exposure to the natural environment, the highways and rail lines should be separated, or screened for sight and noise, from the footpaths and bridle trails. The network provided by this system of routes would be supplemented by open spaces for leisure activities. Facilities for recreational activities would be established on the basis of demand, with the number, location, and size of facilities governed by time-distance and cost-distance standards.

The present open-space pattern would change as follows: the spots and dots of playfields, tot-lots, and vacant lots would be replaced by major and minor networks of open space containing the principal routes. Portions of these networks would be enlarged, at intervals determined by density and topography, to provide open space for recreation.

Should it be established that regular immersion of man in the natural environment, as differentiated from a passing through encased in a climate-controlled car, train, or bus, is salubrious, this could provide impetus for a reconsideration of the arrangement and design of urban land use. It might indicate that, either for many people or for many activities, homes should be within walking distance, through natural open space, of jobs, schools, stores, and social life.

Even in the absence of such evidence, the principle of maximizing variety in the man-made environment calls for a shift in the arrangement of urban activities, although not necessarily at a scale to put many of these activities within walking distance of the home. What may have begun, through zoning, as a filtering out of obnoxious and unhealthy activities has been distorted at the neighborhood scale into a separation of land uses by lot size, by density, and by use. Homes are separated from jobs and shops and from community facilities except, usually, schools and churches. Choice of housing type increases with income but even the rich rarely can choose to live in a neighborhood of mixed housing types and mixed land uses. Although an urban area may encompass great variety, much of the land and many of the people within it are sorted into large, homogeneous blocs, each with an astonishing lack of variety.

Separation of land uses, particularly of housing, has reinforced the tendency of man to establish a pecking order. Man's stratification is by income, race, and, increasingly, age. Possibly restoration of variety of land uses at the neighborhood scale can re-create a sense of community, provided that the urban design is such that residents are focused toward common activities, reinforcing their contact with one another. Provision of variety of housing types will reduce separation by age. Encouragement of neighborhood variety by income and race rests, as do these other changes in urban land-use patterns, on the consensus of society. Hopefully, a more positive public attitude toward variety by income and race can be fostered by building a sense of belonging in a community and so reducing anonymity and insecurity.

ATTAINMENT OF AN ADEQUATE DISTRIBUTION OF OPEN SPACE

Summarizing very briefly what has been said, man is now, and will be, an urban being. The frustration of his open-space needs is a function of his urban condition; his open-space conflicts occur near and within urban areas. In the future there will be an ample supply of non-urban open space; preservation of its quality will be relatively easy because of its low degree of conflict with the man-made environment. Most critical will be a determination of man's need for urban

open space and development of a means for meeting the need.

It is posited here that man, to ensure his health, must have a healthy environment, both natural and man-made, and that the health of his environment is promoted by sustenance of variety. This proposition has the following implications for the future structure of urban areas: (1) they would be concentrated in the temperate zone, particularly where the climate is even and large bodies of water exist; (2) they would be distributed somewhat more broadly than individual preference would indicate in order to protect and provide access to the natural environment; (3) they would have size and density maxima and minima with maxima determined in part by accessibility to open space; (4) they would have an internal mix of land uses and people; and (5) development would be interlaced with a network of open space which incorporates the principal pedestrian and vehicular routes.

Before a system of laws can be enacted and enforced to achieve this distribution of urban open space, two steps are essential. First, it must be established that the approach is a reasonable one to ensure man's health and the health of his environment. Does man really need open space in and near his urban areas? Second, an area of consensus must be reached among the people of this continent that the goal is sound and the cost reasonable in light of the benefits. If this can be achieved, the laws for implementation will follow. President Johnson has said: "A prime national goal must be an environment that is pleasing to the senses and healthy to live in."[2] Do the citizens of North America agree with him?

Acceptance of the goal of maximizing health in the natural and man-made en-

[2] Special Message to Congress on Natural Beauty, President Lyndon B. Johnson, February 8, 1965.

vironments does not violate present legal concepts but does stretch them beyond the present periphery of societal consensus. However, the concern for nature embodied in the goal is anthropocentric and so fits our Western tradition of law.[3] The

scale of action contemplated here is so vast, dealing as it does with control of the pattern of future urban life, that acceptance of the proposals neither can nor should be anticipated without proof of the underlying theory of variety as beneficial for man's health.

[3] For a discussion of a legal presumption favoring the natural condition, see "The Rights and Duties of Beasts and Trees: A Law Teacher's Essay for Landscape Architects," Clarence Morris, 17 Journal of Legal Education 185, 1964.

General Discussion

ORDWAY: I think we can now open the crossfire. We might begin discussion on the problems suggested and the rather interesting and exciting predictions for the future of education and the schools that Brandwein has presented.

MACKAY: I found the paper extremely interesting and the remarks very stimulating, and I think many of us wish we had gone through the conceptual approach. What I'm wondering is how efficient is this in imparting the considerable body of facts that a student must absorb in his secondary and college education. How efficient is the conceptual as opposed to the present system?

BRANDWEIN: The question implies I didn't make clear the notion that the student does the work and that the teacher uses the conceptual framework as the umbilical cord to the scholarly community. The teacher knows these things exist right now, with all kinds of devices—all kinds—such as computerized libraries where a youngster can get vast information, recordings, personal films, programed instruction, a huge new technology of education. There is now planned egress to environments in the community around them that are examples of good environments. The whole emphasis is being placed on work by children, and the teacher is not a regurgitator of the textbook.

I think this notion is important. In twenty-six school systems that I am familiar with in which we have done this kind of experiment—the children have examinations of this kind. You know. The "Twenty Questions." "A planet is: Hercury, Mercury, Tercury, Sercury?" "The green coloring matter in plants is: Chlorophyll, Hemophil, Zoophyll, What You Will?"

He gets a test of about twenty pages, and at the bottom is this statement: "Should you get these twenty correct, at 5 each, you should get 100. But since I am your teacher I consider myself your agent and I will take 10 per cent."

The youngsters readily get to this. That's fine with them. They understand the business ethic. At the bottom is this statement: "Should you wish to earn more, please turn the page."

And there is this statement: "The following twenty tests are taken from the books you have available. For each one that is correct you will get 1. For each one you miss, 2 off, please. Be careful."

The youngsters say, "Do you mean to say if we read ahead we can get a higher grade?"

"Of course. Be our guests."

The evidence is that in almost eight years of working with 1000 teachers generally that youngsters finish the text in one half a year, that the fast youngsters were soon making grades of 150 to 200 on the tests, and that any standard test gave them scores of almost 15 above the average. IQs were raised. The same with reading scores and arithmetic scores.

Dr. Mackay, you have raised an important question, acquisition of facts. And no fact that was true in 1500 is true today. Facts change. Concepts are relatively stable. So we can build a curriculum provided we allow the youngster to do the work and do not rob him of his independence and give him the chance to experience.

ORDWAY: I think you were next, Mr. Glacken.

GLACKEN: I'd like to address this to you too, Paul. You said that mental activity was not directed by problems. What is the history of this widespread conviction that problem solving is a source of knowledge and understanding? Today the criticism is often made of graduate students that they're not problem-oriented. What is the source of this conviction?

BRANDWEIN: It's an important question. It came out of the notion that you presented problems to children that there was a kind of a scientific method than which there was no whicher: the kind a scientist used in solving problems.

It runs something like this, and I can go through it quickly. Problem: to lock that door. What apparatus would you use? The teachers say, "Keys. I happen to have some keys." The teacher has been collecting them for a year. So in that laboratory the problem isn't going to be solved at all, is it? It's going to be done. In short, there was a confusion between problem doing and problem solving.

In problem doing, you can plan the solution of the problem within a laboratory period or a time sequence. In problem solving, you need to take time, because the solution is not known. It will take years perhaps, if an experiment is involved or a design.

So we rarely do experiments in our schools for this reason. We do a lot of observation, reading, a lot of what I call the "calisthenics of discovery," but not problem solving.

You can have problem solving provided a lot of background is given some way. Then you can state a problem. But only if you recognize the object or event. I brought this in because I knew the problem. What do I have here? (*Holds up hand.*)

GLACKEN: A transistor radio.

BRANDWEIN: A transistor radio. I asked this in Nyanza, and they couldn't tell me. They didn't even know what the problem was. You see? All I'm saying is you do not start with a problem. You start with an object, an event, which you place in a concept. Then you can state the problem.

OSBORN: Mr. Chairman, because of the purpose of this gathering, could I ask Paul to give us in a nutshell what he means by teaching conservation through science, and vice versa?

BRANDWEIN: I would merely say that whenever the youngster finds himself out of relation with the community you have a conservation problem to begin with, that I do not need to seek conservation in the wild but seek it wherever an organism is not in relation to the environment. Therefore, if a youngster were to have a discrepant relationship to his classroom, he is not being conserved.

I think Ed Graham said this very well—that there is an economy and ecology in a cornfield, in any relation of a living organism to its environment.

And you can teach the whole concept of balance, interchange, energy-and-matter interrelationship whenever you have an organism and whenever you have the environment, but you cannot teach the concept of beauty unless youngsters get experience with various kinds of beauty and lack of it. And it is there that our problems arise. We must bring youngsters into experiences in relation with different elements. This can be true of a city where there is a slum or a beautiful building. It can also be true of a park. It can also be true of a field. It could also be true of the relation of a man and his dog or reading about the Kabluna Eskimos.

DANSEREAU: Would your system result in the gifted students being kept happily alienated and the others intelligently and lucidly adjusted?

BRANDWEIN: *Touché*, he said as his head rolled off!

The essence of a conceptual framework is that alienation is dissolved, that while one person can know that an egg produces a chick, the other can know that it's the deoxyribonucleic acid in the egg that produces a chick and all the experimental evidence, but they can talk to each other. The one thing that I was concerned with is that we do not have what happened in the German educational economy with its time-binding institutions—that is, that the elite did not talk to the nonelite. The result is they could dominate them. What we want is, if we really believe that all children are of supreme moral worth, education in the conceptual bases of our civilization, with all the data necessary to understand these concepts, for all children. But we recognize that there are some idiosyncratic people who are the innovators of our time, who leap out of the concept to invent new ones. So there is no alienation.

The second point is that you cannot include programs in schools on landscaping or conservation or any new programs that are outside of the existing conceptual basis because the school is a time-binding institution. The first to go in times of economy are the programs that are introduced like conservation and landscape. I have enormous evidence on this.

Therefore, it is most important, if the gifted children are to have experience with our civilization, as well as those who are ordinary but who support the gifted children and therefore have to collaborate with them, that elements of conservation, landscape, beauty, amenity, law, whatever you think is important, have to be integrated conceptually for gifted as well as slow.

GRAHAM: I'd like to get back to this institutional innovation, because I think that, since time is running out on us here in this Conference, we do have to give some consideration to how we might direct our energies and concern after the Conference.

It's rather surprising that in this meeting there has been practically nothing said or no concern expressed over the agricultural landscape. Now, if this meeting had been held twenty years ago, this would have been our primary concern. We would have been worried about erosion and about the defacement and disfiguration of the American landscape in terms of rural environments.

It's probably unfair to say that any one institution has been responsible for this, but it is a fact that at that time we established an institution known as the soil conservation district. Each district was established under state law, but other than that the state had practically nothing to do with its operation because the affiliation of the local people in the district was with the federal government, and you had almost a direct federal government-local community type of endeavor.

The districts were established under state-enabling legislation, to be sure, and now the states are contributing a great deal in the way of funds to the operation of the districts.

The work of the districts has, in fact, changed the agricultural landscape. In many parts of the country now it is a pleasing, a beautiful landscape. When you fly over this country, the erosion, the raw ground you see is around the cities, not in the agricultural areas.

It was soon discovered that the soil conservation district, rurally oriented, and in which assistance was made available to the individual operator, was not sufficient to begin to get at all environmental situations. The next step was the passing of the small-watershed legislation, which led to something like a natural-area basis as opposed to an individual operator's basis.

This legislation in the beginning was directed at the rural landscape, but it was quickly amended to include fish and wildlife facilities. The next amendment was to include recreational facilities. Another one came along to make it possible to provide urban water supply. And so on.

An attempt is now being made, particularly in the northeastern megalopolis, to combine at the local level a concern for both urban environments and rural environments. In Connecticut, for example, you have such things as the regional areas in which the watershed organization, soil conservation district, and the local planning authority are working together.

We need more of this sort of coordination and amalgamation between the rural and urban sectors. But we must be careful about "nationalizing" our conservation effort, as has been suggested, because I don't think that the American public is going to buy this. There are available to us certain tools and certain opportunities for at least beginning to amalgamate various types of interest and concern on the parts of both the urban and the rural public.

In Connecticut, the soil conservation districts, which are run by a group of five local supervisors, are no longer run by five farmers; they are in some cases run entirely by five town businessmen.

In Massachusetts, the town conservation commissions are attempting to solve both rural and urban problems.

It doesn't take the abolition of fifty state governments. You can have national leadership, national assistance, not necessarily on a grant-in-aid basis but of a type that has already been shown to be at least somewhat effective, and have opportunities to use the new concepts, new suggestions, and new thinking that have been expressed in this Conference.

Would it not be reasonable for us to try to achieve our ends through the modification of existing institutions which are available to us rather than to begin to think of entirely new institutions?

I know that the National Association of Soil and Water Conservation Districts, which started out as a strictly agricultural organization, is much concerned with the ways in which it can operate with planning bodies.

In Fairfax County, where I live, the Extension Service, the Soil Conservation District, the other traditionally agricultural groups are providing services not to farmers any longer but to urban groups and to the Planning Commission and to the Board of Supervisors.

I don't know quite where this leads me, except that if you want to get someplace you have to go from where you are at the moment, and at the moment I think we're not in a bad position at all with respect to institutions. If, for instance, you had a new Department of Urban Affairs in the federal government and you had, as was suggested yesterday, a new Department of Urban Affairs in every state government, would this in fact help or would it not? Or would you be superimposing upon existing institutions a still further complex situation?

What Professor Caldwell has been talking about is important, but we're not starting from scratch. We have a lot of lessons already learned. I would like to know whether this Conference couldn't do something in the way of modification of existing facilities, and so forth, to achieve the ends that we have all been worried about.

ORDWAY: Gentlemen, Ann Strong, we have about fifty minutes left of this Conference. We do want to get down to some specifics on institutions. Ed Graham has thrown out an excellent summation of some of the thinking we ought to attack.

And we do want to discuss briefly the implications of the proposed Ecological Survey and the implications of the proposal of the National Academy-Research Council on a kind of Resources Intelligence Agency.

CALDWELL: I think I can do this quite concisely—first of all, because I agree

with Ed Graham. I think he stated what, in fact, inevitably happens—
that the process of innovation is one of evolution.

I would, however, remind us that in 1789, when the Constitution went
into effect, there was no U.S. Department of Agriculture and that the
possibility of creating an Interior Department was debated. A Department
of Home Affairs, as it was called, was rejected. Instead, the proposition
was to divide the home functions among various departments of government. Half a century passed before the nation was ready for the Department of the Interior.

The Soil Conservation Service is, I think, an excellent example of the
fact that we innovate through evolution. I would just suggest one caution.
In this process we have found where the local or state institutions are not
adequate, it is easier to develop or evolve a new institution that superim-
poses on them. We have done this to a very considerable extent in agriculture and in conservation with special-district legislation.

And I would ask the question, although I suggest that we probably not
try to answer it here—it's really a rhetorical question but an important
one, I think—that if we take some of the most vital activities out of general local government, do we not contribute to the devitalization of general
local government? If we create a soil conservation district dealing directly
with the federal government, does this not further lead to the ossification
and deterioration of the American county?

I happen to be basically a conservative person, by nature, and I think
this is perhaps one of the reasons I am interested in conservation. I think
very often we need to innovate on behalf of the things that we want to
conserve. Hence, I would merely say that, given the situation in which we
find ourselves, I think the process of evolution, of building on what we
already have, is probably going to be stepped up quite considerably.

Innovation will have to proceed at a more rapid pace. But this does not
mean an arbitrary break with what we have already accomplished. It does
not mean an endless superimposition of controls out of Washington upon
every village and hamlet and township in the country.

LOWENTHAL: Mrs. Strong, my question concerned a paragraph, perhaps a page
or two, in your paper, to which you adverted this morning briefly, in
which you suggest the regular immersion of man in the natural environment.

Now, my question is: How is this to be accomplished? Does not the
regular immersion of man in a natural environment imply the making of
man-made environments over against or as opposed to natural environments?

Do you not run into the same kind of difficulty that Mr. Eichhorn described with respect to the national parks, for example?

STRONG: No, I don't think this is so at all, because I think, as Paul Brandwein
pointed out, there are all types of qualities. You may have an immersion
in the wilderness, in which case you will have to limit the volume. But

certainly driving or walking along a scenic parkway is not going to destroy the parkway. I think we need to supply within the urban areas or within easy reach of people a variety of types of natural experiences.

One of the most important needs is a transportation latticework in the metropolitan area. This is something Ian [McHarg] and I have been trying to develop in both our Baltimore and Philadelphia studies—the thought that you would try to get people to or from work either on trains or highways through landscaped areas and that you would try to get children to walk to school through this type of area, so that you have a continuing exposure to nature.

ORDWAY: There are two specific proposals that are now in the air for institutional change in the direction that we are concerned with. One is the proposed Ecological Survey, and the other is the recommendation of the National Academy of Sciences-National Research Council for an investigative intelligence agency in the natural resource field which can predict the dangers that lie ahead and warn us in advance and see if action cannot be taken to advance the welfare of the ecosystems.

FOSBERG: Our discussions seemed to have emphasized the fact that our collective ecological knowledge and understanding are extremely inadequate to serve as the basis for our necessary day-to-day judgments in matters affecting our environment. I think this has come out throughout the discussion. However, I don't think that any effective mechanisms or suggested remedies of this situation came out. The ecologists were merely exhorted to get busy and discover everything needed.

Since there is a proposal under consideration in the Department of the Interior to create an agency to promote ecological research, to assemble the knowledge necessary to develop understanding of our environment, it would seem appropriate for this Conference to endorse this proposal.

I would suggest therefore, that the Conference communicate to the Secretary of the Interior our approval of the proposal for an Office of Ecological Research and Survey.

I would like very much to toss this to Henry Caulfield and have him elaborate a bit on the nature of this proposal, since it's basically his idea and it's, I think, in his hands at the moment. Perhaps he could indicate from his viewpoint whether it would be desirable for the Conference to endorse it. And he could probably give us a sufficient indication of the nature of the proposal so that we could decide whether we could endorse it.

CAULFIELD: I will be glad to explain this idea. There is a provision of law someplace I would be violating if I were to lobby for this idea—which has not as yet been fully considered and adopted even in the Department of the Interior. So I will not in any way attempt to lobby, just explain. The idea of an Office of Ecological Research and Survey springs, of course, from the basic concern of those of you here who are ecologists: a belief that much needs to be known that is not now known in order that man may be informed of the consequences of proposed human action upon our natural endowment and try to avoid undesirable consequences.

In the proposal under consideration, we talk about an "office." It could be a "bureau"—not large, but of sufficient size and having its own research and survey program that would justify such an organizational term.

By "survey" we mean something like the Geological Survey in the sense of regularized compilation of specific ecological knowledge of areas, analogous—but only roughly so—to topographic and geologic mapping. This would provide a systematic and continuous means of acquiring ecological knowledge using professionally accepted concepts, methods, theory, and verifications of the science of ecology.

By "research" I mean, as does Mr. Brandwein in his paper, the creation of new knowledge; that is, creating new concepts asserting their relationship to others, and verifying them operationally. This basic research, of course, is most appropriately performed at universities.

In my mind, the "survey" function would be more a government function, while "research" would be more a university function—with financial aid roughly analogous to that provided under the Water Resources Research Act with enactment of the proposed amendment to that act. This financial aid would have the effect of encouraging universities to develop men for survey work as well as to develop concepts and methods which, together with verified basic analytical findings, would back up and support systematized surveys of areas by professional ecologists in government. I don't believe, however, that these distinctions of function between government and universities should be implemented too precisely: government should undertake some "research" and universities should perform some "surveys."

One of the problems of this proposal is this: within the federal government a good deal of work is going on in several departments which can be considered, at least as parts, of ecological surveying. As Ed Graham knows, in the Soil Conservation Service, a great deal of effort has gone into soil surveys. The Forest Service performs surveys of the environment of greatest concern to it. And the Fish and Wildlife Service does a good deal in its fields, too.

In a bureaucratic sense, this fact of ecological survey work underway poses an interesting problem of arriving at agreement that something more is needed. Thus this proposal must be shaped in such a way as to give recognition to existing work underway, that should be separately continued, but coordinated and combined to give a total ecological analysis. Hopefully, a proposal can be developed that is viable administratively and that also catches fire politically. With increasing public concern for environmental quality, this proposal could evolve into governmental processes and decisions relating to our total environment that many people here would think to be good.

ORDWAY: I'm sorry that you weren't here at some of the earlier sessions when the ecologists were pretty roundly taken to task for not knowing enough about what they ought to know about. And I think that there is a pretty general consensus here that we do need much more research.

While there might be some difference of opinion as to the extent that the federal government should be held responsible for it and the extent that other agencies should also dig in harder than they have dug in, I think that our Chairman might well convey to Secretary Udall the thought that we all feel that there is a lack of sufficient knowledge about the ecosystems of this country and the needs for it.

We don't need to have resolutions or formal action, but if anyone here would also like to write to the Secretary, that is his privilege, obviously.

SEARS: May I ask a question as a matter of information? Will this, if it goes through, provide any mechanism for tapping the ability which is now present in non-land-grant and nonwealthy institutions?

CAULFIELD: I know what you have in mind.

SEARS: You see what I mean. Because I think this has an educational potential as well.

CAULFIELD: He is referring to the provisions of the Water Resources Research Act—in case some of you don't know—which tied this research to the land-grant college system, making an analogy of the Hatch Act pertaining to the Department of Agriculture years ago. This has, shall we say, some political appeal to it that has advantages. But there is a section 200 of the Water Resources Research Act which—if the prohibition gets taken out of it with regard to Congressional surveillance—ought to be helpful to the non-land-grant institutions. We haven't in any way prejudiced this question, at least I haven't, and I know of nothing in the proposal at the present time that says it should be land-grant colleges. And I would like personally to avoid this distinction.

SEARS: Yes.

CAULFIELD: However, it puts a burden. If this proposal does go up and it isn't tied to the land-grant college, it puts a great burden on those of you who are in non-land-grant colleges to be as effective politically as land-grant colleges are.

SEARS: That's impossible. (*Laughter*)

CAULFIELD: I just bring that out. That's not a lobbying statement but a factual observation.

Concerning the point that Sam was making here, on the mix of federal and nonfederal activity, my own ideas would be that this be flexible—in the sense that the survey part is more a job of governmental type and the research is more suited to a university.

But I would hate to see us get into a rigid position such that no research could be done of a generalized ecological type by the government —in other words, in house—and I should think the university ought to be brought constructively into the survey work—as the Geological Survey in many ways has tried to do over the years with respect to topographic mapping and so forth.

MEIER: How does one handle the extension in scale, the externalities of the land that is now being settled, when the scale gets so much larger that soil conservation districts, all of our previous precedents, do not really fit any more?

If one could put together a special kind of a forum or assembly whereby the politicians, anyone who has a constituency within the new metropolitan or megalopolitan unit (as it might be at a later stage), would have some continuous representation in the regional assembly where the politicking is done so that agreements can be put together—and at this point you should also be able to funnel in the planning information, the data— one could by continuous meeting manage to get the job done.

Normally we find that this institution-creating process is so fractured that about the time we have created the institution it is already obsolete.

STRONG: Probably these regional agencies should be tied to a changing definition such as the urbanized area of Census.

MEIER: That's right. Add new constituencies.

CALDWELL: We have in connection with the waterways between Canada and the United States an International Joint Commission which does function in the Detroit area and the Buffalo area particularly. Here, too, is something that we have already created for a specific purpose, but it is a model of possible things to come. In the Detroit area you have a metropolitan area that is international.

MEIER: That's right.

MCHARG: I'd like to speak for the necessity for new institutions, too, and simply pose a problem in terms of some numbers.

We could reasonably assume that, even with the urbanization Dick Meier is talking about, perhaps 95 per cent of the United States is going to be nonurbanized. Even though this may include the urbanization of fifty-five million acres, I think we have to know which acres, where, why.

The next problem, if one looks at the Philadelphia standard metropolitan area just to get some idea of numbers, this is 3500 square miles, which is 20 per cent urbanized now. It is likely to be 30 per cent urbanized at the end of the century, which leaves 2500 square miles nonurbanized, a million and a half acres, for which there is no defense at all. They are subject to zoning of some sort but really no defense.

In this land, 15 per cent is prime agricultural soils equal to the best in the United States, 15 per cent of it is flat plain, about 5000 miles of watercourses. And none of these has any defense at all.

If the resources available now were used to purchase land for recreation this might buy 5000 acres. But 5000 acres in a million and a half which are going to be left in the year 2000 means nothing. We might, if we realize all of our dreams, have some guarantee as to the form of the 5000 acres. Oh, we have about 1 per cent open space now. So about 5000 acres protected leave a million and a half acres, with no guarantee, no control, no protection.

So I think we really have got to think about some regulatory devices for 97 per cent of the United States.

Even in metropolitan areas there are substantial areas of open space that need regulation for which no proposals have been made and which I think this meeting must address itself to.

ORDWAY: This comes back, in a way, to the mention that was made yesterday of the virtues of the master plan for a nation, the white spaces mentioned in England that are not to be invaded, and the means that are being taken to preserve them.

I think this meeting could well discuss the obstacles to trying to establish such a map for the United States and some instrumental means of seeing that the various allocations of land, if and when we are able to find them out, should be devoted to the purposes that seem to the planners to be best.

CLAWSON: I'd like to follow up on what Ian has just said. I personally would like very much to see some research carried out on what would be an optimum pattern of rural settlement with the kind of society we are likely to have a generation from now. I go further and just gently crack the door open and say I'm not so sure RFF wouldn't be willing to finance a little bit of it if somebody will come along with some real ideas. I might even be willing to get my own hands dirty on the thing. It's so obvious to me at any rate that the technological changes—social as well as physical—of the past generation have made the existing pattern of occupancy of rural land obsolete and out of date. It is changing rapidly in parts of the United States, but with considerable lag. And future changes are going to make it still more obsolete.

What should it evolve into? Not that I believe now in any centralized, rigid national planning of this thing: I gave a talk last fall to the directors of the agricultural experiment stations at the land-grant-college meeting, and I said to them, "When the farmers of your state come to you and say, 'What is the long-run future of the agricultural structure of our state?' what can you tell them?" Well, not very much. Because we don't know. And I think we need to try to do some research as to what are some of the implications of the current and immediately prospective changes.

ORDWAY: I think this is sound, and I go along with you and say that I think perhaps The Conservation Foundation might chip in slightly to it and we could have both economic and ecological mutuality in seeking this end.

BRINSER: I don't want to be accused of attempting to put a stopper in anybody's prospective cornucopia, but I would like to raise some questions about what is being proposed.

I get frightened when people start talking about "optimum." Maybe they don't mean what they say. But I don't think it's a useful exercise to attempt to make projections into the long-run future about an optimum.

This denies the nature of the processes that we are concerned about—that the future is continuously being created in various stages. I think it is a useful exercise to try to determine what the possibilities are—what the probabilities are—and particularly to focus upon the efficiency of the means that we should use to achieve movement in a direction.

But any attempt to set up any concept of an optimum or of certainty as to what is going to be in the future—except as one of a range of possibilities that gives us some measurement around which we can determine the viability of other possibilities—is a dangerous enterprise. It's the sort of thing that we have done frequently in the past—often by implication—with the consequence that we create a great deal of sterility. We find ourselves in the case of institutions having to talk about institutional innovation, when, as a matter of fact, if we had created viable institutions that were sufficiently responsive, innovation would be built into the system itself.

ORDWAY: This, I understand, is really an attempt to get at the facts that we do not now know in planning for the future.

BRINSER: We can get at facts in various ways. We can assume that there is a set of facts and that all we have got to do is find out what they are. We can also assume that there is a range of probability and possibility and our problem is to become as certain about this as we can. This is a different approach to facts.

BRANDWEIN: I think what Ayers Brinser says is very important, but I don't think we ought to ignore what Caulfield was saying. He was saying that it is necessary not only to get data and projections, but also, to get men.

Now, our guarantee is that if we free enough men—and I think Pierre Dansereau was really getting at this when he spoke of alienation—who are alienated from the present form of institution to question it seriously, they may create new projections which make the old institutions fallible.

And, therefore, in any projection I would like to free the idiosyncratic person who questions those very projections. I think that's one safety catch, if you will.

WHITE: Would it help focus our thinking to ask of Clawson and Meier, McHarg, Graham, and Caulfield whether they think the character of the information and research and training they suggest are needed would be any different if we were confident now that we had to move to a system of a master plan on a national scale than if we were thinking of moving to a highly flexible system by modification of the present administrative organizations and the use of indirect controls? Would you be asking for anything different in one instance than in another?

ORDWAY: Who would like to speak to that?

MEIER: Clawson already said no, and I say no.

CLAWSON: I haven't thought that anybody would raise the kind of issues that Brinser raised—the idea that you could somehow come up with a fixed thing, that this was it and there was nothing else. As I say, I haven't thought such a thing would arise in this argument.

ORDWAY: I don't think that a master plan necessarily has to be inflexible.

BRINSER: I don't think that's the issue I raised, if I may say so.

We don't believe in fixed master plans; we don't believe in putting our future into the iron maiden. On the other hand, I do think there are ways in which we approach this problem of design—and I think this has occurred quite frequently in projection—that go back to Gilbert White's point, in that we could build into the system the capacity for innovation.

MEIER: But the ones we were proposing were just in the opposite directions. That is, how do you propose institutions that have as wide a degree of flexibility and still keep them operable? This is another challenge.

BRINSER: Yes, I would agree.

GRAHAM: Well, if I understand Gilbert's question, I think I would answer it this way: that perhaps if you had the very best of all possible training for people, it wouldn't make much difference whether you had a centralized control or localized control. But I think one of the difficulties we have today is that many of the people we have employed in resource fields have been trained in specialties first. They have been technicians first. As they move up in a resource agency, we then find we need to make administrators out of them—and we wish the administrators had ecological points of view.

I believe it would be better to reverse the training and give the technician a good general education first, which might permit him to obtain what we have been calling an "ecological point of view," and start with an educated man and then ask him to specialize and apply his technology within the framework of that broader education.

ORDWAY: And you would avoid losing a good technician and getting a bad administrator. I'd like to have Dr. Caldwell speak for a few moments on his view of this proposal of the National Academy of Sciences-National Research Council for a resources intelligence agency as another possible instrumentality.

CALDWELL: My thinking on this high-level review-board concept is indebted to Gilbert White, to Paul Weiss, and to proposals developed by the National Resources Planning Board and the Second Hoover Commission.

The proposal—which was developed to some extent in my paper—is one which came out of the National Academy of Sciences report on natural resources; it argues for a high-level continuing commission of inquiry on major problems of resource utilization and the impact of science and technology on the environment and on public policy. Rather than to develop my own thinking on that, I would certainly defer to whatever Professor White might say, because he had suggested such an instrumentality quite a long time before the National Academy of Sciences report came along.

ORDWAY: I might say that my colleagues Wallace Bowman and John Milton and I did review that report and found ourselves in considerable enthusiasm for the proposal.

Would you like to speak to it at all, Gilbert?

WHITE: Only to the extent of saying that it seems to me this Conference is an exercise in a modest, more ephemeral character of the type that the National Academy Committee was proposing should be carried out in a more systematic, continuing fashion—with an effort to identify the emerging questions and to try to sort out what was known and not known about probable effects of certain new actions by man, changes in the environment, and to try to anticipate, through stimulation of research and data collection, the needs which would arise with these changes in both the present and prospect. So, in a way, I would say this excercise today perhaps exemplifies some of the possible gains from and some of the difficulties inherent in such an attempt.

ORDWAY: Thank you.

I think Dr. Dansereau had one further statement.

DANSEREAU: I fail to see how the ecological survey could get off the ground without a master plan. If one of its objectives—not necessarily its most important objective—was to map the natural features, natural vegetation, and possibly other features of the entire country, this cannot just be farmed out to a number of qualified individuals. Some kind of a scheme—a compromise, or adoption of an existing scheme—has to prevail.

There must be some agreement on scale and criteria—and on the eventual users of the map.

As an example, the map that has been done in France on a scale of 1 in 200,000 was begun some ten years ago, and they have mapped about one tenth of the surface of France. This is a multipurpose map. It requires a very special kind of skill, and it obeys a certain number of rules which have to be agreed to by all the participants.

The people who did participate were spread all over the country and operated in different universities.

I would like to ask Dr. Caulfield whether this is an example, although not the principal thing that they want to do but one of them, and if he has any ideas about the master plan.

ORDWAY: I think that Dr. Fosberg would like to speak to that point.

FOSBERG: I think that we are confusing two utterly different uses of the term "master plan."

I think that what you are requiring is the plan for the operation of the Office of Ecological Research and Surveys, while the other mention of a master plan was a master plan for the zoning and future land utilization of the United States. These are not at all the same thing.

DANSEREAU: But they have to be coordinated. And who does the coordinating?

FOSBERG: If there is a master plan to the United States, it should be coordinated with the Office of Ecological Research and Surveys. But this is getting the cart before the horse because you need to know something before you can have a master plan for the zoning of the United States. And perhaps the biggest excuse or the most important reason for the existence of your Office of Ecological Research and Surveys is to provide this information, and then perhaps you can think in terms of a master plan for the United States.

I wanted to say one other thing: these two proposals do not in any way seem to me to be antithetical.

CALDWELL: I agree with that.

FOSBERG: We are not faced with choosing between the Office of Ecological Research and Surveys and the Academy's high-level intelligence body, if you want to call it that, and this is the first time I have heard it so called. But I have heard it discussed. And I think they are complementary bodies rather than exclusive.

CALDWELL: So do I.

CAULFIELD: I'd like to refer back to Gilbert White or at least what I think is the thrust of his remark. I consider the Office of Ecological Research and Surveys as a distinct input into planning that is not in any focused way present in today's United States federal government.

In other words, I don't conceive it as being a body, a group, an institution in some sense engaged in total planning—whatever that phrase means —of the all of society. I still think the President of the United States is the total planner as far as the federal government is concerned.

There is a proposal that Senator Anderson spoke to—some of you may have heard him if you were at the Wilderness Conference in San Francisco last week—for a Council of Resource Advisers. And Senator McGovern has got quite a bit of steam up on it. It comes pretty close in some respects to what people think of in this National Academy—Gilbert White's idea— does it not, Gilbert?

WHITE: Yes.

CAULFIELD: Except it has some institutional difficulties—at least as viewed by the Bureau of the Budget in particular—which may make it founder, given the power of that agency.

We're having real trouble at the moment with an executive order between HHFA and ourselves over the question of the metes and bounds of the Land and Water Conservation Fund Act and the open-space provisions of the authorities and moneys and so forth of HHFA.

But on top of this there is all this poverty planning. There is a bill that has gone up before the Public Works Committees, quite apart from Mr. Shriver, which is a separate operation. This is the type of thing like the Appalachia Commission, to be extended to the Upper Great Lakes, to the Ozarks, to the Southwest, setting up commissions here that are not on a river-basin basis but have some concept of region. Underlying this notion is a realization of underutilization of resources, both physical and human.

The only thing we have today—and this is not adequate in any positive sense of getting to master planning—is the Budget Bureau. This is not a positive agency, if I may say so, Gilbert. I mean I have feelings about that in a disrespectful sense sometimes, but by its nature it is not an agency to be leading, to be a political leader, to be looking outward toward some objective. It's a review agency. It's a controlling agency, trying to make sense out of a lot of other initiative-type agencies.

So, in the federal government, as I see it, we are institutionally in a confusing position.

As a person who has to give advice on these questions hour by hour, minute by minute, day by day, I still find it confusing to know which way to go, as it were—how to get institutional sense that at least approximates what you have in mind by the term "master plan" with all kinds of inputs, among which will be the inputs of ecology.

ORDWAY: Thank you. Our time is running out, gentlemen, and I think it would be appropriate if, before I turn the final words over to our Chairman, we might hear from below the border. And I think Dr. Budowski has a statement he'd like to make.

BUDOWSKI: I will briefly argue why institutional innovation can actually be applied with probably a much greater return for the input than might be the case in the United States. For one reason, institutional change, or adaptation to some kind of relatively small input, may have a much greater response in some of the new developing countries than it may have in the United States. This is the normal procedure in emerging countries. It is much easier to change the state of things than in countries that already have a well established pattern. You can get the necessary people who have much more influence on existing patterns.

To take an example, a man comes back to his country with a Ph.D. degree. He is likely to be one of the three or four who have some ideas on ecology. He's likely to be requested to direct immediately a program like that. It is easy to change. The other thing is that you still have in some countries enough land, land you can get for absolutely nothing from the government if the suitable request is made. It is land with the primitive environment we are arguing for.

But I would like to remind you this is land which after some perhaps two more generations or even less is not going to exist any more. It is something which we have to take now and have to use now and put to the use which we want or we will never have it again, and it will be exceedingly difficult, if ever possible, to reconstruct it. This is the case in countries where you have more than 50 per cent of the land still called national land and which at this time is programed to be "colonized"—that is, to be turned over to farmers, usually without system and usually leading to degradation.

So even if we want to pursue such objectives as those advocated by Nicholson and the IBP, it is perhaps foolish to believe that countries from these areas, just because they sympathize with the IBP program of selecting habitats, will devote money for it. They will not. They think that there are other problems which deserve priority.

It is only if we can get, I wouldn't say only the money, but the necessary pressure applied to the right people that we can get such a program through. If we consider how much the United States has been interested in the past in tropical environments, how much money has been spent and is now spent getting people trained or interested in the tropics—or let us go to a much further site, how much money is spent every year to help those countries as a result of poor ecological planning and how much money is likely to be spent in the future—I feel that for this country it would be one of the most rewarding investments to deal with those problems not only from the political angle but also from the scientific.

You cannot just say, "We will deal with environments of the United States," and ignore some of the other environments next door that will be completely lost in the future. They are a part, in a sense, of the environment of the United States. They don't influence it much now, but they will definitely influence it in a tremendous and costly way in years to come, especially if we let them deteriorate.

ORDWAY: Thank you, Dr. Budowski. That is a well-made point.

I'd like to turn over the final remarks to the Chairman of the Conference, Dr. Darling. And if you feel that you'd like to ask anybody else in the remaining two minutes to make a statement, please do so.

DARLING: I would like Max to make his point, and then I'll finish up very shortly, because there is no need for my making a formal speech. I just want to bring one or two things together.

NICHOLSON: I have listened with acute interest and growing distress to this discussion, because in the Privy Council in London is a charter which is going to create an actual environment research laboratory, called the Natural Resources Research Council, to try to do much of what we have been discussing. I wonder whether I would be really wise to cancel my ticket and stay somewhere out of reach of that task now I hear some of the ramifications.

There are just three points I would like to make. One is that I still think, having heard the discussion, that such an agency can't be just floating about in the air. It must have some particular expertise and status which belongs to it alone and is clearly recognized. I am still dubious whether, unless it has enough scientific staff to rank as one of the scientific family, it will gain such status.

Having said that, I must add that there is a problem which was delicately referred to by Mr. Caulfield about the behavior of an agency coming low in the pecking order; I think we are concerned always with the right gestures and the right methods of disarming the aggressive feelings of agencies higher up in the pecking order.

I think that's important. I'm dubious whether it's wise to commit yourself to many continuing survey problems on a very broad front involving large manpower, or whether it isn't better to have a more in-and-out policy —of going into manageable situations, doing a survey there, and getting out.

I think it's important for a new body like this, rather low in the pecking order, not to be too pretentious to arouse too much resistance among the existing bureaucracy.

The other point, in connection with Dr. Budowski's remarks, is that in this new charter we can act anywhere in the world by agreement where it is considered desirable to do so. Unlike the present charter, this runs world-wide, which is rather significant, I think, and bears out what Dr. Budowski said.

DARLING: Well, here we are four days later, and we have cut ourselves by a couple of hours so that we can't make any sort of going out with a big bang. It's just a case of getting quickly to one or two points.

I think Paul Brandwein this morning brought out a beautiful thought— that freedom of existence is the conservation ethic and that variability and diversity is a measure of freedom. I liked that.

And Ann Louise Strong brought out, too, in her paper that planners and ecologists and economists accept the principle of diversity. This has been one of the recurrent motifs in this Conference—the place of variety and diversity. That's probably the greatest point of agreement within the Conference.

I made an evolutionary analogy at the beginning, wondering if we were going to become an ecosystem within these four days. The Conference has taken different paths altogether. In fact, it has had the freedom of existence in its own right. It has not been pushed around by any teleological deity. It has evolved in its own way. It's perhaps more an "evolutionary cluster."

But we have become something real, I believe, this Conference. I feel that whether you do or not. We shall perhaps feel better about this when we have seen a transcript and can in some measure weigh up that which we have listened to and said.

We have still got the hour when our dear friend Lewis Mumford will give one of his inimitable summings up.

Now, I brought up yesterday morning in a tentative fashion, and I'm going to bring up now a little more firmly and put it to my President and Chairman of Trustees, the possibility of this Conference remaining in existence. Could this be possible? And if you thought so, could we ask the feelings of this Conference as to whether they would like to remain in existence, or have they really had enough and all they want to do is to get away and forget it? I can't think that really after these four days.

But possibly, say, two thirds of those now present might like to continue in existence as a Conference, so that if the chairmen of panels and the panels themselves would perhaps come up in a year's time—with something crystallized from this Conference, a firming up of what it is we have been talking about, we might make some real contribution to the future of this continent, the environment of this continent.

Could I have your feelings on this?

OSBORN: I ask is there any question in anybody's mind as to what Frank Darling means by "remaining in existence"? I think that should be totally clear.

DARLING: Well, I mean the acceptance of the notion that we are an entity and that we haven't dispersed completely. I don't want to put heavy work on busy men.

HUBBERT: If I may make a remark on that, my attitude is quite favorable to the idea. It seems to me the greatest significance of this meeting is not that we have solved anything but that we have met one another, we have kicked problems around, and we have all learned something. I think it's this kicking around that needs to be continued. And out of it I think knowledge and understanding and consensus will gradually emerge.

COWAN: Mr. Chairman, I would like generally to support that view. I think that there is a very large job that hasn't been done. I wanted to make the point earlier, and I'll make it very briefly now. We have been discussing predominantly this morning less than one half the land area of North America. Canada and Mexico are considerably larger than the United States. Mr. Budowski began the point. We have considerable background patterns for multinational cooperation in matters that we are concerned with; the Great Lakes Survey, the International Joint Commission on Waterways, the Salmon Commission, the Migratory Birds Commission, the International Halibut Commission, and so on are operating.

We have recognized here very real problems of a multinational as well as an international nature. To a large degree your citizens make use of our landscape in Canada, and we are sharing the landscape areas that we have been talking about.

I would certainly enjoy the opportunity of thinking over much that I have gained from this Conference and of consulting with some of those whom I have met here, and I'd like to come back to the problems that we face in Canada and have an opportunity to integrate these into the larger pattern that I am sure we all came here to explore.

DARLING: Thank you.

I must adjourn this Conference, and all I can do now is to thank all of you for your patience and courtesy throughout these four days and for coming here at all. It is quite a job to mount a four-day Conference in these days.

And I would like to thank those who have helped me and made my task so very easy, the Deputy Chairmen and my colleagues John Milton and Noel Eichhorn, and Harriet Bennett and Joe Murn. They have done a tremendous amount of work.

SEARS: I think we should reciprocate this appreciation.

PUZZLE

Savannah, mixed of copse and field
Gives us the best biotic yield;
The fruits of tundra or of tropic
Are meager, mixed, and microscopic.

The frozen and the arid lands
Are fragile in our human hands
Because they clearly are not meant
To be warm, wet, or affluent.

The eightfold way of typing soil
Is mostly pretty useless toil.
For land is typed by man's intent,
And classified by paying rent.

We may not save the whooping crane
But all our efforts are not vain,
On tape we'll hear its whoop again,
And code its genes by IBM.

The ingenuity of man
Often improves on nature's plan
Though man's productions are only faeces
From the point of view of other species.

With laissez-faire and price atomic,
Ecology's Uneconomic,
But with another kind of logic
Economy's Unecologic.

The mountains, rivers, lakes, and grass
Are fine for men of middle class
But nature has much less allure
For women and the urban poor.

The thing for which we have to press
Is optimum amounts of stress,
Though even dogs are hard to please
With just the right amount of fleas.

Planners! No matter how you fudge it
A Plan's no good without a budget,
And budgets don't grow very well
Without the power to tax or sell.

K. E. B.

CLOSING STATEMENT

DARLING: It's not only a privilege but an immense personal pleasure, after a good many years of acquaintance—I'd like to say friendship, if I may—with Lewis Mumford, to ask him to wind up this Conference for us, to give us a summation of his reactions to it and the thoughts that have passed through his mind.

May I ask you, please, Lewis, to give us your reactions?

MUMFORD: Well, my friends and colleagues, this is the fourth time I have had the doubtful honor of closing a Conference. We have now come to a point in the Conference which is like the last chapter, I find, in a book. And the last chapter is either a summary of what went before or the beginning of a new book.

I deliberately made notes so that this would be the beginning of a new book and not the end of a Conference, for I am incapable of summarizing these proceedings in any way that would be satisfactory to any of us; and I'm going to concentrate not on the things that were said in this room but on some of the things that were omitted. Though we have traversed a large territory, there are many still unexplored tracts that I think we ought to pay some attention to at least in the future if not now.

And I begin with the title of this Conference—"The Future Environments of North America." In dealing with the future—and here I return to that famous Wenner-Gren Conference—there are two kinds of future that we don't sufficiently discriminate between. One is the probable future based upon the existing institutions and agencies continuing to act in the same way, at the same rate, with the same impact as they have in the past.

The "probable" future is not necessarily the actual future at all. It is always a summary of the past, and all its predictions are predictions about the past, not about the future. The other future is that based on possibility. And instead of a strictly limited number of probabilities, there are n number of possibilities, some coming into existence in an effort to modify or overcome the statistical forecast.

Now, unfortunately, for the effect of its predictions, science necessarily deals with the past, either with what is known or with what can be directly extrapolated from the known factors. But when you concentrate upon probabilities you are under the temptation to take what has happened or is now happening as an instruction for what should happen in future. In other words, you deny yourself possibility.

But if you understand the potentialities of a situation, what you may learn from the past is not that you should continue to conform to it and to push it further and make the dominant forces go faster, but rather that you should stand in the way of it and oppose to it one or another kind of future based not upon statistics, not upon institutional inertia, but upon the human organism itself, what its purposes and values are. Man's autonomous decisions are the only factors that are capable of transforming the future. Otherwise, the future rolls on and we roll with it or roll under it, as the case may be.

Now, I noticed that one or two somewhat dogmatic predictions were made about the future in relation to the city: none the less dogmatic and limited because most people take them to be unchallengeable.

Today we see a smear of population spreading over the Atlantic coast and the Great Lakes area. Many sociologists, following Jean Gottmann, call this "Megalopolis" and say these urbanoid areas are likely to expand and coalesce. Or they look at the statistics of the rate of growth of cities and see that the suburbs are growing much faster than the central area and say that everything will soon be suburban.

Others go further and say that with the technological facilities we now have, if we are crowded for space, we can create urban islands either in the sea or under the sea. And don't think that's something to laugh at. Such proposals have actually been made by sundry bright young architects and planners. And if these forms are in somebody's imagination today, it is likely, if things go on as they are going now, that they will be actually built within twenty-five or fifty years, perhaps even less.

But such predictions about the future are, I repeat, mere extrapolations and projections of the past. Theirs is the "probable" future, not the possible future, and not necessarily the actual future.

Now, why are we tempted to take such a stultifying position with regard to the future? I think it is because we fail to distinguish between three valid aspects of any human environment.

One is the natural physical aspect, whose processes are described by the physical sciences. There we have an enormous amount of knowledge at our disposal and that knowledge is growing geometrically every day. A deep respect for physical processes, particularly for mechanical processes, dominates our mind, because it's associated with our superb achievements in the physical sciences and technics. Hence, the physical sciences have set the pattern of all the other sciences. Accurate observation and statistical prediction prevail here.

Then there is the fact of the organic world. The organic world can't be interpreted solely in terms of physical process. It must be interpreted in terms of organic functions, of modes of growth, of prospective transformations, sometimes not yet visible in the present state of an organism.

Here we rise beyond mere external process toward autonomy and inner control. Physical energies are used by organisms in order to sustain their existence and interact with their environment and fulfill their life pattern.

That takes us a step away from the inevitable future. As soon as you are dealing with an organism, you're dealing with an autonomous creature, who has more than one answer to any given situation: more than one niche open. Even the lowly amoeba has a mind of its own, as Jennings long ago showed. Robert Frost wrote a touching poem about a little mite walking over his writing paper which he was tempted to squash. When he recognized that the tiny insect was running away from his finger, he perceived in that little mite a mind like his own and decided to let it live.

The reactions of both the mite and the man lie outside the world of physics. For human sentiment was brought into play here, which inhibited the first automatic reaction. If we want to preserve the environment, we will have to rely upon getting aid from people who are still capable of having human sentiments.

On that topic we may well be warned by a little essay that Joseph Wood Krutch recently contributed to the *Saturday Review*. He pointed out that students of biology, in the interest of an austere experimental science, are trained to kill creatures and to preside over their death but never to love them or make pets of them. Similarly Dr. Farber told me about his daughter's high school biology class in which the students were trained to insert a needle into the skull of a live frog and carry on that humanly repulsive experiment to the end, without the even dubious justification offered for medical vivisection.

Thus we are training, in the name of experimental science, a race of young exterminators. They are not likely to be more tender toward the organic habitat than they are to a single living frog.

If this is the way we are educating our children—training them to be callous toward, if not hostile to, living organisms—we are not going to save or improve the environment. We may not even be able to save any other form of human life. It is an offense against both life and morals to treat a high-level organism as though it were something insensate. It doesn't matter very much to iron or copper or molybdenum what you do to it, but it does matter even to the lowliest organism when you interfere with its course of life.

Then, finally, of course, we come to another realm, the realm of human society. While based upon physical process and biological function, this area is specifically the realm of purpose, meaning, and value. Physical processes go on all the time in every organism. And we function like other animals, of course; but meaning and value and purpose are what dominate a truly human existence; and when they are absent, even purely organic functions deteriorate.

Now, it's obvious this is a subject for a whole talk, and in the course of the next few minutes I haven't time to explain how it is that the physical sciences, through their very mode of origin in the seventeenth century, displaced man and looked down upon organic processes as somehow inferior, because they don't lend themselves to exact analysis, the kind of analysis that can only take place with a living organism after you have killed it.

There is always something that eludes you when you examine a living organism by the methods of the physical sciences. What eludes you, of course, is life. Life is the factor that you can't understand or control, ultimately, except from within.

The result is that science in the strict sense doesn't really like to deal with organisms as living wholes and isn't at home in the world of the personality, the world of values and purposes and meanings. Even the biological sciences prefer to deal with the genes or with DNA. There is an enormous amount of fascinating activity in both these departments. But the organism and its living environment have dropped out of the picture, since the organism can't be reduced to a tissue of measurable abstractions.

Now, this has a curious practical result. You can't get rid of purpose, but since the scientist has excluded the category of purpose, he is singularly unprepared to recognize or deal with the institutionalized purposes that are actually controlling our society: forces such as finance capitalism, bureaucratic organization, mechanization, and automation. All of these form part of the great technological apparatus of war. The sciences have passively accepted these purposes, as if they did no harm as long as they do not interfere with the pursuit of science and technology. Give the scientist his laboratory, give him his budget, give him his assistants, give him his honors, and he'll work for any government or corporation without challenging the objectives or questioning the social results.

The result is, therefore, that science has become embrangled with all sorts of negative purposes, like nuclear weapons and rockets. And even in the present stage of our ethics, the overexcitement about DNA shows suspicious symptom of a desire to exercise godlike power.

Recently I was frightened when I looked at the CIBA symposium on the "Future of Life" to read the things that Crick, the great exponent of DNA, was saying about what he would do to change the genetic structure of the human race by means of the knowledge and apparatus he might soon have at his command. He would be able to make different kinds of human beings. What examination did he pass to qualify for that task?

Just remember this little illustration. Is it wise to entrust even Nobel prizewinners with godlike powers? If you knew the history of the gods, you'd know that in the early days at least in Mesopotamia and in Egypt the gods were all mad—mad with the lust of power, the desire to control. And when scientists speak the same way as a Mesopotamian god does, we have reason to wonder whether they are speaking in the spirit of pure rationality and under an austere scientific discipline or whether some irrational factor that they have ignored isn't perhaps taking hold of them.

Now, I come back to the theme of this Conference. What is the valid purpose of a Conference like this?

We began, somewhat unfortunately perhaps, with the physical environment. And we might have got off to a surer start, I won't say a quicker start but a surer start, if we had dealt first of all with man himself, for man must first save himself from his own mischievous fantasies and machinations if he is to save the environment. Obviously the purpose of a Conference like this is not just to promote ecology. Ecology is a well-established scientific discipline which by now is self-promoting. Nor can our primary aim be merely to preserve such residual near-primeval habitats as may still be in existence: even less can it be to "restore" them. Such restorations would produce only museum pieces, a sort of scientific Williamsburg.

But the real purpose of a Conference like this—is it not?—is to insure the existence or the replenishment of a sufficiently varied environment to sustain all of life, including human life and thus to widen the ground for man's further conscious development. That ultimately, it seems to me, is what the whole business is about.

Man has developed in the past in a back-and-forth response to an extremely complex organic environment, which, beginning in paleolithic times, he has sampled, staked out, explored, and become increasingly conscious of in all its ramifications. If this planetary habitat had been as uniform, as fixed, as well controlled as a space capsule, man would have undergone no changes whatever. He would have had no incentive to change, no reason to develop, no possibilities beyond what the space capsule itself offered him.

Now, this man-sustaining environment can be variously interpreted. One of the simplest interpretations is that of my old friend Benton Mac-Kaye, he who conceived and planned the Appalachian Trail. He divided the human habitat into the primeval, the rural, and the communal. I find this a very useful classification, because the primeval is the paleolithic environment, the rural is neolithic, and the communal part became highly developed only with the emergence of urban civilizations.

Man became a moral animal in early paleolithic times, and he probably had more cooperative relations with the creatures who shared his habitat than he does today. It's the paleolithic hunter who begs forgiveness of the animal he has to kill for food. Our basic morality, of caring for and nurturing life, goes back even to the mammals, in the care and nurture of the young. That's the rock-bottom basis for all the morality worth calling such.

Then comes the great neolithic process of domestication, a great change that took place slowly, transforming the landscape and making over the whole mode of life. This change gave to sexuality a larger role than it could have had before. In neolithic life the culture of sex, in the domestication of plants and animals and man himself, pervades the whole habitat.

"Home and mother" are written over the cultivated landscape. Man now has a fixed dwelling place, a secure food supply, and the prospect of both biological and cultural continuity.

Then on top of that came the environment of civilization, which is cosmic and urban. Civilization comes in at a time when man observes the stars and the planets long enough to see that his whole life is related not just to the local terrain but to the sun and moon, and to movements and energies that lie far beyond his own immediate habitat.

These are the three great habitats of man. And now we find that all three habitats are disappearing before our eyes. Some are severely threatened, some have already been obliterated. Now, the present danger is not just that a rare wild species or some precious natural feature like the Colorado River gorge may be obliterated. The great threat is to man's own existence.

And what has mainly brought about this danger? The fact that man has now committed himself to an expanding technology in which material processes override human meanings and purposes. This has led to some very curious paradoxes.

All of us in a way, vicariously or directly, are oversensitive about the disappearance of this or that zoological or botanical species. Yet this in itself is not necessarily an evil. Should we mourn the passing of the hairy mammoth or the saber-toothed tiger? Don't forget that some of our most important food plants have disappeared precisely because they have been domesticated. But there is in fact a reason for our overtenderness and apprehension. Because we know that all life is now threatened. In our concern with the whooping crane we are at once symbolizing and concealing a far deeper anxiety—namely, the prospective total extermination of all species. The general silence on this larger subject is strange, and our own silence is even stranger. We have been gathered here for four days and have discussed many things. But has anybody said a word about the fact that the leaders in the Pentagon, if they become even more unreasonable than now, may destroy the major habitats on the planet? That we have not said a word about this fact, that we act as though it were nonexistent, is fantastic.

I don't blame this particular group. I have been fighting this pathological inertia for fifteen years, and I know that it is such a deep-seated inertia, based on such a fundamental fear, that it is very hard to overcome. But man himself is the wild species that is threatened, and it's time we recognize where the threat comes from: not from our enemies but from ourselves.

We all know the patent signs of this threat. The wholesale "normal" pollution of the water and the air. Sewage; industrial waste; lead from gasoline; nuclear waste; herbicides and pesticides. Every habitat is being to one degree or another spoiled or befouled not so much by man's own presence, as by the lethal products of his ever-expanding technology.

We are aware of the desiccation and erosion of the landscape through overpopulation, and I share to the full Mr. Vogt's anxiety about this. We all should be anxious about it. The planet will be a very unpleasant place if the present overproduction of human beings should be maintained. But this evil is magnified by the constant ingestion of chemical poisons which Rachel Carson pointed out. Our life is being poisoned at the source.

After all, one of man's greatest achievements was the invention of food, not just fodder. All animals eat fodder. Man invented food. Food is not merely something that you put in your stomach and digest. Food is an occasion for a social act. It's an occasion for meeting. It's an occasion for conversation. Food is something that stirs the senses. You are pleasantly titillated by good food, while you are disgusted by bad food and bored by mediocre food. The landscape in which a variety of good foods is grown is a healthy landscape for man and beast.

Now, instead of enriching agriculture and horticulture, we have scientists coming along saying, "Don't worry about overpopulation, my dear fellow. Look here: there are plenty of algae! We could even make them out of the sewage if you ask us to. We are already developing this new resource for space capsules. Mankind can learn to swallow this and go on living."

These examples that I am giving you are symptoms of a wider process that will be inevitably destructive of all that ecologists and conservationists are interested in. The result will be the replacement of the natural and human habitat, which is extremely complex, with a simplified, uniform overcontrolled technological environment, in which only equally simplified and underdimensioned human beings will be capable of existing.

Technology has become the Canada thistle of our culture. You remember W. H. Hudson's description of the Pampas in the Argentine when the Canada thistle took over, and overtopped a man riding on horseback, because there wasn't any other plant around or any creature capable of keeping the Canada thistle down.

Mind you, I'm no opponent of technology. I have written two books on technics and its relation to civilization, and I regard an advanced technology as a necessity. But ought we not to take another look at the consequences of this breakup of the ecological pattern by a single factor of our environment? Are we not already paying too high a price for technological and scientific progress?

The basic assumption behind modern technology is that organic functions, human purposes, and cultural values must be reduced to their lowest factor and brought under control. Whose control? The control of the people who are in charge of the technological process. Not a control achieved by a consensus of mankind or by reference to the accumulated values of human history. A control essentially on the basis of one-generation knowledge put together mainly with the aid of five-year-old minds.

You'll find in current literature that the people who are most eager to exercise control are proud of the fact that they are using only raw, recent knowledge, untested for even a generation; and they are prepared to dismiss anybody who hasn't got this five-year-old knowledge, even if he has 500,000 years of knowledge to weigh in the scales against it.

If you are interested in redeeming the human habitat you must deal with this pathological technical syndrome: one exhibits a barely concealed hostility to living organisms, vital functions, organic association. This technology is based on a desire to displace the organic with the synthetic and the prefabricated, the scientifically controlled, and to rule out every aspect of life that isn't amenable to this process.

Along with this goes a subjective tendency—compulsion, rather—to exercise control as though this were the final achievement of mankind, that man should control every aspect in the environment about him. That reminds me by contrast of a sentence Boris Pasternak drops in *Doctor Zhivago*. He says people talk about "controlling life." And he points out that anybody who talks about controlling life has never begun to understand what life is. Life is essentially an autonomous historic process, and the larger part of man's still-active history is beyond the reach of the controllers. Up to a point you can control organisms negatively, by conditioning or confinement, though if you press them too hard they will die. But you can't control them for any length of time positively, because you'll produce reactions of surprising kind, of which the violence we see in our cities today is perhaps one of the symptoms.

At present we are organizing all our activities on a totalitarian mechanical pattern and providing an "ideal" totalitarian habitat, the encapsulated environment—uniform, standardized, machine-fabricated, automatic, under strict control from the moment of birth to the moment of death, from incubator to incinerator, so to speak.

The models for this are all around us. They go from the commonplace chicken farm of today, where no human being dares to enter lest the poor birds panic at the unfamiliar human presence, to the underground rocket silos or to Glacken's transcontinental jet plane, where his contact with the outside environment by eye was denied him so that television or motion pictures could supply a controllable substitute. This is fast becoming the universal environment of our culture.

The natural and the humanized habitat, as a result of the overuse of technological equipment, then becomes either physically unusable or psychologically invisible. People don't see it. They're not aware of the thousand things that we who know something about nature are aware of when we're holding conversation with the environment.

Anybody who is fully alive and who has even a small store of the available scientific knowledge can't be in any kind of environment without engaging in a kind of dialogue, without asking questions and responding to it. The technological environment is by intention a "one-way system." No conversations may take place without permission from the control center. People have begun to accept this as the ideal environment.

One of Loren Eiseley's students said to him: "Why not destroy all organisms and clear the ground for man? Man can make synthetic substitutes for everything the organic world does."

That student curiously forgot in destroying all other organisms he was destroying the possibility of continuing human life. Of course he didn't have enough biological knowledge to realize that. But also he was destroying man's history, without which man cannot make himself fully human. Man's history is associated with the entire organic world. He hasn't been alone. He has had companions: he has had helpers: he has had cooperators. They have taught him many things, more than he has ever up to now been able to teach them.

Wipe this all out and what happens? What happens, of course, is that you lose contact with the real world. Wipe out nature, wipe out human purposes, memories, and expectancies, and the real world disappears. And what's the result of that loss of contact with the real world? The name for it is insanity. Alienation, loss of identity, suicidal depression, irrational hostility, moral insensibility are some of the current symptoms.

The "brave new world" of our totalitarian technics and our machine-made totalitarian habitat lacks essential human dimensions. And one of the things it lacks is sixty million years or so of mammalian experience, and a million or 500,000 years of human experience and memory. We are now busily wiping out every manner of botanical and zoological variety, in order that the machine, or some plastic substitute for a natural species, may flourish.

Fortunately, there is something self-defeating about our technological dynamism: it is unstable almost by definition, because those who further it believe in instability, and do not realize that without continuity nothing that can be called progress is possible. In economic terms, our dominant system calls for constant turnover and constant expansion, whereas organic changes are changes that tend to promote equilibrium and regulate orderly growth. Those who are now making critical decisions for us, in both industry or government, make the mistake of equating power with life, and under this delusion they have been countenancing the mass production of pesticides and the production of nuclear weapons, which may permanently wreck the habitability of the planet—and, ironically, but fatally, bring technology itself to an end.

So now I come back to our central theme. By what means can we preserve and develop the great variety of habitats, primeval, communal, domesticated, and urbane, which modern man needs, now more than ever, to maximize his potentialities for living. We do well to begin with the primeval habitat, the ancestral habit of paleolithic man. For it was in that habitat that *Homo sapiens* developed speech and ritual and art and morals: the foundation of all that can be properly called human.

The purpose we should keep steadfastly in mind, it seems to me, is the maintenance and the furtherance of all these potentialities. Our concern for preserving this or that threatened species, this or that invaded wilderness area, is primarily symbolic. If we say with the poet, Gerard Manley Hopkins, "Wet and wildness, let them be left, let them be left," it is because this wildness remains a precious ingredient in the human soul: not to be surrendered without question to someone with a bulldozer who wants to promote a land development, or stake out a hydroelectric power site.

When we rally to preserve the remaining redwood forests or to protect the whooping crane, we are rallying to preserve ourselves, we are trying to keep in existence the organic variety, the whole span of natural resources, upon which our own further development will be based. If we surrender this variety too easily in one place, we shall lose it everywhere; and we shall find ourselves enclosed in a technological prison, without even the hope that sustains a prisoner in jail—that someday we may get out. Should organic variety disappear, there will be no "out."

Once we define these broad purposes of conservation, we can assign positive values and a positive place to technical improvements. Just as we know now that even in paleolithic times, man's bow and arrow made a necessary contribution toward preserving the balance of species in a habitat favorable for wild creatures, so man's other technical needs have enriched our intercourse with the environment. The question always must be: What essential human need, viewed in historic perspective, is being fulfilled or is being sacrificed?

But we have to challenge the notion that there is something sacred in large-scale technological operations, whether they are for a new superhighway, a new power station, or a new nuclear power plant. There is no wealth, as Ruskin observed, but Life is what gives reason and purpose to technology—not the other way around. We can cordially welcome the machine, so long as it does not dominate us, does not seek to overwhelm us, does not give us instructions how to live.

Too many people today have shown they are ready to submit to having their soil, water, and food polluted, to having the air as choked with noise as their scenery is with motorcar cemeteries, to committing any personal sacrifice of their own life in order to advance the machine. We have taken every technological permission to be a command. Because scientific advances have given us the power to send a rocket to the moon, we are now wasting exorbitant sums on that barren adventure: sums we could use to much better purpose on earth.

One of the best reasons for our conservation movement, with its broad foundations, ever since George Perkins Marsh, in both natural and human history, is that it demonstrates the irrationality of allowing any single factor to dominate the rest of the environment. Our technology has overemphasized, in every sphere of life, the factor of power, of mass production and standardization; it seeks to decrease variety in order to promote quantity. Our aim rather should be to promote variety in order to curb this monotonous quantification.

This brings me back to the theme on which Mr. Brandwein held forth this morning. The need for re-education of ourselves so as to get on top of a technological system that is destroying both organic variety and human choice. And if this is our task, we must perhaps begin to effect a transformation not in wild nature alone, but in the city; for this is where the forces that have undermined both the natural and the historic habitat have assembled. The replenishment of life in our cities and the replenishment of our larger habitat will prosper if these two movements go hand in hand, and interact. But in educational terms, this means that we must provide a curriculum aimed not at producing more technicians, more engineers, more mathematicians, more scientists, but at producing more whole men and women, at home in every part of the environment.

In a word, the conservation of natural resources means nothing less than the conservation of human potentialities. And in that setting, all our present interests take on a wider meaning and open up a larger purpose.

We need to distrust a system of thought that has cut itself off deliberately from the culture and the cultivation of the whole organism and that has acquired an exaggerated respect for the abstract intelligence, even though that intelligence is capable of a more sophisticated kind of thinking than man has ever achieved before.

Don't think I don't admire my superiors when I see them at work, the great mathematicians, the great physical scientists, all those who are capable of this degree of abstraction! I find deficiencies, though, very often, in other parts of their life, and I recognize that the really great ones—the Faradays, the Einsteins, the Clerk Maxwells—bring to their science their whole personality and this is what saves them, and perhaps also adds to their greatness.

Great minds utilize more of their own organism, and have more of the environment at their command than the people who have only learned to live a segmented life and to think in terms of segmented knowledge.

So I now come back to our theme. Our theme is how to preserve and develop a variety of habitats, primitive, domesticated, urbane, how to keep going all that we have acquired from paleolithic man.

Don't forget that we can't leave paleolithic man behind us, because he invented the symbols of language, and if we turn our backs on the paleolithic man and his environment, we are turning our backs upon the possibility of speech, upon the possibility of everything that is derived from his fundamental discoveries of symbols and of morals.

The purpose that we should have in mind, it seems to me, the purpose which we must cling to when we consider the improvement of habitat, is to become more conscious through thought and action and all the works of human art of the possibilities for further human development. It's not just to save the grasslands or the primeval forest, or to save the whooping crane.

Once we accept this premise, we can assign positive human values to technics. Technics itself, of course, has a place to play in every habitat— but not by itself, not to dominate us, not to give us orders as to how to live. It's we, the living, who must tell our technology how much of it is tolerable and how much of it we will put to one side even if it exists. We must take our instructions from human history and the human pros- pect, which is always centered in human beings and has reference to man's whole future development.

So to re-establish a life-favoring environment we must take up the theme Mr. Brandwein amplified this morning. Unless we can re-educate ourselves so as to get on top of this technological system, we shall probably find it impossible to go on for any great length of time in the wasteful, destruc- tive, dehumanized way we are now pursuing. Our habitats will become insignificant and will disappear—and we ourselves along with them.

That means we must begin from the opposite direction. If we want to preserve nature, let's get back to the city and see what makes a man, a man in a human environment. The city as a human environment has been spoiled as badly as the primeval environment by forces that have been acting without our sufficient understanding or control during the last fifty or hundred years. Yet it is in and through the city, with all the resources it offers for the mind that man has created a symbolic counterpart to nature's creativity, variety, and exuberance.

We need the cooperation of all organisms, we need a sense of entire human history in order to root our life once more in realities, not in our abstractions, fantasies, and hallucinations. We mustn't retire into our mind, even the highest kind of mind. We must be able to have inter- course with our fellows, intercourse with the entire environment around us in all their concrete richness.

Man needs the whole cosmos to sustain him. The knowledge of this cosmos and every living part of it enriches him, enables him to know him- self for the first time, to have some sense of the further advantages and the further fulfillments that lie ahead of him if once he gets on top of the forces that now threaten his life.

There, I think, are the conditions under which it will be profitable to examine the future of human environments on the North American continent.

(*Applause*)

DARLING: Thank you indeed, sir.

Index